GRAPHS OF PARENT FUNCTIONS

Linear Function

$f(x) = mx + b$

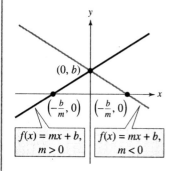

Domain: $(-\infty, \infty)$
Range: $(-\infty, \infty)$
x-intercept: $(-b/m, 0)$
y-intercept: $(0, b)$
Increasing when $m > 0$
Decreasing when $m < 0$

Absolute Value Function

$f(x) = |x| = \begin{cases} x, & x \geq 0 \\ -x, & x < 0 \end{cases}$

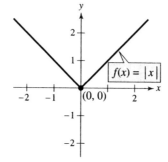

Domain: $(-\infty, \infty)$
Range: $[0, \infty)$
Intercept: $(0, 0)$
Decreasing on $(-\infty, 0)$
Increasing on $(0, \infty)$
Even function
y-axis symmetry

Square Root Function

$f(x) = \sqrt{x}$

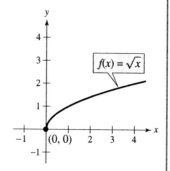

Domain: $[0, \infty)$
Range: $[0, \infty)$
Intercept: $(0, 0)$
Increasing on $(0, \infty)$

Greatest Integer Function

$f(x) = [\![x]\!]$

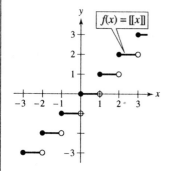

Domain: $(-\infty, \infty)$
Range: the set of integers
x-intercepts: in the interval $[0, 1)$
y-intercept: $(0, 0)$
Constant between each pair of
   consecutive integers
Jumps vertically one unit at
   each integer value

Quadratic (Squaring) Function

$f(x) = ax^2$

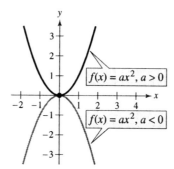

Domain: $(-\infty, \infty)$
Range $(a > 0)$: $[0, \infty)$
Range $(a < 0)$: $(-\infty, 0]$
Intercept: $(0, 0)$
Decreasing on $(-\infty, 0)$ for $a > 0$
Increasing on $(0, \infty)$ for $a > 0$
Increasing on $(-\infty, 0)$ for $a < 0$
Decreasing on $(0, \infty)$ for $a < 0$
Even function
y-axis symmetry
Relative minimum $(a > 0)$,
   relative maximum $(a < 0)$,
   or vertex: $(0, 0)$

Cubic Function

$f(x) = x^3$

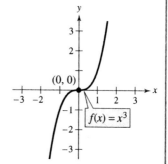

Domain: $(-\infty, \infty)$
Range: $(-\infty, \infty)$
Intercept: $(0, 0)$
Increasing on $(-\infty, \infty)$
Odd function
Origin symmetry

Rational (Reciprocal) Function

$$f(x) = \frac{1}{x}$$

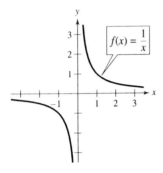

Domain: $(-\infty, 0) \cup (0, \infty)$
Range: $(-\infty, 0) \cup (0, \infty)$
No intercepts
Decreasing on $(-\infty, 0)$ and $(0, \infty)$
Odd function
Origin symmetry
Vertical asymptote: y-axis
Horizontal asymptote: x-axis

Exponential Function

$$f(x) = a^x, \ a > 0, \ a \neq 1$$

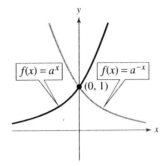

Domain: $(-\infty, \infty)$
Range: $(0, \infty)$
Intercept: $(0, 1)$
Increasing on $(-\infty, \infty)$
  for $f(x) = a^x$
Decreasing on $(-\infty, \infty)$
  for $f(x) = a^{-x}$
Horizontal asymptote: x-axis
Continuous

Logarithmic Function

$$f(x) = \log_a x, \ a > 0, \ a \neq 1$$

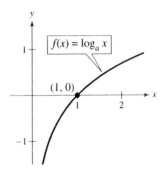

Domain: $(0, \infty)$
Range: $(-\infty, \infty)$
Intercept: $(1, 0)$
Increasing on $(0, \infty)$
Vertical asymptote: y-axis
Continuous
Reflection of graph of $f(x) = a^x$
  in the line $y = x$

Sine Function

$$f(x) = \sin x$$

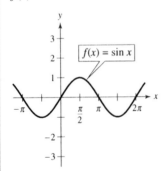

Domain: $(-\infty, \infty)$
Range: $[-1, 1]$
Period: 2π
x-intercepts: $(n\pi, 0)$
y-intercept: $(0, 0)$
Odd function
Origin symmetry

Cosine Function

$$f(x) = \cos x$$

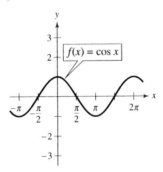

Domain: $(-\infty, \infty)$
Range: $[-1, 1]$
Period: 2π
x-intercepts: $\left(\dfrac{\pi}{2} + n\pi, 0\right)$
y-intercept: $(0, 1)$
Even function
y-axis symmetry

Tangent Function

$$f(x) = \tan x$$

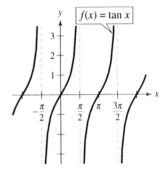

Domain: all $x \neq \dfrac{\pi}{2} + n\pi$
Range: $(-\infty, \infty)$
Period: π
x-intercepts: $(n\pi, 0)$
y-intercept: $(0, 0)$
Vertical asymptotes:
$$x = \frac{\pi}{2} + n\pi$$
Odd function
Origin symmetry

Cosecant Function

$f(x) = \csc x$

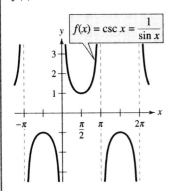

Domain: all $x \neq n\pi$
Range: $(-\infty, -1] \cup [1, \infty)$
Period: 2π
No intercepts
Vertical asymptotes: $x = n\pi$
Odd function
Origin symmetry

Secant Function

$f(x) = \sec x$

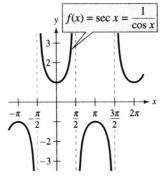

Domain: all $x \neq \dfrac{\pi}{2} + n\pi$

Range: $(-\infty, -1] \cup [1, \infty)$
Period: 2π
y-intercept: $(0, 1)$
Vertical asymptotes:

$$x = \frac{\pi}{2} + n\pi$$

Even function
y-axis symmetry

Cotangent Function

$f(x) = \cot x$

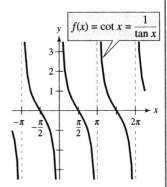

Domain: all $x \neq n\pi$
Range: $(-\infty, \infty)$
Period: π

x-intercepts: $\left(\dfrac{\pi}{2} + n\pi, 0\right)$

Vertical asymptotes: $x = n\pi$
Odd function
Origin symmetry

Inverse Sine Function

$f(x) = \arcsin x$

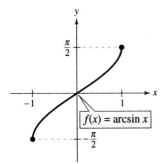

Domain: $[-1, 1]$
Range: $\left[-\dfrac{\pi}{2}, \dfrac{\pi}{2}\right]$
Intercept: $(0, 0)$
Odd function
Origin symmetry

Inverse Cosine Function

$f(x) = \arccos x$

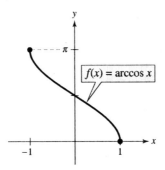

Domain: $[-1, 1]$
Range: $[0, \pi]$

y-intercept: $\left(0, \dfrac{\pi}{2}\right)$

Inverse Tangent Function

$f(x) = \arctan x$

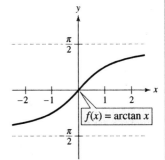

Domain: $(-\infty, \infty)$
Range: $\left(-\dfrac{\pi}{2}, \dfrac{\pi}{2}\right)$
Intercept: $(0, 0)$
Horizontal asymptotes:

$$y = \pm\frac{\pi}{2}$$

Odd function
Origin symmetry

Precalculus
A Concise Course

Ron Larson
The Pennsylvania State University
The Behrend College

Robert Hostetler
The Pennsylvania State University
The Behrend College

With the Assistance of David C. Falvo
The Pennsylvania State University
The Behrend College

Houghton Mifflin Company
Boston   New York

COLLEGE ALGEBRA, SEVENTH EDITION
by Ron Larson and Robert Hostetler
Copyright © 2007 by Houghton Mifflin Company. All rights reserved.

Publisher: Richard Stratton
Sponsoring Editor: Cath Cantin
Development Manager: Maureen Ross
Development Editor: Lisa Collette
Editorial Associate: Elizabeth Kassab
Supervising Editor: Karen Carter
Senior Project Editor: Patty Bergin
Editorial Assistant: Julia Keller
Art and Design Manager: Gary Crespo
Executive Marketing Manager: Brenda Bravener-Grenville
Director Of Manufacturing: Priscilla Manchester
Cover Design Manager: Tony Saizon

Custom Publishing Editor: Dan Luciano
Custom Publishing Production Manager: Tina Kozik
Project Coordinator: Andrea Wagner

Cover Designer: Athea Chen
Cover Image: PhotoDisc

This book contains select works from existing Houghton Mifflin Company resources and was produced by Houghton Mifflin Custom Publishing for collegiate use. As such, those adopting and/or contributing to this work are responsible for editorial content, accuracy, continuity and completeness.

Printed in the United States of America.

ISBN-13: 978-0-618-81843-3
ISBN-10: 0-618-81843-X
N-06916

7 8 9 -CCI- 09 08

 Houghton Mifflin
Custom Publishing

222 Berkeley Street • Boston, MA 02116

Address all correspondence and order information to the above address.

Contents

A Word from the Authors

Welcome to *Precalculus: A Concise Course*. We are pleased to present this new precalculus textbook in which we focus on making the mathematics accessible, supporting student success, and offering instructors flexible teaching options. The purpose of this text is to concisely cover the topics of precalculus. This text covers six chapters: *Functions and Their Graphs*, *Polynomial and Rational Functions*, *Exponential and Logarithmic Functions*, *Trigonometry*, *Analytic Trigonometry*, and *Topics in Analytic Geometry*. Should students need extra help or need to review material from intermediate algebra, the textbook website offers an appendix for review.

Accessible to Students

We have taken care to write this text with the student in mind. Paying careful attention to the presentation, we use precise mathematical language and a clear writing style to develop an effective learning tool. We believe that every student can learn mathematics, and we are committed to providing a text that makes the mathematics of the precalculus course accessible to all students.

Throughout the text, solutions to many examples are presented from multiple perspectives—algebraically, graphically, and numerically. The side-by-side format of this pedagogical feature helps students to see that a problem can be solved in more than one way and to see that different methods yield the same result. The side-by-side format also addresses many different learning styles.

We have found that many precalculus students grasp mathematical concepts more easily when they work with them in the context of real-life situations. Students have numerous opportunities to do this throughout the text. The *Make a Decision* feature further connects real-life data and applications and motivates students. They also offer students the opportunity to generate and analyze mathematical models from large data sets. To reinforce the concept of functions, each function is introduced at the first point of use in the text with a definition and description of basic characteristics. Also, all elementary functions are presented in a summary on the endpapers of the text for convenient reference.

We have carefully written and designed each page to make the book readable and accessible to students. For example, to avoid unnecessary page turning and disruptions to students' thought processes, each example and corresponding solution begins and ends on the same page.

Supports Student Success

During more than 30 years of teaching and writing, we have learned many things about the teaching and learning of mathematics. We have found that students are most successful when they know what they are expected to learn and why it is important to learn the concepts. With that in mind, we have incorporated a thematic study thread throughout *Precalculus: A Concise Course*.

Each chapter begins with a list of applications that are covered in the chapter and serve as a motivational tool by connecting section content to real-life situations. Using the same pedagogical theme, each section begins with a set of section learning objectives—*What You Should Learn.* These are followed by an engaging real-life application—*Why You Should Learn It*—that motivates students and illustrates an area where the mathematical concepts will be applied in an example or exercise in the section. The *Chapter Summary—What Did You Learn?*—at the end of each chapter is a section-by-section overview that ties the learning objectives from the chapter to sets of *Review Exercises* at the end of each chapter.

Throughout the text, other features further improve accessibility. *Study Tips* are provided throughout the text at point-of-use to reinforce concepts and to help students learn how to study mathematics. *Technology, Writing About Mathematics, Historical Notes,* and *Explorations* reinforce mathematical concepts. Each example with worked-out solution is now followed by a *Checkpoint*, which directs the student to work a similar exercise from the exercise set. The *Section Exercises* begin with a *Vocabulary Check*, which gives the students an opportunity to test their understanding of the important terms in the section. A *Prerequisite Skills Review* is offered at the beginning of each exercise set. *Synthesis Exercises* check students' conceptual understanding of the topics in each section. The *Make a Decision* exercises further connect real-life data and applications and motivate students. *Skills Review Exercises* provide additional practice with the concepts in the chapter or previous chapters. *Chapter Tests*, at the end of each chapter, and periodic *Cumulative Tests* offer students frequent opportunities for self-assessment and to develop strong study- and test-taking skills.

The use of technology also supports students with different learning styles. *Technology* notes are provided throughout the text at point-of-use. These notes call attention to the strengths and weaknesses of graphing technology, as well as offer alternative methods for solving or checking a problem using technology. These notes also direct students to the *Graphing Technology Guide*, on the textbook website, for keystroke support that is available for numerous calculator models. The use of technology is optional. This feature and related exercises can be omitted without the loss of continuity in coverage of topics.

Numerous additional text-specific resources are available to help students succeed in the precalculus course. These include "live" online tutoring, instructional DVDs, and a variety of other resources, such as tutorial support and self-assessment, which are available on the HM mathSpace® CD-ROM, the Web, and in Eduspace®. In addition, the *Online Notetaking Guide* is a notetaking guide that helps students organize their class notes and create an effective study and review tool.

Flexible Options for Instructors

From the time we first began writing textbooks in the early 1970s, we have always considered it a critical part of our role as authors to provide instructors with flexible programs. In addition to addressing a variety of learning styles, the optional features within the text allow instructors to design their courses to meet their instructional needs and the needs of their students. For example, the

Explorations throughout the text can be used as a quick introduction to concepts or as a way to reinforce student understanding.

Our goal when developing the exercise sets was to address a wide variety of learning styles and teaching preferences. The *Vocabulary Check* questions are provided at the beginning of every exercise set to help students learn proper mathematical terminology. In each exercise set we have included a variety of exercise types, including questions requiring writing and critical thinking, as well as real-data applications. The problems are carefully graded in difficulty from mastery of basic skills to more challenging exercises. Some of the more challenging exercises include the *Synthesis Exercises* that combine skills and are used to check for conceptual understanding and the *Make a Decision* exercises that further connect real-life data and applications and motivate students. *Skills Review Exercises*, placed at the end of each exercise set, reinforce previously learned skills. In addition, Houghton Mifflin's Eduspace® website offers instructors the option to assign homework and tests online—and also includes the ability to grade these assignments automatically.

Several other print and media resources are also available to support instructors. The *Online Instructor Success Organizer* includes suggested lesson plans and is an especially useful tool for larger departments that want all sections of a course to follow the same outline. The *Instructor's Edition* of the *Student Notetaking Guide* can be used as a lecture outline for every section of the text and includes additional examples for classroom discussion and important definitions. This is another valuable resource for schools trying to have consistent instruction and it can be used as a resource to support less experienced instructors. When used in conjunction with the *Student Notetaking Guide* these resources can save instructors preparation time and help students concentrate on important concepts.

Instructors who stress applications and problem solving, or exploration and technology, coupled with more traditional methods will be able to use this text successfully.

We hope you will enjoy using *Precalculus: A Concise Course* in your precalculus class.

Ron Larson
Robert Hostetler

Acknowledgments

We would like to thank the many people who have helped us prepare the text and the supplements package. Their encouragement, criticisms, and suggestions have been invaluable to us.

Reviewers

Arun Agarwal, *Grambling State University*; Jean Claude Antoine, *Bunker Hill Community College*; W. Edward Bolton, *East Georgia College*; Joanne Brunner, *Joliet Junior College*; Luajean Bryan, *Walker Valley High School*; Nancy Cholvin, *Antelope Valley College*; Amy Daniel, *University of New Orleans*; Nerissa Felder, *Polk Community College*; Kathi Fields, *Blue Ridge Community College*; Edward Green, *North Georgia College & State University*; Karen Guinn, *University of South Carolina Beaufort*; Duane Larson, *Bevill State Community College*; Babette Lowe, *Victoria College (TX)*; Rudy Maglio, *Northwestern University*; Antonio Mazza, *University of Toronto*; Robin McNally, *Reinhardt College*; Constance Meade, *College of Southern Idaho*; Matt Mitchell, *American River College*; Claude Moore, *Danville Community College*; Mark Naber, *Monroe Community College*; Paul Olsen, *Wesley College*; Yewande Olubummo, *Spelman College*; Claudia Pacioni, *Washington State University*; Gary Parker, *Blue Mountain Community College*; Kevin Ratliff, *Blue Ridge Community College*; Michael Simon, *Southern Connecticut State University*; Rick Simon, *University of La Verne*; Delores Smith, *Coppin State University*; Kostas Stroumbakis, *DeVry Institute of Technology*; Michael Tedder, *Jefferson Davis Community College*; Ellen Turnell, *North Harris College*; Pamela Weston, *Tennessee Wesleyan College*

We would like to thank the staff of Larson Texts, Inc. who assisted in preparing the manuscript, rendering the art package, and typesetting and proofreading the pages and supplements.

On a personal level, we are grateful to our wives, Deanna Gilbert Larson and Eloise Hostetler for their love, patience, and support. Also, a special thanks goes to R. Scott O'Neil.

If you have suggestions for improving this text, please feel free to write us. Over the past three decades we have received many useful comments from both instructors and students, and we value these very much.

Ron Larson
Robert Hostetler

Textbook Features and Highlights

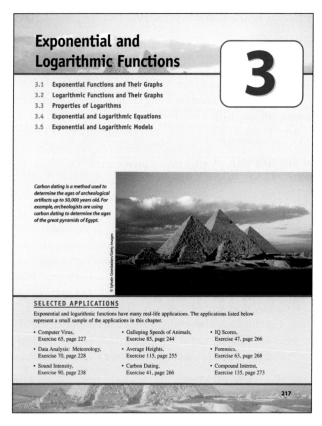

• Chapter Opener

Each chapter begins with a comprehensive overview of the chapter concepts. The photograph and caption illustrate a real-life application of a key concept. Section references help students prepare for the chapter.

• Applications List

An abridged list of applications, covered in the chapter, serve as a motivational tool by connecting section content to real-life situations.

• "What You Should Learn" and "Why You Should Learn It"

Sections begin with *What You Should Learn*, an outline of the main concepts covered in the section, and *Why You Should Learn It*, a real-life application or mathematical reference that illustrates the relevance of the section content.

• Examples

Many examples present side-by-side solutions with multiple approaches—algebraic, graphical, and numerical. This format addresses a variety of learning styles and shows students that different solution methods yield the same result.

• Checkpoint

The *Checkpoint* directs students to work a similar problem in the exercise set for extra practice.

• Explorations

The *Exploration* engages students in active discovery of mathematical concepts, strengthens critical thinking skills, and helps them to develop an intuitive understanding of theoretical concepts.

• Study Tips

Study Tips reinforce concepts and help students learn how to study mathematics.

• Technology

The *Technology* feature gives instructions for graphing utilities at point of use.

• Additional Features

Additional carefully crafted learning tools, designed to connect concepts, are placed throughout the text. These learning tools include *Writing About Mathematics, Historical Notes,* and an extensive art program.

• Real-Life Applications

A wide variety of real-life applications, many using current real data, are integrated throughout the examples and exercises. The 🌐 indicates an example that involves a real-life application.

• Algebra of Calculus

Throughout the text, special emphasis is given to the algebraic techniques used in calculus. Algebra of Calculus examples and exercises are integrated throughout the text and are identified by the symbol ∫.

• Section Exercises

The section exercise sets consist of a variety of computational, conceptual, and applied problems.

• Vocabulary Check

Section exercises begin with a *Vocabulary Check* that serves as a review of the important mathematical terms in each section.

• Prerequisite Skills Review

Extra practice and a review of algebra skills, needed to complete the section exercise sets, are offered to the students and available in Eduspace®.

43. Distance A boat is sailing due east parallel to the shoreline at a speed of 10 miles per hour. At a given time, the bearing to the lighthouse is S 70° E, and 15 minutes later the bearing is S 63° E (see figure). The lighthouse is located at the shoreline. What is the distance from the boat to the shoreline?

Model It

44. Shadow Length The Leaning Tower of Pisa in Italy is characterized by its tilt. The tower leans because it was built on a layer of unstable soil—clay, sand, and water. The tower is approximately 58.36 meters tall from its foundation (see figure). The top of the tower leans about 5.45 meters off center.

5.45 m

58.36 m

Not drawn to scale

(a) Find the angle of lean α of the tower.

(b) Write β as a function of d and θ, where θ is the angle of elevation to the sun.

(c) Use the Law of Sines to write an equation for the length d of the shadow cast by the tower.

(d) Use a graphing utility to complete the table.

θ	10°	20°	30°	40°	50°	60°
d						

Synthesis

True or False? In Exercises 45 and 46, determine whether the statement is true or false. Justify your answer.

45. If a triangle contains an obtuse angle, then it must be oblique.

46. Two angles and one side of a triangle do not necessarily determine a unique triangle.

47. Graphical and Numerical Analysis In the figure, α and β are positive angles.

(a) Write α as a function of β.

(b) Use a graphing utility to graph the function. Determine its domain and range.

(c) Use the result of part (a) to write c as a function of β.

(d) Use a graphing utility to graph the function in part (c). Determine its domain and range.

(e) Complete the table. What can you infer?

β	0.4	0.8	1.2	1.6	2.0	2.4	2.8
α							
c							

18

9

FIGURE FOR 47

20 cm

$\frac{\theta}{2}$

8 cm

30 cm

FIGURE FOR 48

48. Graphical Analysis

(a) Write the area A of the shaded region in the figure as a function of θ.

(b) Use a graphing utility to graph the area function.

(c) Determine the domain of the area function. Explain how the area of the region and the domain of the function would change if the eight-centimeter line segment were decreased in length.

Skills Review

In Exercises 49–52, use the fundamental trigonometric identities to simplify the expression.

49. $\sin x \cot x$

50. $\tan x \cos x \sec x$

51. $1 - \sin^2\left(\dfrac{\pi}{2} - x\right)$

52. $1 + \cot^2\left(\dfrac{\pi}{2} - x\right)$

• Model It

These multi-part applications that involve real data offer students the opportunity to generate and analyze mathematical models.

• Synthesis and Skills Review Exercises

Each exercise set concludes with the two types of exercises.

Synthesis exercises promote further exploration of mathematical concepts, critical thinking skills, and writing about mathematics. The exercises require students to show their understanding of the relationships between many concepts in the section.

Skills Review Exercises reinforce previously learned skills and concepts.

Make a Decision exercises, found in selected sections, further connect real-life data and applications and motivate students. They also offer students the opportunity to generate and analyze mathematical models from large data sets.

Model It

69. Data Analysis: Biology To estimate the amount of defoliation caused by the gypsy moth during a given year, a forester counts the number x of egg masses on $\frac{1}{40}$ of an acre (circle of radius 18.6 feet) in the fall. The percent of defoliation y the next spring is shown in the table. (Source: USDA, Forest Service)

Egg masses, x	Percent of defoliation, y
0	12
25	44
50	81
75	96
100	99

A model for the data is given by

$$y = \frac{100}{1 + 7e^{-0.069x}}.$$

(a) Use a graphing utility to create a scatter plot of the data and graph the model in the same viewing window.

(b) Create a table that compares the model with the sample data.

(c) Estimate the percent of defoliation if 36 egg masses are counted on $\frac{1}{40}$ acre.

(d) You observe that $\frac{2}{3}$ of a forest is defoliated the following spring. Use the graph in part (a) to estimate the number of egg masses per $\frac{1}{40}$ acre.

70. Data Analysis: Meteorology A meteorologist measures the atmospheric pressure P (in pascals) at altitude h (in kilometers). The data are shown in the table.

Altitude, h	Pressure, P
0	101,293
5	54,735
10	23,294
15	12,157
20	5,069

A model for the data is given by $P = 107,428e^{-0.150h}$.

(a) Sketch a scatter plot of the data and graph the model on the same set of axes.

(b) Estimate the atmospheric pressure at a height of 8 kilometers.

Synthesis

True or False? In Exercises 71 and 72, determine whether the statement is true or false. Justify your answer.

71. The line $y = -2$ is an asymptote for the graph of $f(x) = 10^x - 2$.

72. $e = \dfrac{271,801}{99,990}$.

Think About It In Exercises 73–76, use properties of exponents to determine which functions are the same.

73. $f(x) = 3^{x-2}$

$g(x) = 3^x - 9$

$h(x) = \frac{1}{9}(3^x)$

74. $f(x) = 4^x + 12$

$g(x) = 2^{2x+6}$

$h(x) = 64(4^x)$

75. $f(x) = 16(4^{-x})$

$g(x) = \left(\frac{1}{4}\right)^{x-2}$

$h(x) = 16(2^{-2x})$

76. $f(x) = e^{-x} + 3$

$g(x) = e^{3-x}$

$h(x) = -e^{x-3}$

77. Graph the functions given by $y = 3^x$ and $y = 4^x$ and use the graphs to solve each inequality.

(a) $4^x < 3^x$ (b) $4^x > 3^x$

78. Use a graphing utility to graph each function. Use the graph to find where the function is increasing and decreasing, and approximate any relative maximum or minimum values.

(a) $f(x) = x^2 e^{-x}$ (b) $g(x) = x2^{3-x}$

79. Graphical Analysis Use a graphing utility to graph

$$f(x) = \left(1 + \frac{0.5}{x}\right)^x \quad \text{and} \quad g(x) = e^{0.5}$$

in the same viewing window. What is the relationship between f and g as x increases and decreases without bound?

80. Think About It Which functions are exponential?

(a) $3x$ (b) $3x^2$ (c) 3^x (d) 2^{-x}

Skills Review

In Exercises 81 and 82, solve for y.

81. $x^2 + y^2 = 25$

82. $x - |y| = 2$

In Exercises 83 and 84, sketch the graph of the function.

83. $f(x) = \dfrac{2}{9+x}$

84. $f(x) = \sqrt{7-x}$

85. Make a Decision To work an extended application analyzing the population per square mile of the United States, visit this text's website at college.hmco.com. (Data Source: U.S. Census Bureau)

Chapter Summary

The *Chapter Summary "What Did You Learn?"* is a section-by-section overview that ties the learning objectives from the chapter to sets of Review Exercises for extra practice.

Review Exercises

The chapter *Review Exercises* provide additional practice with the concepts covered in the chapter.

Chapter Tests and Cumulative Tests

Chapter Tests, at the end of each chapter, and periodic *Cumulative Tests* offer students frequent opportunities for self-assessment and to develop strong study and test-taking skills.

• Proofs in Mathematics

At the end of every chapter, proofs of important mathematical properties and theorems are presented as well as discussions of various proof techniques.

• P.S. Problem Solving

Each chapter concludes with a collection of thought-provoking and challenging exercises that further explore and expand upon the chapter concepts. These exercises have unusual characteristics that set them apart from traditional text exercises.

Proofs in Mathematics

What does the word *proof* mean to you? In mathematics, the word *proof* is used to mean simply a valid argument. When you are proving a statement or theorem, you must use facts, definitions, and accepted properties in a logical order. You can also use previously proved theorems in your proof. For instance, the Distance Formula is used in the proof of the Midpoint Formula below. There are several different proof methods, which you will see in later chapters.

The Midpoint Formula *(p.)*

The midpoint of the line segment joining the points (x_1, y_1) and (x_2, y_2) is given by the Midpoint Formula

$$\text{Midpoint} = \left(\frac{x_1 + x_2}{2}, \frac{y_1 + y_2}{2} \right).$$

The Cartesian Plane

The Cartesian plane was named after the French mathematician René Descartes (1596–1650). While Descartes was lying in bed, he noticed a fly buzzing around on the square ceiling tiles. He discovered that the position of the fly could be described by which ceiling tile the fly landed on. This led to the development of the Cartesian plane. Descartes felt that a coordinate plane could be used to facilitate description of the positions of objects.

Proof

Using the figure, you must show that $d_1 = d_2$ and $d_1 + d_2 = d_3$.

By the Distance Formula, you obtain

$$d_1 = \sqrt{\left(\frac{x_1 + x_2}{2} - x_1 \right)^2 + \left(\frac{y_1 + y_2}{2} - y_1 \right)^2}$$

$$= \frac{1}{2}\sqrt{(x_2 - x_1)^2 + (y_2 - y_1)^2}$$

$$d_2 = \sqrt{\left(x_2 - \frac{x_1 + x_2}{2} \right)^2 + \left(y_2 - \frac{y_1 + y_2}{2} \right)^2}$$

$$= \frac{1}{2}\sqrt{(x_2 - x_1)^2 + (y_2 - y_1)^2}$$

$$d_3 = \sqrt{(x_2 - x_1)^2 + (y_2 - y_1)^2}$$

So, it follows that $d_1 = d_2$ and $d_1 + d_2 = d_3$.

124

 Problem Solving

This collection of thought-provoking and challenging exercises further explores and expands upon concepts learned in this chapter.

1. As a salesperson, you receive a monthly salary of $2000, plus a commission of 7% of sales. You are offered a new job at $2300 per month, plus a commission of 5% of sales.
   (a) Write a linear equation for your current monthly wage W_1 in terms of your monthly sales S.
   (b) Write a linear equation for the monthly wage W_2 of your new job offer in terms of the monthly sales S.
   (c) Use a graphing utility to graph both equations in the same viewing window. Find the point of intersection. What does it signify?
   (d) You think you can sell $20,000 per month. Should you change jobs? Explain.

2. For the numbers 2 through 9 on a telephone keypad (see figure), create two relations: one mapping numbers onto letters, and the other mapping letters onto numbers. Are both relations functions? Explain.

3. What can be said about the sum and difference of each of the following?
   (a) Two even functions   (b) Two odd functions
   (c) An odd function and an even function

4. The two functions given by
   $$f(x) = x \quad \text{and} \quad g(x) = -x$$
   are their own inverse functions. Graph each function and explain why this is true. Graph other linear functions that are their own inverse functions. Find a general formula for a family of linear functions that are their own inverse functions.

5. Prove that a function of the following form is even.
   $$y = a_{2n}x^{2n} + a_{2n-2}x^{2n-2} + \cdots + a_2x^2 + a_0$$

6. A miniature golf professional is trying to make a hole-in-one on the miniature golf green shown. A coordinate plane is placed over the golf green. The golf ball is at the point (2.5, 2) and the hole is at the point (9.5, 2). The professional wants to bank the ball off the side wall of the green at the point (x, y). Find the coordinates of the point (x, y). Then write an equation for the path of the ball.

FIGURE FOR 6

7. At 2:00 P.M. on April 11, 1912, the *Titanic* left Cobh, Ireland, on her voyage to New York City. At 11:40 P.M. on April 14, the *Titanic* struck an iceberg and sank, having covered only about 2100 miles of the approximately 3400-mile trip.
   (a) What was the total duration of the voyage in hours?
   (b) What was the average speed in miles per hour?
   (c) Write a function relating the distance of the *Titanic* from New York City and the number of hours traveled. Find the domain and range of the function.
   (d) Graph the function from part (c).

8. Consider the function given by $f(x) = -x^2 + 4x - 3$. Find the average rate of change of the function from x_1 to x_2.
   (a) $x_1 = 1, x_2 = 2$ (b) $x_1 = 1, x_2 = 1.5$
   (c) $x_1 = 1, x_2 = 1.25$
   (d) $x_1 = 1, x_2 = 1.125$
   (e) $x_1 = 1, x_2 = 1.0625$
   (f) Does the average rate of change seem to be approaching one value? If so, what value?
   (g) Find the equations of the secant lines through the points $(x_1, f(x_1))$ and $(x_2, f(x_2))$ for parts (a)–(e).
   (h) Find the equation of the line through the point $(1, f(1))$ using your answer from part (f) as the slope of the line.

9. Consider the functions given by $f(x) = 4x$ and $g(x) = x + 6$.
   (a) Find $(f \circ g)(x)$.
   (b) Find $(f \circ g)^{-1}(x)$.
   (c) Find $f^{-1}(x)$ and $g^{-1}(x)$.
   (d) Find $(g^{-1} \circ f^{-1})(x)$ and compare the result with that of part (b).
   (e) Repeat parts (a) through (d) for $f(x) = x^3 + 1$ and $g(x) = 2x$.
   (f) Write two one-to-one functions f and g, and repeat parts (a) through (d) for these functions.
   (g) Make a conjecture about $(f \circ g)^{-1}(x)$ and $(g^{-1} \circ f^{-1})(x)$.

125

---

10. You are in a boat 2 miles from the nearest point on the coast. You are to travel to a point Q, 3 miles down the coast and 1 mile inland (see figure). You can row at 2 miles per hour and you can walk at 4 miles per hour.

   (a) Write the total time T of the trip as a function of x.
   (b) Determine the domain of the function.
   (c) Use a graphing utility to graph the function. Be sure to choose an appropriate viewing window.
   (d) Use the *zoom* and *trace* features to find the value of x that minimizes T.
   (e) Write a brief paragraph interpreting these values.

11. The **Heaviside function** $H(x)$ is widely used in engineering applications. (See figure.) To print an enlarged copy of the graph, go to the website www.mathgraphs.com.

$$H(x) = \begin{cases} 1, & x \geq 0 \\ 0, & x < 0 \end{cases}$$

Sketch the graph of each function by hand.
   (a) $H(x) - 2$ (b) $H(x - 2)$ (c) $-H(x)$
   (d) $H(-x)$ (e) $\frac{1}{2}H(x)$ (f) $-H(x - 2) + 2$

12. Let $f(x) = \dfrac{1}{1 - x}$.
   (a) What are the domain and range of f?
   (b) Find $f(f(x))$. What is the domain of this function?
   (c) Find $f(f(f(x)))$. Is the graph a line? Why or why not?

13. Show that the Associative Property holds for compositions of functions—that is,
   $$(f \circ (g \circ h))(x) = ((f \circ g) \circ h)(x).$$

14. Consider the graph of the function f shown in the figure. Use this graph to sketch the graph of each function. To print an enlarged copy of the graph, go to the website www.mathgraphs.com.
   (a) $f(x + 1)$ (b) $f(x) + 1$ (c) $2f(x)$ (d) $f(-x)$
   (e) $-f(x)$ (f) $|f(x)|$ (g) $f(|x|)$

15. Use the graphs of f and f^{-1} to complete each table of function values.

(a)

x	-4	-2	0	4
$(f(f^{-1}(x))$				

(b)

x	-3	-2	0	1
$(f + f^{-1})(x)$				

(c)

x	-3	-2	0	1
$(f \cdot f^{-1})(x)$				

(d)

x	-4	-3	0	4
$|f^{-1}(x)|$				

126

FEATURES

Supplements

Supplements for the Instructor

Precalculus: A Concise Course has an extensive support package for the instructor that includes:

Instructor's Annotated Edition (IAE)

Online Complete Solutions Guide

Online Instructor Success Organizer

Online Teaching Center: This free companion website contains an abundance of instructor resources.

HM ClassPrep™ with HM Testing (powered by Diploma™): This CD-ROM is a combination of two course management tools.

- *HM Testing* (powered by *Diploma™*) offers instructors a flexible and powerful tool for test generation and test management. Now supported by the Brownstone Research Group's market-leading *Diploma™* software, this new version of *HM Testing* significantly improves on functionality and ease of use by offering all the tools needed to create, author, deliver, and customize multiple types of tests—including authoring and editing algorithmic questions. *Diploma™* is currently in use at thousands of college and university campuses throughout the United States and Canada.

- HM ClassPrep™ also features supplements and text-specific resources for the instructor.

Eduspace®: Eduspace®, powered by Blackboard®, is Houghton Mifflin's customizable and interactive online learning tool. Eduspace® provides instructors with online courses and content. By pairing the widely recognized tools of Blackboard® with quality, text-specific content from Houghton Mifflin Company, Eduspace® makes it easy for instructors to create all or part of a course online. This online learning tool also contains ready-to-use homework exercises, quizzes, tests, tutorials, and supplemental study materials.

Visit *www.eduspace.com* for more information.

Eduspace® with eSolutions: Eduspace® with eSolutions combines all the features of Eduspace® with an electronic version of the textbook exercises and the complete solutions to the odd-numbered exercises, providing students with a convenient and comprehensive way to do homework and view course materials.

Supplements for the Student

Precalculus: A Concise Course has an extensive support package for the student that includes:

Study and Solutions Guide

Online Student Notetaking Guide

Instructional DVDs

Online Study Center: This free companion website contains an abundance of student resources.

HM mathSpace® CD-ROM: This tutorial CD-ROM provides opportunities for self-paced review and practice with algorithmically generated exercises and step-by-step solutions.

Eduspace®: Eduspace®, powered by Blackboard®, is Houghton Mifflin's customizable and interactive online learning tool for instructors and students. Eduspace® is a text-specific, web-based learning environment that your instructor can use to offer students a combination of practice exercises, multimedia tutorials, video explanations, online algorithmic homework and more. Specific content is available 24 hours a day to help you succeed in your course.

Eduspace® with eSolutions: Eduspace® with eSolutions combines all the features of Eduspace® with an electronic version of the textbook exercises and the complete solutions to the odd-numbered exercises. The result is a convenient and comprehensive way to do homework and view your course materials.

Smarthinking®: Houghton Mifflin has partnered with Smarthinking® to provide an easy-to-use, effective, online tutorial service. Through state-of-the-art tools and whiteboard technology, students communicate in real-time with qualified e-instructors who can help the students understand difficult concepts and guide them through the problem-solving process while studying or completing homework.

Three levels of service are offered to the students.

Live Tutorial Help provides real-time, one-on-one instruction.

Question Submission allows students to submit questions to the tutor outside the scheduled hours and receive a reply usually within 24 hours.

Independent Study Resources connects students around-the-clock to additional educational resources, ranging from interactive websites to Frequently Asked Questions.

Visit *smarthinking.com* for more information.

*Limits apply; terms and hours of SMARTHINKING® service are subject to change.

Functions and Their Graphs

1

Functions play a primary role in modeling real-life situations. The estimated growth in the number of digital music sales in the United States can be modeled by a cubic function.

© AP/Wide World Photos

SELECTED APPLICATIONS

Functions have many real-life applications. The applications listed below represent a small sample of the applications in this chapter.

- Data Analysis: Mail,
  Exercise 69, page 12

- Population Statistics,
  Exercise 75, page 24

- College Enrollment,
  Exercise 109, page 37

- Cost, Revenue, and Profit,
  Exercise 97, page 52

- Digital Music Sales,
  Exercise 89, page 64

- Fluid Flow,
  Exercise 70, page 68

- Fuel Use,
  Exercise 67, page 82

- Consumer Awareness,
  Exercise 68, page 92

- Diesel Mechanics,
  Exercise 83, page 102

What you should learn

- Plot points in the Cartesian plane.
- Use the Distance Formula to find the distance between two points.
- Use the Midpoint Formula to find the midpoint of a line segment.
- Use a coordinate plane and geometric formulas to model and solve real-life problems.

Why you should learn it

The Cartesian plane can be used to represent relationships between two variables. For instance, in Exercise 60 on page 12, a graph represents the minimum wage in the United States from 1950 to 2004.

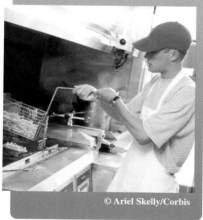

© Ariel Skelly/Corbis

The Cartesian Plane

Just as you can represent real numbers by points on a real number line, you can represent ordered pairs of real numbers by points in a plane called the **rectangular coordinate system,** or the **Cartesian plane,** named after the French mathematician René Descartes (1596–1650).

The Cartesian plane is formed by using two real number lines intersecting at right angles, as shown in Figure 1.1. The horizontal real number line is usually called the **x-axis,** and the vertical real number line is usually called the **y-axis.** The point of intersection of these two axes is the **origin,** and the two axes divide the plane into four parts called **quadrants.**

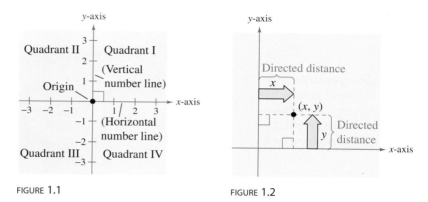

FIGURE 1.1

FIGURE 1.2

Each point in the plane corresponds to an **ordered pair** (x, y) of real numbers x and y, called **coordinates** of the point. The **x-coordinate** represents the directed distance from the y-axis to the point, and the **y-coordinate** represents the directed distance from the x-axis to the point, as shown in Figure 1.2.

The notation (x, y) denotes both a point in the plane and an open interval on the real number line. The context will tell you which meaning is intended.

Example 1   Plotting Points in the Cartesian Plane

Plot the points $(-1, 2)$, $(3, 4)$, $(0, 0)$, $(3, 0)$, and $(-2, -3)$.

Solution

To plot the point $(-1, 2)$, imagine a vertical line through -1 on the x-axis and a horizontal line through 2 on the y-axis. The intersection of these two lines is the point $(-1, 2)$. The other four points can be plotted in a similar way, as shown in Figure 1.3.

✓CHECKPOINT   Now try Exercise 3.

FIGURE 1.3

The beauty of a rectangular coordinate system is that it allows you to *see* relationships between two variables. It would be difficult to overestimate the importance of Descartes's introduction of coordinates in the plane. Today, his ideas are in common use in virtually every scientific and business-related field.

Example 2   Sketching a Scatter Plot

From 1990 through 2003, the amounts *A* (in millions of dollars) spent on skiing equipment in the United States are shown in the table, where *t* represents the year. Sketch a scatter plot of the data. (Source: National Sporting Goods Association)

Solution

To sketch a *scatter plot* of the data shown in the table, you simply represent each pair of values by an ordered pair (t, A) and plot the resulting points, as shown in Figure 1.4. For instance, the first pair of values is represented by the ordered pair (1990, 475). Note that the break in the *t*-axis indicates that the numbers between 0 and 1990 have been omitted.

Year, *t*	Amount, *A*
1990	475
1991	577
1992	521
1993	569
1994	609
1995	562
1996	707
1997	723
1998	718
1999	648
2000	495
2001	476
2002	527
2003	464

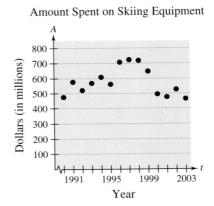

FIGURE 1.4

✓CHECKPOINT   Now try Exercise 21.

In Example 2, you could have let $t = 1$ represent the year 1990. In that case, the horizontal axis would not have been broken, and the tick marks would have been labeled 1 through 14 (instead of 1990 through 2003).

Technology

The scatter plot in Example 2 is only one way to represent the data graphically. You could also represent the data using a bar graph and a line graph. If you have access to a graphing utility, try using it to represent graphically the data given in Example 2.

The *HM mathSpace*® CD-ROM and *Eduspace*® for this text contain additional resources related to the concepts discussed in this chapter.

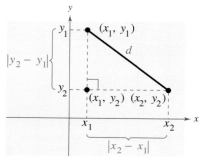

$$a^2 + b^2 = c^2$$

FIGURE 1.5

The Pythagorean Theorem and the Distance Formula

The following famous theorem is used extensively throughout this course.

Pythagorean Theorem

For a right triangle with hypotenuse of length c and sides of lengths a and b, you have $a^2 + b^2 = c^2$, as shown in Figure 1.5. (The converse is also true. That is, if $a^2 + b^2 = c^2$, then the triangle is a right triangle.)

Suppose you want to determine the distance d between two points (x_1, y_1) and (x_2, y_2) in the plane. With these two points, a right triangle can be formed, as shown in Figure 1.6. The length of the vertical side of the triangle is $|y_2 - y_1|$, and the length of the horizontal side is $|x_2 - x_1|$. By the Pythagorean Theorem, you can write

$$d^2 = |x_2 - x_1|^2 + |y_2 - y_1|^2$$
$$d = \sqrt{|x_2 - x_1|^2 + |y_2 - y_1|^2} = \sqrt{(x_2 - x_1)^2 + (y_2 - y_1)^2}.$$

This result is the **Distance Formula.**

FIGURE 1.6

The Distance Formula

The distance d between the points (x_1, y_1) and (x_2, y_2) in the plane is

$$d = \sqrt{(x_2 - x_1)^2 + (y_2 - y_1)^2}.$$

Example 3   Finding a Distance

Find the distance between the points $(-2, 1)$ and $(3, 4)$.

Algebraic Solution

Let $(x_1, y_1) = (-2, 1)$ and $(x_2, y_2) = (3, 4)$. Then apply the Distance Formula.

$$d = \sqrt{(x_2 - x_1)^2 + (y_2 - y_1)^2} \qquad \text{Distance Formula}$$
$$= \sqrt{[3 - (-2)]^2 + (4 - 1)^2} \qquad \text{Substitute for } x_1, y_1, x_2, \text{ and } y_2.$$
$$= \sqrt{(5)^2 + (3)^2} \qquad \text{Simplify.}$$
$$= \sqrt{34} \qquad \text{Simplify.}$$
$$\approx 5.83 \qquad \text{Use a calculator.}$$

So, the distance between the points is about 5.83 units. You can use the Pythagorean Theorem to check that the distance is correct.

$$d^2 \overset{?}{=} 3^2 + 5^2 \qquad \text{Pythagorean Theorem}$$
$$\left(\sqrt{34}\right)^2 \overset{?}{=} 3^2 + 5^2 \qquad \text{Substitute for } d.$$
$$34 = 34 \qquad \text{Distance checks. } \checkmark$$

✓CHECKPOINT   Now try Exercises 31(a) and (b).

Graphical Solution

Use centimeter graph paper to plot the points $A(-2, 1)$ and $B(3, 4)$. Carefully sketch the line segment from A to B. Then use a centimeter ruler to measure the length of the segment.

FIGURE 1.7

The line segment measures about 5.8 centimeters, as shown in Figure 1.7. So, the distance between the points is about 5.8 units.

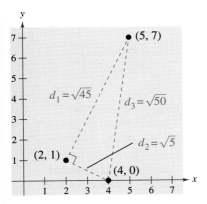

FIGURE **1.8**

Example 4   **Verifying a Right Triangle**

Show that the points $(2, 1)$, $(4, 0)$, and $(5, 7)$ are vertices of a right triangle.

Solution

The three points are plotted in Figure 1.8. Using the Distance Formula, you can find the lengths of the three sides as follows.

$$d_1 = \sqrt{(5 - 2)^2 + (7 - 1)^2} = \sqrt{9 + 36} = \sqrt{45}$$
$$d_2 = \sqrt{(4 - 2)^2 + (0 - 1)^2} = \sqrt{4 + 1} = \sqrt{5}$$
$$d_3 = \sqrt{(5 - 4)^2 + (7 - 0)^2} = \sqrt{1 + 49} = \sqrt{50}$$

Because

$$(d_1)^2 + (d_2)^2 = 45 + 5 = 50 = (d_3)^2$$

you can conclude by the Pythagorean Theorem that the triangle must be a right triangle.

✓CHECKPOINT   Now try Exercise 41.

The Midpoint Formula

To find the **midpoint** of the line segment that joins two points in a coordinate plane, you can simply find the average values of the respective coordinates of the two endpoints using the **Midpoint Formula.**

The Midpoint Formula

The midpoint of the line segment joining the points (x_1, y_1) and (x_2, y_2) is given by the Midpoint Formula

$$\text{Midpoint} = \left(\frac{x_1 + x_2}{2}, \frac{y_1 + y_2}{2}\right).$$

For a proof of the Midpoint Formula, see Proofs in Mathematics on page 124.

Example 5   **Finding a Line Segment's Midpoint**

Find the midpoint of the line segment joining the points $(-5, -3)$ and $(9, 3)$.

Solution

Let $(x_1, y_1) = (-5, -3)$ and $(x_2, y_2) = (9, 3)$.

$$\text{Midpoint} = \left(\frac{x_1 + x_2}{2}, \frac{y_1 + y_2}{2}\right) \quad \text{Midpoint Formula}$$

$$= \left(\frac{-5 + 9}{2}, \frac{-3 + 3}{2}\right) \quad \text{Substitute for } x_1, y_1, x_2, \text{ and } y_2.$$

$$= (2, 0) \quad \text{Simplify.}$$

The midpoint of the line segment is $(2, 0)$, as shown in Figure 1.9.

✓CHECKPOINT   Now try Exercise 31(c).

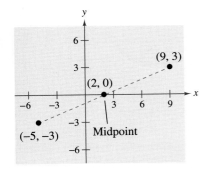

FIGURE **1.9**

Applications

Example 6   Finding the Length of a Pass

During the third quarter of the 2004 Sugar Bowl, the quarterback for Louisiana State University threw a pass from the 28-yard line, 40 yards from the sideline. The pass was caught by a wide receiver on the 5-yard line, 20 yards from the same sideline, as shown in Figure 1.10. How long was the pass?

Solution

You can find the length of the pass by finding the distance between the points (40, 28) and (20, 5).

$$d = \sqrt{(x_2 - x_1)^2 + (y_2 - y_1)^2}$$ Distance Formula

$$= \sqrt{(40 - 20)^2 + (28 - 5)^2}$$ Substitute for x_1, y_1, x_2, and y_2.

$$= \sqrt{400 + 529}$$ Simplify.

$$= \sqrt{929}$$ Simplify.

$$\approx 30$$ Use a calculator.

So, the pass was about 30 yards long.

✓CHECKPOINT   Now try Exercise 47.

In Example 6, the scale along the goal line does not normally appear on a football field. However, when you use coordinate geometry to solve real-life problems, you are free to place the coordinate system in any way that is convenient for the solution of the problem.

Example 7   Estimating Annual Revenue

FedEx Corporation had annual revenues of $20.6 billion in 2002 and $24.7 billion in 2004. Without knowing any additional information, what would you estimate the 2003 revenue to have been?   (Source: FedEx Corp.)

Solution

One solution to the problem is to assume that revenue followed a linear pattern. With this assumption, you can estimate the 2003 revenue by finding the midpoint of the line segment connecting the points (2002, 20.6) and (2004, 24.7).

$$\text{Midpoint} = \left(\frac{x_1 + x_2}{2}, \frac{y_1 + y_2}{2}\right)$$ Midpoint Formula

$$= \left(\frac{2002 + 2004}{2}, \frac{20.6 + 24.7}{2}\right)$$ Substitute for x_1, y_1, x_2, and y_2.

$$= (2003, 22.65)$$ Simplify.

So, you would estimate the 2003 revenue to have been about $22.65 billion, as shown in Figure 1.11. (The actual 2003 revenue was $22.5 billion.)

✓CHECKPOINT   Now try Exercise 49.

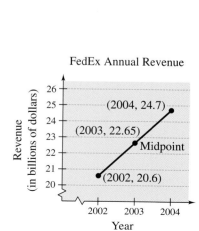

Football Pass

Distance (in yards)

(40, 28)

(20, 5)

Distance (in yards)

FIGURE 1.10

FedEx Annual Revenue

Revenue (in billions of dollars)

(2004, 24.7)

(2003, 22.65)

Midpoint

(2002, 20.6)

2002   2003   2004

Year

FIGURE 1.11

Much of computer graphics, including this computer-generated goldfish tessellation, consists of transformations of points in a coordinate plane. One type of transformation, a translation, is illustrated in Example 8. Other types include reflections, rotations, and stretches.

Example 8   Translating Points in the Plane

The triangle in Figure 1.12 has vertices at the points $(-1, 2)$, $(1, -4)$, and $(2, 3)$. Shift the triangle three units to the right and two units upward and find the vertices of the shifted triangle, as shown in Figure 1.13.

FIGURE 1.12

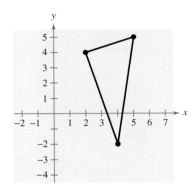

FIGURE 1.13

Solution

To shift the vertices three units to the right, add 3 to each of the x-coordinates. To shift the vertices two units upward, add 2 to each of the y-coordinates.

Original Point	*Translated Point*
$(-1, 2)$	$(-1 + 3, 2 + 2) = (2, 4)$
$(1, -4)$	$(1 + 3, -4 + 2) = (4, -2)$
$(2, 3)$	$(2 + 3, 3 + 2) = (5, 5)$

✓**CHECKPOINT**   Now try Exercise 51.

The figures provided with Example 8 were not really essential to the solution. Nevertheless, it is strongly recommended that you develop the habit of including sketches with your solutions—even if they are not required.

The following geometric formulas are used at various times throughout this course. For your convenience, these formulas along with several others are also provided on the inside back cover of this text.

Common Formulas for Area *A*, Perimeter *P*, Circumference *C*, and Volume *V*

Rectangle	*Circle*	*Triangle*	*Rectangular Solid*	*Circular Cylinder*	*Sphere*
$A = lw$	$A = \pi r^2$	$A = \dfrac{1}{2}bh$	$V = lwh$	$V = \pi r^2 h$	$V = \dfrac{4}{3}\pi r^3$
$P = 2l + 2w$	$C = 2\pi r$	$P = a + b + c$			

←——4 cm——→

h

FIGURE 1.14

Example 9 **Using a Geometric Formula**

A cylindrical can has a volume of 200 cubic centimeters (cm³) and a radius of 4 centimeters (cm), as shown in Figure 1.14. Find the height of the can.

Solution

The formula for the *volume of a cylinder* is $V = \pi r^2 h$. To find the height of the can, solve for h.

$$h = \frac{V}{\pi r^2}$$

Then, using $V = 200$ and $r = 4$, find the height.

$$h = \frac{200}{\pi(4)^2}$$ Substitute 200 for V and 4 for r.

$$= \frac{200}{16\pi}$$ Simplify denominator.

$$\approx 3.98$$ Use a calculator.

Because the value of h was rounded in the solution, a check of the solution will not result in an equality. If the solution is valid, the expressions on each side of the equal sign will be approximately equal to each other.

$$V = \pi r^2 h$$ Write original equation.

$$200 \stackrel{?}{\approx} \pi(4)^2(3.98)$$ Substitute 200 for V, 4 for r, and 3.98 for h.

$$200 \approx 200.06$$ Solution checks. ✓

You can also use unit analysis to check that your answer is reasonable.

$$\frac{200 \text{ cm}^3}{16\pi \text{ cm}^2} \approx 3.98 \text{ cm}$$

✓CHECKPOINT   Now try Exercise 63.

𝒲RITING ABOUT 𝓜ATHEMATICS

Extending the Example Example 8 shows how to translate points in a coordinate plane. Write a short paragraph describing how each of the following transformed points is related to the original point.

Original Point	*Transformed Point*
(x, y)	$(-x, y)$
(x, y)	$(x, -y)$
(x, y)	$(-x, -y)$

<table>
<tr><td>

1.1 | **Exercises**

</td><td>

The *HM mathSpace®* CD-ROM and *Eduspace®* for this text contain step-by-step solutions to all odd-numbered exercises. They also provide Tutorial Exercises for additional help.

</td></tr>
</table>

VOCABULARY CHECK

1. Match each term with its definition.

(a) *x*-axis   (i) point of intersection of vertical axis and horizontal axis

(b) *y*-axis   (ii) directed distance from the *x*-axis

(c) origin   (iii) directed distance from the *y*-axis

(d) quadrants   (iv) four regions of the coordinate plane

(e) *x*-coordinate   (v) horizontal real number line

(f) *y*-coordinate   (vi) vertical real number line

In Exercises 2–4, fill in the blanks.

2. An ordered pair of real numbers can be represented in a plane called the rectangular coordinate system or the _____ plane.

3. The _____ _____ is a result derived from the Pythagorean Theorem.

4. Finding the average values of the representative coordinates of the two endpoints of a line segment in a coordinate plane is also known as using the _____ _____.

PREREQUISITE SKILLS REVIEW: Practice and review algebra skills needed for this section at **www.Eduspace.com.**

In Exercises 1 and 2, approximate the coordinates of the points.

1.

2.

In Exercises 3–6, plot the points in the Cartesian plane.

3. $(-4, 2), (-3, -6), (0, 5), (1, -4)$

4. $(0, 0), (3, 1), (-2, 4), (1, -1)$

5. $(3, 8), (0.5, -1), (5, -6), (-2, 2.5)$

6. $\left(1, -\frac{1}{3}\right), \left(\frac{3}{4}, 3\right), (-3, 4), \left(-\frac{4}{3}, -\frac{3}{2}\right)$

In Exercises 7–10, find the coordinates of the point.

7. The point is located three units to the left of the *y*-axis and four units above the *x*-axis.

8. The point is located eight units below the *x*-axis and four units to the right of the *y*-axis.

9. The point is located five units below the *x*-axis and the coordinates of the point are equal.

10. The point is on the *x*-axis and 12 units to the left of the *y*-axis.

In Exercises 11–20, determine the quadrant(s) in which (x, y) is located so that the condition(s) is (are) satisfied.

11. $x > 0$ and $y < 0$ **12.** $x < 0$ and $y < 0$

13. $x = -4$ and $y > 0$ **14.** $x > 2$ and $y = 3$

15. $y < -5$ **16.** $x > 4$

17. $x < 0$ and $-y > 0$ **18.** $-x > 0$ and $y < 0$

19. $xy > 0$ **20.** $xy < 0$

In Exercises 21 and 22, sketch a scatter plot of the data shown in the table.

21. *Number of Stores* The table shows the number *y* of Wal-Mart stores for each year *x* from 1996 through 2003. (Source: Wal-Mart Stores, Inc.)

Year, *x*	Number of stores, *y*
1996	3054
1997	3406
1998	3599
1999	3985
2000	4189
2001	4414
2002	4688
2003	4906

22. *Meteorology* The table shows the lowest temperature on record y (in degrees Fahrenheit) in Duluth, Minnesota for each month x, where $x = 1$ represents January. (Source: NOAA)

Month, x	Temperature, y
1	-39
2	-39
3	-29
4	-5
5	17
6	27
7	35
8	32
9	22
10	8
11	-23
12	-34

In Exercises 23–26, find the distance between the points. (*Note:* In each case, the two points lie on the same horizontal or vertical line.)

23. $(6, -3), (6, 5)$

24. $(1, 4), (8, 4)$

25. $(-3, -1), (2, -1)$

26. $(-3, -4), (-3, 6)$

In Exercises 27–30, (a) find the length of each side of the right triangle, and (b) show that these lengths satisfy the Pythagorean Theorem.

27.

28.

29.

30.

In Exercises 31–40, (a) plot the points, (b) find the distance between the points, and (c) find the midpoint of the line segment joining the points.

31. $(1, 1), (9, 7)$ 32. $(1, 12), (6, 0)$

33. $(-4, 10), (4, -5)$ 34. $(-7, -4), (2, 8)$

35. $(-1, 2), (5, 4)$ 36. $(2, 10), (10, 2)$

37. $\left(\frac{1}{2}, 1\right), \left(-\frac{5}{2}, \frac{4}{3}\right)$

38. $\left(-\frac{1}{3}, -\frac{1}{3}\right), \left(-\frac{1}{6}, -\frac{1}{2}\right)$

39. $(6.2, 5.4), (-3.7, 1.8)$

40. $(-16.8, 12.3), (5.6, 4.9)$

In Exercises 41 and 42, show that the points form the vertices of the indicated polygon.

41. Right triangle: $(4, 0), (2, 1), (-1, -5)$

42. Isosceles triangle: $(1, -3), (3, 2), (-2, 4)$

43. A line segment has (x_1, y_1) as one endpoint and (x_m, y_m) as its midpoint. Find the other endpoint (x_2, y_2) of the line segment in terms of $x_1, y_1, x_m,$ and y_m.

44. Use the result of Exercise 43 to find the coordinates of the endpoint of a line segment if the coordinates of the other endpoint and midpoint are, respectively,

(a) $(1, -2), (4, -1)$ and (b) $(-5, 11), (2, 4)$.

45. Use the Midpoint Formula three times to find the three points that divide the line segment joining (x_1, y_1) and (x_2, y_2) into four parts.

46. Use the result of Exercise 45 to find the points that divide the line segment joining the given points into four equal parts.

(a) $(1, -2), (4, -1)$ (b) $(-2, -3), (0, 0)$

47. *Sports* A soccer player passes the ball from a point that is 18 yards from the endline and 12 yards from the sideline. The pass is received by a teammate who is 42 yards from the same endline and 50 yards from the same sideline, as shown in the figure. How long is the pass?

48. *Flying Distance* An airplane flies from Naples, Italy in a straight line to Rome, Italy, which is 120 kilometers north and 150 kilometers west of Naples. How far does the plane fly?

Sales   **In Exercises 49 and 50, use the Midpoint Formula to estimate the sales of Big Lots, Inc. and Dollar Tree Stores, Inc. in 2002, given the sales in 2001 and 2003. Assume that the sales followed a linear pattern.**   (Source: Big Lots, Inc.; Dollar Tree Stores, Inc.)

49. Big Lots

Year	Sales (in millions)
2001	$3433
2003	$4174

50. Dollar Tree

Year	Sales (in millions)
2001	$1987
2003	$2800

In Exercises 51–54, the polygon is shifted to a new position in the plane. Find the coordinates of the vertices of the polygon in its new position.

51.

52.

53. Original coordinates of vertices: $(-7, -2), (-2, 2),$
$(-2, -4), (-7, -4)$

Shift: eight units upward, four units to the right

54. Original coordinates of vertices: $(5, 8), (3, 6), (7, 6), (5, 2)$

Shift: 6 units downward, 10 units to the left

Retail Price   **In Exercises 55 and 56, use the graph below, which shows the average retail price of 1 pound of butter from 1995 to 2003.**   (Source: U.S. Bureau of Labor Statistics)

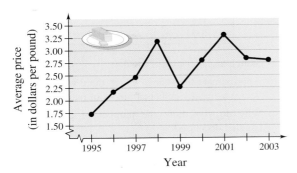

55. Approximate the highest price of a pound of butter shown in the graph. When did this occur?

56. Approximate the percent change in the price of butter from the price in 1995 to the highest price shown in the graph.

Advertising   **In Exercises 57 and 58, use the graph below, which shows the cost of a 30-second television spot (in thousands of dollars) during the Super Bowl from 1989 to 2003.**   (Source: USA Today Research and CNN)

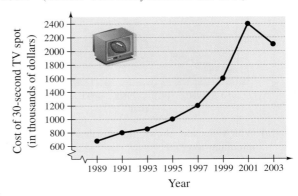

57. Approximate the percent increase in the cost of a 30-second spot from Super Bowl XXIII in 1989 to Super Bowl XXXV in 2001.

58. Estimate the percent increase in the cost of a 30-second spot (a) from Super Bowl XXIII in 1989 to Super Bowl XXVII in 1993 and (b) from Super Bowl XXVII in 1993 to Super Bowl XXXVII in 2003.

59. *Music*   The graph shows the numbers of recording artists who were elected to the Rock and Roll Hall of Fame from 1986 to 2004.

(a) Describe any trends in the data. From these trends, predict the number of artists elected in 2008.

(b) Why do you think the numbers elected in 1986 and 1987 were greater in other years?

Model It

60. Labor Force   Use the graph below, which shows the minimum wage in the United States (in dollars) from 1950 to 2004.   (Source: U.S. Department of Labor)

(a) Which decade shows the greatest increase in minimum wage?

(b) Approximate the percent increases in the minimum wage from 1990 to 1995 and from 1995 to 2004.

(c) Use the percent increase from 1995 to 2004 to predict the minimum wage in 2008.

(d) Do you believe that your prediction in part (c) is reasonable? Explain.

61. Sales   The Coca-Cola Company had sales of $18,546 million in 1996 and $21,900 million in 2004. Use the Midpoint Formula to estimate the sales in 1998, 2000, and 2002. Assume that the sales followed a linear pattern. (Source: The Coca-Cola Company)

62. Data Analysis: Exam Scores   The table shows the mathematics entrance test scores x and the final examination scores y in an algebra course for a sample of 10 students.

x	22	29	35	40	44
y	53	74	57	66	79

x	48	53	58	65	76
y	90	76	93	83	99

(a) Sketch a scatter plot of the data.

(b) Find the entrance exam score of any student with a final exam score in the 80s.

(c) Does a higher entrance exam score imply a higher final exam score? Explain.

63. Volume of a Billiard Ball   A billiard ball has a volume of 5.96 cubic inches. Find the radius of a billiard ball.

64. Length of a Tank   The diameter of a cylindrical propane gas tank is 4 feet. The total volume of the tank is 603.2 cubic feet. Find the length of the tank.

65. Geometry   A "Slow Moving Vehicle" sign has the shape of an equilateral triangle. The sign has a perimeter of 129 centimeters. Find the length of each side of the sign. Find the area of the sign.

66. Geometry   The radius of a traffic cone is 14 centimeters and the lateral surface of the cone is 1617 square centimeters. Find the height of the cone.

67. Dimensions of a Room   A room is 1.5 times as long as it is wide, and its perimeter is 25 meters.

(a) Draw a diagram that represents the problem. Identify the length as l and the width as w.

(b) Write l in terms of w and write an equation for the perimeter in terms of w.

(c) Find the dimensions of the room.

68. Dimensions of a Container   The width of a rectangular storage container is 1.25 times its height. The length of the container is 16 inches and the volume of the container is 2000 cubic inches.

(a) Draw a diagram that represents the problem. Label the height, width, and length accordingly.

(b) Write w in terms of h and write an equation for the volume in terms of h.

(c) Find the dimensions of the container.

69. Data Analysis: Mail   The table shows the number y of pieces of mail handled (in billions) by the U.S. Postal Service for each year x from 1996 through 2003. (Source: U.S. Postal Service)

Year, x	Pieces of mail, y
1996	183
1997	191
1998	197
1999	202
2000	208
2001	207
2002	203
2003	202

(a) Sketch a scatter plot of the data.

(b) Approximate the year in which there was the greatest decrease in the number of pieces of mail handled.

(c) Why do you think the number of pieces of mail handled decreased?

70. *Data Analysis: Athletics*   The table shows the numbers of men's M and women's W college basketball teams for each year x from 1994 through 2003.   (Source: National Collegiate Athletic Association)

Year, x	Men's teams, M	Women's teams, W
1994	858	859
1995	868	864
1996	866	874
1997	865	879
1998	895	911
1999	926	940
2000	932	956
2001	937	958
2002	936	975
2003	967	1009

(a) Sketch scatter plots of these two sets of data on the same set of coordinate axes.

(b) Find the year in which the numbers of men's and women's teams were nearly equal.

(c) Find the year in which the difference between the numbers of men's and women's teams was the greatest. What was this difference?

71. *Make a Conjecture*   Plot the points $(2, 1), (-3, 5)$, and $(7, -3)$ on a rectangular coordinate system. Then change the sign of the x-coordinate of each point and plot the three new points on the same rectangular coordinate system. Make a conjecture about the location of a point when each of the following occurs.

(a) The sign of the x-coordinate is changed.

(b) The sign of the y-coordinate is changed.

(c) The signs of both the x- and y-coordinates are changed.

72. *Collinear Points*   Three or more points are *collinear* if they all lie on the same line. Use the steps below to determine if the set of points $\{A(2, 3), B(2, 6), C(6, 3)\}$ and the set of points $\{A(8, 3), B(5, 2), C(2, 1)\}$ are collinear.

(a) For each set of points, use the Distance Formula to find the distances from A to B, from B to C, and from A to C. What relationship exists among these distances for each set of points?

(b) Plot each set of points in the Cartesian plane. Do all the points of either set appear to lie on the same line?

(c) Compare your conclusions from part (a) with the conclusions you made from the graphs in part (b). Make a general statement about how to use the Distance Formula to determine collinearity.

Synthesis

True or False?   In Exercises 73 and 74, determine whether the statement is true or false. Justify your answer.

73. In order to divide a line segment into 16 equal parts, you would have to use the Midpoint Formula 16 times.

74. The points $(-8, 4), (2, 11)$, and $(-5, 1)$ represent the vertices of an isosceles triangle.

75. *Think About It*   When plotting points on the rectangular coordinate system, is it true that the scales on the x- and y-axes must be the same? Explain.

76. *Proof*   Prove that the diagonals of the parallelogram in the figure intersect at their midpoints.

FIGURE FOR 76   FIGURE FOR 77–80

In Exercises 77–80, use the plot of the point (x_0, y_0) in the figure. Match the transformation of the point with the correct plot. [The plots are labeled (a), (b), (c), and (d).]

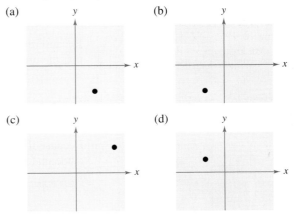

77. $(x_0, -y_0)$

78. $(-2x_0, y_0)$

79. $\left(x_0, \tfrac{1}{2}y_0\right)$

80. $(-x_0, -y_0)$

Skills Review

In Exercises 81–88, solve the equation or inequality.

81. $2x + 1 = 7x - 4$

82. $\tfrac{1}{3}x + 2 = 5 - \tfrac{1}{6}x$

83. $x^2 - 4x - 7 = 0$

84. $2x^2 + 3x - 8 = 0$

85. $3x + 1 < 2(2 - x)$

86. $3x - 8 \geq \tfrac{1}{2}(10x + 7)$

87. $|x - 18| < 4$

88. $|2x + 15| \geq 11$

1.2 Graphs of Equations

What you should learn

- Sketch graphs of equations.
- Find x- and y-intercepts of graphs of equations.
- Use symmetry to sketch graphs of equations.
- Find equations of and sketch graphs of circles.
- Use graphs of equations in solving real-life problems.

Why you should learn it

The graph of an equation can help you see relationships between real-life quantities. For example, in Exercise 75 on page 24, a graph can be used to estimate the life expectancies of children who are born in the years 2005 and 2010.

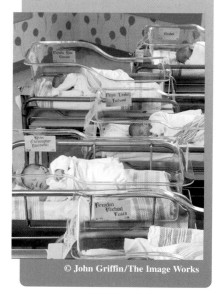

© John Griffin/The Image Works

The Graph of an Equation

In Section 1.1, you used a coordinate system to represent graphically the relationship between two quantities. There, the graphical picture consisted of a collection of points in a coordinate plane.

Frequently, a relationship between two quantities is expressed as an **equation in two variables.** For instance, $y = 7 - 3x$ is an equation in x and y. An ordered pair (a, b) is a **solution** or **solution point** of an equation in x and y if the equation is true when a is substituted for x and b is substituted for y. For instance, $(1, 4)$ is a solution of $y = 7 - 3x$ because $4 = 7 - 3(1)$ is a true statement.

In this section you will review some basic procedures for sketching the graph of an equation in two variables. The **graph of an equation** is the set of all points that are solutions of the equation.

Example 1 Determining Solutions

Determine whether (a) $(2, 13)$ and (b) $(-1, -3)$ are solutions of the equation $y = 10x - 7$.

Solution

a. $y = 10x - 7$ Write original equation.

   $13 \stackrel{?}{=} 10(2) - 7$ Substitute 2 for x and 13 for y.

   $13 = 13$ $(2, 13)$ is a solution. ✓

Because the substitution does satisfy the original equation, you can conclude that the ordered pair $(2, 13)$ *is* a solution of the original equation.

b. $y = 10x - 7$ Write original equation.

   $-3 \stackrel{?}{=} 10(-1) - 7$ Substitute -1 for x and -3 for y.

   $-3 \neq -17$ $(-1, -3)$ is not a solution.

Because the substitution does not satisfy the original equation, you can conclude that the ordered pair $(-1, -3)$ *is not* a solution of the original equation.

✓CHECKPOINT   Now try Exercise 1.

The basic technique used for sketching the graph of an equation is the **point-plotting method.**

Sketching the Graph of an Equation by Point Plotting

1. If possible, rewrite the equation so that one of the variables is isolated on one side of the equation.

2. Make a table of values showing several solution points.

3. Plot these points on a rectangular coordinate system.

4. Connect the points with a smooth curve or line.

Example 2   Sketching the Graph of an Equation

Sketch the graph of

$$y = 7 - 3x.$$

Solution

Because the equation is already solved for y, construct a table of values that consists of several solution points of the equation. For instance, when $x = -1$,

$$y = 7 - 3(-1)$$

$$= 10$$

which implies that $(-1, 10)$ is a solution point of the graph.

x	$y = 7 - 3x$	(x, y)
-1	10	$(-1, 10)$
0	7	$(0, 7)$
1	4	$(1, 4)$
2	1	$(2, 1)$
3	-2	$(3, -2)$
4	-5	$(4, -5)$

From the table, it follows that

$$(-1, 10), (0, 7), (1, 4), (2, 1), (3, -2), \text{ and } (4, -5)$$

are solution points of the equation. After plotting these points, you can see that they appear to lie on a line, as shown in Figure 1.15. The graph of the equation is the line that passes through the six plotted points.

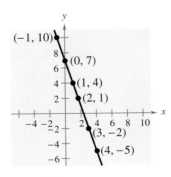

FIGURE 1.15

✓CHECKPOINT   Now try Exercise 5.

| Example 3 | **Sketching the Graph of an Equation** |

Sketch the graph of

$$y = x^2 - 2.$$

Solution

Because the equation is already solved for y, begin by constructing a table of values.

x	-2	-1	0	1	2	3
$y = x^2 - 2$	2	-1	-2	-1	2	7
(x, y)	$(-2, 2)$	$(-1, -1)$	$(0, -2)$	$(1, -1)$	$(2, 2)$	$(3, 7)$

Next, plot the points given in the table, as shown in Figure 1.16. Finally, connect the points with a smooth curve, as shown in Figure 1.17.

FIGURE 1.16

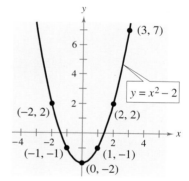

FIGURE 1.17

✓CHECKPOINT   Now try Exercise 7.

The point-plotting method demonstrated in Examples 2 and 3 is easy to use, but it has some shortcomings. With too few solution points, you can misrepresent the graph of an equation. For instance, if only the four points

$$(-2, 2), (-1, -1), (1, -1), \text{ and } (2, 2)$$

in Figure 1.16 were plotted, any one of the three graphs in Figure 1.18 would be reasonable.

FIGURE 1.18

No x-intercepts; one y-intercept

Three x-intercepts; one y-intercept

One x-intercept; two y-intercepts

No intercepts
FIGURE **1.19**

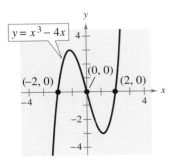

FIGURE **1.20**

> ## Technology
>
> To graph an equation involving x and y on a graphing utility, use the following procedure.
>
> 1. Rewrite the equation so that y is isolated on the left side.
> 2. Enter the equation into the graphing utility.
> 3. Determine a *viewing window* that shows all important features of the graph.
> 4. Graph the equation.
>
> For more extensive instructions on how to use a graphing utility to graph an equation, see the *Graphing Technology Guide* on the text website at *college.hmco.com.*

Intercepts of a Graph

It is often easy to determine the solution points that have zero as either the x-coordinate or the y-coordinate. These points are called **intercepts** because they are the points at which the graph intersects or touches the x- or y-axis. It is possible for a graph to have no intercepts, one intercept, or several intercepts, as shown in Figure 1.19.

Note that an x-intercept can be written as the ordered pair $(x, 0)$ and a y-intercept can be written as the ordered pair $(0, y)$. Some texts denote the x-intercept as the x-coordinate of the point $(a, 0)$ [and the y-intercept as the y-coordinate of the point $(0, b)$] rather than the point itself. Unless it is necessary to make a distinction, we will use the term *intercept* to mean either the point or the coordinate.

> ### Finding Intercepts
>
> 1. To find x-intercepts, let y be zero and solve the equation for x.
>
> 2. To find y-intercepts, let x be zero and solve the equation for y.

Example 4   Finding x- and y-Intercepts

Find the x- and y-intercepts of the graph of $y = x^3 - 4x$.

Solution

Let $y = 0$. Then

$$0 = x^3 - 4x = x(x^2 - 4)$$

has solutions $x = 0$ and $x = \pm 2$.

x-intercepts: $(0, 0), (2, 0), (-2, 0)$

Let $x = 0$. Then

$$y = (0)^3 - 4(0)$$

has one solution, $y = 0$.

y-intercept: $(0, 0)$ See Figure 1.20.

✓**CHECKPOINT**   Now try Exercise 11.

Symmetry

Graphs of equations can have **symmetry** with respect to one of the coordinate axes or with respect to the origin. Symmetry with respect to the *x*-axis means that if the Cartesian plane were folded along the *x*-axis, the portion of the graph above the *x*-axis would coincide with the portion below the *x*-axis. Symmetry with respect to the *y*-axis or the origin can be described in a similar manner, as shown in Figure 1.21.

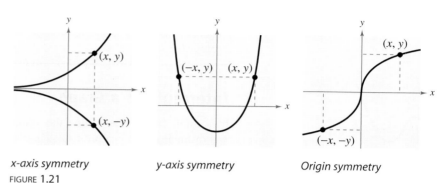

x-axis symmetry   *y-axis symmetry*   *Origin symmetry*

FIGURE **1.21**

Knowing the symmetry of a graph *before* attempting to sketch it is helpful, because then you need only half as many solution points to sketch the graph. There are three basic types of symmetry, described as follows.

Graphical Tests for Symmetry

1. A graph is **symmetric with respect to the *x*-axis** if, whenever (x, y) is on the graph, $(x, -y)$ is also on the graph.

2. A graph is **symmetric with respect to the *y*-axis** if, whenever (x, y) is on the graph, $(-x, y)$ is also on the graph.

3. A graph is **symmetric with respect to the origin** if, whenever (x, y) is on the graph, $(-x, -y)$ is also on the graph.

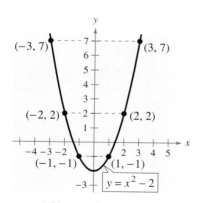

FIGURE **1.22**   *y-axis symmetry*

Example 5   **Testing for Symmetry**

The graph of $y = x^2 - 2$ is symmetric with respect to the *y*-axis because the point $(-x, y)$ is also on the graph of $y = x^2 - 2$. (See Figure 1.22.) The table below confirms that the graph is symmetric with respect to the *y*-axis.

x	-3	-2	-1	1	2	3
y	7	2	-1	-1	2	7
(x, y)	$(-3, 7)$	$(-2, 2)$	$(-1, -1)$	$(1, -1)$	$(2, 2)$	$(3, 7)$

✓CHECKPOINT   Now try Exercise 23.

> **Algebraic Tests for Symmetry**
>
> **1.** The graph of an equation is symmetric with respect to the x-axis if replacing y with $-y$ yields an equivalent equation.
>
> **2.** The graph of an equation is symmetric with respect to the y-axis if replacing x with $-x$ yields an equivalent equation.
>
> **3.** The graph of an equation is symmetric with respect to the origin if replacing x with $-x$ and y with $-y$ yields an equivalent equation.

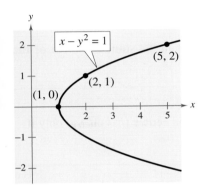

FIGURE **1.23**

Example 6   Using Symmetry as a Sketching Aid

Use symmetry to sketch the graph of

$$x - y^2 = 1.$$

Solution

Of the three tests for symmetry, the only one that is satisfied is the test for x-axis symmetry because $x - (-y)^2 = 1$ is equivalent to $x - y^2 = 1$. So, the graph is symmetric with respect to the x-axis. Using symmetry, you only need to find the solution points above the x-axis and then reflect them to obtain the graph, as shown in Figure 1.23.

y	$x = y^2 + 1$	(x, y)
0	1	$(1, 0)$
1	2	$(2, 1)$
2	5	$(5, 2)$

✓*CHECKPOINT*   Now try Exercise 37.

STUDY TIP

Notice that when creating the table in Example 6, it is easier to choose y-values and then find the corresponding x-values of the ordered pairs.

Example 7   Sketching the Graph of an Equation

Sketch the graph of

$$y = |x - 1|.$$

Solution

This equation fails all three tests for symmetry and consequently its graph is not symmetric with respect to either axis or to the origin. The absolute value sign indicates that y is always nonnegative. Create a table of values and plot the points as shown in Figure 1.24. From the table, you can see that $x = 0$ when $y = 1$. So, the y-intercept is $(0, 1)$. Similarly, $y = 0$ when $x = 1$. So, the x-intercept is $(1, 0)$.

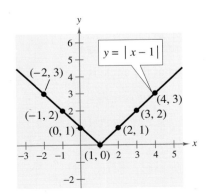

FIGURE **1.24**

x	-2	-1	0	1	2	3	4
$y = |x - 1|$	3	2	1	0	1	2	3
(x, y)	$(-2, 3)$	$(-1, 2)$	$(0, 1)$	$(1, 0)$	$(2, 1)$	$(3, 2)$	$(4, 3)$

✓*CHECKPOINT*   Now try Exercise 41.

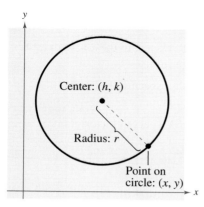

FIGURE **1.25**

Throughout this course, you will learn to recognize several types of graphs from their equations. For instance, you will learn to recognize that the graph of a second-degree equation of the form

$$y = ax^2 + bx + c$$

is a parabola (see Example 3). The graph of a **circle** is also easy to recognize.

Circles

Consider the circle shown in Figure 1.25. A point (x, y) is on the circle if and only if its distance from the center (h, k) is r. By the Distance Formula,

$$\sqrt{(x - h)^2 + (y - k)^2} = r.$$

By squaring each side of this equation, you obtain the **standard form of the equation of a circle.**

> ### Standard Form of the Equation of a Circle
> The point (x, y) lies on the circle of **radius** r and **center** (h, k) if and only if
> $$(x - h)^2 + (y - k)^2 = r^2.$$

STUDY TIP

To find the correct h and k, from the equation of the circle in Example 8, it may be helpful to rewrite the quantities $(x + 1)^2$ and $(y - 2)^2$, using subtraction.

$$(x + 1)^2 = [x - (-1)]^2,$$
$$(y - 2)^2 = [y - (2)]^2$$

So, $h = -1$ and $k = 2$.

From this result, you can see that the standard form of the equation of a circle *with its center at the origin,* $(h, k) = (0, 0)$, is simply

$$x^2 + y^2 = r^2.$$ Circle with center at origin

Example 8   **Finding the Equation of a Circle**

The point $(3, 4)$ lies on a circle whose center is at $(-1, 2)$, as shown in Figure 1.26. Write the standard form of the equation of this circle.

Solution

The radius of the circle is the distance between $(-1, 2)$ and $(3, 4)$.

$$r = \sqrt{(x - h)^2 + (y - k)^2}$$ Distance Formula
$$= \sqrt{[3 - (-1)]^2 + (4 - 2)^2}$$ Substitute for x, y, h, and k.
$$= \sqrt{4^2 + 2^2}$$ Simplify.
$$= \sqrt{16 + 4}$$ Simplify.
$$= \sqrt{20}$$ Radius

Using $(h, k) = (-1, 2)$ and $r = \sqrt{20}$, the equation of the circle is

$$(x - h)^2 + (y - k)^2 = r^2$$ Equation of circle
$$[x - (-1)]^2 + (y - 2)^2 = (\sqrt{20})^2$$ Substitute for h, k, and r.
$$(x + 1)^2 + (y - 2)^2 = 20.$$ Standard form

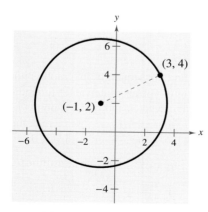

FIGURE **1.26**

✓CHECKPOINT   Now try Exercise 61.

STUDY TIP

You should develop the habit of using at least two approaches to solve every problem. This helps build your intuition and helps you check that your answer is reasonable.

Application

In this course, you will learn that there are many ways to approach a problem. Three common approaches are illustrated in Example 9.

A *Numerical Approach:* Construct and use a table.
A *Graphical Approach:* Draw and use a graph.
An *Algebraic Approach:* Use the rules of algebra.

Example 9   **Recommended Weight**

The median recommended weight y (in pounds) for men of medium frame who are 25 to 59 years old can be approximated by the mathematical model

$$y = 0.073x^2 - 6.99x + 289.0, \quad 62 \le x \le 76$$

where x is the man's height (in inches).   (Source: Metropolitan Life Insurance Company)

a. Construct a table of values that shows the median recommended weights for men with heights of 62, 64, 66, 68, 70, 72, 74, and 76 inches.

b. Use the table of values to sketch a graph of the model. Then use the graph to estimate *graphically* the median recommended weight for a man whose height is 71 inches.

c. Use the model to confirm *algebraically* the estimate you found in part (b).

Solution

a. You can use a calculator to complete the table, as shown at the left.

b. The table of values can be used to sketch the graph of the equation, as shown in Figure 1.27. From the graph, you can estimate that a height of 71 inches corresponds to a weight of about 161 pounds.

Height, x	Weight, y
62	136.2
64	140.6
66	145.6
68	151.2
70	157.4
72	164.2
74	171.5
76	179.4

FIGURE 1.27

c. To confirm algebraically the estimate found in part (b), you can substitute 71 for x in the model.

$$y = 0.073(71)^2 - 6.99(71) + 289.0 \approx 160.70$$

So, the graphical estimate of 161 pounds is fairly good.

✓CHECKPOINT   Now try Exercise 75.

1.2 | Exercises

VOCABULARY CHECK: Fill in the blanks.

1. An ordered pair (a, b) is a _____ of an equation in x and y if the equation is true when a is substituted for x and b is substituted for y.

2. The set of all solution points of an equation is the _____ of the equation.

3. The points at which a graph intersects or touches an axis are called the _____ of the graph.

4. A graph is symmetric with respect to the _____ if, whenever (x, y) is on the graph, $(-x, y)$ is also on the graph.

5. The equation $(x - h)^2 + (y - k)^2 = r^2$ is the standard form of the equation of a _____ with center _____ and radius _____.

6. When you construct and use a table to solve a problem, you are using a _____ approach.

PREREQUISITE SKILLS REVIEW: Practice and review algebra skills needed for this section at **www.Eduspace.com**.

In Exercises 1–4, determine whether each point lies on the graph of the equation.

Equation	Points	
1. $y = \sqrt{x + 4}$	(a) $(0, 2)$	(b) $(5, 3)$
2. $y = x^2 - 3x + 2$	(a) $(2, 0)$	(b) $(-2, 8)$
3. $y = 4 - |x - 2|$	(a) $(1, 5)$	(b) $(6, 0)$
4. $y = \frac{1}{3}x^3 - 2x^2$	(a) $\left(2, -\frac{16}{3}\right)$	(b) $(-3, 9)$

In Exercises 5–8, complete the table. Use the resulting solution points to sketch the graph of the equation.

5. $y = -2x + 5$

x	-1	0	1	2	$\frac{5}{2}$
y					
(x, y)					

6. $y = \frac{3}{4}x - 1$

x	-2	0	1	$\frac{4}{3}$	2
y					
(x, y)					

7. $y = x^2 - 3x$

x	-1	0	1	2	3
y					
(x, y)					

8. $y = 5 - x^2$

x	-2	-1	0	1	2
y					
(x, y)					

In Exercises 9–20, find the x- and y-intercepts of the graph of the equation.

9. $y = 16 - 4x^2$

10. $y = (x + 3)^2$

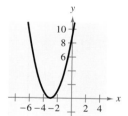

11. $y = 5x - 6$

12. $y = 8 - 3x$

13. $y = \sqrt{x + 4}$

14. $y = \sqrt{2x - 1}$

15. $y = |3x - 7|$

16. $y = -|x + 10|$

17. $y = 2x^3 - 4x^2$

18. $y = x^4 - 25$

19. $y^2 = 6 - x$

20. $y^2 = x + 1$

In Exercises 21–24, assume that the graph has the indicated type of symmetry. Sketch the complete graph of the equation. To print an enlarged copy of the graph, go to the website *www.mathgraphs.com.*

21.

y-axis symmetry

22.

x-axis symmetry

23.

Origin symmetry

24.

y-axis symmetry

In Exercises 25–32, use the algebraic tests to check for symmetry with respect to both axes and the origin.

25. $x^2 - y = 0$

26. $x - y^2 = 0$

27. $y = x^3$

28. $y = x^4 - x^2 + 3$

29. $y = \dfrac{x}{x^2 + 1}$

30. $y = \dfrac{1}{x^2 + 1}$

31. $xy^2 + 10 = 0$

32. $xy = 4$

In Exercises 33–44, use symmetry to sketch the graph of the equation.

33. $y = -3x + 1$

34. $y = 2x - 3$

35. $y = x^2 - 2x$

36. $y = -x^2 - 2x$

37. $y = x^3 + 3$

38. $y = x^3 - 1$

39. $y = \sqrt{x - 3}$

40. $y = \sqrt{1 - x}$

41. $y = |x - 6|$

42. $y = 1 - |x|$

43. $x = y^2 - 1$

44. $x = y^2 - 5$

 In Exercises 45–56, use a graphing utility to graph the equation. Use a standard setting. Approximate any intercepts.

45. $y = 3 - \frac{1}{2}x$

46. $y = \frac{2}{3}x - 1$

47. $y = x^2 - 4x + 3$

48. $y = x^2 + x - 2$

49. $y = \dfrac{2x}{x - 1}$

50. $y = \dfrac{4}{x^2 + 1}$

51. $y = \sqrt[3]{x}$

52. $y = \sqrt[3]{x + 1}$

53. $y = x\sqrt{x + 6}$

54. $y = (6 - x)\sqrt{x}$

55. $y = |x + 3|$

56. $y = 2 - |x|$

In Exercises 57–64, write the standard form of the equation of the circle with the given characteristics.

57. Center: $(0, 0)$; radius: 4

58. Center: $(0, 0)$; radius: 5

59. Center: $(2, -1)$; radius: 4

60. Center: $(-7, -4)$; radius: 7

61. Center: $(-1, 2)$; solution point: $(0, 0)$

62. Center: $(3, -2)$; solution point: $(-1, 1)$

63. Endpoints of a diameter: $(0, 0)$, $(6, 8)$

64. Endpoints of a diameter: $(-4, -1)$, $(4, 1)$

In Exercises 65–70, find the center and radius of the circle, and sketch its graph.

65. $x^2 + y^2 = 25$

66. $x^2 + y^2 = 16$

67. $(x - 1)^2 + (y + 3)^2 = 9$

68. $x^2 + (y - 1)^2 = 1$

69. $\left(x - \frac{1}{2}\right)^2 + \left(y - \frac{1}{2}\right)^2 = \frac{9}{4}$

70. $(x - 2)^2 + (y + 3)^2 = \frac{16}{9}$

71. *Depreciation* A manufacturing plant purchases a new molding machine for \$225,000. The depreciated value y (reduced value) after t years is given by $y = 225{,}000 - 20{,}000t$, $0 \le t \le 8$. Sketch the graph of the equation.

72. *Consumerism* You purchase a jet ski for \$8100. The depreciated value y after t years is given by $y = 8100 - 929t$, $0 \le t \le 6$. Sketch the graph of the equation.

73. *Geometry* A regulation NFL playing field (including the end zones) of length x and width y has a perimeter of $346\frac{2}{3}$ or $\dfrac{1040}{3}$ yards.

(a) Draw a rectangle that gives a visual representation of the problem. Use the specified variables to label the sides of the rectangle.

(b) Show that the width of the rectangle is $y = \dfrac{520}{3} - x$ and its area is $A = x\left(\dfrac{520}{3} - x\right)$.

(c) Use a graphing utility to graph the area equation. Be sure to adjust your window settings.

(d) From the graph in part (c), estimate the dimensions of the rectangle that yield a maximum area.

(e) Use your school's library, the Internet, or some other reference source to find the actual dimensions and area of a regulation NFL playing field and compare your findings with the results of part (d).

The symbol indicates an exercise or a part of an exercise in which you are instructed to use a graphing utility.

74. *Geometry* A soccer playing field of length x and width y has a perimeter of 360 meters.

(a) Draw a rectangle that gives a visual representation of the problem. Use the specified variables to label the sides of the rectangle.

(b) Show that the width of the rectangle is $w = 180 - x$ and its area is $A = x(180 - x)$.

 (c) Use a graphing utility to graph the area equation. Be sure to adjust your window settings.

 (d) From the graph in part (c), estimate the dimensions of the rectangle that yield a maximum area.

(e) Use your school's library, the Internet, or some other reference source to find the actual dimensions and area of a regulation Major League Soccer field and compare your findings with the results of part(d).

Model It

75. *Population Statistics* The table shows the life expectancies of a child (at birth) in the United States for selected years from 1920 to 2000. (Source: U.S. National Center for Health Statistics)

Year	Life expectancy, y
1920	54.1
1930	59.7
1940	62.9
1950	68.2
1960	69.7
1970	70.8
1980	73.7
1990	75.4
2000	77.0

A model for the life expectancy during this period is

$$y = -0.0025t^2 + 0.574t + 44.25, \quad 20 \le t \le 100$$

where y represents the life expectancy and t is the time in years, with $t = 20$ corresponding to 1920.

(a) Sketch a scatter plot of the data.

(b) Graph the model for the data and compare the scatter plot and the graph.

(c) Determine the life expectancy in 1948 both graphically and algebraically.

(d) Use the graph of the model to estimate the life expectancies of a child for the years 2005 and 2010.

(e) Do you think this model can be used to predict the life expectancy of a child 50 years from now? Explain.

76. *Electronics* The resistance y (in ohms) of 1000 feet of solid copper wire at 68 degrees Fahrenheit can be approximated by the model $y = \dfrac{10{,}770}{x^2} - 0.37, \ 5 \le x \le 100$ where x is the diameter of the wire in mils (0.001 inch). (Source: American Wire Gage)

(a) Complete the table.

x	5	10	20	30	40	50
y						

x	60	70	80	90	100
y					

(b) Use the table of values in part (a) to sketch a graph of the model. Then use your graph to estimate the resistance when $x = 85.5$.

(c) Use the model to confirm algebraically the estimate you found in part (b).

(d) What can you conclude in general about the relationship between the diameter of the copper wire and the resistance?

Synthesis

True or False? In Exercises 77 and 78, determine whether the statement is true or false. Justify your answer.

77. A graph is symmetric with respect to the x-axis if, whenever (x, y) is on the graph, $(-x, y)$ is also on the graph.

78. A graph of an equation can have more than one y-intercept.

 79. *Think About It* Suppose you correctly enter an expression for the variable y on a graphing utility. However, no graph appears on the display when you graph the equation. Give a possible explanation and the steps you could take to remedy the problem. Illustrate your explanation with an example.

80. *Think About It* Find a and b if the graph of $y = ax^2 + bx^3$ is symmetric with respect to (a) the y-axis and (b) the origin. (There are many correct answers.)

Skills Review

81. Identify the terms: $9x^5 + 4x^3 - 7$.

82. Rewrite the expression using exponential notation.

$$-(7 \times 7 \times 7 \times 7)$$

In Exercises 83–88, simplify the expression.

83. $\sqrt{18x} - \sqrt{2x}$

84. $\sqrt[4]{x^5}$

85. $\dfrac{70}{\sqrt{7x}}$

86. $\dfrac{55}{\sqrt{20} - 3}$

87. $\sqrt[6]{t^2}$

88. $\sqrt[3]{\sqrt{y}}$

1.3   Linear Equations in Two Variables

What you should learn

- Use slope to graph linear equations in two variables.
- Find slopes of lines.
- Write linear equations in two variables.
- Use slope to identify parallel and perpendicular lines.
- Use slope and linear equations in two variables to model and solve real-life problems.

Why you should learn it

Linear equations in two variables can be used to model and solve real-life problems. For instance, in Exercise 109 on page 37, you will use a linear equation to model student enrollment at the Pennsylvania State University.

Courtesy of Pennsylvania State University

Using Slope

The simplest mathematical model for relating two variables is the **linear equation in two variables** $y = mx + b$. The equation is called *linear* because its graph is a line. (In mathematics, the term *line* means *straight line*.) By letting $x = 0$, you can see that the line crosses the y-axis at $y = b$, as shown in Figure 1.28. In other words, the y-intercept is $(0, b)$. The steepness or slope of the line is m.

$$y = mx + b$$

Slope ——————→   ⌐—— y-Intercept

The **slope** of a nonvertical line is the number of units the line rises (or falls) vertically for each unit of horizontal change from left to right, as shown in Figure 1.28 and Figure 1.29.

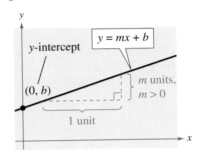

Positive slope, line rises.
FIGURE 1.28

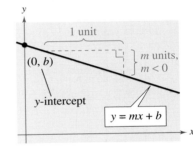

Negative slope, line falls.
FIGURE 1.29

A linear equation that is written in the form $y = mx + b$ is said to be written in **slope-intercept form.**

The Slope-Intercept Form of the Equation of a Line

The graph of the equation

$$y = mx + b$$

is a line whose slope is m and whose y-intercept is $(0, b)$.

Exploration

Use a graphing utility to compare the slopes of the lines $y = mx$, where $m = 0.5, 1, 2,$ and 4. Which line rises most quickly? Now, let $m = -0.5, -1, -2,$ and -4. Which line falls most quickly? Use a square setting to obtain a true geometric perspective. What can you conclude about the slope and the "rate" at which the line rises or falls?

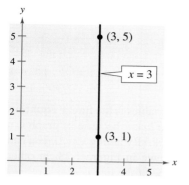

FIGURE 1.30   *Slope is undefined.*

Once you have determined the slope and the *y*-intercept of a line, it is a relatively simple matter to sketch its graph. In the next example, note that none of the lines is vertical. A vertical line has an equation of the form

$$x = a.$$ Vertical line

The equation of a vertical line cannot be written in the form $y = mx + b$ because the slope of a vertical line is undefined, as indicated in Figure 1.30.

Example 1   Graphing a Linear Equation

Sketch the graph of each linear equation.

a. $y = 2x + 1$

b. $y = 2$

c. $x + y = 2$

Solution

a. Because $b = 1$, the *y*-intercept is $(0, 1)$. Moreover, because the slope is $m = 2$, the line *rises* two units for each unit the line moves to the right, as shown in Figure 1.31.

b. By writing this equation in the form $y = (0)x + 2$, you can see that the *y*-intercept is $(0, 2)$ and the slope is zero. A zero slope implies that the line is horizontal—that is, it doesn't rise *or* fall, as shown in Figure 1.32.

c. By writing this equation in slope-intercept form

$$x + y = 2$$ Write original equation.

$$y = -x + 2$$ Subtract *x* from each side.

$$y = (-1)x + 2$$ Write in slope-intercept form.

you can see that the *y*-intercept is $(0, 2)$. Moreover, because the slope is $m = -1$, the line *falls* one unit for each unit the line moves to the right, as shown in Figure 1.33.

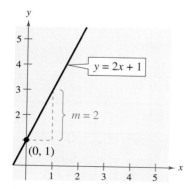

When m is positive, the line rises.

FIGURE 1.31

When m is 0, the line is horizontal.

FIGURE 1.32

When m is negative, the line falls.

FIGURE 1.33

✔**CHECKPOINT**   Now try Exercise 9.

Finding the Slope of a Line

Given an equation of a line, you can find its slope by writing the equation in slope-intercept form. If you are not given an equation, you can still find the slope of a line. For instance, suppose you want to find the slope of the line passing through the points (x_1, y_1) and (x_2, y_2), as shown in Figure 1.34. As you move from left to right along this line, a change of $(y_2 - y_1)$ units in the vertical direction corresponds to a change of $(x_2 - x_1)$ units in the horizontal direction.

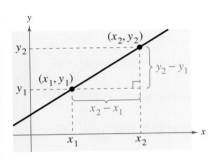

FIGURE 1.34

$$y_2 - y_1 = \text{the change in } y = \text{rise}$$

and

$$x_2 - x_1 = \text{the change in } x = \text{run}$$

The ratio of $(y_2 - y_1)$ to $(x_2 - x_1)$ represents the slope of the line that passes through the points (x_1, y_1) and (x_2, y_2).

$$\text{Slope} = \frac{\text{change in } y}{\text{change in } x}$$

$$= \frac{\text{rise}}{\text{run}}$$

$$= \frac{y_2 - y_1}{x_2 - x_1}$$

The Slope of a Line Passing Through Two Points

The **slope** m of the nonvertical line through (x_1, y_1) and (x_2, y_2) is

$$m = \frac{y_2 - y_1}{x_2 - x_1}$$

where $x_1 \neq x_2$.

When this formula is used for slope, the *order of subtraction* is important. Given two points on a line, you are free to label either one of them as (x_1, y_1) and the other as (x_2, y_2). However, once you have done this, you must form the numerator and denominator using the same order of subtraction.

$$m = \frac{y_2 - y_1}{x_2 - x_1} \qquad m = \frac{y_1 - y_2}{x_1 - x_2} \qquad m = \frac{y_2 - y_1}{x_1 - x_2}$$

Correct   Correct   Incorrect

For instance, the slope of the line passing through the points $(3, 4)$ and $(5, 7)$ can be calculated as

$$m = \frac{7 - 4}{5 - 3} = \frac{3}{2}$$

or, reversing the subtraction order in both the numerator and denominator, as

$$m = \frac{4 - 7}{3 - 5} = \frac{-3}{-2} = \frac{3}{2}.$$

Example 2 Finding the Slope of a Line Through Two Points

Find the slope of the line passing through each pair of points.

a. $(-2, 0)$ and $(3, 1)$ **b.** $(-1, 2)$ and $(2, 2)$
c. $(0, 4)$ and $(1, -1)$ **d.** $(3, 4)$ and $(3, 1)$

Solution

a. Letting $(x_1, y_1) = (-2, 0)$ and $(x_2, y_2) = (3, 1)$, you obtain a slope of

$$m = \frac{y_2 - y_1}{x_2 - x_1} = \frac{1 - 0}{3 - (-2)} = \frac{1}{5}.$$ See Figure 1.35.

b. The slope of the line passing through $(-1, 2)$ and $(2, 2)$ is

$$m = \frac{2 - 2}{2 - (-1)} = \frac{0}{3} = 0.$$ See Figure 1.36.

c. The slope of the line passing through $(0, 4)$ and $(1, -1)$ is

$$m = \frac{-1 - 4}{1 - 0} = \frac{-5}{1} = -5.$$ See Figure 1.37.

d. The slope of the line passing through $(3, 4)$ and $(3, 1)$ is

$$m = \frac{1 - 4}{3 - 3} = \frac{-3}{0}.$$ See Figure 1.38.

Because division by 0 is undefined, the slope is undefined and the line is vertical.

FIGURE 1.35

FIGURE 1.36

FIGURE 1.37

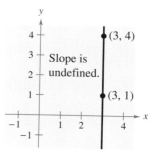

FIGURE 1.38

✓CHECKPOINT   Now try Exercise 21.

Writing Linear Equations in Two Variables

If (x_1, y_1) is a point on a line of slope m and (x, y) is *any other* point on the line, then

$$\frac{y - y_1}{x - x_1} = m.$$

This equation, involving the variables x and y, can be rewritten in the form

$$y - y_1 = m(x - x_1)$$

which is the **point-slope form** of the equation of a line.

Point-Slope Form of the Equation of a Line

The equation of the line with slope m passing through the point (x_1, y_1) is

$$y - y_1 = m(x - x_1).$$

The point-slope form is most useful for *finding* the equation of a line. You should remember this form.

Example 3   Using the Point-Slope Form

Find the slope-intercept form of the equation of the line that has a slope of 3 and passes through the point $(1, -2)$.

Solution

Use the point-slope form with $m = 3$ and $(x_1, y_1) = (1, -2)$.

$$y - y_1 = m(x - x_1) \qquad \text{Point-slope form}$$
$$y - (-2) = 3(x - 1) \qquad \text{Substitute for } m, x_1, \text{ and } y_1.$$
$$y + 2 = 3x - 3 \qquad \text{Simplify.}$$
$$y = 3x - 5 \qquad \text{Write in slope-intercept form.}$$

The slope-intercept form of the equation of the line is $y = 3x - 5$. The graph of this line is shown in Figure 1.39.

✓CHECKPOINT   Now try Exercise 39.

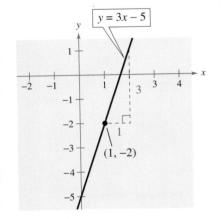

$y = 3x - 5$

FIGURE **1.39**

The point-slope form can be used to find an equation of the line passing through two points (x_1, y_1) and (x_2, y_2). To do this, first find the slope of the line

$$m = \frac{y_2 - y_1}{x_2 - x_1}, \qquad x_1 \neq x_2$$

and then use the point-slope form to obtain the equation

$$y - y_1 = \frac{y_2 - y_1}{x_2 - x_1}(x - x_1). \qquad \text{Two-point form}$$

This is sometimes called the **two-point form** of the equation of a line.

STUDY TIP

When you find an equation of the line that passes through two given points, you only need to substitute the coordinates of one of the points into the point-slope form. It does not matter which point you choose because both points will yield the same result.

Exploration

Find d_1 and d_2 in terms of m_1 and m_2, respectively (see figure). Then use the Pythagorean Theorem to find a relationship between m_1 and m_2.

Parallel and Perpendicular Lines

Slope can be used to decide whether two nonvertical lines in a plane are parallel, perpendicular, or neither.

Parallel and Perpendicular Lines

1. Two distinct nonvertical lines are **parallel** if and only if their slopes are equal. That is, $m_1 = m_2$.

2. Two nonvertical lines are **perpendicular** if and only if their slopes are negative reciprocals of each other. That is, $m_1 = -1/m_2$.

Example 4 Finding Parallel and Perpendicular Lines

Find the slope-intercept forms of the equations of the lines that pass through the point $(2, -1)$ and are (a) parallel to and (b) perpendicular to the line $2x - 3y = 5$.

Solution

By writing the equation of the given line in slope-intercept form

$$2x - 3y = 5 \qquad \text{Write original equation.}$$
$$-3y = -2x + 5 \qquad \text{Subtract } 2x \text{ from each side.}$$
$$y = \tfrac{2}{3}x - \tfrac{5}{3} \qquad \text{Write in slope-intercept form.}$$

you can see that it has a slope of $m = \tfrac{2}{3}$, as shown in Figure 1.40.

a. Any line parallel to the given line must also have a slope of $\tfrac{2}{3}$. So, the line through $(2, -1)$ that is parallel to the given line has the following equation.

$$y - (-1) = \tfrac{2}{3}(x - 2) \qquad \text{Write in point-slope form.}$$
$$3(y + 1) = 2(x - 2) \qquad \text{Multiply each side by 3.}$$
$$3y + 3 = 2x - 4 \qquad \text{Distributive Property}$$
$$y = \tfrac{2}{3}x - \tfrac{7}{3} \qquad \text{Write in slope-intercept form.}$$

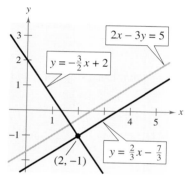

FIGURE 1.40

b. Any line perpendicular to the given line must have a slope of $-\tfrac{3}{2}$ (because $-\tfrac{3}{2}$ is the negative reciprocal of $\tfrac{2}{3}$). So, the line through $(2, -1)$ that is perpendicular to the given line has the following equation.

$$y - (-1) = -\tfrac{3}{2}(x - 2) \qquad \text{Write in point-slope form.}$$
$$2(y + 1) = -3(x - 2) \qquad \text{Multiply each side by 2.}$$
$$2y + 2 = -3x + 6 \qquad \text{Distributive Property}$$
$$y = -\tfrac{3}{2}x + 2 \qquad \text{Write in slope-intercept form.}$$

✓**CHECKPOINT** Now try Exercise 69.

Notice in Example 4 how the slope-intercept form is used to obtain information about the graph of a line, whereas the point-slope form is used to write the equation of a line.

Technology

On a graphing utility, lines will not appear to have the correct slope unless you use a viewing window that has a square setting. For instance, try graphing the lines in Example 4 using the standard setting $-10 \leq x \leq 10$ and $-10 \leq y \leq 10$. Then reset the viewing window with the square setting $-9 \leq x \leq 9$ and $-6 \leq y \leq 6$. On which setting do the lines $y = \tfrac{2}{3}x - \tfrac{5}{3}$ and $y = -\tfrac{3}{2}x + 2$ appear to be perpendicular?

Applications

In real-life problems, the slope of a line can be interpreted as either a *ratio* or a *rate*. If the *x*-axis and *y*-axis have the same unit of measure, then the slope has no units and is a **ratio.** If the *x*-axis and *y*-axis have different units of measure, then the slope is a **rate** or **rate of change.**

Example 5   Using Slope as a Ratio

The maximum recommended slope of a wheelchair ramp is $\frac{1}{12}$. A business is installing a wheelchair ramp that rises 22 inches over a horizontal length of 24 feet. Is the ramp steeper than recommended?   (Source: *Americans with Disabilities Act Handbook*)

Solution

The horizontal length of the ramp is 24 feet or $12(24) = 288$ inches, as shown in Figure 1.41. So, the slope of the ramp is

$$\text{Slope} = \frac{\text{vertical change}}{\text{horizontal change}} = \frac{22 \text{ in.}}{288 \text{ in.}} \approx 0.076.$$

Because $\frac{1}{12} \approx 0.083$, the slope of the ramp is not steeper than recommended.

22 in.

24 ft

FIGURE 1.41

✓CHECKPOINT   Now try Exercise 97.

Example 6   Using Slope as a Rate of Change

A kitchen appliance manufacturing company determines that the total cost in dollars of producing *x* units of a blender is

$$C = 25x + 3500. \qquad \text{Cost equation}$$

Describe the practical significance of the *y*-intercept and slope of this line.

Solution

The *y*-intercept $(0, 3500)$ tells you that the cost of producing zero units is $3500. This is the *fixed cost* of production—it includes costs that must be paid regardless of the number of units produced. The slope of $m = 25$ tells you that the cost of producing each unit is $25, as shown in Figure 1.42. Economists call the cost per unit the *marginal cost*. If the production increases by one unit, then the "margin," or extra amount of cost, is $25. So, the cost increases at a rate of $25 per unit.

✓CHECKPOINT   Now try Exercise 101.

FIGURE 1.42   *Production cost*

Most business expenses can be deducted in the same year they occur. One exception is the cost of property that has a useful life of more than 1 year. Such costs must be *depreciated* (decreased in value) over the useful life of the property. If the *same amount* is depreciated each year, the procedure is called *linear* or *straight-line depreciation*. The *book value* is the difference between the original value and the total amount of depreciation accumulated to date.

Example 7   Straight-Line Depreciation

A college purchased exercise equipment worth $12,000 for the new campus fitness center. The equipment has a useful life of 8 years. The salvage value at the end of 8 years is $2000. Write a linear equation that describes the book value of the equipment each year.

Solution

Let V represent the value of the equipment at the end of year t. You can represent the initial value of the equipment by the data point $(0, 12,000)$ and the salvage value of the equipment by the data point $(8, 2000)$. The slope of the line is

$$m = \frac{2000 - 12,000}{8 - 0} = -\$1250$$

which represents the annual depreciation in *dollars per year*. Using the point-slope form, you can write the equation of the line as follows.

$$V - 12,000 = -1250(t - 0) \qquad \text{Write in point-slope form.}$$

$$V = -1250t + 12,000 \qquad \text{Write in slope-intercept form.}$$

The table shows the book value at the end of each year, and the graph of the equation is shown in Figure 1.43.

FIGURE 1.43   *Straight-line depreciation*

Year, t	Value, V
0	12,000
1	10,750
2	9,500
3	8,250
4	7,000
5	5,750
6	4,500
7	3,250
8	2,000

✓**CHECKPOINT**   Now try Exercise 107.

In many real-life applications, the two data points that determine the line are often given in a disguised form. Note how the data points are described in Example 7.

| Example 8 | **Predicting Sales per Share** | |

The sales per share for Starbucks Corporation were $6.97 in 2001 and $8.47 in 2002. Using only this information, write a linear equation that gives the sales per share in terms of the year. Then predict the sales per share for 2003.   (Source: Starbucks Corporation)

Solution

Let $t = 1$ represent 2001. Then the two given values are represented by the data points $(1, 6.97)$ and $(2, 8.47)$. The slope of the line through these points is

$$m = \frac{8.47 - 6.97}{2 - 1}$$

$$= 1.5.$$

Using the point-slope form, you can find the equation that relates the sales per share y and the year t to be

$$y - 6.97 = 1.5(t - 1) \qquad \text{Write in point-slope form.}$$

$$y = 1.5t + 5.47. \qquad \text{Write in slope-intercept form.}$$

According to this equation, the sales per share in 2003 was $y = 1.5(3) + 5.47 = \$9.97$, as shown in Figure 1.44. (In this case, the prediction is quite good—the actual sales per share in 2003 was $10.35.)

✓**CHECKPOINT**   Now try Exercise 109.

The prediction method illustrated in Example 8 is called **linear extrapolation.** Note in Figure 1.45 that an extrapolated point does not lie between the given points. When the estimated point lies between two given points, as shown in Figure 1.46, the procedure is called **linear interpolation.**

Because the slope of a vertical line is not defined, its equation cannot be written in slope-intercept form. However, every line has an equation that can be written in the **general form**

$$Ax + By + C = 0 \qquad \text{General form}$$

where A and B are not both zero. For instance, the vertical line given by $x = a$ can be represented by the general form $x - a = 0$.

Starbucks Corporation

FIGURE 1.44

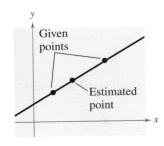

Linear extrapolation

FIGURE 1.45

Linear interpolation

FIGURE 1.46

Summary of Equations of Lines

1. General form: $Ax + By + C = 0$

2. Vertical line: $x = a$

3. Horizontal line: $y = b$

4. Slope-intercept form: $y = mx + b$

5. Point-slope form: $y - y_1 = m(x - x_1)$

6. Two-point form: $y - y_1 = \dfrac{y_2 - y_1}{x_2 - x_1}(x - x_1)$

1.3 | Exercises

VOCABULARY CHECK:

In Exercises 1–6, fill in the blanks.

1. The simplest mathematical model for relating two variables is the _____ equation in two variables $y = mx + b$.

2. For a line, the ratio of the change in y to the change in x is called the _____ of the line.

3. Two lines are _____ if and only if their slopes are equal.

4. Two lines are _____ if and only if their slopes are negative reciprocals of each other.

5. When the x-axis and y-axis have different units of measure, the slope can be interpreted as a _____.

6. The prediction method _____ _____ is the method used to estimate a point on a line that does not lie between the given points.

7. Match each equation of a line with its form.

(a) $Ax + By + C = 0$ (i) Vertical line

(b) $x = a$ (ii) Slope-intercept form

(c) $y = b$ (iii) General form

(d) $y = mx + b$ (iv) Point-slope form

(e) $y - y_1 = m(x - x_1)$ (v) Horizontal line

PREREQUISITE SKILLS REVIEW: Practice and review algebra skills needed for this section at **www.Eduspace.com.**

In Exercises 1 and 2, identify the line that has each slope.

1. (a) $m = \frac{2}{3}$

(b) m is undefined.

(c) $m = -2$

2. (a) $m = 0$

(b) $m = -\frac{3}{4}$

(c) $m = 1$

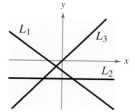

In Exercises 3 and 4, sketch the lines through the point with the indicated slopes on the same set of coordinate axes.

Point	Slopes
3. $(2, 3)$	(a) 0 (b) 1 (c) 2 (d) -3
4. $(-4, 1)$	(a) 3 (b) -3 (c) $\frac{1}{2}$ (d) Undefined

In Exercises 5–8, estimate the slope of the line.

5.

6.

7.

8.

In Exercises 9–20, find the slope and y-intercept (if possible) of the equation of the line. Sketch the line.

9. $y = 5x + 3$

10. $y = x - 10$

11. $y = -\frac{1}{2}x + 4$

12. $y = -\frac{3}{2}x + 6$

13. $5x - 2 = 0$

14. $3y + 5 = 0$

15. $7x + 6y = 30$

16. $2x + 3y = 9$

17. $y - 3 = 0$

18. $y + 4 = 0$

19. $x + 5 = 0$

20. $x - 2 = 0$

In Exercises 21–28, plot the points and find the slope of the line passing through the pair of points.

21. $(-3, -2), (1, 6)$

22. $(2, 4), (4, -4)$

23. $(-6, -1), (-6, 4)$

24. $(0, -10), (-4, 0)$

25. $\left(\frac{11}{2}, -\frac{4}{3}\right), \left(-\frac{3}{2}, -\frac{1}{3}\right)$

26. $\left(\frac{7}{8}, \frac{3}{4}\right), \left(\frac{5}{4}, -\frac{1}{4}\right)$

27. $(4.8, 3.1), (-5.2, 1.6)$

28. $(-1.75, -8.3), (2.25, -2.6)$

In Exercises 29–38, use the point on the line and the slope of the line to find three additional points through which the line passes. (There are many correct answers.)

Point	Slope
29. $(2, 1)$	$m = 0$
30. $(-4, 1)$	m is undefined.
31. $(5, -6)$	$m = 1$
32. $(10, -6)$	$m = -1$
33. $(-8, 1)$	m is undefined.
34. $(-3, -1)$	$m = 0$
35. $(-5, 4)$	$m = 2$
36. $(0, -9)$	$m = -2$
37. $(7, -2)$	$m = \frac{1}{2}$
38. $(-1, -6)$	$m = -\frac{1}{2}$

In Exercises 39–50, find the slope-intercept form of the equation of the line that passes through the given point and has the indicated slope. Sketch the line.

Point	Slope
39. $(0, -2)$	$m = 3$
40. $(0, 10)$	$m = -1$
41. $(-3, 6)$	$m = -2$
42. $(0, 0)$	$m = 4$
43. $(4, 0)$	$m = -\frac{1}{3}$
44. $(-2, -5)$	$m = \frac{3}{4}$
45. $(6, -1)$	m is undefined.
46. $(-10, 4)$	m is undefined.
47. $\left(4, \frac{5}{2}\right)$	$m = 0$
48. $\left(-\frac{1}{2}, \frac{3}{2}\right)$	$m = 0$
49. $(-5.1, 1.8)$	$m = 5$
50. $(2.3, -8.5)$	$m = -\frac{5}{2}$

In Exercises 51–64, find the slope-intercept form of the equation of the line passing through the points. Sketch the line.

51. $(5, -1), (-5, 5)$ **52.** $(4, 3), (-4, -4)$

53. $(-8, 1), (-8, 7)$ **54.** $(-1, 4), (6, 4)$

55. $\left(2, \frac{1}{2}\right), \left(\frac{1}{2}, \frac{5}{4}\right)$ **56.** $\left(1, 1\right), \left(6, -\frac{2}{3}\right)$

57. $\left(-\frac{1}{10}, -\frac{3}{5}\right), \left(\frac{9}{10}, -\frac{9}{5}\right)$ **58.** $\left(\frac{3}{4}, \frac{3}{2}\right), \left(-\frac{4}{3}, \frac{7}{4}\right)$

59. $(1, 0.6), (-2, -0.6)$

60. $(-8, 0.6), (2, -2.4)$

61. $(2, -1), \left(\frac{1}{3}, -1\right)$

62. $\left(\frac{1}{5}, -2\right), (-6, -2)$

63. $\left(\frac{7}{3}, -8\right), \left(\frac{7}{3}, 1\right)$

64. $(1.5, -2), (1.5, 0.2)$

In Exercises 65–68, determine whether the lines L_1 and L_2 passing through the pairs of points are parallel, perpendicular, or neither.

65. L_1: $(0, -1), (5, 9)$ **66.** L_1: $(-2, -1), (1, 5)$
      L_2: $(0, 3), (4, 1)$ L_2: $(1, 3), (5, -5)$

67. L_1: $(3, 6), (-6, 0)$ **68.** L_1: $(4, 8), (-4, 2)$
      L_2: $(0, -1), \left(5, \frac{7}{3}\right)$ L_2: $(3, -5), \left(-1, \frac{1}{3}\right)$

In Exercises 69–78, write the slope-intercept forms of the equations of the lines through the given point (a) parallel to the given line and (b) perpendicular to the given line.

Point	Line
69. $(2, 1)$	$4x - 2y = 3$
70. $(-3, 2)$	$x + y = 7$
71. $\left(-\frac{2}{3}, \frac{7}{8}\right)$	$3x + 4y = 7$
72. $\left(\frac{7}{8}, \frac{3}{4}\right)$	$5x + 3y = 0$
73. $(-1, 0)$	$y = -3$
74. $(4, -2)$	$y = 1$
75. $(2, 5)$	$x = 4$
76. $(-5, 1)$	$x = -2$
77. $(2.5, 6.8)$	$x - y = 4$
78. $(-3.9, -1.4)$	$6x + 2y = 9$

In Exercises 79–84, use the *intercept form* to find the equation of the line with the given intercepts. The intercept form of the equation of a line with intercepts $(a, 0)$ and $(0, b)$ is

$$\frac{x}{a} + \frac{y}{b} = 1, \ a \neq 0, \ b \neq 0.$$

79. x-intercept: $(2, 0)$ **80.** x-intercept: $(-3, 0)$
      y-intercept: $(0, 3)$ y-intercept: $(0, 4)$

81. x-intercept: $\left(-\frac{1}{6}, 0\right)$ **82.** x-intercept: $\left(\frac{2}{3}, 0\right)$
      y-intercept: $\left(0, -\frac{2}{3}\right)$ y-intercept: $(0, -2)$

83. Point on line: $(1, 2)$ **84.** Point on line: $(-3, 4)$
      x-intercept: $(c, 0)$ x-intercept: $(d, 0)$
      y-intercept: $(0, c), \quad c \neq 0$ y-intercept: $(0, d), \quad d \neq 0$

Graphical Interpretation   In Exercises 85–88, identify any relationships that exist among the lines, and then use a graphing utility to graph the three equations in the same viewing window. Adjust the viewing window so that the slope appears visually correct—that is, so that parallel lines appear parallel and perpendicular lines appear to intersect at right angles.

85. (a) $y = 2x$ (b) $y = -2x$ (c) $y = \frac{1}{2}x$

86. (a) $y = \frac{2}{3}x$ (b) $y = -\frac{3}{2}x$ (c) $y = \frac{2}{3}x + 2$

87. (a) $y = -\frac{1}{2}x$ (b) $y = -\frac{1}{2}x + 3$ (c) $y = 2x - 4$

88. (a) $y = x - 8$ (b) $y = x + 1$ (c) $y = -x + 3$

In Exercises 89–92, find a relationship between x and y such that (x, y) is equidistant (the same distance) from the two points.

89. $(4, -1), (-2, 3)$

90. $(6, 5), (1, -8)$

91. $\left(3, \frac{5}{2}\right), (-7, 1)$

92. $\left(-\frac{1}{2}, -4\right), \left(\frac{7}{2}, \frac{5}{4}\right)$

93. Sales The following are the slopes of lines representing annual sales y in terms of time x in years. Use the slopes to interpret any change in annual sales for a one-year increase in time.

(a) The line has a slope of $m = 135$.

(b) The line has a slope of $m = 0$.

(c) The line has a slope of $m = -40$.

94. Revenue The following are the slopes of lines representing daily revenues y in terms of time x in days. Use the slopes to interpret any change in daily revenues for a one-day increase in time.

(a) The line has a slope of $m = 400$.

(b) The line has a slope of $m = 100$.

(c) The line has a slope of $m = 0$.

95. Average Salary The graph shows the average salaries for senior high school principals from 1990 through 2002. (Source: Educational Research Service)

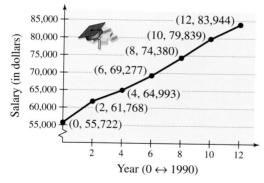

Year $(0 \leftrightarrow 1990)$

(a) Use the slopes to determine the time periods in which the average salary increased the greatest and the least.

(b) Find the slope of the line segment connecting the years 1990 and 2002.

(c) Interpret the meaning of the slope in part (b) in the context of the problem.

96. Net Profit The graph shows the net profits (in millions) for Applebee's International, Inc. for the years 1994 through 2003. (Source: Applebee's International, Inc.)

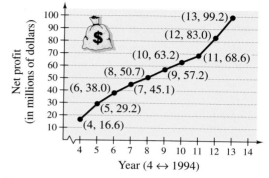

Year $(4 \leftrightarrow 1994)$

(a) Use the slopes to determine the years in which the net profit showed the greatest increase and the least increase.

(b) Find the slope of the line segment connecting the years 1994 and 2003.

(c) Interpret the meaning of the slope in part (b) in the context of the problem.

97. Road Grade You are driving on a road that has a 6% uphill grade (see figure). This means that the slope of the road is $\frac{6}{100}$. Approximate the amount of vertical change in your position if you drive 200 feet.

98. Road Grade From the top of a mountain road, a surveyor takes several horizontal measurements x and several vertical measurements y, as shown in the table (x and y are measured in feet).

x	300	600	900	1200	1500	1800	2100
y	-25	-50	-75	-100	-125	-150	-175

(a) Sketch a scatter plot of the data.

(b) Use a straightedge to sketch the line that you think best fits the data.

(c) Find an equation for the line you sketched in part (b).

(d) Interpret the meaning of the slope of the line in part (c) in the context of the problem.

(e) The surveyor needs to put up a road sign that indicates the steepness of the road. For instance, a surveyor would put up a sign that states "8% grade" on a road with a downhill grade that has a slope of $-\frac{8}{100}$. What should the sign state for the road in this problem?

Rate of Change   In Exercises 99 and 100, you are given the dollar value of a product in 2005 and the rate at which the value of the product is expected to change during the next 5 years. Use this information to write a linear equation that gives the dollar value V of the product in terms of the year t. (Let $t = 5$ represent 2005.)

2005 Value	Rate
99. $2540	$125 decrease per year
100. $156	$4.50 increase per year

Graphical Interpretation   In Exercises 101–104, match the description of the situation with its graph. Also determine the slope and y-intercept of each graph and interpret the slope and y-intercept in the context of the situation. [The graphs are labeled (a), (b), (c), and (d).]

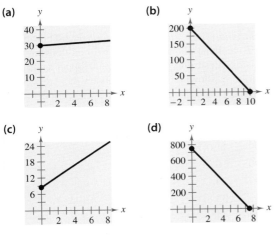

101. A person is paying $20 per week to a friend to repay a $200 loan.

102. An employee is paid $8.50 per hour plus $2 for each unit produced per hour.

103. A sales representative receives $30 per day for food plus $0.32 for each mile traveled.

104. A computer that was purchased for $750 depreciates $100 per year.

105. *Cash Flow per Share*   The cash flow per share for the Timberland Co. was $0.18 in 1995 and $4.04 in 2003. Write a linear equation that gives the cash flow per share in terms of the year. Let $t = 5$ represent 1995. Then predict the cash flows for the years 2008 and 2010. (Source: The Timberland Co.)

106. *Number of Stores*   In 1999 there were 4076 J.C. Penney stores and in 2003 there were 1078 stores. Write a linear equation that gives the number of stores in terms of the year. Let $t = 9$ represent 1999. Then predict the numbers of stores for the years 2008 and 2010. Are your answers reasonable? Explain.   (Source: J.C. Penney Co.)

107. *Depreciation*   A sub shop purchases a used pizza oven for $875. After 5 years, the oven will have to be replaced. Write a linear equation giving the value V of the equipment during the 5 years it will be in use.

108. *Depreciation*   A school district purchases a high-volume printer, copier, and scanner for $25,000. After 10 years, the equipment will have to be replaced. Its value at that time is expected to be $2000. Write a linear equation giving the value V of the equipment during the 10 years it will be in use.

109. *College Enrollment*   The Pennsylvania State University had enrollments of 40,571 students in 2000 and 41,289 students in 2004 at its main campus in University Park, Pennsylvania.   (Source: Penn State Fact Book)

(a) Assuming the enrollment growth is linear, find a linear model that gives the enrollment in terms of the year t, where $t = 0$ corresponds to 2000.

(b) Use your model from part (a) to predict the enrollments in 2008 and 2010.

(c) What is the slope of your model? Explain its meaning in the context of the situation.

110. *College Enrollment*   The University of Florida had enrollments of 36,531 students in 1990 and 48,673 students in 2003.   (Source: University of Florida)

(a) What was the average annual change in enrollment from 1990 to 2003?

(b) Use the average annual change in enrollment to estimate the enrollments in 1994, 1998, and 2002.

(c) Write the equation of a line that represents the given data. What is its slope? Interpret the slope in the context of the problem.

(d) Using the results of parts (a)–(c), write a short paragraph discussing the concepts of *slope* and *average rate of change*.

111. *Sales*   A discount outlet is offering a 15% discount on all items. Write a linear equation giving the sale price S for an item with a list price L.

112. *Hourly Wage*   A microchip manufacturer pays its assembly line workers $11.50 per hour. In addition, workers receive a piecework rate of $0.75 per unit produced. Write a linear equation for the hourly wage W in terms of the number of units x produced per hour.

113. *Cost, Revenue, and Profit*   A roofing contractor purchases a shingle delivery truck with a shingle elevator for $36,500. The vehicle requires an average expenditure of $5.25 per hour for fuel and maintenance, and the operator is paid $11.50 per hour.

(a) Write a linear equation giving the total cost C of operating this equipment for t hours. (Include the purchase cost of the equipment.)

(b) Assuming that customers are charged $27 per hour of machine use, write an equation for the revenue R derived from t hours of use.

(c) Use the formula for profit $(P = R - C)$ to write an equation for the profit derived from t hours of use.

(d) Use the result of part (c) to find the break-even point—that is, the number of hours this equipment must be used to yield a profit of 0 dollars.

114. Rental Demand A real estate office handles an apartment complex with 50 units. When the rent per unit is $580 per month, all 50 units are occupied. However, when the rent is $625 per month, the average number of occupied units drops to 47. Assume that the relationship between the monthly rent p and the demand x is linear.

(a) Write the equation of the line giving the demand x in terms of the rent p.

(b) Use this equation to predict the number of units occupied when the rent is $655.

(c) Predict the number of units occupied when the rent is $595.

115. Geometry The length and width of a rectangular garden are 15 meters and 10 meters, respectively. A walkway of width x surrounds the garden.

(a) Draw a diagram that gives a visual representation of the problem.

(b) Write the equation for the perimeter y of the walkway in terms of x.

(c) Use a graphing utility to graph the equation for the perimeter.

(d) Determine the slope of the graph in part (c). For each additional one-meter increase in the width of the walkway, determine the increase in its perimeter.

116. Monthly Salary A pharmaceutical salesperson receives a monthly salary of $2500 plus a commission of 7% of sales. Write a linear equation for the salesperson's monthly wage W in terms of monthly sales S.

117. Business Costs A sales representative of a company using a personal car receives $120 per day for lodging and meals plus $0.38 per mile driven. Write a linear equation giving the daily cost C to the company in terms of x, the number of miles driven.

118. Sports The median salaries (in thousands of dollars) for players on the Los Angeles Dodgers from 1996 to 2003 are shown in the scatter plot. Find the equation of the line that you think best fits these data. (Let y represent the median salary and let t represent the year, with $t = 6$ corresponding to 1996.) (Source: USA TODAY)

FIGURE FOR **118**

Model It

119. Data Analysis: Cell Phone Suscribers The numbers of cellular phone suscribers y (in millions) in the United States from 1990 through 2002, where x is the year, are shown as data points (x, y). (Source: Cellular Telecommunications & Internet Association)

(1990, 5.3)
(1991, 7.6)
(1992, 11.0)
(1993, 16.0)
(1994, 24.1)
(1995, 33.8)
(1996, 44.0)
(1997, 55.3)
(1998, 69.2)
(1999, 86.0)
(2000, 109.5)
(2001, 128.4)
(2002, 140.8)

(a) Sketch a scatter plot of the data. Let $x = 0$ correspond to 1990.

(b) Use a straightedge to sketch the line that you think best fits the data.

(c) Find the equation of the line from part (b). Explain the procedure you used.

(d) Write a short paragraph explaining the meanings of the slope and y-intercept of the line in terms of the data.

(e) Compare the values obtained using your model with the actual values.

(f) Use your model to estimate the number of cellular phone suscribers in 2008.

120. ***Data Analysis: Average Scores*** An instructor gives regular 20-point quizzes and 100-point exams in an algebra course. Average scores for six students, given as data points (x, y) where x is the average quiz score and y is the average test score, are $(18, 87)$, $(10, 55)$, $(19, 96)$, $(16, 79)$, $(13, 76)$, and $(15, 82)$. [*Note:* There are many correct answers for parts (b)–(d).]

(a) Sketch a scatter plot of the data.

(b) Use a straightedge to sketch the line that you think best fits the data.

(c) Find an equation for the line you sketched in part (b).

(d) Use the equation in part (c) to estimate the average test score for a person with an average quiz score of 17.

(e) The instructor adds 4 points to the average test score of each student in the class. Describe the changes in the positions of the plotted points and the change in the equation of the line.

Synthesis

True or False? **In Exercises 121 and 122, determine whether the statement is true or false. Justify your answer.**

121. A line with a slope of $-\frac{5}{7}$ is steeper than a line with a slope of $-\frac{6}{7}$.

122. The line through $(-8, 2)$ and $(-1, 4)$ and the line through $(0, -4)$ and $(-7, 7)$ are parallel.

123. Explain how you could show that the points $A\,(2, 3)$, $B\,(2, 9)$, and $C\,(4, 3)$ are the vertices of a right triangle.

124. Explain why the slope of a vertical line is said to be undefined.

125. With the information shown in the graphs, is it possible to determine the slope of each line? Is it possible that the lines could have the same slope? Explain.

(a)

(b)

126. The slopes of two lines are -4 and $\frac{5}{2}$. Which is steeper? Explain.

127. The value V of a molding machine t years after it is purchased is

$$V = -4000t + 58{,}500, \quad 0 \le t \le 5.$$

Explain what the V-intercept and slope measure.

128. ***Think About It*** Is it possible for two lines with positive slopes to be perpendicular? Explain.

Skills Review

In Exercises 129–132, match the equation with its graph. [The graphs are labeled (a), (b), (c), and (d).]

(a)

(b)

(c)

(d)

129. $y = 8 - 3x$

130. $y = 8 - \sqrt{x}$

131. $y = \frac{1}{2}x^2 + 2x + 1$

132. $y = |x + 2| - 1$

In Exercises 133–138, find all the solutions of the equation. Check your solution(s) in the original equation.

133. $-7(3 - x) = 14(x - 1)$

134. $\dfrac{8}{2x - 7} = \dfrac{4}{9 - 4x}$

135. $2x^2 - 21x + 49 = 0$

136. $x^2 - 8x + 3 = 0$

137. $\sqrt{x - 9} + 15 = 0$

138. $3x - 16\sqrt{x} + 5 = 0$

139. **Make a Decision** To work an extended application analyzing the numbers of bachelor's degrees earned by women in the United States from 1985 to 2002, visit this text's website at *college.hmco.com*. (*Data Source: U.S. National Center for Education Statistics*)

1.4 Functions

What you should learn

- Determine whether relations between two variables are functions.
- Use function notation and evaluate functions.
- Find the domains of functions.
- Use functions to model and solve real-life problems.
- Evaluate difference quotients.

Why you should learn it

Functions can be used to model and solve real-life problems. For instance, in Exercise 100 on page 52, you will use a function to model the force of water against the face of a dam.

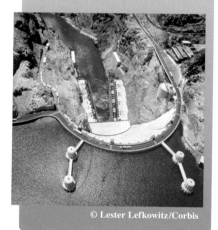

© Lester Lefkowitz/Corbis

Introduction to Functions

Many everyday phenomena involve two quantities that are related to each other by some rule of correspondence. The mathematical term for such a rule of correspondence is a **relation.** In mathematics, relations are often represented by mathematical equations and formulas. For instance, the simple interest I earned on $1000 for 1 year is related to the annual interest rate r by the formula $I = 1000r$.

The formula $I = 1000r$ represents a special kind of relation that matches each item from one set with *exactly one* item from a different set. Such a relation is called a **function.**

Definition of Function

A **function** f from a set A to a set B is a relation that assigns to each element x in the set A exactly one element y in the set B. The set A is the **domain** (or set of inputs) of the function f, and the set B contains the **range** (or set of outputs).

To help understand this definition, look at the function that relates the time of day to the temperature in Figure 1.47.

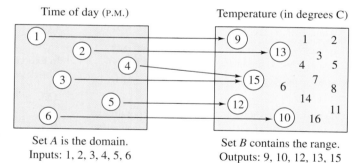

Set A is the domain.
Inputs: 1, 2, 3, 4, 5, 6

Set B contains the range.
Outputs: 9, 10, 12, 13, 15

FIGURE 1.47

This function can be represented by the following ordered pairs, in which the first coordinate (x-value) is the input and the second coordinate (y-value) is the output.

$$\{(1, 9°), (2, 13°), (3, 15°), (4, 15°), (5, 12°), (6, 10°)\}$$

Characteristics of a Function from Set A to Set B

1. Each element in A must be matched with an element in B.

2. Some elements in B may not be matched with any element in A.

3. Two or more elements in A may be matched with the same element in B.

4. An element in A (the domain) cannot be matched with two different elements in B.

Functions are commonly represented in four ways.

> ## Four Ways to Represent a Function
>
> 1. *Verbally* by a sentence that describes how the input variable is related to the output variable
>
> 2. *Numerically* by a table or a list of ordered pairs that matches input values with output values
>
> 3. *Graphically* by points on a graph in a coordinate plane in which the input values are represented by the horizontal axis and the output values are represented by the vertical axis
>
> 4. *Algebraically* by an equation in two variables

To determine whether or not a relation is a function, you must decide whether each input value is matched with exactly one output value. If any input value is matched with two or more output values, the relation is not a function.

Example 1   Testing for Functions

Determine whether the relation represents y as a function of x.

a. The input value x is the number of representatives from a state, and the output value y is the number of senators.

b.

Input, x	Output, y
2	11
2	10
3	8
4	5
5	1

c.

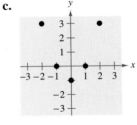

FIGURE 1.48

Solution

a. This verbal description *does* describe y as a function of x. Regardless of the value of x, the value of y is always 2. Such functions are called *constant functions*.

b. This table *does not* describe y as a function of x. The input value 2 is matched with two different y-values.

c. The graph in Figure 1.48 *does* describe y as a function of x. Each input value is matched with exactly one output value.

✓CHECKPOINT   Now try Exercise 5.

Representing functions by sets of ordered pairs is common in *discrete mathematics*. In algebra, however, it is more common to represent functions by equations or formulas involving two variables. For instance, the equation

$$y = x^2 \qquad \text{\small y is a function of x.}$$

represents the variable y as a function of the variable x. In this equation, x is

© Bettmann/Corbis

Historical Note

Leonhard Euler (1707–1783), a Swiss mathematician, is considered to have been the most prolific and productive mathematician in history. One of his greatest influences on mathematics was his use of symbols, or notation. The function notation $y = f(x)$ was introduced by Euler.

the **independent variable** and y is the **dependent variable.** The domain of the function is the set of all values taken on by the independent variable x, and the range of the function is the set of all values taken on by the dependent variable y.

Example 2   Testing for Functions Represented Algebraically

Which of the equations represent(s) y as a function of x?

a. $x^2 + y = 1$ **b.** $-x + y^2 = 1$

Solution

To determine whether y is a function of x, try to solve for y in terms of x.

a. Solving for y yields

$$x^2 + y = 1 \qquad \text{Write original equation.}$$
$$y = 1 - x^2. \qquad \text{Solve for } y.$$

To each value of x there corresponds exactly one value of y. So, y is a function of x.

b. Solving for y yields

$$-x + y^2 = 1 \qquad \text{Write original equation.}$$
$$y^2 = 1 + x \qquad \text{Add } x \text{ to each side.}$$
$$y = \pm\sqrt{1 + x}. \qquad \text{Solve for } y.$$

The $\pm$ indicates that to a given value of x there correspond two values of y. So, y is not a function of x.

✓**CHECKPOINT**   Now try Exercise 15.

Function Notation

When an equation is used to represent a function, it is convenient to name the function so that it can be referenced easily. For example, you know that the equation $y = 1 - x^2$ describes y as a function of x. Suppose you give this function the name "f." Then you can use the following **function notation.**

Input	Output	Equation
x	$f(x)$	$f(x) = 1 - x^2$

The symbol $f(x)$ is read as *the value of f at x* or simply *f of x.* The symbol $f(x)$ corresponds to the y-value for a given x. So, you can write $y = f(x)$. Keep in mind that f is the *name* of the function, whereas $f(x)$ is the *value* of the function at x. For instance, the function given by

$$f(x) = 3 - 2x$$

has *function values* denoted by $f(-1), f(0), f(2)$, and so on. To find these values, substitute the specified input values into the given equation.

For $x = -1$, $f(-1) = 3 - 2(-1) = 3 + 2 = 5.$

For $x = 0$, $f(0) = 3 - 2(0) = 3 - 0 = 3.$

For $x = 2$, $f(2) = 3 - 2(2) = 3 - 4 = -1.$

Although f is often used as a convenient function name and x is often used as the independent variable, you can use other letters. For instance,

$$f(x) = x^2 - 4x + 7, \quad f(t) = t^2 - 4t + 7, \quad \text{and} \quad g(s) = s^2 - 4s + 7$$

all define the same function. In fact, the role of the independent variable is that of a "placeholder." Consequently, the function could be described by

$$f(\quad) = (\quad)^2 - 4(\quad) + 7.$$

STUDY TIP

In Example 3, note that $g(x + 2)$ is not equal to $g(x) + g(2)$. In general, $g(u + v) \neq g(u) + g(v)$.

Example 3   **Evaluating a Function**

Let $g(x) = -x^2 + 4x + 1$. Find each function value.

a. $g(2)$ **b.** $g(t)$ **c.** $g(x + 2)$

Solution

a. Replacing x with 2 in $g(x) = -x^2 + 4x + 1$ yields the following.

$$g(2) = -(2)^2 + 4(2) + 1 = -4 + 8 + 1 = 5$$

b. Replacing x with t yields the following.

$$g(t) = -(t)^2 + 4(t) + 1 = -t^2 + 4t + 1$$

c. Replacing x with $x + 2$ yields the following.

$$\begin{aligned}
g(x + 2) &= -(x + 2)^2 + 4(x + 2) + 1 \\
&= -(x^2 + 4x + 4) + 4x + 8 + 1 \\
&= -x^2 - 4x - 4 + 4x + 8 + 1 \\
&= -x^2 + 5
\end{aligned}$$

✓CHECKPOINT   Now try Exercise 29.

A function defined by two or more equations over a specified domain is called a **piecewise-defined function.**

Example 4   **A Piecewise-Defined Function**

Evaluate the function when $x = -1, 0,$ and 1.

$$f(x) = \begin{cases} x^2 + 1, & x < 0 \\ x - 1, & x \geq 0 \end{cases}$$

Solution

Because $x = -1$ is less than 0, use $f(x) = x^2 + 1$ to obtain

$$f(-1) = (-1)^2 + 1 = 2.$$

For $x = 0$, use $f(x) = x - 1$ to obtain

$$f(0) = (0) - 1 = -1.$$

For $x = 1$, use $f(x) = x - 1$ to obtain

$$f(1) = (1) - 1 = 0.$$

✓CHECKPOINT   Now try Exercise 35.

Technology

Use a graphing utility to graph the functions given by $y = \sqrt{4 - x^2}$ and $y = \sqrt{x^2 - 4}$. What is the domain of each function? Do the domains of these two functions overlap? If so, for what values do the domains overlap?

The Domain of a Function

The domain of a function can be described explicitly or it can be *implied* by the expression used to define the function. The **implied domain** is the set of all real numbers for which the expression is defined. For instance, the function given by

$$f(x) = \frac{1}{x^2 - 4}$$ Domain excludes x-values that result in division by zero.

has an implied domain that consists of all real x other than $x = \pm 2$. These two values are excluded from the domain because division by zero is undefined. Another common type of implied domain is that used to avoid even roots of negative numbers. For example, the function given by

$$f(x) = \sqrt{x}$$ Domain excludes x-values that result in even roots of negative numbers.

is defined only for $x \geq 0$. So, its implied domain is the interval $[0, \infty)$. In general, the domain of a function *excludes* values that would cause division by zero *or* that would result in the even root of a negative number.

Example 5   Finding the Domain of a Function

Find the domain of each function.

a. $f: \{(-3, 0), (-1, 4), (0, 2), (2, 2), (4, -1)\}$ **b.** $g(x) = \dfrac{1}{x + 5}$

c. Volume of a sphere: $V = \frac{4}{3}\pi r^3$ **d.** $h(x) = \sqrt{4 - x^2}$

Solution

a. The domain of f consists of all first coordinates in the set of ordered pairs.

Domain $= \{-3, -1, 0, 2, 4\}$

b. Excluding x-values that yield zero in the denominator, the domain of g is the set of all real numbers x except $x = -5$.

c. Because this function represents the volume of a sphere, the values of the radius r must be positive. So, the domain is the set of all real numbers r such that $r > 0$.

d. This function is defined only for x-values for which

$$4 - x^2 \geq 0.$$

By solving this inequality (see Section 2.7), you can conclude that $-2 \leq x \leq 2$. So, the domain is the interval $[-2, 2]$.

✓**CHECKPOINT**   Now try Exercise 59.

In Example 5(c), note that the domain of a function may be implied by the physical context. For instance, from the equation

$$V = \frac{4}{3}\pi r^3$$

you would have no reason to restrict r to positive values, but the physical context implies that a sphere cannot have a negative or zero radius.

$$\boxed{\frac{h}{r} = 4}$$

FIGURE **1.49**

Applications

Example 6   **The Dimensions of a Container**

You work in the marketing department of a soft-drink company and are experimenting with a new can for iced tea that is slightly narrower and taller than a standard can. For your experimental can, the ratio of the height to the radius is 4, as shown in Figure 1.49.

a. Write the volume of the can as a function of the radius r.

b. Write the volume of the can as a function of the height h.

Solution

a. $V(r) = \pi r^2 h = \pi r^2(4r) = 4\pi r^3$ ⟶ Write V as a function of r.

b. $V(h) = \pi\left(\dfrac{h}{4}\right)^2 h = \dfrac{\pi h^3}{16}$ ⟶ Write V as a function of h.

✓CHECKPOINT   Now try Exercise 87.

Example 7   **The Path of a Baseball**

A baseball is hit at a point 3 feet above ground at a velocity of 100 feet per second and an angle of 45°. The path of the baseball is given by the function

$$f(x) = -0.0032x^2 + x + 3$$

where y and x are measured in feet, as shown in Figure 1.50. Will the baseball clear a 10-foot fence located 300 feet from home plate?

Baseball Path

FIGURE **1.50**

Solution

When $x = 300$, the height of the baseball is

$$f(300) = -0.0032(300)^2 + 300 + 3$$
$$= 15 \text{ feet.}$$

So, the baseball will clear the fence.

✓CHECKPOINT   Now try Exercise 93.

In the equation in Example 7, the height of the baseball is a function of the distance from home plate.

Number of Alternative-Fueled
Vehicles in the U.S.

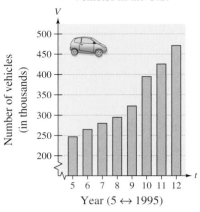

FIGURE 1.51

Example 8 **Alternative-Fueled Vehicles**

The number V (in thousands) of alternative-fueled vehicles in the United States increased in a linear pattern from 1995 to 1999, as shown in Figure 1.51. Then, in 2000, the number of vehicles took a jump and, until 2002, increased in a different linear pattern. These two patterns can be approximated by the function

$$V(t) = \begin{cases} 18.08t + 155.3 & 5 \le t \le 9 \\ 38.20t + 10.2, & 10 \le t \le 12 \end{cases}$$

where t represents the year, with $t = 5$ corresponding to 1995. Use this function to approximate the number of alternative-fueled vehicles for each year from 1995 to 2002. (Source: Science Applications International Corporation; Energy Information Administration)

Solution

From 1995 to 1999, use $V(t) = 18.08t + 155.3$.

245.7	263.8	281.9	299.9	318.0
1995	1996	1997	1998	1999

From 2000 to 2002, use $V(t) = 38.20t + 10.2$.

392.2	430.4	468.6
2000	2001	2002

✓CHECKPOINT Now try Exercise 95.

Difference Quotients

One of the basic definitions in calculus employs the ratio

$$\frac{f(x + h) - f(x)}{h}, \quad h \ne 0.$$

This ratio is called a **difference quotient,** as illustrated in Example 9.

Example 9 **Evaluating a Difference Quotient**

For $f(x) = x^2 - 4x + 7$, find $\dfrac{f(x + h) - f(x)}{h}$.

Solution

$$\frac{f(x + h) - f(x)}{h} = \frac{[(x + h)^2 - 4(x + h) + 7] - (x^2 - 4x + 7)}{h}$$

$$= \frac{x^2 + 2xh + h^2 - 4x - 4h + 7 - x^2 + 4x - 7}{h}$$

$$= \frac{2xh + h^2 - 4h}{h} = \frac{h(2x + h - 4)}{h} = 2x + h - 4, \ h \ne 0$$

✓CHECKPOINT Now try Exercise 79.

The symbol ∫ indicates an example or exercise that highlights algebraic techniques specifically used in calculus.

You may find it easier to calculate the difference quotient in Example 9 by first finding $f(x + h)$, and then substituting the resulting expression into the difference quotient, as follows.

$$f(x + h) = (x + h)^2 - 4(x + h) + 7 = x^2 + 2xh + h^2 - 4x - 4h + 7$$

$$\frac{f(x + h) - f(x)}{h} = \frac{(x^2 + 2xh + h^2 - 4x - 4h + 7) - (x^2 - 4x + 7)}{h}$$

$$= \frac{2xh + h^2 - 4h}{h} = \frac{h(2x + h - 4)}{h} = 2x + h - 4, h \neq 0$$

Summary of Function Terminology

Function: A **function** is a relationship between two variables such that to each value of the independent variable there corresponds exactly one value of the dependent variable.

Function Notation: $y = f(x)$

  f is the *name* of the function.

  y is the **dependent variable.**

  x is the **independent variable.**

  $f(x)$ is the *value of the function at x.*

Domain: The **domain** of a function is the set of all values (inputs) of the independent variable for which the function is defined. If x is in the domain of f, f is said to be *defined* at x. If x is not in the domain of f, f is said to be *undefined* at x.

Range: The **range** of a function is the set of all values (outputs) assumed by the dependent variable (that is, the set of all function values).

Implied Domain: If f is defined by an algebraic expression and the domain is not specified, the **implied domain** consists of all real numbers for which the expression is defined.

---

*W*RITING ABOUT *M*ATHEMATICS

Everyday Functions In groups of two or three, identify common real-life functions. Consider everyday activities, events, and expenses, such as long distance telephone calls and car insurance. Here are two examples.

a. The statement, "Your happiness is a function of the grade you receive in this course" *is not* a correct mathematical use of the word "function." The word "happiness" is ambiguous.

b. The statement, "Your federal income tax is a function of your adjusted gross income" *is* a correct mathematical use of the word "function." Once you have determined your adjusted gross income, your income tax can be determined.

Describe your functions in words. Avoid using ambiguous words. Can you find an example of a piecewise-defined function?

1.4 Exercises

VOCABULARY CHECK: Fill in the blanks.

1. A relation that assigns to each element x from a set of inputs, or _____, exactly one element y in a set of outputs, or _____, is called a _____.

2. Functions are commonly represented in four different ways, _____, _____, _____, and _____.

3. For an equation that represents y as a function of x, the set of all values taken on by the _____ variable x is the domain, and the set of all values taken on by the _____ variable y is the range.

4. The function given by

$$f(x) = \begin{cases} 2x - 1, & x < 0 \\ x^2 + 4, & x \geq 0 \end{cases}$$

is an example of a _____ function.

5. If the domain of the function f is not given, then the set of values of the independent variable for which the expression is defined is called the _____ _____.

6. In calculus, one of the basic definitions is that of a _____ _____, given by $\dfrac{f(x + h) - f(x)}{h}$, $h \neq 0$.

PREREQUISITE SKILLS REVIEW: Practice and review algebra skills needed for this section at **www.Eduspace.com.**

In Exercises 1–4, is the relationship a function?

1.
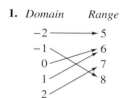

2. Domain   Range

$$\begin{array}{cc} -2 & 3 \\ -1 & 4 \\ 0 & 5 \\ 1 & \\ 2 & \end{array}$$

3.
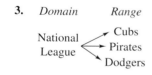

4. Domain   Range
(Year)   (Number of
North Atlantic
tropical storms
and hurricanes)

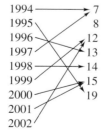

$$\begin{array}{cc} 1994 & 7 \\ 1995 & 8 \\ 1996 & 12 \\ 1997 & 13 \\ 1998 & 14 \\ 1999 & 15 \\ 2000 & 19 \\ 2001 & \\ 2002 & \end{array}$$

In Exercises 5–8, does the table describe a function? Explain your reasoning.

5.

Input value	−2	−1	0	1	2
Output value	−8	−1	0	1	8

6.

Input value	0	1	2	1	0
Output value	−4	−2	0	2	4

7.

Input value	10	7	4	7	10
Output value	3	6	9	12	15

8.

Input value	0	3	9	12	15
Output value	3	3	3	3	3

In Exercises 9 and 10, which sets of ordered pairs represent functions from A to B? Explain.

9. $A = \{0, 1, 2, 3\}$ and $B = \{-2, -1, 0, 1, 2\}$

(a) $\{(0, 1), (1, -2), (2, 0), (3, 2)\}$

(b) $\{(0, -1), (2, 2), (1, -2), (3, 0), (1, 1)\}$

(c) $\{(0, 0), (1, 0), (2, 0), (3, 0)\}$

(d) $\{(0, 2), (3, 0), (1, 1)\}$

10. $A = \{a, b, c\}$ and $B = \{0, 1, 2, 3\}$

(a) $\{(a, 1), (c, 2), (c, 3), (b, 3)\}$

(b) $\{(a, 1), (b, 2), (c, 3)\}$

(c) $\{(1, a), (0, a), (2, c), (3, b)\}$

(d) $\{(c, 0), (b, 0), (a, 3)\}$

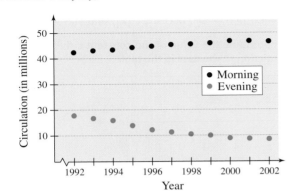

Circulation of Newspapers   In Exercises 11 and 12, use the graph, which shows the circulation (in millions) of daily newspapers in the United States.   (Source: Editor & Publisher Company)

11. Is the circulation of morning newspapers a function of the year? Is the circulation of evening newspapers a function of the year? Explain.

12. Let $f(x)$ represent the circulation of evening newspapers in year x. Find $f(1998)$.

In Exercises 13–24, determine whether the equation represents *y* as a function of *x*.

13. $x^2 + y^2 = 4$

14. $x = y^2$

15. $x^2 + y = 4$

16. $x + y^2 = 4$

17. $2x + 3y = 4$

18. $(x - 2)^2 + y^2 = 4$

19. $y^2 = x^2 - 1$

20. $y = \sqrt{x + 5}$

21. $y = |4 - x|$

22. $|y| = 4 - x$

23. $x = 14$

24. $y = -75$

In Exercises 25–38, evaluate the function at each specified value of the independent variable and simplify.

25. $f(x) = 2x - 3$
   (a) $f(1)$ (b) $f(-3)$ (c) $f(x - 1)$

26. $g(y) = 7 - 3y$
   (a) $g(0)$ (b) $g\left(\frac{7}{3}\right)$ (c) $g(s + 2)$

27. $V(r) = \frac{4}{3}\pi r^3$
   (a) $V(3)$ (b) $V\left(\frac{3}{2}\right)$ (c) $V(2r)$

28. $h(t) = t^2 - 2t$
   (a) $h(2)$ (b) $h(1.5)$ (c) $h(x + 2)$

29. $f(y) = 3 - \sqrt{y}$
   (a) $f(4)$ (b) $f(0.25)$ (c) $f(4x^2)$

30. $f(x) = \sqrt{x + 8} + 2$
   (a) $f(-8)$ (b) $f(1)$ (c) $f(x - 8)$

31. $q(x) = \dfrac{1}{x^2 - 9}$
   (a) $q(0)$ (b) $q(3)$ (c) $q(y + 3)$

32. $q(t) = \dfrac{2t^2 + 3}{t^2}$
   (a) $q(2)$ (b) $q(0)$ (c) $q(-x)$

33. $f(x) = \dfrac{|x|}{x}$
   (a) $f(2)$ (b) $f(-2)$ (c) $f(x - 1)$

34. $f(x) = |x| + 4$
   (a) $f(2)$ (b) $f(-2)$ (c) $f(x^2)$

35. $f(x) = \begin{cases} 2x + 1, & x < 0 \\ 2x + 2, & x \geq 0 \end{cases}$
   (a) $f(-1)$ (b) $f(0)$ (c) $f(2)$

36. $f(x) = \begin{cases} x^2 + 2, & x \leq 1 \\ 2x^2 + 2, & x > 1 \end{cases}$
   (a) $f(-2)$ (b) $f(1)$ (c) $f(2)$

37. $f(x) = \begin{cases} 3x - 1, & x < -1 \\ 4, & -1 \leq x \leq 1 \\ x^2, & x > 1 \end{cases}$
   (a) $f(-2)$ (b) $f\left(-\frac{1}{2}\right)$ (c) $f(3)$

38. $f(x) = \begin{cases} 4 - 5x, & x \leq -2 \\ 0, & -2 < x < 2 \\ x^2 + 1, & x > 2 \end{cases}$
   (a) $f(-3)$ (b) $f(4)$ (c) $f(-1)$

In Exercises 39–44, complete the table.

39. $f(x) = x^2 - 3$

x	-2	-1	0	1	2
$f(x)$					

40. $g(x) = \sqrt{x - 3}$

x	3	4	5	6	7
$g(x)$					

41. $h(t) = \frac{1}{2}|t + 3|$

t	-5	-4	-3	-2	-1
$h(t)$					

42. $f(s) = \dfrac{|s - 2|}{s - 2}$

s	0	1	$\frac{3}{2}$	$\frac{5}{2}$	4
$f(s)$					

43. $f(x) = \begin{cases} -\frac{1}{2}x + 4, & x \le 0 \\ (x-2)^2, & x > 0 \end{cases}$

x	-2	-1	0	1	2
$f(x)$					

44. $f(x) = \begin{cases} 9 - x^2, & x < 3 \\ x - 3, & x \ge 3 \end{cases}$

x	1	2	3	4	5
$f(x)$					

In Exercises 45–52, find all real values of x such that $f(x) = 0$.

45. $f(x) = 15 - 3x$

46. $f(x) = 5x + 1$

47. $f(x) = \dfrac{3x - 4}{5}$

48. $f(x) = \dfrac{12 - x^2}{5}$

49. $f(x) = x^2 - 9$

50. $f(x) = x^2 - 8x + 15$

51. $f(x) = x^3 - x$

52. $f(x) = x^3 - x^2 - 4x + 4$

In Exercises 53–56, find the value(s) of x for which $f(x) = g(x)$.

53. $f(x) = x^2 + 2x + 1, \quad g(x) = 3x + 3$

54. $f(x) = x^4 - 2x^2, \quad g(x) = 2x^2$

55. $f(x) = \sqrt{3x} + 1, \quad g(x) = x + 1$

56. $f(x) = \sqrt{x} - 4, \quad g(x) = 2 - x$

In Exercises 57–70, find the domain of the function.

57. $f(x) = 5x^2 + 2x - 1$

58. $g(x) = 1 - 2x^2$

59. $h(t) = \dfrac{4}{t}$

60. $s(y) = \dfrac{3y}{y + 5}$

61. $g(y) = \sqrt{y - 10}$

62. $f(t) = \sqrt[3]{t + 4}$

63. $f(x) = \sqrt[4]{1 - x^2}$

64. $f(x) = \sqrt[4]{x^2 + 3x}$

65. $g(x) = \dfrac{1}{x} - \dfrac{3}{x + 2}$

66. $h(x) = \dfrac{10}{x^2 - 2x}$

67. $f(s) = \dfrac{\sqrt{s - 1}}{s - 4}$

68. $f(x) = \dfrac{\sqrt{x + 6}}{6 + x}$

69. $f(x) = \dfrac{x - 4}{\sqrt{x}}$

70. $f(x) = \dfrac{x - 5}{\sqrt{x^2 - 9}}$

In Exercises 71–74, assume that the domain of f is the set $A = \{-2, -1, 0, 1, 2\}$. Determine the set of ordered pairs that represents the function f.

71. $f(x) = x^2$

72. $f(x) = x^2 - 3$

73. $f(x) = |x| + 2$

74. $f(x) = |x + 1|$

Exploration   In Exercises 75–78, match the data with one of the following functions

$f(x) = cx, \ g(x) = cx^2, \ h(x) = c\sqrt{|x|}, \text{ and } r(x) = \dfrac{c}{x}$

and determine the value of the constant c that will make the function fit the data in the table.

75.

x	-4	-1	0	1	4
y	-32	-2	0	-2	-32

76.

x	-4	-1	0	1	4
y	-1	$-\frac{1}{4}$	0	$\frac{1}{4}$	1

77.

x	-4	-1	0	1	4
y	-8	-32	Undef.	32	8

78.

x	-4	-1	0	1	4
y	6	3	0	3	6

In Exercises 79–86, find the difference quotient and simplify your answer.

79. $f(x) = x^2 - x + 1, \quad \dfrac{f(2 + h) - f(2)}{h}, h \ne 0$

80. $f(x) = 5x - x^2, \quad \dfrac{f(5 + h) - f(5)}{h}, h \ne 0$

81. $f(x) = x^3 + 3x, \quad \dfrac{f(x + h) - f(x)}{h}, h \ne 0$

82. $f(x) = 4x^2 - 2x, \quad \dfrac{f(x + h) - f(x)}{h}, h \ne 0$

83. $g(x) = \dfrac{1}{x^2}, \quad \dfrac{g(x) - g(3)}{x - 3}, x \ne 3$

84. $f(t) = \dfrac{1}{t - 2}, \quad \dfrac{f(t) - f(1)}{t - 1}, t \ne 1$

85. $f(x) = \sqrt{5x}, \quad \dfrac{f(x) - f(5)}{x - 5}, x \ne 5$

86. $f(x) = x^{2/3} + 1, \quad \dfrac{f(x) - f(8)}{x - 8}, x \ne 8$

87. *Geometry*   Write the area A of a square as a function of its perimeter P.

88. *Geometry*   Write the area A of a circle as a function of its circumference C.

The symbol ∫ indicates an example or exercise that highlights algebraic techniques specifically used in calculus.

89. Maximum Volume   An open box of maximum volume is to be made from a square piece of material 24 centimeters on a side by cutting equal squares from the corners and turning up the sides (see figure).

(a) The table shows the volume V (in cubic centimeters) of the box for various heights x (in centimeters). Use the table to estimate the maximum volume.

Height, x	1	2	3	4	5	6
Volume, V	484	800	972	1024	980	864

(b) Plot the points (x, V) from the table in part (a). Does the relation defined by the ordered pairs represent V as a function of x?

(c) If V is a function of x, write the function and determine its domain.

90. Maximum Profit   The cost per unit in the production of a portable CD player is \$60. The manufacturer charges \$90 per unit for orders of 100 or less. To encourage large orders, the manufacturer reduces the charge by \$0.15 per CD player for each unit ordered in excess of 100 (for example, there would be a charge of \$87 per CD player for an order size of 120).

(a) The table shows the profit P (in dollars) for various numbers of units ordered, x. Use the table to estimate the maximum profit.

Units, x	110	120	130	140
Profit, P	3135	3240	3315	3360

Units, x	150	160	170
Profit, P	3375	3360	3315

(b) Plot the points (x, P) from the table in part (a). Does the relation defined by the ordered pairs represent P as a function of x?

(c) If P is a function of x, write the function and determine its domain.

91. Geometry   A right triangle is formed in the first quadrant by the x- and y-axes and a line through the point $(2, 1)$ (see figure). Write the area A of the triangle as a function of x, and determine the domain of the function.

FIGURE FOR **91**   FIGURE FOR **92**

92. Geometry   A rectangle is bounded by the x-axis and the semicircle $y = \sqrt{36 - x^2}$ (see figure). Write the area A of the rectangle as a function of x, and determine the domain of the function.

93. Path of a Ball   The height y (in feet) of a baseball thrown by a child is

$$y = -\frac{1}{10}x^2 + 3x + 6$$

where x is the horizontal distance (in feet) from where the ball was thrown. Will the ball fly over the head of another child 30 feet away trying to catch the ball? (Assume that the child who is trying to catch the ball holds a baseball glove at a height of 5 feet.)

94. Prescription Drugs   The amounts d (in billions of dollars) spent on prescription drugs in the United States from 1991 to 2002 (see figure) can be approximated by the model

$$d(t) = \begin{cases} 5.0t + 37, & 1 \le t \le 7 \\ 18.7t - 64, & 8 \le t \le 12 \end{cases}$$

where t represents the year, with $t = 1$ corresponding to 1991. Use this model to find the amount spent on prescription drugs in each year from 1991 to 2002. (Source: U.S. Centers for Medicare & Medicaid Services)

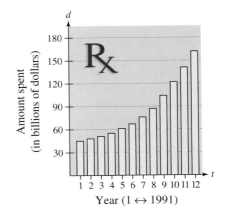

95. *Average Price* The average prices p (in thousands of dollars) of a new mobile home in the United States from 1990 to 2002 (see figure) can be approximated by the model

$$p(t) = \begin{cases} 0.182t^2 + 0.57t + 27.3, & 0 \le t \le 7 \\ 2.50t + 21.3, & 8 \le t \le 12 \end{cases}$$

where t represents the year, with $t = 0$ corresponding to 1990. Use this model to find the average price of a mobile home in each year from 1990 to 2002. (Source: U.S. Census Bureau)

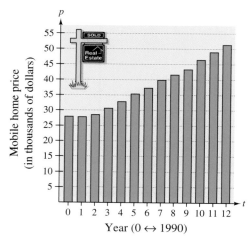

Year (0 ↔ 1990)

96. *Postal Regulations* A rectangular package to be sent by the U.S. Postal Service can have a maximum combined length and girth (perimeter of a cross section) of 108 inches (see figure).

(a) Write the volume V of the package as a function of x. What is the domain of the function?

 (b) Use a graphing utility to graph your function. Be sure to use an appropriate window setting.

(c) What dimensions will maximize the volume of the package? Explain your answer.

97. *Cost, Revenue, and Profit* A company produces a product for which the variable cost is $12.30 per unit and the fixed costs are $98,000. The product sells for $17.98. Let x be the number of units produced and sold.

(a) The total cost for a business is the sum of the variable cost and the fixed costs. Write the total cost C as a function of the number of units produced.

(b) Write the revenue R as a function of the number of units sold.

(c) Write the profit P as a function of the number of units sold. (Note: $P = R - C$)

98. *Average Cost* The inventor of a new game believes that the variable cost for producing the game is $0.95 per unit and the fixed costs are $6000. The inventor sells each game for $1.69. Let x be the number of games sold.

(a) The total cost for a business is the sum of the variable cost and the fixed costs. Write the total cost C as a function of the number of games sold.

(b) Write the average cost per unit $\overline{C} = C/x$ as a function of x.

99. *Transportation* For groups of 80 or more people, a charter bus company determines the rate per person according to the formula

Rate $= 8 - 0.05(n - 80), \quad n \ge 80$

where the rate is given in dollars and n is the number of people.

(a) Write the revenue R for the bus company as a function of n.

(b) Use the function in part (a) to complete the table. What can you conclude?

n	90	100	110	120	130	140	150
$R(n)$							

100. *Physics* The force F (in tons) of water against the face of a dam is estimated by the function $F(y) = 149.76\sqrt{10}\,y^{5/2}$, where y is the depth of the water (in feet).

(a) Complete the table. What can you conclude from the table?

y	5	10	20	30	40
$F(y)$					

(b) Use the table to approximate the depth at which the force against the dam is 1,000,000 tons.

(c) Find the depth at which the force against the dam is 1,000,000 tons algebraically.

101. *Height of a Balloon* A balloon carrying a transmitter ascends vertically from a point 3000 feet from the receiving station.

(a) Draw a diagram that gives a visual representation of the problem. Let h represent the height of the balloon and let d represent the distance between the balloon and the receiving station.

(b) Write the height of the balloon as a function of d. What is the domain of the function?

Model It

102. Wildlife   The graph shows the numbers of threatened and endangered fish species in the world from 1996 through 2003. Let $f(t)$ represent the number of threatened and endangered fish species in the year t. (Source: U.S. Fish and Wildlife Service)

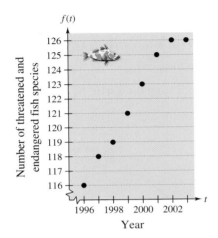

(a) Find $\dfrac{f(2003) - f(1996)}{2003 - 1996}$ and interpret the result in the context of the problem.

(b) Find a linear model for the data algebraically. Let N represent the number of threatened and endangered fish species and let $x = 6$ correspond to 1996.

(c) Use the model found in part (b) to complete the table.

x	6	7	8	9	10	11	12	13
N								

(d) Compare your results from part (c) with the actual data.

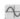 (e) Use a graphing utility to find a linear model for the data. Let $x = 6$ correspond to 1996. How does the model you found in part (b) compare with the model given by the graphing utility?

Synthesis

True or False?   **In Exercises 103 and 104, determine whether the statement is true or false. Justify your answer.**

103. The domain of the function given by $f(x) = x^4 - 1$ is $(-\infty, \infty)$, and the range of $f(x)$ is $(0, \infty)$.

104. The set of ordered pairs $\{(-8, -2), (-6, 0), (-4, 0), (-2, 2), (0, 4), (2, -2)\}$ represents a function.

**105. *Writing*   In your own words, explain the meanings of *domain* and *range*.

**106. *Think About It*   Consider $f(x) = \sqrt{x - 2}$ and $g(x) = \sqrt[3]{x - 2}$. Why are the domains of f and g different?

In Exercises 107 and 108, determine whether the statements use the word *function* in ways that are mathematically correct. Explain your reasoning.

107. (a) The sales tax on a purchased item is a function of the selling price.

(b) Your score on the next algebra exam is a function of the number of hours you study the night before the exam.

108. (a) The amount in your savings account is a function of your salary.

(b) The speed at which a free-falling baseball strikes the ground is a function of the height from which it was dropped.

Skills Review

In Exercises 109–112, solve the equation.

109. $\dfrac{t}{3} + \dfrac{t}{5} = 1$

110. $\dfrac{3}{t} + \dfrac{5}{t} = 1$

111. $\dfrac{3}{x(x + 1)} - \dfrac{4}{x} = \dfrac{1}{x + 1}$

112. $\dfrac{12}{x} - 3 = \dfrac{4}{x} + 9$

In Exercises 113–116, find the equation of the line passing through the pair of points.

113. $(-2, -5), (4, -1)$

114. $(10, 0), (1, 9)$

115. $(-6, 5), (3, -5)$

116. $\left(-\frac{1}{2}, 3\right), \left(\frac{11}{2}, -\frac{1}{3}\right)$

1.5 Analyzing Graphs of Functions

The Graph of a Function

In Section 1.4, you studied functions from an algebraic point of view. In this section, you will study functions from a graphical perspective.

The **graph of a function** f is the collection of ordered pairs $(x, f(x))$ such that x is in the domain of f. As you study this section, remember that

x = the directed distance from the y-axis

$y = f(x)$ = the directed distance from the x-axis

as shown in Figure 1.52.

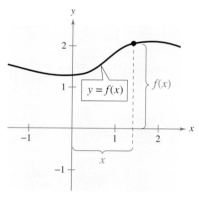

FIGURE 1.52

Example 1   Finding the Domain and Range of a Function

Use the graph of the function f, shown in Figure 1.53, to find (a) the domain of f, (b) the function values $f(-1)$ and $f(2)$, and (c) the range of f.

Solution

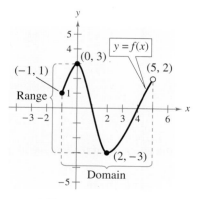

FIGURE 1.53

a. The closed dot at $(-1, 1)$ indicates that $x = -1$ is in the domain of f, whereas the open dot at $(5, 2)$ indicates that $x = 5$ is not in the domain. So, the domain of f is all x in the interval $[-1, 5)$.

b. Because $(-1, 1)$ is a point on the graph of f, it follows that $f(-1) = 1$. Similarly, because $(2, -3)$ is a point on the graph of f, it follows that $f(2) = -3$.

c. Because the graph does not extend below $f(2) = -3$ or above $f(0) = 3$, the range of f is the interval $[-3, 3]$.

✓**CHECKPOINT**   Now try Exercise 1.

The use of dots (open or closed) at the extreme left and right points of a graph indicates that the graph does not extend beyond these points. If no such dots are shown, assume that the graph extends beyond these points.

By the definition of a function, at most one *y*-value corresponds to a given *x*-value. This means that the graph of a function cannot have two or more different points with the same *x*-coordinate, and no two points on the graph of a function can be vertically above or below each other. It follows, then, that a vertical line can intersect the graph of a function at most once. This observation provides a convenient visual test called the **Vertical Line Test** for functions.

Vertical Line Test for Functions

A set of points in a coordinate plane is the graph of *y* as a function of *x* if and only if no *vertical* line intersects the graph at more than one point.

Example 2   **Vertical Line Test for Functions**

Use the Vertical Line Test to decide whether the graphs in Figure 1.54 represent *y* as a function of *x*.

(a)

(b)

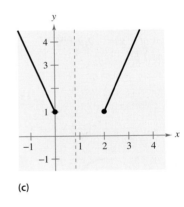

(c)

FIGURE 1.54

Solution

a. This *is not* a graph of *y* as a function of *x*, because you can find a vertical line that intersects the graph twice. That is, for a particular input *x*, there is more than one output *y*.

b. This *is* a graph of *y* as a function of *x*, because every vertical line intersects the graph at most once. That is, for a particular input *x*, there is at most one output *y*.

c. This *is* a graph of *y* as a function of *x*. (Note that if a vertical line does not intersect the graph, it simply means that the function is undefined for that particular value of *x*.) That is, for a particular input *x*, there is at most one output *y*.

✓CHECKPOINT   Now try Exercise 9.

Zeros of a Function

If the graph of a function of x has an x-intercept at $(a, 0)$, then a is a **zero** of the function.

> **Zeros of a Function**
>
> The **zeros of a function** f of x are the x-values for which $f(x) = 0$.

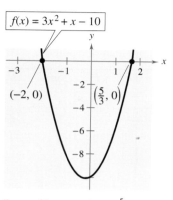

$f(x) = 3x^2 + x - 10$

Zeros of f: $x = -2, x = \frac{5}{3}$

FIGURE **1.55**

Example 3   Finding the Zeros of a Function

Find the zeros of each function.

a. $f(x) = 3x^2 + x - 10$ **b.** $g(x) = \sqrt{10 - x^2}$ **c.** $h(t) = \dfrac{2t - 3}{t + 5}$

Solution

To find the zeros of a function, set the function equal to zero and solve for the independent variable.

a.
$$3x^2 + x - 10 = 0 \qquad \text{Set } f(x) \text{ equal to 0.}$$
$$(3x - 5)(x + 2) = 0 \qquad \text{Factor.}$$
$$3x - 5 = 0 \ \Longrightarrow \ x = \tfrac{5}{3} \qquad \text{Set 1st factor equal to 0.}$$
$$x + 2 = 0 \ \Longrightarrow \ x = -2 \qquad \text{Set 2nd factor equal to 0.}$$

The zeros of f are $x = \frac{5}{3}$ and $x = -2$. In Figure 1.55, note that the graph of f has $\left(\frac{5}{3}, 0\right)$ and $(-2, 0)$ as its x-intercepts.

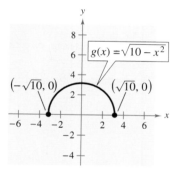

$g(x) = \sqrt{10 - x^2}$

$(-\sqrt{10}, 0)$ $(\sqrt{10}, 0)$

Zeros of g: $x = \pm\sqrt{10}$

FIGURE **1.56**

b.
$$\sqrt{10 - x^2} = 0 \qquad \text{Set } g(x) \text{ equal to 0.}$$
$$10 - x^2 = 0 \qquad \text{Square each side.}$$
$$10 = x^2 \qquad \text{Add } x^2 \text{ to each side.}$$
$$\pm\sqrt{10} = x \qquad \text{Extract square roots.}$$

The zeros of g are $x = -\sqrt{10}$ and $x = \sqrt{10}$. In Figure 1.56, note that the graph of g has $\left(-\sqrt{10}, 0\right)$ and $\left(\sqrt{10}, 0\right)$ as its x-intercepts.

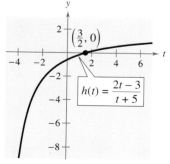

$\left(\frac{3}{2}, 0\right)$

$h(t) = \dfrac{2t - 3}{t + 5}$

Zero of h: $t = \frac{3}{2}$

FIGURE **1.57**

c.
$$\frac{2t - 3}{t + 5} = 0 \qquad \text{Set } h(t) \text{ equal to 0.}$$
$$2t - 3 = 0 \qquad \text{Multiply each side by } t + 5.$$
$$2t = 3 \qquad \text{Add 3 to each side.}$$
$$t = \frac{3}{2} \qquad \text{Divide each side by 2.}$$

The zero of h is $t = \frac{3}{2}$. In Figure 1.57, note that the graph of h has $\left(\frac{3}{2}, 0\right)$ as its t-intercept.

✓**CHECKPOINT**   Now try Exercise 15.

Increasing and Decreasing Functions

The more you know about the graph of a function, the more you know about the function itself. Consider the graph shown in Figure 1.58. As you move from *left to right*, this graph falls from $x = -2$ to $x = 0$, is constant from $x = 0$ to $x = 2$, and rises from $x = 2$ to $x = 4$.

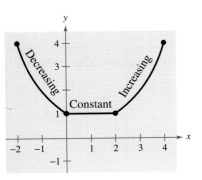

FIGURE **1.58**

> ## Increasing, Decreasing, and Constant Functions
>
> A function f is **increasing** on an interval if, for any x_1 and x_2 in the interval, $x_1 < x_2$ implies $f(x_1) < f(x_2)$.
>
> A function f is **decreasing** on an interval if, for any x_1 and x_2 in the interval, $x_1 < x_2$ implies $f(x_1) > f(x_2)$.
>
> A function f is **constant** on an interval if, for any x_1 and x_2 in the interval, $f(x_1) = f(x_2)$.

Example 4   Increasing and Decreasing Functions

Use the graphs in Figure 1.59 to describe the increasing or decreasing behavior of each function.

Solution

a. This function is increasing over the entire real line.

b. This function is increasing on the interval $(-\infty, -1)$, decreasing on the interval $(-1, 1)$, and increasing on the interval $(1, \infty)$.

c. This function is increasing on the interval $(-\infty, 0)$, constant on the interval $(0, 2)$, and decreasing on the interval $(2, \infty)$.

(a)

(b)

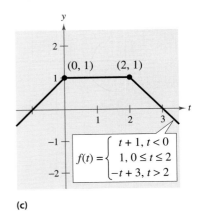

(c)

FIGURE **1.59**

✔CHECKPOINT   Now try Exercise 33.

To help you decide whether a function is increasing, decreasing, or constant on an interval, you can evaluate the function for several values of x. However, calculus is needed to determine, for certain, all intervals on which a function is increasing, decreasing, or constant.

y

Relative maxima

Relative minima

x

FIGURE 1.60

The points at which a function changes its increasing, decreasing, or constant behavior are helpful in determining the **relative minimum** or **relative maximum** values of the function.

> **Definitions of Relative Minimum and Relative Maximum**
>
> A function value $f(a)$ is called a **relative minimum** of f if there exists an interval (x_1, x_2) that contains a such that
>
> $$x_1 < x < x_2 \quad \text{implies} \quad f(a) \le f(x).$$
>
> A function value $f(a)$ is called a **relative maximum** of f if there exists an interval (x_1, x_2) that contains a such that
>
> $$x_1 < x < x_2 \quad \text{implies} \quad f(a) \ge f(x).$$

Figure 1.60 shows several different examples of relative minima and relative maxima. In Section 2.1, you will study a technique for finding the *exact point* at which a second-degree polynomial function has a relative minimum or relative maximum. For the time being, however, you can use a graphing utility to find reasonable approximations of these points.

Example 5 **Approximating a Relative Minimum**

Use a graphing utility to approximate the relative minimum of the function given by $f(x) = 3x^2 - 4x - 2$.

Solution

The graph of f is shown in Figure 1.61. By using the *zoom* and *trace* features or the *minimum* feature of a graphing utility, you can estimate that the function has a relative minimum at the point

$$(0.67, -3.33). \qquad \text{Relative minimum}$$

Later, in Section 2.1, you will be able to determine that the exact point at which the relative minimum occurs is $\left(\frac{2}{3}, -\frac{10}{3}\right)$.

✓CHECKPOINT   Now try Exercise 49.

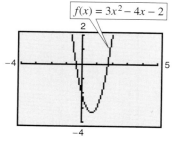

$f(x) = 3x^2 - 4x - 2$

FIGURE 1.61

You can also use the *table* feature of a graphing utility to approximate numerically the relative minimum of the function in Example 5. Using a table that begins at 0.6 and increments the value of x by 0.01, you can approximate that the minimum of $f(x) = 3x^2 - 4x - 2$ occurs at the point $(0.67, -3.33)$.

> **Technology**
>
> If you use a graphing utility to estimate the *x*- and *y*-values of a relative minimum or relative maximum, the *zoom* feature will often produce graphs that are nearly flat. To overcome this problem, you can manually change the vertical setting of the viewing window. The graph will stretch vertically if the values of Ymin and Ymax are closer together.

Average Rate of Change

In Section 1.3, you learned that the slope of a line can be interpreted as a *rate of change*. For a nonlinear graph whose slope changes at each point, the **average rate of change** between any two points $(x_1, f(x_1))$ and $(x_2, f(x_2))$ is the slope of the line through the two points (see Figure 1.62). The line through the two points is called the **secant line**, and the slope of this line is denoted as m_{sec}.

$$\text{Average rate of change of } f \text{ from } x_1 \text{ to } x_2 = \frac{f(x_2) - f(x_1)}{x_2 - x_1}$$

$$= \frac{\text{change in } y}{\text{change in } x}$$

$$= m_{sec}$$

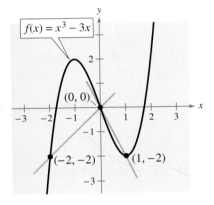

FIGURE 1.62

Example 6   **Average Rate of Change of a Function**

Find the average rates of change of $f(x) = x^3 - 3x$ (a) from $x_1 = -2$ to $x_2 = 0$ and (b) from $x_1 = 0$ to $x_2 = 1$ (see Figure 1.63).

Solution

a. The average rate of change of f from $x_1 = -2$ to $x_2 = 0$ is

$$\frac{f(x_2) - f(x_1)}{x_2 - x_1} = \frac{f(0) - f(-2)}{0 - (-2)} = \frac{0 - (-2)}{2} = 1.$$ Secant line has positive slope.

b. The average rate of change of f from $x_1 = 0$ to $x_2 = 1$ is

$$\frac{f(x_2) - f(x_1)}{x_2 - x_1} = \frac{f(1) - f(0)}{1 - 0} = \frac{-2 - 0}{1} = -2.$$ Secant line has negative slope.

✓CHECKPOINT   Now try Exercise 63.

FIGURE 1.63

Example 7   **Finding Average Speed**

The distance s (in feet) a moving car is from a stoplight is given by the function $s(t) = 20t^{3/2}$, where t is the time (in seconds). Find the average speed of the car (a) from $t_1 = 0$ to $t_2 = 4$ seconds and (b) from $t_1 = 4$ to $t_2 = 9$ seconds.

Solution

a. The average speed of the car from $t_1 = 0$ to $t_2 = 4$ seconds is

$$\frac{s(t_2) - s(t_1)}{t_2 - t_1} = \frac{s(4) - s(0)}{4 - (0)} = \frac{160 - 0}{4} = 40 \text{ feet per second.}$$

b. The average speed of the car from $t_1 = 4$ to $t_2 = 9$ seconds is

$$\frac{s(t_2) - s(t_1)}{t_2 - t_1} = \frac{s(9) - s(4)}{9 - 4} = \frac{540 - 160}{5} = 76 \text{ feet per second.}$$

✓CHECKPOINT   Now try Exercise 89.

Exploration

Use the information in Example 7 to find the average speed of the car from $t_1 = 0$ to $t_2 = 9$ seconds. Explain why the result is less than the value obtained in part (b).

Even and Odd Functions

In Section 1.2, you studied different types of symmetry of a graph. In the terminology of functions, a function is said to be **even** if its graph is symmetric with respect to the y-axis and to be **odd** if its graph is symmetric with respect to the origin. The symmetry tests in Section 1.2 yield the following tests for even and odd functions.

> **Tests for Even and Odd Functions**
>
> A function $y = f(x)$ is **even** if, for each x in the domain of f,
> $$f(-x) = f(x).$$
> A function $y = f(x)$ is **odd** if, for each x in the domain of f,
> $$f(-x) = -f(x).$$

> *Exploration*
>
> Graph each of the functions with a graphing utility. Determine whether the function is *even*, *odd*, or *neither*.
>
> $$f(x) = x^2 - x^4$$
> $$g(x) = 2x^3 + 1$$
> $$h(x) = x^5 - 2x^3 + x$$
> $$j(x) = 2 - x^6 - x^8$$
> $$k(x) = x^5 - 2x^4 + x - 2$$
> $$p(x) = x^9 + 3x^5 - x^3 + x$$
>
> What do you notice about the equations of functions that are odd? What do you notice about the equations of functions that are even? Can you describe a way to identify a function as odd or even by inspecting the equation? Can you describe a way to identify a function as neither odd nor even by inspecting the equation?

Example 8 **Even and Odd Functions**

a. The function $g(x) = x^3 - x$ is odd because $g(-x) = -g(x)$, as follows.

$$g(-x) = (-x)^3 - (-x) \qquad \text{Substitute } -x \text{ for } x.$$
$$= -x^3 + x \qquad \text{Simplify.}$$
$$= -(x^3 - x) \qquad \text{Distributive Property}$$
$$= -g(x) \qquad \text{Test for odd function}$$

b. The function $h(x) = x^2 + 1$ is even because $h(-x) = h(x)$, as follows.

$$h(-x) = (-x)^2 + 1 \qquad \text{Substitute } -x \text{ for } x.$$
$$= x^2 + 1 \qquad \text{Simplify.}$$
$$= h(x) \qquad \text{Test for even function}$$

The graphs and symmetry of these two functions are shown in Figure 1.64.

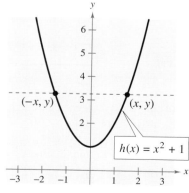

(a) **Symmetric to origin: Odd Function**

(b) **Symmetric to y-axis: Even Function**

FIGURE 1.64

✓**CHECKPOINT**   Now try Exercise 71.

1.5 | Exercises

VOCABULARY CHECK: Fill in the blanks.

1. The graph of a function f is the collection of _____ _____ or $(x, f(x))$ such that x is in the domain of f.

2. The _____ _____ _____ is used to determine whether the graph of an equation is a function of y in terms of x.

3. The _____ of a function f are the values of x for which $f(x) = 0$.

4. A function f is _____ on an interval if, for any x_1 and x_2 in the interval, $x_1 < x_2$ implies $f(x_1) > f(x_2)$.

5. A function value $f(a)$ is a relative _____ of f if there exists an interval (x_1, x_2) containing a such that $x_1 < x < x_2$ implies $f(a) \geq f(x)$.

6. The _____ _____ _____ _____ between any two points $(x_1, f(x_1))$ and $(x_2, f(x_2))$ is the slope of the line through the two points, and this line is called the _____ line.

7. A function f is _____ if for the each x in the domain of f, $f(-x) = -f(x)$.

8. A function f is _____ if its graph is symmetric with respect to the y-axis.

PREREQUISITE SKILLS REVIEW: Practice and review algebra skills needed for this section at **www.Eduspace.com.**

In Exercises 1–4, use the graph of the function to find the domain and range of f.

1.

2.

3.

4.

In Exercises 5–8, use the graph of the function to find the indicated function values.

5. (a) $f(-2)$ (b) $f(-1)$
   (c) $f(\frac{1}{2})$ (d) $f(1)$

6. (a) $f(-1)$ (b) $f(2)$
   (c) $f(0)$ (d) $f(1)$

7. (a) $f(-2)$ (b) $f(1)$
   (c) $f(0)$ (d) $f(2)$

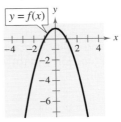

8. (a) $f(2)$ (b) $f(1)$
   (c) $f(3)$ (d) $f(-1)$

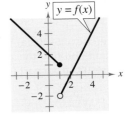

In Exercises 9–14, use the Vertical Line Test to determine whether y is a function of x. To print an enlarged copy of the graph, go to the website www.mathgraphs.com.

9. $y = \frac{1}{2}x^2$

10. $y = \frac{1}{4}x^3$

11. $x - y^2 = 1$

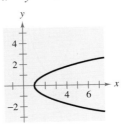

12. $x^2 + y^2 = 25$

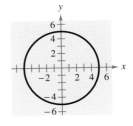

13. $x^2 = 2xy - 1$

14. $x = |y + 2|$

In Exercises 15–24, find the zeros of the function algebraically.

15. $f(x) = 2x^2 - 7x - 30$ **16.** $f(x) = 3x^2 + 22x - 16$

17. $f(x) = \dfrac{x}{9x^2 - 4}$ **18.** $f(x) = \dfrac{x^2 - 9x + 14}{4x}$

19. $f(x) = \frac{1}{2}x^3 - x$

20. $f(x) = x^3 - 4x^2 - 9x + 36$

21. $f(x) = 4x^3 - 24x^2 - x + 6$

22. $f(x) = 9x^4 - 25x^2$

23. $f(x) = \sqrt{2x - 1}$

24. $f(x) = \sqrt{3x + 2}$

In Exercises 25–30, (a) use a graphing utility to graph the function and find the zeros of the function and (b) verify your results from part (a) algebraically.

25. $f(x) = 3 + \dfrac{5}{x}$

26. $f(x) = x(x - 7)$

27. $f(x) = \sqrt{2x + 11}$

28. $f(x) = \sqrt{3x - 14} - 8$

29. $f(x) = \dfrac{3x - 1}{x - 6}$

30. $f(x) = \dfrac{2x^2 - 9}{3 - x}$

In Exercises 31–38, determine the intervals over which the function is increasing, decreasing, or constant.

31. $f(x) = \frac{3}{2}x$ **32.** $f(x) = x^2 - 4x$

33. $f(x) = x^3 - 3x^2 + 2$

34. $f(x) = \sqrt{x^2 - 1}$

35. $f(x) = \begin{cases} x + 3, & x \le 0 \\ 3, & 0 < x \le 2 \\ 2x + 1, & x > 2 \end{cases}$

36. $f(x) = \begin{cases} 2x + 1, & x \le -1 \\ x^2 - 2, & x > -1 \end{cases}$

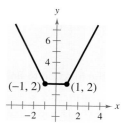

37. $f(x) = |x + 1| + |x - 1|$ **38.** $f(x) = \dfrac{x^2 + x + 1}{x + 1}$

In Exercises 39–48, (a) use a graphing utility to graph the function and visually determine the intervals over which the function is increasing, decreasing, or constant, and (b) make a table of values to verify whether the function is increasing, decreasing, or constant over the intervals you identified in part (a).

39. $f(x) = 3$

40. $g(x) = x$

41. $g(s) = \dfrac{s^2}{4}$

42. $h(x) = x^2 - 4$

43. $f(t) = -t^4$

44. $f(x) = 3x^4 - 6x^2$

45. $f(x) = \sqrt{1-x}$

46. $f(x) = x\sqrt{x+3}$

47. $f(x) = x^{3/2}$

48. $f(x) = x^{2/3}$

In Exercises 49–54, use a graphing utility to graph the function and approximate (to two decimal places) any relative minimum or relative maximum values.

49. $f(x) = (x-4)(x+2)$

50. $f(x) = 3x^2 - 2x - 5$

51. $f(x) = -x^2 + 3x - 2$

52. $f(x) = -2x^2 + 9x$

53. $f(x) = x(x-2)(x+3)$

54. $f(x) = x^3 - 3x^2 - x + 1$

In Exercises 55–62, graph the function and determine the interval(s) for which $f(x) \geq 0$.

55. $f(x) = 4 - x$

56. $f(x) = 4x + 2$

57. $f(x) = x^2 + x$

58. $f(x) = x^2 - 4x$

59. $f(x) = \sqrt{x-1}$

60. $f(x) = \sqrt{x+2}$

61. $f(x) = -\left(1 + |x|\right)$

62. $f(x) = \frac{1}{2}\left(2 + |x|\right)$

In Exercises 63–70, find the average rate of change of the function from x_1 to x_2.

Function	x-Values
63. $f(x) = -2x + 15$	$x_1 = 0, x_2 = 3$
64. $f(x) = 3x + 8$	$x_1 = 0, x_2 = 3$
65. $f(x) = x^2 + 12x - 4$	$x_1 = 1, x_2 = 5$
66. $f(x) = x^2 - 2x + 8$	$x_1 = 1, x_2 = 5$
67. $f(x) = x^3 - 3x^2 - x$	$x_1 = 1, x_2 = 3$
68. $f(x) = -x^3 + 6x^2 + x$	$x_1 = 1, x_2 = 6$
69. $f(x) = -\sqrt{x-2} + 5$	$x_1 = 3, x_2 = 11$
70. $f(x) = -\sqrt{x+1} + 3$	$x_1 = 3, x_2 = 8$

In Exercises 71–76, determine whether the function is even, odd, or neither. Then describe the symmetry.

71. $f(x) = x^6 - 2x^2 + 3$

72. $h(x) = x^3 - 5$

73. $g(x) = x^3 - 5x$

74. $f(x) = x\sqrt{1-x^2}$

75. $f(t) = t^2 + 2t - 3$

76. $g(s) = 4s^{2/3}$

In Exercises 77–80, write the height h of the rectangle as a function of x.

77.

$y = -x^2 + 4x - 1$
$(1, 2)$ $(3, 2)$

78.

$(1, 3)$
$y = 4x - x^2$

79.

$y = 4x - x^2$
$(2, 4)$
$y = 2x$

80.
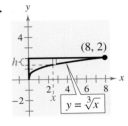
$(8, 2)$
$y = \sqrt[3]{x}$

In Exercises 81–84, write the length L of the rectangle as a function of y.

81.

L
$(8, 4)$
$x = \frac{1}{2}y^2$

82.
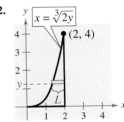
$x = \sqrt[3]{2y}$
$(2, 4)$
L

83.

$x = y^2$
$(4, 2)$
L

84.

$\left(\frac{1}{2}, 4\right)$
$x = \frac{2}{y}$
$(1, 2)$
L

85. ***Electronics*** The number of lumens (time rate of flow of light) L from a fluorescent lamp can be approximated by the model

$$L = -0.294x^2 + 97.744x - 664.875, \quad 20 \leq x \leq 90$$

where x is the wattage of the lamp.

(a) Use a graphing utility to graph the function.

(b) Use the graph from part (a) to estimate the wattage necessary to obtain 2000 lumens.

Model It

86. Data Analysis: Temperature The table shows the temperature y (in degrees Fahrenheit) of a certain city over a 24-hour period. Let x represent the time of day, where $x = 0$ corresponds to 6 A.M.

Time, x	Temperature, y
0	34
2	50
4	60
6	64
8	63
10	59
12	53
14	46
16	40
18	36
20	34
22	37
24	45

A model that represents these data is given by

$$y = 0.026x^3 - 1.03x^2 + 10.2x + 34, \quad 0 \le x \le 24.$$

(a) Use a graphing utility to create a scatter plot of the data. Then graph the model in the same viewing window.

(b) How well does the model fit the data?

(c) Use the graph to approximate the times when the temperature was increasing and decreasing.

(d) Use the graph to approximate the maximum and minimum temperatures during this 24-hour period.

(e) Could this model be used to predict the temperature for the city during the next 24-hour period? Why or why not?

87. Coordinate Axis Scale Each function models the specified data for the years 1995 through 2005, with $t = 5$ corresponding to 1995. Estimate a reasonable scale for the vertical axis (e.g., hundreds, thousands, millions, etc.) of the graph and justify your answer. (There are many correct answers.)

(a) $f(t)$ represents the average salary of college professors.

(b) $f(t)$ represents the U.S. population.

(c) $f(t)$ represents the percent of the civilian work force that is unemployed.

88. Geometry Corners of equal size are cut from a square with sides of length 8 meters (see figure).

(a) Write the area A of the resulting figure as a function of x. Determine the domain of the function.

 (b) Use a graphing utility to graph the area function over its domain. Use the graph to find the range of the function.

(c) Identify the figure that would result if x were chosen to be the maximum value in the domain of the function. What would be the length of each side of the figure?

89. Digital Music Sales The estimated revenues r (in billions of dollars) from sales of digital music from 2002 to 2007 can be approximated by the model

$$r = 15.639t^3 - 104.75t^2 + 303.5t - 301, \quad 2 \le t \le 7$$

where t represents the year, with $t = 2$ corresponding to 2002. (Source: *Fortune*)

 (a) Use a graphing utility to graph the model.

 (b) Find the average rate of change of the model from 2002 to 2007. Interpret your answer in the context of the problem.

90. Foreign College Students The numbers of foreign students F (in thousands) enrolled in colleges in the United States from 1992 to 2002 can be approximated by the model.

$$F = 0.004t^4 + 0.46t^2 + 431.6, \quad 2 \le t \le 12$$

where t represents the year, with $t = 2$ corresponding to 1992. (Source: Institute of International Education)

(a) Use a graphing utility to graph the model.

(b) Find the average rate of change of the model from 1992 to 2002. Interpret your answer in the context of the problem.

(c) Find the five-year time periods when the rate of change was the greatest and the least.

Physics   In Exercises 91–96, (a) use the position equation $s = -16t^2 + v_0t + s_0$ to write a function that represents the situation, (b) use a graphing utility to graph the function, (c) find the average rate of change of the function from t_1 to t_2, (d) interpret your answer to part (c) in the context of the problem, (e) find the equation of the secant line through t_1 and t_2, and (f) graph the secant line in the same viewing window as your position function.

91. An object is thrown upward from a height of 6 feet at a velocity of 64 feet per second.

$t_1 = 0, t_2 = 3$

92. An object is thrown upward from a height of 6.5 feet at a velocity of 72 feet per second.

$t_1 = 0, t_2 = 4$

93. An object is thrown upward from ground level at a velocity of 120 feet per second.

$t_1 = 3, t_2 = 5$

94. An object is thrown upward from ground level at a velocity of 96 feet per second.

$t_1 = 2, t_2 = 5$

95. An object is dropped from a height of 120 feet.

$t_1 = 0, t_2 = 2$

96. An object is dropped from a height of 80 feet.

$t_1 = 1, t_2 = 2$

Synthesis

True or False?   In Exercises 97 and 98, determine whether the statement is true or false. Justify your answer.

97. A function with a square root cannot have a domain that is the set of real numbers.

98. It is possible for an odd function to have the interval $[0, \infty)$ as its domain.

99. If f is an even function, determine whether g is even, odd, or neither. Explain.

(a) $g(x) = -f(x)$

(b) $g(x) = f(-x)$

(c) $g(x) = f(x) - 2$

(d) $g(x) = f(x - 2)$

100. *Think About It*   Does the graph in Exercise 11 represent x as a function of y? Explain.

Think About It   In Exercises 101–104, find the coordinates of a second point on the graph of a function f if the given point is on the graph and the function is (a) even and (b) odd.

101. $\left(-\frac{3}{2}, 4\right)$

102. $\left(-\frac{5}{3}, -7\right)$

103. $(4, 9)$

104. $(5, -1)$

 105. *Writing*   Use a graphing utility to graph each function. Write a paragraph describing any similarities and differences you observe among the graphs.

(a) $y = x$ (b) $y = x^2$

(c) $y = x^3$ (d) $y = x^4$

(e) $y = x^5$ (f) $y = x^6$

106. *Conjecture*   Use the results of Exercise 105 to make a conjecture about the graphs of $y = x^7$ and $y = x^8$. Use a graphing utility to graph the functions and compare the results with your conjecture.

Skills Review

In Exercises 107–110, solve the equation.

107. $x^2 - 10x = 0$

108. $100 - (x - 5)^2 = 0$

109. $x^3 - x = 0$

110. $16x^2 - 40x + 25 = 0$

In Exercises 111–114, evaluate the function at each specified value of the independent variable and simplify.

111. $f(x) = 5x - 8$

(a) $f(9)$ (b) $f(-4)$ (c) $f(x - 7)$

112. $f(x) = x^2 - 10x$

(a) $f(4)$ (b) $f(-8)$ (c) $f(x - 4)$

113. $f(x) = \sqrt{x - 12} - 9$

(a) $f(12)$ (b) $f(40)$ (c) $f\left(-\sqrt{36}\right)$

114. $f(x) = x^4 - x - 5$

(a) $f(-1)$ (b) $f\left(\frac{1}{2}\right)$ (c) $f\left(2\sqrt{3}\right)$

In Exercises 115 and 116, find the difference quotient and simplify your answer.

115. $f(x) = x^2 - 2x + 9$, $\dfrac{f(3 + h) - f(3)}{h}$, $h \neq 0$

116. $f(x) = 5 + 6x - x^2$, $\dfrac{f(6 + h) - f(6)}{h}$, $h \neq 0$

1.6 A Library of Parent Functions

What you should learn

- Identify and graph linear and squaring functions.
- Identify and graph cubic, square root, and reciprocal functions.
- Identify and graph step and other piecewise-defined functions.
- Recognize graphs of parent functions.

Why you should learn it

Step functions can be used to model real-life situations. For instance, in Exercise 63 on page 72, you will use a step function to model the cost of sending an overnight package from Los Angeles to Miami.

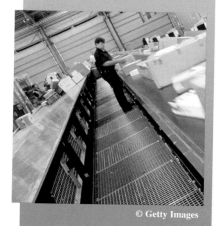

© Getty Images

Linear and Squaring Functions

One of the goals of this text is to enable you to recognize the basic shapes of the graphs of different types of functions. For instance, you know that the graph of the **linear function** $f(x) = ax + b$ is a line with slope $m = a$ and y-intercept at $(0, b)$. The graph of the linear function has the following characteristics.

- The domain of the function is the set of all real numbers.
- The range of the function is the set of all real numbers.
- The graph has an x-intercept of $(-b/m, 0)$ and a y-intercept of $(0, b)$.
- The graph is increasing if $m > 0$, decreasing if $m < 0$, and constant if $m = 0$.

Example 1 Writing a Linear Function

Write the linear function f for which $f(1) = 3$ and $f(4) = 0$.

Solution

To find the equation of the line that passes through $(x_1, y_1) = (1, 3)$ and $(x_2, y_2) = (4, 0)$, first find the slope of the line.

$$m = \frac{y_2 - y_1}{x_2 - x_1} = \frac{0 - 3}{4 - 1} = \frac{-3}{3} = -1$$

Next, use the point-slope form of the equation of a line.

$$y - y_1 = m(x - x_1) \qquad \text{Point-slope form}$$
$$y - 3 = -1(x - 1) \qquad \text{Substitute for } x_1, y_1, \text{ and } m.$$
$$y = -x + 4 \qquad \text{Simplify.}$$
$$f(x) = -x + 4 \qquad \text{Function notation}$$

The graph of this function is shown in Figure 1.65.

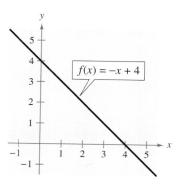

$$f(x) = -x + 4$$

FIGURE 1.65

✓CHECKPOINT Now try Exercise 1.

There are two special types of linear functions, the **constant function** and the **identity function.** A constant function has the form

$$f(x) = c$$

and has the domain of all real numbers with a range consisting of a single real number c. The graph of a constant function is a horizontal line, as shown in Figure 1.66. The identity function has the form

$$f(x) = x.$$

Its domain and range are the set of all real numbers. The identity function has a slope of $m = 1$ and a y-intercept $(0, 0)$. The graph of the identity function is a line for which each x-coordinate equals the corresponding y-coordinate. The graph is always increasing, as shown in Figure 1.67

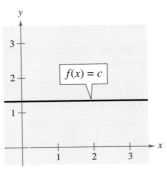

FIGURE 1.66

FIGURE 1.67

The graph of the **squaring function**

$$f(x) = x^2$$

is a U-shaped curve with the following characteristics.

- The domain of the function is the set of all real numbers.
- The range of the function is the set of all nonnegative real numbers.
- The function is even.
- The graph has an intercept at $(0, 0)$.
- The graph is decreasing on the interval $(-\infty, 0)$ and increasing on the interval $(0, \infty)$.
- The graph is symmetric with respect to the y-axis.
- The graph has a relative minimum at $(0, 0)$.

The graph of the squaring function is shown in Figure 1.68.

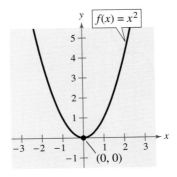

FIGURE 1.68

Cubic, Square Root, and Reciprocal Functions

The basic characteristics of the graphs of the **cubic, square root,** and **reciprocal functions** are summarized below.

1. The graph of the cubic function $f(x) = x^3$ has the following characteristics.

- The domain of the function is the set of all real numbers.
- The range of the function is the set of all real numbers.
- The function is odd.
- The graph has an intercept at $(0, 0)$.
- The graph is increasing on the interval $(-\infty, \infty)$.
- The graph is symmetric with respect to the origin.

The graph of the cubic function is shown in Figure 1.69.

2. The graph of the *square root* function $f(x) = \sqrt{x}$ has the following characteristics.

- The domain of the function is the set of all nonnegative real numbers.
- The range of the function is the set of all nonnegative real numbers.
- The graph has an intercept at $(0, 0)$.
- The graph is increasing on the interval $(0, \infty)$.

The graph of the square root function is shown in Figure 1.70.

3. The graph of the reciprocal function $f(x) = \dfrac{1}{x}$ has the following characteristics.

- The domain of the function is $(-\infty, 0) \cup (0, \infty)$.
- The range of the function is $(-\infty, 0) \cup (0, \infty)$.
- The function is odd.
- The graph does not have any intercepts.
- The graph is decreasing on the intervals $(-\infty, 0)$ and $(0, \infty)$.
- The graph is symmetric with respect to the origin.

The graph of the reciprocal function is shown in Figure 1.71.

Cubic function
FIGURE 1.69

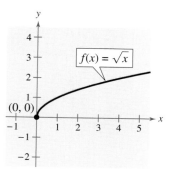

Square root function
FIGURE 1.70

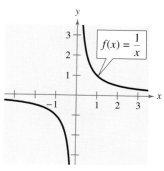

Reciprocal function
FIGURE 1.71

Step and Piecewise-Defined Functions

Functions whose graphs resemble sets of stairsteps are known as **step functions.** The most famous of the step functions is the **greatest integer function,** which is denoted by $[\![x]\!]$ and defined as

$$f(x) = [\![x]\!] = \textit{the greatest integer less than or equal to x.}$$

Some values of the greatest integer function are as follows.

$$[\![-1]\!] = (\text{greatest integer} \le -1) = -1$$

$$\left[\!\left[-\tfrac{1}{2}\right]\!\right] = \left(\text{greatest integer} \le -\tfrac{1}{2}\right) = -1$$

$$\left[\!\left[\tfrac{1}{10}\right]\!\right] = \left(\text{greatest integer} \le \tfrac{1}{10}\right) = 0$$

$$[\![1.5]\!] = (\text{greatest integer} \le 1.5) = 1$$

The graph of the greatest integer function

$$f(x) = [\![x]\!]$$

has the following characteristics, as shown in Figure 1.72.

- The domain of the function is the set of all real numbers.
- The range of the function is the set of all integers.
- The graph has a y-intercept at $(0, 0)$ and x-intercepts in the interval $[0, 1)$.
- The graph is constant between each pair of consecutive integers.
- The graph jumps vertically one unit at each integer value.

FIGURE **1.72**

Technology

When graphing a step function, you should set your graphing utility to *dot* mode.

Example 2   Evaluating a Step Function

Evaluate the function when $x = -1, 2,$ and $\tfrac{3}{2}$.

$$f(x) = [\![x]\!] + 1$$

Solution

For $x = -1$, the greatest integer ≤ -1 is -1, so

$$f(-1) = [\![-1]\!] + 1 = -1 + 1 = 0.$$

For $x = 2$, the greatest integer ≤ 2 is 2, so

$$f(2) = [\![2]\!] + 1 = 2 + 1 = 3.$$

For $x = \tfrac{3}{2}$, the greatest integer $\le \tfrac{3}{2}$ is 1, so

$$f\left(\tfrac{3}{2}\right) = \left[\!\left[\tfrac{3}{2}\right]\!\right] + 1 = 1 + 1 = 2.$$

You can verify your answers by examining the graph of $f(x) = [\![x]\!] + 1$ shown in Figure 1.73.

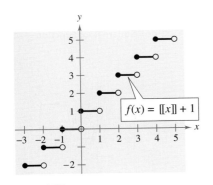

FIGURE **1.73**

✓CHECKPOINT   Now try Exercise 29.

Recall from Section 1.4 that a piecewise-defined function is defined by two or more equations over a specified domain. To graph a piecewise-defined function, graph each equation separately over the specified domain, as shown in Example 3.

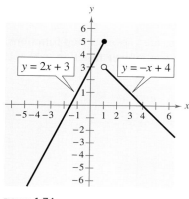

FIGURE **1.74**

Example 3 **Graphing a Piecewise-Defined Function**

Sketch the graph of

$$f(x) = \begin{cases} 2x + 3, & x \le 1 \\ -x + 4, & x > 1 \end{cases}.$$

Solution

This piecewise-defined function is composed of two linear functions. At $x = 1$ and to the left of $x = 1$ the graph is the line $y = 2x + 3$, and to the right of $x = 1$ the graph is the line $y = -x + 4$, as shown in Figure 1.74. Notice that the point $(1, 5)$ is a solid dot and the point $(1, 3)$ is an open dot. This is because $f(1) = 2(1) + 3 = 5$.

✔**CHECKPOINT** Now try Exercise 43.

Parent Functions

The eight graphs shown in Figure 1.75 represent the most commonly used functions in algebra. Familiarity with the basic characteristics of these simple graphs will help you analyze the shapes of more complicated graphs—in particular, graphs obtained from these graphs by the rigid and nonrigid transformations studied in the next section.

(a) Constant Function

(b) Identity Function

(c) Absolute Value Function

(d) Square Root Function

(e) Quadratic Function

(f) Cubic Function

(g) Reciprocal Function

(h) Greatest Integer Function

FIGURE **1.75**

1.6 | Exercises

VOCABULARY CHECK: Match each function with its name.

1. $f(x) = [\![x]\!]$

2. $f(x) = x$

3. $f(x) = \dfrac{1}{x}$

4. $f(x) = x^2$

5. $f(x) = \sqrt{x}$

6. $f(x) = c$

7. $f(x) = |x|$

8. $f(x) = x^3$

9. $f(x) = ax + b$

(a) squaring function

(b) square root function

(c) cubic function

(d) linear function

(e) constant function

(f) absolute value function

(e) greatest integer function

(h) reciprocal function

(i) identity function

PREREQUISITE SKILLS REVIEW: Practice and review algebra skills needed for this section at **www.Eduspace.com.**

In Exercises 1–8, (a) write the linear function f such that it has the indicated function values and (b) sketch the graph of the function.

1. $f(1) = 4,\ f(0) = 6$

2. $f(-3) = -8,\ f(1) = 2$

3. $f(5) = -4,\ f(-2) = 17$

4. $f(3) = 9,\ f(-1) = -11$

5. $f(-5) = -1,\ f(5) = -1$

6. $f(-10) = 12,\ f(16) = -1$

7. $f\left(\tfrac{1}{2}\right) = -6,\ f(4) = -3$

8. $f\left(\tfrac{2}{3}\right) = -\tfrac{15}{2},\ f(-4) = -11$

In Exercises 9–28, use a graphing utility to graph the function. Be sure to choose an appropriate viewing window.

9. $f(x) = -x - \tfrac{3}{4}$

10. $f(x) = 3x - \tfrac{5}{2}$

11. $f(x) = -\tfrac{1}{6}x - \tfrac{5}{2}$

12. $f(x) = \tfrac{5}{6} - \tfrac{2}{3}x$

13. $f(x) = x^2 - 2x$

14. $f(x) = -x^2 + 8x$

15. $h(x) = -x^2 + 4x + 12$

16. $g(x) = x^2 - 6x - 16$

17. $f(x) = x^3 - 1$

18. $f(x) = 8 - x^3$

19. $f(x) = (x - 1)^3 + 2$

20. $g(x) = 2(x + 3)^3 + 1$

21. $f(x) = 4\sqrt{x}$

22. $f(x) = 4 - 2\sqrt{x}$

23. $g(x) = 2 - \sqrt{x + 4}$

24. $h(x) = \sqrt{x + 2} + 3$

25. $f(x) = -\dfrac{1}{x}$

26. $f(x) = 4 + \dfrac{1}{x}$

27. $h(x) = \dfrac{1}{x + 2}$

28. $k(x) = \dfrac{1}{x - 3}$

In Exercises 29–36, evaluate the function for the indicated values.

29. $f(x) = [\![x]\!]$

(a) $f(2.1)$ (b) $f(2.9)$ (c) $f(-3.1)$ (d) $f\left(\tfrac{7}{2}\right)$

30. $g(x) = 2[\![x]\!]$

(a) $g(-3)$ (b) $g(0.25)$ (c) $g(9.5)$ (d) $g\left(\tfrac{11}{3}\right)$

31. $h(x) = [\![x + 3]\!]$

(a) $h(-2)$ (b) $h\left(\tfrac{1}{2}\right)$ (c) $h(4.2)$ (d) $h(-21.6)$

32. $f(x) = 4[\![x]\!] + 7$

(a) $f(0)$ (b) $f(-1.5)$ (c) $f(6)$ (d) $f\left(\tfrac{5}{3}\right)$

33. $h(x) = [\![3x - 1]\!]$

(a) $h(2.5)$ (b) $h(-3.2)$ (c) $h\left(\tfrac{7}{3}\right)$ (d) $h\left(-\tfrac{21}{3}\right)$

34. $k(x) = \left[\!\left[\tfrac{1}{2}x + 6\right]\!\right]$

(a) $k(5)$ (b) $k(-6.1)$ (c) $k(0.1)$ (d) $k(15)$

35. $g(x) = 3[\![x - 2]\!] + 5$

(a) $g(-2.7)$ (b) $g(-1)$ (c) $g(0.8)$ (d) $g(14.5)$

36. $g(x) = -7[\![x + 4]\!] + 6$

(a) $g\left(\tfrac{1}{8}\right)$ (b) $g(9)$ (c) $g(-4)$ (d) $g\left(\tfrac{3}{2}\right)$

In Exercises 37–42, sketch the graph of the function.

37. $g(x) = -[\![x]\!]$

38. $g(x) = 4[\![x]\!]$

39. $g(x) = [\![x]\!] - 2$

40. $g(x) = [\![x]\!] - 1$

41. $g(x) = [\![x + 1]\!]$

42. $g(x) = [\![x - 3]\!]$

In Exercises 43–50, graph the function.

43. $f(x) = \begin{cases} 2x + 3, & x < 0 \\ 3 - x, & x \geq 0 \end{cases}$

44. $g(x) = \begin{cases} x + 6, & x \leq -4 \\ \tfrac{1}{2}x - 4, & x > -4 \end{cases}$

45. $f(x) = \begin{cases} \sqrt{4 + x}, & x < 0 \\ \sqrt{4 - x}, & x \geq 0 \end{cases}$

46. $f(x) = \begin{cases} 1 - (x - 1)^2, & x \leq 2 \\ \sqrt{x - 2}, & x > 2 \end{cases}$

47. $f(x) = \begin{cases} x^2 + 5, & x \leq 1 \\ -x^2 + 4x + 3, & x > 1 \end{cases}$

48. $h(x) = \begin{cases} 3 - x^2, & x < 0 \\ x^2 + 2, & x \geq 0 \end{cases}$

49. $h(x) = \begin{cases} 4 - x^2, & x < -2 \\ 3 + x, & -2 \leq x < 0 \\ x^2 + 1, & x \geq 0 \end{cases}$

50. $k(x) = \begin{cases} 2x + 1, & x \leq -1 \\ 2x^2 - 1, & -1 < x \leq 1 \\ 1 - x^2, & x > 1 \end{cases}$

In Exercises 51 and 52, (a) use a graphing utility to graph the function, (b) state the domain and range of the function, and (c) describe the pattern of the graph.

51. $s(x) = 2\left(\frac{1}{4}x - \left[\!\left[\frac{1}{4}x\right]\!\right]\right)$

52. $g(x) = 2\left(\frac{1}{4}x - \left[\!\left[\frac{1}{4}x\right]\!\right]\right)^2$

In Exercises 53–60, (a) identify the parent function and the transformed parent function shown in the graph, (b) write an equation for the function shown in the graph, and (c) use a graphing utility to verify your answers in parts (a) and (b).

53.

54.

55.

56.

57.

58.

59.

60.

61. *Communications* The cost of a telephone call between Denver and Boise is \$0.60 for the first minute and \$0.42 for each additional minute or portion of a minute. A model for the total cost C (in dollars) of the phone call is $C = 0.60 - 0.42[\![1 - t]\!]$, $t > 0$ where t is the length of the phone call in minutes.

(a) Sketch the graph of the model.

(b) Determine the cost of a call lasting 12 minutes and 30 seconds.

62. *Communications* The cost of using a telephone calling card is \$1.05 for the first minute and \$0.38 for each additional minute or portion of a minute.

(a) A customer needs a model for the cost C of using a calling card for a call lasting t minutes. Which of the following is the appropriate model? Explain.

$C_1(t) = 1.05 + 0.38[\![t - 1]\!]$

$C_2(t) = 1.05 - 0.38[\![-(t - 1)]\!]$

(b) Graph the appropriate model. Determine the cost of a call lasting 18 minutes and 45 seconds.

63. *Delivery Charges* The cost of sending an overnight package from Los Angeles to Miami is \$10.75 for a package weighing up to but not including 1 pound and \$3.95 for each additional pound or portion of a pound. A model for the total cost C (in dollars) of sending the package is $C = 10.75 + 3.95[\![x]\!]$, $x > 0$ where x is the weight in pounds.

(a) Sketch a graph of the model.

(b) Determine the cost of sending a package that weighs 10.33 pounds.

64. *Delivery Charges* The cost of sending an overnight package from New York to Atlanta is \$9.80 for a package weighing up to but not including 1 pound and \$2.50 for each additional pound or portion of a pound.

(a) Use the greatest integer function to create a model for the cost C of overnight delivery of a package weighing x pounds, $x > 0$.

(b) Sketch the graph of the function.

65. *Wages* A mechanic is paid \$12.00 per hour for regular time and time-and-a-half for overtime. The weekly wage function is given by

$$W(h) = \begin{cases} 12h, & 0 < h \leq 40 \\ 18(h - 40) + 480, & h > 40 \end{cases}$$

where h is the number of hours worked in a week.

(a) Evaluate $W(30)$, $W(40)$, $W(45)$, and $W(50)$.

(b) The company increased the regular work week to 45 hours. What is the new weekly wage function?

66. *Snowstorm* During a nine-hour snowstorm, it snows at a rate of 1 inch per hour for the first 2 hours, at a rate of 2 inches per hour for the next 6 hours, and at a rate of 0.5 inch per hour for the final hour. Write and graph a piecewise-defined function that gives the depth of the snow during the snowstorm. How many inches of snow accumulated from the storm?

Model It

67. *Revenue* The table shows the monthly revenue y (in thousands of dollars) of a landscaping business for each month of the year 2005, with $x = 1$ representing January.

Month, x	Revenue, y
1	5.2
2	5.6
3	6.6
4	8.3
5	11.5
6	15.8
7	12.8
8	10.1
9	8.6
10	6.9
11	4.5
12	2.7

A mathematical model that represents these data is

$$f(x) = \begin{cases} -1.97x + 26.3 \\ 0.505x^2 - 1.47x + 6.3 \end{cases}.$$

(a) What is the domain of each part of the piecewise-defined function? How can you tell? Explain your reasoning.

(b) Sketch a graph of the model.

(c) Find $f(5)$ and $f(11)$, and interpret your results in the context of the problem.

(d) How do the values obtained from the model in part (b) compare with the actual data values?

68. *Fluid Flow* The intake pipe of a 100-gallon tank has a flow rate of 10 gallons per minute, and two drainpipes have flow rates of 5 gallons per minute each. The figure shows the volume V of fluid in the tank as a function of time t. Determine the combination of the input pipe and drain pipes in which the fluid is flowing in specific subintervals of the 1 hour of time shown on the graph. (There are many correct answers.)

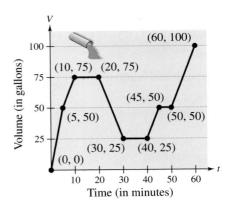

FIGURE FOR 68

Synthesis

True or False? **In Exercises 69 and 70, determine whether the statement is true or false. Justify your answer.**

69. A piecewise-defined function will always have at least one x-intercept or at least one y-intercept.

70. $f(x) = \begin{cases} 2, & 1 \le x < 2 \\ 4, & 2 \le x < 3 \\ 6, & 3 \le x < 4 \end{cases}$

can be rewritten as $f(x) = 2[\![x]\!], \quad 1 \le x < 4.$

Exploration **In Exercises 71 and 72, write equations for the piecewise-defined function shown in the graph.**

71.   **72.**

Skills Review

In Exercises 73 and 74, solve the inequality and sketch the solution on the real number line.

73. $3x + 4 \le 12 - 5x$ **74.** $2x + 1 > 6x - 9$

In Exercises 75 and 76, determine whether the lines L_1 and L_2 passing through the pairs of points are parallel, perpendicular, or neither.

75. L_1: $(-2, -2), (2, 10)$ **76.** L_1: $(-1, -7), (4, 3)$
L_2: $(-1, 3), (3, 9)$ L_2: $(1, 5), (-2, -7)$

1.7 Transformations of Functions

© Ken Fisher/Getty Images

Shifting Graphs

Many functions have graphs that are simple transformations of the parent graphs summarized in Section 1.6. For example, you can obtain the graph of

$$h(x) = x^2 + 2$$

by shifting the graph of $f(x) = x^2$ *upward* two units, as shown in Figure 1.76. In function notation, h and f are related as follows.

$$h(x) = x^2 + 2 = f(x) + 2 \qquad \text{Upward shift of two units}$$

Similarly, you can obtain the graph of

$$g(x) = (x - 2)^2$$

by shifting the graph of $f(x) = x^2$ to the *right* two units, as shown in Figure 1.77. In this case, the functions g and f have the following relationship.

$$g(x) = (x - 2)^2 = f(x - 2) \qquad \text{Right shift of two units}$$

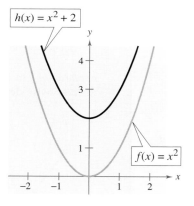

FIGURE 1.76

FIGURE 1.77

The following list summarizes this discussion about horizontal and vertical shifts.

Vertical and Horizontal Shifts

Let c be a positive real number. **Vertical and horizontal shifts** in the graph of $y = f(x)$ are represented as follows.

1. Vertical shift c units *upward:* $\qquad h(x) = f(x) + c$

2. Vertical shift c units *downward:* $\qquad h(x) = f(x) - c$

3. Horizontal shift c units to the *right:* $\qquad h(x) = f(x - c)$

4. Horizontal shift c units to the *left:* $\qquad h(x) = f(x + c)$

Some graphs can be obtained from combinations of vertical and horizontal shifts, as demonstrated in Example 1(b). Vertical and horizontal shifts generate a *family of functions*, each with the same shape but at different locations in the plane.

Example 1   Shifts in the Graphs of a Function

Use the graph of $f(x) = x^3$ to sketch the graph of each function.

a. $g(x) = x^3 - 1$

b. $h(x) = (x + 2)^3 + 1$

Solution

a. Relative to the graph of $f(x) = x^3$, the graph of $g(x) = x^3 - 1$ is a downward shift of one unit, as shown in Figure 1.78.

b. Relative to the graph of $f(x) = x^3$, the graph of $h(x) = (x + 2)^3 + 1$ involves a left shift of two units and an upward shift of one unit, as shown in Figure 1.79.

FIGURE 1.78

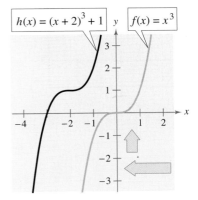

FIGURE 1.79

✓CHECKPOINT   Now try Exercise 1.

In Figure 1.79, notice that the same result is obtained if the vertical shift precedes the horizontal shift *or* if the horizontal shift precedes the vertical shift.

Exploration

Graphing utilities are ideal tools for exploring translations of functions. Graph f, g, and h in same viewing window. Before looking at the graphs, try to predict how the graphs of g and h relate to the graph of f.

a. $f(x) = x^2$, $g(x) = (x - 4)^2$, $h(x) = (x - 4)^2 + 3$

b. $f(x) = x^2$, $g(x) = (x + 1)^2$, $h(x) = (x + 1)^2 - 2$

c. $f(x) = x^2$, $g(x) = (x + 4)^2$, $h(x) = (x + 4)^2 + 2$

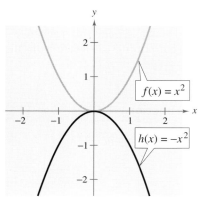

FIGURE **1.80**

Reflecting Graphs

The second common type of transformation is a **reflection.** For instance, if you consider the *x*-axis to be a mirror, the graph of

$$h(x) = -x^2$$

is the mirror image (or reflection) of the graph of

$$f(x) = x^2,$$

as shown in Figure 1.80.

Reflections in the Coordinate Axes

Reflections in the coordinate axes of the graph of $y = f(x)$ are represented as follows.

1. Reflection in the *x*-axis: $\qquad h(x) = -f(x)$

2. Reflection in the *y*-axis: $\qquad h(x) = f(-x)$

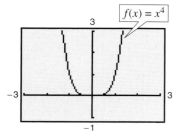

FIGURE **1.81**

Example 2 Finding Equations from Graphs

The graph of the function given by

$$f(x) = x^4$$

is shown in Figure 1.81. Each of the graphs in Figure 1.82 is a transformation of the graph of *f*. Find an equation for each of these functions.

(a)

(b)

FIGURE **1.82**

Solution

a. The graph of *g* is a reflection in the *x*-axis *followed by* an upward shift of two units of the graph of $f(x) = x^4$. So, the equation for *g* is

$$g(x) = -x^4 + 2.$$

b. The graph of *h* is a horizontal shift of three units to the right *followed by* a reflection in the *x*-axis of the graph of $f(x) = x^4$. So, the equation for *h* is

$$h(x) = -(x - 3)^4.$$

✓**CHECKPOINT** Now try Exercise 9.

Exploration

Reverse the order of transformations in Example 2(a). Do you obtain the same graph? Do the same for Example 2(b). Do you obtain the same graph? Explain.

Example 3   Reflections and Shifts

Compare the graph of each function with the graph of $f(x) = \sqrt{x}$.

a. $g(x) = -\sqrt{x}$ **b.** $h(x) = \sqrt{-x}$ **c.** $k(x) = -\sqrt{x+2}$

Algebraic Solution

a. The graph of g is a reflection of the graph of f in the x-axis because

$$g(x) = -\sqrt{x}$$

$$= -f(x).$$

b. The graph of h is a reflection of the graph of f in the y-axis because

$$h(x) = \sqrt{-x}$$

$$= f(-x).$$

c. The graph of k is a left shift of two units followed by a reflection in the x-axis because

$$k(x) = -\sqrt{x+2}$$

$$= -f(x+2).$$

Graphical Solution

a. Graph f and g on the same set of coordinate axes. From the graph in Figure 1.83, you can see that the graph of g is a reflection of the graph of f in the x-axis.

b. Graph f and h on the same set of coordinate axes. From the graph in Figure 1.84, you can see that the graph of h is a reflection of the graph of f in the y-axis.

c. Graph f and k on the same set of coordinate axes. From the graph in Figure 1.85, you can see that the graph of k is a left shift of two units of the graph of f, followed by a reflection in the x-axis.

FIGURE 1.83

FIGURE 1.84

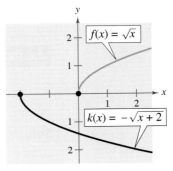

FIGURE 1.85

✔CHECKPOINT   Now try Exercise 19.

When sketching the graphs of functions involving square roots, remember that the domain must be restricted to exclude negative numbers inside the radical. For instance, here are the domains of the functions in Example 3.

Domain of $g(x) = -\sqrt{x}$: $x \geq 0$

Domain of $h(x) = \sqrt{-x}$: $x \leq 0$

Domain of $k(x) = -\sqrt{x+2}$: $x \geq -2$

FIGURE 1.86

FIGURE 1.87

FIGURE 1.88

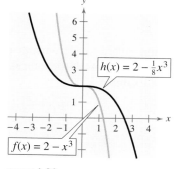

FIGURE 1.89

Nonrigid Transformations

Horizontal shifts, vertical shifts, and reflections are **rigid transformations** because the basic shape of the graph is unchanged. These transformations change only the *position* of the graph in the coordinate plane. **Nonrigid transformations** are those that cause a *distortion*—a change in the shape of the original graph. For instance, a nonrigid transformation of the graph of $y = f(x)$ is represented by $g(x) = cf(x)$, where the transformation is a **vertical stretch** if $c > 1$ and a **vertical shrink** if $0 < c < 1$. Another nonrigid transformation of the graph of $y = f(x)$ is represented by $h(x) = f(cx)$, where the transformation is a **horizontal shrink** if $c > 1$ and a **horizontal stretch** if $0 < c < 1$.

Example 4   Nonrigid Transformations

Compare the graph of each function with the graph of $f(x) = |x|$.

a. $h(x) = 3|x|$ **b.** $g(x) = \frac{1}{3}|x|$

Solution

a. Relative to the graph of $f(x) = |x|$, the graph of

$$h(x) = 3|x| = 3f(x)$$

is a vertical stretch (each y-value is multiplied by 3) of the graph of f. (See Figure 1.86.)

b. Similarly, the graph of

$$g(x) = \tfrac{1}{3}|x| = \tfrac{1}{3}f(x)$$

is a vertical shrink $\left(\text{each } y\text{-value is multiplied by } \tfrac{1}{3}\right)$ of the graph of f. (See Figure 1.87.)

✓**CHECKPOINT**   Now try Exercise 23.

Example 5   Nonrigid Transformations

Compare the graph of each function with the graph of $f(x) = 2 - x^3$.

a. $g(x) = f(2x)$ **b.** $h(x) = f\left(\tfrac{1}{2}x\right)$

Solution

a. Relative to the graph of $f(x) = 2 - x^3$, the graph of

$$g(x) = f(2x) = 2 - (2x)^3 = 2 - 8x^3$$

is a horizontal shrink $(c > 1)$ of the graph of f. (See Figure 1.88.)

b. Similarly, the graph of

$$h(x) = f\left(\tfrac{1}{2}x\right) = 2 - \left(\tfrac{1}{2}x\right)^3 = 2 - \tfrac{1}{8}x^3$$

is a horizontal stretch $(0 < c < 1)$ of the graph of f. (See Figure 1.89.)

✓**CHECKPOINT**   Now try Exercise 27.

1.7 | Exercises

VOCABULARY CHECK:

In Exercises 1–5, fill in the blanks.

1. Horizontal shifts, vertical shifts, and reflections are called _____ transformations.

2. A reflection in the x-axis of $y = f(x)$ is represented by $h(x) = $ _____, while a reflection in the y-axis of $y = f(x)$ is represented by $h(x) = $ _____.

3. Transformations that cause a distortion in the shape of the graph of $y = f(x)$ are called _____ transformations.

4. A nonrigid transformation of $y = f(x)$ represented by $h(x) = f(cx)$ is a _____ _____ if $c > 1$ and a _____ _____ if $0 < c < 1$.

5. A nonrigid transformation of $y = f(x)$ represented by $g(x) = cf(x)$ is a _____ _____ if $c > 1$ and a _____ _____ if $0 < c < 1$.

6. Match the rigid transformation of $y = f(x)$ with the correct representation of the graph of h, where $c > 0$.
   (a) $h(x) = f(x) + c$ (i) A horizontal shift of f, c units to the right
   (b) $h(x) = f(x) - c$ (ii) A vertical shift of f, c units downward
   (c) $h(x) = f(x + c)$ (iii) A horizontal shift of f, c units to the left
   (d) $h(x) = f(x - c)$ (iv) A vertical shift of f, c units upward

PREREQUISITE SKILLS REVIEW: Practice and review algebra skills needed for this section at **www.Eduspace.com.**

1. For each function, sketch (on the same set of coordinate axes) a graph of each function for $c = -1, 1,$ and 3.
   (a) $f(x) = |x| + c$
   (b) $f(x) = |x - c|$
   (c) $f(x) = |x + 4| + c$

2. For each function, sketch (on the same set of coordinate axes) a graph of each function for $c = -3, -1, 1,$ and 3.
   (a) $f(x) = \sqrt{x} + c$
   (b) $f(x) = \sqrt{x - c}$
   (c) $f(x) = \sqrt{x - 3} + c$

3. For each function, sketch (on the same set of coordinate axes) a graph of each function for $c = -2, 0,$ and 2.
   (a) $f(x) = [\![x]\!] + c$
   (b) $f(x) = [\![x + c]\!]$
   (c) $f(x) = [\![x - 1]\!] + c$

4. For each function, sketch (on the same set of coordinate axes) a graph of each function for $c = -3, -1, 1,$ and 3.
   (a) $f(x) = \begin{cases} x^2 + c, & x < 0 \\ -x^2 + c, & x \geq 0 \end{cases}$
   (b) $f(x) = \begin{cases} (x + c)^2, & x < 0 \\ -(x + c)^2, & x \geq 0 \end{cases}$

In Exercises 5–8, use the graph of f to sketch each graph. To print an enlarged copy of the graph go to the website www.mathgraphs.com.

5. (a) $y = f(x) + 2$
   (b) $y = f(x - 2)$
   (c) $y = 2f(x)$
   (d) $y = -f(x)$
   (e) $y = f(x + 3)$
   (f) $y = f(-x)$
   (g) $y = f\left(\frac{1}{2}x\right)$

6. (a) $y = f(-x)$
   (b) $y = f(x) + 4$
   (c) $y = 2f(x)$
   (d) $y = -f(x - 4)$
   (e) $y = f(x) - 3$
   (f) $y = -f(x) - 1$
   (g) $y = f(2x)$

FIGURE FOR 5

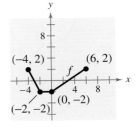

FIGURE FOR 6

7. (a) $y = f(x) - 1$
   (b) $y = f(x - 1)$
   (c) $y = f(-x)$
   (d) $y = f(x + 1)$
   (e) $y = -f(x - 2)$
   (f) $y = \frac{1}{2}f(x)$
   (g) $y = f(2x)$

8. (a) $y = f(x - 5)$
   (b) $y = -f(x) + 3$
   (c) $y = \frac{1}{3}f(x)$
   (d) $y = -f(x + 1)$
   (e) $y = f(-x)$
   (f) $y = f(x) - 10$
   (g) $y = f\left(\frac{1}{3}x\right)$

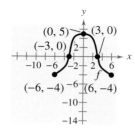

FIGURE FOR 7   FIGURE FOR 8

9. Use the graph of $f(x) = x^2$ to write an equation for each function whose graph is shown.

(a)

(b)

(c)

(d)
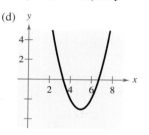

10. Use the graph of $f(x) = x^3$ to write an equation for each function whose graph is shown.

(a)

(b)

(c)

(d)

11. Use the graph of $f(x) = |x|$ to write an equation for each function whose graph is shown.

(a)

(b)

(c)

(d)

12. Use the graph of $f(x) = \sqrt{x}$ to write an equation for each function whose graph is shown.

(a)

(b)

(c)

(d)
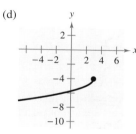

In Exercises 13–18, identify the parent function and the transformation shown in the graph. Write an equation for the function shown in the graph.

13.

14.

15.

16.

17.

18.

In Exercises 19–42, g is related to one of the parent functions described in this chapter. (a) Identify the parent function f. (b) Describe the sequence of tranformations from f to g. (c) Sketch the graph of g. (d) Use function notation to write g in terms of f.

19. $g(x) = 12 - x^2$

20. $g(x) = (x - 8)^2$

21. $g(x) = x^3 + 7$

22. $g(x) = -x^3 - 1$

23. $g(x) = \frac{2}{3}x^2 + 4$

24. $g(x) = 2(x - 7)^2$

25. $g(x) = 2 - (x + 5)^2$

26. $g(x) = -(x + 10)^2 + 5$

27. $g(x) = \sqrt{3x}$

28. $g(x) = \sqrt{\frac{1}{4}x}$

29. $g(x) = (x - 1)^3 + 2$

30. $g(x) = (x + 3)^3 - 10$

31. $g(x) = -|x| - 2$

32. $g(x) = 6 - |x + 5|$

33. $g(x) = -|x + 4| + 8$

34. $g(x) = |-x + 3| + 9$

35. $g(x) = 3 - [\![x]\!]$

36. $g(x) = 2[\![x + 5]\!]$

37. $g(x) = \sqrt{x - 9}$

38. $g(x) = \sqrt{x + 4} + 8$

39. $g(x) = \sqrt{7 - x} - 2$

40. $g(x) = -\sqrt{x + 1} - 6$

41. $g(x) = \sqrt{\frac{1}{2}x} - 4$

42. $g(x) = \sqrt{3x} + 1$

In Exercises 43–50, write an equation for the function that is described by the given characteristics.

43. The shape of $f(x) = x^2$, but moved two units to the right and eight units downward

44. The shape of $f(x) = x^2$, but moved three units to the left, seven units upward, and reflected in the x-axis

45. The shape of $f(x) = x^3$, but moved 13 units to the right

46. The shape of $f(x) = x^3$, but moved six units to the left, six units downward, and reflected in the y-axis

47. The shape of $f(x) = |x|$, but moved 10 units upward and reflected in the x-axis

48. The shape of $f(x) = |x|$, but moved one unit to the left and seven units downward

49. The shape of $f(x) = \sqrt{x}$, but moved six units to the left and reflected in both the x-axis and the y-axis

50. The shape of $f(x) = \sqrt{x}$, but moved nine units downward and reflected in both the x-axis and the y-axis

51. Use the graph of $f(x) = x^2$ to write an equation for each function whose graph is shown.

(a)

(b)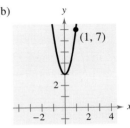

52. Use the graph of $f(x) = x^3$ to write an equation for each function whose graph is shown.

(a)

(b)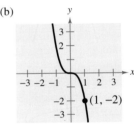

53. Use the graph of $f(x) = |x|$ to write an equation for each function whose graph is shown.

(a)

(b)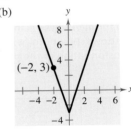

54. Use the graph of $f(x) = \sqrt{x}$ to write an equation for each function whose graph is shown.

(a)

(b)

In Exercises 55–60, identify the parent function and the transformation shown in the graph. Write an equation for the function shown in the graph. Then use a graphing utility to verify your answer.

55.

56.

57.

58.

59.

60.

 Graphical Analysis In Exercises 61–64, use the viewing window shown to write a possible equation for the transformation of the parent function.

61.

62.

63.

64.

Graphical Reasoning In Exercises 65 and 66, use the graph of *f* to sketch the graph of *g*. To print an enlarged copy of the graph, go to the website *www.mathgraphs.com*.

65.

(a) $g(x) = f(x) + 2$ (b) $g(x) = f(x) - 1$
(c) $g(x) = f(-x)$ (d) $g(x) = -2f(x)$
(e) $g(x) = f(4x)$ (f) $g(x) = f\left(\frac{1}{2}x\right)$

66.

(a) $g(x) = f(x) - 5$ (b) $g(x) = f(x) + \frac{1}{2}$
(c) $g(x) = f(-x)$ (d) $g(x) = -4f(x)$
(e) $g(x) = f(2x) + 1$ (f) $g(x) = f\left(\frac{1}{4}x\right) - 2$

Model It

67. **Fuel Use** The amounts of fuel *F* (in billions of gallons) used by trucks from 1980 through 2002 can be approximated by the function

$$F = f(t) = 20.6 + 0.035t^2, \quad 0 \le t \le 22$$

where *t* represents the year, with $t = 0$ corresponding to 1980. (Source: U.S. Federal Highway Administration)

(a) Describe the transformation of the parent function $f(x) = x^2$. Then sketch the graph over the specified domain.

(b) Find the average rate of change of the function from 1980 to 2002. Interpret your answer in the context of the problem.

(c) Rewrite the function so that $t = 0$ represents 1990. Explain how you got your answer.

(d) Use the model from part (c) to predict the amount of fuel used by trucks in 2010. Does your answer seem reasonable? Explain.

68. Finance   The amounts M (in trillions of dollars) of mortgage debt outstanding in the United States from 1990 through 2002 can be approximated by the function

$$M = f(t) = 0.0054(t + 20.396)^2, \quad 0 \le t \le 12$$

where t represents the year, with $t = 0$ corresponding to 1990. (Source: Board of Governors of the Federal Reserve System)

(a) Describe the transformation of the parent function $f(x) = x^2$. Then sketch the graph over the specified domain.

(b) Rewrite the function so that $t = 0$ represents 2000. Explain how you got your answer.

Synthesis

True or False?   In Exercises 69 and 70, determine whether the statement is true or false. Justify your answer.

69. The graphs of

$$f(x) = |x| + 6 \quad \text{and} \quad f(x) = |-x| + 6$$

are identical.

70. If the graph of the parent function $f(x) = x^2$ is moved six units to the right, three units upward, and reflected in the x-axis, then the point $(-2, 19)$ will lie on the graph of the transformation.

71. Describing Profits   Management originally predicted that the profits from the sales of a new product would be approximated by the graph of the function f shown. The actual profits are shown by the function g along with a verbal description. Use the concepts of transformations of graphs to write g in terms of f.

(a) The profits were only three-fourths as large as expected.

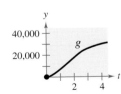

(b) The profits were consistently $10,000 greater than predicted.

(c) There was a two-year delay in the introduction of the product. After sales began, profits grew as expected.

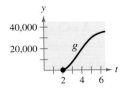

72. Explain why the graph of $y = -f(x)$ is a reflection of the graph of $y = f(x)$ about the x-axis.

73. The graph of $y = f(x)$ passes through the points $(0, 1)$, $(1, 2)$, and $(2, 3)$. Find the corresponding points on the graph of $y = f(x + 2) - 1$.

74. Think About It   You can use either of two methods to graph a function: plotting points or translating a parent function as shown in this section. Which method of graphing do you prefer to use for each function? Explain.

(a) $f(x) = 3x^2 - 4x + 1$ (b) $f(x) = 2(x - 1)^2 - 6$

Skills Review

In Exercises 75–82, perform the operation and simplify.

75. $\dfrac{4}{x} + \dfrac{4}{1 - x}$

76. $\dfrac{2}{x + 5} - \dfrac{2}{x - 5}$

77. $\dfrac{3}{x - 1} - \dfrac{2}{x(x - 1)}$

78. $\dfrac{x}{x - 5} + \dfrac{1}{2}$

79. $(x - 4)\left(\dfrac{1}{\sqrt{x^2 - 4}}\right)$

80. $\left(\dfrac{x}{x^2 - 4}\right)\left(\dfrac{x^2 - x - 2}{x^2}\right)$

81. $(x^2 - 9) \div \left(\dfrac{x + 3}{5}\right)$

82. $\left(\dfrac{x}{x^2 - 3x - 28}\right) \div \left(\dfrac{x^2 + 3x}{x^2 + 5x + 4}\right)$

In Exercises 83 and 84, evaluate the function at the specified values of the independent variable and simplify.

83. $f(x) = x^2 - 6x + 11$

(a) $f(-3)$ (b) $f\left(-\tfrac{1}{2}\right)$ (c) $f(x - 3)$

84. $f(x) = \sqrt{x + 10} - 3$

(a) $f(-10)$ (b) $f(26)$ (c) $f(x - 10)$

In Exercises 85–88, find the domain of the function.

85. $f(x) = \dfrac{2}{11 - x}$

86. $f(x) = \dfrac{\sqrt{x - 3}}{x - 8}$

87. $f(x) = \sqrt{81 - x^2}$

88. $f(x) = \sqrt[3]{4 - x^2}$

1.8 Combinations of Functions: Composite Functions

What you should learn

- Add, subtract, multiply, and divide functions.
- Find the composition of one function with another function.
- Use combinations and compositions of functions to model and solve real-life problems.

Why you should learn it

Compositions of functions can be used to model and solve real-life problems. For instance, in Exercise 68 on page 92, compositions of functions are used to determine the price of a new hybrid car.

Arithmetic Combinations of Functions

Just as two real numbers can be combined by the operations of addition, subtraction, multiplication, and division to form other real numbers, two *functions* can be combined to create new functions. For example, the functions given by $f(x) = 2x - 3$ and $g(x) = x^2 - 1$ can be combined to form the sum, difference, product, and quotient of f and g.

$$f(x) + g(x) = (2x - 3) + (x^2 - 1)$$
$$= x^2 + 2x - 4 \qquad \text{Sum}$$
$$f(x) - g(x) = (2x - 3) - (x^2 - 1)$$
$$= -x^2 + 2x - 2 \qquad \text{Difference}$$
$$f(x)g(x) = (2x - 3)(x^2 - 1)$$
$$= 2x^3 - 3x^2 - 2x + 3 \qquad \text{Product}$$
$$\frac{f(x)}{g(x)} = \frac{2x - 3}{x^2 - 1}, \qquad x \neq \pm 1 \qquad \text{Quotient}$$

The domain of an **arithmetic combination** of functions f and g consists of all real numbers that are common to the domains of f and g. In the case of the quotient $f(x)/g(x)$, there is the further restriction that $g(x) \neq 0$.

Sum, Difference, Product, and Quotient of Functions

Let f and g be two functions with overlapping domains. Then, for all x common to both domains, the *sum*, *difference*, *product*, and *quotient* of f and g are defined as follows.

1. *Sum:* $\qquad (f + g)(x) = f(x) + g(x)$

2. *Difference:* $(f - g)(x) = f(x) - g(x)$

3. *Product:* $\qquad (fg)(x) = f(x) \cdot g(x)$

4. *Quotient:* $\left(\dfrac{f}{g}\right)(x) = \dfrac{f(x)}{g(x)}, \qquad g(x) \neq 0$

Example 1 Finding the Sum of Two Functions

Given $f(x) = 2x + 1$ and $g(x) = x^2 + 2x - 1$, find $(f + g)(x)$.

Solution

$$(f + g)(x) = f(x) + g(x) = (2x + 1) + (x^2 + 2x - 1) = x^2 + 4x$$

✓CHECKPOINT Now try Exercise 5(a).

| **Example 2** | **Finding the Difference of Two Functions** |

Given $f(x) = 2x + 1$ and $g(x) = x^2 + 2x - 1$, find $(f - g)(x)$. Then evaluate the difference when $x = 2$.

Solution

The difference of f and g is

$$(f - g)(x) = f(x) - g(x)$$
$$= (2x + 1) - (x^2 + 2x - 1)$$
$$= -x^2 + 2.$$

When $x = 2$, the value of this difference is

$$(f - g)(2) = -(2)^2 + 2$$
$$= -2.$$

✓CHECKPOINT   Now try Exercise 5(b).

In Examples 1 and 2, both f and g have domains that consist of all real numbers. So, the domains of $(f + g)$ and $(f - g)$ are also the set of all real numbers. Remember that any restrictions on the domains of f and g must be considered when forming the sum, difference, product, or quotient of f and g.

| **Example 3** | **Finding the Domains of Quotients of Functions** |

Find $\left(\dfrac{f}{g}\right)(x)$ and $\left(\dfrac{g}{f}\right)(x)$ for the functions given by

$$f(x) = \sqrt{x} \quad \text{and} \quad g(x) = \sqrt{4 - x^2}.$$

Then find the domains of f/g and g/f.

Solution

The quotient of f and g is

$$\left(\frac{f}{g}\right)(x) = \frac{f(x)}{g(x)} = \frac{\sqrt{x}}{\sqrt{4 - x^2}}$$

and the quotient of g and f is

$$\left(\frac{g}{f}\right)(x) = \frac{g(x)}{f(x)} = \frac{\sqrt{4 - x^2}}{\sqrt{x}}.$$

The domain of f is $[0, \infty)$ and the domain of g is $[-2, 2]$. The intersection of these domains is $[0, 2]$. So, the domains of $\left(\dfrac{f}{g}\right)$ and $\left(\dfrac{g}{f}\right)$ are as follows.

Domain of $\left(\dfrac{f}{g}\right)$: $[0, 2)$ Domain of $\left(\dfrac{g}{f}\right)$: $(0, 2]$

Note that the domain of (f/g) includes $x = 0$, but not $x = 2$, because $x = 2$ yields a zero in the denominator, whereas the domain of (g/f) includes $x = 2$, but not $x = 0$, because $x = 0$ yields a zero in the denominator.

✓CHECKPOINT   Now try Exercise 5(d).

Composition of Functions

Another way of combining two functions is to form the **composition** of one with the other. For instance, if $f(x) = x^2$ and $g(x) = x + 1$, the composition of f with g is

$$f(g(x)) = f(x + 1)$$
$$= (x + 1)^2.$$

This composition is denoted as $(f \circ g)$ and reads as "f composed with g."

Domain of g

Domain of f

FIGURE 1.90

> ### Definition of Composition of Two Functions
>
> The **composition** of the function f with the function g is
>
> $$(f \circ g)(x) = f(g(x)).$$
>
> The domain of $(f \circ g)$ is the set of all x in the domain of g such that $g(x)$ is in the domain of f. (See Figure 1.90.)

Example 4 Composition of Functions

Given $f(x) = x + 2$ and $g(x) = 4 - x^2$, find the following.

a. $(f \circ g)(x)$ **b.** $(g \circ f)(x)$ **c.** $(g \circ f)(-2)$

Solution

a. The composition of f with g is as follows.

$$(f \circ g)(x) = f(g(x))$$ Definition of $f \circ g$

$$= f(4 - x^2)$$ Definition of $g(x)$

$$= (4 - x^2) + 2$$ Definition of $f(x)$

$$= -x^2 + 6$$ Simplify.

b. The composition of g with f is as follows.

$$(g \circ f)(x) = g(f(x))$$ Definition of $g \circ f$

$$= g(x + 2)$$ Definition of $f(x)$

$$= 4 - (x + 2)^2$$ Definition of $g(x)$

$$= 4 - (x^2 + 4x + 4)$$ Expand.

$$= -x^2 - 4x$$ Simplify.

Note that, in this case, $(f \circ g)(x) \neq (g \circ f)(x)$.

c. Using the result of part (b), you can write the following.

$$(g \circ f)(-2) = -(-2)^2 - 4(-2)$$ Substitute.

$$= -4 + 8$$ Simplify.

$$= 4$$ Simplify.

✓CHECKPOINT   Now try Exercise 31.

STUDY TIP

The following tables of values help illustrate the composition $(f \circ g)(x)$ given in Example 4.

x	0	1	2	3
$g(x)$	4	3	0	-5

$g(x)$	4	3	0	-5
$f(g(x))$	6	5	2	-3

x	0	1	2	3
$f(g(x))$	6	5	2	-3

Note that the first two tables can be combined (or "composed") to produce the values given in the third table.

Example 5   Finding the Domain of a Composite Function

Given $f(x) = x^2 - 9$ and $g(x) = \sqrt{9 - x^2}$, find the composition $(f \circ g)(x)$. Then find the domain of $(f \circ g)$.

Solution

$$(f \circ g)(x) = f(g(x))$$

$$= f\left(\sqrt{9 - x^2}\right)$$

$$= \left(\sqrt{9 - x^2}\right)^2 - 9$$

$$= 9 - x^2 - 9$$

$$= -x^2$$

From this, it might appear that the domain of the composition is the set of all real numbers. This, however is not true. Because the domain of f is the set of all real numbers and the domain of g is $-3 \leq x \leq 3$, the domain of $(f \circ g)$ is $-3 \leq x \leq 3$.

✓CHECKPOINT   Now try Exercise 35.

In Examples 4 and 5, you formed the composition of two given functions. In calculus, it is also important to be able to identify two functions that make up a given composite function. For instance, the function h given by

$$h(x) = (3x - 5)^3$$

is the composition of f with g, where $f(x) = x^3$ and $g(x) = 3x - 5$. That is,

$$h(x) = (3x - 5)^3 = [g(x)]^3 = f(g(x)).$$

Basically, to "decompose" a composite function, look for an "inner" function and an "outer" function. In the function h above, $g(x) = 3x - 5$ is the inner function and $f(x) = x^3$ is the outer function.

Example 6   Decomposing a Composite Function

Write the function given by $h(x) = \dfrac{1}{(x - 2)^2}$ as a composition of two functions.

Solution

One way to write h as a composition of two functions is to take the inner function to be $g(x) = x - 2$ and the outer function to be

$$f(x) = \frac{1}{x^2} = x^{-2}.$$

Then you can write

$$h(x) = \frac{1}{(x - 2)^2} = (x - 2)^{-2} = f(x - 2) = f(g(x)).$$

✓CHECKPOINT   Now try Exercise 47.

Application

Example 7   **Bacteria Count**

The number N of bacteria in a refrigerated food is given by

$$N(T) = 20T^2 - 80T + 500, \qquad 2 \le T \le 14$$

where T is the temperature of the food in degrees Celsius. When the food is removed from refrigeration, the temperature of the food is given by

$$T(t) = 4t + 2, \qquad 0 \le t \le 3$$

where t is the time in hours. (a) Find the composition $N(T(t))$ and interpret its meaning in context. (b) Find the time when the bacterial count reaches 2000.

Solution

a. $N(T(t)) = 20(4t + 2)^2 - 80(4t + 2) + 500$

$\qquad\qquad = 20(16t^2 + 16t + 4) - 320t - 160 + 500$

$\qquad\qquad = 320t^2 + 320t + 80 - 320t - 160 + 500$

$\qquad\qquad = 320t^2 + 420$

The composite function $N(T(t))$ represents the number of bacteria in the food as a function of the amount of time the food has been out of refrigeration.

b. The bacterial count will reach 2000 when $320t^2 + 420 = 2000$. Solve this equation to find that the count will reach 2000 when $t \approx 2.2$ hours. When you solve this equation, note that the negative value is rejected because it is not in the domain of the composite function.

✓*CHECKPOINT*   Now try Exercise 65.

---

*W*RITING ABOUT *M*ATHEMATICS

Analyzing Arithmetic Combinations of Functions

a. Use the graphs of f and $(f + g)$ in Figure 1.91 to make a table showing the values of $g(x)$ when $x = 1, 2, 3, 4, 5,$ and 6. Explain your reasoning.

b. Use the graphs of f and $(f - h)$ in Figure 1.91 to make a table showing the values of $h(x)$ when $x = 1, 2, 3, 4, 5,$ and 6. Explain your reasoning.

FIGURE **1.91**

1.8 | Exercises

VOCABULARY CHECK: Fill in the blanks.

1. Two functions f and g can be combined by the arithmetic operations of _____, _____, _____, and _____ to create new functions.

2. The _____ of the function f with g is $(f \circ g)(x) = f(g(x))$.

3. The domain of $(f \circ g)$ is all x in the domain of g such that _____ is in the domain of f.

4. To decompose a composite function, look for an _____ function and an _____ function.

PREREQUISITE SKILLS REVIEW: Practice and review algebra skills needed for this section at **www.Eduspace.com**.

In Exercises 1–4, use the graphs of f and g to graph $h(x) = (f + g)(x)$. To print an enlarged copy of the graph, go to the website **www.mathgraphs.com**.

1.

2.

3.

4.
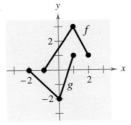

In Exercises 5–12, find (a) $(f + g)(x)$, (b) $(f - g)(x)$, (c) $(fg)(x)$, and (d) $(f/g)(x)$. What is the domain of f/g?

5. $f(x) = x + 2$, $g(x) = x - 2$

6. $f(x) = 2x - 5$, $g(x) = 2 - x$

7. $f(x) = x^2$, $g(x) = 4x - 5$

8. $f(x) = 2x - 5$, $g(x) = 4$

9. $f(x) = x^2 + 6$, $g(x) = \sqrt{1 - x}$

10. $f(x) = \sqrt{x^2 - 4}$, $g(x) = \dfrac{x^2}{x^2 + 1}$

11. $f(x) = \dfrac{1}{x}$, $g(x) = \dfrac{1}{x^2}$

12. $f(x) = \dfrac{x}{x + 1}$, $g(x) = x^3$

In Exercises 13–24, evaluate the indicated function for $f(x) = x^2 + 1$ and $g(x) = x - 4$.

13. $(f + g)(2)$ 14. $(f - g)(-1)$

15. $(f - g)(0)$ 16. $(f + g)(1)$

17. $(f - g)(3t)$ 18. $(f + g)(t - 2)$

19. $(fg)(6)$ 20. $(fg)(-6)$

21. $\left(\dfrac{f}{g}\right)(5)$ 22. $\left(\dfrac{f}{g}\right)(0)$

23. $\left(\dfrac{f}{g}\right)(-1) - g(3)$ 24. $(fg)(5) + f(4)$

In Exercises 25–28, graph the functions f, g, and $f + g$ on the same set of coordinate axes.

25. $f(x) = \tfrac{1}{2}x$, $g(x) = x - 1$

26. $f(x) = \tfrac{1}{3}x$, $g(x) = -x + 4$

27. $f(x) = x^2$, $g(x) = -2x$

28. $f(x) = 4 - x^2$, $g(x) = x$

Graphical Reasoning In Exercises 29 and 30, use a graphing utility to graph f, g, and $f + g$ in the same viewing window. Which function contributes most to the magnitude of the sum when $0 \le x \le 2$? Which function contributes most to the magnitude of the sum when $x > 6$?

29. $f(x) = 3x$, $g(x) = -\dfrac{x^3}{10}$

30. $f(x) = \dfrac{x}{2}$, $g(x) = \sqrt{x}$

In Exercises 31–34, find (a) $f \circ g$, (b) $g \circ f$, and (c) $f \circ f$.

31. $f(x) = x^2$, $g(x) = x - 1$

32. $f(x) = 3x + 5$, $g(x) = 5 - x$

33. $f(x) = \sqrt[3]{x - 1}$, $g(x) = x^3 + 1$

34. $f(x) = x^3$, $g(x) = \dfrac{1}{x}$

In Exercises 35–42, find (a) $f \circ g$ and (b) $g \circ f$. Find the domain of each function and each composite function.

35. $f(x) = \sqrt{x + 4}$, $g(x) = x^2$

36. $f(x) = \sqrt[3]{x - 5}$, $g(x) = x^3 + 1$

37. $f(x) = x^2 + 1$, $g(x) = \sqrt{x}$

38. $f(x) = x^{2/3}$, $g(x) = x^6$

39. $f(x) = |x|$, $g(x) = x + 6$

40. $f(x) = |x - 4|$, $g(x) = 3 - x$

41. $f(x) = \dfrac{1}{x}$, $g(x) = x + 3$

42. $f(x) = \dfrac{3}{x^2 - 1}$, $g(x) = x + 1$

In Exercises 43–46, use the graphs of f and g to evaluate the functions.

43. (a) $(f + g)(3)$ (b) $(f/g)(2)$

44. (a) $(f - g)(1)$ (b) $(fg)(4)$

45. (a) $(f \circ g)(2)$ (b) $(g \circ f)(2)$

46. (a) $(f \circ g)(1)$ (b) $(g \circ f)(3)$

In Exercises 47–54, find two functions f and g such that $(f \circ g)(x) = h(x)$. (There are many correct answers.)

47. $h(x) = (2x + 1)^2$ **48.** $h(x) = (1 - x)^3$

49. $h(x) = \sqrt[3]{x^2 - 4}$ **50.** $h(x) = \sqrt{9 - x}$

51. $h(x) = \dfrac{1}{x + 2}$ **52.** $h(x) = \dfrac{4}{(5x + 2)^2}$

53. $h(x) = \dfrac{-x^2 + 3}{4 - x^2}$ **54.** $h(x) = \dfrac{27x^3 + 6x}{10 - 27x^3}$

55. Stopping Distance The research and development department of an automobile manufacturer has determined that when a driver is required to stop quickly to avoid an accident, the distance (in feet) the car travels during the driver's reaction time is given by $R(x) = \frac{3}{4}x$, where x is the speed of the car in miles per hour. The distance (in feet) traveled while the driver is braking is given by $B(x) = \frac{1}{15}x^2$. Find the function that represents the total stopping distance T. Graph the functions R, B, and T on the same set of coordinate axes for $0 \le x \le 60$.

56. Sales From 2000 to 2005, the sales R_1 (in thousands of dollars) for one of two restaurants owned by the same parent company can be modeled by

$$R_1 = 480 - 8t - 0.8t^2, \qquad t = 0, 1, 2, 3, 4, 5$$

where $t = 0$ represents 2000. During the same six-year period, the sales R_2 (in thousands of dollars) for the second restaurant can be modeled by

$$R_2 = 254 + 0.78t, \qquad t = 0, 1, 2, 3, 4, 5.$$

(a) Write a function R_3 that represents the total sales of the two restaurants owned by the same parent company.

 (b) Use a graphing utility to graph R_1, R_2, and R_3 in the same viewing window.

57. Vital Statistics Let $b(t)$ be the number of births in the United States in year t, and let $d(t)$ represent the number of deaths in the United States in year t, where $t = 0$ corresponds to 2000.

(a) If $p(t)$ is the population of the United States in year t, find the function $c(t)$ that represents the percent change in the population of the United States.

(b) Interpret the value of $c(5)$.

58. Pets Let $d(t)$ be the number of dogs in the United States in year t, and let $c(t)$ be the number of cats in the United States in year t, where $t = 0$ corresponds to 2000.

(a) Find the function $p(t)$ that represents the total number of dogs and cats in the United States.

(b) Interpret the value of $p(5)$.

(c) Let $n(t)$ represent the population of the United States in year t, where $t = 0$ corresponds to 2000. Find and interpret

$$h(t) = \frac{p(t)}{n(t)}.$$

59. Military Personnel The total numbers of Army personnel (in thousands) A and Navy personnel (in thousands) N from 1990 to 2002 can be approximated by the models

$$A(t) = 3.36t^2 - 59.8t + 735$$

and

$$N(t) = 1.95t^2 - 42.2t + 603$$

where t represents the year, with $t = 0$ corresponding to 1990. (Source: Department of Defense)

(a) Find and interpret $(A + N)(t)$. Evaluate this function for $t = 4, 8,$ and 12.

(b) Find and interpret $(A - N)(t)$. Evaluate this function for $t = 4, 8,$ and 12.

60. *Sales* The sales of exercise equipment E (in millions of dollars) in the United States from 1997 to 2003 can be approximated by the function

$$E(t) = 25.95t^2 - 231.2t + 3356$$

and the U.S. population P (in millions) from 1997 to 2003 can be approximated by the function

$$P(t) = 3.02t + 252.0$$

where t represents the year, with $t = 7$ corresponding to 1997. (Source: National Sporting Goods Association, U.S. Census Bureau)

(a) Find and interpret $h(t) = \dfrac{E(t)}{P(t)}$.

(b) Evaluate the function in part (a) for $t = 7$, 10, and 12.

Model It

61. *Health Care Costs* The table shows the total amounts (in billions of dollars) spent on health services and supplies in the United States (including Puerto Rico) for the years 1995 through 2001. The variables y_1, y_2, and y_3 represent out-of-pocket payments, insurance premiums, and other types of payments, respectively. (Source: Centers for Medicare and Medicaid Services)

Year	y_1	y_2	y_3
1995	146.2	329.1	44.8
1996	152.0	344.1	48.1
1997	162.2	359.9	52.1
1998	175.2	382.0	55.6
1999	184.4	412.1	57.8
2000	194.7	449.0	57.4
2001	205.5	496.1	57.8

(a) Use the *regression* feature of a graphing utility to find a linear model for y_1 and quadratic models for y_2 and y_3. Let $t = 5$ represent 1995.

(b) Find $y_1 + y_2 + y_3$. What does this sum represent?

(c) Use a graphing utility to graph y_1, y_2, y_3, and $y_1 + y_2 + y_3$ in the same viewing window.

(d) Use the model from part (b) to estimate the total amounts spent on health services and supplies in the years 2008 and 2010.

---

62. *Graphical Reasoning* An electronically controlled thermostat in a home is programmed to lower the temperature automatically during the night. The temperature in the house T (in degrees Fahrenheit) is given in terms of t, the time in hours on a 24-hour clock (see figure).

(a) Explain why T is a function of t.

(b) Approximate $T(4)$ and $T(15)$.

(c) The thermostat is reprogrammed to produce a temperature H for which $H(t) = T(t - 1)$. How does this change the temperature?

(d) The thermostat is reprogrammed to produce a temperature H for which $H(t) = T(t) - 1$. How does this change the temperature?

(e) Write a piecewise-defined function that represents the graph.

63. *Geometry* A square concrete foundation is prepared as a base for a cylindrical tank (see figure).

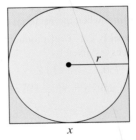

(a) Write the radius r of the tank as a function of the length x of the sides of the square.

(b) Write the area A of the circular base of the tank as a function of the radius r.

(c) Find and interpret $(A \circ r)(x)$.

64. *Physics*   A pebble is dropped into a calm pond, causing ripples in the form of concentric circles (see figure). The radius r (in feet) of the outer ripple is $r(t) = 0.6t$, where t is the time in seconds after the pebble strikes the water. The area A of the circle is given by the function $A(r) = \pi r^2$. Find and interpret $(A \circ r)(t)$.

65. *Bacteria Count*   The number N of bacteria in a refriger-ated food is given by

$$N(T) = 10T^2 - 20T + 600, \quad 1 \le T \le 20$$

where T is the temperature of the food in degrees Celsius. When the food is removed from refrigeration, the tempera-ture of the food is given by

$$T(t) = 3t + 2, \quad 0 \le t \le 6$$

where t is the time in hours.

(a) Find the composition $N(T(t))$ and interpret its meaning in context.

(b) Find the time when the bacterial count reaches 1500.

66. *Cost*   The weekly cost C of producing x units in a manu-facturing process is given by

$$C(x) = 60x + 750.$$

The number of units x produced in t hours is given by

$$x(t) = 50t.$$

(a) Find and interpret $(C \circ x)(t)$.

(b) Find the time that must elapse in order for the cost to increase to \$15,000.

67. *Salary*   You are a sales representative for a clothing manufacturer. You are paid an annual salary, plus a bonus of 3% of your sales over \$500,000. Consider the two functions given by

$$f(x) = x - 500,000 \quad \text{and} \quad g(x) = 0.03x.$$

If x is greater than \$500,000, which of the following repre-sents your bonus? Explain your reasoning.

(a) $f(g(x))$ (b) $g(f(x))$

68. *Consumer Awareness*   The suggested retail price of a new hybrid car is p dollars. The dealership advertises a factory rebate of \$2000 and a 10% discount.

(a) Write a function R in terms of p giving the cost of the hybrid car after receiving the rebate from the factory.

(b) Write a function S in terms of p giving the cost of the hybrid car after receiving the dealership discount.

(c) Form the composite functions $(R \circ S)(p)$ and $(S \circ R)(p)$ and interpret each.

(d) Find $(R \circ S)(20,500)$ and $(S \circ R)(20,500)$. Which yields the lower cost for the hybrid car? Explain.

Synthesis

True or False?   In Exercises 69 and 70, determine whether the statement is true or false. Justify your answer.

69. If $f(x) = x + 1$ and $g(x) = 6x$, then

$$(f \circ g)(x) = (g \circ f)(x).$$

70. If you are given two functions $f(x)$ and $g(x)$, you can calculate $(f \circ g)(x)$ if and only if the range of g is a subset of the domain of f.

71. *Proof*   Prove that the product of two odd functions is an even function, and that the product of two even functions is an even function.

72. *Conjecture*   Use examples to hypothesize whether the product of an odd function and an even function is even or odd. Then prove your hypothesis.

Skills Review

Average Rate of Change   In Exercises 73–76, find the difference quotient

$$\frac{f(x + h) - f(x)}{h}$$

and simplify your answer.

73. $f(x) = 3x - 4$ **74.** $f(x) = 1 - x^2$

75. $f(x) = \dfrac{4}{x}$ **76.** $f(x) = \sqrt{2x + 1}$

In Exercises 77–80, find an equation of the line that passes through the given point and has the indicated slope. Sketch the line.

77. $(2, -4), m = 3$ **78.** $(-6, 3), m = -1$

79. $(8, -1), m = -\frac{3}{2}$ **80.** $(7, 0), m = \frac{5}{7}$

1.9   Inverse Functions

Inverse Functions

Recall from Section 1.4, that a function can be represented by a set of ordered pairs. For instance, the function $f(x) = x + 4$ from the set $A = \{1, 2, 3, 4\}$ to the set $B = \{5, 6, 7, 8\}$ can be written as follows.

$$f(x) = x + 4\text{: }\{(1, 5), (2, 6), (3, 7), (4, 8)\}$$

In this case, by interchanging the first and second coordinates of each of these ordered pairs, you can form the **inverse function** of f, which is denoted by f^{-1}. It is a function from the set B to the set A, and can be written as follows.

$$f^{-1}(x) = x - 4\text{: }\{(5, 1), (6, 2), (7, 3), (8, 4)\}$$

Note that the domain of f is equal to the range of f^{-1}, and vice versa, as shown in Figure 1.92. Also note that the functions f and f^{-1} have the effect of "undoing" each other. In other words, when you form the composition of f with f^{-1} or the composition of f^{-1} with f, you obtain the identity function.

$$f(f^{-1}(x)) = f(x - 4) = (x - 4) + 4 = x$$
$$f^{-1}(f(x)) = f^{-1}(x + 4) = (x + 4) - 4 = x$$

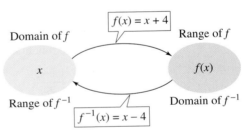

Domain of f $f(x) = x + 4$ Range of f

x $f(x)$

Range of f^{-1} $f^{-1}(x) = x - 4$ Domain of f^{-1}

FIGURE 1.92

Example 1   **Finding Inverse Functions Informally**

Find the inverse function of $f(x) = 4x$. Then verify that both $f(f^{-1}(x))$ and $f^{-1}(f(x))$ are equal to the identity function.

Solution

The function f *multiplies* each input by 4. To "undo" this function, you need to *divide* each input by 4. So, the inverse function of $f(x) = 4x$ is

$$f^{-1}(x) = \frac{x}{4}.$$

You can verify that both $f(f^{-1}(x)) = x$ and $f^{-1}(f(x)) = x$ as follows.

$$f(f^{-1}(x)) = f\left(\frac{x}{4}\right) = 4\left(\frac{x}{4}\right) = x \qquad f^{-1}(f(x)) = f^{-1}(4x) = \frac{4x}{4} = x$$

✓CHECKPOINT   Now try Exercise 1.

Exploration

Consider the functions given by

$$f(x) = x + 2$$

and

$$f^{-1}(x) = x - 2.$$

Evaluate $f(f^{-1}(x))$ and $f^{-1}(f(x))$ for the indicated values of x. What can you conclude about the functions?

x	-10	0	7	45
$f(f^{-1}(x))$				
$f^{-1}(f(x))$				

Definition of Inverse Function

Let f and g be two functions such that

$$f(g(x)) = x \qquad \text{for every } x \text{ in the domain of } g$$

and

$$g(f(x)) = x \qquad \text{for every } x \text{ in the domain of } f.$$

Under these conditions, the function g is the **inverse function** of the function f. The function g is denoted by f^{-1} (read "f-inverse"). So,

$$f(f^{-1}(x)) = x \qquad \text{and} \qquad f^{-1}(f(x)) = x.$$

The domain of f must be equal to the range of f^{-1}, and the range of f must be equal to the domain of f^{-1}.

Don't be confused by the use of -1 to denote the inverse function f^{-1}. In this text, whenever f^{-1} is written, it *always* refers to the inverse function of the function f and *not* to the reciprocal of $f(x)$.

If the function g is the inverse function of the function f, it must also be true that the function f is the inverse function of the function g. For this reason, you can say that the functions f and g are *inverse functions of each other*.

Example 2 Verifying Inverse Functions

Which of the functions is the inverse function of $f(x) = \dfrac{5}{x - 2}$?

$$g(x) = \frac{x - 2}{5} \qquad h(x) = \frac{5}{x} + 2$$

Solution

By forming the composition of f with g, you have

$$f(g(x)) = f\left(\frac{x - 2}{5}\right)$$

$$= \frac{5}{\left(\dfrac{x - 2}{5}\right) - 2} \qquad \text{Substitute } \frac{x - 2}{5} \text{ for } x.$$

$$= \frac{25}{x - 12} \neq x.$$

Because this composition is not equal to the identity function x, it follows that g *is not* the inverse function of f. By forming the composition of f with h, you have

$$f(h(x)) = f\left(\frac{5}{x} + 2\right) = \frac{5}{\left(\dfrac{5}{x} + 2\right) - 2} = \frac{5}{\left(\dfrac{5}{x}\right)} = x.$$

So, it appears that h *is* the inverse function of f. You can confirm this by showing that the composition of h with f is also equal to the identity function.

✓**CHECKPOINT**   Now try Exercise 5.

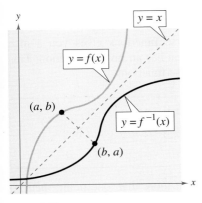

FIGURE **1.93**

The Graph of an Inverse Function

The graphs of a function f and its inverse function f^{-1} are related to each other in the following way. If the point (a, b) lies on the graph of f, then the point (b, a) must lie on the graph of f^{-1}, and vice versa. This means that the graph of f^{-1} is a *reflection* of the graph of f in the line $y = x$, as shown in Figure 1.93.

Example 3   **Finding Inverse Functions Graphically**

Sketch the graphs of the inverse functions $f(x) = 2x - 3$ and $f^{-1}(x) = \frac{1}{2}(x + 3)$ on the same rectangular coordinate system and show that the graphs are reflections of each other in the line $y = x$.

Solution

The graphs of f and f^{-1} are shown in Figure 1.94. It appears that the graphs are reflections of each other in the line $y = x$. You can further verify this reflective property by testing a few points on each graph. Note in the following list that if the point (a, b) is on the graph of f, the point (b, a) is on the graph of f^{-1}.

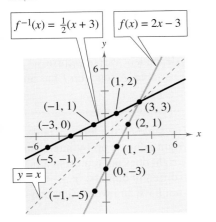

FIGURE **1.94**

Graph of $f(x) = 2x - 3$	Graph of $f^{-1}(x) = \frac{1}{2}(x + 3)$
$(-1, -5)$	$(-5, -1)$
$(0, -3)$	$(-3, 0)$
$(1, -1)$	$(-1, 1)$
$(2, 1)$	$(1, 2)$
$(3, 3)$	$(3, 3)$

✓CHECKPOINT   Now try Exercise 15.

Example 4   **Finding Inverse Functions Graphically**

Sketch the graphs of the inverse functions $f(x) = x^2 \ (x \geq 0)$ and $f^{-1}(x) = \sqrt{x}$ on the same rectangular coordinate system and show that the graphs are reflections of each other in the line $y = x$.

Solution

The graphs of f and f^{-1} are shown in Figure 1.95. It appears that the graphs are reflections of each other in the line $y = x$. You can further verify this reflective property by testing a few points on each graph. Note in the following list that if the point (a, b) is on the graph of f, the point (b, a) is on the graph of f^{-1}.

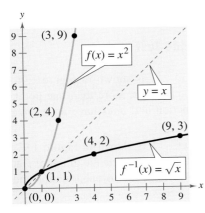

FIGURE **1.95**

Graph of $f(x) = x^2, \quad x \geq 0$	Graph of $f^{-1}(x) = \sqrt{x}$
$(0, 0)$	$(0, 0)$
$(1, 1)$	$(1, 1)$
$(2, 4)$	$(4, 2)$
$(3, 9)$	$(9, 3)$

Try showing that $f(f^{-1}(x)) = x$ and $f^{-1}(f(x)) = x$.

✓CHECKPOINT   Now try Exercise 17.

One-to-One Functions

The reflective property of the graphs of inverse functions gives you a nice *geometric* test for determining whether a function has an inverse function. This test is called the **Horizontal Line Test** for inverse functions.

Horizontal Line Test for Inverse Functions

A function f has an inverse function if and only if no *horizontal* line intersects the graph of f at more than one point.

If no horizontal line intersects the graph of f at more than one point, then no y-value is matched with more than one x-value. This is the essential characteristic of what are called **one-to-one functions.**

One-to-One Functions

A function f is **one-to-one** if each value of the dependent variable corresponds to exactly one value of the independent variable. A function f has an inverse function if and only if f is one-to-one.

Consider the function given by $f(x) = x^2$. The table on the left is a table of values for $f(x) = x^2$. The table of values on the right is made up by interchanging the columns of the first table. The table on the right does not represent a function because the input $x = 4$ is matched with two different outputs: $y = -2$ and $y = 2$. So, $f(x) = x^2$ is not one-to-one and does not have an inverse function.

FIGURE 1.96

x	$f(x) = x^2$
-2	4
-1	1
0	0
1	1
2	4
3	9

x	y
4	-2
1	-1
0	0
1	1
4	2
9	3

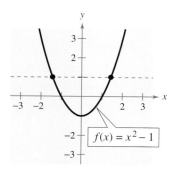

FIGURE 1.97

Example 5 Applying the Horizontal Line Test

a. The graph of the function given by $f(x) = x^3 - 1$ is shown in Figure 1.96. Because no horizontal line intersects the graph of f at more than one point, you can conclude that f *is* a one-to-one function and *does* have an inverse function.

b. The graph of the function given by $f(x) = x^2 - 1$ is shown in Figure 1.97. Because it is possible to find a horizontal line that intersects the graph of f at more than one point, you can conclude that f *is not* a one-to-one function and *does not* have an inverse function.

✓**CHECKPOINT** Now try Exercise 29.

Finding Inverse Functions Algebraically

For simple functions (such as the one in Example 1), you can find inverse functions by inspection. For more complicated functions, however, it is best to use the following guidelines. The key step in these guidelines is Step 3—interchanging the roles of x and y. This step corresponds to the fact that inverse functions have ordered pairs with the coordinates reversed.

> ### Finding an Inverse Function
>
> 1. Use the Horizontal Line Test to decide whether f has an inverse function.
> 2. In the equation for $f(x)$, replace $f(x)$ by y.
> 3. Interchange the roles of x and y, and solve for y.
> 4. Replace y by $f^{-1}(x)$ in the new equation.
> 5. Verify that f and f^{-1} are inverse functions of each other by showing that the domain of f is equal to the range of f^{-1}, the range of f is equal to the domain of f^{-1}, and $f(f^{-1}(x)) = x$ and $f^{-1}(f(x)) = x$.

Example 6   Finding an Inverse Function Algebraically

Find the inverse function of

$$f(x) = \frac{5 - 3x}{2}.$$

Solution

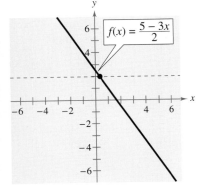

FIGURE **1.98**

The graph of f is a line, as shown in Figure 1.98. This graph passes the Horizontal Line Test. So, you know that f is one-to-one and has an inverse function.

$f(x) = \dfrac{5 - 3x}{2}$		Write original function.
$y = \dfrac{5 - 3x}{2}$		Replace $f(x)$ by y.
$x = \dfrac{5 - 3y}{2}$		Interchange x and y.
$2x = 5 - 3y$		Multiply each side by 2.
$3y = 5 - 2x$		Isolate the y-term.
$y = \dfrac{5 - 2x}{3}$		Solve for y.
$f^{-1}(x) = \dfrac{5 - 2x}{3}$		Replace y by $f^{-1}(x)$.

Note that both f and f^{-1} have domains and ranges that consist of the entire set of real numbers. Check that $f(f^{-1}(x)) = x$ and $f^{-1}(f(x)) = x$.

✓CHECKPOINT   Now try Exercise 55.

Exploration

Restrict the domain of $f(x) = x^2 + 1$ to $x \geq 0$. Use a graphing utility to graph the function. Does the restricted function have an inverse function? Explain.

| Example 7 | **Finding an Inverse Function** |

Find the inverse function of

$$f(x) = \sqrt[3]{x+1}.$$

Solution

The graph of f is a curve, as shown in Figure 1.99. Because this graph passes the Horizontal Line Test, you know that f is one-to-one and has an inverse function.

FIGURE **1.99**

$f(x) = \sqrt[3]{x+1}$	Write original function.
$y = \sqrt[3]{x+1}$	Replace $f(x)$ by y.
$x = \sqrt[3]{y+1}$	Interchange x and y.
$x^3 = y+1$	Cube each side.
$x^3 - 1 = y$	Solve for y.
$x^3 - 1 = f^{-1}(x)$	Replace y by $f^{-1}(x)$.

Both f and f^{-1} have domains and ranges that consist of the entire set of real numbers. You can verify this result numerically as shown in the tables below.

x	$f(x)$
-28	-3
-9	-2
-2	-1
-1	0
0	1
7	2
26	3

x	$f^{-1}(x)$
-3	-28
-2	-9
-1	-2
0	-1
1	0
2	7
3	26

✓CHECKPOINT   Now try Exercise 61.

WRITING ABOUT MATHEMATICS

The Existence of an Inverse Function Write a short paragraph describing why the following functions do or do not have inverse functions.

a. Let x represent the retail price of an item (in dollars), and let f(x) represent the sales tax on the item. Assume that the sales tax is 6% of the retail price *and* that the sales tax is rounded to the nearest cent. Does this function have an inverse function? (*Hint:* Can you undo this function?

For instance, if you know that the sales tax is $0.12, can you determine exactly what the retail price is?)

b. Let x represent the temperature in degrees Celsius, and let f(x) represent the temperature in degrees Fahrenheit. Does this function have an inverse function? (*Hint:* The formula for converting from degrees Celsius to degrees Fahrenheit is $F = \frac{9}{5}C + 32$.)

1.9 Exercises

VOCABULARY CHECK: Fill in the blanks.

1. If the composite functions $f(g(x)) = x$ and $g(f(x)) = x$ then the function g is the _____ function of f.

2. The domain of f is the _____ of f^{-1}, and the _____ of f^{-1} is the range of f.

3. The graphs of f and f^{-1} are reflections of each other in the line _____.

4. A function f is _____ if each value of the dependent variable corresponds to exactly one value of the independent variable.

5. A graphical test for the existence of an inverse function of f is called the _____ Line Test.

PREREQUISITE SKILLS REVIEW: Practice and review algebra skills needed for this section at **www.Eduspace.com**.

In Exercises 1–8, find the inverse function of f informally.
Verify that $f(f^{-1}(x)) = x$ and $f^{-1}(f(x)) = x$.

1. $f(x) = 6x$
2. $f(x) = \frac{1}{3}x$

3. $f(x) = x + 9$
4. $f(x) = x - 4$

5. $f(x) = 3x + 1$
6. $f(x) = \dfrac{x - 1}{5}$

7. $f(x) = \sqrt[3]{x}$
8. $f(x) = x^5$

In Exercises 9–12, match the graph of the function with the graph of its inverse function. [The graphs of the inverse functions are labeled (a), (b), (c), and (d).]

(a)

(b)

(c)

(d)

9.

10.

11.

12.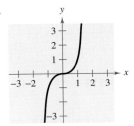

In Exercises 13–24, show that f and g are inverse functions (a) algebraically and (b) graphically.

13. $f(x) = 2x$, $g(x) = \dfrac{x}{2}$

14. $f(x) = x - 5$, $g(x) = x + 5$

15. $f(x) = 7x + 1$, $g(x) = \dfrac{x - 1}{7}$

16. $f(x) = 3 - 4x$, $g(x) = \dfrac{3 - x}{4}$

17. $f(x) = \dfrac{x^3}{8}$, $g(x) = \sqrt[3]{8x}$

18. $f(x) = \dfrac{1}{x}$, $g(x) = \dfrac{1}{x}$

19. $f(x) = \sqrt{x - 4}$, $g(x) = x^2 + 4$, $x \ge 0$

20. $f(x) = 1 - x^3$, $g(x) = \sqrt[3]{1 - x}$

21. $f(x) = 9 - x^2$, $x \ge 0$, $g(x) = \sqrt{9 - x}$, $x \le 9$

22. $f(x) = \dfrac{1}{1 + x}$, $x \ge 0$, $g(x) = \dfrac{1 - x}{x}$, $0 < x \le 1$

23. $f(x) = \dfrac{x - 1}{x + 5}$, $g(x) = -\dfrac{5x + 1}{x - 1}$

24. $f(x) = \dfrac{x + 3}{x - 2}$, $g(x) = \dfrac{2x + 3}{x - 1}$

In Exercises 25 and 26, does the function have an inverse function?

25.

x	-1	0	1	2	3	4
$f(x)$	-2	1	2	1	-2	-6

26.

x	-3	-2	-1	0	2	3
$f(x)$	10	6	4	1	-3	-10

In Exercises 27 and 28, use the table of values for $y = f(x)$ to complete a table for $y = f^{-1}(x)$.

27.

x	-2	-1	0	1	2	3
$f(x)$	-2	0	2	4	6	8

28.

x	-3	-2	-1	0	1	2
$f(x)$	-10	-7	-4	-1	2	5

In Exercises 29–32, does the function have an inverse function?

29.

30.

31.

32.

In Exercises 33–38, use a graphing utility to graph the function, and use the Horizontal Line Test to determine whether the function is one-to-one and so has an inverse function.

33. $g(x) = \dfrac{4 - x}{6}$

34. $f(x) = 10$

35. $h(x) = |x + 4| - |x - 4|$

36. $g(x) = (x + 5)^3$

37. $f(x) = -2x\sqrt{16 - x^2}$

38. $f(x) = \frac{1}{8}(x + 2)^2 - 1$

In Exercises 39–54, (a) find the inverse function of f, (b) graph both f and f^{-1} on the same set of coordinate axes, (c) describe the relationship between the graphs of f and f^{-1}, and (d) state the domain and range of f and f^{-1}.

39. $f(x) = 2x - 3$

40. $f(x) = 3x + 1$

41. $f(x) = x^5 - 2$

42. $f(x) = x^3 + 1$

43. $f(x) = \sqrt{x}$

44. $f(x) = x^2, \quad x \geq 0$

45. $f(x) = \sqrt{4 - x^2}, \quad 0 \leq x \leq 2$

46. $f(x) = x^2 - 2, \quad x \leq 0$

47. $f(x) = \dfrac{4}{x}$

48. $f(x) = -\dfrac{2}{x}$

49. $f(x) = \dfrac{x + 1}{x - 2}$

50. $f(x) = \dfrac{x - 3}{x + 2}$

51. $f(x) = \sqrt[3]{x - 1}$

52. $f(x) = x^{3/5}$

53. $f(x) = \dfrac{6x + 4}{4x + 5}$

54. $f(x) = \dfrac{8x - 4}{2x + 6}$

In Exercises 55–68, determine whether the function has an inverse function. If it does, find the inverse function.

55. $f(x) = x^4$

56. $f(x) = \dfrac{1}{x^2}$

57. $g(x) = \dfrac{x}{8}$

58. $f(x) = 3x + 5$

59. $p(x) = -4$

60. $f(x) = \dfrac{3x + 4}{5}$

61. $f(x) = (x + 3)^2, \quad x \geq -3$

62. $q(x) = (x - 5)^2$

63. $f(x) = \begin{cases} x + 3, & x < 0 \\ 6 - x, & x \geq 0 \end{cases}$

64. $f(x) = \begin{cases} -x, & x \leq 0 \\ x^2 - 3x, & x > 0 \end{cases}$

65. $h(x) = -\dfrac{4}{x^2}$

66. $f(x) = |x - 2|, \quad x \leq 2$

67. $f(x) = \sqrt{2x + 3}$

68. $f(x) = \sqrt{x - 2}$

In Exercises 69–74, use the functions given by $f(x) = \frac{1}{8}x - 3$ and $g(x) = x^3$ to find the indicated value or function.

69. $(f^{-1} \circ g^{-1})(1)$

70. $(g^{-1} \circ f^{-1})(-3)$

71. $(f^{-1} \circ f^{-1})(6)$

72. $(g^{-1} \circ g^{-1})(-4)$

73. $(f \circ g)^{-1}$

74. $g^{-1} \circ f^{-1}$

In Exercises 75–78, use the functions given by $f(x) = x + 4$ and $g(x) = 2x - 5$ to find the specified function.

75. $g^{-1} \circ f^{-1}$

76. $f^{-1} \circ g^{-1}$

77. $(f \circ g)^{-1}$

78. $(g \circ f)^{-1}$

Model It

79. *U.S. Households*   The numbers of households f (in thousands) in the United States from 1995 to 2003 are shown in the table. The time (in years) is given by t, with $t = 5$ corresponding to 1995. (Source: U.S. Census Bureau)

Year, t	Households, $f(t)$
5	98,990
6	99,627
7	101,018
8	102,528
9	103,874
10	104,705
11	108,209
12	109,297
13	111,278

(a) Find $f^{-1}(108,209)$.

(b) What does f^{-1} mean in the context of the problem?

(c) Use the *regression* feature of a graphing utility to find a linear model for the data, $y = mx + b$. (Round m and b to two decimal places.)

(d) Algebraically find the inverse function of the linear model in part (c).

(e) Use the inverse function of the linear model you found in part (d) to approximate $f^{-1}(117, 022)$.

(f) Use the inverse function of the linear model you found in part (d) to approximate $f^{-1}(108,209)$. How does this value compare with the original data shown in the table?

80. *Digital Camera Sales*   The factory sales f (in millions of dollars) of digital cameras in the United States from 1998 through 2003 are shown in the table. The time (in years) is given by t, with $t = 8$ corresponding to 1998. (Source: Consumer Electronincs Association)

Year, t	Sales, $f(t)$
8	519
9	1209
10	1825
11	1972
12	2794
13	3421

(a) Does f^{-1} exist?

(b) If f^{-1} exists, what does it represent in the context of the problem?

(c) If f^{-1} exists, find $f^{-1}(1825)$.

(d) If the table was extended to 2004 and if the factory sales of digital cameras for that year was $2794 million, would f^{-1} exist? Explain.

81. *Miles Traveled*   The total numbers f (in billions) of miles traveled by motor vehicles in the United States from 1995 through 2002 are shown in the table. The time (in years) is given by t, with $t = 5$ corresponding to 1995. (Source: U.S. Federal Highway Administration)

Year, t	Miles traveled, $f(t)$
5	2423
6	2486
7	2562
8	2632
9	2691
10	2747
11	2797
12	2856

(a) Does f^{-1} exist?

(b) If f^{-1} exists, what does it mean in the context of the problem?

(c) If f^{-1} exists, find $f^{-1}(2632)$.

(d) If the table was extended to 2003 and if the total number of miles traveled by motor vehicles for that year was 2747 billion, would f^{-1} exist? Explain.

82. *Hourly Wage* Your wage is $8.00 per hour plus $0.75 for each unit produced per hour. So, your hourly wage y in terms of the number of units produced is

$$y = 8 + 0.75x.$$

(a) Find the inverse function.

(b) What does each variable represent in the inverse function?

(c) Determine the number of units produced when your hourly wage is $22.25.

83. *Diesel Mechanics* The function given by

$$y = 0.03x^2 + 245.50, \qquad 0 < x < 100$$

approximates the exhaust temperature y in degrees Fahrenheit, where x is the percent load for a diesel engine.

(a) Find the inverse function. What does each variable represent in the inverse function?

 (b) Use a graphing utility to graph the inverse function.

(c) The exhaust temperature of the engine must not exceed 500 degrees Fahrenheit. What is the percent load interval?

84. *Cost* You need a total of 50 pounds of two types of ground beef costing $1.25 and $1.60 per pound, respectively. A model for the total cost y of the two types of beef is

$$y = 1.25x + 1.60(50 - x)$$

where x is the number of pounds of the less expensive ground beef.

(a) Find the inverse function of the cost function. What does each variable represent in the inverse function?

(b) Use the context of the problem to determine the domain of the inverse function.

(c) Determine the number of pounds of the less expensive ground beef purchased when the total cost is $73.

Synthesis

True or False? In Exercises 85 and 86, determine whether the statement is true or false. Justify your answer.

85. If f is an even function, f^{-1} exists.

86. If the inverse function of f exists and the graph of f has a y-intercept, the y-intercept of f is an x-intercept of f^{-1}.

87. *Proof* Prove that if f and g are one-to-one functions, then $(f \circ g)^{-1}(x) = (g^{-1} \circ f^{-1})(x)$.

88. *Proof* Prove that if f is a one-to-one odd function, then f^{-1} is an odd function.

In Exercises 89–92, use the graph of the function f to create a table of values for the given points. Then create a second table that can be used to find f^{-1}, and sketch the graph of f^{-1} if possible.

89.

90.

91.

92.

93. *Think About It* The function given by

$$f(x) = k(2 - x - x^3)$$

has an inverse function, and $f^{-1}(3) = -2$. Find k.

94. *Think About It* The function given by

$$f(x) = k(x^3 + 3x - 4)$$

has an inverse function, and $f^{-1}(-5) = 2$. Find k.

Skills Review

In Exercises 95–102, solve the equation using any convenient method.

95. $x^2 = 64$

96. $(x - 5)^2 = 8$

97. $4x^2 - 12x + 9 = 0$

98. $9x^2 + 12x + 3 = 0$

99. $x^2 - 6x + 4 = 0$

100. $2x^2 - 4x - 6 = 0$

101. $50 + 5x = 3x^2$

102. $2x^2 + 4x - 9 = 2(x - 1)^2$

103. Find two consecutive positive even integers whose product is 288.

104. *Geometry* A triangular sign has a height that is twice its base. The area of the sign is 10 square feet. Find the base and height of the sign.

1.10 Mathematical Modeling and Variation

Introduction

You have already studied some techniques for fitting models to data. For instance, in Section 1.3, you learned how to find the equation of a line that passes through two points. In this section, you will study other techniques for fitting models to data: *least squares regression* and *direct and inverse variation*. The resulting models are either polynomial functions or rational functions. (Rational functions will be studied in Chapter 2.)

Example 1   A Mathematical Model

The numbers of insured commercial banks y (in thousands) in the United States for the years 1996 to 2001 are shown in the table.   (Source: Federal Deposit Insurance Corporation)

Year	Insured commercial banks, y
1996	9.53
1997	9.14
1998	8.77
1999	8.58
2000	8.32
2001	8.08

A linear model that approximates the data is $y = -0.283t + 11.14$ for $6 \le t \le 11$, where t is the year, with $t = 6$ corresponding to 1996. Plot the actual data *and* the model on the same graph. How closely does the model represent the data?

Solution

The actual data are plotted in Figure 1.100, along with the graph of the linear model. From the graph, it appears that the model is a "good fit" for the actual data. You can see how well the model fits by comparing the actual values of y with the values of y given by the model. The values given by the model are labeled $y*$ in the table below.

t	6	7	8	9	10	11
y	9.53	9.14	8.77	8.58	8.32	8.08
$y*$	9.44	9.16	8.88	8.59	8.31	8.03

✓CHECKPOINT   Now try Exercise 1.

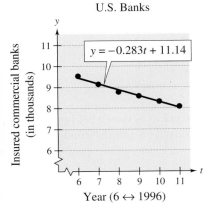

FIGURE 1.100

Note in Example 1 that you could have chosen any two points to find a line that fits the data. However, the given linear model was found using the *regression* feature of a graphing utility and is the line that *best* fits the data. This concept of a "best-fitting" line is discussed on the next page.

Least Squares Regression and Graphing Utilities

So far in this text, you have worked with many different types of mathematical models that approximate real-life data. In some instances the model was given (as in Example 1), whereas in other instances you were asked to find the model using simple algebraic techniques or a graphing utility.

To find a model that approximates the data most accurately, statisticians use a measure called the **sum of square differences,** which is the sum of the squares of the differences between actual data values and model values. The "best-fitting" linear model, called the **least squares regression line,** is the one with the least sum of square differences. Recall that you can approximate this line visually by plotting the data points and drawing the line that appears to fit best—or you can enter the data points into a calculator or computer and use the *linear regression* feature of the calculator or computer. When you use the *regression* feauture of a graphing calculator or computer program, you will notice that the program may also output an "r-value." This r-value is the **correlation coefficient** of the data and gives a measure of how well the model fits the data. The closer the value of $|r|$ is to 1, the better the fit.

Example 2 Finding a Least Squares Regression Line

The amounts p (in millions of dollars) of total annual prize money awarded at the Indianapolis 500 race from 1995 to 2004 are shown in the table. Construct a scatter plot that represents the data and find the least squares regression line for the data. (Source: indy500.com)

Indianapolis 500

FIGURE 1.101

Year	Prize money, p
1995	8.06
1996	8.11
1997	8.61
1998	8.72
1999	9.05
2000	9.48
2001	9.61
2002	10.03
2003	10.15
2004	10.25

Solution

Let $t = 5$ represent 1995. The scatter plot for the points is shown in Figure 1.101. Using the *regression* feature of a graphing utility, you can determine that the equation of the least squares regression line is

$$p = 0.268t + 6.66.$$

To check this model, compare the actual p-values with the p-values given by the model, which are labeled $p*$ in the table at the left. The correlation coefficient for this model is $r \approx 0.991$, which implies that the model is a good fit.

t	p	$p*$
5	8.06	8.00
6	8.11	8.27
7	8.61	8.54
8	8.72	8.80
9	9.05	9.07
10	9.48	9.34
11	9.61	9.61
12	10.03	9.88
13	10.15	10.14
14	10.25	10.41

✓CHECKPOINT Now try Exercise 7.

Direct Variation

There are two basic types of linear models. The more general model has a *y*-intercept that is nonzero.

$$y = mx + b, \quad b \neq 0$$

The simpler model

$$y = kx$$

has a *y*-intercept that is zero. In the simpler model, *y* is said to **vary directly** as *x*, or to be **directly proportional** to *x*.

Direct Variation

The following statements are equivalent.

1. *y* **varies directly** as *x*.

2. *y* is **directly proportional** to *x*.

3. $y = kx$ for some nonzero constant *k*.

k is the **constant of variation** or the **constant of proportionality.**

Example 3   **Direct Variation**

In Pennsylvania, the state income tax is directly proportional to *gross income*. You are working in Pennsylvania and your state income tax deduction is $46.05 for a gross monthly income of $1500. Find a mathematical model that gives the Pennsylvania state income tax in terms of gross income.

Solution

Verbal Model:	State income tax $= k \cdot$ Gross income

Labels: State income tax $= y$ (dollars)
Gross income $= x$ (dollars)
Income tax rate $= k$ (percent in decimal form)

Equation: $y = kx$

To solve for *k*, substitute the given information into the equation $y = kx$, and then solve for *k*.

$$y = kx \qquad \text{Write direct variation model.}$$

$$46.05 = k(1500) \qquad \text{Substitute } y = 46.05 \text{ and } x = 1500.$$

$$0.0307 = k \qquad \text{Simplify.}$$

So, the equation (or model) for state income tax in Pennsylvania is

$$y = 0.0307x.$$

In other words, Pennsylvania has a state income tax rate of 3.07% of gross income. The graph of this equation is shown in Figure 1.102.

✓CHECKPOINT   Now try Exercise 33.

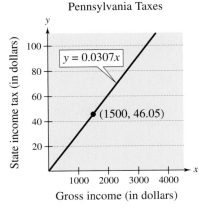

Pennsylvania Taxes

$y = 0.0307x$

(1500, 46.05)

State income tax (in dollars)

Gross income (in dollars)

FIGURE 1.102

Direct Variation as an *n*th Power

Another type of direct variation relates one variable to a *power* of another variable. For example, in the formula for the area of a circle

$$A = \pi r^2$$

the area A is directly proportional to the square of the radius r. Note that for this formula, π is the constant of proportionality.

STUDY TIP

Note that the direct variation model $y = kx$ is a special case of $y = kx^n$ with $n = 1$.

> ### Direct Variation as an *n*th Power
>
> The following statements are equivalent.
>
> **1.** y **varies directly as the *n*th power** of x.
>
> **2.** y is **directly proportional to the *n*th power** of x.
>
> **3.** $y = kx^n$ for some constant k.

Example 4   Direct Variation as *n*th Power

The distance a ball rolls down an inclined plane is directly proportional to the square of the time it rolls. During the first second, the ball rolls 8 feet. (See Figure 1.103.)

a. Write an equation relating the distance traveled to the time.

b. How far will the ball roll during the first 3 seconds?

$t = 0$ sec
$t = 1$ sec
$t = 3$ sec

FIGURE 1.103

Solution

a. Letting d be the distance (in feet) the ball rolls and letting t be the time (in seconds), you have

$$d = kt^2.$$

Now, because $d = 8$ when $t = 1$, you can see that $k = 8$, as follows.

$$d = kt^2$$
$$8 = k(1)^2$$
$$8 = k$$

So, the equation relating distance to time is

$$d = 8t^2.$$

b. When $t = 3$, the distance traveled is $d = 8(3)^2 = 8(9) = 72$ feet.

✔**CHECKPOINT**   Now try Exercise 63.

In Examples 3 and 4, the direct variations are such that an *increase* in one variable corresponds to an *increase* in the other variable. This is also true in the model $d = \frac{1}{5}F$, $F > 0$, where an increase in F results in an increase in d. You should not, however, assume that this always occurs with direct variation. For example, in the model $y = -3x$, an increase in x results in a *decrease* in y, and yet y is said to vary directly as x.

Inverse Variation

> ### Inverse Variation
>
> The following statements are equivalent.
>
> **1.** y **varies inversely** as x.   **2.** y is **inversely proportional** to x.
>
> **3.** $y = \dfrac{k}{x}$ for some constant k.

If x and y are related by an equation of the form $y = k/x^n$, then y varies inversely as the nth power of x (or y is inversely proportional to the nth power of x).

Some applications of variation involve problems with *both* direct and inverse variation in the same model. These types of models are said to have **combined variation.**

Example 5   Direct and Inverse Variation

A gas law states that the volume of an enclosed gas varies directly as the temperature *and* inversely as the pressure, as shown in Figure 1.104. The pressure of a gas is 0.75 kilogram per square centimeter when the temperature is 294 K and the volume is 8000 cubic centimeters. (a) Write an equation relating pressure, temperature, and volume. (b) Find the pressure when the temperature is 300 K and the volume is 7000 cubic centimeters.

Solution

a. Let V be volume (in cubic centimeters), let P be pressure (in kilograms per square centimeter), and let T be temperature (in Kelvin). Because V varies directly as T and inversely as P, you have

$$V = \frac{kT}{P}.$$

Now, because $P = 0.75$ when $T = 294$ and $V = 8000$, you have

$$8000 = \frac{k(294)}{0.75}$$

$$k = \frac{6000}{294} = \frac{1000}{49}.$$

So, the equation relating pressure, temperature, and volume is

$$V = \frac{1000}{49}\left(\frac{T}{P}\right).$$

b. When $T = 300$ and $V = 7000$, the pressure is

$$P = \frac{1000}{49}\left(\frac{300}{7000}\right) = \frac{300}{343} \approx 0.87 \text{ kilogram per square centimeter.}$$

✔CHECKPOINT   Now try Exercise 65.

P_1

P_2

V_1

V_2

$P_2 > P_1$ then $V_2 < V_1$

FIGURE 1.104   *If the temperature is held constant and pressure increases, volume decreases.*

Joint Variation

In Example 5, note that when a direct variation and an inverse variation occur in the same statement, they are coupled with the word "and." To describe two different *direct* variations in the same statement, the word **jointly** is used.

Joint Variation

The following statements are equivalent.

1. z **varies jointly** as x and y.

2. z is **jointly proportional** to x and y.

3. $z = kxy$ for some constant k.

If x, y, and z are related by an equation of the form

$$z = kx^n y^m$$

then z varies jointly as the nth power of x and the mth power of y.

Example 6   Joint Variation

The *simple* interest for a certain savings account is jointly proportional to the time and the principal. After one quarter (3 months), the interest on a principal of $5000 is $43.75.

a. Write an equation relating the interest, principal, and time.

b. Find the interest after three quarters.

Solution

a. Let I = interest (in dollars), P = principal (in dollars), and t = time (in years). Because I is jointly proportional to P and t, you have

$$I = kPt.$$

For $I = 43.75$, $P = 5000$, and $t = \frac{1}{4}$, you have

$$43.75 = k(5000)\left(\frac{1}{4}\right)$$

which implies that $k = 4(43.75)/5000 = 0.035$. So, the equation relating interest, principal, and time is

$$I = 0.035Pt$$

which is the familiar equation for simple interest where the constant of proportionality, 0.035, represents an annual interest rate of 3.5%.

b. When $P = \$5000$ and $t = \frac{3}{4}$, the interest is

$$I = (0.035)(5000)\left(\frac{3}{4}\right)$$

$$= \$131.25.$$

✓*CHECKPOINT*   Now try Exercise 67.

1.10 Exercises

VOCABULARY CHECK: Fill in the blanks.

1. Two techniques for fitting models to data are called direct _____ and least squares _____.

2. Statisticians use a measure called _____ of_____ _____ to find a model that approximates a set of data most accurately.

3. An r-value of a set of data, also called a _____ _____, gives a measure of how well a model fits a set of data.

4. Direct variation models can be described as y varies directly as x, or y is _____ _____ to x.

5. In direct variation models of the form $y = kx$, k is called the _____ of _____.

6. The direct variation model $y = kx^n$ can be described as y varies directly as the nth power of x, or y is _____ _____ to the nth power of x.

7. The mathematical model $y = \dfrac{k}{x}$ is an example of _____ variation.

8. Mathematical models that involve both direct and inverse variation are said to have _____ variation.

9. The joint variation model $z = kxy$ can be described as z varies jointly as x and y, or z is _____ _____ to x and y.

PREREQUISITE SKILLS REVIEW: Practice and review algebra skills needed for this section at **www.Eduspace.com.**

---

1. *Employment* The total numbers of employees (in thousands) in the United States from 1992 to 2002 are given by the following ordered pairs.

(1992, 128,105)	(1998, 137,673)
(1993, 129,200)	(1999, 139,368)
(1994, 131,056)	(2000, 142,583)
(1995, 132,304)	(2001, 143,734)
(1996, 133,943)	(2002, 144,683)
(1997, 136,297)	

A linear model that approximates the data is $y = 1767.0t + 123{,}916$, where y represents the number of employees (in thousands) and $t = 2$ represents 1992. Plot the actual data and the model on the same set of coordinate axes. How closely does the model represent the data? (Source: U.S. Bureau of Labor Statistics)

2. *Sports* The winning times (in minutes) in the women's 400-meter freestyle swimming event in the Olympics from 1948 to 2004 are given by the following ordered pairs.

(1948, 5.30)	(1980, 4.15)
(1952, 5.20)	(1984, 4.12)
(1956, 4.91)	(1988, 4.06)
(1960, 4.84)	(1992, 4.12)
(1964, 4.72)	(1996, 4.12)
(1968, 4.53)	(2000, 4.10)
(1972, 4.32)	(2004, 4.09)
(1976, 4.16)	

A linear model that approximates the data is $y = -0.022t + 5.03$, where y represents the winning time (in minutes) and $t = 0$ represents 1950. Plot the actual data and the model on the same set of coordinate axes. How closely does the model represent the data? Does it appear that another type of model may be a better fit? Explain.   (Source: *The World Almanac and Book of Facts*)

In Exercises 3–6, sketch the line that you think best approximates the data in the scatter plot. Then find an equation of the line. To print an enlarged copy of the graph, go to the website *www.mathgraphs.com*.

3.

4.

5.

6.

7. *Sports*   The lengths (in feet) of the winning men's discus throws in the Olympics from 1912 to 2004 are listed below.   (Source: *The World Almanac and Book of Facts*)

1912	148.3	1952	180.5	1980	218.7
1920	146.6	1956	184.9	1984	218.5
1924	151.3	1960	194.2	1988	225.8
1928	155.3	1964	200.1	1992	213.7
1932	162.3	1968	212.5	1996	227.7
1936	165.6	1972	211.3	2000	227.3
1948	173.2	1976	221.5	2004	229.3

(a) Sketch a scatter plot of the data. Let y represent the length of the winning discus throw (in feet) and let $t = 12$ represent 1912.

(b) Use a straightedge to sketch the best-fitting line through the points and find an equation of the line.

(c) Use the *regression* feature of a graphing utility to find the least squares regression line that fits the data.

(d) Compare the linear model you found in part (b) with the linear model given by the graphing utility in part (c).

(e) Use the models from parts (b) and (c) to estimate the winning men's discus throw in the year 2008.

(f) Use your school's library, the Internet, or some other reference source to analyze the accuracy of the estimate in part (e).

8. *Revenue*   The total revenues (in millions of dollars) for Outback Steakhouse from 1995 to 2003 are listed below. (Source: Outback Steakhouse, Inc.)

1995	664.0	2000	1906.0
1996	937.4	2001	2127.0
1997	1151.6	2002	2362.1
1998	1358.9	2003	2744.4
1999	1646.0		

(a) Sketch a scatter plot of the data. Let y represent the total revenue (in millions of dollars) and let $t = 5$ represent 1995.

(b) Use a straightedge to sketch the best-fitting line through the points and find an equation of the line.

(c) Use the *regression* feature of a graphing utility to find the least squares regression line that fits the data.

(d) Compare the linear model you found in part (b) with the linear model given by the graphing utility in part (c).

(e) Use the models from parts (b) and (c) to estimate the revenues of Outback Steakhouse in 2005.

(f) Use your school's library, the Internet, or some other reference source to analyze the accuracy of the estimate in part (e).

9. *Data Analysis: Broadway Shows*   The table shows the annual gross ticket sales S (in millions of dollars) for Broadway shows in New York City from 1995 through 2004.   (Source: The League of American Theatres and Producers, Inc.)

Year	Sales, S
1995	406
1996	436
1997	499
1998	558
1999	588
2000	603
2001	666
2002	643
2003	721
2004	771

(a) Use a graphing utility to create a scatter plot of the data. Let $t = 5$ represent 1995.

(b) Use the *regression* feature of a graphing utility to find the equation of the least squares regression line that fits the data.

(c) Use the graphing utility to graph the scatter plot you found in part (a) and the model you found in part (b) in the same viewing window. How closely does the model represent the data?

(d) Use the model to estimate the annual gross ticket sales in 2005 and 2007.

(e) Interpret the meaning of the slope of the linear model in the context of the problem.

10. *Data Analysis: Television Households*   The table shows the numbers x (in millions) of households with cable television and the numbers y (in millions) of households with color television sets in the United States from 1995 through 2002.   (Source: Nielson Media Research; Television Bureau of Advertising, Inc.)

Households with cable, x	Households with color TV, y
63	94
65	95
66	97
67	98
75	99
77	101
80	102
86	105

(a) Use the *regression* feature of a graphing utility to find the equation of the least squares regression line that fits the data.

(b) Use the graphing utility to create a scatter plot of the data. Then graph the model you found in part (a) and the scatter plot in the same viewing window. How closely does the model represent the data?

(c) Use the model to estimate the number of households with color television sets if the number of households with cable television is 90 million.

(d) Interpret the meaning of the slope of the linear model in the context of the problem.

Think About It   In Exercises 11 and 12, use the graph to determine whether y varies directly as some power of x or inversely as some power of x. Explain.

11.

12.
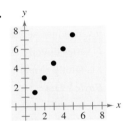

In Exercises 13–16, use the given value of k to complete the table for the direct variation model $y = kx^2$. Plot the points on a rectangular coordinate system.

x	2	4	6	8	10
$y = kx^2$					

13. $k = 1$

15. $k = \frac{1}{2}$

14. $k = 2$

16. $k = \frac{1}{4}$

In Exercises 17–20, use the given value of k to complete the table for the inverse variation model

$$y = \frac{k}{x^2}.$$

Plot the points on a rectangular coordinate system.

x	2	4	6	8	10
$y = \dfrac{k}{x^2}$					

17. $k = 2$

19. $k = 10$

18. $k = 5$

20. $k = 20$

In Exercises 21–24, determine whether the variation model is of the form $y = kx$ or $y = k/x$, and find k.

21.

x	5	10	15	20	25
y	1	$\frac{1}{2}$	$\frac{1}{3}$	$\frac{1}{4}$	$\frac{1}{5}$

22.

x	5	10	15	20	25
y	2	4	6	8	10

23.

x	5	10	15	20	25
y	-3.5	-7	-10.5	-14	-17.5

24.

x	5	10	15	20	25
y	24	12	8	6	$\frac{24}{5}$

Direct Variation   In Exercises 25–28, assume that y is directly proportional to x. Use the given x-value and y-value to find a linear model that relates y and x.

25. $x = 5, y = 12$

26. $x = 2, y = 14$

27. $x = 10, y = 2050$

28. $x = 6, y = 580$

29. *Simple Interest*   The simple interest on an investment is directly proportional to the amount of the investment. By investing $2500 in a certain bond issue, you obtained an interest payment of $87.50 after 1 year. Find a mathematical model that gives the interest I for this bond issue after 1 year in terms of the amount invested P.

30. *Simple Interest*   The simple interest on an investment is directly proportional to the amount of the investment. By investing $5000 in a municipal bond, you obtained an interest payment of $187.50 after 1 year. Find a mathematical model that gives the interest I for this municipal bond after 1 year in terms of the amount invested P.

31. *Measurement*   On a yardstick with scales in inches and centimeters, you notice that 13 inches is approximately the same length as 33 centimeters. Use this information to find a mathematical model that relates centimeters to inches. Then use the model to find the numbers of centimeters in 10 inches and 20 inches.

32. *Measurement*   When buying gasoline, you notice that 14 gallons of gasoline is approximately the same amount of gasoline as 53 liters. Then use this information to find a linear model that relates gallons to liters. Then use the model to find the numbers of liters in 5 gallons and 25 gallons.

33. *Taxes* Property tax is based on the assessed value of a property. A house that has an assessed value of $150,000 has a property tax of $5520. Find a mathematical model that gives the amount of property tax y in terms of the assessed value x of the property. Use the model to find the property tax on a house that has an assessed value of $200,000.

34. *Taxes* State sales tax is based on retail price. An item that sells for $145.99 has a sales tax of $10.22. Find a mathematical model that gives the amount of sales tax y in terms of the retail price x. Use the model to find the sales tax on a $540.50 purchase.

Hooke's Law **In Exercises 35–38, use Hooke's Law for springs, which states that the distance a spring is stretched (or compressed) varies directly as the force on the spring.**

35. A force of 265 newtons stretches a spring 0.15 meter (see figure).

Equilibrium

0.15 meter

265 newtons

(a) How far will a force of 90 newtons stretch the spring?

(b) What force is required to stretch the spring 0.1 meter?

36. A force of 220 newtons stretches a spring 0.12 meter. What force is required to stretch the spring 0.16 meter?

37. The coiled spring of a toy supports the weight of a child. The spring is compressed a distance of 1.9 inches by the weight of a 25-pound child. The toy will not work properly if its spring is compressed more than 3 inches. What is the weight of the heaviest child who should be allowed to use the toy?

38. An overhead garage door has two springs, one on each side of the door (see figure). A force of 15 pounds is required to stretch each spring 1 foot. Because of a pulley system, the springs stretch only one-half the distance the door travels. The door moves a total of 8 feet, and the springs are at their natural length when the door is open. Find the combined lifting force applied to the door by the springs when the door is closed.

8 ft

FIGURE FOR 38

In Exercises 39–48, find a mathematical model for the verbal statement.

39. A varies directly as the square of r.

40. V varies directly as the cube of e.

41. y varies inversely as the square of x.

42. h varies inversely as the square root of s.

43. F varies directly as g and inversely as r^2.

44. z is jointly proportional to the square of x and the cube of y.

45. *Boyle's Law:* For a constant temperature, the pressure P of a gas is inversely proportional to the volume V of the gas.

46. *Newton's Law of Cooling:* The rate of change R of the temperature of an object is proportional to the difference between the temperature T of the object and the temperature T_e of the environment in which the object is placed.

47. *Newton's Law of Universal Gravitation:* The gravitational attraction F between two objects of masses m_1 and m_2 is proportional to the product of the masses and inversely proportional to the square of the distance r between the objects.

48. *Logistic Growth:* The rate of growth R of a population is jointly proportional to the size S of the population and the difference between S and the maximum population size L that the environment can support.

In Exercises 49–54, write a sentence using the variation terminology of this section to describe the formula.

49. *Area of a triangle:* $A = \frac{1}{2}bh$

50. *Surface area of a sphere:* $S = 4\pi r^2$

51. *Volume of a sphere:* $V = \frac{4}{3}\pi r^3$

52. *Volume of a right circular cylinder:* $V = \pi r^2 h$

53. *Average speed:* $r = \dfrac{d}{t}$

54. *Free vibrations:* $\omega = \sqrt{\dfrac{kg}{W}}$

In Exercises 55–62, find a mathematical model representing the statement. (In each case, determine the constant of proportionality.)

55. A varies directly as r^2. ($A = 9\pi$ when $r = 3$.)

56. y varies inversely as x. ($y = 3$ when $x = 25$.)

57. y is inversely proportional to x. ($y = 7$ when $x = 4$.)

58. z varies jointly as x and y. ($z = 64$ when $x = 4$ and $y = 8$.)

59. F is jointly proportional to r and the third power of s. ($F = 4158$ when $r = 11$ and $s = 3$.)

60. P varies directly as x and inversely as the square of y. $\left(P = \frac{28}{3}\text{ when }x = 42\text{ and }y = 9.\right)$

61. z varies directly as the square of x and inversely as y. ($z = 6$ when $x = 6$ and $y = 4$.)

62. v varies jointly as p and q and inversely as the square of s. ($v = 1.5$ when $p = 4.1$, $q = 6.3$, and $s = 1.2$.)

Ecology   **In Exercises 63 and 64, use the fact that the diameter of the largest particle that can be moved by a stream varies approximately directly as the square of the velocity of the stream.**

63. A stream with a velocity of $\frac{1}{4}$ mile per hour can move coarse sand particles about 0.02 inch in diameter. Approximate the velocity required to carry particles 0.12 inch in diameter.

64. A stream of velocity v can move particles of diameter d or less. By what factor does d increase when the velocity is doubled?

Resistance   **In Exercises 65 and 66, use the fact that the resistance of a wire carrying an electrical current is directly proportional to its length and inversely proportional to its cross-sectional area.**

65. If #28 copper wire (which has a diameter of 0.0126 inch) has a resistance of 66.17 ohms per thousand feet, what length of #28 copper wire will produce a resistance of 33.5 ohms?

66. A 14-foot piece of copper wire produces a resistance of 0.05 ohm. Use the constant of proportionality from Exercise 65 to find the diameter of the wire.

67. *Work*   The work W (in joules) done when lifting an object varies jointly with the mass m (in kilograms) of the object and the height h (in meters) that the object is lifted. The work done when a 120-kilogram object is lifted 1.8 meters is 2116.8 joules. How much work is done when lifting a 100-kilogram object 1.5 meters?

68. *Spending*   The prices of three sizes of pizza at a pizza shop are as follows.

9-inch: $8.78, 12-inch: $11.78, 15-inch: $14.18

You would expect that the price of a certain size of pizza would be directly proportional to its surface area. Is that the case for this pizza shop? If not, which size of pizza is the best buy?

69. *Fluid Flow*   The velocity v of a fluid flowing in a conduit is inversely proportional to the cross-sectional area of the conduit. (Assume that the volume of the flow per unit of time is held constant.) Determine the change in the velocity of water flowing from a hose when a person places a finger over the end of the hose to decrease its cross-sectional area by 25%.

70. *Beam Load*   The maximum load that can be safely supported by a horizontal beam varies jointly as the width of the beam and the square of its depth, and inversely as the length of the beam. Determine the changes in the maximum safe load under the following conditions.

(a) The width and length of the beam are doubled.

(b) The width and depth of the beam are doubled.

(c) All three of the dimensions are doubled.

(d) The depth of the beam is halved.

Model It

71. *Data Analysis: Ocean Temperatures*   An oceanographer took readings of the water temperatures C (in degrees Celsius) at several depths d (in meters). The data collected are shown in the table.

Depth, d	Temperature, C
1000	4.2°
2000	1.9°
3000	1.4°
4000	1.2°
5000	0.9°

(a) Sketch a scatter plot of the data.

(b) Does it appear that the data can be modeled by the inverse variation model $C = k/d$? If so, find k for each pair of coordinates.

(c) Determine the mean value of k from part (b) to find the inverse variation model $C = k/d$.

 (d) Use a graphing utility to plot the data points and the inverse model in part (c).

(e) Use the model to approximate the depth at which the water temperature is 3°C.

72. *Data Analysis: Physics Experiment* An experiment in a physics lab requires a student to measure the compressed lengths y (in centimeters) of a spring when various forces of F pounds are applied. The data are shown in the table.

Force, F	Length, y
0	0
2	1.15
4	2.3
6	3.45
8	4.6
10	5.75
12	6.9

(a) Sketch a scatter plot of the data.

(b) Does it appear that the data can be modeled by Hooke's Law? If so, estimate k. (See Exercises 35–38.)

(c) Use the model in part (b) to approximate the force required to compress the spring 9 centimeters.

73. *Data Analysis: Light Intensity* A light probe is located x centimeters from a light source, and the intensity y (in microwatts per square centimeter) of the light is measured. The results are shown as ordered pairs (x, y).

(30, 0.1881)   (34, 0.1543)   (38, 0.1172)

(42, 0.0998)   (46, 0.0775)   (50, 0.0645)

A model for the data is $y = 262.76/x^{2.12}$.

(a) Use a graphing utility to plot the data points and the model in the same viewing window.

(b) Use the model to approximate the light intensity 25 centimeters from the light source.

74. *Illumination* The illumination from a light source varies inversely as the square of the distance from the light source. When the distance from a light source is doubled, how does the illumination change? Discuss this model in terms of the data given in Exercise 73. Give a possible explanation of the difference.

Synthesis

True or False? **In Exercises 75–77, decide whether the statement is true or false. Justify your answer.**

75. If y varies directly as x, then if x increases, y will increase as well.

76. In the equation for kinetic energy, $E = \frac{1}{2}mv^2$, the amount of kinetic energy E is directly proportional to the mass m of an object and the square of its velocity v.

77. If the correlation coefficient for a least squares regression line is close to -1, the regression line cannot be used to describe the data.

78. Discuss how well the data shown in each scatter plot can be approximated by a linear model.

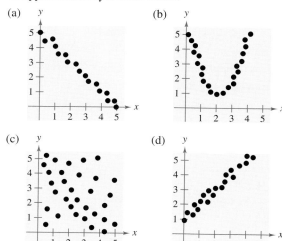

79. *Writing* A linear mathematical model for predicting prize winnings at a race is based on data for 3 years. Write a paragraph discussing the potential accuracy or inaccuracy of such a model.

80. *Research Project* Use your school's library, the Internet, or some other reference source to find data that you think describe a linear relationship. Create a scatter plot of the data and find the least squares regression line that represents the data points. Interpret the slope and y-intercept in the context of the data. Write a summary of your findings.

Skills Review

In Exercises 81–84, solve the inequality and graph the solution on the real number line.

81. $3x + 2 > 17$

82. $-7x + 10 \leq -1 + x$

83. $|2x - 1| < 9$ **84.** $|4 - 3x| + 7 \geq 12$

In Exercises 85 and 86, evaluate the function at each value of the independent variable and simplify.

85. $f(x) = \dfrac{x^2 + 5}{x - 3}$

(a) $f(0)$ (b) $f(-3)$ (c) $f(4)$

86. $f(x) = \begin{cases} -x^2 + 10, & x \geq -2 \\ 6x^2 - 1, & x < -2 \end{cases}$

(a) $f(-2)$ (b) $f(1)$ (c) $f(-8)$

87. Make a Decision To work an extended application analyzing registered voters in United States, visit this text's website at *college.hmco.com*. (*Data Source: U.S. Census Bureau*)

1   Chapter Summary

What did you learn?

	Review Exercises

Section 1.1
☐ Plot points on the Cartesian plane *(p. 2)*.   1–4
☐ Use the Distance Formula to find the distance between two points *(p. 4)*.   5–8
☐ Use the Midpoint Formula to find the midpoint of a line segment *(p. 5)*.   5–8
☐ Use a coordinate plane and geometric formulas to model and solve real-life problems *(p. 6)*.   9–14

Section 1.2
☐ Sketch graphs of equations *(p. 14)*.   15–24
☐ Find *x*- and *y*-intercepts of graphs of equations *(p. 17)*.   25–28
☐ Use symmetry to sketch graphs of equations *(p. 18)*.   29–36
☐ Find equations of and sketch graphs of circles *(p. 20)*.   37–44
☐ Use graphs of equations in solving real-life problems *(p. 21)*.   45, 46

Section 1.3
☐ Use slope to graph linear equations in two variables *(p. 25)*.   47–50
☐ Find slopes of lines *(p. 27)*.   51–54
☐ Write linear equations in two variables *(p. 29)*.   55–62
☐ Use slope to identify parallel and perpendicular lines *(p. 30)*.   63, 64
☐ Use slope and linear equations in two variables to model and solve real-life problems *(p. 31)*.   65, 66

Section 1.4
☐ Determine whether relations between two variables are functions *(p. 40)*.   67–70
☐ Use function notation and evaluate functions *(p. 42)*.   71, 72
☐ Find the domains of functions *(p. 44)*.   73–76
☐ Use functions to model and solve real-life problems *(p. 45)*.   77, 78
☐ Evaluate difference quotients *(p. 46)*.   79, 80

Section 1.5
☐ Use the Vertical Line Test for functions *(p. 54)*.   81–84
☐ Find the zeros of functions *(p. 56)*.   85–88
☐ Determine intervals on which functions are increasing or decreasing and determine relative maximum and relative minimum values of functions *(p. 57)*.   89–94
☐ Determine the average rate of change of a function *(p. 59)*.   95–98
☐ Identify even and odd functions *(p. 60)*.   99–102

1 Review Exercises

1.1 In Exercises 1 and 2, plot the points in the Cartesian plane.

1. $(2, 2), (0, -4), (-3, 6), (-1, -7)$
2. $(5, 0), (8, 1), (4, -2), (-3, -3)$

In Exercises 3 and 4, determine the quadrant(s) in which (x, y) is located so that the condition(s) is (are) satisfied.

3. $x > 0$ and $y = -2$
4. $y > 0$

In Exercises 5–8, (a) plot the points, (b) find the distance between the points, and (c) find the midpoint of the line segment joining the points.

5. $(-3, 8), (1, 5)$
6. $(-2, 6), (4, -3)$
7. $(5.6, 0), (0, 8.2)$
8. $(0, -1.2), (-3.6, 0)$

In Exercises 9 and 10, the polygon is shifted to a new position in the plane. Find the coordinates of the vertices of the polygon in its new position.

9. Original coordinates of vertices:

   $(4, 8), (6, 8), (4, 3), (6, 3)$

   Shift: three units downward, two units to the left

10. Original coordinates of vertices:

    $(0, 1), (3, 3), (0, 5), (-3, 3)$

    Shift: five units upward, four units to the left

11. **Sales** The Cheesecake Factory had annual sales of $539.1 million in 2001 and $773.8 million in 2003. Use the Midpoint Formula to estimate the sales in 2002. (Source: The Cheesecake Factory, Inc.)

12. **Meteorology** The apparent temperature is a measure of relative discomfort to a person from heat and high humidity. The table shows the actual temperatures x (in degrees Fahrenheit) versus the apparent temperatures y (in degrees Fahrenheit) for a relative humidity of 75%.

x	70	75	80	85	90	95	100
y	70	77	85	95	109	130	150

(a) Sketch a scatter plot of the data shown in the table.

(b) Find the change in the apparent temperature when the actual temperature changes from 70°F to 100°F.

13. **Geometry** The volume of a globe is about 47,712.94 cubic centimeters. Find the radius of the globe.

14. **Geometry** The volume of a rectangular package is 2304 cubic inches. The length of the package is 3 times its width, and the height is 1.5 times its width.

(a) Draw a diagram that represents the problem. Label the height, width, and length accordingly.

(b) Find the dimensions of the package.

1.2 In Exercises 15–18, complete a table of values. Use the solution points to sketch the graph of the equation.

15. $y = 3x - 5$
16. $y = -\frac{1}{2}x + 2$
17. $y = x^2 - 3x$
18. $y = 2x^2 - x - 9$

In Exercises 19–24, sketch the graph by hand.

19. $y - 2x - 3 = 0$
20. $3x + 2y + 6 = 0$
21. $y = \sqrt{5 - x}$
22. $y = \sqrt{x + 2}$
23. $y + 2x^2 = 0$
24. $y = x^2 - 4x$

In Exercises 25–28, find the x- and y-intercepts of the graph of the equation.

25. $y = 2x + 7$
26. $y = |x + 1| - 3$
27. $y = (x - 3)^2 - 4$
28. $y = x\sqrt{4 - x^2}$

In Exercises 29–36, use the algebraic tests to check for symmetry with respect to both axes and the origin. Then sketch the graph of the equation.

29. $y = -4x + 1$
30. $y = 5x - 6$
31. $y = 5 - x^2$
32. $y = x^2 - 10$
33. $y = x^3 + 3$
34. $y = -6 - x^3$
35. $y = \sqrt{x + 5}$
36. $y = |x| + 9$

In Exercises 37–42, find the center and radius of the circle and sketch its graph.

37. $x^2 + y^2 = 9$

38. $x^2 + y^2 = 4$

39. $(x + 2)^2 + y^2 = 16$

40. $x^2 + (y - 8)^2 = 81$

41. $\left(x - \frac{1}{2}\right)^2 + (y + 1)^2 = 36$

42. $(x + 4)^2 + \left(y - \frac{3}{2}\right)^2 = 100$

43. Find the standard form of the equation of the circle for which the endpoints of a diameter are $(0, 0)$ and $(4, -6)$.

44. Find the standard form of the equation of the circle for which the endpoints of a diameter are $(-2, -3)$ and $(4, -10)$.

45. *Physics*   The force F (in pounds) required to stretch a spring x inches from its natural length (see figure) is

$$F = \frac{5}{4}x, \ 0 \le x \le 20.$$

(a) Use the model to complete the table.

x	0	4	8	12	16	20
Force, F						

(b) Sketch a graph of the model.

(c) Use the graph to estimate the force necessary to stretch the spring 10 inches.

46. *Number of Stores*   The numbers N of Target stores for the years 1994 to 2003 can be approximated by the model

$$N = 3.69t^2 + 939, \ 4 \le t \le 13$$

where t is the time (in years), with $t = 4$ corresponding to 1994.   (Source: Target Corp.)

(a) Sketch a graph of the model.

(b) Use the graph to estimate the year in which the number of stores was 1300.

1.3 In Exercises 47–50, find the slope and y-intercept (if possible) of the equation of the line. Sketch the line.

47. $y = 6$

48. $x = -3$

49. $y = 3x + 13$

50. $y = -10x + 9$

In Exercises 51–54, plot the points and find the slope of the line passing through the pair of points.

51. $(3, -4), (-7, 1)$

52. $(-1, 8), (6, 5)$

53. $(-4.5, 6), (2.1, 3)$

54. $(-3, 2), (8, 2)$

In Exercises 55–58, find the slope-intercept form of the equation of the line that passes through the given point and has the indicated slope. Sketch the line.

	Point	Slope
55.	$(0, -5)$	$m = \frac{3}{2}$
56.	$(-2, 6)$	$m = 0$
57.	$(10, -3)$	$m = -\frac{1}{2}$
58.	$(-8, 5)$	m is undefined.

In Exercises 59–62, find the slope-intercept form of the equation of the line passing through the points.

59. $(0, 0), (0, 10)$

60. $(2, 5), (-2, -1)$

61. $(-1, 4), (2, 0)$

62. $(11, -2), (6, -1)$

In Exercises 63 and 64, write the slope-intercept forms of the equations of the lines through the given point (a) parallel to the given line and (b) perpendicular to the given line.

	Point	Line
63.	$(3, -2)$	$5x - 4y = 8$
64.	$(-8, 3)$	$2x + 3y = 5$

Rate of Change In Exercises 65 and 66, you are given the dollar value of a product in 2006 and the rate at which the value of the product is expected to change during the next 5 years. Use this information to write a linear equation that gives the dollar value V of the product in terms of the year t. (Let $t = 6$ represent 2006.)

	2006 Value	Rate
65.	$12,500	$850 increase per year
66.	$72.95	$5.15 increase per year

1.4 In Exercises 67–70, determine whether the equation represents y as a function of x.

67. $16x - y^4 = 0$

68. $2x - y - 3 = 0$

69. $y = \sqrt{1 - x}$

70. $|y| = x + 2$

In Exercises 71 and 72, evaluate the function at each specified value of the independent variable and simplify.

71. $f(x) = x^2 + 1$

    (a) $f(2)$ (b) $f(-4)$ (c) $f(t^2)$ (d) $f(t + 1)$

72. $h(x) = \begin{cases} 2x + 1, & x \le -1 \\ x^2 + 2, & x > -1 \end{cases}$

    (a) $h(-2)$ (b) $h(-1)$ (c) $h(0)$ (d) $h(2)$

In Exercises 73–76, find the domain of the function. Verify your result with a graph.

73. $f(x) = \sqrt{25 - x^2}$

74. $f(x) = 3x + 4$

75. $h(x) = \dfrac{x}{x^2 - x - 6}$

76. $h(t) = |t + 1|$

77. *Physics* The velocity of a ball projected upward from ground level is given by $v(t) = -32t + 48$, where t is the time in seconds and v is the velocity in feet per second.

    (a) Find the velocity when $t = 1$.

    (b) Find the time when the ball reaches its maximum height. [*Hint:* Find the time when $v(t) = 0$.]

    (c) Find the velocity when $t = 2$.

78. *Mixture Problem* From a full 50-liter container of a 40% concentration of acid, x liters is removed and replaced with 100% acid.

    (a) Write the amount of acid in the final mixture as a function of x.

    (b) Determine the domain and range of the function.

    (c) Determine x if the final mixture is 50% acid.

In Exercises 79 and 80, find the difference quotient and simplify your answer.

79. $f(x) = 2x^2 + 3x - 1$, $\quad \dfrac{f(x + h) - f(x)}{h}$, $\quad h \ne 0$

80. $f(x) = x^3 - 5x^2 + x$, $\quad \dfrac{f(x + h) - f(x)}{h}$, $\quad h \ne 0$

1.5 In Exercises 81–84, use the Vertical Line Test to determine whether y is a function of x. To print an enlarged copy of the graph, go to the website *www.mathgraphs.com*.

81. $y = (x - 3)^2$

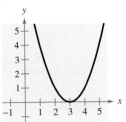

82. $y = -\frac{3}{5}x^3 - 2x + 1$

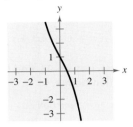

83. $x - 4 = y^2$

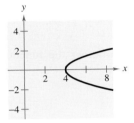

84. $x = -|4 - y|$

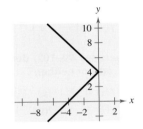

In Exercises 85–88, find the zeros of the function algebraically.

85. $f(x) = 3x^2 - 16x + 21$

86. $f(x) = 5x^2 + 4x - 1$

87. $f(x) = \dfrac{8x + 3}{11 - x}$

88. $f(x) = x^3 - x^2 - 25x + 25$

In Exercises 89 and 90, determine the intervals over which the function is increasing, decreasing, or constant.

89. $f(x) = |x| + |x + 1|$

90. $f(x) = (x^2 - 4)^2$

In Exercises 91–94, use a graphing utility to graph the function and approximate (to two decimal places) any relative minimum or relative maximum values.

91. $f(x) = -x^2 + 2x + 1$

92. $f(x) = x^4 - 4x^2 - 2$

93. $f(x) = x^3 - 6x^4$

94. $f(x) = x^3 - 4x^2 + x - 1$

In Exercises 95–98, find the average rate of change of the function from x_1 to x_2.

Function	x-Values
95. $f(x) = -x^2 + 8x - 4$	$x_1 = 0, x_2 = 4$
96. $f(x) = x^3 + 12x - 2$	$x_1 = 0, x_2 = 4$
97. $f(x) = 2 - \sqrt{x+1}$	$x_1 = 3, x_2 = 7$
98. $f(x) = 1 - \sqrt{x+3}$	$x_1 = 1, x_2 = 6$

In Exercises 99–102, determine whether the function is even, odd, or neither.

99. $f(x) = x^5 + 4x - 7$

100. $f(x) = x^4 - 20x^2$

101. $f(x) = 2x\sqrt{x^2 + 3}$

102. $f(x) = \sqrt[5]{6x^2}$

1.6 **In Exercises 103–104, write the linear function f such that it has the indicated function values. Then sketch the graph of the function.**

103. $f(2) = -6, \ f(-1) = 3$

104. $f(0) = -5, \ f(4) = -8$

In Exercises 105–114, graph the function.

105. $f(x) = 3 - x^2$

106. $h(x) = x^3 - 2$

107. $f(x) = -\sqrt{x}$

108. $f(x) = \sqrt{x+1}$

109. $g(x) = \dfrac{3}{x}$

110. $g(x) = \dfrac{1}{x+5}$

111. $f(x) = [\![x]\!] - 2$

112. $g(x) = [\![x+4]\!]$

113. $f(x) = \begin{cases} 5x - 3, & x \geq -1 \\ -4x + 5, & x < -1 \end{cases}$

114. $f(x) = \begin{cases} x^2 - 2, & x < -2 \\ 5, & -2 \leq x \leq 0 \\ 8x - 5, & x > 0 \end{cases}$

In Exercises 115 and 116, the figure shows the graph of a transformed parent function. Identify the parent function.

115.

116.

1.7 **In Exercises 117–130, h is related to one of the parent functions described in this chapter. (a) Identify the parent function f. (b) Describe the sequence of transformations from f to h. (c) Sketch the graph of h. (d) Use function notation to write h in terms of f.**

117. $h(x) = x^2 - 9$

118. $h(x) = (x - 2)^3 + 2$

119. $h(x) = \sqrt{x - 7}$

120. $h(x) = |x + 3| - 5$

121. $h(x) = -(x + 3)^2 + 1$

122. $h(x) = -(x - 5)^3 - 5$

123. $h(x) = -[\![x]\!] + 6$

124. $h(x) = -\sqrt{x + 1} + 9$

125. $h(x) = -|-x + 4| + 6$

126. $h(x) = -(x + 1)^2 - 3$

127. $h(x) = 5[\![x - 9]\!]$

128. $h(x) = -\frac{1}{3}x^3$

129. $h(x) = -2\sqrt{x - 4}$

130. $h(x) = \frac{1}{2}|x| - 1$

1.8 **In Exercises 131 and 132, find (a) $(f + g)(x)$, (b) $(f - g)(x)$, (c) $(fg)(x)$, and (d) $(f/g)(x)$. What is the domain of f/g?**

131. $f(x) = x^2 + 3, \quad g(x) = 2x - 1$

132. $f(x) = x^2 - 4, \quad g(x) = \sqrt{3 - x}$

In Exercises 133 and 134, find (a) $f \circ g$ and (b) $g \circ f$. Find the domain of each function and each composite function.

133. $f(x) = \frac{1}{3}x - 3, \quad g(x) = 3x + 1$

134. $f(x) = x^3 - 4, \quad g(x) = \sqrt[3]{x + 7}$

In Exercises 135 and 136, find two functions f and g such that $(f \circ g)(x) = h(x)$. (There are many correct answers.)

135. $h(x) = (6x - 5)^3$

136. $h(x) = \sqrt[3]{x + 2}$

137. *Electronics Sales* The factory sales (in millions of dollars) for VCRs $v(t)$ and DVD players $d(t)$ from 1997 to 2003 can be approximated by the functions

$$v(t) = -31.86t^2 + 233.6t + 2594$$

and

$$d(t) = -4.18t^2 + 571.0t - 3706$$

where t represents the year, with $t = 7$ corresponding to 1997. (Source: Consumer Electronics Association)

(a) Find and interpret $(v + d)(t)$.

 (b) Use a graphing utility to graph $v(t)$, $d(t)$, and the function from part (a) in the same viewing window.

 (c) Find $(v + d)(10)$. Use the graph in part (b) to verify your result.

138. *Bacteria Count* The number N of bacteria in a refrigerated food is given by

$$N(T) = 25T^2 - 50T + 300, \quad 2 \le T \le 20$$

where T is the temperature of the food in degrees Celsius. When the food is removed from refrigeration, the temperature of the food is given by

$$T(t) = 2t + 1, \quad 0 \le t \le 9$$

where t is the time in hours (a) Find the composition $N(T(t))$, and interpret its meaning in context, and (b) find the time when the bacterial count reaches 750.

1.9 In Exercises 139 and 140, find the inverse function of f informally. Verify that $f(f^{-1}(x)) = x$ and $f^{-1}(f(x)) = x$.

139. $f(x) = x - 7$

140. $f(x) = x + 5$

In Exercises 141 and 142, determine whether the function has an inverse function.

141.

142.

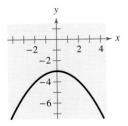

☑ **In Exercises 143–146, use a graphing utility to graph the function, and use the Horizontal Line Test to determine whether the function is one-to-one and so has an inverse function.**

143. $f(x) = 4 - \frac{1}{3}x$

144. $f(x) = (x - 1)^2$

145. $h(t) = \dfrac{2}{t - 3}$

146. $g(x) = \sqrt{x + 6}$

In Exercises 147–150, (a) find the inverse function of f, (b) graph both f and f^{-1} on the same set of coordinate axes, (c) describe the relationship between the graphs of f and f^{-1}, and (d) state the domains and ranges of f and f^{-1}.

147. $f(x) = \frac{1}{2}x - 3$

148. $f(x) = 5x - 7$

149. $f(x) = \sqrt{x + 1}$

150. $f(x) = x^3 + 2$

In Exercises 151 and 152, restrict the domain of the function f to an interval over which the function is increasing and determine f^{-1} over that interval.

151. $f(x) = 2(x - 4)^2$

152. $f(x) = |x - 2|$

1.10 **153.** *Median Income* The median incomes I (in thousands of dollars) for married-couple families in the United States from 1995 through 2002 are shown in the table. A linear model that approximates these data is

$$I = 2.09t + 37.2$$

where t represents the year, with $t = 5$ corresponding to 1995. (Source: U.S. Census Bureau)

Year	Median income, I
1995	47.1
1996	49.7
1997	51.6
1998	54.2
1999	56.5
2000	59.1
2001	60.3
2002	61.1

(a) Plot the actual data and the model on the same set of coordinate axes.

(b) How closely does the model represent the data?

154. *Data Analysis: Electronic Games* The table shows the factory sales S (in millions of dollars) of electronic gaming software in the United States from 1995 through 2003. (Source: Consumer Electronics Association)

Year	Sales, S
1995	3000
1996	3500
1997	3900
1998	4480
1999	5100
2000	5850
2001	6725
2002	7375
2003	7744

(a) Use a graphing utility to create a scatter plot of the data. Let t represent the year, with $t = 5$ corresponding to 1995.

(b) Use the *regression* feature of the graphing utility to find the equation of the least squares regression line that fits the data. Then graph the model and the scatter plot you found in part (a) in the same viewing window. How closely does the model represent the data?

(c) Use the model to estimate the factory sales of electronic gaming software in the year 2008.

(d) Interpret the meaning of the slope of the linear model in the context of the problem.

155. *Measurement* You notice a billboard indicating that it is 2.5 miles or 4 kilometers to the next restaurant of a national fast-food chain. Use this information to find a mathematical model that relates miles to kilometers. Then use the model to find the numbers of kilometers in 2 miles and 10 miles.

156. *Energy* The power P produced by a wind turbine is proportional to the cube of the wind speed S. A wind speed of 27 miles per hour produces a power output of 750 kilowatts. Find the output for a wind speed of 40 miles per hour.

157. *Frictional Force* The frictional force F between the tires and the road required to keep a car on a curved section of a highway is directly proportional to the square of the speed s of the car. If the speed of the car is doubled, the force will change by what factor?

158. *Demand* A company has found that the daily demand x for its boxes of chocolates is inversely proportional to the price p. When the price is $5, the demand is 800 boxes. Approximate the demand when the price is increased to $6.

159. *Travel Time* The travel time between two cities is inversely proportional to the average speed. A train travels between the cities in 3 hours at an average speed of 65 miles per hour. How long would it take to travel between the cities at an average speed of 80 miles per hour?

160. *Cost* The cost of constructing a wooden box with a square base varies jointly as the height of the box and the square of the width of the box. A box of height 16 inches and width 6 inches costs $28.80. How much would a box of height 14 inches and width 8 inches cost?

Synthesis

True or False? **In Exercises 161–163, determine whether the statement is true or false. Justify your answer.**

161. Relative to the graph of $f(x) = \sqrt{x}$, the function given by $h(x) = -\sqrt{x + 9} - 13$ is shifted 9 units to the left and 13 units downward, then reflected in the x-axis.

162. If f and g are two inverse functions, then the domain of g is equal to the range of f.

163. If y is directly proportional to x, then x is directly proportional to y.

164. *Writing* Explain the difference between the Vertical Line Test and the Horizontal Line Test.

165. *Writing* Explain how to tell whether a relation between two variables is a function.

Take this test as you would take a test in class. When you are finished, check your work against the answers given in the back of the book.

1. Plot the points $(-2, 5)$ and $(6, 0)$. Find the coordinates of the midpoint of the line segment joining the points and the distance between the points.

2. A cylindrical can has a volume of 600 cubic centimeters and a radius of 4 centimeters. Find the height of the can.

In Exercises 3–5, use intercepts and symmetry to sketch the graph of the equation.

3. $y = 3 - 5x$ 　　　　4. $y = 4 - |x|$ 　　　　5. $y = x^2 - 1$

6. Write the standard form of the equation of the circle shown at the left.

In Exercises 7 and 8, find an equation of the line passing through the points.

7. $(2, -3), (-4, 9)$ 　　　　8. $(3, 0.8), (7, -6)$

9. Find equations of the lines that pass through the point $(3, 8)$ and are (a) parallel to and (b) perpendicular to the line $-4x + 7y = -5$.

10. Evaluate $f(x) = \dfrac{\sqrt{x + 9}}{x^2 - 81}$ at each value: (a) $f(7)$ (b) $f(-5)$ (c) $f(x - 9)$.

11. Determine the domain of $f(x) = \sqrt{100 - x^2}$.

FIGURE FOR 6

In Exercises 12–14, (a) find the zeros of the function, (b) use a graphing utility to graph the function, (c) approximate the intervals over which the function is increasing, decreasing, or constant, and (d) determine whether the function is even, odd, or neither.

12. $f(x) = 2x^6 + 5x^4 - x^2$ 　　13. $f(x) = 4x\sqrt{3 - x}$ 　　　14. $f(x) = |x + 5|$

15. Sketch the graph of $f(x) = \begin{cases} 3x + 7, & x \le -3 \\ 4x^2 - 1, & x > -3 \end{cases}$.

In Exercises 16 and 17, identify the parent function in the transformation. Then sketch a graph of the function.

16. $h(x) = -[\![x]\!]$ 　　　　　　　　17. $h(x) = -\sqrt{x + 5} + 8$

In Exercises 18 and 19, find (a) $(f + g)(x)$, (b) $(f - g)(x)$, (c) $(fg)(x)$, (d) $(f/g)(x)$, (e) $(f \circ g)(x)$, and (f) $(g \circ f)(x)$.

18. $f(x) = 3x^2 - 7, \quad g(x) = -x^2 - 4x + 5$ 　　　19. $f(x) = \dfrac{1}{x}, \quad g(x) = 2\sqrt{x}$

In Exercises 20–22, determine whether or not the function has an inverse function, and if so, find the inverse function.

20. $f(x) = x^3 + 8$ 　　　　21. $f(x) = |x^2 - 3| + 6$ 　　　　22. $f(x) = 3x\sqrt{x}$

In Exercises 23–25, find a mathematical model representing the statement. (In each case, determine the constant of proportionality.)

23. v varies directly as the square root of s. ($v = 24$ when $s = 16$.)

24. A varies jointly as x and y. ($A = 500$ when $x = 15$ and $y = 8$.)

25. b varies inversely as a. ($b = 32$ when $a = 1.5$.)

Proofs in Mathematics

What does the word *proof* mean to you? In mathematics, the word *proof* is used to mean simply a valid argument. When you are proving a statement or theorem, you must use facts, definitions, and accepted properties in a logical order. You can also use previously proved theorems in your proof. For instance, the Distance Formula is used in the proof of the Midpoint Formula below. There are several different proof methods, which you will see in later chapters.

> ## The Midpoint Formula   *(p. 5)*
>
> The midpoint of the line segment joining the points (x_1, y_1) and (x_2, y_2) is given by the Midpoint Formula
>
> $$\text{Midpoint} = \left(\frac{x_1 + x_2}{2}, \frac{y_1 + y_2}{2} \right).$$

The Cartesian Plane

The Cartesian plane was named after the French mathematician René Descartes (1596–1650). While Descartes was lying in bed, he noticed a fly buzzing around on the square ceiling tiles. He discovered that the position of the fly could be described by which ceiling tile the fly landed on. This led to the development of the Cartesian plane. Descartes felt that a coordinate plane could be used to facilitate description of the positions of objects.

Proof

Using the figure, you must show that $d_1 = d_2$ and $d_1 + d_2 = d_3$.

By the Distance Formula, you obtain

$$d_1 = \sqrt{\left(\frac{x_1 + x_2}{2} - x_1\right)^2 + \left(\frac{y_1 + y_2}{2} - y_1\right)^2}$$

$$= \frac{1}{2}\sqrt{(x_2 - x_1)^2 + (y_2 - y_1)^2}$$

$$d_2 = \sqrt{\left(x_2 - \frac{x_1 + x_2}{2}\right)^2 + \left(y_2 - \frac{y_1 + y_2}{2}\right)^2}$$

$$= \frac{1}{2}\sqrt{(x_2 - x_1)^2 + (y_2 - y_1)^2}$$

$$d_3 = \sqrt{(x_2 - x_1)^2 + (y_2 - y_1)^2}$$

So, it follows that $d_1 = d_2$ and $d_1 + d_2 = d_3$.

P.S. Problem Solving

This collection of thought-provoking and challenging exercises further explores and expands upon concepts learned in this chapter.

1. As a salesperson, you receive a monthly salary of $2000, plus a commission of 7% of sales. You are offered a new job at $2300 per month, plus a commission of 5% of sales.

   (a) Write a linear equation for your current monthly wage W_1 in terms of your monthly sales S.

   (b) Write a linear equation for the monthly wage W_2 of your new job offer in terms of the monthly sales S.

   (c) Use a graphing utility to graph both equations in the same viewing window. Find the point of intersection. What does it signify?

   (d) You think you can sell $20,000 per month. Should you change jobs? Explain.

2. For the numbers 2 through 9 on a telephone keypad (see figure), create two relations: one mapping numbers onto letters, and the other mapping letters onto numbers. Are both relations functions? Explain.

3. What can be said about the sum and difference of each of the following?

   (a) Two even functions   (b) Two odd functions

   (c) An odd function and an even function

4. The two functions given by

   $$f(x) = x \quad \text{and} \quad g(x) = -x$$

   are their own inverse functions. Graph each function and explain why this is true. Graph other linear functions that are their own inverse functions. Find a general formula for a family of linear functions that are their own inverse functions.

5. Prove that a function of the following form is even.

   $$y = a_{2n}x^{2n} + a_{2n-2}x^{2n-2} + \cdots + a_2x^2 + a_0$$

6. A miniature golf professional is trying to make a hole-in-one on the miniature golf green shown. A coordinate plane is placed over the golf green. The golf ball is at the point $(2.5, 2)$ and the hole is at the point $(9.5, 2)$. The professional wants to bank the ball off the side wall of the green at the point (x, y). Find the coordinates of the point (x, y). Then write an equation for the path of the ball.

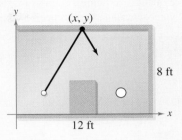

FIGURE FOR 6

7. At 2:00 P.M. on April 11, 1912, the *Titanic* left Cobh, Ireland, on her voyage to New York City. At 11:40 P.M. on April 14, the *Titanic* struck an iceberg and sank, having covered only about 2100 miles of the approximately 3400-mile trip.

   (a) What was the total duration of the voyage in hours?

   (b) What was the average speed in miles per hour?

   (c) Write a function relating the distance of the *Titantic* from New York City and the number of hours traveled. Find the domain and range of the function.

   (d) Graph the function from part (c).

8. Consider the function given by $f(x) = -x^2 + 4x - 3$. Find the average rate of change of the function from x_1 to x_2.

   (a) $x_1 = 1, x_2 = 2$ (b) $x_1 = 1, x_2 = 1.5$

   (c) $x_1 = 1, x_2 = 1.25$

   (d) $x_1 = 1, x_2 = 1.125$

   (e) $x_1 = 1, x_2 = 1.0625$

   (f) Does the average rate of change seem to be approaching one value? If so, what value?

   (g) Find the equations of the secant lines through the points $(x_1, f(x_1))$ and $(x_2, f(x_2))$ for parts (a)–(e).

   (h) Find the equation of the line through the point $(1, f(1))$ using your answer from part (f) as the slope of the line.

9. Consider the functions given by $f(x) = 4x$ and $g(x) = x + 6$.

   (a) Find $(f \circ g)(x)$.

   (b) Find $(f \circ g)^{-1}(x)$.

   (c) Find $f^{-1}(x)$ and $g^{-1}(x)$.

   (d) Find $(g^{-1} \circ f^{-1})(x)$ and compare the result with that of part (b).

   (e) Repeat parts (a) through (d) for $f(x) = x^3 + 1$ and $g(x) = 2x$.

   (f) Write two one-to-one functions f and g, and repeat parts (a) through (d) for these functions.

   (g) Make a conjecture about $(f \circ g)^{-1}(x)$ and $(g^{-1} \circ f^{-1})(x)$.

10. You are in a boat 2 miles from the nearest point on the coast. You are to travel to a point Q, 3 miles down the coast and 1 mile inland (see figure). You can row at 2 miles per hour and you can walk at 4 miles per hour.

Not drawn to scale.

(a) Write the total time T of the trip as a function of x.

(b) Determine the domain of the function.

 (c) Use a graphing utility to graph the function. Be sure to choose an appropriate viewing window.

 (d) Use the *zoom* and *trace* features to find the value of x that minimizes T.

 (e) Write a brief paragraph interpreting these values.

11. The **Heaviside function** $H(x)$ is widely used in engineering applications. (See figure.) To print an enlarged copy of the graph, go to the website *www.mathgraphs.com*.

$$H(x) = \begin{cases} 1, & x \geq 0 \\ 0, & x < 0 \end{cases}$$

Sketch the graph of each function by hand.

(a) $H(x) - 2$ (b) $H(x - 2)$ (c) $-H(x)$

(d) $H(-x)$ (e) $\frac{1}{2}H(x)$ (f) $-H(x - 2) + 2$

12. Let $f(x) = \dfrac{1}{1 - x}$.

(a) What are the domain and range of f?

(b) Find $f(f(x))$. What is the domain of this function?

(c) Find $f(f(f(x)))$. Is the graph a line? Why or why not?

13. Show that the Associative Property holds for compositions of functions—that is,

$$(f \circ (g \circ h))(x) = ((f \circ g) \circ h)(x).$$

14. Consider the graph of the function f shown in the figure. Use this graph to sketch the graph of each function. To print an enlarged copy of the graph, go to the website *www.mathgraphs.com*.

(a) $f(x + 1)$ (b) $f(x) + 1$ (c) $2f(x)$ (d) $f(-x)$

(e) $-f(x)$ (f) $|f(x)|$ (g) $f(|x|)$

15. Use the graphs of f and f^{-1} to complete each table of function values.

(a)

x	-4	-2	0	4
$(f(f^{-1}(x)))$				

(b)

x	-3	-2	0	1
$(f + f^{-1})(x)$				

(c)

x	-3	-2	0	1
$(f \cdot f^{-1})(x)$				

(d)

x	-4	-3	0	4
$|f^{-1}(x)|$				

Polynomial and Rational Functions

2

Quadratic functions are often used to model real-life phenomena, such as the path of a diver.

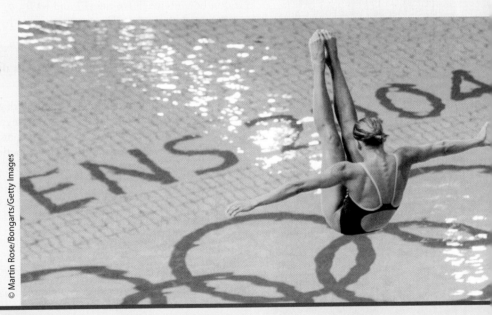

© Martin Rose/Bongarts/Getty Images

SELECTED APPLICATIONS

Polynomial and rational functions have many real-life applications. The applications listed below represent a small sample of the applications in this chapter.

2.1   Quadratic Functions and Models

What you should learn

- Analyze graphs of quadratic functions.
- Write quadratic functions in standard form and use the results to sketch graphs of functions.
- Use quadratic functions to model and solve real-life problems.

Why you should learn it

Quadratic functions can be used to model data to analyze consumer behavior. For instance, in Exercise 83 on page 137, you will use a quadratic function to model the revenue earned from manufacturing handheld video games.

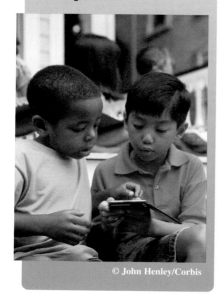

© John Henley/Corbis

The *HM mathSpace*® CD-ROM and *Eduspace*® for this text contain additional resources related to the concepts discussed in this chapter.

The Graph of a Quadratic Function

In this and the next section, you will study the graphs of polynomial functions. In Section 1.6, you were introduced to the following basic functions.

$$f(x) = ax + b \qquad \text{Linear function}$$

$$f(x) = c \qquad \text{Constant function}$$

$$f(x) = x^2 \qquad \text{Squaring function}$$

These functions are examples of **polynomial functions.**

Definition of Polynomial Function

Let n be a nonnegative integer and let $a_n, a_{n-1}, \ldots, a_2, a_1, a_0$ be real numbers with $a_n \neq 0$. The function given by

$$f(x) = a_n x^n + a_{n-1} x^{n-1} + \cdots + a_2 x^2 + a_1 x + a_0$$

is called a **polynomial function of x with degree n.**

Polynomial functions are classified by degree. For instance, a constant function has degree 0 and a linear function has degree 1. In this section, you will study second-degree polynomial functions, which are called **quadratic functions.**

For instance, each of the following functions is a quadratic function.

$$f(x) = x^2 + 6x + 2$$

$$g(x) = 2(x + 1)^2 - 3$$

$$h(x) = 9 + \tfrac{1}{4}x^2$$

$$k(x) = -3x^2 + 4$$

$$m(x) = (x - 2)(x + 1)$$

Note that the squaring function is a simple quadratic function that has degree 2.

Definition of Quadratic Function

Let a, b, and c be real numbers with $a \neq 0$. The function given by

$$f(x) = ax^2 + bx + c \qquad \text{Quadratic function}$$

is called a **quadratic function.**

The graph of a quadratic function is a special type of "U"-shaped curve called a **parabola.** Parabolas occur in many real-life applications—especially those involving reflective properties of satellite dishes and flashlight reflectors. You will study these properties in Section 10.2.

All parabolas are symmetric with respect to a line called the **axis of symmetry,** or simply the **axis** of the parabola. The point where the axis intersects the parabola is the **vertex** of the parabola, as shown in Figure 2.1. If the leading coefficient is positive, the graph of

$$f(x) = ax^2 + bx + c$$

is a parabola that opens upward. If the leading coefficient is negative, the graph of

$$f(x) = ax^2 + bx + c$$

is a parabola that opens downward.

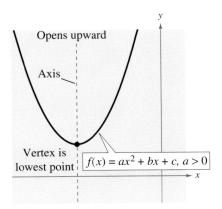

Leading coefficient is positive.
FIGURE 2.1

Leading coefficient is negative.

The simplest type of quadratic function is

$$f(x) = ax^2.$$

Its graph is a parabola whose vertex is $(0, 0)$. If $a > 0$, the vertex is the point with the *minimum* y-value on the graph, and if $a < 0$, the vertex is the point with the *maximum* y-value on the graph, as shown in Figure 2.2.

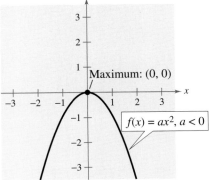

Leading coefficient is positive.
FIGURE 2.2

Leading coefficient is negative.

Exploration

Graph $y = ax^2$ for $a = -2, -1, -0.5, 0.5, 1,$ and 2. How does changing the value of a affect the graph?

Graph $y = (x - h)^2$ for $h = -4, -2, 2,$ and 4. How does changing the value of h affect the graph?

Graph $y = x^2 + k$ for $k = -4, -2, 2,$ and 4. How does changing the value of k affect the graph?

When sketching the graph of $f(x) = ax^2$, it is helpful to use the graph of $y = x^2$ as a reference, as discussed in Section 1.7.

Example 1   **Sketching Graphs of Quadratic Functions**

a. Compare the graphs of $y = x^2$ and $f(x) = \frac{1}{3}x^2$.

b. Compare the graphs of $y = x^2$ and $g(x) = 2x^2$.

Solution

a. Compared with $y = x^2$, each output of $f(x) = \frac{1}{3}x^2$ "shrinks" by a factor of $\frac{1}{3}$, creating the broader parabola shown in Figure 2.3.

b. Compared with $y = x^2$, each output of $g(x) = 2x^2$ "stretches" by a factor of 2, creating the narrower parabola shown in Figure 2.4.

FIGURE **2.3**

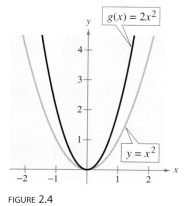

FIGURE **2.4**

✓CHECKPOINT   Now try Exercise 9.

In Example 1, note that the coefficient a determines how widely the parabola given by $f(x) = ax^2$ opens. If $|a|$ is small, the parabola opens more widely than if $|a|$ is large.

Recall from Section 1.7 that the graphs of $y = f(x \pm c)$, $y = f(x) \pm c$, $y = f(-x)$, and $y = -f(x)$ are rigid transformations of the graph of $y = f(x)$. For instance, in Figure 2.5, notice how the graph of $y = x^2$ can be transformed to produce the graphs of $f(x) = -x^2 + 1$ and $g(x) = (x + 2)^2 - 3$.

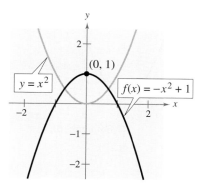

Reflection in x-axis followed by an upward shift of one unit

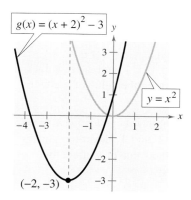

Left shift of two units followed by a downward shift of three units

FIGURE **2.5**

The Standard Form of a Quadratic Function

The **standard form** of a quadratic function is $f(x) = a(x - h)^2 + k$. This form is especially convenient for sketching a parabola because it identifies the vertex of the parabola as (h, k).

Standard Form of a Quadratic Function

The quadratic function given by

$$f(x) = a(x - h)^2 + k, \quad a \neq 0$$

is in **standard form.** The graph of f is a parabola whose axis is the vertical line $x = h$ and whose vertex is the point (h, k). If $a > 0$, the parabola opens upward, and if $a < 0$, the parabola opens downward.

To graph a parabola, it is helpful to begin by writing the quadratic function in standard form using the process of completing the square, as illustrated in Example 2. In this example, notice that when completing the square, you *add and subtract* the square of half the coefficient of x within the parentheses instead of adding the value to each side of the equation as is done in Appendix A.5.

Example 2   Graphing a Parabola in Standard Form

Sketch the graph of $f(x) = 2x^2 + 8x + 7$ and identify the vertex and the axis of the parabola.

Solution

Begin by writing the quadratic function in standard form. Notice that the first step in completing the square is to factor out any coefficient of x^2 that is not 1.

$$f(x) = 2x^2 + 8x + 7 \qquad \text{Write original function.}$$

$$= 2(x^2 + 4x) + 7 \qquad \text{Factor 2 out of } x\text{-terms.}$$

$$= 2(x^2 + 4x + 4 - 4) + 7 \qquad \text{Add and subtract 4 within parentheses.}$$

$$\underbrace{\qquad}_{(4/2)^2}$$

After adding and subtracting 4 within the parentheses, you must now regroup the terms to form a perfect square trinomial. The -4 can be removed from inside the parentheses; however, because of the 2 outside of the parentheses, you must multiply -4 by 2, as shown below.

$$f(x) = 2(x^2 + 4x + 4) - 2(4) + 7 \qquad \text{Regroup terms.}$$

$$= 2(x^2 + 4x + 4) - 8 + 7 \qquad \text{Simplify.}$$

$$= 2(x + 2)^2 - 1 \qquad \text{Write in standard form.}$$

From this form, you can see that the graph of f is a parabola that opens upward and has its vertex at $(-2, -1)$. This corresponds to a left shift of two units and a downward shift of one unit relative to the graph of $y = 2x^2$, as shown in Figure 2.6. In the figure, you can see that the axis of the parabola is the vertical line through the vertex, $x = -2$.

✓CHECKPOINT   Now try Exercise 13.

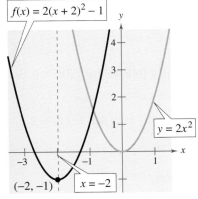

FIGURE 2.6

To find the x-intercepts of the graph of $f(x) = ax^2 + bx + c$, you must solve the equation $ax^2 + bx + c = 0$. If $ax^2 + bx + c$ does not factor, you can use the Quadratic Formula to find the x-intercepts. Remember, however, that a parabola may not have x-intercepts.

Example 3 Finding the Vertex and x-Intercepts of a Parabola

Sketch the graph of $f(x) = -x^2 + 6x - 8$ and identify the vertex and x-intercepts.

Solution

$$
\begin{aligned}
f(x) &= -x^2 + 6x - 8 && \text{Write original function.}\\
&= -(x^2 - 6x) - 8 && \text{Factor } -1 \text{ out of } x\text{-terms.}\\
&= -(x^2 - 6x + 9 - 9) - 8 && \text{Add and subtract 9 within}\\
& && \text{parentheses.}
\end{aligned}
$$

$$(-6/2)^2$$

$$
\begin{aligned}
&= -(x^2 - 6x + 9) - (-9) - 8 && \text{Regroup terms.}\\
&= -(x - 3)^2 + 1 && \text{Write in standard form.}
\end{aligned}
$$

From this form, you can see that f is a parabola that opens downward with vertex $(3, 1)$. The x-intercepts of the graph are determined as follows.

$$
\begin{aligned}
-(x^2 - 6x + 8) &= 0 && \text{Factor out } -1.\\
-(x - 2)(x - 4) &= 0 && \text{Factor.}\\
x - 2 = 0 \quad &\Longrightarrow \quad x = 2 && \text{Set 1st factor equal to 0.}\\
x - 4 = 0 \quad &\Longrightarrow \quad x = 4 && \text{Set 2nd factor equal to 0.}
\end{aligned}
$$

So, the x-intercepts are $(2, 0)$ and $(4, 0)$, as shown in Figure 2.7.

✔CHECKPOINT   Now try Exercise 19.

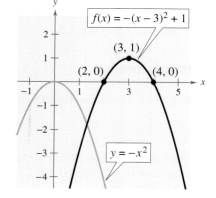

FIGURE **2.7**

Example 4 Writing the Equation of a Parabola

Write the standard form of the equation of the parabola whose vertex is $(1, 2)$ and that passes through the point $(0, 0)$, as shown in Figure 2.8.

Solution

Because the vertex of the parabola is at $(h, k) = (1, 2)$, the equation has the form

$$f(x) = a(x - 1)^2 + 2. \qquad \text{Substitute for } h \text{ and } k \text{ in standard form.}$$

Because the parabola passes through the point $(0, 0)$, it follows that $f(0) = 0$. So,

$$0 = a(0 - 1)^2 + 2 \quad \Longrightarrow \quad a = -2 \qquad \text{Substitute 0 for } x; \text{ solve for } a.$$

which implies that the equation in standard form is $f(x) = -2(x - 1)^2 + 2$.

✔CHECKPOINT   Now try Exercise 43.

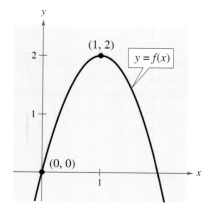

FIGURE **2.8**

Applications

Many applications involve finding the maximum or minimum value of a quadratic function. You can find the maximum or minimum value of a quadratic function by locating the vertex of the graph of the function.

Vertex of a Parabola

The vertex of the graph of $f(x) = ax^2 + bx + c$ is $\left(-\dfrac{b}{2a}, f\left(-\dfrac{b}{2a}\right)\right)$.

1. If $a > 0$, has a *minimum* at $x = -\dfrac{b}{2a}$.

2. If $a < 0$, has a *maximum* at $x = -\dfrac{b}{2a}$.

Example 5   The Maximum Height of a Baseball

A baseball is hit at a point 3 feet above the ground at a velocity of 100 feet per second and at an angle of 45° with respect to the ground. The path of the baseball is given by the function $f(x) = -0.0032x^2 + x + 3$, where $f(x)$ is the height of the baseball (in feet) and x is the horizontal distance from home plate (in feet). What is the maximum height reached by the baseball?

Solution

From the given function, you can see that $a = -0.0032$ and $b = 1$. Because the function has a maximum when $x = -b/(2a)$, you can conclude that the baseball reaches its maximum height when it is x feet from home plate, where x is

$$x = -\frac{b}{2a}x = -\frac{b}{2a} = -\frac{1}{2(-0.0032)} = 156.25 \text{ feet.}$$

At this distance, the maximum height is $f(156.25) = -0.0032(156.25)^2 + 156.25 + 3 = 81.125$ feet. The path of the baseball is shown in Figure 2.9.

✓CHECKPOINT   Now try Exercise 77.

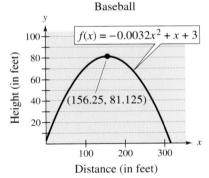

Baseball

$f(x) = -0.0032x^2 + x + 3$

(156.25, 81.125)

FIGURE 2.9

Example 6   Minimizing Cost

A small local soft-drink manufacturer has daily production costs of $C = 70,000 - 120x + 0.075x^2$, where C is the total cost (in dollars) and x is the number of units produced. How many units should be produced each day to yield a minimum cost?

Solution

Use the fact that the function has a minimum when $x = -b/(2a)$. From the given function you can see that $a = 0.075$ and $b = -120$. So, producing

$$x = -\frac{b}{2a} = -\frac{-120}{2(0.075)} = 800 \text{ units}$$

each day will yield a minimum cost.

✓CHECKPOINT   Now try Exercise 83.

2.1 Exercises

The *HM mathSpace®* CD-ROM and *Eduspace®* for this text contain step-by-step solutions to all odd-numbered exercises. They also provide Tutorial Exercises for additional help.

VOCABULARY CHECK: Fill in the blanks.

1. A polynomial function of degree n and leading coefficient a_n is a function of the form
$f(x) = a_n x^n + a_{n-1} x^{n-1} + \cdots + a_1 x + a_0 \ (a_n \neq 0)$ where n is a _____ _____ and a_1 are _____ numbers.

2. A _____ function is a second-degree polynomial function, and its graph is called a _____.

3. The graph of a quadratic function is symmetric about its _____.

4. If the graph of a quadratic function opens upward, then its leading coefficient is _____ and the vertex of the graph is a _____.

5. If the graph of a quadratic function opens downward, then its leading coefficient is _____ and the vertex of the graph is a _____.

PREREQUISITE SKILLS REVIEW: Practice and review algebra skills needed for this section at **www.Eduspace.com.**

In Exercises 1–8, match the quadratic function with its graph. [The graphs are labeled (a), (b), (c), (d), (e), (f), (g), and (h).]

1. $f(x) = (x - 2)^2$
2. $f(x) = (x + 4)^2$
3. $f(x) = x^2 - 2$
4. $f(x) = 3 - x^2$
5. $f(x) = 4 - (x - 2)^2$
6. $f(x) = (x + 1)^2 - 2$
7. $f(x) = -(x - 3)^2 - 2$
8. $f(x) = -(x - 4)^2$

(a)

(b)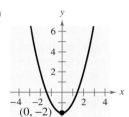

In Exercises 9–12, graph each function. Compare the graph of each function with the graph of $y = x^2$.

9. (a) $f(x) = \frac{1}{2}x^2$ (b) $g(x) = -\frac{1}{8}x^2$
   (c) $h(x) = \frac{3}{2}x^2$ (d) $k(x) = -3x^2$

10. (a) $f(x) = x^2 + 1$ (b) $g(x) = x^2 - 1$
    (c) $h(x) = x^2 + 3$ (d) $k(x) = x^2 - 3$

(c)

(d)

11. (a) $f(x) = (x - 1)^2$ (b) $g(x) = (3x)^2 + 1$
    (c) $h(x) = \left(\frac{1}{3}x\right)^2 - 3$ (d) $k(x) = (x + 3)^2$

12. (a) $f(x) = -\frac{1}{2}(x - 2)^2 + 1$
    (b) $g(x) = \left[\frac{1}{2}(x - 1)\right]^2 - 3$
    (c) $h(x) = -\frac{1}{2}(x + 2)^2 - 1$
    (d) $k(x) = [2(x + 1)]^2 + 4$

(e)

(f)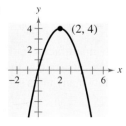

In Exercises 13–28, sketch the graph of the quadratic function without using a graphing utility. Identify the vertex, axis of symmetry, and x-intercept(s).

13. $f(x) = x^2 - 5$
14. $h(x) = 25 - x^2$
15. $f(x) = \frac{1}{2}x^2 - 4$
16. $f(x) = 16 - \frac{1}{4}x^2$
17. $f(x) = (x + 5)^2 - 6$
18. $f(x) = (x - 6)^2 + 3$
19. $h(x) = x^2 - 8x + 16$
20. $g(x) = x^2 + 2x + 1$
21. $f(x) = x^2 - x + \frac{5}{4}$
22. $f(x) = x^2 + 3x + \frac{1}{4}$
23. $f(x) = -x^2 + 2x + 5$
24. $f(x) = -x^2 - 4x + 1$
25. $h(x) = 4x^2 - 4x + 21$
26. $f(x) = 2x^2 - x + 1$
27. $f(x) = \frac{1}{4}x^2 - 2x - 12$
28. $f(x) = -\frac{1}{3}x^2 + 3x - 6$

(g)

(h)

In Exercises 29–36, use a graphing utility to graph the quadratic function. Identify the vertex, axis of symmetry, and x-intercepts. Then check your results algebraically by writing the quadratic function in standard form.

29. $f(x) = -(x^2 + 2x - 3)$ **30.** $f(x) = -(x^2 + x - 30)$

31. $g(x) = x^2 + 8x + 11$ **32.** $f(x) = x^2 + 10x + 14$

33. $f(x) = 2x^2 - 16x + 31$ **34.** $f(x) = -4x^2 + 24x - 41$

35. $g(x) = \frac{1}{2}(x^2 + 4x - 2)$ **36.** $f(x) = \frac{3}{5}(x^2 + 6x - 5)$

In Exercises 37–42, find the standard form of the quadratic function.

37.

38.

39.

40.

41.

42.

In Exercises 43–52, write the standard form of the equation of the parabola that has the indicated vertex and whose graph passes through the given point.

43. Vertex: $(-2, 5)$; point: $(0, 9)$

44. Vertex: $(4, -1)$; point: $(2, 3)$

45. Vertex: $(3, 4)$; point: $(1, 2)$

46. Vertex: $(2, 3)$; point: $(0, 2)$

47. Vertex: $(5, 12)$; point: $(7, 15)$

48. Vertex: $(-2, -2)$; point: $(-1, 0)$

49. Vertex: $\left(-\frac{1}{4}, \frac{3}{2}\right)$; point: $(-2, 0)$

50. Vertex: $\left(\frac{5}{2}, -\frac{3}{4}\right)$; point: $(-2, 4)$

51. Vertex: $\left(-\frac{5}{2}, 0\right)$; point: $\left(-\frac{7}{2}, -\frac{16}{3}\right)$

52. Vertex: $(6, 6)$; point: $\left(\frac{61}{10}, \frac{3}{2}\right)$

Graphical Reasoning   **In Exercises 53–56, determine the x-intercept(s) of the graph visually. Then find the x-intercepts algebraically to confirm your results.**

53. $y = x^2 - 16$

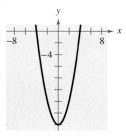

54. $y = x^2 - 6x + 9$

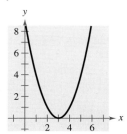

55. $y = x^2 - 4x - 5$

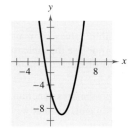

56. $y = 2x^2 + 5x - 3$

In Exercises 57–64, use a graphing utility to graph the quadratic function. Find the x-intercepts of the graph and compare them with the solutions of the corresponding quadratic equation when $f(x) = 0$.

57. $f(x) = x^2 - 4x$

58. $f(x) = -2x^2 + 10x$

59. $f(x) = x^2 - 9x + 18$

60. $f(x) = x^2 - 8x - 20$

61. $f(x) = 2x^2 - 7x - 30$

62. $f(x) = 4x^2 + 25x - 21$

63. $f(x) = -\frac{1}{2}(x^2 - 6x - 7)$

64. $f(x) = \frac{7}{10}(x^2 + 12x - 45)$

In Exercises 65–70, find two quadratic functions, one that opens upward and one that opens downward, whose graphs have the given x-intercepts. (There are many correct answers.)

65. $(-1, 0), (3, 0)$ **66.** $(-5, 0), (5, 0)$

67. $(0, 0), (10, 0)$ **68.** $(4, 0), (8, 0)$

69. $(-3, 0), \left(-\frac{1}{2}, 0\right)$ **70.** $\left(-\frac{5}{2}, 0\right), (2, 0)$

In Exercises 71–74, find two positive real numbers whose product is a maximum.

71. The sum is 110.

72. The sum is S.

73. The sum of the first and twice the second is 24.

74. The sum of the first and three times the second is 42.

75. *Numerical, Graphical, and Analytical Analysis* A rancher has 200 feet of fencing to enclose two adjacent rectangular corrals (see figure).

(a) Write the area A of the corral as a function of x.

(b) Create a table showing possible values of x and the corresponding areas of the corral. Use the table to estimate the dimensions that will produce the maximum enclosed area.

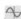 (c) Use a graphing utility to graph the area function. Use the graph to approximate the dimensions that will produce the maximum enclosed area.

(d) Write the area function in standard form to find analytically the dimensions that will produce the maximum area.

(e) Compare your results from parts (b), (c), and (d).

76. *Geometry* An indoor physical fitness room consists of a rectangular region with a semicircle on each end (see figure). The perimeter of the room is to be a 200-meter single-lane running track.

(a) Determine the radius of the semicircular ends of the room. Determine the distance, in terms of y, around the inside edge of the two semicircular parts of the track.

(b) Use the result of part (a) to write an equation, in terms of x and y, for the distance traveled in one lap around the track. Solve for y.

(c) Use the result of part (b) to write the area A of the rectangular region as a function of x. What dimensions will produce a maximum area of the rectangle?

77. *Path of a Diver* The path of a diver is given by

$$y = -\frac{4}{9}x^2 + \frac{24}{9}x + 12$$

where y is the height (in feet) and x is the horizontal distance from the end of the diving board (in feet). What is the maximum height of the diver?

78. *Height of a Ball* The height y (in feet) of a punted football is given by

$$y = -\frac{16}{2025}x^2 + \frac{9}{5}x + 1.5$$

where x is the horizontal distance (in feet) from the point at which the ball is punted (see figure).

Not drawn to scale

(a) How high is the ball when it is punted?

(b) What is the maximum height of the punt?

(c) How long is the punt?

79. *Minimum Cost* A manufacturer of lighting fixtures has daily production costs of

$$C = 800 - 10x + 0.25x^2$$

where C is the total cost (in dollars) and x is the number of units produced. How many fixtures should be produced each day to yield a minimum cost?

80. *Minimum Cost* A textile manufacturer has daily production costs of

$$C = 100,000 - 110x + 0.045x^2$$

where C is the total cost (in dollars) and x is the number of units produced. How many units should be produced each day to yield a minimum cost?

81. *Maximum Profit* The profit P (in dollars) for a company that produces antivirus and system utilities software is

$$P = -0.0002x^2 + 140x - 250,000$$

where x is the number of units sold. What sales level will yield a maximum profit?

82. *Maximum Profit* The profit P (in hundreds of dollars) that a company makes depends on the amount x (in hundreds of dollars) the company spends on advertising according to the model

$$P = 230 + 20x - 0.5x^2.$$

What expenditure for advertising will yield a maximum profit?

83. *Maximum Revenue* The total revenue R earned (in thousands of dollars) from manufacturing handheld video games is given by

$$R(p) = -25p^2 + 1200p$$

where p is the price per unit (in dollars).

(a) Find the revenue earned for each price per unit given below.

$20

$25

$30

(b) Find the unit price that will yield a maximum revenue. What is the maximum revenue? Explain your results.

84. *Maximum Revenue* The total revenue R earned per day (in dollars) from a pet-sitting service is given by

$$R(p) = -12p^2 + 150p$$

where p is the price charged per pet (in dollars).

(a) Find the revenue earned for each price per pet given below.

$4

$6

$8

(b) Find the price that will yield a maximum revenue. What is the maximum revenue? Explain your results.

85. *Graphical Analysis* From 1960 to 2003, the per capita consumption C of cigarettes by Americans (age 18 and older) can be modeled by

$$C = 4299 - 1.8t - 1.36t^2, \quad 0 \le t \le 43$$

where t is the year, with $t = 0$ corresponding to 1960. (Source: *Tobacco Outlook Report*)

(a) Use a graphing utility to graph the model.

(b) Use the graph of the model to approximate the maximum average annual consumption. Beginning in 1966, all cigarette packages were required by law to carry a health warning. Do you think the warning had any effect? Explain.

(c) In 2000, the U.S. population (age 18 and over) was 209,128,094. Of those, about 48,308,590 were smokers. What was the average annual cigarette consumption *per smoker* in 2000? What was the average daily cigarette consumption *per smoker*?

Model It

86. *Data Analysis* The numbers y (in thousands) of hairdressers and cosmetologists in the United States for the years 1994 through 2002 are shown in the table. (Source: U.S. Bureau of Labor Statistics)

Year	Number of hairdressers and cosmetologists, y
1994	753
1995	750
1996	737
1997	748
1998	763
1999	784
2000	820
2001	854
2002	908

(a) Use a graphing utility to create a scatter plot of the data. Let x represent the year, with $x = 4$ corresponding to 1994.

(b) Use the *regression* feature of a graphing utility to find a quadratic model for the data.

(c) Use a graphing utility to graph the model in the same viewing window as the scatter plot. How well does the model fit the data?

(d) Use the *trace* feature of the graphing utility to approximate the year in which the number of hairdressers and cosmetologists was the least.

(e) Verify your answer to part (d) algebraically.

(f) Use the model to predict the number of hairdressers and cosmetologists in 2008.

87. *Wind Drag* 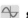 The number of horsepower y required to overcome wind drag on an automobile is approximated by

$$y = 0.002s^2 + 0.005s - 0.029, \quad 0 \le s \le 100$$

where s is the speed of the car (in miles per hour).

(a) Use a graphing utility to graph the function.

(b) Graphically estimate the maximum speed of the car if the power required to overcome wind drag is not to exceed 10 horsepower. Verify your estimate algebraically.

88. Maximum Fuel Economy A study was done to compare the speed x (in miles per hour) with the mileage y (in miles per gallon) of an automobile. The results are shown in the table. (Source: Federal Highway Administration)

Speed, x	Mileage, y
15	22.3
20	25.5
25	27.5
30	29.0
35	28.8
40	30.0
45	29.9
50	30.2
55	30.4
60	28.8
65	27.4
70	25.3
75	23.3

(a) Use a graphing utility to create a scatter plot of the data.

(b) Use the *regression* feature of a graphing utility to find a quadratic model for the data.

(c) Use a graphing utility to graph the model in the same viewing window as the scatter plot.

(d) Estimate the speed for which the miles per gallon is greatest.

Synthesis

True or False? In Exercises 89 and 90, determine whether the statement is true or false. Justify your answer.

89. The function given by $f(x) = -12x^2 - 1$ has no x-intercepts.

90. The graphs of

$$f(x) = -4x^2 - 10x + 7$$

and

$$g(x) = 12x^2 + 30x + 1$$

have the same axis of symmetry.

91. Write the quadratic function

$$f(x) = ax^2 + bx + c$$

in standard form to verify that the vertex occurs at

$$\left(-\frac{b}{2a}, \, f\left(-\frac{b}{2a}\right)\right).$$

92. Profit The profit P (in millions of dollars) for a recreational vehicle retailer is modeled by a quadratic function of the form

$$P = at^2 + bt + c$$

where t represents the year. If you were president of the company, which of the models below would you prefer? Explain your reasoning.

(a) a is positive and $-b/(2a) \le t$.

(b) a is positive and $t \le -b/(2a)$.

(c) a is negative and $-b/(2a) \le t$.

(d) a is negative and $t \le -b/(2a)$.

93. Is it possible for a quadratic equation to have only one x-intercept? Explain.

94. Assume that the function given by

$$f(x) = ax^2 + bx + c, \quad a \ne 0$$

has two real zeros. Show that the x-coordinate of the vertex of the graph is the average of the zeros of f. (*Hint:* Use the Quadratic Formula.)

Skills Review

In Exercises 95–98, find the equation of the line in slope-intercept form that has the given characteristics.

95. Passes through the points $(-4, 3)$ and $(2, 1)$

96. Passes through the point $\left(\frac{7}{2}, 2\right)$ and has a slope of $\frac{3}{2}$

97. Passes through the point $(0, 3)$ and is perpendicular to the line $4x + 5y = 10$

98. Passes through the point $(-8, 4)$ and is parallel to the line $y = -3x + 2$

In Exercises 99–104, let $f(x) = 14x - 3$ and let $g(x) = 8x^2$. Find the indicated value.

99. $(f + g)(-3)$

100. $(g - f)(2)$

101. $(fg)\left(-\frac{4}{7}\right)$

102. $\left(\dfrac{f}{g}\right)(-1.5)$

103. $(f \circ g)(-1)$

104. $(g \circ f)(0)$

105. Make a Decision To work an extended application analyzing the height of a basketball after it has been dropped, visit this text's website at *college.hmco.com*.

2.2   Polynomial Functions of Higher Degree

Graphs of Polynomial Functions

In this section, you will study basic features of the graphs of polynomial functions. The first feature is that the graph of a polynomial function is **continuous.** Essentially, this means that the graph of a polynomial function has no breaks, holes, or gaps, as shown in Figure 2.10(a). The graph shown in Figure 2.10(b) is an example of a piecewise-defined function that is not continuous.

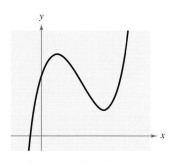

(a) Polynomial functions have continuous graphs.

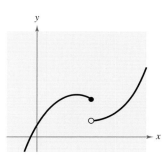

(b) Functions with graphs that are not continuous are not polynomial functions.

FIGURE 2.10

The second feature is that the graph of a polynomial function has only smooth, rounded turns, as shown in Figure 2.11. A polynomial function cannot have a sharp turn. For instance, the function given by $f(x) = |x|$, which has a sharp turn at the point $(0, 0)$, as shown in Figure 2.12, is not a polynomial function.

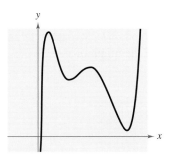

Polynomial functions have graphs with smooth rounded turns.
FIGURE 2.11

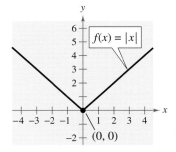

Graphs of polynomial functions cannot have sharp turns.
FIGURE 2.12

The graphs of polynomial functions of degree greater than 2 are more difficult to analyze than the graphs of polynomials of degree 0, 1, or 2. However, using the features presented in this section, coupled with your knowledge of point plotting, intercepts, and symmetry, you should be able to make reasonably accurate sketches *by hand*.

The polynomial functions that have the simplest graphs are monomials of the form $f(x) = x^n$, where n is an integer greater than zero. From Figure 2.13, you can see that when n is *even*, the graph is similar to the graph of $f(x) = x^2$, and when n is *odd*, the graph is similar to the graph of $f(x) = x^3$. Moreover, the greater the value of n, the flatter the graph near the origin. Polynomial functions of the form $f(x) = x^n$ are often referred to as **power functions.**

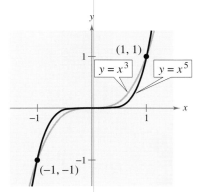

(a) If n is even, the graph of $y = x^n$ touches the axis at the x-intercept.

(b) If n is odd, the graph of $y = x^n$ crosses the axis at the x-intercept.

FIGURE 2.13

Example 1   Sketching Transformations of Monomial Functions

Sketch the graph of each function.

a. $f(x) = -x^5$ **b.** $h(x) = (x + 1)^4$

Solution

a. Because the degree of $f(x) = -x^5$ is odd, its graph is similar to the graph of $y = x^3$. In Figure 2.14, note that the negative coefficient has the effect of reflecting the graph in the x-axis.

b. The graph of $h(x) = (x + 1)^4$, as shown in Figure 2.15, is a left shift by one unit of the graph of $y = x^4$.

FIGURE 2.14

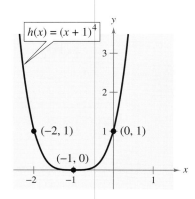

FIGURE 2.15

✓*CHECKPOINT*   Now try Exercise 9.

The Leading Coefficient Test

In Example 1, note that both graphs eventually rise or fall without bound as x moves to the right. Whether the graph of a polynomial function eventually rises or falls can be determined by the function's degree (even or odd) and by its leading coefficient, as indicated in the **Leading Coefficient Test.**

Leading Coefficient Test

As x moves without bound to the left or to the right, the graph of the polynomial function $f(x) = a_n x^n + \cdots + a_1 x + a_0$ eventually rises or falls in the following manner.

1. When n is *odd:*

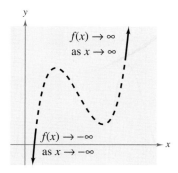

If the leading coefficient is positive ($a_n > 0$), the graph falls to the left and rises to the right.

If the leading coefficient is negative ($a_n < 0$), the graph rises to the left and falls to the right.

2. When n is *even:*

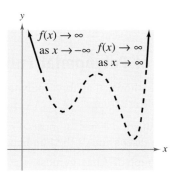

If the leading coefficient is positive ($a_n > 0$), the graph rises to the left and right.

If the leading coefficient is negative ($a_n < 0$), the graph falls to the left and right.

The dashed portions of the graphs indicate that the test determines *only* the right-hand and left-hand behavior of the graph.

Example 2 **Applying the Leading Coefficient Test**

Describe the right-hand and left-hand behavior of the graph of each function.

a. $f(x) = -x^3 + 4x$ **b.** $f(x) = x^4 - 5x^2 + 4$ **c.** $f(x) = x^5 - x$

Solution

a. Because the degree is odd and the leading coefficient is negative, the graph rises to the left and falls to the right, as shown in Figure 2.16.

b. Because the degree is even and the leading coefficient is positive, the graph rises to the left and right, as shown in Figure 2.17.

c. Because the degree is odd and the leading coefficient is positive, the graph falls to the left and rises to the right, as shown in Figure 2.18.

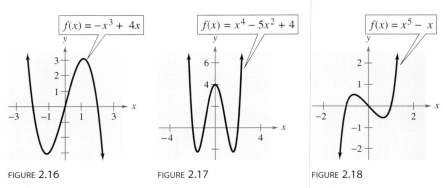

FIGURE 2.16   FIGURE 2.17   FIGURE 2.18

✓CHECKPOINT   Now try Exercise 15.

In Example 2, note that the Leading Coefficient Test tells you only whether the graph *eventually* rises or falls to the right or left. Other characteristics of the graph, such as intercepts and minimum and maximum points, must be determined by other tests.

Zeros of Polynomial Functions

It can be shown that for a polynomial function f of degree n, the following statements are true.

1. The function f has, at most, n real zeros. (You will study this result in detail in the discussion of the Fundamental Theorem of Algebra in Section 2.5.)

2. The graph of f has, at most, $n - 1$ turning points. (Turning points, also called relative minima or relative maxima, are points at which the graph changes from increasing to decreasing or vice versa.)

Finding the zeros of polynomial functions is one of the most important problems in algebra. There is a strong interplay between graphical and algebraic approaches to this problem. Sometimes you can use information about the graph of a function to help find its zeros, and in other cases you can use information about the zeros of a function to help sketch its graph. Finding zeros of polynomial functions is closely related to factoring and finding x-intercepts.

> **Real Zeros of Polynomial Functions**
>
> If f is a polynomial function and a is a real number, the following statements are equivalent.
>
> **1.** $x = a$ is a *zero* of the function f.
>
> **2.** $x = a$ is a *solution* of the polynomial equation $f(x) = 0$.
>
> **3.** $(x - a)$ is a *factor* of the polynomial $f(x)$.
>
> **4.** $(a, 0)$ is an *x-intercept* of the graph of f.

Example 3   Finding the Zeros of a Polynomial Function

Find all real zeros of

$$f(x) = -2x^4 + 2x^2.$$

Then determine the number of turning points of the graph of the function.

Algebraic Solution

To find the real zeros of the function, set $f(x)$ equal to zero and solve for x.

$$-2x^4 + 2x^2 = 0 \qquad \text{Set } f(x) \text{ equal to 0.}$$

$$-2x^2(x^2 - 1) = 0 \qquad \text{Remove common monomial factor.}$$

$$-2x^2(x - 1)(x + 1) = 0 \qquad \text{Factor completely.}$$

So, the real zeros are $x = 0$, $x = 1$, and $x = -1$. Because the function is a fourth-degree polynomial, the graph of f can have at most $4 - 1 = 3$ turning points.

Graphical Solution

Use a graphing utility to graph $y = -2x^4 + 2x^2$. In Figure 2.19, the graph appears to have zeros at $(0, 0)$, $(1, 0)$, and $(-1, 0)$. Use the *zero* or *root* feature, or the *zoom* and *trace* features, of the graphing utility to verify these zeros. So, the real zeros are $x = 0$, $x = 1$, and $x = -1$. From the figure, you can see that the graph has three turning points. This is consistent with the fact that a fourth-degree polynomial can have at most three turning points.

FIGURE 2.19

✓CHECKPOINT   Now try Exercise 27.

In Example 3, note that because k is even, the factor $-2x^2$ yields the *repeated* zero $x = 0$. The graph touches the x-axis at $x = 0$, as shown in Figure 2.19.

> **Repeated Zeros**
>
> A factor $(x - a)^k$, $k > 1$, yields a **repeated zero** $x = a$ of **multiplicity** k.
>
> **1.** If k is odd, the graph *crosses* the x-axis at $x = a$.
>
> **2.** If k is even, the graph *touches* the x-axis (but does not cross the x-axis) at $x = a$.

Technology

Example 4 uses an *algebraic approach* to describe the graph of the function. A graphing utility is a complement to this approach. Remember that an important aspect of using a graphing utility is to find a viewing window that shows all significant features of the graph. For instance, the viewing window in part (a) illustrates all of the significant features of the function in Example 4.

a.

b.

To graph polynomial functions, you can use the fact that a polynomial function can change signs only at its zeros. Between two consecutive zeros, a polynomial must be entirely positive or entirely negative. This means that when the real zeros of a polynomial function are put in order, they divide the real number line into intervals in which the function has no sign changes. These resulting intervals are **test intervals** in which a representative x-value in the interval is chosen to determine if the value of the polynomial function is positive (the graph lies above the x-axis) or negative (the graph lies below the x-axis).

Example 4   Sketching the Graph of a Polynomial Function

Sketch the graph of $f(x) = 3x^4 - 4x^3$.

Solution

1. *Apply the Leading Coefficient Test.* Because the leading coefficient is positive and the degree is even, you know that the graph eventually rises to the left and to the right (see Figure 2.20).

2. *Find the Zeros of the Polynomial.* By factoring $f(x) = 3x^4 - 4x^3$ as $f(x) = x^3(3x - 4)$, you can see that the zeros of f are $x = 0$ and $x = \frac{4}{3}$ (both of odd multiplicity). So, the x-intercepts occur at $(0, 0)$ and $\left(\frac{4}{3}, 0\right)$. Add these points to your graph, as shown in Figure 2.20.

3. *Plot a Few Additional Points.* Use the zeros of the polynomial to find the test intervals. In each test interval, choose a representative x-value and evaluate the polynomial function, as shown in the table.

Test interval	Representative x-value	Value of f	Sign	Point on graph
$(-\infty, 0)$	-1	$f(-1) = 7$	Positive	$(-1, 7)$
$\left(0, \frac{4}{3}\right)$	1	$f(1) = -1$	Negative	$(1, -1)$
$\left(\frac{4}{3}, \infty\right)$	1.5	$f(1.5) = 1.6875$	Positive	$(1.5, 1.6875)$

4. *Draw the Graph.* Draw a continuous curve through the points, as shown in Figure 2.21. Because both zeros are of odd multiplicity, you know that the graph should cross the x-axis at $x = 0$ and $x = \frac{4}{3}$.

STUDY TIP

If you are unsure of the shape of a portion of the graph of a polynomial function, plot some additional points, such as the point $(0.5, -0.3125)$ as shown in Figure 2.21.

FIGURE 2.20

FIGURE 2.21

  ✔CHECKPOINT   Now try Exercise 67.

Example 5   Sketching the Graph of a Polynomial Function

Sketch the graph of $f(x) = -2x^3 + 6x^2 - \frac{9}{2}x$.

Solution

1. *Apply the Leading Coefficient Test.*   Because the leading coefficient is negative and the degree is odd, you know that the graph eventually rises to the left and falls to the right (see Figure 2.22).

2. *Find the Zeros of the Polynomial.*   By factoring

$$f(x) = -2x^3 + 6x^2 - \frac{9}{2}x$$

$$= -\frac{1}{2}x(4x^2 - 12x + 9)$$

$$= -\frac{1}{2}x(2x - 3)^2$$

you can see that the zeros of f are $x = 0$ (odd multiplicity) and $x = \frac{3}{2}$ (even multiplicity). So, the x-intercepts occur at $(0, 0)$ and $\left(\frac{3}{2}, 0\right)$. Add these points to your graph, as shown in Figure 2.22.

3. *Plot a Few Additional Points.*   Use the zeros of the polynomial to find the test intervals. In each test interval, choose a representative x-value and evaluate the polynomial function, as shown in the table.

Observe in Example 5 that the sign of $f(x)$ is positive to the left of and negative to the right of the zero $x = 0$. Similarly, the sign of $f(x)$ is negative to the left and to the right of the zero $x = \frac{3}{2}$. This suggests that if the zero of a polynomial function is of *odd* multiplicity, then the sign of $f(x)$ changes from one side of the zero to the other side. If the zero is of *even* multiplicity, then the sign of $f(x)$ does not change from one side of the zero to the other side.

Test interval	Representative x-value	Value of f	Sign	Point on graph
$(-\infty, 0)$	-0.5	$f(-0.5) = 4$	Positive	$(-0.5, 4)$
$\left(0, \frac{3}{2}\right)$	0.5	$f(0.5) = -1$	Negative	$(0.5, -1)$
$\left(\frac{3}{2}, \infty\right)$	2	$f(2) = -1$	Negative	$(2, -1)$

4. *Draw the Graph.*   Draw a continuous curve through the points, as shown in Figure 2.23. As indicated by the multiplicities of the zeros, the graph crosses the x-axis at $(0, 0)$ but does not cross the x-axis at $\left(\frac{3}{2}, 0\right)$.

FIGURE **2.22**

FIGURE **2.23**

✓CHECKPOINT   Now try Exercise 69.

The Intermediate Value Theorem

The next theorem, called the **Intermediate Value Theorem,** illustrates the existence of real zeros of polynomial functions. This theorem implies that if $(a, f(a))$ and $(b, f(b))$ are two points on the graph of a polynomial function such that $f(a) \neq f(b)$, then for any number d between $f(a)$ and $f(b)$ there must be a number c between a and b such that $f(c) = d$. (See Figure 2.24.)

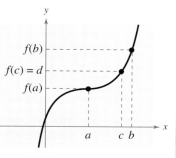

FIGURE 2.24

Intermediate Value Theorem

Let a and b be real numbers such that $a < b$. If f is a polynomial function such that $f(a) \neq f(b)$, then, in the interval $[a, b]$, f takes on every value between $f(a)$ and $f(b)$.

The Intermediate Value Theorem helps you locate the real zeros of a polynomial function in the following way. If you can find a value $x = a$ at which a polynomial function is positive, and another value $x = b$ at which it is negative, you can conclude that the function has at least one real zero between these two values. For example, the function given by $f(x) = x^3 + x^2 + 1$ is negative when $x = -2$ and positive when $x = -1$. Therefore, it follows from the Intermediate Value Theorem that f must have a real zero somewhere between -2 and -1, as shown in Figure 2.25.

FIGURE 2.25

By continuing this line of reasoning, you can approximate any real zeros of a polynomial function to any desired accuracy. This concept is further demonstrated in Example 6.

Example 6   **Approximating a Zero of a Polynomial Function**

Use the Intermediate Value Theorem to approximate the real zero of

$$f(x) = x^3 - x^2 + 1.$$

Solution

Begin by computing a few function values, as follows.

x	$f(x)$
-2	-11
-1	-1
0	1
1	1

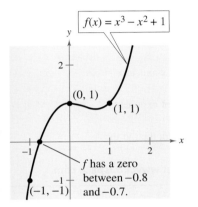

$f(x) = x^3 - x^2 + 1$

$(0, 1)$

$(1, 1)$

f has a zero
between -0.8
and -0.7.

$(-1, -1)$

FIGURE 2.26

Because $f(-1)$ is negative and $f(0)$ is positive, you can apply the Intermediate Value Theorem to conclude that the function has a zero between -1 and 0. To pinpoint this zero more closely, divide the interval $[-1, 0]$ into tenths and evaluate the function at each point. When you do this, you will find that

$$f(-0.8) = -0.152 \qquad \text{and} \qquad f(-0.7) = 0.167.$$

So, f must have a zero between -0.8 and -0.7, as shown in Figure 2.26. For a more accurate approximation, compute function values between $f(-0.8)$ and $f(-0.7)$ and apply the Intermediate Value Theorem again. By continuing this process, you can approximate this zero to any desired accuracy.

✓*CHECKPOINT*   Now try Exercise 85.

Technology

You can use the *table* feature of a graphing utility to approximate the zeros of a polynomial function. For instance, for the function given by

$$f(x) = -2x^3 - 3x^2 + 3$$

create a table that shows the function values for $-20 \le x \le 20$, as shown in the first table at the right. Scroll through the table looking for consecutive function values that differ in sign. From the table, you can see that $f(0)$ and $f(1)$ differ in sign. So, you can conclude from the Intermediate Value Theorem that the function has a zero between 0 and 1. You can adjust your table to show function values for $0 \le x \le 1$ using increments of 0.1, as shown in the second table at the right. By scrolling through the table you can see that $f(0.8)$ and $f(0.9)$ differ in sign. So, the function has a zero between 0.8 and 0.9. If you repeat this process several times, you should obtain $x \approx 0.806$ as the zero of the function. Use the *zero* or *root* feature of a graphing utility to confirm this result.

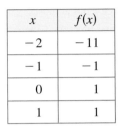

2.2 | Exercises

VOCABULARY CHECK: Fill in the blanks.

1. The graphs of all polynomial functions are _____, which means that the graphs have no breaks, holes, or gaps.

2. The _____ _____ _____ is used to determine the left-hand and right-hand behavior of the graph of a polynomial function.

3. A polynomial function of degree n has at most _____ real zeros and at most _____ turning points.

4. If $x = a$ is a zero of a polynomial function f, then the following three statements are true.

(a) $x = a$ is a _____ of the polynomial equation $f(x) = 0$.

(b) _____ is a factor of the polynomial $f(x)$.

(c) $(a, 0)$ is an _____ of the graph f.

5. If a real zero of a polynomial function is of even multiplicity, then the graph of f _____ the x-axis at $x = a$, and if it is of odd multiplicity then the graph of f _____ the x-axis at $x = a$.

6. A polynomial function is written in _____ form if its terms are written in descending order of exponents from left to right.

7. The _____ _____ Theorem states that if f is a polynomial function such that $f(a) \neq f(b)$, then in the interval $[a, b]$, f takes on every value between $f(a)$ and $f(b)$.

PREREQUISITE SKILLS REVIEW: Practice and review algebra skills needed for this section at **www.Eduspace.com**.

In Exercises 1–8, match the polynomial function with its graph. [The graphs are labeled (a), (b), (c), (d), (e), (f), (g), and (h).]

(a)

(b)

(c)

(d)

(e)

(f)

(g)

(h)

1. $f(x) = -2x + 3$

2. $f(x) = x^2 - 4x$

3. $f(x) = -2x^2 - 5x$

4. $f(x) = 2x^3 - 3x + 1$

5. $f(x) = -\frac{1}{4}x^4 + 3x^2$

6. $f(x) = -\frac{1}{3}x^3 + x^2 - \frac{4}{3}$

7. $f(x) = x^4 + 2x^3$

8. $f(x) = \frac{1}{5}x^5 - 2x^3 + \frac{9}{5}x$

In Exercises 9–12, sketch the graph of $y = x^n$ and each transformation.

9. $y = x^3$

(a) $f(x) = (x - 2)^3$

(b) $f(x) = x^3 - 2$

(c) $f(x) = -\frac{1}{2}x^3$

(d) $f(x) = (x - 2)^3 - 2$

10. $y = x^5$

(a) $f(x) = (x + 1)^5$

(b) $f(x) = x^5 + 1$

(c) $f(x) = 1 - \frac{1}{2}x^5$

(d) $f(x) = -\frac{1}{2}(x + 1)^5$

11. $y = x^4$

(a) $f(x) = (x + 3)^4$

(b) $f(x) = x^4 - 3$

(c) $f(x) = 4 - x^4$

(d) $f(x) = \frac{1}{2}(x - 1)^4$

(e) $f(x) = (2x)^4 + 1$

(f) $f(x) = \left(\frac{1}{2}x\right)^4 - 2$

12. $y = x^6$

   (a) $f(x) = -\frac{1}{8}x^6$ (b) $f(x) = (x + 2)^6 - 4$

   (c) $f(x) = x^6 - 4$ (d) $f(x) = -\frac{1}{4}x^6 + 1$

   (e) $f(x) = \left(\frac{1}{4}x\right)^6 - 2$ (f) $f(x) = (2x)^6 - 1$

In Exercises 13–22, describe the right-hand and left-hand behavior of the graph of the polynomial function.

13. $f(x) = \frac{1}{3}x^3 + 5x$ **14.** $f(x) = 2x^2 - 3x + 1$

15. $g(x) = 5 - \frac{7}{2}x - 3x^2$ **16.** $h(x) = 1 - x^6$

17. $f(x) = -2.1x^5 + 4x^3 - 2$

18. $f(x) = 2x^5 - 5x + 7.5$

19. $f(x) = 6 - 2x + 4x^2 - 5x^3$

20. $f(x) = \dfrac{3x^4 - 2x + 5}{4}$

21. $h(t) = -\frac{2}{3}(t^2 - 5t + 3)$

22. $f(s) = -\frac{7}{8}(s^3 + 5s^2 - 7s + 1)$

Graphical Analysis **In Exercises 23–26, use a graphing utility to graph the functions f and g in the same viewing window. Zoom out sufficiently far to show that the right-hand and left-hand behaviors of f and g appear identical.**

23. $f(x) = 3x^3 - 9x + 1$, $g(x) = 3x^3$

24. $f(x) = -\frac{1}{3}(x^3 - 3x + 2)$, $g(x) = -\frac{1}{3}x^3$

25. $f(x) = -(x^4 - 4x^3 + 16x)$, $g(x) = -x^4$

26. $f(x) = 3x^4 - 6x^2$, $g(x) = 3x^4$

In Exercises 27–42, (a) find all the real zeros of the polynomial function, (b) determine the multiplicity of each zero and the number of turning points of the graph of the function, and (c) use a graphing utility to graph the function and verify your answers.

27. $f(x) = x^2 - 25$ **28.** $f(x) = 49 - x^2$

29. $h(t) = t^2 - 6t + 9$ **30.** $f(x) = x^2 + 10x + 25$

31. $f(x) = \frac{1}{3}x^2 + \frac{1}{3}x - \frac{2}{3}$

32. $f(x) = \frac{1}{2}x^2 + \frac{5}{2}x - \frac{3}{2}$

33. $f(x) = 3x^3 - 12x^2 + 3x$

34. $g(x) = 5x(x^2 - 2x - 1)$

35. $f(t) = t^3 - 4t^2 + 4t$

36. $f(x) = x^4 - x^3 - 20x^2$

37. $g(t) = t^5 - 6t^3 + 9t$

38. $f(x) = x^5 + x^3 - 6x$

39. $f(x) = 5x^4 + 15x^2 + 10$

40. $f(x) = 2x^4 - 2x^2 - 40$

41. $g(x) = x^3 + 3x^2 - 4x - 12$

42. $f(x) = x^3 - 4x^2 - 25x + 100$

Graphical Analysis **In Exercises 43–46, (a) use a graphing utility to graph the function, (b) use the graph to approximate any x-intercepts of the graph, (c) set $y = 0$ and solve the resulting equation, and (d) compare the results of part (c) with any x-intercepts of the graph.**

43. $y = 4x^3 - 20x^2 + 25x$

44. $y = 4x^3 + 4x^2 - 8x + 8$

45. $y = x^5 - 5x^3 + 4x$

46. $y = \frac{1}{4}x^3(x^2 - 9)$

In Exercises 47–56, find a polynomial function that has the given zeros. (There are many correct answers.)

47. $0, 10$ **48.** $0, -3$

49. $2, -6$ **50.** $-4, 5$

51. $0, -2, -3$ **52.** $0, 2, 5$

53. $4, -3, 3, 0$ **54.** $-2, -1, 0, 1, 2$

55. $1 + \sqrt{3}, 1 - \sqrt{3}$ **56.** $2, 4 + \sqrt{5}, 4 - \sqrt{5}$

In Exercises 57–66, find a polynomial of degree n that has the given zero(s). (There are many correct answers.)

Zero(s)	Degree
57. $x = -2$	$n = 2$
58. $x = -8, -4$	$n = 2$
59. $x = -3, 0, 1$	$n = 3$
60. $x = -2, 4, 7$	$n = 3$
61. $x = 0, \sqrt{3}, -\sqrt{3}$	$n = 3$
62. $x = 9$	$n = 3$
63. $x = -5, 1, 2$	$n = 4$
64. $x = -4, -1, 3, 6$	$n = 4$
65. $x = 0, -4$	$n = 5$
66. $x = -3, 1, 5, 6$	$n = 5$

In Exercises 67–80, sketch the graph of the function by (a) applying the Leading Coefficient Test, (b) finding the zeros of the polynomial, (c) plotting sufficient solution points, and (d) drawing a continuous curve through the points.

67. $f(x) = x^3 - 9x$ **68.** $g(x) = x^4 - 4x^2$

69. $f(t) = \frac{1}{4}(t^2 - 2t + 15)$

70. $g(x) = -x^2 + 10x - 16$

71. $f(x) = x^3 - 3x^2$ **72.** $f(x) = 1 - x^3$

73. $f(x) = 3x^3 - 15x^2 + 18x$

74. $f(x) = -4x^3 + 4x^2 + 15x$

75. $f(x) = -5x^2 - x^3$ **76.** $f(x) = -48x^2 + 3x^4$

77. $f(x) = x^2(x - 4)$ **78.** $h(x) = \frac{1}{3}x^3(x - 4)^2$

79. $g(t) = -\frac{1}{4}(t - 2)^2(t + 2)^2$

80. $g(x) = \frac{1}{10}(x + 1)^2(x - 3)^3$

In Exercises 81–84, use a graphing utility to graph the function. Use the *zero* or *root* feature to approximate the real zeros of the function. Then determine the multiplicity of each zero.

81. $f(x) = x^3 - 4x$

82. $f(x) = \frac{1}{4}x^4 - 2x^2$

83. $g(x) = \frac{1}{5}(x + 1)^2(x - 3)(2x - 9)$

84. $h(x) = \frac{1}{5}(x + 2)^2(3x - 5)^2$

In Exercises 85–88, use the Intermediate Value Theorem and the *table* feature of a graphing utility to find intervals one unit in length in which the polynomial function is guaranteed to have a zero. Adjust the table to approximate the zeros of the function. Use the *zero* or *root* feature of a graphing utility to verify your results.

85. $f(x) = x^3 - 3x^2 + 3$

86. $f(x) = 0.11x^3 - 2.07x^2 + 9.81x - 6.88$

87. $g(x) = 3x^4 + 4x^3 - 3$

88. $h(x) = x^4 - 10x^2 + 3$

89. Numerical and Graphical Analysis   An open box is to be made from a square piece of material, 36 inches on a side, by cutting equal squares with sides of length x from the corners and turning up the sides (see figure).

(a) Verify that the volume of the box is given by the function

$$V(x) = x(36 - 2x)^2.$$

(b) Determine the domain of the function.

 (c) Use a graphing utility to create a table that shows the box height x and the corresponding volumes V. Use the table to estimate the dimensions that will produce a maximum volume.

 (d) Use a graphing utility to graph V and use the graph to estimate the value of x for which $V(x)$ is maximum. Compare your result with that of part (c).

90. Maximum Volume   An open box with locking tabs is to be made from a square piece of material 24 inches on a side. This is to be done by cutting equal squares from the corners and folding along the dashed lines shown in the figure.

(a) Verify that the volume of the box is given by the function

$$V(x) = 8x(6 - x)(12 - x).$$

(b) Determine the domain of the function V.

(c) Sketch a graph of the function and estimate the value of x for which $V(x)$ is maximum.

91. Construction   A roofing contractor is fabricating gutters from 12-inch aluminum sheeting. The contractor plans to use an aluminum siding folding press to create the gutter by creasing equal lengths for the sidewalls (see figure).

(a) Let x represent the height of the sidewall of the gutter. Write a function A that represents the cross-sectional area of the gutter.

(b) The length of the aluminum sheeting is 16 feet. Write a function V that represents the volume of one run of gutter in terms of x.

(c) Determine the domain of the function in part (b).

 (d) Use a graphing utility to create a table that shows the sidewall height x and the corresponding volumes V. Use the table to estimate the dimensions that will produce a maximum volume.

 (e) Use a graphing utility to graph V. Use the graph to estimate the value of x for which $V(x)$ is a maximum. Compare your result with that of part (d).

(f) Would the value of x change if the aluminum sheeting were of different lengths? Explain.

92. *Construction*   An industrial propane tank is formed by adjoining two hemispheres to the ends of a right circular cylinder. The length of the cylindrical portion of the tank is four times the radius of the hemispherical components (see figure).

(a) Write a function that represents the total volume V of the tank in terms of r.

(b) Find the domain of the function.

(c) Use a graphing utility to graph the function.

(d) The total volume of the tank is to be 120 cubic feet. Use the graph from part (c) to estimate the radius and length of the cylindrical portion of the tank.

Data Analysis: Home Prices   In Exercise 93–96, use the table, which shows the median prices (in thousands of dollars) of new privately owned U.S. homes in the Midwest y_1 and in the South y_2 for the years 1997 through 2003. The data can be approximated by the following models.

$$y_1 = 0.139t^3 - 4.42t^2 + 51.1t - 39$$

$$y_2 = 0.056t^3 - 1.73t^2 + 23.8t + 29$$

In the models, t represents the year, with $t = 7$ corresponding to 1997. (Source: U.S. Census Bureau; U.S. Department of Housing and Urban Development)

Year, t	y_1	y_2
7	150	130
8	158	136
9	164	146
10	170	148
11	173	155
12	178	163
13	184	168

93. Use a graphing utility to plot the data and graph the model for y_1 in the same viewing window. How closely does the model represent the data?

94. Use a graphing utility to plot the data and graph the model for y_2 in the same viewing window. How closely does the model represent the data?

95. Use the models to predict the median prices of a new privately owned home in both regions in 2008. Do your answers seem reasonable? Explain.

96. Use the graphs of the models in Exercises 93 and 94 to write a short paragraph about the relationship between the median prices of homes in the two regions.

Model It

97. *Tree Growth*   The growth of a red oak tree is approximated by the function

$$G = -0.003t^3 + 0.137t^2 + 0.458t - 0.839$$

where G is the height of the tree (in feet) and t ($2 \leq t \leq 34$) is its age (in years).

(a) Use a graphing utility to graph the function. (*Hint:* Use a viewing window in which $-10 \leq x \leq 45$ and $-5 \leq y \leq 60$.)

(b) Estimate the age of the tree when it is growing most rapidly. This point is called the *point of diminishing returns* because the increase in size will be less with each additional year.

(c) Using calculus, the point of diminishing returns can also be found by finding the vertex of the parabola given by

$$y = -0.009t^2 + 0.274t + 0.458.$$

Find the vertex of this parabola.

(d) Compare your results from parts (b) and (c).

98. *Revenue*   The total revenue R (in millions of dollars) for a company is related to its advertising expense by the function

$$R = \frac{1}{100,000}(-x^3 + 600x^2), \qquad 0 \leq x \leq 400$$

where x is the amount spent on advertising (in tens of thousands of dollars). Use the graph of this function, shown in the figure, to estimate the point on the graph at which the function is increasing most rapidly. This point is called the *point of diminishing returns* because any expense above this amount will yield less return per dollar invested in advertising.

Synthesis

True or False? **In Exercises 99–101, determine whether the statement is true or false. Justify your answer.**

99. A fifth-degree polynomial can have five turning points in its graph.

100. It is possible for a sixth-degree polynomial to have only one solution.

101. The graph of the function given by

$$f(x) = 2 + x - x^2 + x^3 - x^4 + x^5 + x^6 - x^7$$

rises to the left and falls to the right.

102. ***Graphical Analysis*** For each graph, describe a polynomial function that could represent the graph. (Indicate the degree of the function and the sign of its leading coefficient.)

(a)

(b)

(c)

(d)

103. ***Graphical Reasoning*** Sketch a graph of the function given by $f(x) = x^4$. Explain how the graph of each function g differs (if it does) from the graph of each function f. Determine whether g is odd, even, or neither.

(a) $g(x) = f(x) + 2$

(b) $g(x) = f(x + 2)$

(c) $g(x) = f(-x)$

(d) $g(x) = -f(x)$

(e) $g(x) = f\left(\frac{1}{2}x\right)$

(f) $g(x) = \frac{1}{2}f(x)$

(g) $g(x) = f\left(x^{3/4}\right)$

(h) $g(x) = (f \circ f)(x)$

104. ***Exploration*** Explore the transformations of the form $g(x) = a(x - h)^5 + k$.

 (a) Use a graphing utility to graph the functions given by

$$y_1 = -\frac{1}{3}(x - 2)^5 + 1$$

and

$$y_2 = \frac{3}{5}(x + 2)^5 - 3.$$

Determine whether the graphs are increasing or decreasing. Explain.

(b) Will the graph of g always be increasing or decreasing? If so, is this behavior determined by a, h, or k? Explain.

(c) Use a graphing utility to graph the function given by

$$H(x) = x^5 - 3x^3 + 2x + 1.$$

Use the graph and the result of part (b) to determine whether H can be written in the form $H(x) = a(x - h)^5 + k$. Explain.

Skills Review

In Exercises 105–108, factor the expression completely.

105. $5x^2 + 7x - 24$

106. $6x^3 - 61x^2 + 10x$

107. $4x^4 - 7x^3 - 15x^2$

108. $y^3 + 216$

In Exercises 109–112, solve the equation by factoring.

109. $2x^2 - x - 28 = 0$

110. $3x^2 - 22x - 16 = 0$

111. $12x^2 + 11x - 5 = 0$

112. $x^2 + 24x + 144 = 0$

In Exercises 113–116, solve the equation by completing the square.

113. $x^2 - 2x - 21 = 0$

114. $x^2 - 8x + 2 = 0$

115. $2x^2 + 5x - 20 = 0$

116. $3x^2 + 4x - 9 = 0$

In Exercises 117–122, describe the transformation from a common function that occurs in $f(x)$. Then sketch its graph.

117. $f(x) = (x + 4)^2$

118. $f(x) = 3 - x^2$

119. $f(x) = \sqrt{x + 1} - 5$

120. $f(x) = 7 - \sqrt{x - 6}$

121. $f(x) = 2[\![x]\!] + 9$

122. $f(x) = 10 - \frac{1}{3}[\![x + 3]\!]$

The Remainder and Factor Theorems

The remainder obtained in the synthetic division process has an important interpretation, as described in the **Remainder Theorem.**

The Remainder Theorem

If a polynomial $f(x)$ is divided by $x - k$, the remainder is

$$r = f(k).$$

For a proof of the Remainder Theorem, see Proofs in Mathematics on page 213.

The Remainder Theorem tells you that synthetic division can be used to evaluate a polynomial function. That is, to evaluate a polynomial function $f(x)$ when $x = k$, divide $f(x)$ by $x - k$. The remainder will be $f(k)$, as illustrated in Example 5.

Example 5   Using the Remainder Theorem

Use the Remainder Theorem to evaluate the following function at $x = -2$.

$$f(x) = 3x^3 + 8x^2 + 5x - 7$$

Solution

Using synthetic division, you obtain the following.

$$
\begin{array}{r|rrrr}
-2 & 3 & 8 & 5 & -7 \\
   &   & -6 & -4 & -2 \\
\hline
   & 3 & 2 & 1 & -9
\end{array}
$$

Because the remainder is $r = -9$, you can conclude that

$$f(-2) = -9. \qquad {\scriptstyle r = f(k)}$$

This means that $(-2, -9)$ is a point on the graph of f. You can check this by substituting $x = -2$ in the original function.

Check

$$f(-2) = 3(-2)^3 + 8(-2)^2 + 5(-2) - 7$$
$$= 3(-8) + 8(4) - 10 - 7 = -9$$

✓CHECKPOINT   Now try Exercise 45.

Another important theorem is the **Factor Theorem,** stated below. This theorem states that you can test to see whether a polynomial has $(x - k)$ as a factor by evaluating the polynomial at $x = k$. If the result is 0, $(x - k)$ is a factor.

The Factor Theorem

A polynomial $f(x)$ has a factor $(x - k)$ if and only if $f(k) = 0$.

For a proof of the Factor Theorem, see Proofs in Mathematics on page 213.

Example 6   **Factoring a Polynomial: Repeated Division**

Show that $(x - 2)$ and $(x + 3)$ are factors of

$$f(x) = 2x^4 + 7x^3 - 4x^2 - 27x - 18.$$

Then find the remaining factors of $f(x)$.

Solution

Using synthetic division with the factor $(x - 2)$, you obtain the following.

$$
\begin{array}{r|rrrrr}
2 & 2 & 7 & -4 & -27 & -18 \\
  &   & 4 & 22 & 36 & 18 \\
\hline
  & 2 & 11 & 18 & 9 & 0
\end{array}
$$
$\longrightarrow$ 0 remainder, so $f(2) = 0$ and
$(x - 2)$ is a factor.

Take the result of this division and perform synthetic division again using the factor $(x + 3)$.

$$
\begin{array}{r|rrrr}
-3 & 2 & 11 & 18 & 9 \\
   &   & -6 & -15 & -9 \\
\hline
   & 2 & 5 & 3 & 0
\end{array}
$$
$\longrightarrow$ 0 remainder, so $f(-3) = 0$
and $(x + 3)$ is a factor.

Because the resulting quadratic expression factors as

$$2x^2 + 5x + 3 = (2x + 3)(x + 1)$$

the complete factorization of $f(x)$ is

$$f(x) = (x - 2)(x + 3)(2x + 3)(x + 1).$$

Note that this factorization implies that f has four real zeros:

$$x = 2, \ x = -3, \ x = -\tfrac{3}{2}, \ \text{and} \ x = -1.$$

This is confirmed by the graph of f, which is shown in Figure 2.28.

✔CHECKPOINT   Now try Exercise 57.

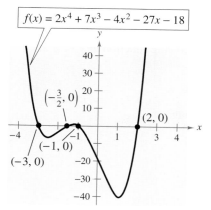

$f(x) = 2x^4 + 7x^3 - 4x^2 - 27x - 18$

$\left(-\tfrac{3}{2}, 0\right)$

$(2, 0)$

$(-1, 0)$

$(-3, 0)$

FIGURE 2.28

Uses of the Remainder in Synthetic Division

The remainder r, obtained in the synthetic division of $f(x)$ by $x - k$, provides the following information.

1. The remainder r gives the value of f at $x = k$. That is, $r = f(k)$.

2. If $r = 0$, $(x - k)$ is a factor of $f(x)$.

3. If $r = 0$, $(k, 0)$ is an x-intercept of the graph of f.

Throughout this text, the importance of developing several problem-solving strategies is emphasized. In the exercises for this section, try using more than one strategy to solve several of the exercises. For instance, if you find that $x - k$ divides evenly into $f(x)$ (with no remainder), try sketching the graph of f. You should find that $(k, 0)$ is an x-intercept of the graph.

2.3 | Exercises

VOCABULARY CHECK:

1. Two forms of the Division Algorithm are shown below. Identify and label each term or function.

$$f(x) = d(x)q(x) + r(x) \qquad \frac{f(x)}{d(x)} = q(x) + \frac{r(x)}{d(x)}$$

In Exercises 2–5, fill in the blanks.

2. The rational expression $p(x)/q(x)$ is called _____ if the degree of the numerator is greater than or equal to that of the denominator, and is called _____ if the degree of the numerator is less than that of the denominator.

3. An alternative method to long division of polynomials is called _____ _____, in which the divisor must be of the form $x - k$.

4. The _____ Theorem states that a polynomial $f(x)$ has a factor $(x - k)$ if and only if $f(k) = 0$.

5. The _____ Theorem states that if a polynomial $f(x)$ is divided by $x - k$, the remainder is $r = f(k)$.

PREREQUISITE SKILLS REVIEW: Practice and review algebra skills needed for this section at **www.Eduspace.com.**

Analytical Analysis   **In Exercises 1 and 2, use long division to verify that $y_1 = y_2$.**

1. $y_1 = \dfrac{x^2}{x + 2}, \quad y_2 = x - 2 + \dfrac{4}{x + 2}$

2. $y_1 = \dfrac{x^4 - 3x^2 - 1}{x^2 + 5}, \quad y_2 = x^2 - 8 + \dfrac{39}{x^2 + 5}$

Graphical Analysis   **In Exercises 3 and 4, (a) use a graphing utility to graph the two equations in the same viewing window, (b) use the graphs to verify that the expressions are equivalent, and (c) use long division to verify the results algebraically.**

3. $y_1 = \dfrac{x^5 - 3x^3}{x^2 + 1}, \quad y_2 = x^3 - 4x + \dfrac{4x}{x^2 + 1}$

4. $y_1 = \dfrac{x^3 - 2x^2 + 5}{x^2 + x + 1}, \quad y_2 = x - 3 + \dfrac{2(x + 4)}{x^2 + x + 1}$

In Exercises 5–18, use long division to divide.

5. $(2x^2 + 10x + 12) \div (x + 3)$

6. $(5x^2 - 17x - 12) \div (x - 4)$

7. $(4x^3 - 7x^2 - 11x + 5) \div (4x + 5)$

8. $(6x^3 - 16x^2 + 17x - 6) \div (3x - 2)$

9. $(x^4 + 5x^3 + 6x^2 - x - 2) \div (x + 2)$

10. $(x^3 + 4x^2 - 3x - 12) \div (x - 3)$

11. $(7x + 3) \div (x + 2)$ **12.** $(8x - 5) \div (2x + 1)$

13. $(6x^3 + 10x^2 + x + 8) \div (2x^2 + 1)$

14. $(x^3 - 9) \div (x^2 + 1)$

15. $(x^4 + 3x^2 + 1) \div (x^2 - 2x + 3)$

16. $(x^5 + 7) \div (x^3 - 1)$

17. $\dfrac{x^4}{(x - 1)^3}$ **18.** $\dfrac{2x^3 - 4x^2 - 15x + 5}{(x - 1)^2}$

In Exercises 19–36, use synthetic division to divide.

19. $(3x^3 - 17x^2 + 15x - 25) \div (x - 5)$

20. $(5x^3 + 18x^2 + 7x - 6) \div (x + 3)$

21. $(4x^3 - 9x + 8x^2 - 18) \div (x + 2)$

22. $(9x^3 - 16x - 18x^2 + 32) \div (x - 2)$

23. $(-x^3 + 75x - 250) \div (x + 10)$

24. $(3x^3 - 16x^2 - 72) \div (x - 6)$

25. $(5x^3 - 6x^2 + 8) \div (x - 4)$

26. $(5x^3 + 6x + 8) \div (x + 2)$

27. $\dfrac{10x^4 - 50x^3 - 800}{x - 6}$ **28.** $\dfrac{x^5 - 13x^4 - 120x + 80}{x + 3}$

29. $\dfrac{x^3 + 512}{x + 8}$ **30.** $\dfrac{x^3 - 729}{x - 9}$

31. $\dfrac{-3x^4}{x - 2}$ **32.** $\dfrac{-3x^4}{x + 2}$

33. $\dfrac{180x - x^4}{x - 6}$ **34.** $\dfrac{5 - 3x + 2x^2 - x^3}{x + 1}$

35. $\dfrac{4x^3 + 16x^2 - 23x - 15}{x + \frac{1}{2}}$ **36.** $\dfrac{3x^3 - 4x^2 + 5}{x - \frac{3}{2}}$

In Exercises 37–44, write the function in the form $f(x) = (x - k)q(x) + r$ for the given value of k, and demonstrate that $f(k) = r$.

Function	*Value of k*
37. $f(x) = x^3 - x^2 - 14x + 11$	$k = 4$
38. $f(x) = x^3 - 5x^2 - 11x + 8$	$k = -2$

Function	Value of k
39. $f(x) = 15x^4 + 10x^3 - 6x^2 + 14$	$k = -\frac{2}{3}$
40. $f(x) = 10x^3 - 22x^2 - 3x + 4$	$k = \frac{1}{5}$
41. $f(x) = x^3 + 3x^2 - 2x - 14$	$k = \sqrt{2}$
42. $f(x) = x^3 + 2x^2 - 5x - 4$	$k = -\sqrt{5}$
43. $f(x) = -4x^3 + 6x^2 + 12x + 4$	$k = 1 - \sqrt{3}$
44. $f(x) = -3x^3 + 8x^2 + 10x - 8$	$k = 2 + \sqrt{2}$

In Exercises 45–48, use synthetic division to find each function value. Verify your answers using another method.

45. $f(x) = 4x^3 - 13x + 10$

    (a) $f(1)$ (b) $f(-2)$ (c) $f\left(\frac{1}{2}\right)$ (d) $f(8)$

46. $g(x) = x^6 - 4x^4 + 3x^2 + 2$

    (a) $g(2)$ (b) $g(-4)$ (c) $g(3)$ (d) $g(-1)$

47. $h(x) = 3x^3 + 5x^2 - 10x + 1$

    (a) $h(3)$ (b) $h\left(\frac{1}{3}\right)$ (c) $h(-2)$ (d) $h(-5)$

48. $f(x) = 0.4x^4 - 1.6x^3 + 0.7x^2 - 2$

    (a) $f(1)$ (b) $f(-2)$ (c) $f(5)$ (d) $f(-10)$

In Exercises 49–56, use synthetic division to show that x is a solution of the third-degree polynomial equation, and use the result to factor the polynomial completely. List all real solutions of the equation.

Polynomial Equation	Value of x
49. $x^3 - 7x + 6 = 0$	$x = 2$
50. $x^3 - 28x - 48 = 0$	$x = -4$
51. $2x^3 - 15x^2 + 27x - 10 = 0$	$x = \frac{1}{2}$
52. $48x^3 - 80x^2 + 41x - 6 = 0$	$x = \frac{2}{3}$
53. $x^3 + 2x^2 - 3x - 6 = 0$	$x = \sqrt{3}$
54. $x^3 + 2x^2 - 2x - 4 = 0$	$x = \sqrt{2}$
55. $x^3 - 3x^2 + 2 = 0$	$x = 1 + \sqrt{3}$
56. $x^3 - x^2 - 13x - 3 = 0$	$x = 2 - \sqrt{5}$

In Exercises 57–64, (a) verify the given factors of the function f, (b) find the remaining factors of f, (c) use your results to write the complete factorization of f, (d) list all real zeros of f, and (e) confirm your results by using a graphing utility to graph the function.

Function	Factors
57. $f(x) = 2x^3 + x^2 - 5x + 2$	$(x + 2), (x - 1)$
58. $f(x) = 3x^3 + 2x^2 - 19x + 6$	$(x + 3), (x - 2)$
59. $f(x) = x^4 - 4x^3 - 15x^2$ $+ 58x - 40$	$(x - 5), (x + 4)$
60. $f(x) = 8x^4 - 14x^3 - 71x^2$ $- 10x + 24$	$(x + 2), (x - 4)$

Function	Factors
61. $f(x) = 6x^3 + 41x^2 - 9x - 14$	$(2x + 1), (3x - 2)$
62. $f(x) = 10x^3 - 11x^2 - 72x + 45$	$(2x + 5), (5x - 3)$
63. $f(x) = 2x^3 - x^2 - 10x + 5$	$(2x - 1), (x + \sqrt{5})$
64. $f(x) = x^3 + 3x^2 - 48x - 144$	$(x + 4\sqrt{3}), (x + 3)$

Graphical Analysis In Exercises 65–68, (a) use the *zero* or *root* feature of a graphing utility to approximate the zeros of the function accurate to three decimal places, (b) determine one of the exact zeros, and (c) use synthetic division to verify your result from part (b), and then factor the polynomial completely.

65. $f(x) = x^3 - 2x^2 - 5x + 10$

66. $g(x) = x^3 - 4x^2 - 2x + 8$

67. $h(t) = t^3 - 2t^2 - 7t + 2$

68. $f(s) = s^3 - 12s^2 + 40s - 24$

In Exercises 69–72, simplify the rational expression by using long division or synthetic division.

69. $\dfrac{4x^3 - 8x^2 + x + 3}{2x - 3}$ **70.** $\dfrac{x^3 + x^2 - 64x - 64}{x + 8}$

71. $\dfrac{x^4 + 6x^3 + 11x^2 + 6x}{x^2 + 3x + 2}$ **72.** $\dfrac{x^4 + 9x^3 - 5x^2 - 36x + 4}{x^2 - 4}$

Model It

73. *Data Analysis: Military Personnel* The numbers M (in thousands) of United States military personnel on active duty for the years 1993 through 2003 are shown in the table, where t represents the year, with $t = 3$ corresponding to 1993. (Source: U.S. Department of Defense)

Year, t	Military personnel, M
3	1705
4	1611
5	1518
6	1472
7	1439
8	1407
9	1386
10	1384
11	1385
12	1412
13	1434

Model It (continued)

(a) Use a graphing utility to create a scatter plot of the data.

(b) Use the *regression* feature of the graphing utility to find a cubic model for the data. Graph the model in the same viewing window as the scatter plot.

(c) Use the model to create a table of estimated values of M. Compare the model with the original data.

(d) Use synthetic division to evaluate the model for the year 2008. Even though the model is relatively accurate for estimating the given data, would you use this model to predict the number of military personnel in the future? Explain.

---

74. *Data Analysis: Cable Television*   The average monthly basic rates R (in dollars) for cable television in the United States for the years 1992 through 2002 are shown in the table, where t represents the year, with $t = 2$ corresponding to 1992.   (Source: Kagan Research LLC)

Year, t	Basic rate, R
2	19.08
3	19.39
4	21.62
5	23.07
6	24.41
7	26.48
8	27.81
9	28.92
10	30.37
11	32.87
12	34.71

(a) Use a graphing utility to create a scatter plot of the data.

(b) Use the *regression* feature of the graphing utility to find a cubic model for the data. Then graph the model in the same viewing window as the scatter plot. Compare the model with the data.

(c) Use synthetic division to evaluate the model for the year 2008.

Synthesis

True or False?   In Exercises 75–77, determine whether the statement is true or false. Justify your answer.

75. If $(7x + 4)$ is a factor of some polynomial function f, then $\frac{4}{7}$ is a zero of f.

76. $(2x - 1)$ is a factor of the polynomial

$$6x^6 + x^5 - 92x^4 + 45x^3 + 184x^2 + 4x - 48.$$

77. The rational expression

$$\frac{x^3 + 2x^2 - 13x + 10}{x^2 - 4x - 12}$$

is improper.

78. *Exploration*   Use the form $f(x) = (x - k)q(x) + r$ to create a cubic function that (a) passes through the point $(2, 5)$ and rises to the right, and (b) passes through the point $(-3, 1)$ and falls to the right. (There are many correct answers.)

Think About It   In Exercises 79 and 80, perform the division by assuming that n is a positive integer.

79. $\dfrac{x^{3n} + 9x^{2n} + 27x^n + 27}{x^n + 3}$ **80.** $\dfrac{x^{3n} - 3x^{2n} + 5x^n - 6}{x^n - 2}$

81. *Writing*   Briefly explain what it means for a divisor to divide evenly into a dividend.

82. *Writing*   Briefly explain how to check polynomial division, and justify your reasoning. Give an example.

Exploration   In Exercises 83 and 84, find the constant c such that the denominator will divide evenly into the numerator.

83. $\dfrac{x^3 + 4x^2 - 3x + c}{x - 5}$ **84.** $\dfrac{x^5 - 2x^2 + x + c}{x + 2}$

Think About It   In Exercises 85 and 86, answer the questions about the division $f(x) \div (x - k)$, where $f(x) = (x + 3)^2(x - 3)(x + 1)^3$.

85. What is the remainder when $k = -3$? Explain.

86. If it is necessary to find $f(2)$, is it easier to evaluate the function directly or to use synthetic division? Explain.

Skills Review

In Exercises 87–92, use any method to solve the quadratic equation.

87. $9x^2 - 25 = 0$ **88.** $16x^2 - 21 = 0$

89. $5x^2 - 3x - 14 = 0$ **90.** $8x^2 - 22x + 15 = 0$

91. $2x^2 + 6x + 3 = 0$ **92.** $x^2 + 3x - 3 = 0$

In Exercises 93–96, find a polynomial function that has the given zeros. (There are many correct answers.)

93. $0, 3, 4$ **94.** $-6, 1$

95. $-3, 1 + \sqrt{2}, 1 - \sqrt{2}$ **96.** $1, -2, 2 + \sqrt{3}, 2 - \sqrt{3}$

2.4   Complex Numbers

What you should learn

- Use the imaginary unit *i* to write complex numbers.
- Add, subtract, and multiply complex numbers.
- Use complex conjugates to write the quotient of two complex numbers in standard form.
- Find complex solutions of quadratic equations.

Why you should learn it

You can use complex numbers to model and solve real-life problems in electronics. For instance, in Exercise 83 on page 168, you will learn how to use complex numbers to find the impedance of an electrical circuit.

© Richard Megna/Fundamental Photographs

The Imaginary Unit *i*

You have learned that some quadratic equations have no real solutions. For instance, the quadratic equation $x^2 + 1 = 0$ has no real solution because there is no real number x that can be squared to produce -1. To overcome this deficiency, mathematicians created an expanded system of numbers using the **imaginary unit *i*,** defined as

$$i = \sqrt{-1} \qquad \text{Imaginary unit}$$

where $i^2 = -1$. By adding real numbers to real multiples of this imaginary unit, the set of **complex numbers** is obtained. Each complex number can be written in the **standard form** $a + bi$. For instance, the standard form of the complex number $-5 + \sqrt{-9}$ is $-5 + 3i$ because

$$-5 + \sqrt{-9} = -5 + \sqrt{3^2(-1)} = -5 + 3\sqrt{-1} = -5 + 3i.$$

In the standard form $a + bi$, the real number a is called the **real part** of the **complex number $a + bi$,** and the number bi (where b is a real number) is called the **imaginary part** of the complex number.

Definition of a Complex Number

If a and b are real numbers, the number $a + bi$ is a **complex number,** and it is said to be written in **standard form.** If $b = 0$, the number $a + bi = a$ is a real number. If $b \neq 0$, the number $a + bi$ is called an **imaginary number.** A number of the form bi, where $b \neq 0$, is called a **pure imaginary number.**

The set of real numbers is a subset of the set of complex numbers, as shown in Figure 2.29. This is true because every real number a can be written as a complex number using $b = 0$. That is, for every real number a, you can write $a = a + 0i$.

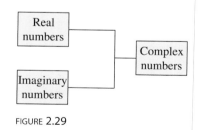

FIGURE 2.29

Equality of Complex Numbers

Two complex numbers $a + bi$ and $c + di$, written in standard form, are equal to each other

$$a + bi = c + di \qquad \text{Equality of two complex numbers}$$

if and only if $a = c$ and $b = d$.

Operations with Complex Numbers

To add (or subtract) two complex numbers, you add (or subtract) the real and imaginary parts of the numbers separately.

> ### Addition and Subtraction of Complex Numbers
>
> If $a + bi$ and $c + di$ are two complex numbers written in standard form, their sum and difference are defined as follows.
>
> Sum: $(a + bi) + (c + di) = (a + c) + (b + d)i$
>
> Difference: $(a + bi) - (c + di) = (a - c) + (b - d)i$

The **additive identity** in the complex number system is zero (the same as in the real number system). Furthermore, the **additive inverse** of the complex number $a + bi$ is

$$-(a + bi) = -a - bi. \qquad \text{Additive inverse}$$

So, you have

$$(a + bi) + (-a - bi) = 0 + 0i = 0.$$

Example 1   Adding and Subtracting Complex Numbers

a. $(4 + 7i) + (1 - 6i) = 4 + 7i + 1 - 6i$ Remove parentheses.

$$= (4 + 1) + (7i - 6i) \qquad \text{Group like terms.}$$

$$= 5 + i \qquad \text{Write in standard form.}$$

b. $(1 + 2i) - (4 + 2i) = 1 + 2i - 4 - 2i$ Remove parentheses.

$$= (1 - 4) + (2i - 2i) \qquad \text{Group like terms.}$$

$$= -3 + 0 \qquad \text{Simplify.}$$

$$= -3 \qquad \text{Write in standard form.}$$

c. $3i - (-2 + 3i) - (2 + 5i) = 3i + 2 - 3i - 2 - 5i$

$$= (2 - 2) + (3i - 3i - 5i)$$

$$= 0 - 5i$$

$$= -5i$$

d. $(3 + 2i) + (4 - i) - (7 + i) = 3 + 2i + 4 - i - 7 - i$

$$= (3 + 4 - 7) + (2i - i - i)$$

$$= 0 + 0i$$

$$= 0$$

✓CHECKPOINT   Now try Exercise 17.

Note in Examples 1(b) and 1(d) that the sum of two complex numbers can be a real number.

Many of the properties of real numbers are valid for complex numbers as well. Here are some examples.

Associative Properties of Addition and Multiplication

Commutative Properties of Addition and Multiplication

Distributive Property of Multiplication Over Addition

Notice below how these properties are used when two complex numbers are multiplied.

$$(a + bi)(c + di) = a(c + di) + bi(c + di) \qquad \text{Distributive Property}$$
$$= ac + (ad)i + (bc)i + (bd)i^2 \qquad \text{Distributive Property}$$
$$= ac + (ad)i + (bc)i + (bd)(-1) \qquad i^2 = -1$$
$$= ac - bd + (ad)i + (bc)i \qquad \text{Commutative Property}$$
$$= (ac - bd) + (ad + bc)i \qquad \text{Associative Property}$$

Rather than trying to memorize this multiplication rule, you should simply remember how the Distributive Property is used to multiply two complex numbers.

Example 2 **Multiplying Complex Numbers**

a. $4(-2 + 3i) = 4(-2) + 4(3i)$ Distributive Property

$= -8 + 12i$ Simplify.

b. $(2 - i)(4 + 3i) = 2(4 + 3i) - i(4 + 3i)$ Distributive Property

$= 8 + 6i - 4i - 3i^2$ Distributive Property

$= 8 + 6i - 4i - 3(-1)$ $i^2 = -1$

$= (8 + 3) + (6i - 4i)$ Group like terms.

$= 11 + 2i$ Write in standard form.

c. $(3 + 2i)(3 - 2i) = 3(3 - 2i) + 2i(3 - 2i)$ Distributive Property

$= 9 - 6i + 6i - 4i^2$ Distributive Property

$= 9 - 6i + 6i - 4(-1)$ $i^2 = -1$

$= 9 + 4$ Simplify.

$= 13$ Write in standard form.

d. $(3 + 2i)^2 = (3 + 2i)(3 + 2i)$ Square of a binomial

$= 3(3 + 2i) + 2i(3 + 2i)$ Distributive Property

$= 9 + 6i + 6i + 4i^2$ Distributive Property

$= 9 + 6i + 6i + 4(-1)$ $i^2 = -1$

$= 9 + 12i - 4$ Simplify.

$= 5 + 12i$ Write in standard form.

✓**CHECKPOINT**   Now try Exercise 27.

STUDY TIP

The procedure described above is similar to multiplying two polynomials and combining like terms, as in the FOIL Method shown in Appendix A.3. For instance, you can use the FOIL Method to multiply the two complex numbers from Example 2(b).

$$\overset{\text{F}\quad\text{O}\quad\text{I}\quad\text{L}}{(2 - i)(4 + 3i) = 8 + 6i - 4i - 3i^2}$$

Complex Conjugates

Notice in Example 2(c) that the product of two complex numbers can be a real number. This occurs with pairs of complex numbers of the form $a + bi$ and $a - bi$, called **complex conjugates.**

$$(a + bi)(a - bi) = a^2 - abi + abi - b^2i^2$$
$$= a^2 - b^2(-1)$$
$$= a^2 + b^2$$

Example 3   **Multiplying Conjugates**

Multiply each complex number by its complex conjugate.

a. $1 + i$ **b.** $4 - 3i$

Solution

a. The complex conjugate of $1 + i$ is $1 - i$.
$$(1 + i)(1 - i) = 1^2 - i^2 = 1 - (-1) = 2$$

b. The complex conjugate of $4 - 3i$ is $4 + 3i$.
$$(4 - 3i)(4 + 3i) = 4^2 - (3i)^2 = 16 - 9i^2 = 16 - 9(-1) = 25$$

✓CHECKPOINT   Now try Exercise 37.

To write the quotient of $a + bi$ and $c + di$ in standard form, where c and d are not both zero, multiply the numerator and denominator by the complex conjugate of the *denominator* to obtain

$$\frac{a + bi}{c + di} = \frac{a + bi}{c + di}\left(\frac{c - di}{c - di}\right)$$
$$= \frac{(ac + bd) + (bc - ad)i}{c^2 + d^2}. \qquad \text{Standard form}$$

STUDY TIP

Note that when you multiply the numerator and denominator of a quotient of complex numbers by

$$\frac{c - di}{c - di}$$

you are actually multiplying the quotient by a form of 1. You are not changing the original expression, you are only creating an expression that is equivalent to the original expression.

Example 4   **Writing a Quotient of Complex Numbers in Standard Form**

$$\frac{2 + 3i}{4 - 2i} = \frac{2 + 3i}{4 - 2i}\left(\frac{4 + 2i}{4 + 2i}\right) \qquad \text{Multiply numerator and denominator by complex conjugate of denominator.}$$

$$= \frac{8 + 4i + 12i + 6i^2}{16 - 4i^2} \qquad \text{Expand.}$$

$$= \frac{8 - 6 + 16i}{16 + 4} \qquad i^2 = -1$$

$$= \frac{2 + 16i}{20} \qquad \text{Simplify.}$$

$$= \frac{1}{10} + \frac{4}{5}i \qquad \text{Write in standard form.}$$

✓CHECKPOINT   Now try Exercise 49.

Complex Solutions of Quadratic Equations

When using the Quadratic Formula to solve a quadratic equation, you often obtain a result such as $\sqrt{-3}$, which you know is not a real number. By factoring out $i = \sqrt{-1}$, you can write this number in standard form.

$$\sqrt{-3} = \sqrt{3(-1)} = \sqrt{3}\sqrt{-1} = \sqrt{3}\,i$$

The number $\sqrt{3}\,i$ is called the *principal square root* of -3.

STUDY TIP

The definition of principal square root uses the rule

$$\sqrt{ab} = \sqrt{a}\sqrt{b}$$

for $a > 0$ and $b < 0$. This rule is not valid if *both* a and b are negative. For example,

$$\sqrt{-5}\sqrt{-5} = \sqrt{5(-1)}\sqrt{5(-1)}$$
$$= \sqrt{5}\,i\sqrt{5}\,i$$
$$= \sqrt{25}\,i^2$$
$$= 5i^2 = -5$$

whereas

$$\sqrt{(-5)(-5)} = \sqrt{25} = 5.$$

To avoid problems with square roots of negative numbers, be sure to convert complex numbers to standard form *before* multiplying.

> **Principal Square Root of a Negative Number**
>
> If a is a positive number, the **principal square root** of the negative number $-a$ is defined as
>
> $$\sqrt{-a} = \sqrt{a}\,i.$$

Example 5   **Writing Complex Numbers in Standard Form**

a. $\sqrt{-3}\sqrt{-12} = \sqrt{3}\,i\sqrt{12}\,i = \sqrt{36}\,i^2 = 6(-1) = -6$

b. $\sqrt{-48} - \sqrt{-27} = \sqrt{48}\,i - \sqrt{27}\,i = 4\sqrt{3}\,i - 3\sqrt{3}\,i = \sqrt{3}\,i$

c. $\left(-1 + \sqrt{-3}\right)^2 = \left(-1 + \sqrt{3}\,i\right)^2$

$$= (-1)^2 - 2\sqrt{3}\,i + \left(\sqrt{3}\right)^2(i^2)$$
$$= 1 - 2\sqrt{3}\,i + 3(-1)$$
$$= -2 - 2\sqrt{3}\,i$$

✓*CHECKPOINT*   Now try Exercise 59.

Example 6   **Complex Solutions of a Quadratic Equation**

Solve (a) $x^2 + 4 = 0$ and (b) $3x^2 - 2x + 5 = 0$.

Solution

a. $x^2 + 4 = 0$ Write original equation.

$x^2 = -4$ Subtract 4 from each side.

$x = \pm 2i$ Extract square roots.

b. $3x^2 - 2x + 5 = 0$ Write original equation.

$$x = \frac{-(-2) \pm \sqrt{(-2)^2 - 4(3)(5)}}{2(3)}$$ Quadratic Formula

$$= \frac{2 \pm \sqrt{-56}}{6}$$ Simplify.

$$= \frac{2 \pm 2\sqrt{14}\,i}{6}$$ Write $\sqrt{-56}$ in standard form.

$$= \frac{1}{3} \pm \frac{\sqrt{14}}{3}\,i$$ Write in standard form.

✓*CHECKPOINT*   Now try Exercise 65.

2.4 Exercises

VOCABULARY CHECK:

1. Match the type of complex number with its definition.

(a) Real Number   (i) $a + bi$, $a \neq 0$, $b \neq 0$

(b) Imaginary number   (ii) $a + bi$, $a = 0$, $b \neq 0$

(c) Pure imaginary number   (iii) $a + bi$, $b = 0$

In Exercises 2–4, fill in the blanks.

2. The imaginary unit i is defined as $i =$ _____, where $i^2 =$ _____.

3. If a is a positive number, the _____ _____ root of the negative number $-a$ is defined as $\sqrt{-a} = \sqrt{a}\,i$.

4. The numbers $a + bi$ and $a - bi$ are called _____ _____, and their product is a real number $a^2 + b^2$.

PREREQUISITE SKILLS REVIEW: Practice and review algebra skills needed for this section at **www.Eduspace.com.**

In Exercises 1–4, find real numbers a and b such that the equation is true.

1. $a + bi = -10 + 6i$ **2.** $a + bi = 13 + 4i$

3. $(a - 1) + (b + 3)i = 5 + 8i$

4. $(a + 6) + 2bi = 6 - 5i$

In Exercises 5–16, write the complex number in standard form.

5. $4 + \sqrt{-9}$ **6.** $3 + \sqrt{-16}$

7. $2 - \sqrt{-27}$ **8.** $1 + \sqrt{-8}$

9. $\sqrt{-75}$ **10.** $\sqrt{-4}$

11. 8 **12.** 45

13. $-6i + i^2$ **14.** $-4i^2 + 2i$

15. $\sqrt{-0.09}$ **16.** $\sqrt{-0.0004}$

In Exercises 17–26, perform the addition or subtraction and write the result in standard form.

17. $(5 + i) + (6 - 2i)$ **18.** $(13 - 2i) + (-5 + 6i)$

19. $(8 - i) - (4 - i)$ **20.** $(3 + 2i) - (6 + 13i)$

21. $\left(-2 + \sqrt{-8}\right) + \left(5 - \sqrt{-50}\right)$

22. $\left(8 + \sqrt{-18}\right) - \left(4 + 3\sqrt{2}\,i\right)$

23. $13i - (14 - 7i)$ **24.** $22 + (-5 + 8i) + 10i$

25. $-\left(\frac{3}{2} + \frac{5}{2}i\right) + \left(\frac{5}{3} + \frac{11}{3}i\right)$

26. $(1.6 + 3.2i) + (-5.8 + 4.3i)$

In Exercises 27–36, perform the operation and write the result in standard form.

27. $(1 + i)(3 - 2i)$ **28.** $(6 - 2i)(2 - 3i)$

29. $6i(5 - 2i)$ **30.** $-8i(9 + 4i)$

31. $\left(\sqrt{14} + \sqrt{10}\,i\right)\left(\sqrt{14} - \sqrt{10}\,i\right)$

32. $\left(\sqrt{3} + \sqrt{15}\,i\right)\left(\sqrt{3} - \sqrt{15}\,i\right)$

33. $(4 + 5i)^2$ **34.** $(2 - 3i)^2$

35. $(2 + 3i)^2 + (2 - 3i)^2$ **36.** $(1 - 2i)^2 - (1 + 2i)^2$

In Exercises 37–44, write the complex conjugate of the complex number. Then multiply the number by its complex conjugate.

37. $6 + 3i$ **38.** $7 - 12i$

39. $-1 - \sqrt{5}\,i$ **40.** $-3 + \sqrt{2}\,i$

41. $\sqrt{-20}$ **42.** $\sqrt{-15}$

43. $\sqrt{8}$ **44.** $1 + \sqrt{8}$

In Exercises 45–54, write the quotient in standard form.

45. $\dfrac{5}{i}$ **46.** $-\dfrac{14}{2i}$

47. $\dfrac{2}{4 - 5i}$ **48.** $\dfrac{5}{1 - i}$

49. $\dfrac{3 + i}{3 - i}$ **50.** $\dfrac{6 - 7i}{1 - 2i}$

51. $\dfrac{6 - 5i}{i}$ **52.** $\dfrac{8 + 16i}{2i}$

53. $\dfrac{3i}{(4 - 5i)^2}$ **54.** $\dfrac{5i}{(2 + 3i)^2}$

In Exercises 55–58, perform the operation and write the result in standard form.

55. $\dfrac{2}{1 + i} - \dfrac{3}{1 - i}$ **56.** $\dfrac{2i}{2 + i} + \dfrac{5}{2 - i}$

57. $\dfrac{i}{3 - 2i} + \dfrac{2i}{3 + 8i}$ **58.** $\dfrac{1 + i}{i} - \dfrac{3}{4 - i}$

In Exercises 59–64, write the complex number in standard form.

59. $\sqrt{-6} \cdot \sqrt{-2}$

60. $\sqrt{-5} \cdot \sqrt{-10}$

61. $\left(\sqrt{-10}\right)^2$

62. $\left(\sqrt{-75}\right)^2$

63. $\left(3 + \sqrt{-5}\right)\left(7 - \sqrt{-10}\right)$

64. $\left(2 - \sqrt{-6}\right)^2$

In Exercises 65–74, use the Quadratic Formula to solve the quadratic equation.

65. $x^2 - 2x + 2 = 0$

66. $x^2 + 6x + 10 = 0$

67. $4x^2 + 16x + 17 = 0$

68. $9x^2 - 6x + 37 = 0$

69. $4x^2 + 16x + 15 = 0$

70. $16t^2 - 4t + 3 = 0$

71. $\frac{3}{2}x^2 - 6x + 9 = 0$

72. $\frac{7}{8}x^2 - \frac{3}{4}x + \frac{5}{16} = 0$

73. $1.4x^2 - 2x - 10 = 0$

74. $4.5x^2 - 3x + 12 = 0$

In Exercises 75–82, simplify the complex number and write it in standard form.

75. $-6i^3 + i^2$

76. $4i^2 - 2i^3$

77. $-5i^5$

78. $(-i)^3$

79. $\left(\sqrt{-75}\right)^3$

80. $\left(\sqrt{-2}\right)^6$

81. $\dfrac{1}{i^3}$

82. $\dfrac{1}{(2i)^3}$

Model It

83. *Impedance* The opposition to current in an electrical circuit is called its impedance. The impedance z in a parallel circuit with two pathways satisfies the equation

$$\frac{1}{z} = \frac{1}{z_1} + \frac{1}{z_2}$$

where z_1 is the impedance (in ohms) of pathway 1 and z_2 is the impedance of pathway 2.

(a) The impedance of each pathway in a parallel circuit is found by adding the impedances of all components in the pathway. Use the table to find z_1 and z_2.

(b) Find the impedance z.

	Resistor	Inductor	Capacitor
Symbol	$a\Omega$	$b\Omega$	$c\Omega$
Impedance	a	bi	$-ci$

---

84. Cube each complex number.

(a) 2   (b) $-1 + \sqrt{3}i$ (c) $-1 - \sqrt{3}i$

85. Raise each complex number to the fourth power.

(a) 2   (b) -2 (c) $2i$ (d) $-2i$

86. Write each of the powers of i as i, $-i$, 1, or -1.

(a) i^{40} (b) i^{25} (c) i^{50} (d) i^{67}

Synthesis

True or False? **In Exercises 87–89, determine whether the statement is true or false. Justify your answer.**

87. There is no complex number that is equal to its complex conjugate.

88. $-i\sqrt{6}$ is a solution of $x^4 - x^2 + 14 = 56$.

89. $i^{44} + i^{150} - i^{74} - i^{109} + i^{61} = -1$

90. *Error Analysis* Describe the error.

$$\sqrt{-6}\sqrt{-6} = \sqrt{(-6)(-6)} = \sqrt{36} = 6$$

91. *Proof* Prove that the complex conjugate of the product of two complex numbers $a_1 + b_1i$ and $a_2 + b_2i$ is the product of their complex conjugates.

92. *Proof* Prove that the complex conjugate of the sum of two complex numbers $a_1 + b_1i$ and $a_2 + b_2i$ is the sum of their complex conjugates.

Skills Review

In Exercises 93–96, perform the operation and write the result in standard form.

93. $(4 + 3x) + (8 - 6x - x^2)$

94. $(x^3 - 3x^2) - (6 - 2x - 4x^2)$

95. $\left(3x - \frac{1}{2}\right)(x + 4)$

96. $(2x - 5)^2$

In Exercises 97–100, solve the equation and check your solution.

97. $-x - 12 = 19$

98. $8 - 3x = -34$

99. $4(5x - 6) - 3(6x + 1) = 0$

100. $5[x - (3x + 11)] = 20x - 15$

101. *Volume of an Oblate Spheroid*

Solve for a: $V = \frac{4}{3}\pi a^2 b$

102. *Newton's Law of Universal Gravitation*

Solve for r: $F = \alpha\dfrac{m_1 m_2}{r^2}$

103. *Mixture Problem* A five-liter container contains a mixture with a concentration of 50%. How much of this mixture must be withdrawn and replaced by 100% concentrate to bring the mixture up to 60% concentration?

2.5 Zeros of Polynomial Functions

What you should learn

- Use the Fundamental Theorem of Algebra to determine the number of zeros of polynomial functions.
- Find rational zeros of polynomial functions.
- Find conjugate pairs of complex zeros.
- Find zeros of polynomials by factoring.
- Use Descartes's Rule of Signs and the Upper and Lower Bound Rules to find zeros of polynomials.

Why you should learn it

Finding zeros of polynomial functions is an important part of solving real-life problems. For instance, in Exercise 112 on page 182, the zeros of a polynomial function can help you analyze the attendance at women's college basketball games.

The Fundamental Theorem of Algebra

You know that an nth-degree polynomial can have at most n real zeros. In the complex number system, this statement can be improved. That is, in the complex number system, every nth-degree polynomial function has *precisely* n zeros. This important result is derived from the **Fundamental Theorem of Algebra,** first proved by the German mathematician Carl Friedrich Gauss (1777–1855).

The Fundamental Theorem of Algebra

If $f(x)$ is a polynomial of degree n, where $n > 0$, then f has at least one zero in the complex number system.

Using the Fundamental Theorem of Algebra and the equivalence of zeros and factors, you obtain the **Linear Factorization Theorem.**

Linear Factorization Theorem

If $f(x)$ is a polynomial of degree n, where $n > 0$, then f has precisely n linear factors

$$f(x) = a_n(x - c_1)(x - c_2) \cdots (x - c_n)$$

where $c_1, c_2, \ldots, c_n$ are complex numbers.

For a proof of the Linear Factorization Theorem, see Proofs in Mathematics on page 214.

Note that the Fundamental Theorem of Algebra and the Linear Factorization Theorem tell you only that the zeros or factors of a polynomial exist, not how to find them. Such theorems are called *existence theorems*.

Example 1 Zeros of Polynomial Functions

a. The first-degree polynomial $f(x) = x - 2$ has exactly *one* zero: $x = 2$.

b. Counting multiplicity, the second-degree polynomial function

$$f(x) = x^2 - 6x + 9 = (x - 3)(x - 3)$$

has exactly *two* zeros: $x = 3$ and $x = 3$. (This is called a *repeated zero*.)

c. The third-degree polynomial function

$$f(x) = x^3 + 4x = x(x^2 + 4) = x(x - 2i)(x + 2i)$$

has exactly *three* zeros: $x = 0$, $x = 2i$, and $x = -2i$.

d. The fourth-degree polynomial function

$$f(x) = x^4 - 1 = (x - 1)(x + 1)(x - i)(x + i)$$

has exactly *four* zeros: $x = 1$, $x = -1$, $x = i$, and $x = -i$.

✓CHECKPOINT   Now try Exercise 1.

STUDY TIP

Recall that in order to find the zeros of a function $f(x)$, set $f(x)$ equal to 0 and solve the resulting equation for x. For instance, the function in Example 1(a) has a zero at $x = 2$ because

$$x - 2 = 0$$
$$x = 2.$$

The Rational Zero Test

The **Rational Zero Test** relates the possible rational zeros of a polynomial (having integer coefficients) to the leading coefficient and to the constant term of the polynomial.

Fogg Art Museum

Historical Note
Although they were not contemporaries, Jean Le Rond d'Alembert (1717–1783) worked independently of Carl Gauss in trying to prove the Fundamental Theorem of Algebra. His efforts were such that, in France, the Fundamental Theorem of Algebra is frequently known as the Theorem of d'Alembert.

The Rational Zero Test

If the polynomial $f(x) = a_n x^n + a_{n-1} x^{n-1} + \cdots + a_2 x^2 + a_1 x + a_0$ has *integer* coefficients, every rational zero of f has the form

$$\text{Rational zero} = \frac{p}{q}$$

where p and q have no common factors other than 1, and

p = a factor of the constant term a_0

q = a factor of the leading coefficient a_n.

To use the Rational Zero Test, you should first list all rational numbers whose numerators are factors of the constant term and whose denominators are factors of the leading coefficient.

$$\text{Possible rational zeros} = \frac{\text{factors of constant term}}{\text{factors of leading coefficient}}$$

Having formed this list of *possible rational zeros*, use a trial-and-error method to determine which, if any, are actual zeros of the polynomial. Note that when the leading coefficient is 1, the possible rational zeros are simply the factors of the constant term.

Example 2 Rational Zero Test with Leading Coefficient of 1

Find the rational zeros of

$$f(x) = x^3 + x + 1.$$

Solution

Because the leading coefficient is 1, the possible rational zeros are ± 1, the factors of the constant term. By testing these possible zeros, you can see that neither works.

$$f(1) = (1)^3 + 1 + 1$$
$$= 3$$
$$f(-1) = (-1)^3 + (-1) + 1$$
$$= -1$$

So, you can conclude that the given polynomial has *no* rational zeros. Note from the graph of f in Figure 2.30 that f does have one real zero between -1 and 0. However, by the Rational Zero Test, you know that this real zero is *not* a rational number.

✓CHECKPOINT Now try Exercise 7.

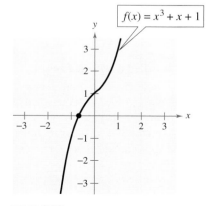

$f(x) = x^3 + x + 1$

FIGURE 2.30

STUDY TIP

When the list of possible rational zeros is small, as in Example 2, it may be quicker to test the zeros by evaluating the function. When the list of possible rational zeros is large, as in Example 3, it may be quicker to use a different approach to test the zeros, such as using synthetic division or sketching a graph.

Example 3   **Rational Zero Test with Leading Coefficient of 1**

Find the rational zeros of $f(x) = x^4 - x^3 + x^2 - 3x - 6$.

Solution

Because the leading coefficient is 1, the possible rational zeros are the factors of the constant term.

   Possible rational zeros: $\pm 1, \pm 2, \pm 3, \pm 6$

By applying synthetic division successively, you can determine that $x = -1$ and $x = 2$ are the only two rational zeros.

$$
\begin{array}{r|rrrrr}
-1 & 1 & -1 & 1 & -3 & -6 \\
   &   & -1 & 2 & -3 & 6 \\
\hline
   & 1 & -2 & 3 & -6 & 0
\end{array}
\longrightarrow \text{0 remainder, so } x = -1 \text{ is a zero.}
$$

$$
\begin{array}{r|rrrr}
2 & 1 & -2 & 3 & -6 \\
  &   & 2 & 0 & 6 \\
\hline
  & 1 & 0 & 3 & 0
\end{array}
\longrightarrow \text{0 remainder, so } x = 2 \text{ is a zero.}
$$

So, $f(x)$ factors as

$$f(x) = (x + 1)(x - 2)(x^2 + 3).$$

Because the factor $(x^2 + 3)$ produces no real zeros, you can conclude that $x = -1$ and $x = 2$ are the only *real* zeros of f, which is verified in Figure 2.31.

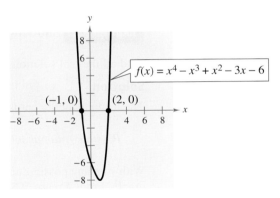

FIGURE **2.31**

✔CHECKPOINT   Now try Exercise 11.

   If the leading coefficient of a polynomial is not 1, the list of possible rational zeros can increase dramatically. In such cases, the search can be shortened in several ways: (1) a programmable calculator can be used to speed up the calculations; (2) a graph, drawn either by hand or with a graphing utility, can give a good estimate of the locations of the zeros; (3) the Intermediate Value Theorem along with a table generated by a graphing utility can give approximations of zeros; and (4) synthetic division can be used to test the possible rational zeros.

   Finding the first zero is often the most difficult part. After that, the search is simplified by working with the lower-degree polynomial obtained in synthetic division, as shown in Example 3.

Example 4 **Using the Rational Zero Test**

Find the rational zeros of $f(x) = 2x^3 + 3x^2 - 8x + 3$.

Solution

The leading coefficient is 2 and the constant term is 3.

$$\text{Possible rational zeros: } \frac{\text{Factors of } 3}{\text{Factors of } 2} = \frac{\pm 1, \pm 3}{\pm 1, \pm 2} = \pm 1, \pm 3, \pm \frac{1}{2}, \pm \frac{3}{2}$$

By synthetic division, you can determine that $x = 1$ is a rational zero.

$$
\begin{array}{r|rrrr}
1 & 2 & 3 & -8 & 3 \\
  &   & 2 & 5 & -3 \\
\hline
  & 2 & 5 & -3 & 0
\end{array}
$$

So, $f(x)$ factors as

$$f(x) = (x - 1)(2x^2 + 5x - 3)$$
$$= (x - 1)(2x - 1)(x + 3)$$

and you can conclude that the rational zeros of f are $x = 1$, $x = \frac{1}{2}$, and $x = -3$.

✓*CHECKPOINT*   Now try Exercise 17.

Recall from Section 2.2 that if $x = a$ is a zero of the polynomial function f, then $x = a$ is a solution of the polynomial equation $f(x) = 0$.

Example 5 **Solving a Polynomial Equation**

Find all the real solutions of $-10x^3 + 15x^2 + 16x - 12 = 0$.

Solution

The leading coefficient is -10 and the constant term is -12.

$$\text{Possible rational solutions: } \frac{\text{Factors of } -12}{\text{Factors of } -10} = \frac{\pm 1, \pm 2, \pm 3, \pm 4, \pm 6, \pm 12}{\pm 1, \pm 2, \pm 5, \pm 10}$$

With so many possibilities (32, in fact), it is worth your time to stop and sketch a graph. From Figure 2.32, it looks like three reasonable solutions would be $x = -\frac{6}{5}$, $x = \frac{1}{2}$, and $x = 2$. Testing these by synthetic division shows that $x = 2$ is the only rational solution. So, you have

$$(x - 2)(-10x^2 - 5x + 6) = 0.$$

Using the Quadratic Formula for the second factor, you find that the two additional solutions are irrational numbers.

$$x = \frac{-5 - \sqrt{265}}{20} \approx -1.0639$$

and

$$x = \frac{-5 + \sqrt{265}}{20} \approx 0.5639$$

✓*CHECKPOINT*   Now try Exercise 23.

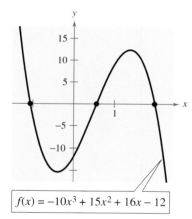

$f(x) = -10x^3 + 15x^2 + 16x - 12$

FIGURE **2.32**

Conjugate Pairs

In Example 1(c) and (d), note that the pairs of complex zeros are **conjugates.** That is, they are of the form $a + bi$ and $a - bi$.

Complex Zeros Occur in Conjugate Pairs

Let $f(x)$ be a polynomial function that has *real coefficients*. If $a + bi$, where $b \neq 0$, is a zero of the function, the conjugate $a - bi$ is also a zero of the function.

Be sure you see that this result is true only if the polynomial function has *real coefficients*. For instance, the result applies to the function given by $f(x) = x^2 + 1$ but not to the function given by $g(x) = x - i$.

Example 6   Finding a Polynomial with Given Zeros

Find a fourth-degree polynomial function with real coefficients that has -1, -1, and $3i$ as zeros.

Solution

Because $3i$ is a zero *and* the polynomial is stated to have real coefficients, you know that the conjugate $-3i$ must also be a zero. So, from the Linear Factorization Theorem, $f(x)$ can be written as

$$f(x) = a(x + 1)(x + 1)(x - 3i)(x + 3i).$$

For simplicity, let $a = 1$ to obtain

$$f(x) = (x^2 + 2x + 1)(x^2 + 9)$$
$$= x^4 + 2x^3 + 10x^2 + 18x + 9.$$

✓CHECKPOINT   Now try Exercise 37.

Factoring a Polynomial

The Linear Factorization Theorem shows that you can write any nth-degree polynomial as the product of n linear factors.

$$f(x) = a_n(x - c_1)(x - c_2)(x - c_3) \cdots (x - c_n)$$

However, this result includes the possibility that some of the values of c_i are complex. The following theorem says that even if you do not want to get involved with "complex factors," you can still write $f(x)$ as the product of linear and/or quadratic factors. For a proof of this theorem, see Proofs in Mathematics on page 214.

Factors of a Polynomial

Every polynomial of degree $n > 0$ with real coefficients can be written as the product of linear and quadratic factors with real coefficients, where the quadratic factors have no real zeros.

A quadratic factor with no real zeros is said to be *prime* or **irreducible over the reals.** Be sure you see that this is not the same as being *irreducible over the rationals.* For example, the quadratic $x^2 + 1 = (x - i)(x + i)$ is irreducible over the reals (and therefore over the rationals). On the other hand, the quadratic $x^2 - 2 = \left(x - \sqrt{2}\right)\left(x + \sqrt{2}\right)$ is irreducible over the rationals but *reducible* over the reals.

Example 7   Finding the Zeros of a Polynomial Function

Find all the zeros of $f(x) = x^4 - 3x^3 + 6x^2 + 2x - 60$ given that $1 + 3i$ is a zero of f.

Algebraic Solution

Because complex zeros occur in conjugate pairs, you know that $1 - 3i$ is also a zero of f. This means that both

$$[x - (1 + 3i)] \quad \text{and} \quad [x - (1 - 3i)]$$

are factors of f. Multiplying these two factors produces

$$[x - (1 + 3i)][x - (1 - 3i)] = [(x - 1) - 3i][(x - 1) + 3i]$$
$$= (x - 1)^2 - 9i^2$$
$$= x^2 - 2x + 10.$$

Using long division, you can divide $x^2 - 2x + 10$ into f to obtain the following.

$$
\begin{array}{r}
x^2 - x - 6 \\
x^2 - 2x + 10 \overline{\smash{)}\, x^4 - 3x^3 + 6x^2 + 2x - 60} \\
\underline{x^4 - 2x^3 + 10x^2 } \\
-x^3 - 4x^2 + 2x \\
\underline{-x^3 + 2x^2 - 10x } \\
-6x^2 + 12x - 60 \\
\underline{-6x^2 + 12x - 60} \\
0
\end{array}
$$

So, you have

$$f(x) = (x^2 - 2x + 10)(x^2 - x - 6)$$
$$= (x^2 - 2x + 10)(x - 3)(x + 2)$$

and you can conclude that the zeros of f are $x = 1 + 3i$, $x = 1 - 3i$, $x = 3$, and $x = -2$.

✓*CHECKPOINT*   Now try Exercise 47.

Graphical Solution

Because complex zeros always occur in conjugate pairs, you know that $1 - 3i$ is also a zero of f. Because the polynomial is a fourth-degree polynomial, you know that there are at most two other zeros of the function. Use a graphing utility to graph

$$y = x^4 - 3x^3 + 6x^2 + 2x - 60$$

as shown in Figure 2.33.

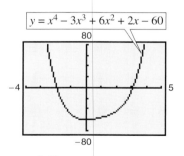

$y = x^4 - 3x^3 + 6x^2 + 2x - 60$

FIGURE 2.33

You can see that -2 and 3 appear to be zeros of the graph of the function. Use the *zero* or *root* feature or the *zoom* and *trace* features of the graphing utility to confirm that $x = -2$ and $x = 3$ are zeros of the graph. So, you can conclude that the zeros of f are $x = 1 + 3i$, $x = 1 - 3i$, $x = 3$, and $x = -2$.

In Example 7, if you were not told that $1 + 3i$ is a zero of f, you could still find all zeros of the function by using synthetic division to find the real zeros -2 and 3. Then you could factor the polynomial as $(x + 2)(x - 3)(x^2 - 2x + 10)$. Finally, by using the Quadratic Formula, you could determine that the zeros are $x = -2$, $x = 3$, $x = 1 + 3i$, and $x = 1 - 3i$.

Example 8 shows how to find all the zeros of a polynomial function, including complex zeros.

STUDY TIP

In Example 8, the fifth-degree polynomial function has three real zeros. In such cases, you can use the *zoom* and *trace* features or the *zero* or *root* feature of a graphing utility to approximate the real zeros. You can then use these real zeros to determine the complex zeros algebraically.

Example 8 Finding the Zeros of a Polynomial Function

Write $f(x) = x^5 + x^3 + 2x^2 - 12x + 8$ as the product of linear factors, and list all of its zeros.

Solution

The possible rational zeros are $\pm 1, \pm 2, \pm 4,$ and ± 8. Synthetic division produces the following.

$$
\begin{array}{r|rrrrrr}
1 & 1 & 0 & 1 & 2 & -12 & 8 \\
  &   & 1 & 1 & 2 & 4 & -8 \\
\hline
  & 1 & 1 & 2 & 4 & -8 & 0 \\
\end{array}
\quad\longrightarrow\quad 1 \text{ is a zero.}
$$

$$
\begin{array}{r|rrrrr}
-2 & 1 & 1 & 2 & 4 & -8 \\
   &   & -2 & 2 & -8 & 8 \\
\hline
   & 1 & -1 & 4 & -4 & 0 \\
\end{array}
\quad\longrightarrow\quad -2 \text{ is a zero.}
$$

So, you have

$$f(x) = x^5 + x^3 + 2x^2 - 12x + 8$$
$$= (x - 1)(x + 2)(x^3 - x^2 + 4x - 4).$$

You can factor $x^3 - x^2 + 4x - 4$ as $(x - 1)(x^2 + 4)$, and by factoring $x^2 + 4$ as

$$x^2 - (-4) = \left(x - \sqrt{-4}\right)\left(x + \sqrt{-4}\right)$$
$$= (x - 2i)(x + 2i)$$

you obtain

$$f(x) = (x - 1)(x - 1)(x + 2)(x - 2i)(x + 2i)$$

which gives the following five zeros of f.

$$x = 1, \ x = 1, \ x = -2, \ x = 2i, \quad \text{and} \quad x = -2i$$

From the graph of f shown in Figure 2.34, you can see that the *real* zeros are the only ones that appear as x-intercepts. Note that $x = 1$ is a repeated zero.

✓CHECKPOINT   Now try Exercise 63.

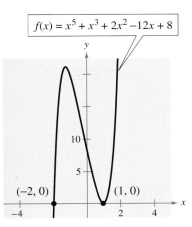

$f(x) = x^5 + x^3 + 2x^2 - 12x + 8$

$(-2, 0)$ $(1, 0)$

FIGURE 2.34

Technology

You can use the *table* feature of a graphing utility to help you determine which of the possible rational zeros are zeros of the polynomial in Example 8. The table should be set to *ask* mode. Then enter each of the possible rational zeros in the table. When you do this, you will see that there are two rational zeros, -2 and 1, as shown at the right.

X	Y1
-8	-33048
-4	-1000
-2	0
-1	20
1	0
2	32
4	1080

X=4

Other Tests for Zeros of Polynomials

You know that an nth-degree polynomial function can have *at most n* real zeros. Of course, many nth-degree polynomials do not have that many real zeros. For instance, $f(x) = x^2 + 1$ has no real zeros, and $f(x) = x^3 + 1$ has only one real zero. The following theorem, called **Descartes's Rule of Signs,** sheds more light on the number of real zeros of a polynomial.

Descartes's Rule of Signs

Let $f(x) = a_n x^n + a_{n-1} x^{n-1} + \cdots + a_2 x^2 + a_1 x + a_0$ be a polynomial with real coefficients and $a_0 \neq 0$.

1. The number of *positive real zeros* of f is either equal to the number of variations in sign of $f(x)$ or less than that number by an even integer.

2. The number of *negative real zeros* of f is either equal to the number of variations in sign of $f(-x)$ or less than that number by an even integer.

A **variation in sign** means that two consecutive coefficients have opposite signs.

When using Descartes's Rule of Signs, a zero of multiplicity k should be counted as k zeros. For instance, the polynomial $x^3 - 3x + 2$ has two variations in sign, and so has either two positive or no positive real zeros. Because

$$x^3 - 3x + 2 = (x - 1)(x - 1)(x + 2)$$

you can see that the two positive real zeros are $x = 1$ of multiplicity 2.

Example 9 **Using Descartes's Rule of Signs**

Describe the possible real zeros of

$$f(x) = 3x^3 - 5x^2 + 6x - 4.$$

Solution

The original polynomial has *three* variations in sign.

The polynomial

$$f(-x) = 3(-x)^3 - 5(-x)^2 + 6(-x) - 4$$
$$= -3x^3 - 5x^2 - 6x - 4$$

has no variations in sign. So, from Descartes's Rule of Signs, the polynomial $f(x) = 3x^3 - 5x^2 + 6x - 4$ has either three positive real zeros or one positive real zero, and has no negative real zeros. From the graph in Figure 2.35, you can see that the function has only one real zero (it is a positive number, near $x = 1$).

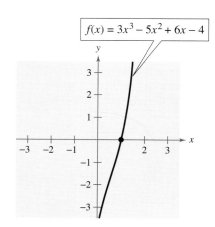

$f(x) = 3x^3 - 5x^2 + 6x - 4$

FIGURE 2.35

✓CHECKPOINT Now try Exercise 79.

Another test for zeros of a polynomial function is related to the sign pattern in the last row of the synthetic division array. This test can give you an upper or lower bound of the real zeros of f. A real number b is an **upper bound** for the real zeros of f if no zeros are greater than b. Similarly, b is a **lower bound** if no real zeros of f are less than b.

Upper and Lower Bound Rules

Let $f(x)$ be a polynomial with real coefficients and a positive leading coefficient. Suppose $f(x)$ is divided by $x - c$, using synthetic division.

1. If $c > 0$ and each number in the last row is either positive or zero, c is an **upper bound** for the real zeros of f.

2. If $c < 0$ and the numbers in the last row are alternately positive and negative (zero entries count as positive or negative), c is a **lower bound** for the real zeros of f.

Example 10   Finding the Zeros of a Polynomial Function

Find the real zeros of $f(x) = 6x^3 - 4x^2 + 3x - 2$.

Solution

The possible real zeros are as follows.

$$\frac{\text{Factors of } 2}{\text{Factors of } 6} = \frac{\pm 1, \pm 2}{\pm 1, \pm 2, \pm 3, \pm 6} = \pm 1, \pm\frac{1}{2}, \pm\frac{1}{3}, \pm\frac{1}{6}, \pm\frac{2}{3}, \pm 2$$

The original polynomial $f(x)$ has three variations in sign. The polynomial

$$f(-x) = 6(-x)^3 - 4(-x)^2 + 3(-x) - 2$$
$$= -6x^3 - 4x^2 - 3x - 2$$

has no variations in sign. As a result of these two findings, you can apply Descartes's Rule of Signs to conclude that there are three positive real zeros or one positive real zero, and no negative zeros. Trying $x = 1$ produces the following.

$$
\begin{array}{r|rrrr}
1 & 6 & -4 & 3 & -2 \\
  &   & 6 & 2 & 5 \\
\hline
  & 6 & 2 & 5 & 3
\end{array}
$$

So, $x = 1$ is not a zero, but because the last row has all positive entries, you know that $x = 1$ is an upper bound for the real zeros. So, you can restrict the search to zeros between 0 and 1. By trial and error, you can determine that $x = \frac{2}{3}$ is a zero. So,

$$f(x) = \left(x - \frac{2}{3}\right)(6x^2 + 3).$$

Because $6x^2 + 3$ has no real zeros, it follows that $x = \frac{2}{3}$ is the only real zero.

✓**CHECKPOINT**   Now try Exercise 87.

Before concluding this section, here are two additional hints that can help you find the real zeros of a polynomial.

1. If the terms of $f(x)$ have a common monomial factor, it should be factored out before applying the tests in this section. For instance, by writing

$$f(x) = x^4 - 5x^3 + 3x^2 + x$$
$$= x(x^3 - 5x^2 + 3x + 1)$$

you can see that $x = 0$ is a zero of f and that the remaining zeros can be obtained by analyzing the cubic factor.

2. If you are able to find all but two zeros of $f(x)$, you can always use the Quadratic Formula on the remaining quadratic factor. For instance, if you succeeded in writing

$$f(x) = x^4 - 5x^3 + 3x^2 + x$$
$$= x(x - 1)(x^2 - 4x - 1)$$

you can apply the Quadratic Formula to $x^2 - 4x - 1$ to conclude that the two remaining zeros are $x = 2 + \sqrt{5}$ and $x = 2 - \sqrt{5}$.

Example 11   Using a Polynomial Model

You are designing candle-making kits. Each kit contains 25 cubic inches of candle wax and a mold for making a pyramid-shaped candle. You want the height of the candle to be 2 inches less than the length of each side of the candle's square base. What should the dimensions of your candle mold be?

Solution

The volume of a pyramid is $V = \frac{1}{3}Bh$, where B is the area of the base and h is the height. The area of the base is x^2 and the height is $(x - 2)$. So, the volume of the pyramid is $V = \frac{1}{3}x^2(x - 2)$. Substituting 25 for the volume yields the following.

$$25 = \frac{1}{3}x^2(x - 2) \qquad \text{Substitute 25 for } V.$$

$$75 = x^3 - 2x^2 \qquad \text{Multiply each side by 3.}$$

$$0 = x^3 - 2x^2 - 75 \qquad \text{Write in general form.}$$

The possible rational solutions are $x = \pm 1, \pm 3, \pm 5, \pm 15, \pm 25, \pm 75$. Use synthetic division to test some of the possible solutions. Note that in this case, it makes sense to test only positive x-values. Using synthetic division, you can determine that $x = 5$ is a solution.

$$
\begin{array}{r|rrrr}
5 & 1 & -2 & 0 & -75 \\
  &   & 5 & 15 & 75 \\
\hline
  & 1 & 3 & 15 & 0
\end{array}
$$

The other two solutions, which satisfy $x^2 + 3x + 15 = 0$, are imaginary and can be discarded. You can conclude that the base of the candle mold should be 5 inches by 5 inches and the height of the mold should be $5 - 2 = 3$ inches.

✔CHECKPOINT   Now try Exercise 107.

2.5 Exercises

VOCABULARY CHECK: Fill in the blanks.

1. The _____ _____ of _____ states that if $f(x)$ is a polynomial of degree n ($n > 0$), then f has at least one zero in the complex number system.

2. The _____ _____ _____ states that if $f(x)$ is a polynomial of degree n ($n > 0$), then f has precisely n linear factors $f(x) = a_n(x - c_1)(x - c_2) \cdots (x - c_n)$ where $c_1, c_2, \ldots, c_n$ are complex numbers.

3. The test that gives a list of the possible rational zeros of a polynomial function is called the _____ _____ Test.

4. If $a + bi$ is a complex zero of a polynomial with real coefficients, then so is its _____, $a - bi$.

5. A quadratic factor that cannot be factored further as a product of linear factors containing real numbers is said to be _____ over the _____.

6. The theorem that can be used to determine the possible numbers of positive real zeros and negative real zeros of a function is called _____ _____ of _____.

7. A real number b is a(n) _____ bound for the real zeros of f if no real zeros are less than b, and is a(n) _____ bound if no real zeros are greater than b.

PREREQUISITE SKILLS REVIEW: Practice and review algebra skills needed for this section at **www.Eduspace.com.**

In Exercises 1–6, find all the zeros of the function.

1. $f(x) = x(x - 6)^2$
2. $f(x) = x^2(x + 3)(x^2 - 1)$
3. $g(x) = (x - 2)(x + 4)^3$
4. $f(x) = (x + 5)(x - 8)^2$
5. $f(x) = (x + 6)(x + i)(x - i)$
6. $h(t) = (t - 3)(t - 2)(t - 3i)(t + 3i)$

In Exercises 7–10, use the Rational Zero Test to list all possible rational zeros of f. Verify that the zeros of f shown on the graph are contained in the list.

7. $f(x) = x^3 + 3x^2 - x - 3$

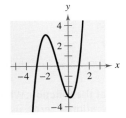

8. $f(x) = x^3 - 4x^2 - 4x + 16$

9. $f(x) = 2x^4 - 17x^3 + 35x^2 + 9x - 45$

10. $f(x) = 4x^5 - 8x^4 - 5x^3 + 10x^2 + x - 2$

In Exercises 11–20, find all the rational zeros of the function.

11. $f(x) = x^3 - 6x^2 + 11x - 6$
12. $f(x) = x^3 - 7x - 6$
13. $g(x) = x^3 - 4x^2 - x + 4$
14. $h(x) = x^3 - 9x^2 + 20x - 12$
15. $h(t) = t^3 + 12t^2 + 21t + 10$
16. $p(x) = x^3 - 9x^2 + 27x - 27$
17. $C(x) = 2x^3 + 3x^2 - 1$
18. $f(x) = 3x^3 - 19x^2 + 33x - 9$
19. $f(x) = 9x^4 - 9x^3 - 58x^2 + 4x + 24$
20. $f(x) = 2x^4 - 15x^3 + 23x^2 + 15x - 25$

In Exercises 21–24, find all real solutions of the polynomial equation.

21. $z^4 - z^3 - 2z - 4 = 0$

22. $x^4 - 13x^2 - 12x = 0$

23. $2y^4 + 7y^3 - 26y^2 + 23y - 6 = 0$

24. $x^5 - x^4 - 3x^3 + 5x^2 - 2x = 0$

In Exercises 25–28, (a) list the possible rational zeros of f, (b) sketch the graph of f so that some of the possible zeros in part (a) can be disregarded, and then (c) determine all real zeros of f.

25. $f(x) = x^3 + x^2 - 4x - 4$

26. $f(x) = -3x^3 + 20x^2 - 36x + 16$

27. $f(x) = -4x^3 + 15x^2 - 8x - 3$

28. $f(x) = 4x^3 - 12x^2 - x + 15$

 In Exercises 29–32, (a) list the possible rational zeros of f, (b) use a graphing utility to graph f so that some of the possible zeros in part (a) can be disregarded, and then (c) determine all real zeros of f.

29. $f(x) = -2x^4 + 13x^3 - 21x^2 + 2x + 8$

30. $f(x) = 4x^4 - 17x^2 + 4$

31. $f(x) = 32x^3 - 52x^2 + 17x + 3$

32. $f(x) = 4x^3 + 7x^2 - 11x - 18$

 Graphical Analysis In Exercises 33–36, (a) use the *zero* or *root* feature of a graphing utility to approximate the zeros of the function accurate to three decimal places, (b) determine one of the exact zeros (use synthetic division to verify your result), and (c) factor the polynomial completely.

33. $f(x) = x^4 - 3x^2 + 2$ **34.** $P(t) = t^4 - 7t^2 + 12$

35. $h(x) = x^5 - 7x^4 + 10x^3 + 14x^2 - 24x$

36. $g(x) = 6x^4 - 11x^3 - 51x^2 + 99x - 27$

In Exercises 37–42, find a polynomial function with real coefficients that has the given zeros. (There are many correct answers.)

37. $1, 5i, -5i$

38. $4, 3i, -3i$

39. $6, -5 + 2i, -5 - 2i$

40. $2, 4 + i, 4 - i$

41. $\frac{2}{3}, -1, 3 + \sqrt{2}i$

42. $-5, -5, 1 + \sqrt{3}i$

In Exercises 43–46, write the polynomial (a) as the product of factors that are irreducible over the *rationals*, (b) as the product of linear and quadratic factors that are irreducible over the *reals*, and (c) in completely factored form.

43. $f(x) = x^4 + 6x^2 - 27$

44. $f(x) = x^4 - 2x^3 - 3x^2 + 12x - 18$
(*Hint:* One factor is $x^2 - 6$.)

45. $f(x) = x^4 - 4x^3 + 5x^2 - 2x - 6$
(*Hint:* One factor is $x^2 - 2x - 2$.)

46. $f(x) = x^4 - 3x^3 - x^2 - 12x - 20$
(*Hint:* One factor is $x^2 + 4$.)

In Exercises 47–54, use the given zero to find all the zeros of the function.

Function	Zero
47. $f(x) = 2x^3 + 3x^2 + 50x + 75$	$5i$
48. $f(x) = x^3 + x^2 + 9x + 9$	$3i$
49. $f(x) = 2x^4 - x^3 + 7x^2 - 4x - 4$	$2i$
50. $g(x) = x^3 - 7x^2 - x + 87$	$5 + 2i$
51. $g(x) = 4x^3 + 23x^2 + 34x - 10$	$-3 + i$
52. $h(x) = 3x^3 - 4x^2 + 8x + 8$	$1 - \sqrt{3}i$
53. $f(x) = x^4 + 3x^3 - 5x^2 - 21x + 22$	$-3 + \sqrt{2}i$
54. $f(x) = x^3 + 4x^2 + 14x + 20$	$-1 - 3i$

In Exercises 55–72, find all the zeros of the function and write the polynomial as a product of linear factors.

55. $f(x) = x^2 + 25$ **56.** $f(x) = x^2 - x + 56$

57. $h(x) = x^2 - 4x + 1$ **58.** $g(x) = x^2 + 10x + 23$

59. $f(x) = x^4 - 81$

60. $f(y) = y^4 - 625$

61. $f(z) = z^2 - 2z + 2$

62. $h(x) = x^3 - 3x^2 + 4x - 2$

63. $g(x) = x^3 - 6x^2 + 13x - 10$

64. $f(x) = x^3 - 2x^2 - 11x + 52$

65. $h(x) = x^3 - x + 6$

66. $h(x) = x^3 + 9x^2 + 27x + 35$

67. $f(x) = 5x^3 - 9x^2 + 28x + 6$

68. $g(x) = 3x^3 - 4x^2 + 8x + 8$

69. $g(x) = x^4 - 4x^3 + 8x^2 - 16x + 16$

70. $h(x) = x^4 + 6x^3 + 10x^2 + 6x + 9$

71. $f(x) = x^4 + 10x^2 + 9$ **72.** $f(x) = x^4 + 29x^2 + 100$

 In Exercises 73–78, find all the zeros of the function. When there is an extended list of possible rational zeros, use a graphing utility to graph the function in order to discard any rational zeros that are obviously not zeros of the function.

73. $f(x) = x^3 + 24x^2 + 214x + 740$

74. $f(s) = 2s^3 - 5s^2 + 12s - 5$

75. $f(x) = 16x^3 - 20x^2 - 4x + 15$

76. $f(x) = 9x^3 - 15x^2 + 11x - 5$

77. $f(x) = 2x^4 + 5x^3 + 4x^2 + 5x + 2$

78. $g(x) = x^5 - 8x^4 + 28x^3 - 56x^2 + 64x - 32$

In Exercises 79–86, use Descartes's Rule of Signs to determine the possible numbers of positive and negative zeros of the function.

79. $g(x) = 5x^5 + 10x$

80. $h(x) = 4x^2 - 8x + 3$

81. $h(x) = 3x^4 + 2x^2 + 1$

82. $h(x) = 2x^4 - 3x + 2$

83. $g(x) = 2x^3 - 3x^2 - 3$

84. $f(x) = 4x^3 - 3x^2 + 2x - 1$

85. $f(x) = -5x^3 + x^2 - x + 5$

86. $f(x) = 3x^3 + 2x^2 + x + 3$

In Exercises 87–90, use synthetic division to verify the upper and lower bounds of the real zeros of f.

87. $f(x) = x^4 - 4x^3 + 15$

   (a) Upper: $x = 4$ (b) Lower: $x = -1$

88. $f(x) = 2x^3 - 3x^2 - 12x + 8$

   (a) Upper: $x = 4$ (b) Lower: $x = -3$

89. $f(x) = x^4 - 4x^3 + 16x - 16$

   (a) Upper: $x = 5$ (b) Lower: $x = -3$

90. $f(x) = 2x^4 - 8x + 3$

   (a) Upper: $x = 3$ (b) Lower: $x = -4$

In Exercises 91–94, find all the real zeros of the function.

91. $f(x) = 4x^3 - 3x - 1$

92. $f(z) = 12z^3 - 4z^2 - 27z + 9$

93. $f(y) = 4y^3 + 3y^2 + 8y + 6$

94. $g(x) = 3x^3 - 2x^2 + 15x - 10$

In Exercises 95–98, find all the rational zeros of the polynomial function.

95. $P(x) = x^4 - \frac{25}{4}x^2 + 9 = \frac{1}{4}(4x^4 - 25x^2 + 36)$

96. $f(x) = x^3 - \frac{3}{2}x^2 - \frac{23}{2}x + 6 = \frac{1}{2}(2x^3 - 3x^2 - 23x + 12)$

97. $f(x) = x^3 - \frac{1}{4}x^2 - x + \frac{1}{4} = \frac{1}{4}(4x^3 - x^2 - 4x + 1)$

98. $f(z) = z^3 + \frac{11}{6}z^2 - \frac{1}{2}z - \frac{1}{3} = \frac{1}{6}(6z^3 + 11z^2 - 3z - 2)$

In Exercises 99–102, match the cubic function with the numbers of rational and irrational zeros.

(a) Rational zeros: 0; irrational zeros: 1

(b) Rational zeros: 3; irrational zeros: 0

(c) Rational zeros: 1; irrational zeros: 2

(d) Rational zeros: 1; irrational zeros: 0

99. $f(x) = x^3 - 1$

100. $f(x) = x^3 - 2$

101. $f(x) = x^3 - x$

102. $f(x) = x^3 - 2x$

103. *Geometry*   An open box is to be made from a rectangular piece of material, 15 centimeters by 9 centimeters, by cutting equal squares from the corners and turning up the sides.

(a) Let x represent the length of the sides of the squares removed. Draw a diagram showing the squares removed from the original piece of material and the resulting dimensions of the open box.

(b) Use the diagram to write the volume V of the box as a function of x. Determine the domain of the function.

(c) Sketch the graph of the function and approximate the dimensions of the box that will yield a maximum volume.

(d) Find values of x such that $V = 56$. Which of these values is a physical impossibility in the construction of the box? Explain.

104. *Geometry*   A rectangular package to be sent by a delivery service (see figure) can have a maximum combined length and girth (perimeter of a cross section) of 120 inches.

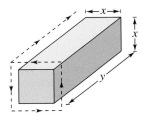

(a) Show that the volume of the package is

$$V(x) = 4x^2(30 - x).$$

 (b) Use a graphing utility to graph the function and approximate the dimensions of the package that will yield a maximum volume.

(c) Find values of x such that $V = 13{,}500$. Which of these values is a physical impossibility in the construction of the package? Explain.

105. *Advertising Cost*   A company that produces MP3 players estimates that the profit P (in dollars) for selling a particular model is given by

$$P = -76x^3 + 4830x^2 - 320{,}000, \quad 0 \le x \le 60$$

where x is the advertising expense (in tens of thousands of dollars). Using this model, find the smaller of two advertising amounts that will yield a profit of $2,500,000.

106. *Advertising Cost*   A company that manufactures bicycles estimates that the profit P (in dollars) for selling a particular model is given by

$$P = -45x^3 + 2500x^2 - 275{,}000, \quad 0 \le x \le 50$$

where x is the advertising expense (in tens of thousands of dollars). Using this model, find the smaller of two advertising amounts that will yield a profit of $800,000.

107. *Geometry* A bulk food storage bin with dimensions 2 feet by 3 feet by 4 feet needs to be increased in size to hold five times as much food as the current bin. (Assume each dimension is increased by the same amount.)

  (a) Write a function that represents the volume V of the new bin.

  (b) Find the dimensions of the new bin.

108. *Geometry* A rancher wants to enlarge an existing rectangular corral such that the total area of the new corral is 1.5 times that of the original corral. The current corral's dimensions are 250 feet by 160 feet. The rancher wants to increase each dimension by the same amount.

  (a) Write a function that represents the area A of the new corral.

  (b) Find the dimensions of the new corral.

  (c) A rancher wants to add a length to the sides of the corral that are 160 feet, and twice the length to the sides that are 250 feet, such that the total area of the new corral is 1.5 times that of the original corral. Repeat parts (a) and (b). Explain your results.

109. *Cost* The ordering and transportation cost C (in thousands of dollars) for the components used in manufacturing a product is given by

$$C = 100\left(\frac{200}{x^2} + \frac{x}{x + 30}\right), \quad x \geq 1$$

where x is the order size (in hundreds). In calculus, it can be shown that the cost is a minimum when

$$3x^3 - 40x^2 - 2400x - 36{,}000 = 0.$$

Use a calculator to approximate the optimal order size to the nearest hundred units.

110. *Height of a Baseball* A baseball is thrown upward from a height of 6 feet with an initial velocity of 48 feet per second, and its height h (in feet) is

$$h(t) = -16t^2 + 48t + 6, \quad 0 \leq t \leq 3$$

where t is the time (in seconds). You are told the ball reaches a height of 64 feet. Is this possible?

111. *Profit* The demand equation for a certain product is $p = 140 - 0.0001x$, where p is the unit price (in dollars) of the product and x is the number of units produced and sold. The cost equation for the product is $C = 80x + 150{,}000$, where C is the total cost (in dollars) and x is the number of units produced. The total profit obtained by producing and selling x units is

$$P = R - C = xp - C.$$

You are working in the marketing department of the company that produces this product, and you are asked to determine a price p that will yield a profit of 9 million dollars. Is this possible? Explain.

Model It

112. *Athletics* The attendance A (in millions) at NCAA women's college basketball games for the years 1997 through 2003 is shown in the table, where t represents the year, with $t = 7$ corresponding to 1997. (Source: National Collegiate Athletic Association)

Year, t	Attendance, A
7	6.7
8	7.4
9	8.0
10	8.7
11	8.8
12	9.5
13	10.2

  (a) Use the *regression* feature of a graphing utility to find a cubic model for the data.

  (b) Use the graphing utility to create a scatter plot of the data. Then graph the model and the scatter plot in the same viewing window. How do they compare?

  (c) According to the model found in part (a), in what year did attendance reach 8.5 million?

  (d) According to the model found in part (a), in what year did attendance reach 9 million?

  (e) According to the right-hand behavior of the model, will the attendance continue to increase? Explain.

Synthesis

True or False? In Exercises 113 and 114, decide whether the statement is true or false. Justify your answer.

113. It is possible for a third-degree polynomial function with integer coefficients to have no real zeros.

114. If $x = -i$ is a zero of the function given by

$$f(x) = x^3 + ix^2 + ix - 1$$

then $x = i$ must also be a zero of f.

Think About It In Exercises 115–120, determine (if possible) the zeros of the function g if the function f has zeros at $x = r_1, x = r_2,$ and $x = r_3$.

115. $g(x) = -f(x)$ **116.** $g(x) = 3f(x)$

117. $g(x) = f(x - 5)$

118. $g(x) = f(2x)$

119. $g(x) = 3 + f(x)$

120. $g(x) = f(-x)$

121. *Exploration* Use a graphing utility to graph the function given by $f(x) = x^4 - 4x^2 + k$ for different values of k. Find values of k such that the zeros of f satisfy the specified characteristics. (Some parts do not have unique answers.)

(a) Four real zeros

(b) Two real zeros, each of multiplicity 2

(c) Two real zeros and two complex zeros

(d) Four complex zeros

122. *Think About It* Will the answers to Exercise 121 change for the function g?

(a) $g(x) = f(x - 2)$ (b) $g(x) = f(2x)$

123. *Think About It* A third-degree polynomial function f has real zeros $-2, \frac{1}{2}$, and 3, and its leading coefficient is negative. Write an equation for f. Sketch the graph of f. How many different polynomial functions are possible for f?

124. *Think About It* Sketch the graph of a fifth-degree polynomial function whose leading coefficient is positive and that has one zero at $x = 3$ of multiplicity 2.

125. *Writing* Compile a list of all the various techniques for factoring a polynomial that have been covered so far in the text. Give an example illustrating each technique, and write a paragraph discussing when the use of each technique is appropriate.

126. Use the information in the table to answer each question.

Interval	Value of $f(x)$
$(-\infty, -2)$	Positive
$(-2, 1)$	Negative
$(1, 4)$	Negative
$(4, \infty)$	Positive

(a) What are the three real zeros of the polynomial function f?

(b) What can be said about the behavior of the graph of f at $x = 1$?

(c) What is the least possible degree of f? Explain. Can the degree of f ever be odd? Explain.

(d) Is the leading coefficient of f positive or negative? Explain.

(e) Write an equation for f. (There are many correct answers.)

(f) Sketch a graph of the equation you wrote in part (e).

127. (a) Find a quadratic function f (with integer coefficients) that has $\pm \sqrt{b}i$ as zeros. Assume that b is a positive integer.

(b) Find a quadratic function f (with integer coefficients) that has $a \pm bi$ as zeros. Assume that b is a positive integer.

128. *Graphical Reasoning* The graph of one of the following functions is shown below. Identify the function shown in the graph. Explain why each of the others is not the correct function. Use a graphing utility to verify your result.

(a) $f(x) = x^2(x + 2)(x - 3.5)$

(b) $g(x) = (x + 2)(x - 3.5)$

(c) $h(x) = (x + 2)(x - 3.5)(x^2 + 1)$

(d) $k(x) = (x + 1)(x + 2)(x - 3.5)$

Skills Review

In Exercises 129–132, perform the operation and simplify.

129. $(-3 + 6i) - (8 - 3i)$

130. $(12 - 5i) + 16i$

131. $(6 - 2i)(1 + 7i)$

132. $(9 - 5i)(9 + 5i)$

In Exercises 133–138, use the graph of f to sketch the graph of g. To print an enlarged copy of the graph, go to the website *www.mathgraphs.com*.

133. $g(x) = f(x - 2)$

134. $g(x) = f(x) - 2$

135. $g(x) = 2f(x)$

136. $g(x) = f(-x)$

137. $g(x) = f(2x)$

138. $g(x) = f\left(\frac{1}{2}x\right)$

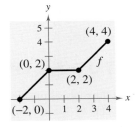

2.6   Rational Functions

What you should learn

- Find the domains of rational functions.
- Find the horizontal and vertical asymptotes of graphs of rational functions.
- Analyze and sketch graphs of rational functions.
- Sketch graphs of rational functions that have slant asymptotes.
- Use rational functions to model and solve real-life problems.

Why you should learn it

Rational functions can be used to model and solve real-life problems relating to business. For instance, in Exercise 79 on page 196, a rational function is used to model average speed over a distance.

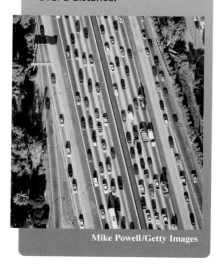

Mike Powell/Getty Images

Introduction

A **rational function** can be written in the form

$$f(x) = \frac{N(x)}{D(x)}$$

where $N(x)$ and $D(x)$ are polynomials and $D(x)$ is not the zero polynomial.

In general, the *domain* of a rational function of x includes all real numbers except x-values that make the denominator zero. Much of the discussion of rational functions will focus on their graphical behavior near the x-values excluded from the domain.

Example 1   **Finding the Domain of a Rational Function**

Find the domain of $f(x) = \dfrac{1}{x}$ and discuss the behavior of f near any excluded x-values.

Solution

Because the denominator is zero when $x = 0$, the domain of f is all real numbers except $x = 0$. To determine the behavior of f near this excluded value, evaluate $f(x)$ to the left and right of $x = 0$, as indicated in the following tables.

x	-1	-0.5	-0.1	-0.01	-0.001	$\longrightarrow 0$
$f(x)$	-1	-2	-10	-100	-1000	$\longrightarrow -\infty$

x	$0 \longleftarrow$	0.001	0.01	0.1	0.5	1
$f(x)$	$\infty \longleftarrow$	1000	100	10	2	1

Note that as x approaches 0 *from the left*, $f(x)$ decreases without bound. In contrast, as x approaches 0 *from the right*, $f(x)$ increases without bound. The graph of f is shown in Figure 2.36.

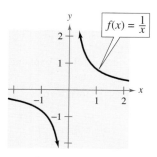

FIGURE 2.36

✓CHECKPOINT   Now try Exercise 1.

STUDY TIP

Note that the rational function given by $f(x) = 1/x$ is also referred to as the reciprocal function discussed in Section 1.6.

FIGURE 2.37

Horizontal and Vertical Asymptotes

In Example 1, the behavior of f near $x = 0$ is denoted as follows.

$$f(x) \longrightarrow -\infty \text{ as } x \longrightarrow 0^- \qquad f(x) \longrightarrow \infty \text{ as } x \longrightarrow 0^+$$

$\underbrace{\qquad\qquad}$ $f(x)$ decreases without bound as x approaches 0 from the left. $\underbrace{\qquad\qquad}$ $f(x)$ increases without bound as x approaches 0 from the right.

The line $x = 0$ is a **vertical asymptote** of the graph of f, as shown in Figure 2.37. From this figure, you can see that the graph of f also has a **horizontal asymptote**— the line $y = 0$. This means that the values of $f(x) = 1/x$ approach zero as x increases or decreases without bound.

$$f(x) \longrightarrow 0 \text{ as } x \longrightarrow -\infty \qquad f(x) \longrightarrow 0 \text{ as } x \longrightarrow \infty$$

$\underbrace{\qquad\qquad}$ $f(x)$ approaches 0 as x decreases without bound. $\underbrace{\qquad\qquad}$ $f(x)$ approaches 0 as x increases without bound.

Definitions of Vertical and Horizontal Asymptotes

1. The line $x = a$ is a **vertical asymptote** of the graph of f if

$$f(x) \longrightarrow \infty \quad \text{or} \quad f(x) \longrightarrow -\infty$$

as $x \longrightarrow a$, either from the right or from the left.

2. The line $y = b$ is a **horizontal asymptote** of the graph of f if

$$f(x) \longrightarrow b$$

as $x \longrightarrow \infty$ or $x \longrightarrow -\infty$.

Eventually (as $x \longrightarrow \infty$ or $x \longrightarrow -\infty$), the distance between the horizontal asymptote and the points on the graph must approach zero. Figure 2.38 shows the horizontal and vertical asymptotes of the graphs of three rational functions.

(a)

(b)

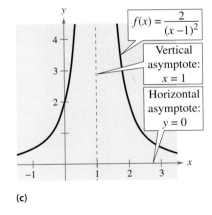

(c)

FIGURE 2.38

The graphs of $f(x) = 1/x$ in Figure 2.37 and $f(x) = (2x + 1)/(x + 1)$ in Figure 2.38(a) are **hyperbolas.** You will study hyperbolas in Section 10.4.

Asymptotes of a Rational Function

Let f be the rational function given by

$$f(x) = \frac{N(x)}{D(x)} = \frac{a_n x^n + a_{n-1} x^{n-1} + \cdots + a_1 x + a_0}{b_m x^m + b_{m-1} x^{m-1} + \cdots + b_1 x + b_0}$$

where $N(x)$ and $D(x)$ have no common factors.

1. The graph of f has *vertical* asymptotes at the zeros of $D(x)$.

2. The graph of f has one or no *horizontal* asymptote determined by comparing the degrees of $N(x)$ and $D(x)$.

    a. If $n < m$, the graph of f has the line $y = 0$ (the x-axis) as a horizontal asymptote.

    b. If $n = m$, the graph of f has the line $y = a_n/b_m$ (ratio of the leading coefficients) as a horizontal asymptote.

    c. If $n > m$, the graph of f has no horizontal asymptote.

Example 2   Finding Horizontal and Vertical Asymptotes

Find all horizontal and vertical asymptotes of the graph of each rational function.

a. $f(x) = \dfrac{2x^2}{x^2 - 1}$ **b.** $f(x) = \dfrac{x^2 + x - 2}{x^2 - x - 6}$

Solution

a. For this rational function, the degree of the numerator is *equal to* the degree of the denominator. The leading coefficient of the numerator is 2 and the leading coefficient of the denominator is 1, so the graph has the line $y = 2$ as a horizontal asymptote. To find any vertical asymptotes, set the denominator equal to zero and solve the resulting equation for x.

$$x^2 - 1 = 0 \qquad \text{Set denominator equal to zero.}$$

$$(x + 1)(x - 1) = 0 \qquad \text{Factor.}$$

$$x + 1 = 0 \implies x = -1 \qquad \text{Set 1st factor equal to 0.}$$

$$x - 1 = 0 \implies x = 1 \qquad \text{Set 2nd factor equal to 0.}$$

This equation has two real solutions $x = -1$ and $x = 1$, so the graph has the lines $x = -1$ and $x = 1$ as vertical asymptotes. The graph of the function is shown in Figure 2.39.

b. For this rational function, the degree of the numerator is *equal to* the degree of the denominator. The leading coefficient of both the numerator and denominator is 1, so the graph has the line $y = 1$ as a horizontal asymptote. To find any vertical asymptotes, first factor the numerator and denominator as follows.

$$f(x) = \frac{x^2 + x - 2}{x^2 - x - 6} = \frac{(x - 1)(x + 2)}{(x + 2)(x - 3)} = \frac{x - 1}{x - 3}, \quad x \neq 2$$

By setting the denominator $x - 3$ (of the simplified function) equal to zero, you can determine that the graph has the line $x = 3$ as a vertical asymptote.

✓**CHECKPOINT**   Now try Exercise 9.

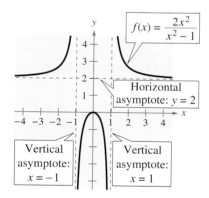

Horizontal asymptote: $y = 2$

Vertical asymptote: $x = -1$

Vertical asymptote: $x = 1$

FIGURE 2.39

Analyzing Graphs of Rational Functions

To sketch the graph of a rational function, use the following guidelines.

STUDY TIP

You may also want to test for symmetry when graphing rational functions, especially for simple rational functions. Recall from Section 1.6 that the graph of

$$f(x) = \frac{1}{x}$$

is symmetric with respect to the origin.

Guidelines for Analyzing Graphs of Rational Functions

Let $f(x) = N(x)/D(x)$, where $N(x)$ and $D(x)$ are polynomials.

1. Simplify f, if possible.

2. Find and plot the y-intercept (if any) by evaluating $f(0)$.

3. Find the zeros of the numerator (if any) by solving the equation $N(x) = 0$. Then plot the corresponding x-intercepts.

4. Find the zeros of the denominator (if any) by solving the equation $D(x) = 0$. Then sketch the corresponding vertical asymptotes.

5. Find and sketch the horizontal asymptote (if any) by using the rule for finding the horizontal asymptote of a rational function.

6. Plot at least one point *between* and one point *beyond* each x-intercept and vertical asymptote.

7. Use smooth curves to complete the graph between and beyond the vertical asymptotes.

Technology

Some graphing utilities have difficulty graphing rational functions that have vertical asymptotes. Often, the utility will connect parts of the graph that are not supposed to be connected. For instance, the top screen on the right shows the graph of

$$f(x) = \frac{1}{x - 2}.$$

Notice that the graph should consist of two unconnected portions—one to the left of $x = 2$ and the other to the right of $x = 2$. To eliminate this problem, you can try changing the mode of the graphing utility to *dot mode*. The problem with this is that the graph is then represented as a collection of dots (as shown in the bottom screen on the right) rather than as a smooth curve.

The concept of *test intervals* from Section 2.2 can be extended to graphing of rational functions. To do this, use the fact that a rational function can change signs only at its zeros and its undefined values (the x-values for which its denominator is zero). Between two consecutive zeros of the numerator and the denominator, a rational function must be entirely positive or entirely negative. This means that when the zeros of the numerator and the denominator of a rational function are put in order, they divide the real number line into test intervals in which the function has no sign changes. A representative x-value is chosen to determine if the value of the rational function is positive (the graph lies above the x-axis) or negative (the graph lies below the x-axis).

Example 3   Sketching the Graph of a Rational Function

Sketch the graph of $g(x) = \dfrac{3}{x - 2}$ and state its domain.

Solution

y-intercept:	$\left(0, -\frac{3}{2}\right)$, because $g(0) = -\frac{3}{2}$
x-intercept:	None, because $3 \neq 0$
Vertical asymptote:	$x = 2$, zero of denominator
Horizontal asymptote:	$y = 0$, because degree of $N(x) <$ degree of $D(x)$
Additional points:	

Test interval	Representative x-value	Value of g	Sign	Point on graph
$(-\infty, 2)$	-4	$g(-4) = -0.5$	Negative	$(-4, -0.5)$
$(2, \infty)$	3	$g(3) = 3$	Positive	$(3, 3)$

By plotting the intercepts, asymptotes, and a few additional points, you can obtain the graph shown in Figure 2.40. The domain of g is all real numbers x except $x = 2$.

✓CHECKPOINT   Now try Exercise 27.

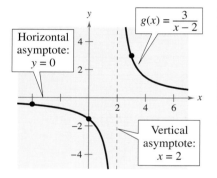

Horizontal asymptote: $y = 0$

$g(x) = \dfrac{3}{x - 2}$

Vertical asymptote: $x = 2$

FIGURE 2.40

Example 4   Sketching the Graph of a Rational Function

Sketch the graph of

$$f(x) = \frac{2x - 1}{x}$$

and state its domain.

Solution

y-intercept:	None, because $x = 0$ is not in the domain
x-intercept:	$\left(\frac{1}{2}, 0\right)$, because $2x - 1 = 0$
Vertical asymptote:	$x = 0$, zero of denominator
Horizontal asymptote:	$y = 2$, because degree of $N(x) =$ degree of $D(x)$
Additional points:	

Test interval	Representative x-value	Value of f	Sign	Point on graph
$(-\infty, 0)$	-1	$f(-1) = 3$	Positive	$(-1, 3)$
$\left(0, \frac{1}{2}\right)$	$\frac{1}{4}$	$f\left(\frac{1}{4}\right) = -2$	Negative	$\left(\frac{1}{4}, -2\right)$
$\left(\frac{1}{2}, \infty\right)$	4	$f(4) = 1.75$	Positive	$(4, 1.75)$

By plotting the intercepts, asymptotes, and a few additional points, you can obtain the graph shown in Figure 2.41. The domain of f is all real numbers x except $x = 0$.

✓CHECKPOINT   Now try Exercise 31.

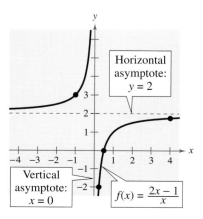

Horizontal asymptote: $y = 2$

Vertical asymptote: $x = 0$

$f(x) = \dfrac{2x - 1}{x}$

FIGURE 2.41

Example 5   Sketching the Graph of a Rational Function

Sketch the graph of $f(x) = x/(x^2 - x - 2)$.

Solution

Factoring the denominator, you have $f(x) = \dfrac{x}{(x + 1)(x - 2)}$.

y-intercept:	$(0, 0)$, because $f(0) = 0$
x-intercept:	$(0, 0)$
Vertical asymptotes:	$x = -1$, $x = 2$, zeros of denominator
Horizontal asymptote:	$y = 0$, because degree of $N(x)$ < degree of $D(x)$

Additional points:

Test interval	Representative x-value	Value of f	Sign	Point on graph
$(-\infty, -1)$	-3	$f(-3) = -0.3$	Negative	$(-3, -0.3)$
$(-1, 0)$	-0.5	$f(-0.5) = 0.4$	Positive	$(-0.5, 0.4)$
$(0, 2)$	1	$f(1) = -0.5$	Negative	$(1, -0.5)$
$(2, \infty)$	3	$f(3) = 0.75$	Positive	$(3, 0.75)$

The graph is shown in Figure 2.42.

✓CHECKPOINT   Now try Exercise 35.

Vertical asymptote: $x = -1$

Vertical asymptote: $x = 2$

Horizontal asymptote: $y = 0$

$f(x) = \dfrac{x}{x^2 - x - 2}$

FIGURE 2.42

STUDY TIP

If you are unsure of the shape of a portion of the graph of a rational function, plot some additional points. Also note that when the numerator and the denominator of a rational function have a common factor, the graph of the function has a *hole* at the zero of the common factor (see Example 6).

Example 6   A Rational Function with Common Factors

Sketch the graph of $f(x) = (x^2 - 9)/(x^2 - 2x - 3)$.

Solution

By factoring the numerator and denominator, you have

$$f(x) = \frac{x^2 - 9}{x^2 - 2x - 3} = \frac{(x - 3)(x + 3)}{(x - 3)(x + 1)} = \frac{x + 3}{x + 1}, \quad x \neq 3.$$

y-intercept:	$(0, 3)$, because $f(0) = 3$
x-intercept:	$(-3, 0)$, because $f(-3) = 0$
Vertical asymptote:	$x = -1$, zero of (simplified) denominator
Horizontal asymptote:	$y = 1$, because degree of $N(x)$ = degree of $D(x)$

Additional points:

Test interval	Representative x-value	Value of f	Sign	Point on graph
$(-\infty, -3)$	-4	$f(-4) = 0.33$	Positive	$(-4, -0.33)$
$(-3, -1)$	-2	$f(-2) = -1$	Negative	$(-2, -1)$
$(-1, \infty)$	2	$f(2) = 1.67$	Positive	$(2, 1.67)$

The graph is shown in Figure 2.43. Notice that there is a hole in the graph at $x = 3$ because the function is not defined when $x = 3$.

✓CHECKPOINT   Now try Exercise 41.

Horizontal asymptote: $y = 1$

$f(x) = \dfrac{x^2 - 9}{x^2 - 2x - 3}$

Vertical asymptote: $x = -1$

FIGURE 2.43   HOLE AT x = 3

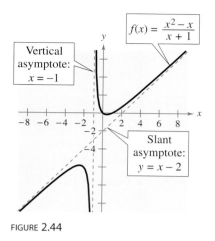

Vertical asymptote: $x = -1$

$f(x) = \dfrac{x^2 - x}{x + 1}$

Slant asymptote: $y = x - 2$

FIGURE 2.44

Slant Asymptotes

Consider a rational function whose denominator is of degree 1 or greater. If the degree of the numerator is exactly *one more* than the degree of the denominator, the graph of the function has a **slant** (or **oblique**) **asymptote.** For example, the graph of

$$f(x) = \frac{x^2 - x}{x + 1}$$

has a slant asymptote, as shown in Figure 2.44. To find the equation of a slant asymptote, use long division. For instance, by dividing $x + 1$ into $x^2 - x$, you obtain

$$f(x) = \frac{x^2 - x}{x + 1} = \underbrace{x - 2}_{\substack{\text{Slant asymptote} \\ (y = x - 2)}} + \frac{2}{x + 1}.$$

As x increases or decreases without bound, the remainder term $2/(x + 1)$ approaches 0, so the graph of f approaches the line $y = x - 2$, as shown in Figure 2.44.

Example 7 A Rational Function with a Slant Asymptote

Sketch the graph of $f(x) = (x^2 - x - 2)/(x - 1)$.

Solution

Factoring the numerator as $(x - 2)(x + 1)$ allows you to recognize the *x*-intercepts. Using long division

$$f(x) = \frac{x^2 - x - 2}{x - 1} = x - \frac{2}{x - 1}$$

allows you to recognize that the line $y = x$ is a slant asymptote of the graph.

y-intercept:	$(0, 2)$, because $f(0) = 2$
x-intercepts:	$(-1, 0)$ and $(2, 0)$
Vertical asymptote:	$x = 1$, zero of denominator
Slant asymptote:	$y = x$

Additional points:

Test interval	Representative x-value	Value of f	Sign	Point on graph
$(-\infty, -1)$	-2	$f(-2) = -1.33$	Negative	$(-2, -1.33)$
$(-1, 1)$	0.5	$f(0.5) = 4.5$	Positive	$(0.5, 4.5)$
$(1, 2)$	1.5	$f(1.5) = -2.5$	Negative	$(1.5, -2.5)$
$(2, \infty)$	3	$f(3) = 2$	Positive	$(3, 2)$

The graph is shown in Figure 2.45.

✓**CHECKPOINT**   Now try Exercise 61.

Slant asymptote: $y = x$

Vertical asymptote: $x = 1$

$f(x) = \dfrac{x^2 - x - 2}{x - 1}$

FIGURE 2.45

Applications

There are many examples of asymptotic behavior in real life. For instance, Example 8 shows how a vertical asymptote can be used to analyze the cost of removing pollutants from smokestack emissions.

Example 8   Cost-Benefit Model

A utility company burns coal to generate electricity. The cost C (in dollars) of removing $p\%$ of the smokestack pollutants is given by

$$C = \frac{80{,}000p}{100 - p}$$

for $0 \le p < 100$. Sketch the graph of this function. You are a member of a state legislature considering a law that would require utility companies to remove 90% of the pollutants from their smokestack emissions. The current law requires 85% removal. How much additional cost would the utility company incur as a result of the new law?

Solution

The graph of this function is shown in Figure 2.46. Note that the graph has a vertical asymptote at $p = 100$. Because the current law requires 85% removal, the current cost to the utility company is

$$C = \frac{80{,}000(85)}{100 - 85} \approx \$453{,}333. \qquad \text{Evaluate } C \text{ when } p = 85.$$

If the new law increases the percent removal to 90%, the cost will be

$$C = \frac{80{,}000(90)}{100 - 90} = \$720{,}000. \qquad \text{Evaluate } C \text{ when } p = 90.$$

So, the new law would require the utility company to spend an additional

$$720{,}000 - 453{,}333 = \$266{,}667. \qquad \begin{array}{l}\text{Subtract 85\% removal cost}\\ \text{from 90\% removal cost.}\end{array}$$

FIGURE 2.46

✓CHECKPOINT   Now try Exercise 73.

Example 9   Finding a Minimum Area

A rectangular page is designed to contain 48 square inches of print. The margins at the top and bottom of the page are each 1 inch deep. The margins on each side are $1\frac{1}{2}$ inches wide. What should the dimensions of the page be so that the least amount of paper is used?

FIGURE 2.47

Graphical Solution

Let A be the area to be minimized. From Figure 2.47, you can write

$$A = (x + 3)(y + 2).$$

The printed area inside the margins is modeled by $48 = xy$ or $y = 48/x$. To find the minimum area, rewrite the equation for A in terms of just one variable by substituting $48/x$ for y.

$$A = (x + 3)\left(\frac{48}{x} + 2\right)$$

$$= \frac{(x + 3)(48 + 2x)}{x}, \quad x > 0$$

The graph of this rational function is shown in Figure 2.48. Because x represents the width of the printed area, you need consider only the portion of the graph for which x is positive. Using a graphing utility, you can approximate the minimum value of A to occur when $x \approx 8.5$ inches. The corresponding value of y is $48/8.5 \approx 5.6$ inches. So, the dimensions should be

$$x + 3 \approx 11.5 \text{ inches} \quad \text{by} \quad y + 2 \approx 7.6 \text{ inches}.$$

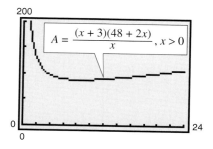

FIGURE 2.48

Numerical Solution

Let A be the area to be minimized. From Figure 2.47, you can write

$$A = (x + 3)(y + 2).$$

The printed area inside the margins is modeled by $48 = xy$ or $y = 48/x$. To find the minimum area, rewrite the equation for A in terms of just one variable by substituting $48/x$ for y.

$$A = (x + 3)\left(\frac{48}{x} + 2\right)$$

$$= \frac{(x + 3)(48 + 2x)}{x}, \quad x > 0$$

Use the *table* feature of a graphing utility to create a table of values for the function

$$y_1 = \frac{(x + 3)(48 + 2x)}{x}$$

beginning at $x = 1$. From the table, you can see that the minimum value of y_1 occurs when x is somewhere between 8 and 9, as shown in Figure 2.49. To approximate the minimum value of y_1 to one decimal place, change the table so that it starts at $x = 8$ and increases by 0.1. The minimum value of y_1 occurs when $x \approx 8.5$, as shown in Figure 2.50. The corresponding value of y is $48/8.5 \approx 5.6$ inches. So, the dimensions should be $x + 3 \approx 11.5$ inches by $y + 2 \approx 7.6$ inches.

X	Y₁
6	90
7	88.571
8	88
9	88
10	88.4
11	89.091
12	90
X=8	

FIGURE 2.49

X	Y₁
8.2	87.961
8.3	87.949
8.4	87.943
8.5	87.941
8.6	87.944
8.7	87.952
8.8	87.964
X=8.5	

FIGURE 2.50

✓CHECKPOINT   Now try Exercise 77.

If you go on to take a course in calculus, you will learn an analytic technique for finding the exact value of x that produces a minimum area. In this case, that value is $x = 6\sqrt{2} \approx 8.485$.

2.6 | Exercises

VOCABULARY CHECK: Fill in the blanks.

1. Functions of the form $f(x) = N(x)/D(x)$, where $N(x)$ and $D(x)$ are polynomials and $D(x)$ is not the zero polynomial, are called _____ _____.

2. If $f(x) \to \pm\infty$ as $x \to a$ from the left or the right, then $x = a$ is a _____ _____ of the graph of f.

3. If $f(x) \to b$ as $x \to \pm\infty$, then $y = b$ is a _____ _____ of the graph of f.

4. For the rational function given by $f(x) = N(x)/D(x)$, if the degree of $N(x)$ is exactly one more than the degree of $D(x)$, then the graph of f has a _____ (or oblique) _____.

PREREQUISITE SKILLS REVIEW: Practice and review algebra skills needed for this section at **www.Eduspace.com.**

In Exercises 1–4, (a) complete each table for the function, (b) determine the vertical and horizontal asymptotes of the graph of the function, and (c) find the domain of the function.

x	$f(x)$
0.5	
0.9	
0.99	
0.999	

x	$f(x)$
1.5	
1.1	
1.01	
1.001	

x	$f(x)$
5	
10	
100	
1000	

1. $f(x) = \dfrac{1}{x-1}$

2. $f(x) = \dfrac{5x}{x-1}$

3. $f(x) = \dfrac{3x^2}{x^2-1}$

4. $f(x) = \dfrac{4x}{x^2-1}$

In Exercises 5–12, find the domain of the function and identify any horizontal and vertical asymptotes.

5. $f(x) = \dfrac{1}{x^2}$

6. $f(x) = \dfrac{4}{(x-2)^3}$

7. $f(x) = \dfrac{2+x}{2-x}$

8. $f(x) = \dfrac{1-5x}{1+2x}$

9. $f(x) = \dfrac{x^3}{x^2-1}$

10. $f(x) = \dfrac{2x^2}{x+1}$

11. $f(x) = \dfrac{3x^2+1}{x^2+x+9}$

12. $f(x) = \dfrac{3x^2+x-5}{x^2+1}$

In Exercises 13–16, match the rational function with its graph. [The graphs are labeled (a), (b), (c), and (d).]

(a)

(b)

(c)

(d)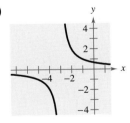

13. $f(x) = \dfrac{2}{x+3}$

14. $f(x) = \dfrac{1}{x-5}$

15. $f(x) = \dfrac{x-1}{x-4}$

16. $f(x) = -\dfrac{x+2}{x+4}$

In Exercises 17–20, find the zeros (if any) of the rational function.

17. $g(x) = \dfrac{x^2-1}{x+1}$

18. $h(x) = 2 + \dfrac{5}{x^2+2}$

19. $f(x) = 1 - \dfrac{3}{x-3}$

20. $g(x) = \dfrac{x^3-8}{x^2+1}$

In Exercises 21–26, find the domain of the function and identify any horizontal and vertical asymptotes.

21. $f(x) = \dfrac{x - 4}{x^2 - 16}$

22. $f(x) = \dfrac{x + 3}{x^2 - 9}$

23. $f(x) = \dfrac{x^2 - 1}{x^2 - 2x - 3}$

24. $f(x) = \dfrac{x^2 - 4}{x^2 - 3x + 2}$

25. $f(x) = \dfrac{x^2 - 3x - 4}{2x^2 + x - 1}$

26. $f(x) = \dfrac{6x^2 - 11x + 3}{6x^2 - 7x - 3}$

In Exercises 27–46, (a) state the domain of the function, (b) identify all intercepts, (c) find any vertical and horizontal asymptotes, and (d) plot additional solution points as needed to sketch the graph of the rational function.

27. $f(x) = \dfrac{1}{x + 2}$

28. $f(x) = \dfrac{1}{x - 3}$

29. $h(x) = \dfrac{-1}{x + 2}$

30. $g(x) = \dfrac{1}{3 - x}$

31. $C(x) = \dfrac{5 + 2x}{1 + x}$

32. $P(x) = \dfrac{1 - 3x}{1 - x}$

33. $f(x) = \dfrac{x^2}{x^2 + 9}$

34. $f(t) = \dfrac{1 - 2t}{t}$

35. $g(s) = \dfrac{s}{s^2 + 1}$

36. $f(x) = -\dfrac{1}{(x - 2)^2}$

37. $h(x) = \dfrac{x^2 - 5x + 4}{x^2 - 4}$

38. $g(x) = \dfrac{x^2 - 2x - 8}{x^2 - 9}$

39. $f(x) = \dfrac{2x^2 - 5x - 3}{x^3 - 2x^2 - x + 2}$

40. $f(x) = \dfrac{x^2 - x - 2}{x^3 - 2x^2 - 5x + 6}$

41. $f(x) = \dfrac{x^2 + 3x}{x^2 + x - 6}$

42. $f(x) = \dfrac{5(x + 4)}{x^2 + x - 12}$

43. $f(x) = \dfrac{2x^2 - 5x + 2}{2x^2 - x - 6}$

44. $f(x) = \dfrac{3x^2 - 8x + 4}{2x^2 - 3x - 2}$

45. $f(t) = \dfrac{t^2 - 1}{t + 1}$

46. $f(x) = \dfrac{x^2 - 16}{x - 4}$

Analytical, Numerical, and Graphical Analysis In Exercises 47–50, do the following.

(a) Determine the domains of f and g.

(b) Simplify f and find any vertical asymptotes of the graph of f.

(c) Compare the functions by completing the table.

 (d) Use a graphing utility to graph f and g in the same viewing window.

 (e) Explain why the graphing utility may not show the difference in the domains of f and g.

47. $f(x) = \dfrac{x^2 - 1}{x + 1}, \quad g(x) = x - 1$

x	-3	-2	-1.5	-1	-0.5	0	1
$f(x)$							
$g(x)$							

48. $f(x) = \dfrac{x^2(x - 2)}{x^2 - 2x}, \quad g(x) = x$

x	-1	0	1	1.5	2	2.5	3
$f(x)$							
$g(x)$							

49. $f(x) = \dfrac{x - 2}{x^2 - 2x}, \quad g(x) = \dfrac{1}{x}$

x	-0.5	0	0.5	1	1.5	2	3
$f(x)$							
$g(x)$							

50. $f(x) = \dfrac{2x - 6}{x^2 - 7x + 12}, \quad g(x) = \dfrac{2}{x - 4}$

x	0	1	2	3	4	5	6
$f(x)$							
$g(x)$							

In Exercises 51–64, (a) state the domain of the function, (b) identify all intercepts, (c) identify any vertical and slant asymptotes, and (d) plot additional solution points as needed to sketch the graph of the rational function.

51. $h(x) = \dfrac{x^2 - 4}{x}$

52. $g(x) = \dfrac{x^2 + 5}{x}$

53. $f(x) = \dfrac{2x^2 + 1}{x}$

54. $f(x) = \dfrac{1 - x^2}{x}$

55. $g(x) = \dfrac{x^2 + 1}{x}$

56. $h(x) = \dfrac{x^2}{x - 1}$

57. $f(t) = -\dfrac{t^2 + 1}{t + 5}$

58. $f(x) = \dfrac{x^2}{3x + 1}$

59. $f(x) = \dfrac{x^3}{x^2 - 1}$

60. $g(x) = \dfrac{x^3}{2x^2 - 8}$

61. $f(x) = \dfrac{x^2 - x + 1}{x - 1}$

62. $f(x) = \dfrac{2x^2 - 5x + 5}{x - 2}$

63. $f(x) = \dfrac{2x^3 - x^2 - 2x + 1}{x^2 + 3x + 2}$

64. $f(x) = \dfrac{2x^3 + x^2 - 8x - 4}{x^2 - 3x + 2}$

In Exercises 65–68, use a graphing utility to graph the rational function. Give the domain of the function and identify any asymptotes. Then zoom out sufficiently far so that the graph appears as a line. Identify the line.

65. $f(x) = \dfrac{x^2 + 5x + 8}{x + 3}$

66. $f(x) = \dfrac{2x^2 + x}{x + 1}$

67. $g(x) = \dfrac{1 + 3x^2 - x^3}{x^2}$

68. $h(x) = \dfrac{12 - 2x - x^2}{2(4 + x)}$

Graphical Reasoning   In Exercises 69–72, (a) use the graph to determine any x-intercepts of the graph of the rational function and (b) set y = 0 and solve the resulting equation to confirm your result in part (a).

69. $y = \dfrac{x + 1}{x - 3}$

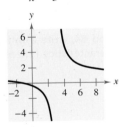

70. $y = \dfrac{2x}{x - 3}$

71. $y = \dfrac{1}{x} - x$

72. $y = x - 3 + \dfrac{2}{x}$

73. *Pollution*   The cost C (in millions of dollars) of removing $p\%$ of the industrial and municipal pollutants discharged into a river is given by

$$C = \dfrac{255p}{100 - p}, \quad 0 \le p < 100.$$

(a) Use a graphing utility to graph the cost function.

(b) Find the costs of removing 10%, 40%, and 75% of the pollutants.

(c) According to this model, would it be possible to remove 100% of the pollutants? Explain.

74. *Recycling*   In a pilot project, a rural township is given recycling bins for separating and storing recyclable products. The cost C (in dollars) for supplying bins to $p\%$ of the population is given by

$$C = \dfrac{25{,}000p}{100 - p}, \quad 0 \le p < 100.$$

(a) Use a graphing utility to graph the cost function.

(b) Find the costs of supplying bins to 15%, 50%, and 90% of the population.

(c) According to this model, would it be possible to supply bins to 100% of the residents? Explain.

75. *Population Growth*   The game commission introduces 100 deer into newly acquired state game lands. The population N of the herd is modeled by

$$N = \dfrac{20(5 + 3t)}{1 + 0.04t}, \quad t \ge 0$$

where t is the time in years (see figure).

(a) Find the populations when $t = 5$, $t = 10$, and $t = 25$.

(b) What is the limiting size of the herd as time increases?

76. *Concentration of a Mixture*   A 1000-liter tank contains 50 liters of a 25% brine solution. You add x liters of a 75% brine solution to the tank.

(a) Show that the concentration C, the proportion of brine to total solution, in the final mixture is

$$C = \dfrac{3x + 50}{4(x + 50)}.$$

(b) Determine the domain of the function based on the physical constraints of the problem.

(c) Sketch a graph of the concentration function.

(d) As the tank is filled, what happens to the rate at which the concentration of brine is increasing? What percent does the concentration of brine appear to approach?

77. Page Design A page that is x inches wide and y inches high contains 30 square inches of print. The top and bottom margins are 1 inch deep and the margins on each side are 2 inches wide (see figure).

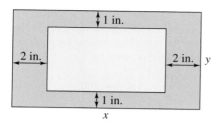

(a) Show that the total area A on the page is

$$A = \frac{2x(x + 11)}{x - 4}.$$

(b) Determine the domain of the function based on the physical constraints of the problem.

 (c) Use a graphing utility to graph the area function and approximate the page size for which the least amount of paper will be used. Verify your answer numerically using the *table* feature of the graphing utility.

78. Page Design A rectangular page is designed to contain 64 square inches of print. The margins at the top and bottom of the page are each 1 inch deep. The margins on each side are $1\frac{1}{2}$ inches wide. What should the dimensions of the page be so that the least amount of paper is used?

Model It

79. Average Speed A driver averaged 50 miles per hour on the round trip between Akron, Ohio, and Columbus, Ohio, 100 miles away. The average speeds for going and returning were x and y miles per hour, respectively.

(a) Show that $y = \dfrac{25x}{x - 25}$.

(b) Determine the vertical and horizontal asymptotes of the graph of the function.

 (c) Use a graphing utility to graph the function.

(d) Complete the table.

x	30	35	40	45	50	55	60
y							

(e) Are the results in the table what you expected? Explain.

(f) Is it possible to average 20 miles per hour in one direction and still average 50 miles per hour on the round trip? Explain.

---

80. Sales The sales S (in millions of dollars) for the Yankee Candle Company in the years 1998 through 2003 are shown in the table. (Source: The Yankee Candle Company)

1998 184.5	1999 256.6	2000 338.8
2001 379.8	2002 444.8	2003 508.6

A model for these data is given by

$$S = \frac{5.816t^2 - 130.68}{0.004t^2 + 1.00}, \quad 8 \le t \le 13$$

where t represents the year, with $t = 8$ corresponding to 1998.

 (a) Use a graphing utility to plot the data and graph the model in the same viewing window. How well does the model fit the data?

(b) Use the model to estimate the sales for the Yankee Candle Company in 2008.

(c) Would this model be useful for estimating sales after 2008? Explain.

Synthesis

True or False? In Exercises 81 and 82, determine whether the statement is true or false. Justify your answer.

81. A polynomial can have infinitely many vertical asymptotes.

82. The graph of a rational function can never cross one of its asymptotes.

Think About It In Exercises 83 and 84, write a rational function f that has the specified characteristics. (There are many correct answers.)

83. Vertical asymptote: None
  Horizontal asymptote: $y = 2$

84. Vertical asymptote: $x = -2$, $x = 1$
  Horizontal asymptote: None

Skills Review

In Exercises 85–88, completely factor the expression.

85. $x^2 - 15x + 56$

86. $3x^2 + 23x - 36$

87. $x^3 - 5x^2 + 4x - 20$

88. $x^3 + 6x^2 - 2x - 12$

In Exercises 89–92, solve the inequality and graph the solution on the real number line.

89. $10 - 3x \le 0$

90. $5 - 2x > 5(x + 1)$

91. $|4(x - 2)| < 20$

92. $\frac{1}{2}|2x + 3| \ge 5$

93. Make a Decision To work an extended application analyzing the total manpower of the Department of Defense, visit this text's website at *college.hmco.com*. (Data Source: U.S. Department of Defense)

2.7 Nonlinear Inequalities

What you should learn

• Solve polynomial inequalities.
• Solve rational inequalities.
• Use inequalities to model and solve real-life problems.

Why you should learn it

Inequalities can be used to model and solve real-life problems. For instance, in Exercise 73 on page 205, a polynomial inequality is used to model the percent of households that own a television and have cable in the United States.

Polynomial Inequalities

To solve a polynomial inequality such as $x^2 - 2x - 3 < 0$, you can use the fact that a polynomial can change signs only at its **zeros** (the x-values that make the polynomial equal to zero). Between two consecutive zeros, a polynomial must be entirely positive or entirely negative. This means that when the real zeros of a polynomial are put in order, they divide the real number line into intervals in which the polynomial has no sign changes. These zeros are the **critical numbers** of the inequality, and the resulting intervals are the **test intervals** for the inequality. For instance, the polynomial above factors as

$$x^2 - 2x - 3 = (x + 1)(x - 3)$$

and has two zeros, $x = -1$ and $x = 3$. These zeros divide the real number line into three test intervals:

$$(-\infty, -1), \quad (-1, 3), \quad \text{and} \quad (3, \infty). \quad \text{(See Figure 2.51.)}$$

So, to solve the inequality $x^2 - 2x - 3 < 0$, you need only test one value from each of these test intervals to determine whether the value satisfies the original inequality. If so, you can conclude that the interval is a solution of the inequality.

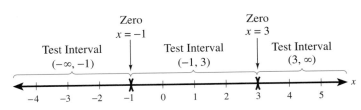

FIGURE 2.51 *Three test intervals for $x^2 - 2x - 3$*

You can use the same basic approach to determine the test intervals for any polynomial.

Finding Test Intervals for a Polynomial

To determine the intervals on which the values of a polynomial are entirely negative or entirely positive, use the following steps.

1. Find all real zeros of the polynomial, and arrange the zeros in increasing order (from smallest to largest). These zeros are the critical numbers of the polynomial.

2. Use the critical numbers of the polynomial to determine its test intervals.

3. Choose one representative x-value in each test interval and evaluate the polynomial at that value. If the value of the polynomial is negative, the polynomial will have negative values for every x-value in the interval. If the value of the polynomial is positive, the polynomial will have positive values for every x-value in the interval.

| Example 1 | Solving a Polynomial Inequality |

Solve

$$x^2 - x - 6 < 0.$$

Solution

By factoring the polynomial as

$$x^2 - x - 6 = (x + 2)(x - 3)$$

you can see that the critical numbers are $x = -2$ and $x = 3$. So, the polynomial's test intervals are

$$(-\infty, -2), \quad (-2, 3), \quad \text{and} \quad (3, \infty). \qquad \text{Test intervals}$$

In each test interval, choose a representative x-value and evaluate the polynomial.

Test Interval	x-Value	Polynomial Value	Conclusion
$(-\infty, -2)$	$x = -3$	$(-3)^2 - (-3) - 6 = 6$	Positive
$(-2, 3)$	$x = 0$	$(0)^2 - (0) - 6 = -6$	Negative
$(3, \infty)$	$x = 4$	$(4)^2 - (4) - 6 = 6$	Positive

From this you can conclude that the inequality is satisfied for all x-values in $(-2, 3)$. This implies that the solution of the inequality $x^2 - x - 6 < 0$ is the interval $(-2, 3)$, as shown in Figure 2.52. Note that the original inequality contains a less than symbol. This means that the solution set does not contain the endpoints of the test interval $(-2, 3)$.

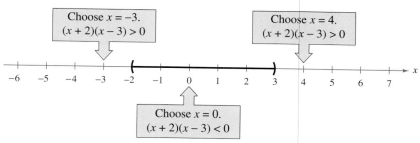

FIGURE 2.52

✓CHECKPOINT   Now try Exercise 13.

As with linear inequalities, you can check the reasonableness of a solution by substituting x-values into the original inequality. For instance, to check the solution found in Example 1, try substituting several x-values from the interval $(-2, 3)$ into the inequality

$$x^2 - x - 6 < 0.$$

Regardless of which x-values you choose, the inequality should be satisfied. You can also use a graph to check the result of Example 1. Sketch the graph of $y = x^2 - x - 6$, as shown in Figure 2.53. Notice that the graph is below the x-axis on the interval $(-2, 3)$.

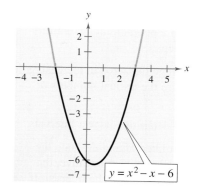

FIGURE 2.53

In Example 1, the polynomial inequality was given in general form (with the polynomial on one side and zero on the other). Whenever this is not the case, you should begin the solution process by writing the inequality in general form.

Example 2 Solving a Polynomial Inequality

Solve $2x^3 - 3x^2 - 32x > -48$.

Solution

Begin by writing the inequality in general form.

$$2x^3 - 3x^2 - 32x > -48 \qquad \text{Write original inequality.}$$

$$2x^3 - 3x^2 - 32x + 48 > 0 \qquad \text{Write in general form.}$$

$$(x - 4)(x + 4)(2x - 3) > 0 \qquad \text{Factor.}$$

The critical numbers are $x = -4$, $x = \frac{3}{2}$, and $x = 4$, and the test intervals are $(-\infty, -4)$, $\left(-4, \frac{3}{2}\right)$, $\left(\frac{3}{2}, 4\right)$, and $(4, \infty)$.

Test Interval	x-Value	Polynomial Value	Conclusion
$(-\infty, -4)$	$x = -5$	$2(-5)^3 - 3(-5)^2 - 32(-5) + 48$	Negative
$\left(-4, \frac{3}{2}\right)$	$x = 0$	$2(0)^3 - 3(0)^2 - 32(0) + 48$	Positive
$\left(\frac{3}{2}, 4\right)$	$x = 2$	$2(2)^3 - 3(2)^2 - 32(2) + 48$	Negative
$(4, \infty)$	$x = 5$	$2(5)^3 - 3(5)^2 - 32(5) + 48$	Positive

From this you can conclude that the inequality is satisfied on the open intervals $\left(-4, \frac{3}{2}\right)$ and $(4, \infty)$. Therefore, the solution set consists of all real numbers in the intervals $\left(-4, \frac{3}{2}\right)$ and $(4, \infty)$, as shown in Figure 2.54.

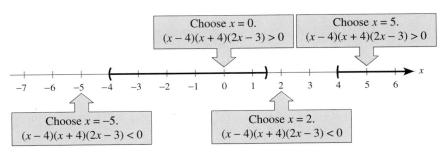

FIGURE **2.54**

✓CHECKPOINT   Now try Exercise 21.

When solving a polynomial inequality, be sure you have accounted for the particular type of inequality symbol given in the inequality. For instance, in Example 2, note that the original inequality contained a "greater than" symbol and the solution consisted of two open intervals. If the original inequality had been

$$2x^3 - 3x^2 - 32x \geq -48$$

the solution would have consisted of the closed interval $\left[-4, \frac{3}{2}\right]$ and the interval $[4, \infty)$.

STUDY TIP

You may find it easier to determine the sign of a polynomial from its *factored* form. For instance, in Example 2, if the test value $x = 2$ is substituted into the factored form

$$(x - 4)(x + 4)(2x - 3)$$

you can see that the sign pattern of the factors is

$$(-)(+)(+)$$

which yields a negative result. Try using the factored forms of the polynomials to determine the signs of the polynomials in the test intervals of the other examples in this section.

Each of the polynomial inequalities in Examples 1 and 2 has a solution set that consists of a single interval or the union of two intervals. When solving the exercises for this section, watch for unusual solution sets, as illustrated in Example 3.

Example 3   Unusual Solution Sets

a. The solution set of the following inequality consists of the entire set of real numbers, $(-\infty, \infty)$. In other words, the value of the quadratic $x^2 + 2x + 4$ is positive for every real value of x.

$$x^2 + 2x + 4 > 0$$

b. The solution set of the following inequality consists of the single real number $\{-1\}$, because the quadratic $x^2 + 2x + 1$ has only one critical number, $x = -1$, and it is the only value that satisfies the inequality.

$$x^2 + 2x + 1 \le 0$$

c. The solution set of the following inequality is empty. In other words, the quadratic $x^2 + 3x + 5$ is not less than zero for any value of x.

$$x^2 + 3x + 5 < 0$$

d. The solution set of the following inequality consists of all real numbers except $x = 2$. In interval notation, this solution set can be written as $(-\infty, 2) \cup (2, \infty)$.

$$x^2 - 4x + 4 > 0$$

✓**CHECKPOINT**   Now try Exercise 25.

Exploration

You can use a graphing utility to verify the results in Example 3. For instance, the graph of $y = x^2 + 2x + 4$ is shown below. Notice that the y-values are greater than 0 for all values of x, as stated in Example 3(a). Use the graphing utility to graph the following:

$$y = x^2 + 2x + 1 \qquad y = x^2 + 3x + 5 \qquad y = x^2 - 4x + 4$$

Explain how you can use the graphs to verify the results of parts (b), (c), and (d) of Example 3.

Rational Inequalities

The concepts of critical numbers and test intervals can be extended to rational inequalities. To do this, use the fact that the value of a rational expression can change sign only at its *zeros* (the x-values for which its numerator is zero) and its *undefined values* (the x-values for which its denominator is zero). These two types of numbers make up the *critical numbers* of a rational inequality. When solving a rational inequality, begin by writing the inequality in general form with the rational expression on the left and zero on the right.

Example 4   Solving a Rational Inequality

Solve $\dfrac{2x - 7}{x - 5} \le 3$.

Solution

$$\frac{2x - 7}{x - 5} \le 3 \qquad\qquad \text{Write original inequality.}$$

$$\frac{2x - 7}{x - 5} - 3 \le 0 \qquad\qquad \text{Write in general form.}$$

$$\frac{2x - 7 - 3x + 15}{x - 5} \le 0 \qquad\qquad \text{Find the LCD and add fractions.}$$

$$\frac{-x + 8}{x - 5} \le 0 \qquad\qquad \text{Simplify.}$$

Critical numbers: $x = 5, x = 8$ Zeros and undefined values of rational expression

Test intervals: $(-\infty, 5), (5, 8), (8, \infty)$

Test: Is $\dfrac{-x + 8}{x - 5} \le 0$?

After testing these intervals, as shown in Figure 2.55, you can see that the inequality is satisfied on the open intervals $(-\infty, 5)$ and $(8, \infty)$. Moreover, because $(-x + 8)/(x - 5) = 0$ when $x = 8$, you can conclude that the solution set consists of all real numbers in the intervals $(-\infty, 5) \cup [8, \infty)$. (Be sure to use a closed interval to indicate that x can equal 8.)

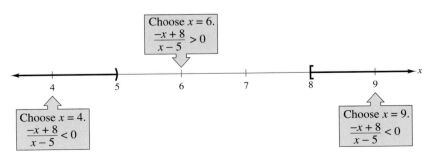

FIGURE 2.55

✓CHECKPOINT   Now try Exercise 39.

Applications

One common application of inequalities comes from business and involves profit, revenue, and cost. The formula that relates these three quantities is

$$\text{Profit} = \text{Revenue} - \text{Cost}$$
$$P = R - C.$$

Example 5 Increasing the Profit for a Product

The marketing department of a calculator manufacturer has determined that the demand for a new model of calculator is

$$p = 100 - 0.00001x, \qquad 0 \le x \le 10{,}000{,}000 \qquad \text{Demand equation}$$

where p is the price per calculator (in dollars) and x represents the number of calculators sold. (If this model is accurate, no one would be willing to pay $100 for the calculator. At the other extreme, the company couldn't sell more than 10 million calculators.) The revenue for selling x calculators is

$$R = xp = x(100 - 0.00001x) \qquad \text{Revenue equation}$$

as shown in Figure 2.56. The total cost of producing x calculators is $10 per calculator plus a development cost of $2,500,000. So, the total cost is

$$C = 10x + 2{,}500{,}000. \qquad \text{Cost equation}$$

What price should the company charge per calculator to obtain a profit of at least $190,000,000?

Solution

Verbal Model: $\quad \text{Profit} = \text{Revenue} - \text{Cost}$

Equation: $\quad P = R - C$

$$P = 100x - 0.00001x^2 - (10x + 2{,}500{,}000)$$
$$P = -0.00001x^2 + 90x - 2{,}500{,}000$$

To answer the question, solve the inequality

$$P \ge 190{,}000{,}000$$
$$-0.00001x^2 + 90x - 2{,}500{,}000 \ge 190{,}000{,}000.$$

When you write the inequality in general form, find the critical numbers and the test intervals, and then test a value in each test interval, you can find the solution to be

$$3{,}500{,}000 \le x \le 5{,}500{,}000$$

as shown in Figure 2.57. Substituting the x-values in the original price equation shows that prices of

$$\$45.00 \le p \le \$65.00$$

will yield a profit of at least $190,000,000.

✓**CHECKPOINT** Now try Exercise 71.

FIGURE **2.56**

FIGURE **2.57**

Another common application of inequalities is finding the domain of an expression that involves a square root, as shown in Example 6.

Example 6   Finding the Domain of an Expression

Find the domain of $\sqrt{64 - 4x^2}$.

Algebraic Solution

Remember that the domain of an expression is the set of all x-values for which the expression is defined. Because $\sqrt{64 - 4x^2}$ is defined (has real values) only if $64 - 4x^2$ is nonnegative, the domain is given by $64 - 4x^2 \geq 0$.

$$64 - 4x^2 \geq 0 \qquad \text{Write in general form.}$$
$$16 - x^2 \geq 0 \qquad \text{Divide each side by 4.}$$
$$(4 - x)(4 + x) \geq 0 \qquad \text{Write in factored form.}$$

So, the inequality has two critical numbers: $x = -4$ and $x = 4$. You can use these two numbers to test the inequality as follows.

Critical numbers: $x = -4, x = 4$

Test intervals: $(-\infty, -4), (-4, 4), (4, \infty)$

Test: For what values of x is $\sqrt{64 - 4x^2} \geq 0$?

A test shows that the inequality is satisfied in the *closed interval* $[-4, 4]$. So, the domain of the expression $\sqrt{64 - 4x^2}$ is the interval $[-4, 4]$.

✓**CHECKPOINT**   Now try Exercise 55.

Graphical Solution

Begin by sketching the graph of the equation $y = \sqrt{64 - 4x^2}$, as shown in Figure 2.58. From the graph, you can determine that the x-values extend from -4 to 4 (including -4 and 4). So, the domain of the expression $\sqrt{64 - 4x^2}$ is the interval $[-4, 4]$.

FIGURE **2.58**

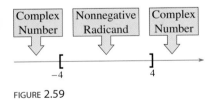

FIGURE **2.59**

To analyze a test interval, choose a representative x-value in the interval and evaluate the expression at that value. For instance, in Example 6, if you substitute any number from the interval $[-4, 4]$ into the expression $\sqrt{64 - 4x^2}$ you will obtain a nonnegative number under the radical symbol that simplifies to a real number. If you substitute any number from the intervals $(-\infty, -4)$ and $(4, \infty)$ you will obtain a complex number. It might be helpful to draw a visual representation of the intervals as shown in Figure 2.59.

WRITING ABOUT **M**ATHEMATICS

Profit Analysis   Consider the relationship

$$P = R - C$$

described on page 202. Write a paragraph discussing why it might be beneficial to solve $P < 0$ if you owned a business. Use the situation described in Example 5 to illustrate your reasoning.

2.7 | Exercises

VOCABULARY CHECK: Fill in the blanks.

1. To solve a polynomial inequality, find the _____ numbers of the polynomial, and use these numbers to create _____ _____ for the inequality.

2. The critical numbers of a rational expression are its _____ and its _____ _____.

3. The formula that relates cost, revenue, and profit is _____.

PREREQUISITE SKILLS REVIEW: Practice and review algebra skills needed for this section at **www.Eduspace.com.**

In Exercises 1–4, determine whether each value of x is a solution of the inequality.

Inequality   *Values*

1. $x^2 - 3 < 0$ (a) $x = 3$ (b) $x = 0$
          (c) $x = \frac{3}{2}$ (d) $x = -5$

2. $x^2 - x - 12 \geq 0$ (a) $x = 5$ (b) $x = 0$
          (c) $x = -4$ (d) $x = -3$

3. $\dfrac{x + 2}{x - 4} \geq 3$ (a) $x = 5$ (b) $x = 4$
          (c) $x = -\frac{9}{2}$ (d) $x = \frac{9}{2}$

4. $\dfrac{3x^2}{x^2 + 4} < 1$ (a) $x = -2$ (b) $x = -1$
          (c) $x = 0$ (d) $x = 3$

In Exercises 5–8, find the critical numbers of the expression.

5. $2x^2 - x - 6$ 6. $9x^3 - 25x^2$

7. $2 + \dfrac{3}{x - 5}$ 8. $\dfrac{x}{x + 2} - \dfrac{2}{x - 1}$

In Exercises 9–26, solve the inequality and graph the solution on the real number line.

9. $x^2 \leq 9$ 10. $x^2 < 36$

11. $(x + 2)^2 < 25$ 12. $(x - 3)^2 \geq 1$

13. $x^2 + 4x + 4 \geq 9$ 14. $x^2 - 6x + 9 < 16$

15. $x^2 + x < 6$ 16. $x^2 + 2x > 3$

17. $x^2 + 2x - 3 < 0$

18. $x^2 - 4x - 1 > 0$

19. $x^2 + 8x - 5 \geq 0$

20. $-2x^2 + 6x + 15 \leq 0$

21. $x^3 - 3x^2 - x + 3 > 0$

22. $x^3 + 2x^2 - 4x - 8 \leq 0$

23. $x^3 - 2x^2 - 9x - 2 \geq -20$

24. $2x^3 + 13x^2 - 8x - 46 \geq 6$

25. $4x^2 - 4x + 1 \leq 0$

26. $x^2 + 3x + 8 > 0$

In Exercises 27–32, solve the inequality and write the solution set in interval notation.

27. $4x^3 - 6x^2 < 0$ 28. $4x^3 - 12x^2 > 0$

29. $x^3 - 4x \geq 0$ 30. $2x^3 - x^4 \leq 0$

31. $(x - 1)^2(x + 2)^3 \geq 0$ 32. $x^4(x - 3) \leq 0$

Graphical Analysis In Exercises 33–36, use a graphing utility to graph the equation. Use the graph to approximate the values of x that satisfy each inequality.

Equation   *Inequalities*

33. $y = -x^2 + 2x + 3$ (a) $y \leq 0$ (b) $y \geq 3$

34. $y = \frac{1}{2}x^2 - 2x + 1$ (a) $y \leq 0$ (b) $y \geq 7$

35. $y = \frac{1}{8}x^3 - \frac{1}{2}x$ (a) $y \geq 0$ (b) $y \leq 6$

36. $y = x^3 - x^2 - 16x + 16$ (a) $y \leq 0$ (b) $y \geq 36$

In Exercises 37–50, solve the inequality and graph the solution on the real number line.

37. $\dfrac{1}{x} - x > 0$ 38. $\dfrac{1}{x} - 4 < 0$

39. $\dfrac{x + 6}{x + 1} - 2 < 0$ 40. $\dfrac{x + 12}{x + 2} - 3 \geq 0$

41. $\dfrac{3x - 5}{x - 5} > 4$ 42. $\dfrac{5 + 7x}{1 + 2x} < 4$

43. $\dfrac{4}{x + 5} > \dfrac{1}{2x + 3}$ 44. $\dfrac{5}{x - 6} > \dfrac{3}{x + 2}$

45. $\dfrac{1}{x - 3} \leq \dfrac{9}{4x + 3}$ 46. $\dfrac{1}{x} \geq \dfrac{1}{x + 3}$

47. $\dfrac{x^2 + 2x}{x^2 - 9} \leq 0$

48. $\dfrac{x^2 + x - 6}{x} \geq 0$

49. $\dfrac{5}{x - 1} - \dfrac{2x}{x + 1} < 1$

50. $\dfrac{3x}{x - 1} \leq \dfrac{x}{x + 4} + 3$

Graphical Analysis   In Exercises 51–54, use a graphing utility to graph the equation. Use the graph to approximate the values of *x* that satisfy each inequality.

Equation	*Inequalities*
51. $y = \dfrac{3x}{x-2}$	(a) $y \le 0$ (b) $y \ge 6$
52. $y = \dfrac{2(x-2)}{x+1}$	(a) $y \le 0$ (b) $y \ge 8$
53. $y = \dfrac{2x^2}{x^2+4}$	(a) $y \ge 1$ (b) $y \le 2$
54. $y = \dfrac{5x}{x^2+4}$	(a) $y \ge 1$ (b) $y \le 0$

In Exercises 55–60, find the domain of *x* in the expression. Use a graphing utility to verify your result.

55. $\sqrt{4-x^2}$ **56.** $\sqrt{x^2-4}$

57. $\sqrt{x^2-7x+12}$ **58.** $\sqrt{144-9x^2}$

59. $\sqrt{\dfrac{x}{x^2-2x-35}}$ **60.** $\sqrt{\dfrac{x}{x^2-9}}$

In Exercises 61–66, solve the inequality. (Round your answers to two decimal places.)

61. $0.4x^2 + 5.26 < 10.2$

62. $-1.3x^2 + 3.78 > 2.12$

63. $-0.5x^2 + 12.5x + 1.6 > 0$

64. $1.2x^2 + 4.8x + 3.1 < 5.3$

65. $\dfrac{1}{2.3x - 5.2} > 3.4$

66. $\dfrac{2}{3.1x - 3.7} > 5.8$

67. *Height of a Projectile*   A projectile is fired straight upward from ground level with an initial velocity of 160 feet per second.

(a) At what instant will it be back at ground level?

(b) When will the height exceed 384 feet?

68. *Height of a Projectile*   A projectile is fired straight upward from ground level with an initial velocity of 128 feet per second.

(a) At what instant will it be back at ground level?

(b) When will the height be less than 128 feet?

69. *Geometry*   A rectangular playing field with a perimeter of 100 meters is to have an area of at least 500 square meters. Within what bounds must the length of the rectangle lie?

70. *Geometry*   A rectangular parking lot with a perimeter of 440 feet is to have an area of at least 8000 square feet. Within what bounds must the length of the rectangle lie?

71. *Cost, Revenue, and Profit*   The revenue and cost equations for a product are

$$R = x(75 - 0.0005x) \quad \text{and} \quad C = 30x + 250{,}000$$

where *R* and *C* are measured in dollars and *x* represents the number of units sold. How many units must be sold to obtain a profit of at least $750,000? What is the price per unit?

72. *Cost, Revenue, and Profit*   The revenue and cost equations for a product are

$$R = x(50 - 0.0002x) \quad \text{and} \quad C = 12x + 150{,}000$$

where *R* and *C* are measured in dollars and *x* represents the number of units sold. How many units must be sold to obtain a profit of at least $1,650,000? What is the price per unit?

Model It

73. *Cable Television*   The percents *C* of households in the United States that owned a television and had cable from 1980 to 2003 can be modeled by

$$C = 0.0031t^3 - 0.216t^2 + 5.54t + 19.1,$$
$$0 \le t \le 23$$

where *t* is the year, with $t = 0$ corresponding to 1980.
(Source: Nielsen Media Research)

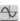 (a) Use a graphing utility to graph the equation.

(b) Complete the table to determine the year in which the percent of households that own a television and have cable will exceed 75%.

t	24	26	28	30	32	34
C						

 (c) Use the *trace* feature of a graphing utility to verify your answer to part (b).

(d) Complete the table to determine the years during which the percent of households that own a television and have cable will be between 85% and 100%.

t	36	37	38	39	40	41	42	43
C								

 (e) Use the *trace* feature of a graphing utility to verify your answer to part (d).

(f) Explain why the model may give values greater than 100% even though such values are not reasonable.

74. *Safe Load* The maximum safe load uniformly distributed over a one-foot section of a two-inch-wide wooden beam is approximated by the model Load $= 168.5d^2 - 472.1$, where d is the depth of the beam.

(a) Evaluate the model for $d = 4$, $d = 6$, $d = 8$, $d = 10$, and $d = 12$. Use the results to create a bar graph.

(b) Determine the minimum depth of the beam that will safely support a load of 2000 pounds.

75. *Resistors* When two resistors of resistances R_1 and R_2 are connected in parallel (see figure), the total resistance R satisfies the equation

$$\frac{1}{R} = \frac{1}{R_1} + \frac{1}{R_2}.$$

Find R_1 for a parallel circuit in which $R_2 = 2$ ohms and R must be at least 1 ohm.

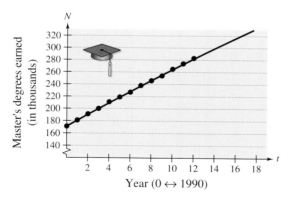

76. *Education* The numbers N (in thousands) of master's degrees earned by women in the United States from 1990 to 2002 are approximated by the model

$$N = -0.03t^2 + 9.6t + 172$$

where t represents the year, with $t = 0$ corresponding to 1990 (see figure). (Source: U.S. National Center for Education Statistics)

Year ($0 \leftrightarrow 1990$)

(a) According to the model, during what year did the number of master's degrees earned by women exceed 220,000?

(b) Use the graph to verify the result of part (a).

(c) According to the model, during what year will the number of master's degrees earned by women exceed 320,000?

(d) Use the graph to verify the result of part (c).

Synthesis

True or False? **In Exercises 77 and 78, determine whether the statement is true or false. Justify your answer.**

77. The zeros of the polynomial $x^3 - 2x^2 - 11x + 12 \geq 0$ divide the real number line into four test intervals.

78. The solution set of the inequality $\frac{3}{2}x^2 + 3x + 6 \geq 0$ is the entire set of real numbers.

Exploration **In Exercises 79–82, find the interval for b such that the equation has at least one real solution.**

79. $x^2 + bx + 4 = 0$

80. $x^2 + bx - 4 = 0$

81. $3x^2 + bx + 10 = 0$

82. $2x^2 + bx + 5 = 0$

83. (a) Write a conjecture about the intervals for b in Exercises 79–82. Explain your reasoning.

(b) What is the center of each interval for b in Exercises 79–82?

84. Consider the polynomial $(x - a)(x - b)$ and the real number line shown below.

(a) Identify the points on the line at which the polynomial is zero.

(b) In each of the three subintervals of the line, write the sign of each factor and the sign of the product.

(c) For what x-values does the polynomial change signs?

Skills Review

In Exercises 85–88, factor the expression completely.

85. $4x^2 + 20x + 25$

86. $(x + 3)^2 - 16$

87. $x^2(x + 3) - 4(x + 3)$

88. $2x^4 - 54x$

In Exercises 89 and 90, write an expression for the area of the region.

89.

90.

2 Chapter Summary

What did you learn?

2 Review Exercises

2.1 In Exercises 1 and 2, graph each function. Compare the graph of each function with the graph of $y = x^2$.

1. (a) $f(x) = 2x^2$

   (b) $g(x) = -2x^2$

   (c) $h(x) = x^2 + 2$

   (d) $k(x) = (x + 2)^2$

2. (a) $f(x) = x^2 - 4$

   (b) $g(x) = 4 - x^2$

   (c) $h(x) = (x - 3)^2$

   (d) $k(x) = \frac{1}{2}x^2 - 1$

In Exercises 3–14, write the quadratic function in standard form and sketch its graph. Identify the vertex, axis of symmetry, and x-intercept(s).

3. $g(x) = x^2 - 2x$

4. $f(x) = 6x - x^2$

5. $f(x) = x^2 + 8x + 10$

6. $h(x) = 3 + 4x - x^2$

7. $f(t) = -2t^2 + 4t + 1$

8. $f(x) = x^2 - 8x + 12$

9. $h(x) = 4x^2 + 4x + 13$

10. $f(x) = x^2 - 6x + 1$

11. $h(x) = x^2 + 5x - 4$

12. $f(x) = 4x^2 + 4x + 5$

13. $f(x) = \frac{1}{3}(x^2 + 5x - 4)$

14. $f(x) = \frac{1}{2}(6x^2 - 24x + 22)$

In Exercises 15–18, write the standard form of the equation of the parabola that has the indicated vertex and whose graph passes through the given point.

15.

16.

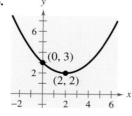

17. Vertex: $(1, -4)$; point: $(2, -3)$

18. Vertex: $(2, 3)$; point: $(-1, 6)$

19. *Geometry* The perimeter of a rectangle is 200 meters.

   (a) Draw a diagram that gives a visual representation of the problem. Label the length and width as x and y, respectively.

   (b) Write y as a function of x. Use the result to write the area as a function of x.

   (c) Of all possible rectangles with perimeters of 200 meters, find the dimensions of the one with the maximum area.

20. *Maximum Revenue* The total revenue R earned (in dollars) from producing a gift box of candles is given by

$$R(p) = -10p^2 + 800p$$

where p is the price per unit (in dollars).

   (a) Find the revenues when the prices per box are \$20, \$25, and \$30.

   (b) Find the unit price that will yield a maximum revenue. What is the maximum revenue? Explain your results.

21. *Minimum Cost* A soft-drink manufacturer has daily production costs of

$$C = 70,000 - 120x + 0.055x^2$$

where C is the total cost (in dollars) and x is the number of units produced. How many units should be produced each day to yield a minimum cost?

22. *Sociology* The average age of the groom at a first marriage for a given age of the bride can be approximated by the model

$$y = -0.107x^2 + 5.68x - 48.5, \quad 20 \le x \le 25$$

where y is the age of the groom and x is the age of the bride. Sketch a graph of the model. For what age of the bride is the average age of the groom 26? (Source: U.S. Census Bureau)

2.2 In Exercises 23–28, sketch the graphs of $y = x^n$ and the transformation.

23. $y = x^3$, $\quad f(x) = -(x - 4)^3$

24. $y = x^3$, $\quad f(x) = -4x^3$

25. $y = x^4$, $\quad f(x) = 2 - x^4$

26. $y = x^4$, $\quad f(x) = 2(x - 2)^4$

27. $y = x^5$, $\quad f(x) = (x - 3)^5$

28. $y = x^5$, $\quad f(x) = \frac{1}{2}x^5 + 3$

In Exercises 29–32, describe the right-hand and left-hand behavior of the graph of the polynomial function.

29. $f(x) = -x^2 + 6x + 9$

30. $f(x) = \frac{1}{2}x^3 + 2x$

31. $g(x) = \frac{3}{4}(x^4 + 3x^2 + 2)$

32. $h(x) = -x^5 - 7x^2 + 10x$

In Exercises 33–38, find all the real zeros of the polynomial function. Determine the multiplicity of each zero and the number of turning points of the graph of the function. Use a graphing utility to verify your answers.

33. $f(x) = 2x^2 + 11x - 21$

34. $f(x) = x(x + 3)^2$

35. $f(t) = t^3 - 3t$

36. $f(x) = x^3 - 8x^2$

37. $f(x) = -12x^3 + 20x^2$

38. $g(x) = x^4 - x^3 - 2x^2$

In Exercises 39–42, sketch the graph of the function by (a) applying the Leading Coefficient Test, (b) finding the zeros of the polynomial, (c) plotting sufficient solution points, and (d) drawing a continuous curve through the points.

39. $f(x) = -x^3 + x^2 - 2$

40. $g(x) = 2x^3 + 4x^2$

41. $f(x) = x(x^3 + x^2 - 5x + 3)$

42. $h(x) = 3x^2 - x^4$

In Exercises 43–46, (a) use the Intermediate Value Theorem and the *table* feature of a graphing utility to find intervals one unit in length in which the polynomial function is guaranteed to have a zero. (b) Adjust the table to approximate the zeros of the function. Use the *zero* or *root* feature of the graphing utility to verify your results.

43. $f(x) = 3x^3 - x^2 + 3$

44. $f(x) = 0.25x^3 - 3.65x + 6.12$

45. $f(x) = x^4 - 5x - 1$

46. $f(x) = 7x^4 + 3x^3 - 8x^2 + 2$

2.3 In Exercises 47–52, use long division to divide.

47. $\dfrac{24x^2 - x - 8}{3x - 2}$

48. $\dfrac{4x + 7}{3x - 2}$

49. $\dfrac{5x^3 - 13x^2 - x + 2}{x^2 - 3x + 1}$

50. $\dfrac{3x^4}{x^2 - 1}$

51. $\dfrac{x^4 - 3x^3 + 4x^2 - 6x + 3}{x^2 + 2}$

52. $\dfrac{6x^4 + 10x^3 + 13x^2 - 5x + 2}{2x^2 - 1}$

In Exercises 53–56, use synthetic division to divide.

53. $\dfrac{6x^4 - 4x^3 - 27x^2 + 18x}{x - 2}$

54. $\dfrac{0.1x^3 + 0.3x^2 - 0.5}{x - 5}$

55. $\dfrac{2x^3 - 19x^2 + 38x + 24}{x - 4}$

56. $\dfrac{3x^3 + 20x^2 + 29x - 12}{x + 3}$

In Exercises 57 and 58, use synthetic division to determine whether the given values of *x* are zeros of the function.

57. $f(x) = 20x^4 + 9x^3 - 14x^2 - 3x$

    (a) $x = -1$ (b) $x = \frac{3}{4}$ (c) $x = 0$ (d) $x = 1$

58. $f(x) = 3x^3 - 8x^2 - 20x + 16$

    (a) $x = 4$ (b) $x = -4$ (c) $x = \frac{2}{3}$ (d) $x = -1$

In Exercises 59 and 60, use synthetic division to find each function value.

59. $f(x) = x^4 + 10x^3 - 24x^2 + 20x + 44$

    (a) $f(-3)$ (b) $f(-1)$

60. $g(t) = 2t^5 - 5t^4 - 8t + 20$

    (a) $g(-4)$ (b) $g(\sqrt{2})$

In Exercises 61–64, (a) verify the given factor(s) of the function *f*, (b) find the remaining factors of *f*, (c) use your results to write the complete factorization of *f*, (d) list all real zeros of *f*, and (e) confirm your results by using a graphing utility to graph the function.

Function	Factor(s)
61. $f(x) = x^3 + 4x^2 - 25x - 28$	$(x - 4)$
62. $f(x) = 2x^3 + 11x^2 - 21x - 90$	$(x + 6)$
63. $f(x) = x^4 - 4x^3 - 7x^2 + 22x + 24$	$(x + 2)(x - 3)$
64. $f(x) = x^4 - 11x^3 + 41x^2 - 61x + 30$	$(x - 2)(x - 5)$

2.4 In Exercises 65–68, write the complex number in standard form.

65. $6 + \sqrt{-4}$

66. $3 - \sqrt{-25}$

67. $i^2 + 3i$

68. $-5i + i^2$

In Exercises 69–74, perform the operation and write the result in standard form.

69. $(7 + 5i) + (-4 + 2i)$

70. $\left(\dfrac{\sqrt{2}}{2} - \dfrac{\sqrt{2}}{2}i\right) - \left(\dfrac{\sqrt{2}}{2} + \dfrac{\sqrt{2}}{2}i\right)$

71. $5i(13 - 8i)$

72. $(1 + 6i)(5 - 2i)$

73. $(10 - 8i)(2 - 3i)$

74. $i(6 + i)(3 - 2i)$

In Exercises 75 and 76, write the quotient in standard form.

75. $\dfrac{6 + i}{4 - i}$

76. $\dfrac{3 + 2i}{5 + i}$

In Exercises 77 and 78, perform the operation and write the result in standard form.

77. $\dfrac{4}{2 - 3i} + \dfrac{2}{1 + i}$

78. $\dfrac{1}{2 + i} - \dfrac{5}{1 + 4i}$

In Exercises 79–82, find all solutions of the equation.

79. $3x^2 + 1 = 0$

80. $2 + 8x^2 = 0$

81. $x^2 - 2x + 10 = 0$

82. $6x^2 + 3x + 27 = 0$

2.5 **In Exercises 83–88, find all the zeros of the function.**

83. $f(x) = 3x(x - 2)^2$

84. $f(x) = (x - 4)(x + 9)^2$

85. $f(x) = x^2 - 9x + 8$

86. $f(x) = x^3 + 6x$

87. $f(x) = (x + 4)(x - 6)(x - 2i)(x + 2i)$

88. $f(x) = (x - 8)(x - 5)^2(x - 3 + i)(x - 3 - i)$

In Exercises 89 and 90, use the Rational Zero Test to list all possible rational zeros of f.

89. $f(x) = -4x^3 + 8x^2 - 3x + 15$

90. $f(x) = 3x^4 + 4x^3 - 5x^2 - 8$

In Exercises 91–96, find all the rational zeros of the function.

91. $f(x) = x^3 - 2x^2 - 21x - 18$

92. $f(x) = 3x^3 - 20x^2 + 7x + 30$

93. $f(x) = x^3 - 10x^2 + 17x - 8$

94. $f(x) = x^3 + 9x^2 + 24x + 20$

95. $f(x) = x^4 + x^3 - 11x^2 + x - 12$

96. $f(x) = 25x^4 + 25x^3 - 154x^2 - 4x + 24$

In Exercises 97 and 98, find a polynomial function with real coefficients that has the given zeros. (There are many correct answers.)

97. $\frac{2}{3}, 4, \sqrt{3}\,i$

98. $2, -3, 1 - 2i$

In Exercises 99–102, use the given zero to find all the zeros of the function.

	Function	*Zero*
99.	$f(x) = x^3 - 4x^2 + x - 4$	i
100.	$h(x) = -x^3 + 2x^2 - 16x + 32$	$-4i$
101.	$g(x) = 2x^4 - 3x^3 - 13x^2 + 37x - 15$	$2 + i$
102.	$f(x) = 4x^4 - 11x^3 + 14x^2 - 6x$	$1 - i$

In Exercises 103–106, find all the zeros of the function and write the polynomial as a product of linear factors.

103. $f(x) = x^3 + 4x^2 - 5x$

104. $g(x) = x^3 - 7x^2 + 36$

105. $g(x) = x^4 + 4x^3 - 3x^2 + 40x + 208$

106. $f(x) = x^4 + 8x^3 + 8x^2 - 72x - 153$

In Exercises 107 and 108, use Descartes's Rule of Signs to determine the possible numbers of positive and negative zeros of the function.

107. $g(x) = 5x^3 + 3x^2 - 6x + 9$

108. $h(x) = -2x^5 + 4x^3 - 2x^2 + 5$

In Exercises 109 and 110, use synthetic division to verify the upper and lower bounds of the real zeros of f.

109. $f(x) = 4x^3 - 3x^2 + 4x - 3$

    (a) Upper: $x = 1$

    (b) Lower: $x = -\frac{1}{4}$

110. $f(x) = 2x^3 - 5x^2 - 14x + 8$

    (a) Upper: $x = 8$

    (b) Lower: $x = -4$

2.6 **In Exercises 111–114, find the domain of the rational function.**

111. $f(x) = \dfrac{5x}{x + 12}$

112. $f(x) = \dfrac{3x^2}{1 + 3x}$

113. $f(x) = \dfrac{8}{x^2 - 10x + 24}$

114. $f(x) = \dfrac{x^2 + x - 2}{x^2 + 4}$

In Exercises 115–118, identify any horizontal or vertical asymptotes.

115. $f(x) = \dfrac{4}{x + 3}$

116. $f(x) = \dfrac{2x^2 + 5x - 3}{x^2 + 2}$

117. $h(x) = \dfrac{2x - 10}{x^2 - 2x - 15}$

118. $h(x) = \dfrac{x^3 - 4x^2}{x^2 + 3x + 2}$

In Exercises 119–130, (a) state the domain of the function, (b) identify all intercepts, (c) find any vertical and horizontal asymptotes, and (d) plot additional solution points as needed to sketch the graph of the rational function.

119. $f(x) = \dfrac{-5}{x^2}$

120. $f(x) = \dfrac{4}{x}$

121. $g(x) = \dfrac{2 + x}{1 - x}$

122. $h(x) = \dfrac{x - 3}{x - 2}$

123. $p(x) = \dfrac{x^2}{x^2 + 1}$

124. $f(x) = \dfrac{2x}{x^2 + 4}$

125. $f(x) = \dfrac{x}{x^2 + 1}$

126. $h(x) = \dfrac{4}{(x - 1)^2}$

127. $f(x) = \dfrac{-6x^2}{x^2 + 1}$

128. $y = \dfrac{2x^2}{x^2 - 4}$

129. $f(x) = \dfrac{6x^2 - 11x + 3}{3x^2 - x}$

130. $f(x) = \dfrac{6x^2 - 7x + 2}{4x^2 - 1}$

In Exercises 131–134, (a) state the domain of the function, (b) identify all intercepts, (c) identify any vertical and slant asymptotes, and (d) plot additional solution points as needed to sketch the graph of the rational function.

131. $f(x) = \dfrac{2x^3}{x^2 + 1}$

132. $f(x) = \dfrac{x^2 + 1}{x + 1}$

133. $f(x) = \dfrac{3x^3 - 2x^2 - 3x + 2}{3x^2 - x - 4}$

134. $f(x) = \dfrac{3x^3 - 4x^2 - 12x + 16}{3x^2 + 5x - 2}$

135. *Average Cost* A business has a production cost of $C = 0.5x + 500$ for producing x units of a product. The average cost per unit, $\overline{C}$, is given by

$$\overline{C} = \frac{C}{x} = \frac{0.5x + 500}{x}, \quad x > 0.$$

Determine the average cost per unit as x increases without bound. (Find the horizontal asymptote.)

136. *Seizure of Illegal Drugs* The cost C (in millions of dollars) for the federal government to seize $p\%$ of an illegal drug as it enters the country is given by

$$C = \frac{528p}{100 - p}, \quad 0 \le p < 100.$$

(a) Use a graphing utility to graph the cost function.

(b) Find the costs of seizing 25%, 50%, and 75% of the drug.

(c) According to this model, would it be possible to seize 100% of the drug?

137. *Page Design* A page that is x inches wide and y inches high contains 30 square inches of print. The top and bottom margins are 2 inches deep and the margins on each side are 2 inches wide.

(a) Draw a diagram that gives a visual representation of the problem.

(b) Show that the total area A on the page is

$$A = \frac{2x(2x + 7)}{x - 4}.$$

(c) Determine the domain of the function based on the physical constraints of the problem.

(d) Use a graphing utility to graph the area function and approximate the page size for which the least amount of paper will be used. Verify your answer numerically using the *table* feature of the graphing utility.

138. *Photosynthesis* The amount y of CO_2 uptake (in milligrams per square decimeter per hour) at optimal temperatures and with the natural supply of CO_2 is approximated by the model

$$y = \frac{18.47x - 2.96}{0.23x + 1}, \quad x > 0$$

where x is the light intensity (in watts per square meter). Use a graphing utility to graph the function and determine the limiting amount of CO_2 uptake.

2.7 In Exercises 139–146, solve the inequality.

139. $6x^2 + 5x < 4$

140. $2x^2 + x \ge 15$

141. $x^3 - 16x \ge 0$

142. $12x^3 - 20x^2 < 0$

143. $\dfrac{2}{x + 1} \le \dfrac{3}{x - 1}$

144. $\dfrac{x - 5}{3 - x} < 0$

145. $\dfrac{x^2 + 7x + 12}{x} \ge 0$

146. $\dfrac{1}{x - 2} > \dfrac{1}{x}$

147. *Investment* P dollars invested at interest rate r compounded annually increases to an amount

$$A = P(1 + r)^2$$

in 2 years. An investment of \$5000 is to increase to an amount greater than \$5500 in 2 years. The interest rate must be greater than what percent?

148. *Population of a Species* A biologist introduces 200 ladybugs into a crop field. The population P of the ladybugs is approximated by the model

$$P = \frac{1000(1 + 3t)}{5 + t}$$

where t is the time in days. Find the time required for the population to increase to at least 2000 ladybugs.

Synthesis

True or False? In Exercises 149 and 150, determine whether the statement is true or false. Justify your answer.

149. A fourth-degree polynomial with real coefficients can have -5, $-8i$, $4i$, and 5 as its zeros.

150. The domain of a rational function can never be the set of all real numbers.

151. *Writing* Explain how to determine the maximum or minimum value of a quadratic function.

152. *Writing* Explain the connections among factors of a polynomial, zeros of a polynomial function, and solutions of a polynomial equation.

153. *Writing* Describe what is meant by an asymptote of a graph.

2 Chapter Test

Take this test as you would take a test in class. When you are finished, check your work against the answers given in the back of the book.

1. Describe how the graph of g differs from the graph of $f(x) = x^2$.

(a) $g(x) = 2 - x^2$ (b) $g(x) = \left(x - \frac{3}{2}\right)^2$

2. Find an equation of the parabola shown in the figure at the left.

3. The path of a ball is given by $y = -\frac{1}{20}x^2 + 3x + 5$, where y is the height (in feet) of the ball and x is the horizontal distance (in feet) from where the ball was thrown.

(a) Find the maximum height of the ball.

(b) Which number determines the height at which the ball was thrown? Does changing this value change the coordinates of the maximum height of the ball? Explain.

4. Determine the right-hand and left-hand behavior of the graph of the function $h(t) = -\frac{3}{4}t^5 + 2t^2$. Then sketch its graph.

5. Divide using long division.   **6.** Divide using synthetic division.

$$\frac{3x^3 + 4x - 1}{x^2 + 1}$$ $$\frac{2x^4 - 5x^2 - 3}{x - 2}$$

7. Use synthetic division to show that $x = \sqrt{3}$ is a zero of the function given by

$$f(x) = 4x^3 - x^2 - 12x + 3.$$

Use the result to factor the polynomial function completely and list all the real zeros of the function.

8. Perform each operation and write the result in standard form.

(a) $10i - \left(3 + \sqrt{-25}\right)$ (b) $\left(2 + \sqrt{3}\,i\right)\left(2 - \sqrt{3}\,i\right)$

9. Write the quotient in standard form: $\dfrac{5}{2 + i}$.

In Exercises 10 and 11, find a polynomial function with real coefficients that has the given zeros. (There are many correct answers.)

10. $0, 3, 3 + i, 3 - i$ **11.** $1 + \sqrt{3}\,i, 1 - \sqrt{3}\,i, 2, 2$

In Exercises 12 and 13, find all the zeros of the function.

12. $f(x) = x^3 + 2x^2 + 5x + 10$ **13.** $f(x) = x^4 - 9x^2 - 22x - 24$

In Exercises 14–16, identify any intercepts and asymptotes of the graph the function. Then sketch a graph of the function.

14. $h(x) = \dfrac{4}{x^2} - 1$ **15.** $f(x) = \dfrac{2x^2 - 5x - 12}{x^2 - 16}$ **16.** $g(x) = \dfrac{x^2 + 2}{x - 1}$

In Exercises 17 and 18, solve the inequality. Sketch the solution set on the real number line.

17. $2x^2 + 5x > 12$ **18.** $\dfrac{2}{x} > \dfrac{5}{x + 6}$

---

y

$(0, 3)$

$(3, -6)$

FIGURE FOR **2**

Proofs in Mathematics

These two pages contain proofs of four important theorems about polynomial functions. The first two theorems are from Section 2.3, and the second two theorems are from Section 2.5.

> ## The Remainder Theorem   *(p. 157)*
> If a polynomial $f(x)$ is divided by $x - k$, the remainder is
> $$r = f(k).$$

Proof

From the Division Algorithm, you have

$$f(x) = (x - k)q(x) + r(x)$$

and because either $r(x) = 0$ or the degree of $r(x)$ is less than the degree of $x - k$, you know that $r(x)$ must be a constant. That is, $r(x) = r$. Now, by evaluating $f(x)$ at $x = k$, you have

$$f(k) = (k - k)q(k) + r$$
$$= (0)q(k) + r = r.$$

To be successful in algebra, it is important that you understand the connection among *factors* of a polynomial, *zeros* of a polynomial function, and *solutions* or *roots* of a polynomial equation. The Factor Theorem is the basis for this connection.

> ## The Factor Theorem   *(p. 157)*
> A polynomial $f(x)$ has a factor $(x - k)$ if and only if $f(k) = 0$.

Proof

Using the Division Algorithm with the factor $(x - k)$, you have

$$f(x) = (x - k)q(x) + r(x).$$

By the Remainder Theorem, $r(x) = r = f(k)$, and you have

$$f(x) = (x - k)q(x) + f(k)$$

where $q(x)$ is a polynomial of lesser degree than $f(x)$. If $f(k) = 0$, then

$$f(x) = (x - k)q(x)$$

and you see that $(x - k)$ is a factor of $f(x)$. Conversely, if $(x - k)$ is a factor of $f(x)$, division of $f(x)$ by $(x - k)$ yields a remainder of 0. So, by the Remainder Theorem, you have $f(k) = 0$.

Proofs in Mathematics

Linear Factorization Theorem   *(p. 169)*

If $f(x)$ is a polynomial of degree n, where $n > 0$, then f has precisely n linear factors

$$f(x) = a_n(x - c_1)(x - c_2) \cdots (x - c_n)$$

where $c_1, c_2, \ldots, c_n$ are complex numbers.

The Fundamental Theorem of Algebra

The Linear Factorization Theorem is closely related to the Fundamental Theorem of Algebra. The Fundamental Theorem of Algebra has a long and interesting history. In the early work with polynomial equations, The Fundamental Theorem of Algebra was thought to have been not true, because imaginary solutions were not considered. In fact, in the very early work by mathematicians such as Abu al-Khwarizmi (c. 800 A.D.), negative solutions were also not considered.

Once imaginary numbers were accepted, several mathematicians attempted to give a general proof of the Fundamental Theorem of Algebra. These included Gottfried von Leibniz (1702), Jean d'Alembert (1746), Leonhard Euler (1749), Joseph-Louis Lagrange (1772), and Pierre Simon Laplace (1795). The mathematician usually credited with the first correct proof of the Fundamental Theorem of Algebra is Carl Friedrich Gauss, who published the proof in his doctoral thesis in 1799.

Proof

Using the Fundamental Theorem of Algebra, you know that f must have at least one zero, c_1. Consequently, $(x - c_1)$ is a factor of $f(x)$, and you have

$$f(x) = (x - c_1)f_1(x).$$

If the degree of $f_1(x)$ is greater than zero, you again apply the Fundamental Theorem to conclude that f_1 must have a zero c_2, which implies that

$$f(x) = (x - c_1)(x - c_2)f_2(x).$$

It is clear that the degree of $f_1(x)$ is $n - 1$, that the degree of $f_2(x)$ is $n - 2$, and that you can repeatedly apply the Fundamental Theorem n times until you obtain

$$f(x) = a_n(x - c_1)(x - c_2) \cdots (x - c_n)$$

where a_n is the leading coefficient of the polynomial $f(x)$.

Factors of a Polynomial   *(p. 173)*

Every polynomial of degree $n > 0$ with real coefficients can be written as the product of linear and quadratic factors with real coefficients, where the quadratic factors have no real zeros.

Proof

To begin, you use the Linear Factorization Theorem to conclude that $f(x)$ can be *completely* factored in the form

$$f(x) = d(x - c_1)(x - c_2)(x - c_3) \cdots (x - c_n).$$

If each c_i is real, there is nothing more to prove. If any c_i is complex ($c_i = a + bi$, $b \neq 0$), then, because the coefficients of $f(x)$ are real, you know that the conjugate $c_j = a - bi$ is also a zero. By multiplying the corresponding factors, you obtain

$$(x - c_i)(x - c_j) = [x - (a + bi)][x - (a - bi)]$$
$$= x^2 - 2ax + (a^2 + b^2)$$

where each coefficient is real.

P.S. Problem Solving

This collection of thought-provoking and challenging exercises further explores and expands upon concepts learned in this chapter.

1. Show that if $f(x) = ax^3 + bx^2 + cx + d$ then $f(k) = r$, where $r = ak^3 + bk^2 + ck + d$ using long division. In other words, verify the Remainder Theorem for a third-degree polynomial function.

2. In 2000 B.C., the Babylonians solved polynomial equations by referring to tables of values. One such table gave the values of $y^3 + y^2$. To be able to use this table, the Babylonians sometimes had to manipulate the equation as shown below.

$$ax^3 + bx^2 = c \qquad \text{Original equation}$$

$$\frac{a^3 x^3}{b^3} + \frac{a^2 x^2}{b^2} = \frac{a^2 c}{b^3} \qquad \text{Multiply each side by } \frac{a^2}{b^3}.$$

$$\left(\frac{ax}{b}\right)^3 + \left(\frac{ax}{b}\right)^2 = \frac{a^2 c}{b^3} \qquad \text{Rewrite.}$$

Then they would find $(a^2 c)/b^3$ in the $y^3 + y^2$ column of the table. Because they knew that the corresponding y-value was equal to $(ax)/b$, they could conclude that $x = (by)/a$.

(a) Calculate $y^3 + y^2$ for $y = 1, 2, 3, \ldots, 10$. Record the values in a table.

Use the table from part (a) and the method above to solve each equation.

(b) $x^3 + x^2 = 252$

(c) $x^3 + 2x^2 = 288$

(d) $3x^3 + x^2 = 90$

(e) $2x^3 + 5x^2 = 2500$

(f) $7x^3 + 6x^2 = 1728$

(g) $10x^3 + 3x^2 = 297$

Using the methods from this chapter, verify your solution to each equation.

3. At a glassware factory, molten cobalt glass is poured into molds to make paperweights. Each mold is a rectangular prism whose height is 3 inches greater than the length of each side of the square base. A machine pours 20 cubic inches of liquid glass into each mold. What are the dimensions of the mold?

4. Determine whether the statement is true or false. If false, provide one or more reasons why the statement is false and correct the statement. Let $f(x) = ax^3 + bx^2 + cx + d$, $a \neq 0$, and let $f(2) = -1$. Then

$$\frac{f(x)}{x + 1} = q(x) + \frac{2}{x + 1}$$

where $q(x)$ is a second-degree polynomial.

5. The parabola shown in the figure has an equation of the form $y = ax^2 + bx + c$. Find the equation of this parabola by the following methods. (a) Find the equation analytically. (b) Use the *regression* feature of a graphing utility to find the equation.

6. One of the fundamental themes of calculus is to find the slope of the tangent line to a curve at a point. To see how this can be done, consider the point $(2, 4)$ on the graph of the quadratic function $f(x) = x^2$.

(a) Find the slope of the line joining $(2, 4)$ and $(3, 9)$. Is the slope of the tangent line at $(2, 4)$ greater than or less than the slope of the line through $(2, 4)$ and $(3, 9)$?

(b) Find the slope of the line joining $(2, 4)$ and $(1, 1)$. Is the slope of the tangent line at $(2, 4)$ greater than or less than the slope of the line through $(2, 4)$ and $(1, 1)$?

(c) Find the slope of the line joining $(2, 4)$ and $(2.1, 4.41)$. Is the slope of the tangent line at $(2, 4)$ greater than or less than the slope of the line through $(2, 4)$ and $(2.1, 4.41)$?

(d) Find the slope of the line joining $(2, 4)$ and $(2 + h, f(2 + h))$ in terms of the nonzero number h.

(e) Evaluate the slope formula from part (d) for $h = -1$, 1, and 0.1. Compare these values with those in parts (a)–(c).

(f) What can you conclude the slope of the tangent line at $(2, 4)$ to be? Explain your answer.

7. Use the form $f(x) = (x - k)q(x) + r$ to create a cubic function that (a) passes through the point $(2, 5)$ and rises to the right and (b) passes through the point $(-3, 1)$ and falls to the right. (There are many correct answers.)

8. The multiplicative inverse of z is a complex number z_m such that $z \cdot z_m = 1$. Find the multiplicative inverse of each complex number.

   (a) $z = 1 + i$ (b) $z = 3 - i$ (c) $z = -2 + 8i$

9. Prove that the product of a complex number $a + bi$ and its complex conjugate is a real number.

10. Match the graph of the rational function given by

$$f(x) = \frac{ax + b}{cx + d}$$

with the given conditions.

(a)

(b)

(c)

(d)

(i) $a > 0$ (ii) $a > 0$ (iii) $a < 0$ (iv) $a > 0$
$\quad\;\; b < 0$ $\quad\;\;\; b > 0$ $\quad\;\;\;\; b > 0$ $\quad\;\;\; b < 0$
$\quad\;\; c > 0$ $\quad\;\;\; c < 0$ $\quad\;\;\;\; c > 0$ $\quad\;\;\; c > 0$
$\quad\;\; d < 0$ $\quad\;\;\; d < 0$ $\quad\;\;\;\; d < 0$ $\quad\;\;\; d > 0$

11. Consider the function given by

$$f(x) = \frac{ax}{(x - b)^2}.$$

(a) Determine the effect on the graph of f if $b \neq 0$ and a is varied. Consider cases in which a is positive and a is negative.

(b) Determine the effect on the graph of f if $a \neq 0$ and b is varied.

12. The endpoints of the interval over which distinct vision is possible is called the *near point* and *far point* of the eye (see figure). With increasing age, these points normally change. The table shows the approximate near points y (in inches) for various ages x (in years).

FIGURE FOR 12

Age, x	Near point, y
16	3.0
32	4.7
44	9.8
50	19.7
60	39.4

(a) Use the *regression* feature of a graphing utility to find a quadratic model for the data. Use a graphing utility to plot the data and graph the model in the same viewing window.

(b) Find a rational model for the data. Take the reciprocals of the near points to generate the points $(x, 1/y)$. Use the *regression* feature of a graphing utility to find a linear model for the data. The resulting line has the form

$$\frac{1}{y} = ax + b.$$

Solve for y. Use a graphing utility to plot the data and graph the model in the same viewing window.

(c) Use the *table* feature of a graphing utility to create a table showing the predicted near point based on each model for each of the ages in the original table. How well do the models fit the original data?

(d) Use both models to estimate the near point for a person who is 25 years old. Which model is a better fit?

(e) Do you think either model can be used to predict the near point for a person who is 70 years old? Explain.

Exponential and Logarithmic Functions

3

- **3.1** Exponential Functions and Their Graphs
- **3.2** Logarithmic Functions and Their Graphs
- **3.3** Properties of Logarithms
- **3.4** Exponential and Logarithmic Equations
- **3.5** Exponential and Logarithmic Models

Carbon dating is a method used to determine the ages of archeological artifacts up to 50,000 years old. For example, archeologists are using carbon dating to determine the ages of the great pyramids of Egypt.

© Sylvain Grandadam/Getty Images

SELECTED APPLICATIONS

Exponential and logarithmic functions have many real-life applications. The applications listed below represent a small sample of the applications in this chapter.

- Computer Virus,
  Exercise 65, page 227

- Data Analysis: Meteorology,
  Exercise 70, page 228

- Sound Intensity,
  Exercise 90, page 238

- Galloping Speeds of Animals,
  Exercise 85, page 244

- Average Heights,
  Exercise 115, page 255

- Carbon Dating,
  Exercise 41, page 266

- IQ Scores,
  Exercise 47, page 266

- Forensics,
  Exercise 63, page 268

- Compound Interest,
  Exercise 135, page 273

3.1 Exponential Functions and Their Graphs

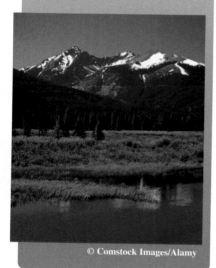

© Comstock Images/Alamy

Exponential Functions

So far, this text has dealt mainly with **algebraic functions,** which include polynomial functions and rational functions. In this chapter, you will study two types of nonalgebraic functions—*exponential functions* and *logarithmic functions.* These functions are examples of **transcendental functions.**

> **Definition of Exponential Function**
>
> The **exponential function f with base a** is denoted by
>
> $$f(x) = a^x$$
>
> where $a > 0$, $a \neq 1$, and x is any real number.

The base $a = 1$ is excluded because it yields $f(x) = 1^x = 1$. This is a constant function, not an exponential function.

You have evaluated a^x for integer and rational values of x. For example, you know that $4^3 = 64$ and $4^{1/2} = 2$. However, to evaluate 4^x for any real number x, you need to interpret forms with *irrational* exponents. For the purposes of this text, it is sufficient to think of

$$a^{\sqrt{2}} \quad \text{(where } \sqrt{2} \approx 1.41421356)$$

as the number that has the successively closer approximations

$$a^{1.4}, a^{1.41}, a^{1.414}, a^{1.4142}, a^{1.41421}, \ldots.$$

Example 1 Evaluating Exponential Functions

Use a calculator to evaluate each function at the indicated value of x.

	Function	*Value*
a.	$f(x) = 2^x$	$x = -3.1$
b.	$f(x) = 2^{-x}$	$x = \pi$
c.	$f(x) = 0.6^x$	$x = \frac{3}{2}$

Solution

	Function Value	*Graphing Calculator Keystrokes*	*Display*
a.	$f(-3.1) = 2^{-3.1}$	2 [^] [(-)] 3.1 [ENTER]	0.1166291
b.	$f(\pi) = 2^{-\pi}$	2 [^] [(-)] π [ENTER]	0.1133147
c.	$f\left(\frac{3}{2}\right) = (0.6)^{3/2}$	.6 [^] [(] 3 [÷] 2 [)] [ENTER]	0.4647580

✓CHECKPOINT   Now try Exercise 1.

When evaluating exponential functions with a calculator, remember to enclose fractional exponents in parentheses. Because the calculator follows the order of operations, parentheses are crucial in order to obtain the correct result.

Graphs of Exponential Functions

The graphs of all exponential functions have similar characteristics, as shown in Examples 2, 3, and 5.

Example 2   Graphs of $y = a^x$

In the same coordinate plane, sketch the graph of each function.

a. $f(x) = 2^x$ **b.** $g(x) = 4^x$

Solution

The table below lists some values for each function, and Figure 3.1 shows the graphs of the two functions. Note that both graphs are increasing. Moreover, the graph of $g(x) = 4^x$ is increasing more rapidly than the graph of $f(x) = 2^x$.

x	-3	-2	-1	0	1	2
2^x	$\frac{1}{8}$	$\frac{1}{4}$	$\frac{1}{2}$	1	2	4
4^x	$\frac{1}{64}$	$\frac{1}{16}$	$\frac{1}{4}$	1	4	16

✓CHECKPOINT   Now try Exercise 11.

The table in Example 2 was evaluated by hand. You could, of course, use a graphing utility to construct tables with even more values.

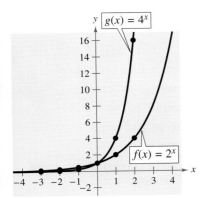

FIGURE 3.1

Example 3   Graphs of $y = a^{-x}$

In the same coordinate plane, sketch the graph of each function.

a. $F(x) = 2^{-x}$ **b.** $G(x) = 4^{-x}$

Solution

The table below lists some values for each function, and Figure 3.2 shows the graphs of the two functions. Note that both graphs are decreasing. Moreover, the graph of $G(x) = 4^{-x}$ is decreasing more rapidly than the graph of $F(x) = 2^{-x}$.

x	-2	-1	0	1	2	3
2^{-x}	4	2	1	$\frac{1}{2}$	$\frac{1}{4}$	$\frac{1}{8}$
4^{-x}	16	4	1	$\frac{1}{4}$	$\frac{1}{16}$	$\frac{1}{64}$

✓CHECKPOINT   Now try Exercise 13.

In Example 3, note that by using one of the properties of exponents, the functions $F(x) = 2^{-x}$ and $G(x) = 4^{-x}$ can be rewritten with positive exponents.

$$F(x) = 2^{-x} = \frac{1}{2^x} = \left(\frac{1}{2}\right)^x \quad \text{and} \quad G(x) = 4^{-x} = \frac{1}{4^x} = \left(\frac{1}{4}\right)^x$$

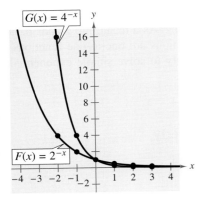

FIGURE 3.2

Comparing the functions in Examples 2 and 3, observe that

$$F(x) = 2^{-x} = f(-x) \qquad \text{and} \qquad G(x) = 4^{-x} = g(-x).$$

Consequently, the graph of F is a reflection (in the y-axis) of the graph of f. The graphs of G and g have the same relationship. The graphs in Figures 3.1 and 3.2 are typical of the exponential functions $y = a^x$ and $y = a^{-x}$. They have one y-intercept and one horizontal asymptote (the x-axis), and they are continuous. The basic characteristics of these exponential functions are summarized in Figures 3.3 and 3.4.

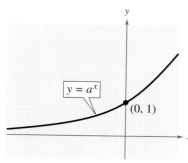

FIGURE 3.3

Graph of $y = a^x$, $a > 1$
- Domain: $(-\infty, \infty)$
- Range: $(0, \infty)$
- Intercept: $(0, 1)$
- Increasing
- x-axis is a horizontal asymptote $(a^x \to 0$ as $x \to -\infty)$
- Continuous

FIGURE 3.4

Graph of $y = a^{-x}$, $a > 1$
- Domain: $(-\infty, \infty)$
- Range: $(0, \infty)$
- Intercept: $(0, 1)$
- Decreasing
- x-axis is a horizontal asymptote $(a^{-x} \to 0$ as $x \to \infty)$
- Continuous

From Figures 3.3 and 3.4, you can see that the graph of an exponential function is always increasing or always decreasing. As a result, the graphs pass the Horizontal Line Test, and therefore the functions are one-to-one functions. You can use the following **One-to-One Property** to solve simple exponential equations.

For $a > 0$ and $a \neq 1$, $a^x = a^y$ if and only if $x = y$.   One-to-One Property

Example 4   **Using the One-to-One Property**

a.
$$\begin{aligned}
9 &= 3^{x+1} &&\text{Original equation} \\
3^2 &= 3^{x+1} &&9 = 3^2 \\
2 &= x + 1 &&\text{One-to-One Property} \\
1 &= x &&\text{Solve for } x.
\end{aligned}$$

b. $\left(\frac{1}{2}\right)^x = 8 \Longrightarrow 2^{-x} = 2^3 \Longrightarrow x = -3$

✓**CHECKPOINT**   Now try Exercise 45.

In the following example, notice how the graph of $y = a^x$ can be used to sketch the graphs of functions of the form $f(x) = b \pm a^{x+c}$.

Example 5   Transformations of Graphs of Exponential Functions

Each of the following graphs is a transformation of the graph of $f(x) = 3^x$.

a. Because $g(x) = 3^{x+1} = f(x + 1)$, the graph of g can be obtained by shifting the graph of f one unit to the *left*, as shown in Figure 3.5.

b. Because $h(x) = 3^x - 2 = f(x) - 2$, the graph of h can be obtained by shifting the graph of f *downward* two units, as shown in Figure 3.6.

c. Because $k(x) = -3^x = -f(x)$, the graph of k can be obtained by *reflecting* the graph of f in the x-axis, as shown in Figure 3.7.

d. Because $j(x) = 3^{-x} = f(-x)$, the graph of j can be obtained by *reflecting* the graph of f in the y-axis, as shown in Figure 3.8.

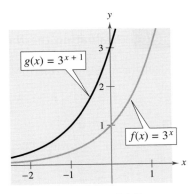

FIGURE **3.5**   *Horizontal shift*

FIGURE **3.6**   *Vertical shift*

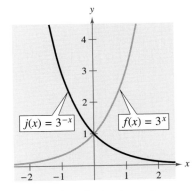

FIGURE **3.7**   *Reflection in x-axis*

FIGURE **3.8**   *Reflection in y-axis*

✔CHECKPOINT   Now try Exercise 17.

Notice that the transformations in Figures 3.5, 3.7, and 3.8 keep the x-axis as a horizontal asymptote, but the transformation in Figure 3.6 yields a new horizontal asymptote of $y = -2$. Also, be sure to note how the y-intercept is affected by each transformation.

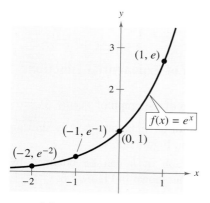

FIGURE **3.9**

The Natural Base e

In many applications, the most convenient choice for a base is the irrational number

$$e \approx 2.718281828 \ldots .$$

This number is called the **natural base.** The function given by $f(x) = e^x$ is called the **natural exponential function.** Its graph is shown in Figure 3.9. Be sure you see that for the exponential function $f(x) = e^x$, e is the constant $2.718281828 \ldots$, whereas x is the variable.

> ## Exploration
>
> Use a graphing utility to graph $y_1 = (1 + 1/x)^x$ and $y_2 = e$ in the same viewing window. Using the *trace* feature, explain what happens to the graph of y_1 as x increases.

Example 6 Evaluating the Natural Exponential Function

Use a calculator to evaluate the function given by $f(x) = e^x$ at each indicated value of x.

a. $x = -2$ **b.** $x = -1$ **c.** $x = 0.25$ **d.** $x = -0.3$

Solution

Function Value	Graphing Calculator Keystrokes	Display
a. $f(-2) = e^{-2}$	$\boxed{e^x}$ $\boxed{(-)}$ 2 $\boxed{\text{ENTER}}$	0.1353353
b. $f(-1) = e^{-1}$	$\boxed{e^x}$ $\boxed{(-)}$ 1 $\boxed{\text{ENTER}}$	0.3678794
c. $f(0.25) = e^{0.25}$	$\boxed{e^x}$ 0.25 $\boxed{\text{ENTER}}$	1.2840254
d. $f(-0.3) = e^{-0.3}$	$\boxed{e^x}$ $\boxed{(-)}$ 0.3 $\boxed{\text{ENTER}}$	0.7408182

✓*CHECKPOINT* Now try Exercise 27.

FIGURE **3.10**

Example 7 Graphing Natural Exponential Functions

Sketch the graph of each natural exponential function.

a. $f(x) = 2e^{0.24x}$ **b.** $g(x) = \frac{1}{2}e^{-0.58x}$

Solution

To sketch these two graphs, you can use a graphing utility to construct a table of values, as shown below. After constructing the table, plot the points and connect them with smooth curves, as shown in Figures 3.10 and 3.11. Note that the graph in Figure 3.10 is increasing, whereas the graph in Figure 3.11 is decreasing.

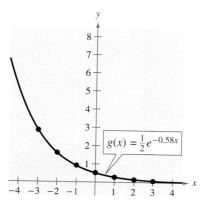

FIGURE **3.11**

x	-3	-2	-1	0	1	2	3
$f(x)$	0.974	1.238	1.573	2.000	2.542	3.232	4.109
$g(x)$	2.849	1.595	0.893	0.500	0.280	0.157	0.088

✓*CHECKPOINT* Now try Exercise 35.

Exploration

Use the formula

$$A = P\left(1 + \frac{r}{n}\right)^{nt}$$

to calculate the amount in an account when $P = \$3000$, $r = 6\%$, $t = 10$ years, and compounding is done (a) by the day, (b) by the hour, (c) by the minute, and (d) by the second. Does increasing the number of compoundings per year result in unlimited growth of the amount in the account? Explain.

Applications

One of the most familiar examples of exponential growth is that of an investment earning *continuously compounded interest.* Using exponential functions, you can *develop* a formula for interest compounded n times per year and show how it leads to continuous compounding.

Suppose a principal P is invested at an annual interest rate r, compounded once a year. If the interest is added to the principal at the end of the year, the new balance P_1 is

$$P_1 = P + Pr$$
$$= P(1 + r).$$

This pattern of multiplying the previous principal by $1 + r$ is then repeated each successive year, as shown below.

Year	Balance After Each Compounding
0	$P = P$
1	$P_1 = P(1 + r)$
2	$P_2 = P_1(1 + r) = P(1 + r)(1 + r) = P(1 + r)^2$
3	$P_3 = P_2(1 + r) = P(1 + r)^2(1 + r) = P(1 + r)^3$
$\vdots$	$\vdots$
t	$P_t = P(1 + r)^t$

To accommodate more frequent (quarterly, monthly, or daily) compounding of interest, let n be the number of compoundings per year and let t be the number of years. Then the rate per compounding is r/n and the account balance after t years is

$$A = P\left(1 + \frac{r}{n}\right)^{nt}. \qquad \text{Amount (balance) with } n \text{ compoundings per year}$$

If you let the number of compoundings n increase without bound, the process approaches what is called **continuous compounding.** In the formula for n compoundings per year, let $m = n/r$. This produces

$$A = P\left(1 + \frac{r}{n}\right)^{nt} \qquad \text{Amount with } n \text{ compoundings per year}$$

$$= P\left(1 + \frac{r}{mr}\right)^{mrt} \qquad \text{Substitute } mr \text{ for } n.$$

$$= P\left(1 + \frac{1}{m}\right)^{mrt} \qquad \text{Simplify.}$$

$$= P\left[\left(1 + \frac{1}{m}\right)^{m}\right]^{rt}. \qquad \text{Property of exponents}$$

m	$\left(1 + \dfrac{1}{m}\right)^{m}$
1	2
10	2.59374246
100	2.704813829
1,000	2.716923932
10,000	2.718145927
100,000	2.718268237
1,000,000	2.718280469
10,000,000	2.718281693
$\downarrow$	$\downarrow$
∞	e

As m increases without bound, the table at the left shows that $[1 + (1/m)]^{m} \to e$ as $m \to \infty$. From this, you can conclude that the formula for continuous compounding is

$$A = Pe^{rt}. \qquad \text{Substitute } e \text{ for } (1 + 1/m)^{m}.$$

STUDY TIP

Be sure you see that the annual interest rate must be written in decimal form. For instance, 6% should be written as 0.06.

Formulas for Compound Interest

After t years, the balance A in an account with principal P and annual interest rate r (in decimal form) is given by the following formulas.

1. For n compoundings per year: $A = P\left(1 + \dfrac{r}{n}\right)^{nt}$

2. For continuous compounding: $A = Pe^{rt}$

Example 8 **Compound Interest**

A total of $12,000 is invested at an annual interest rate of 9%. Find the balance after 5 years if it is compounded

a. quarterly.

b. monthly.

c. continuously.

Solution

a. For quarterly compounding, you have $n = 4$. So, in 5 years at 9%, the balance is

$$A = P\left(1 + \frac{r}{n}\right)^{nt}$$ Formula for compound interest

$$= 12{,}000\left(1 + \frac{0.09}{4}\right)^{4(5)}$$ Substitute for P, r, n, and t.

$$\approx \$18{,}726.11.$$ Use a calculator.

b. For monthly compounding, you have $n = 12$. So, in 5 years at 9%, the balance is

$$A = P\left(1 + \frac{r}{n}\right)^{nt}$$ Formula for compound interest

$$= 12{,}000\left(1 + \frac{0.09}{12}\right)^{12(5)}$$ Substitute for P, r, n, and t.

$$\approx \$18{,}788.17.$$ Use a calculator.

c. For continuous compounding, the balance is

$$A = Pe^{rt}$$ Formula for continuous compounding

$$= 12{,}000e^{0.09(5)}$$ Substitute for P, r, and t.

$$\approx \$18{,}819.75.$$ Use a calculator.

✓CHECKPOINT   Now try Exercise 53.

In Example 8, note that continuous compounding yields more than quarterly or monthly compounding. This is typical of the two types of compounding. That is, for a given principal, interest rate, and time, continuous compounding will always yield a larger balance than compounding n times a year.

Example 9   Radioactive Decay

In 1986, a nuclear reactor accident occurred in Chernobyl in what was then the Soviet Union. The explosion spread highly toxic radioactive chemicals, such as plutonium, over hundreds of square miles, and the government evacuated the city and the surrounding area. To see why the city is now uninhabited, consider the model

$$P = 10\left(\frac{1}{2}\right)^{t/24,100}$$

which represents the amount of plutonium P that remains (from an initial amount of 10 pounds) after t years. Sketch the graph of this function over the interval from $t = 0$ to $t = 100,000$, where $t = 0$ represents 1986. How much of the 10 pounds will remain in the year 2010? How much of the 10 pounds will remain after 100,000 years?

Solution

The graph of this function is shown in Figure 3.12. Note from this graph that plutonium has a *half-life* of about 24,100 years. That is, after 24,100 years, *half* of the original amount will remain. After another 24,100 years, one-quarter of the original amount will remain, and so on. In the year 2010 ($t = 24$), there will still be

$$P = 10\left(\frac{1}{2}\right)^{24/24,100} \approx 10\left(\frac{1}{2}\right)^{0.0009959} \approx 9.993 \text{ pounds}$$

of plutonium remaining. After 100,000 years, there will still be

$$P = 10\left(\frac{1}{2}\right)^{100,000/24,100} \approx 10\left(\frac{1}{2}\right)^{4.1494} \approx 0.564 \text{ pound}$$

of plutonium remaining.

✓CHECKPOINT   Now try Exercise 67.

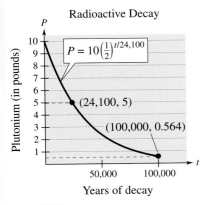

Radioactive Decay

$$P = 10\left(\frac{1}{2}\right)^{t/24,100}$$

(24,100, 5)

(100,000, 0.564)

FIGURE **3.12**

---

*W*RITING ABOUT *M*ATHEMATICS

Identifying Exponential Functions Which of the following functions generated the two tables below? Discuss how you were able to decide. What do these functions have in common? Are any of them the same? If so, explain why.

a. $f_1(x) = 2^{(x+3)}$ **b.** $f_2(x) = 8\left(\frac{1}{2}\right)^x$ **c.** $f_3(x) = \left(\frac{1}{2}\right)^{(x-3)}$

d. $f_4(x) = \left(\frac{1}{2}\right)^x + 7$ **e.** $f_5(x) = 7 + 2^x$ **f.** $f_6(x) = (8)2^x$

x	-1	0	1	2	3
$g(x)$	7.5	8	9	11	15

x	-2	-1	0	1	2
$h(x)$	32	16	8	4	2

Create two different exponential functions of the forms $y = a(b)^x$ and $y = c^x + d$ with y-intercepts of $(0, -3)$.

3.1 | Exercises

The *HM mathSpace®* CD-ROM and *Eduspace®* for this text contain step-by-step solutions to all odd-numbered exercises. They also provide Tutorial Exercises for additional help.

VOCABULARY CHECK: Fill in the blanks.

1. Polynomials and rational functions are examples of _____ functions.

2. Exponential and logarithmic functions are examples of nonalgebraic functions, also called _____ functions.

3. The exponential function given by $f(x) = e^x$ is called the _____ _____ function, and the base e is called the _____ base.

4. To find the amount A in an account after t years with principal P and an annual interest rate r compounded n times per year, you can use the formula _____.

5. To find the amount A in an account after t years with principal P and an annual interest rate r compounded continuously, you can use the formula _____.

PREREQUISITE SKILLS REVIEW: Practice and review algebra skills needed for this section at **www.Eduspace.com**.

In Exercises 1–6, evaluate the function at the indicated value of x. Round your result to three decimal places.

Function	Value
1. $f(x) = 3.4^x$	$x = 5.6$
2. $f(x) = 2.3^x$	$x = \frac{3}{2}$
3. $f(x) = 5^x$	$x = -\pi$
4. $f(x) = \left(\frac{2}{3}\right)^{5x}$	$x = \frac{3}{10}$
5. $g(x) = 5000(2^x)$	$x = -1.5$
6. $f(x) = 200(1.2)^{12x}$	$x = 24$

In Exercises 7–10, match the exponential function with its graph. [The graphs are labeled (a), (b), (c), and (d).]

(a)

(b)

(c)

(d)

7. $f(x) = 2^x$

8. $f(x) = 2^x + 1$

9. $f(x) = 2^{-x}$

10. $f(x) = 2^{x-2}$

In Exercises 11–16, use a graphing utility to construct a table of values for the function. Then sketch the graph of the function.

11. $f(x) = \left(\frac{1}{2}\right)^x$ **12.** $f(x) = \left(\frac{1}{2}\right)^{-x}$

13. $f(x) = 6^{-x}$ **14.** $f(x) = 6^x$

15. $f(x) = 2^{x-1}$ **16.** $f(x) = 4^{x-3} + 3$

In Exercises 17–22, use the graph of *f* to describe the transformation that yields the graph of *g*.

17. $f(x) = 3^x$, $g(x) = 3^{x-4}$

18. $f(x) = 4^x$, $g(x) = 4^x + 1$

19. $f(x) = -2^x$, $g(x) = 5 - 2^x$

20. $f(x) = 10^x$, $g(x) = 10^{-x+3}$

21. $f(x) = \left(\frac{7}{2}\right)^x$, $g(x) = -\left(\frac{7}{2}\right)^{-x+6}$

22. $f(x) = 0.3^x$, $g(x) = -0.3^x + 5$

In Exercises 23–26, use a graphing utility to graph the exponential function.

23. $y = 2^{-x^2}$ **24.** $y = 3^{-|x|}$

25. $y = 3^{x-2} + 1$ **26.** $y = 4^{x+1} - 2$

In Exercises 27–32, evaluate the function at the indicated value of x. Round your result to three decimal places.

Function	Value
27. $h(x) = e^{-x}$	$x = \frac{3}{4}$
28. $f(x) = e^x$	$x = 3.2$
29. $f(x) = 2e^{-5x}$	$x = 10$
30. $f(x) = 1.5e^{x/2}$	$x = 240$
31. $f(x) = 5000e^{0.06x}$	$x = 6$
32. $f(x) = 250e^{0.05x}$	$x = 20$

In Exercises 33–38, use a graphing utility to construct a table of values for the function. Then sketch the graph of the function.

33. $f(x) = e^x$

34. $f(x) = e^{-x}$

35. $f(x) = 3e^{x+4}$

36. $f(x) = 2e^{-0.5x}$

37. $f(x) = 2e^{x-2} + 4$

38. $f(x) = 2 + e^{x-5}$

In Exercises 39–44, use a graphing utility to graph the exponential function.

39. $y = 1.08^{-5x}$

40. $y = 1.08^{5x}$

41. $s(t) = 2e^{0.12t}$

42. $s(t) = 3e^{-0.2t}$

43. $g(x) = 1 + e^{-x}$

44. $h(x) = e^{x-2}$

In Exercise 45–52, use the One-to-One Property to solve the equation for x.

45. $3^{x+1} = 27$

46. $2^{x-3} = 16$

47. $2^{x-2} = \dfrac{1}{32}$

48. $\left(\dfrac{1}{5}\right)^{x+1} = 125$

49. $e^{3x+2} = e^3$

50. $e^{2x-1} = e^4$

51. $e^{x^2-3} = e^{2x}$

52. $e^{x^2+6} = e^{5x}$

Compound Interest   **In Exercises 53–56, complete the table to determine the balance A for P dollars invested at rate r for t years and compounded n times per year.**

n	1	2	4	12	365	Continuous
A						

53. $P = \$2500, r = 2.5\%, t = 10$ years

54. $P = \$1000, r = 4\%, t = 10$ years

55. $P = \$2500, r = 3\%, t = 20$ years

56. $P = \$1000, r = 6\%, t = 40$ years

Compound Interest   **In Exercises 57–60, complete the table to determine the balance A for \$12,000 invested at rate r for t years, compounded continuously.**

t	10	20	30	40	50
A					

57. $r = 4\%$

58. $r = 6\%$

59. $r = 6.5\%$

60. $r = 3.5\%$

61. *Trust Fund*   On the day of a child's birth, a deposit of \$25,000 is made in a trust fund that pays 8.75% interest, compounded continuously. Determine the balance in this account on the child's 25th birthday.

62. *Trust Fund*   A deposit of \$5000 is made in a trust fund that pays 7.5% interest, compounded continuously. It is specified that the balance will be given to the college from which the donor graduated after the money has earned interest for 50 years. How much will the college receive?

63. *Inflation*   If the annual rate of inflation averages 4% over the next 10 years, the approximate costs C of goods or services during any year in that decade will be modeled by $C(t) = P(1.04)^t$, where t is the time in years and P is the present cost. The price of an oil change for your car is presently \$23.95. Estimate the price 10 years from now.

64. *Demand*   The demand equation for a product is given by

$$p = 5000\left(1 - \frac{4}{4 + e^{-0.002x}}\right)$$

where p is the price and x is the number of units.

 (a) Use a graphing utility to graph the demand function for $x > 0$ and $p > 0$.

(b) Find the price p for a demand of $x = 500$ units.

 (c) Use the graph in part (a) to approximate the greatest price that will still yield a demand of at least 600 units.

65. *Computer Virus*   The number V of computers infected by a computer virus increases according to the model $V(t) = 100e^{4.6052t}$, where t is the time in hours. Find (a) $V(1)$, (b) $V(1.5)$, and (c) $V(2)$.

66. *Population*   The population P (in millions) of Russia from 1996 to 2004 can be approximated by the model $P = 152.26e^{-0.0039t}$, where t represents the year, with $t = 6$ corresponding to 1996. (Source: Census Bureau, International Data Base)

(a) According to the model, is the population of Russia increasing or decreasing? Explain.

(b) Find the population of Russia in 1998 and 2000.

(c) Use the model to predict the population of Russia in 2010.

67. *Radioactive Decay*   Let Q represent a mass of radioactive radium (^{226}Ra) (in grams), whose half-life is 1599 years. The quantity of radium present after t years is $Q = 25\left(\frac{1}{2}\right)^{t/1599}$.

(a) Determine the initial quantity (when $t = 0$).

(b) Determine the quantity present after 1000 years.

 (c) Use a graphing utility to graph the function over the interval $t = 0$ to $t = 5000$.

68. *Radioactive Decay*   Let Q represent a mass of carbon 14 (^{14}C) (in grams), whose half-life is 5715 years. The quantity of carbon 14 present after t years is $Q = 10\left(\frac{1}{2}\right)^{t/5715}$.

(a) Determine the initial quantity (when $t = 0$).

(b) Determine the quantity present after 2000 years.

(c) Sketch the graph of this function over the interval $t = 0$ to $t = 10,000$.

Model It

69. Data Analysis: Biology To estimate the amount of defoliation caused by the gypsy moth during a given year, a forester counts the number x of egg masses on $\frac{1}{40}$ of an acre (circle of radius 18.6 feet) in the fall. The percent of defoliation y the next spring is shown in the table. (Source: USDA, Forest Service)

Egg masses, x	Percent of defoliation, y
0	12
25	44
50	81
75	96
100	99

A model for the data is given by

$$y = \frac{100}{1 + 7e^{-0.069x}}.$$

 (a) Use a graphing utility to create a scatter plot of the data and graph the model in the same viewing window.

(b) Create a table that compares the model with the sample data.

(c) Estimate the percent of defoliation if 36 egg masses are counted on $\frac{1}{40}$ acre.

 (d) You observe that $\frac{2}{3}$ of a forest is defoliated the following spring. Use the graph in part (a) to estimate the number of egg masses per $\frac{1}{40}$ acre.

70. Data Analysis: Meteorology A meteorologist measures the atmospheric pressure P (in pascals) at altitude h (in kilometers). The data are shown in the table.

Altitude, h	Pressure, P
0	101,293
5	54,735
10	23,294
15	12,157
20	5,069

A model for the data is given by $P = 107,428e^{-0.150h}$.

(a) Sketch a scatter plot of the data and graph the model on the same set of axes.

(b) Estimate the atmospheric pressure at a height of 8 kilometers.

Synthesis

True or False? In Exercises 71 and 72, determine whether the statement is true or false. Justify your answer.

71. The line $y = -2$ is an asymptote for the graph of $f(x) = 10^x - 2$.

72. $e = \frac{271,801}{99,990}$.

Think About It In Exercises 73–76, use properties of exponents to determine which functions (if any) are the same.

73. $f(x) = 3^{x-2}$
$g(x) = 3^x - 9$
$h(x) = \frac{1}{9}(3^x)$

74. $f(x) = 4^x + 12$
$g(x) = 2^{2x+6}$
$h(x) = 64(4^x)$

75. $f(x) = 16(4^{-x})$
$g(x) = \left(\frac{1}{4}\right)^{x-2}$
$h(x) = 16(2^{-2x})$

76. $f(x) = e^{-x} + 3$
$g(x) = e^{3-x}$
$h(x) = -e^{x-3}$

77. Graph the functions given by $y = 3^x$ and $y = 4^x$ and use the graphs to solve each inequality.
(a) $4^x < 3^x$ (b) $4^x > 3^x$

78. Use a graphing utility to graph each function. Use the graph to find where the function is increasing and decreasing, and approximate any relative maximum or minimum values.
(a) $f(x) = x^2e^{-x}$ (b) $g(x) = x2^{3-x}$

79. Graphical Analysis Use a graphing utility to graph
$$f(x) = \left(1 + \frac{0.5}{x}\right)^x \quad \text{and} \quad g(x) = e^{0.5}$$
in the same viewing window. What is the relationship between f and g as x increases and decreases without bound?

80. Think About It Which functions are exponential?
(a) $3x$ (b) $3x^2$ (c) 3^x (d) 2^{-x}

Skills Review

In Exercises 81 and 82, solve for y.

81. $x^2 + y^2 = 25$ **82.** $x - |y| = 2$

In Exercises 83 and 84, sketch the graph of the function.

83. $f(x) = \frac{2}{9 + x}$ **84.** $f(x) = \sqrt{7 - x}$

85. Make a Decision To work an extended application analyzing the population per square mile of the United States, visit this text's website at *college.hmco.com*. (Data Source: U.S. Census Bureau)

What you should learn

- Recognize and evaluate logarithmic functions with base a.
- Graph logarithmic functions.
- Recognize, evaluate, and graph natural logarithmic functions.
- Use logarithmic functions to model and solve real-life problems.

Why you should learn it

Logarithmic functions are often used to model scientific observations. For instance, in Exercise 89 on page 238, a logarithmic function is used to model human memory.

© Ariel Skelley/Corbis

Logarithmic Functions

In Section 1.9, you studied the concept of an inverse function. There, you learned that if a function is one-to-one—that is, if the function has the property that no horizontal line intersects the graph of the function more than once—the function must have an inverse function. By looking back at the graphs of the exponential functions introduced in Section 3.1, you will see that every function of the form $f(x) = a^x$ passes the Horizontal Line Test and therefore must have an inverse function. This inverse function is called the **logarithmic function with base** a.

Definition of Logarithmic Function with Base a

For $x > 0$, $a > 0$, and $a \neq 1$,

$$y = \log_a x \text{ if and only if } x = a^y.$$

The function given by

$$f(x) = \log_a x \qquad \text{Read as "log base } a \text{ of } x.\text{"}$$

is called the **logarithmic function with base** a.

The equations

$$y = \log_a x \qquad \text{and} \qquad x = a^y$$

are equivalent. The first equation is in logarithmic form and the second is in exponential form. For example, the logarithmic equation $2 = \log_3 9$ can be rewritten in exponential form as $9 = 3^2$. The exponential equation $5^3 = 125$ can be rewritten in logarithmic form as $\log_5 125 = 3$.

When evaluating logarithms, remember that *a logarithm is an exponent.* This means that $\log_a x$ is the exponent to which a must be raised to obtain x. For instance, $\log_2 8 = 3$ because 2 must be raised to the third power to get 8.

Example 1   **Evaluating Logarithms**

Use the definition of logarithmic function to evaluate each logarithm at the indicated value of x.

a. $f(x) = \log_2 x, \quad x = 32$ **b.** $f(x) = \log_3 x, \quad x = 1$

c. $f(x) = \log_4 x, \quad x = 2$ **d.** $f(x) = \log_{10} x, \quad x = \frac{1}{100}$

Solution

a. $f(32) = \log_2 32 = 5$ 　　　because $2^5 = 32$.

b. $f(1) = \log_3 1 = 0$ 　　　because $3^0 = 1$.

c. $f(2) = \log_4 2 = \frac{1}{2}$ 　　　because $4^{1/2} = \sqrt{4} = 2$.

d. $f\left(\frac{1}{100}\right) = \log_{10} \frac{1}{100} = -2$ 　　　because $10^{-2} = \frac{1}{10^2} = \frac{1}{100}$.

✓CHECKPOINT   Now try Exercise 17.

Exploration

Complete the table for $f(x) = 10^x$.

x	-2	-1	0	1	2
$f(x)$					

Complete the table for $f(x) = \log x$.

x	$\frac{1}{100}$	$\frac{1}{10}$	1	10	100
$f(x)$					

Compare the two tables. What is the relationship between $f(x) = 10^x$ and $f(x) = \log x$?

The logarithmic function with base 10 is called the **common logarithmic function.** It is denoted by $\log_{10}$ or simply by log. On most calculators, this function is denoted by $\boxed{\text{LOG}}$. Example 2 shows how to use a calculator to evaluate common logarithmic functions. You will learn how to use a calculator to calculate logarithms to any base in the next section.

Example 2 **Evaluating Common Logarithms on a Calculator**

Use a calculator to evaluate the function given by $f(x) = \log x$ at each value of x.

a. $x = 10$ **b.** $x = \frac{1}{3}$ **c.** $x = 2.5$ **d.** $x = -2$

Solution

Function Value	*Graphing Calculator Keystrokes*	*Display*
a. $f(10) = \log 10$	$\boxed{\text{LOG}}$ 10 $\boxed{\text{ENTER}}$	1
b. $f\left(\frac{1}{3}\right) = \log\frac{1}{3}$	$\boxed{\text{LOG}}$ $\boxed{(}$ 1 $\boxed{\div}$ 3 $\boxed{)}$ $\boxed{\text{ENTER}}$	-0.4771213
c. $f(2.5) = \log 2.5$	$\boxed{\text{LOG}}$ 2.5 $\boxed{\text{ENTER}}$	0.3979400
d. $f(-2) = \log(-2)$	$\boxed{\text{LOG}}$ $\boxed{(-)}$ 2 $\boxed{\text{ENTER}}$	ERROR

Note that the calculator displays an error message (or a complex number) when you try to evaluate $\log(-2)$. The reason for this is that there is no real number power to which 10 can be raised to obtain -2.

✓CHECKPOINT   Now try Exercise 23.

The following properties follow directly from the definition of the logarithmic function with base a.

Properties of Logarithms

1. $\log_a 1 = 0$ because $a^0 = 1$.

2. $\log_a a = 1$ because $a^1 = a$.

3. $\log_a a^x = x$ and $a^{\log_a x} = x$ Inverse Properties

4. If $\log_a x = \log_a y$, then $x = y$.   One-to-One Property

---

Example 3 **Using Properties of Logarithms**

a. Simplify: $\log_4 1$ **b.** Simplify: $\log_{\sqrt{7}} \sqrt{7}$ **c.** Simplify: $6^{\log_6 20}$

Solution

a. Using Property 1, it follows that $\log_4 1 = 0$.

b. Using Property 2, you can conclude that $\log_{\sqrt{7}} \sqrt{7} = 1$.

c. Using the Inverse Property (Property 3), it follows that $6^{\log_6 20} = 20$.

✓CHECKPOINT   Now try Exercise 27.

You can use the One-to-One Property (Property 4) to solve simple logarithmic equations, as shown in Example 4.

Example 4   Using the One-to-One Property

a. $\log_3 x = \log_3 12$ Original equation

$ x = 12$ One-to-One Property

b. $\log(2x + 1) = \log x \Rightarrow 2x + 1 = x \Rightarrow x = -1$

c. $\log_4(x^2 - 6) = \log_4 10 \Rightarrow x^2 - 6 = 10 \Rightarrow x^2 = 16 \Rightarrow x = \pm 4$

✓CHECKPOINT   Now try Exercise 79.

Graphs of Logarithmic Functions

To sketch the graph of $y = \log_a x$, you can use the fact that the graphs of inverse functions are reflections of each other in the line $y = x$.

Example 5   Graphs of Exponential and Logarithmic Functions

In the same coordinate plane, sketch the graph of each function.

a. $f(x) = 2^x$ **b.** $g(x) = \log_2 x$

Solution

a. For $f(x) = 2^x$, construct a table of values. By plotting these points and connecting them with a smooth curve, you obtain the graph shown in Figure 3.13.

x	-2	-1	0	1	2	3
$f(x) = 2^x$	$\frac{1}{4}$	$\frac{1}{2}$	1	2	4	8

b. Because $g(x) = \log_2 x$ is the inverse function of $f(x) = 2^x$, the graph of g is obtained by plotting the points $(f(x), x)$ and connecting them with a smooth curve. The graph of g is a reflection of the graph of f in the line $y = x$, as shown in Figure 3.13.

✓CHECKPOINT   Now try Exercise 31.

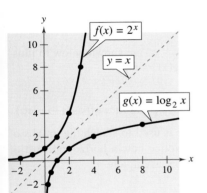

FIGURE **3.13**

Example 6   Sketching the Graph of a Logarithmic Function

Sketch the graph of the common logarithmic function $f(x) = \log x$. Identify the vertical asymptote.

Solution

Begin by constructing a table of values. Note that some of the values can be obtained without a calculator by using the Inverse Property of Logarithms. Others require a calculator. Next, plot the points and connect them with a smooth curve, as shown in Figure 3.14. The vertical asymptote is $x = 0$ (y-axis).

FIGURE **3.14**

	Without calculator				With calculator		
x	$\frac{1}{100}$	$\frac{1}{10}$	1	10	2	5	8
$f(x) = \log x$	-2	-1	0	1	0.301	0.699	0.903

✓CHECKPOINT   Now try Exercise 37.

The nature of the graph in Figure 3.14 is typical of functions of the form $f(x) = \log_a x, a > 1$. They have one x-intercept and one vertical asymptote. Notice how slowly the graph rises for $x > 1$. The basic characteristics of logarithmic graphs are summarized in Figure 3.15.

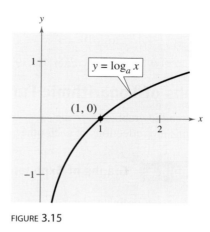

FIGURE 3.15

Graph of $y = \log_a x, a > 1$
- Domain: $(0, \infty)$
- Range: $(-\infty, \infty)$
- x-intercept: $(1, 0)$
- Increasing
- One-to-one, therefore has an inverse function
- y-axis is a vertical asymptote ($\log_a x \to -\infty$ as $x \to 0^+$).
- Continuous
- Reflection of graph of $y = a^x$ about the line $y = x$

The basic characteristics of the graph of $f(x) = a^x$ are shown below to illustrate the inverse relation between $f(x) = a^x$ and $g(x) = \log_a x$.

- Domain: $(-\infty, \infty)$ • Range: $(0, \infty)$
- y-intercept: $(0, 1)$ • x-axis is a horizontal asymptote ($a^x \to 0$ as $x \to -\infty$).

In the next example, the graph of $y = \log_a x$ is used to sketch the graphs of functions of the form $f(x) = b \pm \log_a(x + c)$. Notice how a horizontal shift of the graph results in a horizontal shift of the vertical asymptote.

Example 7 **Shifting Graphs of Logarithmic Functions**

The graph of each of the functions is similar to the graph of $f(x) = \log x$.

a. Because $g(x) = \log(x - 1) = f(x - 1)$, the graph of g can be obtained by shifting the graph of f one unit to the right, as shown in Figure 3.16.

b. Because $h(x) = 2 + \log x = 2 + f(x)$, the graph of h can be obtained by shifting the graph of f two units upward, as shown in Figure 3.17.

FIGURE 3.16

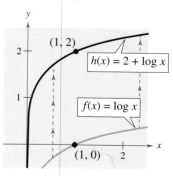

FIGURE 3.17

✓CHECKPOINT Now try Exercise 39.

The Natural Logarithmic Function

By looking back at the graph of the natural exponential function introduced in Section 3.1 on page 388, you will see that $f(x) = e^x$ is one-to-one and so has an inverse function. This inverse function is called the **natural logarithmic function** and is denoted by the special symbol ln x, read as "the natural log of x" or "el en of x." Note that the natural logarithm is written without a base. The base is understood to be e.

The Natural Logarithmic Function

The function defined by

$$f(x) = \log_e x = \ln x, \quad x > 0$$

is called the **natural logarithmic function.**

The definition above implies that the natural logarithmic function and the natural exponential function are inverse functions of each other. So, every logarithmic equation can be written in an equivalent exponential form and every exponential equation can be written in logarithmic form. That is, $y = \ln x$ and $x = e^y$ are equivalent equations.

Because the functions given by $f(x) = e^x$ and $g(x) = \ln x$ are inverse functions of each other, their graphs are reflections of each other in the line $y = x$. This reflective property is illustrated in Figure 3.18.

On most calculators, the natural logarithm is denoted by $\boxed{\text{LN}}$, as illustrated in Example 8.

Reflection of graph of $f(x) = e^x$ about the line $y = x$

FIGURE 3.18

STUDY TIP

Notice that as with every other logarithmic function, the domain of the natural logarithmic function is the set of *positive real numbers*—be sure you see that ln x is not defined for zero or for negative numbers.

Example 8   Evaluating the Natural Logarithmic Function

Use a calculator to evaluate the function given by $f(x) = \ln x$ for each value of x.

a. $x = 2$ **b.** $x = 0.3$ **c.** $x = -1$ **d.** $x = 1 + \sqrt{2}$

Solution

Function Value	Graphing Calculator Keystrokes	Display
a. $f(2) = \ln 2$	$\boxed{\text{LN}}$ 2 $\boxed{\text{ENTER}}$	0.6931472
b. $f(0.3) = \ln 0.3$	$\boxed{\text{LN}}$ .3 $\boxed{\text{ENTER}}$	−1.2039728
c. $f(-1) = \ln(-1)$	$\boxed{\text{LN}}$ $\boxed{(-)}$ 1 $\boxed{\text{ENTER}}$	ERROR
d. $f(1 + \sqrt{2}) = \ln(1 + \sqrt{2})$	$\boxed{\text{LN}}$ $\boxed{(}$ 1 $\boxed{+}$ $\boxed{\sqrt{\ }}$ 2 $\boxed{)}$ $\boxed{\text{ENTER}}$	0.8813736

✓CHECKPOINT   Now try Exercise 61.

In Example 8, be sure you see that $\ln(-1)$ gives an error message on most calculators. (Some calculators may display a complex number.) This occurs because the domain of ln x is the set of positive real numbers (see Figure 3.18). So, $\ln(-1)$ is undefined.

The four properties of logarithms listed on page 230 are also valid for natural logarithms.

Properties of Natural Logarithms

1. $\ln 1 = 0$ because $e^0 = 1$.

2. $\ln e = 1$ because $e^1 = e$.

3. $\ln e^x = x$ and $e^{\ln x} = x$ Inverse Properties

4. If $\ln x = \ln y$, then $x = y$.   One-to-One Property

Example 9   **Using Properties of Natural Logarithms**

Use the properties of natural logarithms to simplify each expression.

a. $\ln \dfrac{1}{e}$ **b.** $e^{\ln 5}$ **c.** $\dfrac{\ln 1}{3}$ **d.** $2 \ln e$

Solution

a. $\ln \dfrac{1}{e} = \ln e^{-1} = -1$ Inverse Property   **b.** $e^{\ln 5} = 5$ Inverse Property

c. $\dfrac{\ln 1}{3} = \dfrac{0}{3} = 0$ Property 1   **d.** $2 \ln e = 2(1) = 2$ Property 2

✓**CHECKPOINT**   Now try Exercise 65.

Example 10   **Finding the Domains of Logarithmic Functions**

Find the domain of each function.

a. $f(x) = \ln(x - 2)$ **b.** $g(x) = \ln(2 - x)$ **c.** $h(x) = \ln x^2$

Solution

a. Because $\ln(x - 2)$ is defined only if $x - 2 > 0$, it follows that the domain of f is $(2, \infty)$. The graph of f is shown in Figure 3.19.

b. Because $\ln(2 - x)$ is defined only if $2 - x > 0$, it follows that the domain of g is $(-\infty, 2)$. The graph of g is shown in Figure 3.20.

c. Because $\ln x^2$ is defined only if $x^2 > 0$, it follows that the domain of h is all real numbers except $x = 0$. The graph of h is shown in Figure 3.21.

FIGURE 3.19

FIGURE 3.20

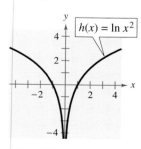

FIGURE 3.21

✓**CHECKPOINT**   Now try Exercise 69.

Memory Model

FIGURE **3.22**

Application

Example 11   Human Memory Model

Students participating in a psychology experiment attended several lectures on a subject and were given an exam. Every month for a year after the exam, the students were retested to see how much of the material they remembered. The average scores for the group are given by the *human memory model*

$$f(t) = 75 - 6 \ln(t + 1), \quad 0 \le t \le 12$$

where t is the time in months. The graph of f is shown in Figure 3.22.

a. What was the average score on the original ($t = 0$) exam?

b. What was the average score at the end of $t = 2$ months?

c. What was the average score at the end of $t = 6$ months?

Solution

a. The original average score was

$$f(0) = 75 - 6 \ln(0 + 1) \qquad \text{Substitute 0 for } t.$$

$$= 75 - 6 \ln 1 \qquad \text{Simplify.}$$

$$= 75 - 6(0) \qquad \text{Property of natural logarithms}$$

$$= 75. \qquad \text{Solution}$$

b. After 2 months, the average score was

$$f(2) = 75 - 6 \ln(2 + 1) \qquad \text{Substitute 2 for } t.$$

$$= 75 - 6 \ln 3 \qquad \text{Simplify.}$$

$$\approx 75 - 6(1.0986) \qquad \text{Use a calculator.}$$

$$\approx 68.4. \qquad \text{Solution}$$

c. After 6 months, the average score was

$$f(6) = 75 - 6 \ln(6 + 1) \qquad \text{Substitute 6 for } t.$$

$$= 75 - 6 \ln 7 \qquad \text{Simplify.}$$

$$\approx 75 - 6(1.9459) \qquad \text{Use a calculator.}$$

$$\approx 63.3. \qquad \text{Solution}$$

✓CHECKPOINT   Now try Exercise 89.

---

*W*RITING ABOUT *M*ATHEMATICS

Analyzing a Human Memory Model Use a graphing utility to determine the time in months when the average score in Example 11 was 60. Explain your method of solving the problem. Describe another way that you can use a graphing utility to determine the answer.

3.2 | Exercises

VOCABULARY CHECK: Fill in the blanks.

1. The inverse function of the exponential function given by $f(x) = a^x$ is called the _____ function with base a.
2. The common logarithmic function has base _____ .
3. The logarithmic function given by $f(x) = \ln x$ is called the _____ logarithmic function and has base _____.
4. The Inverse Property of logarithms and exponentials states that $\log_a a^x = x$ and _____.
5. The One-to-One Property of natural logarithms states that if $\ln x = \ln y$, then _____.

PREREQUISITE SKILLS REVIEW: Practice and review algebra skills needed for this section at **www.Eduspace.com**.

In Exercises 1–8, write the logarithmic equation in exponential form. For example, the exponential form of $\log_5 25 = 2$ is $5^2 = 25$.

1. $\log_4 64 = 3$ **2.** $\log_3 81 = 4$
3. $\log_7 \frac{1}{49} = -2$ **4.** $\log \frac{1}{1000} = -3$
5. $\log_{32} 4 = \frac{2}{5}$ **6.** $\log_{16} 8 = \frac{3}{4}$
7. $\log_{36} 6 = \frac{1}{2}$ **8.** $\log_8 4 = \frac{2}{3}$

In Exercises 9–16, write the exponential equation in logarithmic form. For example, the logarithmic form of $2^3 = 8$ is $\log_2 8 = 3$.

9. $5^3 = 125$ **10.** $8^2 = 64$
11. $81^{1/4} = 3$ **12.** $9^{3/2} = 27$
13. $6^{-2} = \frac{1}{36}$ **14.** $4^{-3} = \frac{1}{64}$
15. $7^0 = 1$ **16.** $10^{-3} = 0.001$

In Exercises 17–22, evaluate the function at the indicated value of x without using a calculator.

Function	Value
17. $f(x) = \log_2 x$	$x = 16$
18. $f(x) = \log_{16} x$	$x = 4$
19. $f(x) = \log_7 x$	$x = 1$
20. $f(x) = \log x$	$x = 10$
21. $g(x) = \log_a x$	$x = a^2$
22. $g(x) = \log_b x$	$x = b^{-3}$

 In Exercises 23–26, use a calculator to evaluate $f(x) = \log x$ at the indicated value of x. Round your result to three decimal places.

23. $x = \frac{4}{5}$ **24.** $x = \frac{1}{500}$
25. $x = 12.5$ **26.** $x = 75.25$

In Exercises 27–30, use the properties of logarithms to simplify the expression.

27. $\log_3 3^4$ **28.** $\log_{1.5} 1$
29. $\log_\pi \pi$ **30.** $9^{\log_9 15}$

In Exercises 31–38, find the domain, x-intercept, and vertical asymptote of the logarithmic function and sketch its graph.

31. $f(x) = \log_4 x$ **32.** $g(x) = \log_6 x$
33. $y = -\log_3 x + 2$ **34.** $h(x) = \log_4(x - 3)$
35. $f(x) = -\log_6(x + 2)$ **36.** $y = \log_5(x - 1) + 4$
37. $y = \log\left(\dfrac{x}{5}\right)$ **38.** $y = \log(-x)$

In Exercises 39–44, use the graph of $g(x) = \log_3 x$ to match the given function with its graph. Then describe the relationship between the graphs of f and g. [The graphs are labeled (a), (b), (c), (d), (e), and (f).]

(a)

(b)

(c)

(d)

(e)

(f)
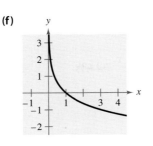

39. $f(x) = \log_3 x + 2$

40. $f(x) = -\log_3 x$

41. $f(x) = -\log_3(x + 2)$

42. $f(x) = \log_3(x - 1)$

43. $f(x) = \log_3(1 - x)$

44. $f(x) = -\log_3(-x)$

In Exercises 45–52, write the logarithmic equation in exponential form.

45. $\ln \frac{1}{2} = -0.693 \ldots$

46. $\ln \frac{2}{5} = -0.916 \ldots$

47. $\ln 4 = 1.386 \ldots$

48. $\ln 10 = 2.302 \ldots$

49. $\ln 250 = 5.521 \ldots$

50. $\ln 679 = 6.520 \ldots$

51. $\ln 1 = 0$

52. $\ln e = 1$

In Exercises 53–60, write the exponential equation in logarithmic form.

53. $e^3 = 20.0855 \ldots$

54. $e^2 = 7.3890 \ldots$

55. $e^{1/2} = 1.6487 \ldots$

56. $e^{1/3} = 1.3956 \ldots$

57. $e^{-0.5} = 0.6065 \ldots$

58. $e^{-4.1} = 0.0165 \ldots$

59. $e^x = 4$

60. $e^{2x} = 3$

In Exercises 61–64, use a calculator to evaluate the function at the indicated value of x. Round your result to three decimal places.

Function	Value
61. $f(x) = \ln x$	$x = 18.42$
62. $f(x) = 3 \ln x$	$x = 0.32$
63. $g(x) = 2 \ln x$	$x = 0.75$
64. $g(x) = -\ln x$	$x = \frac{1}{2}$

In Exercises 65–68, evaluate $g(x) = \ln x$ at the indicated value of x without using a calculator.

65. $x = e^3$

66. $x = e^{-2}$

67. $x = e^{-2/3}$

68. $x = e^{-5/2}$

In Exercises 69–72, find the domain, x-intercept, and vertical asymptote of the logarithmic function and sketch its graph.

69. $f(x) = \ln(x - 1)$

70. $h(x) = \ln(x + 1)$

71. $g(x) = \ln(-x)$

72. $f(x) = \ln(3 - x)$

 In Exercises 73–78, use a graphing utility to graph the function. Be sure to use an appropriate viewing window.

73. $f(x) = \log(x + 1)$

74. $f(x) = \log(x - 1)$

75. $f(x) = \ln(x - 1)$

76. $f(x) = \ln(x + 2)$

77. $f(x) = \ln x + 2$

78. $f(x) = 3 \ln x - 1$

In Exercises 79–86, use the One-to-One Property to solve the equation for x.

79. $\log_2(x + 1) = \log_2 4$

80. $\log_2(x - 3) = \log_2 9$

81. $\log(2x + 1) = \log 15$

82. $\log(5x + 3) = \log 12$

83. $\ln(x + 2) = \ln 6$

84. $\ln(x - 4) = \ln 2$

85. $\ln(x^2 - 2) = \ln 23$

86. $\ln(x^2 - x) = \ln 6$

Model It

87. *Monthly Payment* The model

$$t = 12.542 \ln\left(\frac{x}{x - 1000}\right), \quad x > 1000$$

approximates the length of a home mortgage of $150,000 at 8% in terms of the monthly payment. In the model, t is the length of the mortgage in years and x is the monthly payment in dollars (see figure).

(a) Use the model to approximate the lengths of a $150,000 mortgage at 8% when the monthly payment is $1100.65 and when the monthly payment is $1254.68.

(b) Approximate the total amounts paid over the term of the mortgage with a monthly payment of $1100.65 and with a monthly payment of $1254.68.

(c) Approximate the total interest charges for a monthly payment of $1100.65 and for a monthly payment of $1254.68.

(d) What is the vertical asymptote for the model? Interpret its meaning in the context of the problem.

88. *Compound Interest* A principal P, invested at $9\frac{1}{2}\%$ and compounded continuously, increases to an amount K times the original principal after t years, where t is given by $t = (\ln K)/0.095$.

(a) Complete the table and interpret your results.

K	1	2	4	6	8	10	12
t							

(b) Sketch a graph of the function.

89. *Human Memory Model* Students in a mathematics class were given an exam and then retested monthly with an equivalent exam. The average scores for the class are given by the human memory model $f(t) = 80 - 17\log(t + 1)$, $0 \le t \le 12$ where t is the time in months.

 (a) Use a graphing utility to graph the model over the specified domain.

(b) What was the average score on the original exam $(t = 0)$?

(c) What was the average score after 4 months?

(d) What was the average score after 10 months?

90. *Sound Intensity* The relationship between the number of decibels β and the intensity of a sound I in watts per square meter is

$$\beta = 10\log\left(\frac{I}{10^{-12}}\right).$$

(a) Determine the number of decibels of a sound with an intensity of 1 watt per square meter.

(b) Determine the number of decibels of a sound with an intensity of 10^{-2} watt per square meter.

(c) The intensity of the sound in part (a) is 100 times as great as that in part (b). Is the number of decibels 100 times as great? Explain.

Synthesis

True or False? In Exercises 91 and 92, determine whether the statement is true or false. Justify your answer.

91. You can determine the graph of $f(x) = \log_6 x$ by graphing $g(x) = 6^x$ and reflecting it about the x-axis.

92. The graph of $f(x) = \log_3 x$ contains the point $(27, 3)$.

In Exercises 93–96, sketch the graph of f and g and describe the relationship between the graphs of f and g. What is the relationship between the functions f and g?

93. $f(x) = 3^x$, $g(x) = \log_3 x$

94. $f(x) = 5^x$, $g(x) = \log_5 x$

95. $f(x) = e^x$, $g(x) = \ln x$

96. $f(x) = 10^x$, $g(x) = \log x$

 97. *Graphical Analysis* Use a graphing utility to graph f and g in the same viewing window and determine which is increasing at the greater rate as x approaches $+\infty$. What can you conclude about the rate of growth of the natural logarithmic function?

(a) $f(x) = \ln x$, $g(x) = \sqrt{x}$

(b) $f(x) = \ln x$, $g(x) = \sqrt[4]{x}$

98. (a) Complete the table for the function given by

$$f(x) = \frac{\ln x}{x}.$$

x	1	5	10	10^2	10^4	10^6
$f(x)$						

(b) Use the table in part (a) to determine what value $f(x)$ approaches as x increases without bound.

(c) Use a graphing utility to confirm the result of part (b).

99. *Think About It* The table of values was obtained by evaluating a function. Determine which of the statements may be true and which must be false.

x	1	2	8
y	0	1	3

(a) y is an exponential function of x.

(b) y is a logarithmic function of x.

(c) x is an exponential function of y.

(d) y is a linear function of x.

100. *Writing* Explain why $\log_a x$ is defined only for $0 < a < 1$ and $a > 1$.

 In Exercises 101 and 102, (a) use a graphing utility to graph the function, (b) use the graph to determine the intervals in which the function is increasing and decreasing, and (c) approximate any relative maximum or minimum values of the function.

101. $f(x) = |\ln x|$

102. $h(x) = \ln(x^2 + 1)$

Skills Review

In Exercises 103–108, evaluate the function for $f(x) = 3x + 2$ and $g(x) = x^3 - 1$.

103. $(f + g)(2)$

104. $(f - g)(-1)$

105. $(fg)(6)$

106. $\left(\dfrac{f}{g}\right)(0)$

107. $(f \circ g)(7)$

108. $(g \circ f)(-3)$

3.3   Properties of Logarithms

What you should learn

• Use the change-of-base formula to rewrite and evaluate logarithmic expressions.
• Use properties of logarithms to evaluate or rewrite logarithmic expressions.
• Use properties of logarithms to expand or condense logarithmic expressions.
• Use logarithmic functions to model and solve real-life problems.

Why you should learn it

Logarithmic functions can be used to model and solve real-life problems. For instance, in Exercises 81–83 on page 244, a logarithmic function is used to model the relationship between the number of decibels and the intensity of a sound.

AP Photo/Stephen Chernin

Change of Base

Most calculators have only two types of log keys, one for common logarithms (base 10) and one for natural logarithms (base e). Although common logs and natural logs are the most frequently used, you may occasionally need to evaluate logarithms to other bases. To do this, you can use the following **change-of-base formula.**

> ### Change-of-Base Formula
>
> Let a, b, and x be positive real numbers such that $a \neq 1$ and $b \neq 1$. Then $\log_a x$ can be converted to a different base as follows.
>
> | Base b | Base 10 | Base e |
> |----------|---------|----------|
> | $\log_a x = \dfrac{\log_b x}{\log_b a}$ | $\log_a x = \dfrac{\log x}{\log a}$ | $\log_a x = \dfrac{\ln x}{\ln a}$ |

One way to look at the change-of-base formula is that logarithms to base a are simply *constant multiples* of logarithms to base b. The constant multiplier is $1/(\log_b a)$.

Example 1   Changing Bases Using Common Logarithms

a. $\log_4 25 = \dfrac{\log 25}{\log 4}$ $\log_a x = \dfrac{\log x}{\log a}$

$\approx \dfrac{1.39794}{0.60206}$ Use a calculator.

≈ 2.3219 Simplify.

b. $\log_2 12 = \dfrac{\log 12}{\log 2} \approx \dfrac{1.07918}{0.30103} \approx 3.5850$

✓CHECKPOINT   Now try Exercise 1(a).

Example 2   Changing Bases Using Natural Logarithms

a. $\log_4 25 = \dfrac{\ln 25}{\ln 4}$ $\log_a x = \dfrac{\ln x}{\ln a}$

$\approx \dfrac{3.21888}{1.38629}$ Use a calculator.

≈ 2.3219 Simplify.

b. $\log_2 12 = \dfrac{\ln 12}{\ln 2} \approx \dfrac{2.48491}{0.69315} \approx 3.5850$

✓CHECKPOINT   Now try Exercise 1(b).

Properties of Logarithms

You know from the preceding section that the logarithmic function with base a is the *inverse function* of the exponential function with base a. So, it makes sense that the properties of exponents should have corresponding properties involving logarithms. For instance, the exponential property $a^0 = 1$ has the corresponding logarithmic property $\log_a 1 = 0$.

Properties of Logarithms

Let a be a positive number such that $a \neq 1$, and let n be a real number. If u and v are positive real numbers, the following properties are true.

	Logarithm with Base a	*Natural Logarithm*
1. Product Property:	$\log_a(uv) = \log_a u + \log_a v$	$\ln(uv) = \ln u + \ln v$
2. Quotient Property:	$\log_a \dfrac{u}{v} = \log_a u - \log_a v$	$\ln \dfrac{u}{v} = \ln u - \ln v$
3. Power Property:	$\log_a u^n = n \log_a u$	$\ln u^n = n \ln u$

For proofs of the properties listed above, see Proofs in Mathematics on page 278.

Example 3   **Using Properties of Logarithms**

Write each logarithm in terms of $\ln 2$ and $\ln 3$.

a. $\ln 6$ **b.** $\ln \dfrac{2}{27}$

Solution

a. $\ln 6 = \ln(2 \cdot 3)$ $\qquad$ Rewrite 6 as $2 \cdot 3$.

$\qquad = \ln 2 + \ln 3$ $\qquad$ Product Property

b. $\ln \dfrac{2}{27} = \ln 2 - \ln 27$ $\qquad$ Quotient Property

$\qquad = \ln 2 - \ln 3^3$ $\qquad$ Rewrite 27 as 3^3.

$\qquad = \ln 2 - 3 \ln 3$ $\qquad$ Power Property

✓CHECKPOINT   Now try Exercise 17.

Example 4   **Using Properties of Logarithms**

Find the exact value of each expression without using a calculator.

a. $\log_5 \sqrt[3]{5}$ **b.** $\ln e^6 - \ln e^2$

Solution

a. $\log_5 \sqrt[3]{5} = \log_5 5^{1/3} = \frac{1}{3} \log_5 5 = \frac{1}{3}(1) = \frac{1}{3}$

b. $\ln e^6 - \ln e^2 = \ln \dfrac{e^6}{e^2} = \ln e^4 = 4 \ln e = 4(1) = 4$

✓CHECKPOINT   Now try Exercise 23.

The Granger Collection

Historical Note
John Napier, a Scottish mathematician, developed logarithms as a way to simplify some of the tedious calculations of his day. Beginning in 1594, Napier worked about 20 years on the invention of logarithms. Napier was only partially successful in his quest to simplify tedious calculations. Nonetheless, the development of logarithms was a step forward and received immediate recognition.

Rewriting Logarithmic Expressions

The properties of logarithms are useful for rewriting logarithmic expressions in forms that simplify the operations of algebra. This is true because these properties convert complicated products, quotients, and exponential forms into simpler sums, differences, and products, respectively.

Example 5   Expanding Logarithmic Expressions

Expand each logarithmic expression.

a. $\log_4 5x^3 y$ **b.** $\ln \dfrac{\sqrt{3x-5}}{7}$

Solution

a. $\log_4 5x^3 y = \log_4 5 + \log_4 x^3 + \log_4 y$ Product Property

$\qquad\qquad\quad = \log_4 5 + 3\log_4 x + \log_4 y$ Power Property

b. $\ln \dfrac{\sqrt{3x-5}}{7} = \ln \dfrac{(3x-5)^{1/2}}{7}$ Rewrite using rational exponent.

$\qquad\qquad\quad = \ln(3x - 5)^{1/2} - \ln 7$ Quotient Property

$\qquad\qquad\quad = \dfrac{1}{2}\ln(3x - 5) - \ln 7$ Power Property

✓**CHECKPOINT**   Now try Exercise 47.

In Example 5, the properties of logarithms were used to *expand* logarithmic expressions. In Example 6, this procedure is reversed and the properties of logarithms are used to *condense* logarithmic expressions.

Example 6   Condensing Logarithmic Expressions

Condense each logarithmic expression.

a. $\frac{1}{2}\log x + 3\log(x + 1)$ **b.** $2\ln(x + 2) - \ln x$

c. $\frac{1}{3}[\log_2 x + \log_2(x + 1)]$

Solution

a. $\frac{1}{2}\log x + 3\log(x + 1) = \log x^{1/2} + \log(x + 1)^3$ Power Property

$\qquad\qquad\qquad\qquad = \log\left[\sqrt{x}(x + 1)^3\right]$ Product Property

b. $2\ln(x + 2) - \ln x = \ln(x + 2)^2 - \ln x$ Power Property

$\qquad\qquad\qquad\quad = \ln \dfrac{(x + 2)^2}{x}$ Quotient Property

c. $\frac{1}{3}[\log_2 x + \log_2(x + 1)] = \frac{1}{3}\{\log_2[x(x + 1)]\}$ Product Property

$\qquad\qquad\qquad\qquad = \log_2[x(x + 1)]^{1/3}$ Power Property

$\qquad\qquad\qquad\qquad = \log_2 \sqrt[3]{x(x + 1)}$ Rewrite with a radical.

✓**CHECKPOINT**   Now try Exercise 69.

Application

One method of determining how the x- and y-values for a set of nonlinear data are related is to take the natural logarithm of each of the x- and y-values. If the points are graphed and fall on a line, then you can determine that the x- and y-values are related by the equation

$$\ln y = m \ln x$$

where m is the slope of the line.

Example 7   Finding a Mathematical Model

The table shows the mean distance x and the period (the time it takes a planet to orbit the sun) y for each of the six planets that are closest to the sun. In the table, the mean distance is given in terms of astronomical units (where Earth's mean distance is defined as 1.0), and the period is given in years. Find an equation that relates y and x.

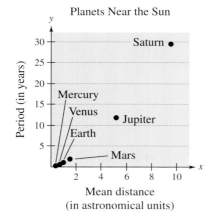

Planets Near the Sun

Period (in years) vs Mean distance (in astronomical units)

FIGURE 3.23

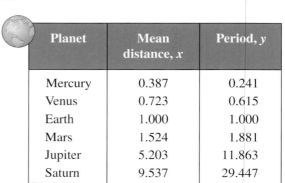

Planet	Mean distance, x	Period, y
Mercury	0.387	0.241
Venus	0.723	0.615
Earth	1.000	1.000
Mars	1.524	1.881
Jupiter	5.203	11.863
Saturn	9.537	29.447

Solution

The points in the table above are plotted in Figure 3.23. From this figure it is not clear how to find an equation that relates y and x. To solve this problem, take the natural logarithm of each of the x- and y-values in the table. This produces the following results.

Planet	Mercury	Venus	Earth	Mars	Jupiter	Saturn
ln x	−0.949	−0.324	0.000	0.421	1.649	2.255
ln y	−1.423	−0.486	0.000	0.632	2.473	3.383

Now, by plotting the points in the second table, you can see that all six of the points appear to lie in a line (see Figure 3.24). Choose any two points to determine the slope of the line. Using the two points $(0.421, 0.632)$ and $(0, 0)$, you can determine that the slope of the line is

$$m = \frac{0.632 - 0}{0.421 - 0} \approx 1.5 = \frac{3}{2}.$$

By the point-slope form, the equation of the line is $Y = \frac{3}{2}X$, where $Y = \ln y$ and $X = \ln x$. You can therefore conclude that $\ln y = \frac{3}{2} \ln x$.

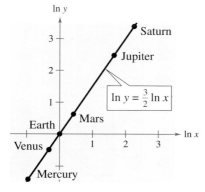

FIGURE 3.24

✓**CHECKPOINT**   Now try Exercise 85.

3.3 | Exercises

VOCABULARY CHECK:

In Exercises 1 and 2, fill in the blanks.

1. To evaluate a logarithm to any base, you can use the _____ formula.

2. The change-of-base formula for base e is given by $\log_a x =$ _____.

In Exercises 3–5, match the property of logarithms with its name.

3. $\log_a(uv) = \log_a u + \log_a v$ (a) Power Property

4. $\ln u^n = n \ln u$ (b) Quotient Property

5. $\log_a \dfrac{u}{v} = \log_a u - \log_a v$ (c) Product Property

PREREQUISITE SKILLS REVIEW: Practice and review algebra skills needed for this section at **www.Eduspace.com.**

In Exercises 1–8, rewrite the logarithm as a ratio of (a) common logarithms and (b) natural logarithms.

1. $\log_5 x$

2. $\log_3 x$

3. $\log_{1/5} x$

4. $\log_{1/3} x$

5. $\log_x \frac{3}{10}$

6. $\log_x \frac{3}{4}$

7. $\log_{2.6} x$

8. $\log_{7.1} x$

In Exercises 9–16, evaluate the logarithm using the change-of-base formula. Round your result to three decimal places.

9. $\log_3 7$

10. $\log_7 4$

11. $\log_{1/2} 4$

12. $\log_{1/4} 5$

13. $\log_9 0.4$

14. $\log_{20} 0.125$

15. $\log_{15} 1250$

16. $\log_3 0.015$

In Exercises 17–22, use the properties of logarithms to rewrite and simplify the logarithmic expression.

17. $\log_4 8$

18. $\log_2(4^2 \cdot 3^4)$

19. $\log_5 \frac{1}{250}$

20. $\log \frac{9}{300}$

21. $\ln(5e^6)$

22. $\ln \dfrac{6}{e^2}$

In Exercises 23–38, find the exact value of the logarithmic expression without using a calculator. (If this is not possible, state the reason.)

23. $\log_3 9$

24. $\log_5 \frac{1}{125}$

25. $\log_2 \sqrt[4]{8}$

26. $\log_6 \sqrt[3]{6}$

27. $\log_4 16^{1.2}$

28. $\log_3 81^{-0.2}$

29. $\log_3(-9)$

30. $\log_2(-16)$

31. $\ln e^{4.5}$

32. $3 \ln e^4$

33. $\ln \dfrac{1}{\sqrt{e}}$

34. $\ln \sqrt[4]{e^3}$

35. $\ln e^2 + \ln e^5$

36. $2 \ln e^6 - \ln e^5$

37. $\log_5 75 - \log_5 3$

38. $\log_4 2 + \log_4 32$

In Exercises 39–60, use the properties of logarithms to expand the expression as a sum, difference, and/or constant multiple of logarithms. (Assume all variables are positive.)

39. $\log_4 5x$

40. $\log_3 10z$

41. $\log_8 x^4$

42. $\log_{10} \dfrac{y}{2}$

43. $\log_5 \dfrac{5}{x}$

44. $\log_6 \dfrac{1}{z^3}$

45. $\ln \sqrt{z}$

46. $\ln \sqrt[3]{t}$

47. $\ln xyz^2$

48. $\log 4x^2 y$

49. $\ln z(z-1)^2$, $z > 1$

50. $\ln\left(\dfrac{x^2-1}{x^3}\right)$, $x > 1$

51. $\log_2 \dfrac{\sqrt{a-1}}{9}$, $a > 1$

52. $\ln \dfrac{6}{\sqrt{x^2+1}}$

53. $\ln \sqrt[3]{\dfrac{x}{y}}$

54. $\ln \sqrt{\dfrac{x^2}{y^3}}$

55. $\ln \dfrac{x^4 \sqrt{y}}{z^5}$

56. $\log_2 \dfrac{\sqrt{x}\, y^4}{z^4}$

57. $\log_5 \dfrac{x^2}{y^2 z^3}$

58. $\log_{10} \dfrac{xy^4}{z^5}$

59. $\ln \sqrt[4]{x^3(x^2+3)}$

60. $\ln \sqrt{x^2(x+2)}$

In Exercises 61–78, condense the expression to the logarithm of a single quantity.

61. $\ln x + \ln 3$

62. $\ln y + \ln t$

63. $\log_4 z - \log_4 y$

64. $\log_5 8 - \log_5 t$

65. $2 \log_2(x + 4)$

66. $\frac{2}{3} \log_7(z - 2)$

67. $\frac{1}{4} \log_3 5x$

68. $-4 \log_6 2x$

69. $\ln x - 3 \ln(x + 1)$

70. $2 \ln 8 + 5 \ln(z - 4)$

71. $\log x - 2 \log y + 3 \log z$

72. $3 \log_3 x + 4 \log_3 y - 4 \log_3 z$

73. $\ln x - 4[\ln(x + 2) + \ln(x - 2)]$

74. $4[\ln z + \ln(z + 5)] - 2 \ln(z - 5)$

75. $\frac{1}{3}[2 \ln(x + 3) + \ln x - \ln(x^2 - 1)]$

76. $2[3 \ln x - \ln(x + 1) - \ln(x - 1)]$

77. $\frac{1}{3}[\log_8 y + 2 \log_8(y + 4)] - \log_8(y - 1)$

78. $\frac{1}{2}[\log_4(x + 1) + 2 \log_4(x - 1)] + 6 \log_4 x$

In Exercises 79 and 80, compare the logarithmic quantities. If two are equal, explain why.

79. $\dfrac{\log_2 32}{\log_2 4}, \quad \log_2 \dfrac{32}{4}, \quad \log_2 32 - \log_2 4$

80. $\log_7 \sqrt{70}, \quad \log_7 35, \quad \frac{1}{2} + \log_7 \sqrt{10}$

Sound Intensity **In Exercises 81–83, use the following information. The relationship between the number of decibels β and the intensity of a sound I in watts per square meter is given by**

$$\beta = 10 \log\left(\frac{I}{10^{-12}}\right).$$

81. Use the properties of logarithms to write the formula in simpler form, and determine the number of decibels of a sound with an intensity of 10^{-6} watt per square meter.

82. Find the difference in loudness between an average office with an intensity of 1.26×10^{-7} watt per square meter and a broadcast studio with an intensity of 3.16×10^{-5} watt per square meter.

83. You and your roommate are playing your stereos at the same time and at the same intensity. How much louder is the music when both stereos are playing compared with just one stereo playing?

Model It

84. ***Human Memory Model*** Students participating in a psychology experiment attended several lectures and were given an exam. Every month for a year after the exam, the students were retested to see how much of the material they remembered. The average scores for the group can be modeled by the human memory model

$$f(t) = 90 - 15 \log(t + 1), \quad 0 \le t \le 12$$

where t is the time in months.

(a) Use the properties of logarithms to write the function in another form.

(b) What was the average score on the original exam $(t = 0)$?

(c) What was the average score after 4 months?

(d) What was the average score after 12 months?

 (e) Use a graphing utility to graph the function over the specified domain.

(f) Use the graph in part (e) to determine when the average score will decrease to 75.

(g) Verify your answer to part (f) numerically.

85. ***Galloping Speeds of Animals*** Four-legged animals run with two different types of motion: trotting and galloping. An animal that is trotting has at least one foot on the ground at all times, whereas an animal that is galloping has all four feet off the ground at some point in its stride. The number of strides per minute at which an animal breaks from a trot to a gallop depends on the weight of the animal. Use the table to find a logarithmic equation that relates an animal's weight x (in pounds) and its lowest galloping speed y (in strides per minute).

Weight, x	Galloping Speed, y
25	191.5
35	182.7
50	173.8
75	164.2
500	125.9
1000	114.2

86. ***Comparing Models***   A cup of water at an initial temperature of 78° C is placed in a room at a constant temperature of 21° C. The temperature of the water is measured every 5 minutes during a half-hour period. The results are recorded as ordered pairs of the form (t, T), where t is the time (in minutes) and T is the temperature (in degrees Celsius).

(0, 78.0°), (5, 66.0°), (10, 57.5°), (15, 51.2°), (20, 46.3°), (25, 42.4°), (30, 39.6°)

(a) The graph of the model for the data should be asymptotic with the graph of the temperature of the room. Subtract the room temperature from each of the temperatures in the ordered pairs. Use a graphing utility to plot the data points (t, T) and $(t, T - 21)$.

(b) An exponential model for the data $(t, T - 21)$ is given by

$$T - 21 = 54.4(0.964)^t.$$

Solve for T and graph the model. Compare the result with the plot of the original data.

(c) Take the natural logarithms of the revised temperatures. Use a graphing utility to plot the points $(t, \ln(T - 21))$ and observe that the points appear to be linear. Use the *regression* feature of the graphing utility to fit a line to these data. This resulting line has the form

$$\ln(T - 21) = at + b.$$

Use the properties of the logarithms to solve for T. Verify that the result is equivalent to the model in part (b).

(d) Fit a rational model to the data. Take the reciprocals of the y-coordinates of the revised data points to generate the points

$$\left(t, \frac{1}{T - 21}\right).$$

Use a graphing utility to graph these points and observe that they appear to be linear. Use the *regression* feature of a graphing utility to fit a line to these data. The resulting line has the form

$$\frac{1}{T - 21} = at + b.$$

Solve for T, and use a graphing utility to graph the rational function and the original data points.

(e) Write a short paragraph explaining why the transformations of the data were necessary to obtain each model. Why did taking the logarithms of the temperatures lead to a linear scatter plot? Why did taking the reciprocals of the temperature lead to a linear scatter plot?

Synthesis

True or False?   In Exercises 87–92, determine whether the statement is true or false given that $f(x) = \ln x$. Justify your answer.

87. $f(0) = 0$

88. $f(ax) = f(a) + f(x), \quad a > 0, x > 0$

89. $f(x - 2) = f(x) - f(2), \quad x > 2$

90. $\sqrt{f(x)} = \frac{1}{2}f(x)$

91. If $f(u) = 2f(v)$, then $v = u^2$.

92. If $f(x) < 0$, then $0 < x < 1$.

93. ***Proof***   Prove that $\log_b \dfrac{u}{v} = \log_b u - \log_b v$.

94. ***Proof***   Prove that $\log_b u^n = n \log_b u$.

In Exercises 95–100, use the change-of-base formula to rewrite the logarithm as a ratio of logarithms. Then use a graphing utility to graph both functions in the same viewing window to verify that the functions are equivalent.

95. $f(x) = \log_2 x$

96. $f(x) = \log_4 x$

97. $f(x) = \log_{1/2} x$

98. $f(x) = \log_{1/4} x$

99. $f(x) = \log_{11.8} x$

100. $f(x) = \log_{12.4} x$

101. ***Think About It***   Consider the functions below.

$$f(x) = \ln \frac{x}{2}, \quad g(x) = \frac{\ln x}{\ln 2}, \quad h(x) = \ln x - \ln 2$$

Which two functions should have identical graphs? Verify your answer by sketching the graphs of all three functions on the same set of coordinate axes.

102. ***Exploration***   For how many integers between 1 and 20 can the natural logarithms be approximated given that $\ln 2 \approx 0.6931$, $\ln 3 \approx 1.0986$,   and $\ln 5 \approx 1.6094$? Approximate these logarithms (do not use a calculator).

Skills Review

In Exercises 103–106, simplify the expression.

103. $\dfrac{24xy^{-2}}{16x^{-3}y}$

104. $\left(\dfrac{2x^2}{3y}\right)^{-3}$

105. $(18x^3y^4)^{-3}(18x^3y^4)^3$

106. $xy(x^{-1} + y^{-1})^{-1}$

In Exercises 107–110, solve the equation.

107. $3x^2 + 2x - 1 = 0$

108. $4x^2 - 5x + 1 = 0$

109. $\dfrac{2}{3x + 1} = \dfrac{x}{4}$

110. $\dfrac{5}{x - 1} = \dfrac{2x}{3}$

3.4 Exponential and Logarithmic Equations

What you should learn

- Solve simple exponential and logarithmic equations.
- Solve more complicated exponential equations.
- Solve more complicated logarithmic equations.
- Use exponential and logarithmic equations to model and solve real-life problems.

Why you should learn it

Exponential and logarithmic equations are used to model and solve life science applications. For instance, in Exercise 112, on page 255, a logarithmic function is used to model the number of trees per acre given the average diameter of the trees.

© James Marshall/Corbis

Introduction

So far in this chapter, you have studied the definitions, graphs, and properties of exponential and logarithmic functions. In this section, you will study procedures for *solving equations* involving these exponential and logarithmic functions.

There are two basic strategies for solving exponential or logarithmic equations. The first is based on the One-to-One Properties and was used to solve simple exponential and logarithmic equations in Sections 3.1 and 3.2. The second is based on the Inverse Properties. For $a > 0$ and $a \neq 1$, the following properties are true for all x and y for which $\log_a x$ and $\log_a y$ are defined.

One-to-One Properties

$a^x = a^y$ if and only if $x = y$.

$\log_a x = \log_a y$ if and only if $x = y$.

Inverse Properties

$a^{\log_a x} = x$

$\log_a a^x = x$

Example 1 Solving Simple Equations

	Original Equation	Rewritten Equation	Solution	Property
a.	$2^x = 32$	$2^x = 2^5$	$x = 5$	One-to-One
b.	$\ln x - \ln 3 = 0$	$\ln x = \ln 3$	$x = 3$	One-to-One
c.	$\left(\frac{1}{3}\right)^x = 9$	$3^{-x} = 3^2$	$x = -2$	One-to-One
d.	$e^x = 7$	$\ln e^x = \ln 7$	$x = \ln 7$	Inverse
e.	$\ln x = -3$	$e^{\ln x} = e^{-3}$	$x = e^{-3}$	Inverse
f.	$\log x = -1$	$10^{\log x} = 10^{-1}$	$x = 10^{-1} = \frac{1}{10}$	Inverse

✓CHECKPOINT Now try Exercise 13.

The strategies used in Example 1 are summarized as follows.

Strategies for Solving Exponential and Logarithmic Equations

1. Rewrite the original equation in a form that allows the use of the One-to-One Properties of exponential or logarithmic functions.

2. Rewrite an *exponential* equation in logarithmic form and apply the Inverse Property of logarithmic functions.

3. Rewrite a *logarithmic* equation in exponential form and apply the Inverse Property of exponential functions.

Solving Exponential Equations

Example 2 **Solving Exponential Equations**

Solve each equation and approximate the result to three decimal places if necessary.

a. $e^{-x^2} = e^{-3x-4}$ **b.** $3(2^x) = 42$

Solution

a.

$e^{-x^2} = e^{-3x-4}$	Write original equation.
$-x^2 = -3x - 4$	One-to-One Property
$x^2 - 3x - 4 = 0$	Write in general form.
$(x + 1)(x - 4) = 0$	Factor.
$(x + 1) = 0 \Longrightarrow x = -1$	Set 1st factor equal to 0.
$(x - 4) = 0 \Longrightarrow x = 4$	Set 2nd factor equal to 0.

The solutions are $x = -1$ and $x = 4$. Check these in the original equation.

b.

$3(2^x) = 42$	Write original equation.
$2^x = 14$	Divide each side by 3.
$\log_2 2^x = \log_2 14$	Take log (base 2) of each side.
$x = \log_2 14$	Inverse Property
$x = \dfrac{\ln 14}{\ln 2} \approx 3.807$	Change-of-base formula

The solution is $x = \log_2 14 \approx 3.807$. Check this in the original equation.

✔**CHECKPOINT**   Now try Exercise 25.

In Example 2(b), the exact solution is $x = \log_2 14$ and the approximate solution is $x \approx 3.807$. An exact answer is preferred when the solution is an intermediate step in a larger problem. For a final answer, an approximate solution is easier to comprehend.

Example 3 **Solving an Exponential Equation**

Solve $e^x + 5 = 60$ and approximate the result to three decimal places.

Solution

$e^x + 5 = 60$	Write original equation.
$e^x = 55$	Subtract 5 from each side.
$\ln e^x = \ln 55$	Take natural log of each side.
$x = \ln 55 \approx 4.007$	Inverse Property

The solution is $x = \ln 55 \approx 4.007$. Check this in the original equation.

✔**CHECKPOINT**   Now try Exercise 51.

STUDY TIP

Remember that the natural logarithmic function has a base of e.

Example 4   **Solving an Exponential Equation**

Solve $2(3^{2t-5}) - 4 = 11$ and approximate the result to three decimal places.

Solution

$$2(3^{2t-5}) - 4 = 11 \qquad \text{Write original equation.}$$

$$2(3^{2t-5}) = 15 \qquad \text{Add 4 to each side.}$$

$$3^{2t-5} = \frac{15}{2} \qquad \text{Divide each side by 2.}$$

$$\log_3 3^{2t-5} = \log_3 \frac{15}{2} \qquad \text{Take log (base 3) of each side.}$$

$$2t - 5 = \log_3 \frac{15}{2} \qquad \text{Inverse Property}$$

$$2t = 5 + \log_3 7.5 \qquad \text{Add 5 to each side.}$$

$$t = \frac{5}{2} + \frac{1}{2}\log_3 7.5 \qquad \text{Divide each side by 2.}$$

$$t \approx 3.417 \qquad \text{Use a calculator.}$$

The solution is $t = \frac{5}{2} + \frac{1}{2}\log_3 7.5 \approx 3.417$. Check this in the original equation.

✓**CHECKPOINT**   Now try Exercise 53.

> **STUDY TIP**
>
> Remember that to evaluate a logarithm such as $\log_3 7.5$, you need to use the change-of-base formula.
>
> $$\log_3 7.5 = \frac{\ln 7.5}{\ln 3} \approx 1.834$$

When an equation involves two or more exponential expressions, you can still use a procedure similar to that demonstrated in Examples 2, 3, and 4. However, the algebra is a bit more complicated.

Example 5   **Solving an Exponential Equation of Quadratic Type**

Solve $e^{2x} - 3e^x + 2 = 0$.

Algebraic Solution

$$e^{2x} - 3e^x + 2 = 0 \qquad \text{Write original equation.}$$

$$(e^x)^2 - 3e^x + 2 = 0 \qquad \text{Write in quadratic form.}$$

$$(e^x - 2)(e^x - 1) = 0 \qquad \text{Factor.}$$

$$e^x - 2 = 0 \qquad \text{Set 1st factor equal to 0.}$$

$$x = \ln 2 \qquad \text{Solution}$$

$$e^x - 1 = 0 \qquad \text{Set 2nd factor equal to 0.}$$

$$x = 0 \qquad \text{Solution}$$

The solutions are $x = \ln 2 \approx 0.693$ and $x = 0$. Check these in the original equation.

✓**CHECKPOINT**   Now try Exercise 67.

Graphical Solution

Use a graphing utility to graph $y = e^{2x} - 3e^x + 2$. Use the *zero* or *root* feature or the *zoom* and *trace* features of the graphing utility to approximate the values of x for which $y = 0$. In Figure 3.25, you can see that the zeros occur at $x = 0$ and at $x \approx 0.693$. So, the solutions are $x = 0$ and $x \approx 0.693$.

FIGURE 3.25

Solving Logarithmic Equations

To solve a logarithmic equation, you can write it in exponential form.

$\ln x = 3$	Logarithmic form
$e^{\ln x} = e^3$	Exponentiate each side.
$x = e^3$	Exponential form

This procedure is called *exponentiating* each side of an equation.

Example 6   Solving Logarithmic Equations

a. $\ln x = 2$ Original equation

$e^{\ln x} = e^2$ Exponentiate each side.

$x = e^2$ Inverse Property

b. $\log_3(5x - 1) = \log_3(x + 7)$ Original equation

$5x - 1 = x + 7$ One-to-One Property

$4x = 8$ Add $-x$ and 1 to each side.

$x = 2$ Divide each side by 4.

c. $\log_6(3x + 14) - \log_6 5 = \log_6 2x$ Original equation

 $\log_6\left(\dfrac{3x + 14}{5}\right) = \log_6 2x$ Quotient Property of Logarithms

$\dfrac{3x + 14}{5} = 2x$ One-to-One Property

$3x + 14 = 10x$ Cross multiply.

$-7x = -14$ Isolate x.

$x = 2$ Divide each side by -7.

✓CHECKPOINT   Now try Exercise 77.

Example 7   Solving a Logarithmic Equation

Solve $5 + 2 \ln x = 4$ and approximate the result to three decimal places.

Solution

$5 + 2 \ln x = 4$	Write original equation.
$2 \ln x = -1$	Subtract 5 from each side.
$\ln x = -\dfrac{1}{2}$	Divide each side by 2.
$e^{\ln x} = e^{-1/2}$	Exponentiate each side.
$x = e^{-1/2}$	Inverse Property
$x \approx 0.607$	Use a calculator.

✓CHECKPOINT   Now try Exercise 85.

Example 8   **Solving a Logarithmic Equation**

Solve $2 \log_5 3x = 4$.

Solution

$$2 \log_5 3x = 4 \qquad \text{Write original equation.}$$

$$\log_5 3x = 2 \qquad \text{Divide each side by 2.}$$

$$5^{\log_5 3x} = 5^2 \qquad \text{Exponentiate each side (base 5).}$$

$$3x = 25 \qquad \text{Inverse Property}$$

$$x = \frac{25}{3} \qquad \text{Divide each side by 3.}$$

The solution is $x = \frac{25}{3}$. Check this in the original equation.

✓*CHECKPOINT*   Now try Exercise 87.

Because the domain of a logarithmic function generally does not include all real numbers, you should be sure to check for extraneous solutions of logarithmic equations.

> **STUDY TIP**
>
> Notice in Example 9 that the logarithmic part of the equation is condensed into a single logarithm before exponentiating each side of the equation.

Example 9   **Checking for Extraneous Solutions**

Solve $\log 5x + \log(x - 1) = 2$.

Algebraic Solution

$$\log 5x + \log(x - 1) = 2 \qquad \text{Write original equation.}$$

$$\log[5x(x - 1)] = 2 \qquad \text{Product Property of Logarithms}$$

$$10^{\log(5x^2 - 5x)} = 10^2 \qquad \text{Exponentiate each side (base 10).}$$

$$5x^2 - 5x = 100 \qquad \text{Inverse Property}$$

$$x^2 - x - 20 = 0 \qquad \text{Write in general form.}$$

$$(x - 5)(x + 4) = 0 \qquad \text{Factor.}$$

$$x - 5 = 0 \qquad \text{Set 1st factor equal to 0.}$$

$$x = 5 \qquad \text{Solution}$$

$$x + 4 = 0 \qquad \text{Set 2nd factor equal to 0.}$$

$$x = -4 \qquad \text{Solution}$$

The solutions appear to be $x = 5$ and $x = -4$. However, when you check these in the original equation, you can see that $x = 5$ is the only solution.

✓*CHECKPOINT*   Now try Exercise 99.

Graphical Solution

Use a graphing utility to graph $y_1 = \log 5x + \log(x - 1)$ and $y_2 = 2$ in the same viewing window. From the graph shown in Figure 3.26, it appears that the graphs intersect at one point. Use the *intersect* feature or the *zoom* and *trace* features to determine that the graphs intersect at approximately $(5, 2)$. So, the solution is $x = 5$. Verify that 5 is an exact solution algebraically.

FIGURE **3.26**

In Example 9, the domain of $\log 5x$ is $x > 0$ and the domain of $\log(x - 1)$ is $x > 1$, so the domain of the original equation is $x > 1$. Because the domain is all real numbers greater than 1, the solution $x = -4$ is extraneous. The graph in Figure 3.26 verifies this concept.

Applications

Example 10   **Doubling an Investment**

You have deposited $500 in an account that pays 6.75% interest, compounded continuously. How long will it take your money to double?

Solution

Using the formula for continuous compounding, you can find that the balance in the account is

$$A = Pe^{rt}$$

$$A = 500e^{0.0675t}.$$

To find the time required for the balance to double, let $A = 1000$ and solve the resulting equation for t.

$500e^{0.0675t} = 1000$	Let $A = 1000$.
$e^{0.0675t} = 2$	Divide each side by 500.
$\ln e^{0.0675t} = \ln 2$	Take natural log of each side.
$0.0675t = \ln 2$	Inverse Property
$t = \dfrac{\ln 2}{0.0675}$	Divide each side by 0.0675.
$t \approx 10.27$	Use a calculator.

The balance in the account will double after approximately 10.27 years. This result is demonstrated graphically in Figure 3.27.

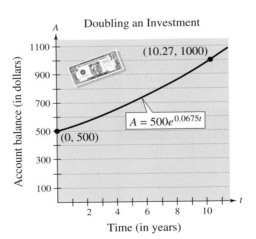

FIGURE 3.27

✓CHECKPOINT   Now try Exercise 107.

In Example 10, an approximate answer of 10.27 years is given. Within the context of the problem, the exact solution, $(\ln 2)/0.0675$ years, does not make sense as an answer.

Endangered Animal Species

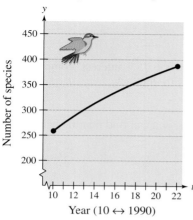

FIGURE 3.28

Example 11   **Endangered Animals**

The number y of endangered animal species in the United States from 1990 to 2002 can be modeled by

$$y = -119 + 164 \ln t, \quad 10 \le t \le 22$$

where t represents the year, with $t = 10$ corresponding to 1990 (see Figure 3.28). During which year did the number of endangered animal species reach 357? (Source: U.S. Fish and Wildlife Service)

Solution

$-119 + 164 \ln t = y$	Write original equation.
$-119 + 164 \ln t = 357$	Substitute 357 for y.
$164 \ln t = 476$	Add 119 to each side.
$\ln t = \dfrac{476}{164}$	Divide each side by 164.
$e^{\ln t} \approx e^{476/164}$	Exponentiate each side.
$t \approx e^{476/164}$	Inverse Property
$t \approx 18$	Use a calculator.

The solution is $t \approx 18$. Because $t = 10$ represents 1990, it follows that the number of endangered animals reached 357 in 1998.

✓CHECKPOINT   Now try Exercise 113.

WRITING ABOUT MATHEMATICS

Comparing Mathematical Models The table shows the U.S. Postal Service rates y for sending an express mail package for selected years from 1985 through 2002, where $x = 5$ represents 1985.   (Source: U.S. Postal Service)

Year, x	Rate, y
5	10.75
8	12.00
11	13.95
15	15.00
19	15.75
21	16.00
22	17.85

a. Create a scatter plot of the data. Find a linear model for the data, and add its graph to your scatter plot. According to this model, when will the rate for sending an express mail package reach $19.00?

b. Create a new table showing values for ln x and ln y and create a scatter plot of these transformed data. Use the method illustrated in Example 7 in Section 3.3 to find a model for the transformed data, and add its graph to your scatter plot. According to this model, when will the rate for sending an express mail package reach $19.00?

c. Solve the model in part (b) for y, and add its graph to your scatter plot in part (a). Which model better fits the original data? Which model will better predict future rates? Explain.

3.4 | Exercises

VOCABULARY CHECK: Fill in the blanks.

1. To _____ an equation in x means to find all values of x for which the equation is true.

2. To solve exponential and logarithmic equations, you can use the following One-to-One and Inverse Properties.

(a) $a^x = a^y$ if and only if _____.

(b) $\log_a x = \log_a y$ if and only if _____.

(c) $a^{\log_a x} =$ _____

(d) $\log_a a^x =$ _____

3. An _____ solution does not satisfy the original equation.

PREREQUISITE SKILLS REVIEW: Practice and review algebra skills needed for this section at **www.Eduspace.com.**

In Exercises 1–8, determine whether each x-value is a solution (or an approximate solution) of the equation.

1. $4^{2x-7} = 64$

   (a) $x = 5$

   (b) $x = 2$

2. $2^{3x+1} = 32$

   (a) $x = -1$

   (b) $x = 2$

3. $3e^{x+2} = 75$

   (a) $x = -2 + e^{25}$

   (b) $x = -2 + \ln 25$

   (c) $x \approx 1.219$

4. $2e^{5x+2} = 12$

   (a) $x = \frac{1}{5}(-2 + \ln 6)$

   (b) $x = \dfrac{\ln 6}{5 \ln 2}$

   (c) $x \approx -0.0416$

5. $\log_4(3x) = 3$

   (a) $x \approx 21.333$

   (b) $x = -4$

   (c) $x = \frac{64}{3}$

6. $\log_2(x + 3) = 10$

   (a) $x = 1021$

   (b) $x = 17$

   (c) $x = 10^2 - 3$

7. $\ln(2x + 3) = 5.8$

   (a) $x = \frac{1}{2}(-3 + \ln 5.8)$

   (b) $x = \frac{1}{2}(-3 + e^{5.8})$

   (c) $x \approx 163.650$

8. $\ln(x - 1) = 3.8$

   (a) $x = 1 + e^{3.8}$

   (b) $x \approx 45.701$

   (c) $x = 1 + \ln 3.8$

In Exercises 9–20, solve for x.

9. $4^x = 16$

10. $3^x = 243$

11. $\left(\frac{1}{2}\right)^x = 32$

12. $\left(\frac{1}{4}\right)^x = 64$

13. $\ln x - \ln 2 = 0$

14. $\ln x - \ln 5 = 0$

15. $e^x = 2$

16. $e^x = 4$

17. $\ln x = -1$

18. $\ln x = -7$

19. $\log_4 x = 3$

20. $\log_5 x = -3$

In Exercises 21–24, approximate the point of intersection of the graphs of f and g. Then solve the equation $f(x) = g(x)$ algebraically to verify your approximation.

21. $f(x) = 2^x$

   $g(x) = 8$

22. $f(x) = 27^x$

   $g(x) = 9$

23. $f(x) = \log_3 x$

   $g(x) = 2$

24. $f(x) = \ln(x - 4)$

   $g(x) = 0$

In Exercises 25–66, solve the exponential equation algebraically. Approximate the result to three decimal places.

25. $e^x = e^{x^2 - 2}$

26. $e^{2x} = e^{x^2 - 8}$

27. $e^{x^2 - 3} = e^{x - 2}$

28. $e^{-x^2} = e^{x^2 - 2x}$

29. $4(3^x) = 20$

30. $2(5^x) = 32$

31. $2e^x = 10$

32. $4e^x = 91$

33. $e^x - 9 = 19$

34. $6^x + 10 = 47$

35. $3^{2x} = 80$

36. $6^{5x} = 3000$

37. $5^{-t/2} = 0.20$

38. $4^{-3t} = 0.10$

39. $3^{x-1} = 27$

40. $2^{x-3} = 32$

41. $2^{3-x} = 565$

42. $8^{-2-x} = 431$

43. $8(10^{3x}) = 12$

44. $5(10^{x-6}) = 7$

45. $3(5^{x-1}) = 21$

46. $8(3^{6-x}) = 40$

47. $e^{3x} = 12$

48. $e^{2x} = 50$

49. $500e^{-x} = 300$

50. $1000e^{-4x} = 75$

51. $7 - 2e^x = 5$

52. $-14 + 3e^x = 11$

53. $6(2^{3x-1}) - 7 = 9$

54. $8(4^{6-2x}) + 13 = 41$

55. $e^{2x} - 4e^x - 5 = 0$

56. $e^{2x} - 5e^x + 6 = 0$

57. $e^{2x} - 3e^x - 4 = 0$

58. $e^{2x} + 9e^x + 36 = 0$

59. $\dfrac{500}{100 - e^{x/2}} = 20$

60. $\dfrac{400}{1 + e^{-x}} = 350$

61. $\dfrac{3000}{2 + e^{2x}} = 2$

62. $\dfrac{119}{e^{6x} - 14} = 7$

63. $\left(1 + \dfrac{0.065}{365}\right)^{365t} = 4$

64. $\left(4 - \dfrac{2.471}{40}\right)^{9t} = 21$

65. $\left(1 + \dfrac{0.10}{12}\right)^{12t} = 2$

66. $\left(16 - \dfrac{0.878}{26}\right)^{3t} = 30$

 In Exercises 67–74, use a graphing utility to graph and solve the equation. Approximate the result to three decimal places. Verify your result algebraically.

67. $6e^{1-x} = 25$

68. $-4e^{-x-1} + 15 = 0$

69. $3e^{3x/2} = 962$

70. $8e^{-2x/3} = 11$

71. $e^{0.09t} = 3$

72. $-e^{1.8x} + 7 = 0$

73. $e^{0.125t} - 8 = 0$

74. $e^{2.724x} = 29$

In Exercises 75–102, solve the logarithmic equation algebraically. Approximate the result to three decimal places.

75. $\ln x = -3$

76. $\ln x = 2$

77. $\ln 2x = 2.4$

78. $\ln 4x = 1$

79. $\log x = 6$

80. $\log 3z = 2$

81. $3 \ln 5x = 10$

82. $2 \ln x = 7$

83. $\ln \sqrt{x + 2} = 1$

84. $\ln \sqrt{x - 8} = 5$

85. $7 + 3 \ln x = 5$

86. $2 - 6 \ln x = 10$

87. $6 \log_3(0.5x) = 11$

88. $5 \log_{10}(x - 2) = 11$

89. $\ln x - \ln(x + 1) = 2$

90. $\ln x + \ln(x + 1) = 1$

91. $\ln x + \ln(x - 2) = 1$

92. $\ln x + \ln(x + 3) = 1$

93. $\ln(x + 5) = \ln(x - 1) - \ln(x + 1)$

94. $\ln(x + 1) - \ln(x - 2) = \ln x$

95. $\log_2(2x - 3) = \log_2(x + 4)$

96. $\log(x - 6) = \log(2x + 1)$

97. $\log(x + 4) - \log x = \log(x + 2)$

98. $\log_2 x + \log_2(x + 2) = \log_2(x + 6)$

99. $\log_4 x - \log_4(x - 1) = \dfrac{1}{2}$

100. $\log_3 x + \log_3(x - 8) = 2$

101. $\log 8x - \log(1 + \sqrt{x}) = 2$

102. $\log 4x - \log(12 + \sqrt{x}) = 2$

 In Exercises 103–106, use a graphing utility to graph and solve the equation. Approximate the result to three decimal places. Verify your result algebraically.

103. $7 = 2^x$

104. $500 = 1500e^{-x/2}$

105. $3 - \ln x = 0$

106. $10 - 4 \ln(x - 2) = 0$

Compound Interest In Exercises 107 and 108, $2500 is invested in an account at interest rate r, compounded continuously. Find the time required for the amount to (a) double and (b) triple.

107. $r = 0.085$

108. $r = 0.12$

109. *Demand* The demand equation for a microwave oven is given by

$$p = 500 - 0.5(e^{0.004x}).$$

Find the demand x for a price of (a) $p = \$350$ and (b) $p = \$300$.

110. *Demand* The demand equation for a hand-held electronic organizer is

$$p = 5000\left(1 - \dfrac{4}{4 + e^{-0.002x}}\right).$$

Find the demand x for a price of (a) $p = \$600$ and (b) $p = \$400$.

111. *Forest Yield* The yield V (in millions of cubic feet per acre) for a forest at age t years is given by

$$V = 6.7e^{-48.1/t}.$$

 (a) Use a graphing utility to graph the function.

(b) Determine the horizontal asymptote of the function. Interpret its meaning in the context of the problem.

(c) Find the time necessary to obtain a yield of 1.3 million cubic feet.

112. Trees per Acre The number N of trees of a given species per acre is approximated by the model $N = 68(10^{-0.04x})$, $5 \leq x \leq 40$ where x is the average diameter of the trees (in inches) 3 feet above the ground. Use the model to approximate the average diameter of the trees in a test plot when $N = 21$.

113. Medicine The number y of hospitals in the United States from 1995 to 2002 can be modeled by

$$y = 7312 - 630.0 \ln t, \quad 5 \leq t \leq 12$$

where t represents the year, with $t = 5$ corresponding to 1995. During which year did the number of hospitals reach 5800? (Source: Health Forum)

114. Sports The number y of daily fee golf facilities in the United States from 1995 to 2003 can be modeled by $y = 4381 + 1883.6 \ln t$, $5 \leq t \leq 13$ where t represents the year, with $t = 5$ corresponding to 1995. During which year did the number of daily fee golf facilities reach 9000? (Source: National Golf Foundation)

115. Average Heights The percent m of American males between the ages of 18 and 24 who are no more than x inches tall is modeled by

$$m(x) = \frac{100}{1 + e^{-0.6114(x - 69.71)}}$$

and the percent f of American females between the ages of 18 and 24 who are no more than x inches tall is modeled by

$$f(x) = \frac{100}{1 + e^{-0.66607(x - 64.51)}}.$$

(Source: U.S. National Center for Health Statistics)

(a) Use the graph to determine any horizontal asymptotes of the graphs of the functions. Interpret the meaning in the context of the problem.

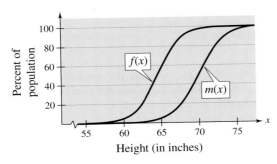

Height (in inches)

(b) What is the average height of each sex?

116. Learning Curve In a group project in learning theory, a mathematical model for the proportion P of correct responses after n trials was found to be

$$P = \frac{0.83}{1 + e^{-0.2n}}.$$

 (a) Use a graphing utility to graph the function.

(b) Use the graph to determine any horizontal asymptotes of the graph of the function. Interpret the meaning of the upper asymptote in the context of this problem.

(c) After how many trials will 60% of the responses be correct?

Model It

117. Automobiles Automobiles are designed with crumple zones that help protect their occupants in crashes. The crumple zones allow the occupants to move short distances when the automobiles come to abrupt stops. The greater the distance moved, the fewer g's the crash victims experience. (One g is equal to the acceleration due to gravity. For very short periods of time, humans have withstood as much as 40 g's.) In crash tests with vehicles moving at 90 kilometers per hour, analysts measured the numbers of g's experienced during deceleration by crash dummies that were permitted to move x meters during impact. The data are shown in the table.

x	g's
0.2	158
0.4	80
0.6	53
0.8	40
1.0	32

A model for the data is given by

$$y = -3.00 + 11.88 \ln x + \frac{36.94}{x}$$

where y is the number of g's.

(a) Complete the table using the model.

x	0.2	0.4	0.6	0.8	1.0
y					

 (b) Use a graphing utility to graph the data points and the model in the same viewing window. How do they compare?

(c) Use the model to estimate the distance traveled during impact if the passenger deceleration must not exceed 30 g's.

(d) Do you think it is practical to lower the number of g's experienced during impact to fewer than 23? Explain your reasoning.

118. **Data Analysis** An object at a temperature of 160°C was removed from a furnace and placed in a room at 20°C. The temperature T of the object was measured each hour h and recorded in the table. A model for the data is given by $T = 20[1 + 7(2^{-h})]$. The graph of this model is shown in the figure.

Hour, h	Temperature, T
0	160°
1	90°
2	56°
3	38°
4	29°
5	24°

(a) Use the graph to identify the horizontal asymptote of the model and interpret the asymptote in the context of the problem.

(b) Use the model to approximate the time when the temperature of the object was 100°C.

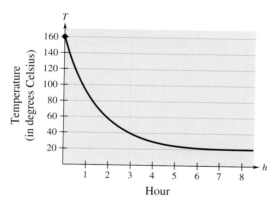

Synthesis

True or False? In Exercises 119–122, rewrite each verbal statement as an equation. Then decide whether the statement is true or false. Justify your answer.

119. The logarithm of the product of two numbers is equal to the sum of the logarithms of the numbers.

120. The logarithm of the sum of two numbers is equal to the product of the logarithms of the numbers.

121. The logarithm of the difference of two numbers is equal to the difference of the logarithms of the numbers.

122. The logarithm of the quotient of two numbers is equal to the difference of the logarithms of the numbers.

123. **Think About It** Is it possible for a logarithmic equation to have more than one extraneous solution? Explain.

124. **Finance** You are investing P dollars at an annual interest rate of r, compounded continuously, for t years. Which of the following would result in the highest value of the investment? Explain your reasoning.

(a) Double the amount you invest.

(b) Double your interest rate.

(c) Double the number of years.

125. **Think About It** Are the times required for the investments in Exercises 107 and 108 to quadruple twice as long as the times for them to double? Give a reason for your answer and verify your answer algebraically.

126. **Writing** Write two or three sentences stating the general guidelines that you follow when solving (a) exponential equations and (b) logarithmic equations.

Skills Review

In Exercises 127–130, simplify the expression.

127. $\sqrt{48x^2y^5}$

128. $\sqrt{32} - 2\sqrt{25}$

129. $\sqrt[3]{25} \cdot \sqrt[3]{15}$

130. $\dfrac{3}{\sqrt{10} - 2}$

In Exercises 131–134, sketch a graph of the function.

131. $f(x) = |x| + 9$

132. $f(x) = |x + 2| - 8$

133. $g(x) = \begin{cases} 2x, & x < 0 \\ -x^2 + 4, & x \geq 0 \end{cases}$

134. $g(x) = \begin{cases} x - 3, & x \leq -1 \\ x^2 + 1, & x > -1 \end{cases}$

In Exercises 135–138, evaluate the logarithm using the change-of-base formula. Approximate your result to three decimal places.

135. $\log_6 9$

136. $\log_3 4$

137. $\log_{3/4} 5$

138. $\log_8 22$

3.5 Exponential and Logarithmic Models

What you should learn

- Recognize the five most common types of models involving exponential and logarithmic functions.
- Use exponential growth and decay functions to model and solve real-life problems.
- Use Gaussian functions to model and solve real-life problems.
- Use logistic growth functions to model and solve real-life problems.
- Use logarithmic functions to model and solve real-life problems.

Why you should learn it

Exponential growth and decay models are often used to model the population of a country. For instance, in Exercise 36 on page 265, you will use exponential growth and decay models to compare the populations of several countries.

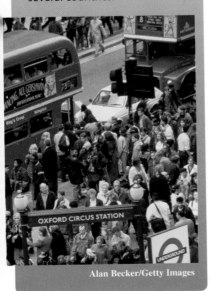

Introduction

The five most common types of mathematical models involving exponential functions and logarithmic functions are as follows.

1. **Exponential growth model:** $y = ae^{bx}, \quad b > 0$
2. **Exponential decay model:** $y = ae^{-bx}, \quad b > 0$
3. **Gaussian model:** $y = ae^{-(x-b)^2/c}$
4. **Logistic growth model:** $y = \dfrac{a}{1 + be^{-rx}}$
5. **Logarithmic models:** $y = a + b \ln x, \quad y = a + b \log x$

The basic shapes of the graphs of these functions are shown in Figure 3.29.

EXPONENTIAL GROWTH MODEL

EXPONENTIAL DECAY MODEL

GAUSSIAN MODEL

LOGISTIC GROWTH MODEL

FIGURE 3.29

NATURAL LOGARITHMIC MODEL

COMMON LOGARITHMIC MODEL

You can often gain quite a bit of insight into a situation modeled by an exponential or logarithmic function by identifying and interpreting the function's asymptotes. Use the graphs in Figure 3.29 to identify the asymptotes of the graph of each function.

Exponential Growth and Decay

Example 1   **Digital Television**

Estimates of the numbers (in millions) of U.S. households with digital television from 2003 through 2007 are shown in the table. The scatter plot of the data is shown in Figure 3.30.   (Source: eMarketer)

Digital Television

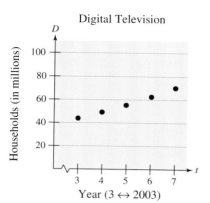

Households (in millions)

Year (3 ↔ 2003)

FIGURE 3.30

Year	Households
2003	44.2
2004	49.0
2005	55.5
2006	62.5
2007	70.3

An exponential growth model that approximates these data is given by

$$D = 30.92e^{0.1171t}, \quad 3 \le t \le 7$$

where D is the number of households (in millions) and $t = 3$ represents 2003. Compare the values given by the model with the estimates shown in the table. According to this model, when will the number of U.S. households with digital television reach 100 million?

Solution

The following table compares the two sets of figures. The graph of the model and the original data are shown in Figure 3.31.

Digital Television

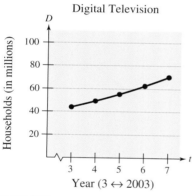

Households (in millions)

Year (3 ↔ 2003)

FIGURE 3.31

Year	2003	2004	2005	2006	2007
Households	44.2	49.0	55.5	62.5	70.3
Model	43.9	49.4	55.5	62.4	70.2

To find when the number of U.S. households with digital television will reach 100 million, let $D = 100$ in the model and solve for t.

$30.92e^{0.1171t} = D$	Write original model.
$30.92e^{0.1171t} = 100$	Let $D = 100$.
$e^{0.1171t} \approx 3.2342$	Divide each side by 30.92.
$\ln e^{0.1171t} \approx \ln 3.2342$	Take natural log of each side.
$0.1171t \approx 1.1738$	Inverse Property
$t \approx 10.0$	Divide each side by 0.1171.

According to the model, the number of U.S. households with digital television will reach 100 million in 2010.

 CHECKPOINT   Now try Exercise 35.

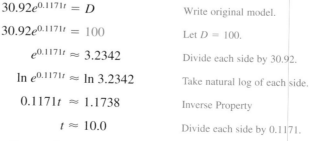

Technology

Some graphing utilities have an *exponential regression* feature that can be used to find exponential models that represent data. If you have such a graphing utility, try using it to find an exponential model for the data given in Example 1. How does your model compare with the model given in Example 1?

In Example 1, you were given the exponential growth model. But suppose this model were not given; how could you find such a model? One technique for doing this is demonstrated in Example 2.

Example 2   Modeling Population Growth

In a research experiment, a population of fruit flies is increasing according to the law of exponential growth. After 2 days there are 100 flies, and after 4 days there are 300 flies. How many flies will there be after 5 days?

Solution

Let y be the number of flies at time t. From the given information, you know that $y = 100$ when $t = 2$ and $y = 300$ when $t = 4$. Substituting this information into the model $y = ae^{bt}$ produces

$$100 = ae^{2b} \quad \text{and} \quad 300 = ae^{4b}.$$

To solve for b, solve for a in the first equation.

$$100 = ae^{2b} \quad \Longrightarrow \quad a = \frac{100}{e^{2b}} \qquad \text{Solve for } a \text{ in the first equation.}$$

Then substitute the result into the second equation.

$$300 = ae^{4b} \qquad\qquad\qquad \text{Write second equation.}$$

$$300 = \left(\frac{100}{e^{2b}}\right)e^{4b} \qquad\qquad \text{Substitute } 100/e^{2b} \text{ for } a.$$

$$\frac{300}{100} = e^{2b} \qquad\qquad\qquad \text{Divide each side by 100.}$$

$$\ln 3 = 2b \qquad\qquad\qquad \text{Take natural log of each side.}$$

$$\frac{1}{2} \ln 3 = b \qquad\qquad\qquad \text{Solve for } b.$$

Using $b = \frac{1}{2} \ln 3$ and the equation you found for a, you can determine that

$$a = \frac{100}{e^{2[(1/2)\ln 3]}} \qquad\qquad \text{Substitute } \tfrac{1}{2} \ln 3 \text{ for } b.$$

$$= \frac{100}{e^{\ln 3}} \qquad\qquad\qquad \text{Simplify.}$$

$$= \frac{100}{3} \qquad\qquad\qquad \text{Inverse Property}$$

$$\approx 33.33. \qquad\qquad\qquad \text{Simplify.}$$

So, with $a \approx 33.33$ and $b = \frac{1}{2} \ln 3 \approx 0.5493$, the exponential growth model is

$$y = 33.33e^{0.5493t}$$

as shown in Figure 3.32. This implies that, after 5 days, the population will be

$$y = 33.33e^{0.5493(5)} \approx 520 \text{ flies.}$$

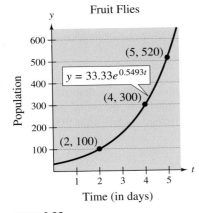

Fruit Flies

$(5, 520)$

$y = 33.33e^{0.5493t}$

$(4, 300)$

$(2, 100)$

Time (in days)

FIGURE 3.32

✓CHECKPOINT   Now try Exercise 37.

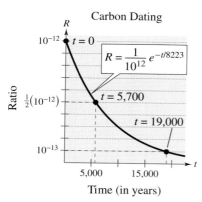

FIGURE 3.33

In living organic material, the ratio of the number of radioactive carbon isotopes (carbon 14) to the number of nonradioactive carbon isotopes (carbon 12) is about 1 to 10^{12}. When organic material dies, its carbon 12 content remains fixed, whereas its radioactive carbon 14 begins to decay with a half-life of about 5700 years. To estimate the age of dead organic material, scientists use the following formula, which denotes the ratio of carbon 14 to carbon 12 present at any time t (in years).

$$R = \frac{1}{10^{12}} e^{-t/8223} \qquad \text{Carbon dating model}$$

The graph of R is shown in Figure 3.33. Note that R decreases as t increases.

Example 3 Carbon Dating

Estimate the age of a newly discovered fossil in which the ratio of carbon 14 to carbon 12 is

$$R = \frac{1}{10^{13}}.$$

Solution

In the carbon dating model, substitute the given value of R to obtain the following.

$$\frac{1}{10^{12}} e^{-t/8223} = R \qquad \text{Write original model.}$$

$$\frac{e^{-t/8223}}{10^{12}} = \frac{1}{10^{13}} \qquad \text{Let } R = \frac{1}{10^{13}}.$$

$$e^{-t/8223} = \frac{1}{10} \qquad \text{Multiply each side by } 10^{12}.$$

$$\ln e^{-t/8223} = \ln \frac{1}{10} \qquad \text{Take natural log of each side.}$$

$$-\frac{t}{8223} \approx -2.3026 \qquad \text{Inverse Property}$$

$$t \approx 18{,}934 \qquad \text{Multiply each side by } -8223.$$

So, to the nearest thousand years, the age of the fossil is about 19,000 years.

✓CHECKPOINT   Now try Exercise 41.

The value of b in the exponential decay model $y = ae^{-bt}$ determines the *decay* of radioactive isotopes. For instance, to find how much of an initial 10 grams of ^{226}Ra isotope with a half-life of 1599 years is left after 500 years, substitute this information into the model $y = ae^{-bt}$.

$$\frac{1}{2}(10) = 10e^{-b(1599)} \implies \ln \frac{1}{2} = -1599b \implies b = -\frac{\ln \frac{1}{2}}{1599}$$

Using the value of b found above and $a = 10$, the amount left is

$$y = 10e^{-[-\ln(1/2)/1599](500)} \approx 8.05 \text{ grams.}$$

STUDY TIP

The carbon dating model in Example 3 assumed that the carbon 14 to carbon 12 ratio was one part in 10,000,000,000,000. Suppose an error in measurement occurred and the actual ratio was one part in 8,000,000,000,000. The fossil age corresponding to the actual ratio would then be approximately 17,000 years. Try checking this result.

Gaussian Models

As mentioned at the beginning of this section, Gaussian models are of the form

$$y = ae^{-(x-b)^2/c}.$$

This type of model is commonly used in probability and statistics to represent populations that are **normally distributed.** The graph of a Gaussian model is called a **bell-shaped curve.** Try graphing the normal distribution with a graphing utility. Can you see why it is called a bell-shaped curve?

For *standard* normal distributions, the model takes the form

$$y = \frac{1}{\sqrt{2\pi}}e^{-x^2/2}.$$

The **average value** for a population can be found from the bell-shaped curve by observing where the maximum y-value of the function occurs. The x-value corresponding to the maximum y-value of the function represents the average value of the independent variable—in this case, x.

Example 4   SAT Scores

In 2004, the Scholastic Aptitude Test (SAT) math scores for college-bound seniors roughly followed the normal distribution given by

$$y = 0.0035e^{-(x-518)^2/25,992}, \quad 200 \le x \le 800$$

where x is the SAT score for mathematics. Sketch the graph of this function. From the graph, estimate the average SAT score.   (Source: College Board)

Solution

The graph of the function is shown in Figure 3.34. On this bell-shaped curve, the maximum value of the curve represents the average score. From the graph, you can estimate that the average mathematics score for college-bound seniors in 2004 was 518.

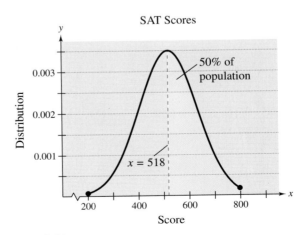

FIGURE 3.34

✓CHECKPOINT   Now try Exercise 47.

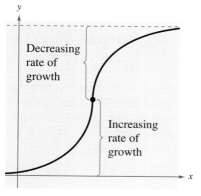

FIGURE **3.35**

Logistic Growth Models

Some populations initially have rapid growth, followed by a declining rate of growth, as indicated by the graph in Figure 3.35. One model for describing this type of growth pattern is the **logistic curve** given by the function

$$y = \frac{a}{1 + be^{-rx}}$$

where y is the population size and x is the time. An example is a bacteria culture that is initially allowed to grow under ideal conditions, and then under less favorable conditions that inhibit growth. A logistic growth curve is also called a **sigmoidal curve.**

Example 5   Spread of a Virus

On a college campus of 5000 students, one student returns from vacation with a contagious and long-lasting flu virus. The spread of the virus is modeled by

$$y = \frac{5000}{1 + 4999e^{-0.8t}}, \quad t \geq 0$$

where y is the total number of students infected after t days. The college will cancel classes when 40% or more of the students are infected.

a. How many students are infected after 5 days?

b. After how many days will the college cancel classes?

Solution

a. After 5 days, the number of students infected is

$$y = \frac{5000}{1 + 4999e^{-0.8(5)}} = \frac{5000}{1 + 4999e^{-4}} \approx 54.$$

b. Classes are canceled when the number infected is $(0.40)(5000) = 2000$.

$$2000 = \frac{5000}{1 + 4999e^{-0.8t}}$$

$$1 + 4999e^{-0.8t} = 2.5$$

$$e^{-0.8t} = \frac{1.5}{4999}$$

$$\ln e^{-0.8t} = \ln \frac{1.5}{4999}$$

$$-0.8t = \ln \frac{1.5}{4999}$$

$$t = -\frac{1}{0.8} \ln \frac{1.5}{4999}$$

$$t \approx 10.1$$

So, after about 10 days, at least 40% of the students will be infected, and the college will cancel classes. The graph of the function is shown in Figure 3.36.

Flu Virus

(graph) (10.1, 2000)   (5, 54)

Students infected — Time (in days)

FIGURE **3.36**

✔*CHECKPOINT*   Now try Exercise 49.

On December 26, 2004, an earthquake of magnitude 9.0 struck northern Sumatra and many other Asian countries. This earthquake caused a deadly tsunami and was the fourth largest earthquake in the world since 1900.

t	Year	Population, P
1	1910	92.23
2	1920	106.02
3	1930	123.20
4	1940	132.16
5	1950	151.33
6	1960	179.32
7	1970	203.30
8	1980	226.54
9	1990	248.72
10	2000	281.42

Logarithmic Models

Example 6   Magnitudes of Earthquakes

On the Richter scale, the magnitude R of an earthquake of intensity I is given by

$$R = \log \frac{I}{I_0}$$

where $I_0 = 1$ is the minimum intensity used for comparison. Find the intensities per unit of area for each earthquake. (Intensity is a measure of the wave energy of an earthquake.)

a. Northern Sumatra in 2004: $R = 9.0$

b. Southeastern Alaska in 2004: $R = 6.8$

Solution

a. Because $I_0 = 1$ and $R = 9.0$, you have

$$9.0 = \log \frac{I}{1}$$ Substitute 1 for I_0 and 9.0 for R.

$$10^{9.0} = 10^{\log I}$$ Exponentiate each side.

$$I = 10^{9.0} \approx 100{,}000{,}000.$$ Inverse Property

b. For $R = 6.8$, you have

$$6.8 = \log \frac{I}{1}$$ Substitute 1 for I_0 and 6.8 for R.

$$10^{6.8} = 10^{\log I}$$ Exponentiate each side.

$$I = 10^{6.8} \approx 6{,}310{,}000.$$ Inverse Property

Note that an increase of 2.2 units on the Richter scale (from 6.8 to 9.0) represents an increase in intensity by a factor of

$$\frac{1{,}000{,}000{,}000}{6{,}310{,}000} \approx 158.$$

In other words, the intensity of the earthquake in Sumatra was about 158 times greater than that of the earthquake in Alaska.

✓CHECKPOINT   Now try Exercise 51.

𝒲RITING ABOUT 𝓜ATHEMATICS

Comparing Population Models The populations P (in millions) of the United States for the census years from 1910 to 2000 are shown in the table at the left. Least squares regression analysis gives the best quadratic model for these data as $P = 1.0328t^2 + 9.607t + 81.82$, and the best exponential model for these data as $P = 82.677e^{0.124t}$. Which model better fits the data? Describe how you reached your conclusion.   (Source: U.S. Census Bureau)

3.5 | Exercises

VOCABULARY CHECK: Fill in the blanks.

1. An exponential growth model has the form _____ and an exponential decay model has the form _____.
2. A logarithmic model has the form _____ or _____.
3. Gaussian models are commonly used in probability and statistics to represent populations that are _____ _____.
4. The graph of a Gaussian model is _____ shaped, where the _____ _____ is the maximum y-value of the graph.
5. A logistic curve is also called a _____ curve.

PREREQUISITE SKILLS REVIEW: Practice and review algebra skills needed for this section at **www.Eduspace.com.**

In Exercises 1–6, match the function with its graph. [The graphs are labeled (a), (b), (c), (d), (e), and (f).]

(a)

(b)

(c)

(d)

(e)

(f)

1. $y = 2e^{x/4}$

2. $y = 6e^{-x/4}$

3. $y = 6 + \log(x + 2)$

4. $y = 3e^{-(x-2)^2/5}$

5. $y = \ln(x + 1)$

6. $y = \dfrac{4}{1 + e^{-2x}}$

Compound Interest   In Exercises 7–14, complete the table for a savings account in which interest is compounded continuously.

	Initial Investment	Annual % Rate	Time to Double	Amount After 10 Years
7.	$1000	3.5%		
8.	$750	$10\frac{1}{2}\%$		
9.	$750		$7\frac{3}{4}$ yr	
10.	$10,000		12 yr	
11.	$500			$1505.00
12.	$600			$19,205.00
13.		4.5%		$10,000.00
14.		2%		$2000.00

Compound Interest   In Exercises 15 and 16, determine the principal P that must be invested at rate r, compounded monthly, so that $500,000 will be available for retirement in t years.

15. $r = 7\frac{1}{2}\%, t = 20$

16. $r = 12\%, t = 40$

Compound Interest   In Exercises 17 and 18, determine the time necessary for $1000 to double if it is invested at interest rate r compounded (a) annually, (b) monthly, (c) daily, and (d) continuously.

17. $r = 11\%$

18. $r = 10\frac{1}{2}\%$

19. **Compound Interest** Complete the table for the time t necessary for P dollars to triple if interest is compounded continuously at rate r.

r	2%	4%	6%	8%	10%	12%
t						

 20. **Modeling Data** Draw a scatter plot of the data in Exercise 19. Use the *regression* feature of a graphing utility to find a model for the data.

21. *Compound Interest*   Complete the table for the time t necessary for P dollars to triple if interest is compounded annually at rate r.

r	2%	4%	6%	8%	10%	12%
t						

22. *Modeling Data*   Draw a scatter plot of the data in Exercise 21. Use the *regression* feature of a graphing utility to find a model for the data.

23. *Comparing Models*   If \$1 is invested in an account over a 10-year period, the amount in the account, where t represents the time in years, is given by $A = 1 + 0.075[\![t]\!]$ or $A = e^{0.07t}$ depending on whether the account pays simple interest at $7\frac{1}{2}\%$ or continuous compound interest at 7%. Graph each function on the same set of axes. Which grows at a higher rate? (Remember that $[\![t]\!]$ is the greatest integer function discussed in Section 1.6.)

24. *Comparing Models*   If \$1 is invested in an account over a 10-year period, the amount in the account, where t represents the time in years, is given by

$$A = 1 + 0.06[\![t]\!] \quad \text{or} \quad A = \left(1 + \frac{0.055}{365}\right)^{[\![365t]\!]}$$

depending on whether the account pays simple interest at 6% or compound interest at $5\frac{1}{2}\%$ compounded daily. Use a graphing utility to graph each function in the same viewing window. Which grows at a higher rate?

Radioactive Decay   **In Exercises 25–30, complete the table for the radioactive isotope.**

Isotope	Half-life (years)	Initial Quantity	Amount After 1000 Years
25. ^{226}Ra	1599	10 g	
26. ^{226}Ra	1599		1.5 g
27. ^{14}C	5715		2 g
28. ^{14}C	5715	3 g	
29. ^{239}Pu	24,100		2.1 g
30. ^{239}Pu	24,100		0.4 g

In Exercises 31–34, find the exponential model $y = ae^{bx}$ that fits the points shown in the graph or table.

31.

32.

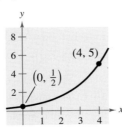

33.

x	0	4
y	5	1

34.

x	0	3
y	1	$\frac{1}{4}$

35. *Population*   The population P (in thousands) of Pittsburgh, Pennsylvania from 2000 through 2003 can be modeled by $P = 2430e^{-0.0029t}$, where t represents the year, with $t = 0$ corresponding to 2000.   (Source: U.S. Census Bureau)

(a) According to the model, was the population of Pittsburgh increasing or decreasing from 2000 to 2003? Explain your reasoning.

(b) What were the populations of Pittsburgh in 2000 and 2003?

(c) According to the model, when will the population be approximately 2.3 million?

Model It

36. *Population*   The table shows the populations (in millions) of five countries in 2000 and the projected populations (in millions) for the year 2010.   (Source: U.S. Census Bureau)

Country	2000	2010
Bulgaria	7.8	7.1
Canada	31.3	34.3
China	1268.9	1347.6
United Kingdom	59.5	61.2
United States	282.3	309.2

(a) Find the exponential growth or decay model $y = ae^{bt}$ or $y = ae^{-bt}$ for the population of each country by letting $t = 0$ correspond to 2000. Use the model to predict the population of each country in 2030.

(b) You can see that the populations of the United States and the United Kingdom are growing at different rates. What constant in the equation $y = ae^{bt}$ is determined by these different growth rates? Discuss the relationship between the different growth rates and the magnitude of the constant.

(c) You can see that the population of China is increasing while the population of Bulgaria is decreasing. What constant in the equation $y = ae^{bt}$ reflects this difference? Explain.

37. Website Growth   The number y of hits a new search-engine website receives each month can be modeled by

$$y = 4080e^{kt}$$

where t represents the number of months the website has been operating. In the website's third month, there were 10,000 hits. Find the value of k, and use this result to predict the number of hits the website will receive after 24 months.

38. Value of a Painting   The value V (in millions of dollars) of a famous painting can be modeled by

$$V = 10e^{kt}$$

where t represents the year, with $t = 0$ corresponding to 1990. In 2004, the same painting was sold for $65 million. Find the value of k, and use this result to predict the value of the painting in 2010.

39. Bacteria Growth   The number N of bacteria in a culture is modeled by

$$N = 100e^{kt}$$

where t is the time in hours. If $N = 300$ when $t = 5$, estimate the time required for the population to double in size.

40. Bacteria Growth   The number N of bacteria in a culture is modeled by

$$N = 250e^{kt}$$

where t is the time in hours. If $N = 280$ when $t = 10$, estimate the time required for the population to double in size.

41. Carbon Dating

(a) The ratio of carbon 14 to carbon 12 in a piece of wood discovered in a cave is $R = 1/8^{14}$. Estimate the age of the piece of wood.

(b) The ratio of carbon 14 to carbon 12 in a piece of paper buried in a tomb is $R = 1/13^{11}$. Estimate the age of the piece of paper.

42. Radioactive Decay   Carbon 14 dating assumes that the carbon dioxide on Earth today has the same radioactive content as it did centuries ago. If this is true, the amount of ^{14}C absorbed by a tree that grew several centuries ago should be the same as the amount of ^{14}C absorbed by a tree growing today. A piece of ancient charcoal contains only 15% as much radioactive carbon as a piece of modern charcoal. How long ago was the tree burned to make the ancient charcoal if the half-life of ^{14}C is 5715 years?

43. Depreciation   A 2005 Jeep Wrangler that costs $30,788 new has a book value of $18,000 after 2 years.

(a) Find the linear model $V = mt + b$.

(b) Find the exponential model $V = ae^{kt}$.

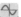 (c) Use a graphing utility to graph the two models in the same viewing window. Which model depreciates faster in the first 2 years?

(d) Find the book values of the vehicle after 1 year and after 3 years using each model.

(e) Explain the advantages and disadvantages of using each model to a buyer and a seller.

44. Depreciation   A Dell Inspiron 8600 laptop computer that costs $1150 new has a book value of $550 after 2 years.

(a) Find the linear model $V = mt + b$.

(b) Find the exponential model $V = ae^{kt}$.

 (c) Use a graphing utility to graph the two models in the same viewing window. Which model depreciates faster in the first 2 years?

(d) Find the book values of the computer after 1 year and after 3 years using each model.

(e) Explain the advantages and disadvantages to a buyer and a seller of using each model.

45. Sales   The sales S (in thousands of units) of a new CD burner after it has been on the market for t years are modeled by

$$S(t) = 100(1 - e^{kt}).$$

Fifteen thousand units of the new product were sold the first year.

(a) Complete the model by solving for k.

(b) Sketch the graph of the model.

(c) Use the model to estimate the number of units sold after 5 years.

46. Learning Curve   The management at a plastics factory has found that the maximum number of units a worker can produce in a day is 30. The learning curve for the number N of units produced per day after a new employee has worked t days is modeled by

$$N = 30(1 - e^{kt}).$$

After 20 days on the job, a new employee produces 19 units.

(a) Find the learning curve for this employee (first, find the value of k).

(b) How many days should pass before this employee is producing 25 units per day?

 47. IQ Scores   The IQ scores from a sample of a class of returning adult students at a small northeastern college roughly follow the normal distribution

$$y = 0.0266e^{-(x - 100)^2/450}, \quad 70 \le x \le 115$$

where x is the IQ score.

(a) Use a graphing utility to graph the function.

(b) From the graph in part (a), estimate the average IQ score of an adult student.

48. *Education* The time (in hours per week) a student utilizes a math-tutoring center roughly follows the normal distribution

$$y = 0.7979e^{-(x-5.4)^2/0.5}, \quad 4 \le x \le 7$$

where x is the number of hours.

(a) Use a graphing utility to graph the function.

(b) From the graph in part (a), estimate the average number of hours per week a student uses the tutor center.

49. *Population Growth* A conservation organization releases 100 animals of an endangered species into a game preserve. The organization believes that the preserve has a carrying capacity of 1000 animals and that the growth of the pack will be modeled by the logistic curve

$$p(t) = \frac{1000}{1 + 9e^{-0.1656t}}$$

where t is measured in months (see figure).

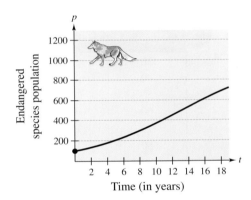

(a) Estimate the population after 5 months.

(b) After how many months will the population be 500?

(c) Use a graphing utility to graph the function. Use the graph to determine the horizontal asymptotes, and interpret the meaning of the larger p-value in the context of the problem.

50. *Sales* After discontinuing all advertising for a tool kit in 2000, the manufacturer noted that sales began to drop according to the model

$$S = \frac{500,000}{1 + 0.6e^{kt}}$$

where S represents the number of units sold and $t = 0$ represents 2000. In 2004, the company sold 300,000 units.

(a) Complete the model by solving for k.

(b) Estimate sales in 2008.

Geology **In Exercises 51 and 52, use the Richter scale**

$$R = \log \frac{I}{I_0}$$

for measuring the magnitudes of earthquakes.

51. Find the intensity I of an earthquake measuring R on the Richter scale (let $I_0 = 1$).

(a) Central Alaska in 2002, $R = 7.9$

(b) Hokkaido, Japan in 2003, $R = 8.3$

(c) Illinois in 2004, $R = 4.2$

52. Find the magnitude R of each earthquake of intensity I (let $I_0 = 1$).

(a) $I = 80,500,000$ (b) $I = 48,275,000$

(c) $I = 251,200$

Intensity of Sound **In Exercises 53–56, use the following information for determining sound intensity. The level of sound β, in decibels, with an intensity of I, is given by**

$$\beta = 10 \log \frac{I}{I_0}$$

where I_0 is an intensity of 10^{-12} watt per square meter, corresponding roughly to the faintest sound that can be heard by the human ear. In Exercises 53 and 54, find the level of sound β.

53. (a) $I = 10^{-10}$ watt per m^2 (quiet room)

(b) $I = 10^{-5}$ watt per m^2 (busy street corner)

(c) $I = 10^{-8}$ watt per m^2 (quiet radio)

(d) $I = 10^0$ watt per m^2 (threshold of pain)

54. (a) $I = 10^{-11}$ watt per m^2 (rustle of leaves)

(b) $I = 10^2$ watt per m^2 (jet at 30 meters)

(c) $I = 10^{-4}$ watt per m^2 (door slamming)

(d) $I = 10^{-2}$ watt per m^2 (siren at 30 meters)

55. Due to the installation of noise suppression materials, the noise level in an auditorium was reduced from 93 to 80 decibels. Find the percent decrease in the intensity level of the noise as a result of the installation of these materials.

56. Due to the installation of a muffler, the noise level of an engine was reduced from 88 to 72 decibels. Find the percent decrease in the intensity level of the noise as a result of the installation of the muffler.

pH Levels **In Exercises 57–62, use the acidity model given by pH $= -\log[H^+]$, where acidity (pH) is a measure of the hydrogen ion concentration $[H^+]$ (measured in moles of hydrogen per liter) of a solution.**

57. Find the pH if $[H^+] = 2.3 \times 10^{-5}$.

58. Find the pH if $[H^+] = 11.3 \times 10^{-6}$.

59. Compute $[H^+]$ for a solution in which pH $= 5.8$.

60. Compute $[H^+]$ for a solution in which pH $= 3.2$.

61. Apple juice has a pH of 2.9 and drinking water has a pH of 8.0. The hydrogen ion concentration of the apple juice is how many times the concentration of drinking water?

62. The pH of a solution is decreased by one unit. The hydrogen ion concentration is increased by what factor?

63. *Forensics*   At 8:30 A.M., a coroner was called to the home of a person who had died during the night. In order to estimate the time of death, the coroner took the person's temperature twice. At 9:00 A.M. the temperature was 85.7°F, and at 11:00 a.m. the temperature was 82.8°F. From these two temperatures, the coroner was able to determine that the time elapsed since death and the body temperature were related by the formula

$$t = -10 \ln \frac{T - 70}{98.6 - 70}$$

where t is the time in hours elapsed since the person died and T is the temperature (in degrees Fahrenheit) of the person's body. Assume that the person had a normal body temperature of 98.6°F at death, and that the room temperature was a constant 70°F. (This formula is derived from a general cooling principle called *Newton's Law of Cooling*.) Use the formula to estimate the time of death of the person.

 64. *Home Mortgage*   A $120,000 home mortgage for 35 years at $7\frac{1}{2}\%$ has a monthly payment of $809.39. Part of the monthly payment is paid toward the interest charge on the unpaid balance, and the remainder of the payment is used to reduce the principal. The amount that is paid toward the interest is

$$u = M - \left(M - \frac{Pr}{12}\right)\left(1 + \frac{r}{12}\right)^{12t}$$

and the amount that is paid toward the reduction of the principal is

$$v = \left(M - \frac{Pr}{12}\right)\left(1 + \frac{r}{12}\right)^{12t}.$$

In these formulas, P is the size of the mortgage, r is the interest rate, M is the monthly payment, and t is the time in years.

(a) Use a graphing utility to graph each function in the same viewing window. (The viewing window should show all 35 years of mortgage payments.)

(b) In the early years of the mortgage, is the larger part of the monthly payment paid toward the interest or the principal? Approximate the time when the monthly payment is evenly divided between interest and principal reduction.

(c) Repeat parts (a) and (b) for a repayment period of 20 years ($M = \$966.71$). What can you conclude?

65. *Home Mortgage*   The total interest u paid on a home mortgage of P dollars at interest rate r for t years is

$$u = P\left[\frac{rt}{1 - \left(\dfrac{1}{1 + r/12}\right)^{12t}} - 1\right].$$

Consider a $120,000 home mortgage at $7\frac{1}{2}\%$.

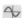 (a) Use a graphing utility to graph the total interest function.

(b) Approximate the length of the mortgage for which the total interest paid is the same as the size of the mortgage. Is it possible that some people are paying twice as much in interest charges as the size of the mortgage?

 66. *Data Analysis*   The table shows the time t (in seconds) required to attain a speed of s miles per hour from a standing start for a car.

Speed, s	Time, t
30	3.4
40	5.0
50	7.0
60	9.3
70	12.0
80	15.8
90	20.0

Two models for these data are as follows.

$$t_1 = 40.757 + 0.556s - 15.817 \ln s$$

$$t_2 = 1.2259 + 0.0023s^2$$

(a) Use the *regression* feature of a graphing utility to find a linear model t_3 and an exponential model t_4 for the data.

(b) Use a graphing utility to graph the data and each model in the same viewing window.

(c) Create a table comparing the data with estimates obtained from each model.

(d) Use the results of part (c) to find the sum of the absolute values of the differences between the data and the estimated values given by each model. Based on the four sums, which model do you think better fits the data? Explain.

Synthesis

True or False?   **In Exercises 67–70, determine whether the statement is true or false. Justify your answer.**

67. The domain of a logistic growth function cannot be the set of real numbers.

68. A logistic growth function will always have an x-intercept.

69. The graph of

$$f(x) = \frac{4}{1 + 6e^{-2x}} + 5$$

is the graph of

$$g(x) = \frac{4}{1 + 6e^{-2x}}$$

shifted to the right five units.

70. The graph of a Gaussian model will never have an x-intercept.

71. Identify each model as linear, logarithmic, exponential, logistic, or none of the above. Explain your reasoning.

(a)

(b)

(c)

(d)

(e)

(f)
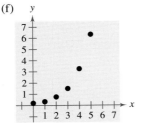

72. *Writing*   Use your school's library, the Internet, or some other reference source to write a paper describing John Napier's work with logarithms.

Skills Review

In Exercises 73–78, (a) plot the points, (b) find the distance between the points, (c) find the midpoint of the line segment joining the points, and (d) find the slope of the line passing through the points.

73. $(-1, 2), (0, 5)$

74. $(4, -3), (-6, 1)$

75. $(3, 3), (14, -2)$

76. $(7, 0), (10, 4)$

77. $\left(\frac{1}{2}, -\frac{1}{4}\right), \left(\frac{3}{4}, 0\right)$

78. $\left(\frac{7}{3}, \frac{1}{6}\right), \left(-\frac{2}{3}, -\frac{1}{3}\right)$

In Exercises 79–88, sketch the graph of the equation.

79. $y = 10 - 3x$

80. $y = -4x - 1$

81. $y = -2x^2 - 3$

82. $y = 2x^2 - 7x - 30$

83. $3x^2 - 4y = 0$

84. $-x^2 - 8y = 0$

85. $y = \dfrac{4}{1 - 3x}$

86. $y = \dfrac{x^2}{-x - 2}$

87. $x^2 + (y - 8)^2 = 25$

88. $(x - 4)^2 + (y + 7) = 4$

In Exercises 89–92, graph the exponential function.

89. $f(x) = 2^{x-1} + 5$

90. $f(x) = -2^{-x-1} - 1$

91. $f(x) = 3^x - 4$

92. $f(x) = -3^x + 4$

93. **Make a Decision**   To work an extended application analyzing the net sales for Kohl's Corporation from 1992 to 2004, visit this text's website at *college.hmco.com.*   *(Data Source: Kohl's Illinois, Inc.)*

3 | Chapter Summary

What did you learn?

	Review Exercises
Section 3.1	
☐ Recognize and evaluate exponential functions with base a (p. 218).	1–6
☐ Graph exponential functions and use the One-to-One Property (p. 219).	7–26
☐ Recognize, evaluate, and graph exponential functions with base e (p. 222).	27–34
☐ Use exponential functions to model and solve real-life problems (p. 223).	35–40
Section 3.2	
☐ Recognize and evaluate logarithmic functions with base a (p. 229).	41–52
☐ Graph logarithmic functions (p. 231).	53–58
☐ Recognize, evaluate, and graph natural logarithmic functions (p. 233).	59–68
☐ Use logarithmic functions to model and solve real-life problems (p. 235).	69, 70
Section 3.3	
☐ Use the change-of-base formula to rewrite and evaluate logarithmic expressions (p. 239).	71–74
☐ Use properties of logarithms to evaluate or rewrite logarithmic expressions (p. 240).	75–78
☐ Use properties of logarithms to expand or condense logarithmic expressions (p. 241).	79–94
☐ Use logarithmic functions to model and solve real-life problems (p. 242).	95, 96
Section 3.4	
☐ Solve simple exponential and logarithmic equations (p. 246).	97–104
☐ Solve more complicated exponential equations (p. 247).	105–118
☐ Solve more complicated logarithmic equations (p. 249).	119–134
☐ Use exponential and logarithmic equations to model and solve real-life problems (p. 251).	135, 136
Section 3.5	
☐ Recognize the five most common types of models involving exponential and logarithmic functions (p. 257).	137–142
☐ Use exponential growth and decay functions to model and solve real-life problems (p. 258).	143–148
☐ Use Gaussian functions to model and solve real-life problems (p. 261).	149
☐ Use logistic growth functions to model and solve real-life problems (p. 262).	150
☐ Use logarithmic functions to model and solve real-life problems (p. 263).	151, 152

3 Review Exercises

3.1 In Exercises 1–6, evaluate the function at the indicated value of *x*. Round your result to three decimal places.

Function	Value
1. $f(x) = 6.1^x$	$x = 2.4$
2. $f(x) = 30^x$	$x = \sqrt{3}$
3. $f(x) = 2^{-0.5x}$	$x = \pi$
4. $f(x) = 1278^{x/5}$	$x = 1$
5. $f(x) = 7(0.2^x)$	$x = -\sqrt{11}$
6. $f(x) = -14(5^x)$	$x = -0.8$

In Exercises 7–10, match the function with its graph. [The graphs are labeled (a), (b), (c), and (d).]

(a)

(b)

(c)

(d)

7. $f(x) = 4^x$

8. $f(x) = 4^{-x}$

9. $f(x) = -4^x$

10. $f(x) = 4^x + 1$

In Exercises 11–14, use the graph of *f* to describe the transformation that yields the graph of *g*.

11. $f(x) = 5^x$, $g(x) = 5^{x-1}$

12. $f(x) = 4^x$, $g(x) = 4^x - 3$

13. $f(x) = \left(\frac{1}{2}\right)^x$, $g(x) = -\left(\frac{1}{2}\right)^{x+2}$

14. $f(x) = \left(\frac{2}{3}\right)^x$, $g(x) = 8 - \left(\frac{2}{3}\right)^x$

In Exercises 15–22, use a graphing utility to construct a table of values for the function. Then sketch the graph of the function.

15. $f(x) = 4^{-x} + 4$

16. $f(x) = -4^x - 3$

17. $f(x) = -2.65^{x+1}$

18. $f(x) = 2.65^{x-1}$

19. $f(x) = 5^{x-2} + 4$

20. $f(x) = 2^{x-6} - 5$

21. $f(x) = \left(\frac{1}{2}\right)^{-x} + 3$

22. $f(x) = \left(\frac{1}{8}\right)^{x+2} - 5$

In Exercises 23–26, use the One-to-One Property to solve the equation for *x*.

23. $3^{x+2} = \dfrac{1}{9}$

24. $\left(\dfrac{1}{3}\right)^{x-2} = 81$

25. $e^{5x-7} = e^{15}$

26. $e^{8-2x} = e^{-3}$

In Exercises 27–30, evaluate the function given by $f(x) = e^x$ at the indicated value of *x*. Round your result to three decimal places.

27. $x = 8$

28. $x = \frac{5}{8}$

29. $x = -1.7$

30. $x = 0.278$

In Exercises 31–34, use a graphing utility to construct a table of values for the function. Then sketch the graph of the function.

31. $h(x) = e^{-x/2}$

32. $h(x) = 2 - e^{-x/2}$

33. $f(x) = e^{x+2}$

34. $s(t) = 4e^{-2/t}$, $t > 0$

Compound Interest In Exercises 35 and 36, complete the table to determine the balance *A* for *P* dollars invested at rate *r* for *t* years and compounded *n* times per year.

n	1	2	4	12	365	Continuous
A						

35. $P = \$3500$, $r = 6.5\%$, $t = 10$ years

36. $P = \$2000$, $r = 5\%$, $t = 30$ years

37. ***Waiting Times*** The average time between incoming calls at a switchboard is 3 minutes. The probability *F* of waiting less than *t* minutes until the next incoming call is approximated by the model $F(t) = 1 - e^{-t/3}$. A call has just come in. Find the probability that the next call will be within

(a) $\frac{1}{2}$ minute.   (b) 2 minutes.   (c) 5 minutes.

38. ***Depreciation*** After *t* years, the value *V* of a car that originally cost $14,000 is given by $V(t) = 14{,}000\left(\frac{3}{4}\right)^t$.

 (a) Use a graphing utility to graph the function.

(b) Find the value of the car 2 years after it was purchased.

(c) According to the model, when does the car depreciate most rapidly? Is this realistic? Explain.

39. Trust Fund On the day a person is born, a deposit of $50,000 is made in a trust fund that pays 8.75% interest, compounded continuously.

(a) Find the balance on the person's 35th birthday.

(b) How much longer would the person have to wait for the balance in the trust fund to double?

40. Radioactive Decay Let Q represent a mass of plutonium 241 (^{241}Pu) (in grams), whose half-life is 14.4 years. The quantity of plutonium 241 present after t years is given by $Q = 100\left(\frac{1}{2}\right)^{t/14.4}$.

(a) Determine the initial quantity (when $t = 0$).

(b) Determine the quantity present after 10 years.

(c) Sketch the graph of this function over the interval $t = 0$ to $t = 100$.

3.2 In Exercises 41–44, write the exponential equation in logarithmic form.

41. $4^3 = 64$

42. $25^{3/2} = 125$

43. $e^{0.8} = 2.2255\ldots$

44. $e^0 = 1$

In Exercises 45–48, evaluate the function at the indicated value of x without using a calculator.

Function	Value
45. $f(x) = \log x$	$x = 1000$
46. $g(x) = \log_9 x$	$x = 3$
47. $g(x) = \log_2 x$	$x = \frac{1}{8}$
48. $f(x) = \log_4 x$	$x = \frac{1}{4}$

In Exercises 49–52, use the One-to-One Property to solve the equation for x.

49. $\log_4(x + 7) = \log_4 14$

50. $\log_8(3x - 10) = \log_8 5$

51. $\ln(x + 9) = \ln 4$

52. $\ln(2x - 1) = \ln 11$

In Exercises 53–58, find the domain, x-intercept, and vertical asymptote of the logarithmic function and sketch its graph.

53. $g(x) = \log_7 x$

54. $g(x) = \log_5 x$

55. $f(x) = \log\left(\frac{x}{3}\right)$

56. $f(x) = 6 + \log x$

57. $f(x) = 4 - \log(x + 5)$

58. $f(x) = \log(x - 3) + 1$

 In Exercises 59–64, use a calculator to evaluate the function given by $f(x) = \ln x$ at the indicated value of x. Round your result to three decimal places if necessary.

59. $x = 22.6$

60. $x = 0.98$

61. $x = e^{-12}$

62. $x = e^7$

63. $x = \sqrt{7} + 5$

64. $x = \frac{\sqrt{3}}{8}$

In Exercises 65–68, find the domain, x-intercept, and vertical asymptote of the logarithmic function and sketch its graph.

65. $f(x) = \ln x + 3$

66. $f(x) = \ln(x - 3)$

67. $h(x) = \ln(x^2)$

68. $f(x) = \frac{1}{4}\ln x$

69. Antler Spread The antler spread a (in inches) and shoulder height h (in inches) of an adult male American elk are related by the model $h = 116 \log(a + 40) - 176$. Approximate the shoulder height of a male American elk with an antler spread of 55 inches.

70. Snow Removal The number of miles s of roads cleared of snow is approximated by the model

$$s = 25 - \frac{13 \ln(h/12)}{\ln 3}, \quad 2 \le h \le 15$$

where h is the depth of the snow in inches. Use this model to find s when $h = 10$ inches.

3.3 In Exercises 71–74, evaluate the logarithm using the change-of-base formula. Do each exercise twice, once with common logarithms and once with natural logarithms. Round your the results to three decimal places.

71. $\log_4 9$

72. $\log_{12} 200$

73. $\log_{1/2} 5$

74. $\log_3 0.28$

In Exercises 75–78, use the properties of logarithms to rewrite and simplify the logarithmic expression.

75. $\log 18$

76. $\log_2\left(\frac{1}{12}\right)$

77. $\ln 20$

78. $\ln(3e^{-4})$

In Exercises 79–86, use the properties of logarithms to expand the expression as a sum, difference, and/or constant multiple of logarithms. (Assume all variables are positive.)

79. $\log_5 5x^2$

80. $\log 7x^4$

81. $\log_3 \dfrac{6}{\sqrt[3]{x}}$

82. $\log_7 \dfrac{\sqrt{x}}{4}$

83. $\ln x^2 y^2 z$

84. $\ln 3xy^2$

85. $\ln\left(\dfrac{x + 3}{xy}\right)$

86. $\ln\left(\dfrac{y - 1}{4}\right)^2, \quad y > 1$

In Exercises 87–94, condense the expression to the logarithm of a single quantity.

87. $\log_2 5 + \log_2 x$

88. $\log_6 y - 2 \log_6 z$

89. $\ln x - \frac{1}{4} \ln y$

90. $3 \ln x + 2 \ln(x + 1)$

91. $\frac{1}{3} \log_8(x + 4) + 7 \log_8 y$

92. $-2 \log x - 5 \log(x + 6)$

93. $\frac{1}{2} \ln(2x - 1) - 2 \ln(x + 1)$

94. $5 \ln(x - 2) - \ln(x + 2) - 3 \ln x$

95. Climb Rate The time t (in minutes) for a small plane to climb to an altitude of h feet is modeled by

$$t = 50 \log \frac{18{,}000}{18{,}000 - h}$$

where 18,000 feet is the plane's absolute ceiling.

(a) Determine the domain of the function in the context of the problem.

 (b) Use a graphing utility to graph the function and identify any asymptotes.

(c) As the plane approaches its absolute ceiling, what can be said about the time required to increase its altitude?

(d) Find the time for the plane to climb to an altitude of 4000 feet.

96. Human Memory Model Students in a learning theory study were given an exam and then retested monthly for 6 months with an equivalent exam. The data obtained in the study are given as the ordered pairs (t, s), where t is the time in months after the initial exam and s is the average score for the class. Use these data to find a logarithmic equation that relates t and s.

(1, 84.2), (2, 78.4), (3, 72.1),

(4, 68.5), (5, 67.1), (6, 65.3)

3.4 **In Exercises 97–104, solve for x.**

97. $8^x = 512$

98. $6^x = \frac{1}{216}$

99. $e^x = 3$

100. $e^x = 6$

101. $\log_4 x = 2$

102. $\log_6 x = -1$

103. $\ln x = 4$

104. $\ln x = -3$

In Exercises 105–114, solve the exponential equation algebraically. Approximate your result to three decimal places.

105. $e^x = 12$

106. $e^{3x} = 25$

107. $e^{4x} = e^{x^2 + 3}$

108. $14e^{3x+2} = 560$

109. $2^x + 13 = 35$

110. $6^x - 28 = -8$

111. $-4(5^x) = -68$

112. $2(12^x) = 190$

113. $e^{2x} - 7e^x + 10 = 0$

114. $e^{2x} - 6e^x + 8 = 0$

In Exercises 115–118, use a graphing utility to graph and solve the equation. Approximate the result to three decimal places.

115. $2^{0.6x} - 3x = 0$

116. $4^{-0.2x} + x = 0$

117. $25e^{-0.3x} = 12$

118. $4e^{1.2x} = 9$

In Exercises 119–130, solve the logarithmic equation algebraically. Approximate the result to three decimal places.

119. $\ln 3x = 8.2$

120. $\ln 5x = 7.2$

121. $2 \ln 4x = 15$

122. $4 \ln 3x = 15$

123. $\ln x - \ln 3 = 2$

124. $\ln \sqrt{x + 8} = 3$

125. $\ln \sqrt{x + 1} = 2$

126. $\ln x - \ln 5 = 4$

127. $\log_8(x - 1) = \log_8(x - 2) - \log_8(x + 2)$

128. $\log_6(x + 2) - \log_6 x = \log_6(x + 5)$

129. $\log(1 - x) = -1$

130. $\log(-x - 4) = 2$

 In Exercises 131–134, use a graphing utility to graph and solve the equation. Approximate the result to three decimal places.

131. $2 \ln(x + 3) + 3x = 8$

132. $6 \log(x^2 + 1) - x = 0$

133. $4 \ln(x + 5) - x = 10$

134. $x - 2 \log(x + 4) = 0$

135. Compound Interest You deposit \$7550 in an account that pays 7.25% interest, compounded continuously. How long will it take for the money to triple?

136. Meteorology The speed of the wind S (in miles per hour) near the center of a tornado and the distance d (in miles) the tornado travels are related by the model $S = 93 \log d + 65$. On March 18, 1925, a large tornado struck portions of Missouri, Illinois, and Indiana with a wind speed at the center of about 283 miles per hour. Approximate the distance traveled by this tornado.

3.5 **In Exercises 137–142, match the function with its graph. [The graphs are labeled (a), (b), (c), (d), (e), and (f).]**

(a)

(b)

(c)

(d)

(e)

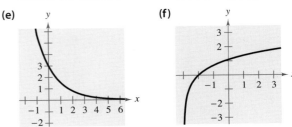

(f)

137. $y = 3e^{-2x/3}$ **138.** $y = 4e^{2x/3}$

139. $y = \ln(x + 3)$ **140.** $y = 7 - \log(x + 3)$

141. $y = 2e^{-(x+4)^2/3}$ **142.** $y = \dfrac{6}{1 + 2e^{-2x}}$

In Exercises 143 and 144, find the exponential model $y = ae^{bx}$ that passes through the points.

143. $(0, 2), (4, 3)$ **144.** $\left(0, \tfrac{1}{2}\right), (5, 5)$

145. *Population* The population P of South Carolina (in thousands) from 1990 through 2003 can be modeled by $P = 3499e^{0.0135t}$, where t represents the year, with $t = 0$ corresponding to 1990. According to this model, when will the population reach 4.5 million? (Source: U.S. Census Bureau)

146. *Radioactive Decay* The half-life of radioactive uranium II (^{234}U) is about 250,000 years. What percent of a present amount of radioactive uranium II will remain after 5000 years?

147. *Compound Interest* A deposit of $10,000 is made in a savings account for which the interest is compounded continuously. The balance will double in 5 years.

(a) What is the annual interest rate for this account?

(b) Find the balance after 1 year.

148. *Wildlife Population* A species of bat is in danger of becoming extinct. Five years ago, the total population of the species was 2000. Two years ago, the total population of the species was 1400. What was the total population of the species one year ago?

  149. *Test Scores* The test scores for a biology test follow a normal distribution modeled by

$$y = 0.0499e^{-(x-71)^2/128}, \quad 40 \le x \le 100$$

where x is the test score.

(a) Use a graphing utility to graph the equation.

(b) From the graph in part (a), estimate the average test score.

150. *Typing Speed* In a typing class, the average number N of words per minute typed after t weeks of lessons was found to be

$$N = \frac{157}{1 + 5.4e^{-0.12t}}.$$

Find the time necessary to type (a) 50 words per minute and (b) 75 words per minute.

151. *Sound Intensity* The relationship between the number of decibels β and the intensity of a sound I in watts per square centimeter is

$$\beta = 10 \log\!\left(\frac{I}{10^{-16}}\right).$$

Determine the intensity of a sound in watts per square centimeter if the decibel level is 125.

152. *Geology* On the Richter scale, the magnitude R of an earthquake of intensity I is given by

$$R = \log \frac{I}{I_0}$$

where $I_0 = 1$ is the minimum intensity used for comparison. Find the intensity per unit of area for each value of R.

(a) $R = 8.4$ (b) $R = 6.85$ (c) $R = 9.1$

Synthesis

True or False? **In Exercises 153 and 154, determine whether the equation is true or false. Justify your answer.**

153. $\log_b b^{2x} = 2x$

154. $\ln(x + y) = \ln x + \ln y$

155. The graphs of $y = e^{kt}$ are shown where $k = a, b, c,$ and d. Which of the four values are negative? Which are positive? Explain your reasoning.

(a)

(b)

(c)

(d)

3 | Chapter Test

Take this test as you would take a test in class. When you are finished, check your work against the answers given in the back of the book.

In Exercises 1–4, evaluate the expression. Approximate your result to three decimal places.

1. $12.4^{2.79}$ **2.** $4^{3\pi/2}$ **3.** $e^{-7/10}$ **4.** $e^{3.1}$

In Exercises 5–7, construct a table of values. Then sketch the graph of the function.

5. $f(x) = 10^{-x}$ **6.** $f(x) = -6^{x-2}$ **7.** $f(x) = 1 - e^{2x}$

8. Evaluate (a) $\log_7 7^{-0.89}$ and (b) $4.6 \ln e^2$.

In Exercises 9–11, construct a table of values. Then sketch the graph of the function. Identify any asymptotes.

9. $f(x) = -\log x - 6$ **10.** $f(x) = \ln(x - 4)$ **11.** $f(x) = 1 + \ln(x + 6)$

In Exercises 12–14, evaluate the logarithm using the change-of-base formula. Round your result to three decimal places.

12. $\log_7 44$ **13.** $\log_{2/5} 0.9$ **14.** $\log_{24} 68$

In Exercises 15–17, use the properties of logarithms to expand the expression as a sum, difference, and/or constant multiple of logarithms.

15. $\log_2 3a^4$ **16.** $\ln \dfrac{5\sqrt{x}}{6}$ **17.** $\log \dfrac{7x^2}{yz^3}$

In Exercises 18–20, condense the expression to the logarithm of a single quantity.

18. $\log_3 13 + \log_3 y$ **19.** $4 \ln x - 4 \ln y$

20. $2 \ln x + \ln(x - 5) - 3 \ln y$

In Exercises 21–26, solve the equation algebraically. Approximate your result to three decimal places.

21. $5^x = \dfrac{1}{25}$ **22.** $3e^{-5x} = 132$

23. $\dfrac{1025}{8 + e^{4x}} = 5$ **24.** $\ln x = \dfrac{1}{2}$

25. $18 + 4 \ln x = 7$ **26.** $\log x - \log(8 - 5x) = 2$

Exponential Growth

$(9, 11{,}277)$

$(0, 2745)$

FIGURE FOR **27**

27. Find an exponential growth model for the graph shown in the figure.

28. The half-life of radioactive actinium (^{227}Ac) is 21.77 years. What percent of a present amount of radioactive actinium will remain after 19 years?

29. A model that can be used for predicting the height H (in centimeters) of a child based on his or her age is $H = 70.228 + 5.104x + 9.222 \ln x$, $\frac{1}{4} \le x \le 6$, where x is the age of the child in years.   (Source: Snapshots of Applications in Mathematics)

(a) Construct a table of values. Then sketch the graph of the model.

(b) Use the graph from part (a) to estimate the height of a four-year-old child. Then calculate the actual height using the model.

3 | Cumulative Test for Chapters 1–3

Take this test to review the material from earlier chapters. When you are finished, check your work against the answers given in the back of the book.

1. Plot the points $(3, 4)$ and $(-1, -1)$. Find the coordinates of the midpoint of the line segment joining the points and the distance between the points.

In Exercises 2–4, graph the equation without using a graphing utility.

2. $x - 3y + 12 = 0$ **3.** $y = x^2 - 9$ **4.** $y = \sqrt{4 - x}$

5. Find an equation of the line passing through $\left(-\frac{1}{2}, 1\right)$ and $(3, 8)$.

6. Explain why the graph at the left does not represent y as a function of x.

7. Evaluate (if possible) the function given by $f(x) = \dfrac{x}{x - 2}$ for each value.

   (a) $f(6)$ (b) $f(2)$ (c) $f(s + 2)$

8. Compare the graph of each function with the graph of $y = \sqrt[3]{x}$. (*Note:* It is not necessary to sketch the graphs.)

   (a) $r(x) = \frac{1}{2}\sqrt[3]{x}$ (b) $h(x) = \sqrt[3]{x} + 2$ (c) $g(x) = \sqrt[3]{x + 2}$

In Exercises 9 and 10, find (a) $(f + g)(x)$, (b) $(f - g)(x)$, (c) $(fg)(x)$, and (d) $(f/g)(x)$. What is the domain of f/g?

9. $f(x) = x - 3, \quad g(x) = 4x + 1$ **10.** $f(x) = \sqrt{x - 1}, \quad g(x) = x^2 + 1$

In Exercises 11 and 12, find (a) $f \circ g$ and (b) $g \circ f$. Find the domain of each composite function.

11. $f(x) = 2x^2, \quad g(x) = \sqrt{x + 6}$ **12.** $f(x) = x - 2, \quad g(x) = |x|$

13. Determine whether $h(x) = 5x - 2$ has an inverse function. If so, find the inverse function.

14. The power P produced by a wind turbine is proportional to the cube of the wind speed S. A wind speed of 27 miles per hour produces a power output of 750 kilowatts. Find the output for a wind speed of 40 miles per hour.

15. Find the quadratic function whose graph has a vertex at $(-8, 5)$ and passes through the point $(-4, -7)$.

In Exercises 16–18, sketch the graph of the function without the aid of a graphing utility.

16. $h(x) = -(x^2 + 4x)$ **17.** $f(t) = \frac{1}{4}t(t - 2)^2$ **18.** $g(s) = s^2 + 4s + 10$

In Exercises 19–21, find all the zeros of the function and write the function as a product of linear factors.

19. $f(x) = x^3 + 2x^2 + 4x + 8$

20. $f(x) = x^4 + 4x^3 - 21x^2$

21. $f(x) = 2x^4 - 11x^3 + 30x^2 - 62x - 40$

FIGURE FOR **6**

22. Use long division to divide $6x^3 - 4x^2$ by $2x^2 + 1$.

23. Use synthetic division to divide $2x^4 + 3x^3 - 6x + 5$ by $x + 2$.

24. Use the Intermediate Value Theorem and a graphing utility to find intervals one unit in length in which the function $g(x) = x^3 + 3x^2 - 6$ is guaranteed to have a zero. Approximate the real zeros of the function.

In Exercises 25–27, sketch the graph of the rational function by hand. Be sure to identify all intercepts and asymptotes.

25. $f(x) = \dfrac{2x}{x^2 - 9}$

26. $f(x) = \dfrac{x^2 - 4x + 3}{x^2 - 2x - 3}$

27. $f(x) = \dfrac{x^3 + 3x^2 - 4x - 12}{x^2 - x - 2}$

In Exercises 28 and 29, solve the inequality. Sketch the solution set on the real number line.

28. $3x^3 - 12x \le 0$

29. $\dfrac{1}{x + 1} \ge \dfrac{1}{x + 5}$

In Exercises 30 and 31, use the graph of f to describe the transformation that yields the graph of g.

30. $f(x) = \left(\tfrac{2}{5}\right)^x, \quad g(x) = -\left(\tfrac{2}{5}\right)^{-x+3}$

31. $f(x) = 2.2^x, \quad g(x) = -2.2^x + 4$

In Exercises 32–35, use a calculator to evaluate the expression. Round your result to three decimal places.

32. $\log 98$

33. $\log\!\left(\tfrac{6}{7}\right)$

34. $\ln\sqrt{31}$

35. $\ln\!\left(\sqrt{40} - 5\right)$

36. Use the properties of logarithms to expand $\ln\!\left(\dfrac{x^2 - 16}{x^4}\right)$, where $x > 4$.

37. Write $2\ln x - \tfrac{1}{2}\ln(x + 5)$ as a logarithm of a single quantity.

In Exercises 38–40, solve the equation algebraically. Approximate the result to three decimal places.

38. $6e^{2x} = 72$

39. $e^{2x} - 11e^x + 24 = 0$

40. $\ln\sqrt{x + 2} = 3$

Year	Sales, S
1997	35.5
1998	35.6
1999	36.0
2000	37.2
2001	38.4
2002	42.0
2003	43.5

TABLE FOR 41

41. The sales S (in billions of dollars) of lottery tickets in the United States from 1997 through 2003 are shown in the table. (Source: TLF Publications, Inc.)

    (a) Use a graphing utility to create a scatter plot of the data. Let t represent the year, with $t = 7$ corresponding to 1997.

    (b) Use the *regression* feature of the graphing utility to find a quadratic model for the data.

    (c) Use the graphing utility to graph the model in the same viewing window used for the scatter plot. How well does the model fit the data?

    (d) Use the model to predict the sales of lottery tickets in 2008. Does your answer seem reasonable? Explain.

42. The number N of bacteria in a culture is given by the model $N = 175e^{kt}$, where t is the time in hours. If $N = 420$ when $t = 8$, estimate the time required for the population to double in size.

Proofs in Mathematics

Each of the following three properties of logarithms can be proved by using properties of exponential functions.

Properties of Logarithms *(p. 240)*

Let a be a positive number such that $a \neq 1$, and let n be a real number. If u and v are positive real numbers, the following properties are true.

	Logarithm with Base a	*Natural Logarithm*
1. Product Property:	$\log_a(uv) = \log_a u + \log_a v$	$\ln(uv) = \ln u + \ln v$
2. Quotient Property:	$\log_a \dfrac{u}{v} = \log_a u - \log_a v$	$\ln \dfrac{u}{v} = \ln u - \ln v$
3. Power Property:	$\log_a u^n = n \log_a u$	$\ln u^n = n \ln u$

Proof

Let

$$x = \log_a u \quad \text{and} \quad y = \log_a v.$$

The corresponding exponential forms of these two equations are

$$a^x = u \quad \text{and} \quad a^y = v.$$

To prove the Product Property, multiply u and v to obtain

$$uv = a^x a^y = a^{x+y}.$$

The corresponding logarithmic form of $uv = a^{x+y}$ is $\log_a(uv) = x + y$. So,

$$\log_a(uv) = \log_a u + \log_a v.$$

To prove the Quotient Property, divide u by v to obtain

$$\frac{u}{v} = \frac{a^x}{a^y} = a^{x-y}.$$

The corresponding logarithmic form of $u/v = a^{x-y}$ is $\log_a(u/v) = x - y$. So,

$$\log_a \frac{u}{v} = \log_a u - \log_a v.$$

To prove the Power Property, substitute a^x for u in the expression $\log_a u^n$, as follows.

$$\log_a u^n = \log_a(a^x)^n \qquad \text{Substitute } a^x \text{ for } u.$$
$$= \log_a a^{nx} \qquad \text{Property of exponents}$$
$$= nx \qquad \text{Inverse Property of Logarithms}$$
$$= n \log_a u \qquad \text{Substitute } \log_a u \text{ for } x.$$

So, $\log_a u^n = n \log_a u.$

This collection of thought-provoking and challenging exercises further explores
and expands upon concepts learned in this chapter.

1. Graph the exponential function given by $y = a^x$ for $a = 0.5$, 1.2, and 2.0. Which of these curves intersects the line $y = x$? Determine all positive numbers a for which the curve $y = a^x$ intersects the line $y = x$.

2. Use a graphing utility to graph $y_1 = e^x$ and each of the functions $y_2 = x^2$, $y_3 = x^3$, $y_4 = \sqrt{x}$, and $y_5 = |x|$. Which function increases at the greatest rate as x approaches $+\infty$?

3. Use the result of Exercise 2 to make a conjecture about the rate of growth of $y_1 = e^x$ and $y = x^n$, where n is a natural number and x approaches $+\infty$.

4. Use the results of Exercises 2 and 3 to describe what is implied when it is stated that a quantity is growing exponentially.

5. Given the exponential function

$$f(x) = a^x$$

show that

(a) $f(u + v) = f(u) \cdot f(v)$.

(b) $f(2x) = [f(x)]^2$.

6. Given that

$$f(x) = \frac{e^x + e^{-x}}{2} \text{ and } g(x) = \frac{e^x - e^{-x}}{2}$$

show that

$$[f(x)]^2 - [g(x)]^2 = 1.$$

7. Use a graphing utility to compare the graph of the function given by $y = e^x$ with the graph of each given function. [$n!$ (read "n factorial") is defined as $n! = 1 \cdot 2 \cdot 3 \cdots (n - 1) \cdot n$.]

(a) $y_1 = 1 + \dfrac{x}{1!}$

(b) $y_2 = 1 + \dfrac{x}{1!} + \dfrac{x^2}{2!}$

(c) $y_3 = 1 + \dfrac{x}{1!} + \dfrac{x^2}{2!} + \dfrac{x^3}{3!}$

8. Identify the pattern of successive polynomials given in Exercise 7. Extend the pattern one more term and compare the graph of the resulting polynomial function with the graph of $y = e^x$. What do you think this pattern implies?

9. Graph the function given by

$$f(x) = e^x - e^{-x}.$$

From the graph, the function appears to be one-to-one. Assuming that the function has an inverse function, find $f^{-1}(x)$.

10. Find a pattern for $f^{-1}(x)$ if

$$f(x) = \frac{a^x + 1}{a^x - 1}$$

where $a > 0$, $a \neq 1$.

11. By observation, identify the equation that corresponds to the graph. Explain your reasoning.

(a) $y = 6e^{-x^2/2}$

(b) $y = \dfrac{6}{1 + e^{-x/2}}$

(c) $y = 6(1 - e^{-x^2/2})$

12. You have two options for investing $500. The first earns 7% compounded annually and the second earns 7% simple interest. The figure shows the growth of each investment over a 30-year period.

(a) Identify which graph represents each type of investment. Explain your reasoning.

(b) Verify your answer in part (a) by finding the equations that model the investment growth and graphing the models.

(c) Which option would you choose? Explain your reasoning.

13. Two different samples of radioactive isotopes are decaying. The isotopes have initial amounts of c_1 and c_2, as well as half-lives of k_1 and k_2, respectively. Find the time required for the samples to decay to equal amounts.

14. A lab culture initially contains 500 bacteria. Two hours later, the number of bacteria has decreased to 200. Find the exponential decay model of the form

$$B = B_0 a^{kt}$$

that can be used to approximate the number of bacteria after t hours.

15. The table shows the colonial population estimates of the American colonies from 1700 to 1780. (Source: U.S. Census Bureau)

Year	Population
1700	250,900
1710	331,700
1720	466,200
1730	629,400
1740	905,600
1750	1,170,800
1760	1,593,600
1770	2,148,100
1780	2,780,400

In each of the following, let y represent the population in the year t, with $t = 0$ corresponding to 1700.

(a) Use the *regression* feature of a graphing utility to find an exponential model for the data.

(b) Use the *regression* feature of the graphing utility to find a quadratic model for the data.

(c) Use the graphing utility to plot the data and the models from parts (a) and (b) in the same viewing window.

(d) Which model is a better fit for the data? Would you use this model to predict the population of the United States in 2010? Explain your reasoning.

16. Show that $\dfrac{\log_a x}{\log_{a/b} x} = 1 + \log_a \dfrac{1}{b}$.

17. Solve $(\ln x)^2 = \ln x^2$.

18. Use a graphing utility to compare the graph of the function given by $y = \ln x$ with the graph of each given function.

(a) $y_1 = x - 1$

(b) $y_2 = (x - 1) - \frac{1}{2}(x - 1)^2$

(c) $y_3 = (x - 1) - \frac{1}{2}(x - 1)^2 + \frac{1}{3}(x - 1)^3$

19. Identify the pattern of successive polynomials given in Exercise 18. Extend the pattern one more term and compare the graph of the resulting polynomial function with the graph of $y = \ln x$. What do you think the pattern implies?

20. Using

$$y = ab^x \qquad \text{and} \qquad y = ax^b$$

take the natural logarithm of each side of each equation. What are the slope and y-intercept of the line relating x and $\ln y$ for $y = ab^x$? What are the slope and y-intercept of the line relating $\ln x$ and $\ln y$ for $y = ax^b$?

In Exercises 21 and 22, use the model

$$y = 80.4 - 11 \ln x, \quad 100 \le x \le 1500$$

which approximates the minimum required ventilation rate in terms of the air space per child in a public school classroom. In the model, x is the air space per child in cubic feet and y is the ventilation rate per child in cubic feet per minute.

21. Use a graphing utility to graph the model and approximate the required ventilation rate if there is 300 cubic feet of air space per child.

22. A classroom is designed for 30 students. The air conditioning system in the room has the capacity of moving 450 cubic feet of air per minute.

(a) Determine the ventilation rate per child, assuming that the room is filled to capacity.

(b) Estimate the air space required per child.

(c) Determine the minimum number of square feet of floor space required for the room if the ceiling height is 30 feet.

In Exercises 23–26, (a) use a graphing utility to create a scatter plot of the data, (b) decide whether the data could best be modeled by a linear model, an exponential model, or a logarithmic model, (c) explain why you chose the model you did in part (b), (d) use the *regression* feature of a graphing utility to find the model you chose in part (b) for the data and graph the model with the scatter plot, and (e) determine how well the model you chose fits the data.

23. $(1, 2.0), (1.5, 3.5), (2, 4.0), (4, 5.8), (6, 7.0), (8, 7.8)$

24. $(1, 4.4), (1.5, 4.7), (2, 5.5), (4, 9.9), (6, 18.1), (8, 33.0)$

25. $(1, 7.5), (1.5, 7.0), (2, 6.8), (4, 5.0), (6, 3.5), (8, 2.0)$

26. $(1, 5.0), (1.5, 6.0), (2, 6.4), (4, 7.8), (6, 8.6), (8, 9.0)$

Trigonometry

Airport runways are named on the basis of the angles they form with due north, measured in a clockwise direction. These angles are called bearings and can be determined using trigonometry.

Rajs/Photonica/Getty Images

SELECTED APPLICATIONS

Trigonometric functions have many real-life applications. The applications listed below represent a small sample of the applications in this chapter.

4.1   Radian and Degree Measure

What you should learn

- Describe angles.
- Use radian measure.
- Use degree measure.
- Use angles to model and solve real-life problems.

Why you should learn it

You can use angles to model and solve real-life problems. For instance, in Exercise 108 on page 293, you are asked to use angles to find the speed of a bicycle.

© Wolfgang Rattay/Reuters/Corbis

Angles

As derived from the Greek language, the word **trigonometry** means "measurement of triangles." Initially, trigonometry dealt with relationships among the sides and angles of triangles and was used in the development of astronomy, navigation, and surveying. With the development of calculus and the physical sciences in the 17th century, a different perspective arose—one that viewed the classic trigonometric relationships as *functions* with the set of real numbers as their domains. Consequently, the applications of trigonometry expanded to include a vast number of physical phenomena involving rotations and vibrations. These phenomena include sound waves, light rays, planetary orbits, vibrating strings, pendulums, and orbits of atomic particles.

The approach in this text incorporates *both* perspectives, starting with angles and their measure.

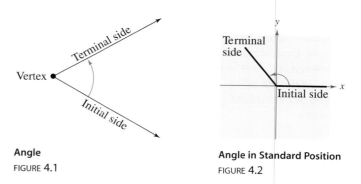

Angle
FIGURE **4.1**

Angle in Standard Position
FIGURE **4.2**

An **angle** is determined by rotating a ray (half-line) about its endpoint. The starting position of the ray is the **initial side** of the angle, and the position after rotation is the **terminal side,** as shown in Figure 4.1. The endpoint of the ray is the **vertex** of the angle. This perception of an angle fits a coordinate system in which the origin is the vertex and the initial side coincides with the positive *x*-axis. Such an angle is in **standard position,** as shown in Figure 4.2. **Positive angles** are generated by counterclockwise rotation, and **negative angles** by clockwise rotation, as shown in Figure 4.3. Angles are labeled with Greek letters α (alpha), β (beta), and θ (theta), as well as uppercase letters A, B, and C. In Figure 4.4, note that angles α and β have the same initial and terminal sides. Such angles are **coterminal.**

The *HM mathSpace®* CD-ROM and *Eduspace®* for this text contain additional resources related to the concepts discussed in this chapter.

FIGURE **4.3**

FIGURE **4.4**   *Coterminal Angles*

Radian Measure

The **measure of an angle** is determined by the amount of rotation from the initial side to the terminal side. One way to measure angles is in *radians*. This type of measure is especially useful in calculus. To define a radian, you can use a **central angle** of a circle, one whose vertex is the center of the circle, as shown in Figure 4.5.

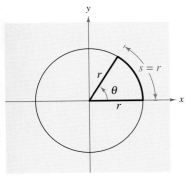

Arc length = radius when θ = 1 radian

FIGURE **4.5**

Definition of Radian

One **radian** is the measure of a central angle θ that intercepts an arc s equal in length to the radius r of the circle. See Figure 4.5. Algebraically, this means that

$$\theta = \frac{s}{r}$$

where θ is measured in radians.

Because the circumference of a circle is $2\pi r$ units, it follows that a central angle of one full revolution (counterclockwise) corresponds to an arc length of

$$s = 2\pi r.$$

Moreover, because $2\pi \approx 6.28$, there are just over six radius lengths in a full circle, as shown in Figure 4.6. Because the units of measure for s and r are the same, the ratio s/r has no units—it is simply a real number.

Because the radian measure of an angle of one full revolution is 2π, you can obtain the following.

$$\frac{1}{2} \text{ revolution} = \frac{2\pi}{2} = \pi \text{ radians}$$

$$\frac{1}{4} \text{ revolution} = \frac{2\pi}{4} = \frac{\pi}{2} \text{ radians}$$

$$\frac{1}{6} \text{ revolution} = \frac{2\pi}{6} = \frac{\pi}{3} \text{ radians}$$

These and other common angles are shown in Figure 4.7.

FIGURE **4.6**

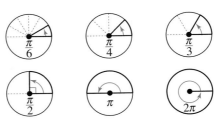

FIGURE **4.7**

Recall that the four quadrants in a coordinate system are numbered I, II, III, and IV. Figure 4.8 on page 284 shows which angles between 0 and 2π lie in each of the four quadrants. Note that angles between 0 and $\pi/2$ are **acute** angles and angles between $\pi/2$ and π are **obtuse** angles.

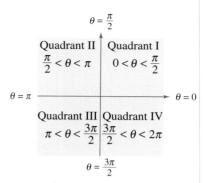

FIGURE 4.8

Two angles are coterminal if they have the same initial and terminal sides. For instance, the angles 0 and 2π are coterminal, as are the angles $\pi/6$ and $13\pi/6$. You can find an angle that is coterminal to a given angle θ by adding or subtracting 2π (one revolution), as demonstrated in Example 1. A given angle θ has infinitely many coterminal angles. For instance, $\theta = \pi/6$ is coterminal with

$$\frac{\pi}{6} + 2n\pi$$

where n is an integer.

Example 1 **Sketching and Finding Coterminal Angles**

a. For the positive angle $13\pi/6$, subtract 2π to obtain a coterminal angle

$$\frac{13\pi}{6} - 2\pi = \frac{\pi}{6}. \qquad \text{See Figure 4.9.}$$

b. For the positive angle $3\pi/4$, subtract 2π to obtain a coterminal angle

$$\frac{3\pi}{4} - 2\pi = -\frac{5\pi}{4}. \qquad \text{See Figure 4.10.}$$

c. For the negative angle $-2\pi/3$, add 2π to obtain a coterminal angle

$$-\frac{2\pi}{3} + 2\pi = \frac{4\pi}{3}. \qquad \text{See Figure 4.11.}$$

FIGURE 4.9

FIGURE 4.10

FIGURE 4.11

✓CHECKPOINT Now try Exercise 17.

Two positive angles α and β are **complementary** (complements of each other) if their sum is $\pi/2$. Two positive angles are **supplementary** (supplements of each other) if their sum is π. See Figure 4.12.

    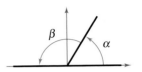

Complementary Angles   *Supplementary Angles*

FIGURE 4.12

Example 2   **Complementary and Supplementary Angles**

If possible, find the complement and the supplement of (a) $2\pi/5$ and (b) $4\pi/5$.

Solution

a. The complement of $2\pi/5$ is

$$\frac{\pi}{2} - \frac{2\pi}{5} = \frac{5\pi}{10} - \frac{4\pi}{10} = \frac{\pi}{10}.$$

The supplement of $2\pi/5$ is

$$\pi - \frac{2\pi}{5} = \frac{5\pi}{5} - \frac{2\pi}{5} = \frac{3\pi}{5}.$$

b. Because $4\pi/5$ is greater than $\pi/2$, it has no complement. (Remember that complements are *positive* angles.) The supplement is

$$\pi - \frac{4\pi}{5} = \frac{5\pi}{5} - \frac{4\pi}{5} = \frac{\pi}{5}.$$

✓CHECKPOINT   Now try Exercise 21.

Degree Measure

A second way to measure angles is in terms of **degrees,** denoted by the symbol $^\circ$. A measure of one degree (1°) is equivalent to a rotation of $\frac{1}{360}$ of a complete revolution about the vertex. To measure angles, it is convenient to mark degrees on the circumference of a circle, as shown in Figure 4.13. So, a full revolution (counterclockwise) corresponds to 360°, a half revolution to 180°, a quarter revolution to 90°, and so on.

Because 2π radians corresponds to one complete revolution, degrees and radians are related by the equations

$$360^\circ = 2\pi \text{ rad} \qquad \text{and} \qquad 180^\circ = \pi \text{ rad}.$$

From the latter equation, you obtain

$$1^\circ = \frac{\pi}{180} \text{ rad} \qquad \text{and} \qquad 1 \text{ rad} = \left(\frac{180^\circ}{\pi}\right)$$

which lead to the conversion rules at the top of the next page.

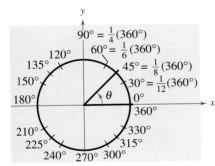

FIGURE 4.13

> **Conversions Between Degrees and Radians**
>
> **1.** To convert degrees to radians, multiply degrees by $\dfrac{\pi \text{ rad}}{180°}$.
>
> **2.** To convert radians to degrees, multiply radians by $\dfrac{180°}{\pi \text{ rad}}$.
>
> To apply these two conversion rules, use the basic relationship $\pi \text{ rad} = 180°$.
> (See Figure 4.14.)

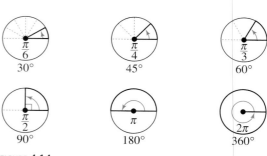

FIGURE **4.14**

When no units of angle measure are specified, *radian measure is implied.*
For instance, if you write $\theta = 2$, you imply that $\theta = 2$ radians.

Example 3   Converting from Degrees to Radians

a. $135° = (135 \deg)\left(\dfrac{\pi \text{ rad}}{180 \deg}\right) = \dfrac{3\pi}{4}$ radians   Multiply by $\pi/180$.

b. $540° = (540 \deg)\left(\dfrac{\pi \text{ rad}}{180 \deg}\right) = 3\pi$ radians   Multiply by $\pi/180$.

c. $-270° = (-270 \deg)\left(\dfrac{\pi \text{ rad}}{180 \deg}\right) = -\dfrac{3\pi}{2}$ radians   Multiply by $\pi/180$.

✓CHECKPOINT   Now try Exercise 47.

Example 4   Converting from Radians to Degrees

a. $-\dfrac{\pi}{2} \text{ rad} = \left(-\dfrac{\pi}{2} \text{ rad}\right)\left(\dfrac{180 \deg}{\pi \text{ rad}}\right) = -90°$ Multiply by $180/\pi$.

b. $\dfrac{9\pi}{2} \text{ rad} = \left(\dfrac{9\pi}{2} \text{ rad}\right)\left(\dfrac{180 \deg}{\pi \text{ rad}}\right) = 810°$ Multiply by $180/\pi$.

c. $2 \text{ rad} = (2 \text{ rad})\left(\dfrac{180 \deg}{\pi \text{ rad}}\right) = \dfrac{360°}{\pi} \approx 114.59°$ Multiply by $180/\pi$.

✓CHECKPOINT   Now try Exercise 51.

If you have a calculator with a "radian-to-degree" conversion key, try using
it to verify the result shown in part (c) of Example 4.

Technology

With calculators it is convenient
to use *decimal* degrees to denote
fractional parts of degrees.
Historically, however, fractional
parts of degrees were expressed
in *minutes* and *seconds*, using the
prime (′) and double prime (″)
notations, respectively. That is,

$1' = $ one minute $= \frac{1}{60}(1°)$

$1'' = $ one second $= \frac{1}{3600}(1°)$

Consequently, an angle of 64
degrees, 32 minutes, and 47 seconds
is represented by $\theta = 64°\, 32'\, 47''$.
Many calculators have special keys
for converting an angle in degrees,
minutes, and seconds (D° M′ S″)
to decimal degree form, and
vice versa.

Applications

The *radian measure* formula, $\theta = s/r$, can be used to measure arc length along a circle.

> ### Arc Length
>
> For a circle of radius r, a central angle θ intercepts an arc of length s given by
>
> $$s = r\theta \qquad\qquad \text{Length of circular arc}$$
>
> where θ is measured in radians. Note that if $r = 1$, then $s = \theta$, and the radian measure of θ equals the arc length.

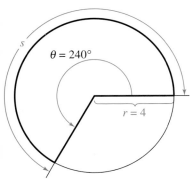

$\theta = 240°$

$r = 4$

FIGURE **4.15**

Example 5   Finding Arc Length

A circle has a radius of 4 inches. Find the length of the arc intercepted by a central angle of 240°, as shown in Figure 4.15.

Solution

To use the formula $s = r\theta$, first convert 240° to radian measure.

$$240° = (240 \text{ deg})\left(\frac{\pi \text{ rad}}{180 \text{ deg}}\right) = \frac{4\pi}{3} \text{ radians}$$

Then, using a radius of $r = 4$ inches, you can find the arc length to be

$$s = r\theta = 4\left(\frac{4\pi}{3}\right) = \frac{16\pi}{3} \approx 16.76 \text{ inches.}$$

Note that the units for $r\theta$ are determined by the units for r because θ is given in radian measure, which has no units.

✓**CHECKPOINT**   Now try Exercise 87.

The formula for the length of a circular arc can be used to analyze the motion of a particle moving at a *constant speed* along a circular path.

STUDY TIP

Linear speed measures how fast the particle moves, and angular speed measures how fast the angle changes. By dividing the formula for arc length by t, you can establish a relationship between linear speed v and angular speed ω, as shown.

$$s = r\theta$$

$$\frac{s}{t} = \frac{r\theta}{t}$$

$$v = r\omega$$

> ### Linear and Angular Speeds
>
> Consider a particle moving at a constant speed along a circular arc of radius r. If s is the length of the arc traveled in time t, then the **linear speed** v of the particle is
>
> $$\text{Linear speed } v = \frac{\text{arc length}}{\text{time}} = \frac{s}{t}.$$
>
> Moreover, if θ is the angle (in radian measure) corresponding to the arc length s, then the **angular speed** ω (the lowercase Greek letter omega) of the particle is
>
> $$\text{Angular speed } \omega = \frac{\text{central angle}}{\text{time}} = \frac{\theta}{t}.$$

FIGURE **4.16**

FIGURE **4.17**

Example 6 **Finding Linear Speed**

The second hand of a clock is 10.2 centimeters long, as shown in Figure 4.16. Find the linear speed of the tip of this second hand as it passes around the clock face.

Solution

In one revolution, the arc length traveled is

$$s = 2\pi r$$
$$= 2\pi(10.2) \qquad \text{Substitute for } r.$$
$$= 20.4\pi \text{ centimeters.}$$

The time required for the second hand to travel this distance is

$$t = 1 \text{ minute} = 60 \text{ seconds.}$$

So, the linear speed of the tip of the second hand is

$$\text{Linear speed} = \frac{s}{t}$$
$$= \frac{20.4\pi \text{ centimeters}}{60 \text{ seconds}}$$
$$\approx 1.068 \text{ centimeters per second.}$$

✓CHECKPOINT   Now try Exercise 103.

Example 7 **Finding Angular and Linear Speeds**

A Ferris wheel with a 50-foot radius (see Figure 4.17) makes 1.5 revolutions per minute.

a. Find the angular speed of the Ferris wheel in radians per minute.

b. Find the linear speed of the Ferris wheel.

Solution

a. Because each revolution generates 2π radians, it follows that the wheel turns $(1.5)(2\pi) = 3\pi$ radians per minute. In other words, the angular speed is

$$\text{Angular speed} = \frac{\theta}{t}$$
$$= \frac{3\pi \text{ radians}}{1 \text{ minute}} = 3\pi \text{ radians per minute.}$$

b. The linear speed is

$$\text{Linear speed} = \frac{s}{t}$$
$$= \frac{r\theta}{t}$$
$$= \frac{50(3\pi) \text{ feet}}{1 \text{ minute}} \approx 471.2 \text{ feet per minute.}$$

✓CHECKPOINT   Now try Exercise 105.

A **sector** of a circle is the region bounded by two radii of the circle and their intercepted arc (see Figure 4.18).

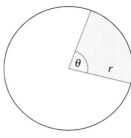

FIGURE **4.18**

Area of a Sector of a Circle

For a circle of radius r, the area A of a sector of the circle with central angle θ is given by

$$A = \frac{1}{2}r^2\theta$$

where θ is measured in radians.

Example 8   **Area of a Sector of a Circle**

A sprinkler on a golf course fairway is set to spray water over a distance of 70 feet and rotates through an angle of $120°$ (see Figure 4.19). Find the area of the fairway watered by the sprinkler.

Solution

First convert $120°$ to radian measure as follows.

$$\theta = 120°$$

$$= (120 \text{ deg})\left(\frac{\pi \text{ rad}}{180 \text{ deg}}\right) \qquad \text{Multiply by } \pi/180.$$

$$= \frac{2\pi}{3} \text{ radians}$$

Then, using $\theta = 2\pi/3$ and $r = 70$, the area is

$$A = \frac{1}{2}r^2\theta \qquad \text{Formula for the area of a sector of a circle}$$

$$= \frac{1}{2}(70)^2\left(\frac{2\pi}{3}\right) \qquad \text{Substitute for } r \text{ and } \theta.$$

$$= \frac{4900\pi}{3} \qquad \text{Simplify.}$$

$$\approx 5131 \text{ square feet.} \qquad \text{Simplify.}$$

✓CHECKPOINT   Now try Exercise 107.

FIGURE **4.19**

120°

70 ft

4.1 | Exercises

The *HM mathSpace®* CD-ROM and *Eduspace®* for this text contain step-by-step solutions to all odd-numbered exercises. They also provide Tutorial Exercises for additional help.

VOCABULARY CHECK: Fill in the blanks.

1. _____ means "measurement of triangles."

2. An _____ is determined by rotating a ray about its endpoint.

3. Two angles that have the same initial and terminal sides are _____.

4. One _____ is the measure of a central angle that intercepts an arc equal to the radius of the circle.

5. Angles that measure between 0 and $\pi/2$ are _____ angles, and angles that measure between $\pi/2$ and π are _____ angles.

6. Two positive angles that have a sum of $\pi/2$ are _____ angles, whereas two positive angles that have a sum of π are _____ angles.

7. The angle measure that is equivalent to $\frac{1}{360}$ of a complete revolution about an angle's vertex is one _____.

8. The _____ speed of a particle is the ratio of the arc length traveled to the time traveled.

9. The _____ speed of a particle is the ratio of the change in the central angle to time.

10. The area of a sector of a circle with radius r and central angle θ, where θ is measured in radians, is given by the formula _____.

PREREQUISITE SKILLS REVIEW: Practice and review algebra skills needed for this section at **www.Eduspace.com.**

In Exercises 1–6, estimate the angle to the nearest one-half radian.

1.

2.

3.

4.

5.

6.

In Exercises 7–12, determine the quadrant in which each angle lies. (The angle measure is given in radians.)

7. (a) $\dfrac{\pi}{5}$ (b) $\dfrac{7\pi}{5}$

8. (a) $\dfrac{11\pi}{8}$ (b) $\dfrac{9\pi}{8}$

9. (a) $-\dfrac{\pi}{12}$ (b) -2

10. (a) -1 (b) $-\dfrac{11\pi}{9}$

11. (a) 3.5 (b) 2.25

12. (a) 6.02 (b) -4.25

In Exercises 13–16, sketch each angle in standard position.

13. (a) $\dfrac{5\pi}{4}$ (b) $-\dfrac{2\pi}{3}$ 14. (a) $-\dfrac{7\pi}{4}$ (b) $\dfrac{5\pi}{2}$

15. (a) $\dfrac{11\pi}{6}$ (b) -3 16. (a) 4 (b) 7π

In Exercises 17–20, determine two coterminal angles (one positive and one negative) for each angle. Give your answers in radians.

17. (a) (b)

$\theta = \dfrac{\pi}{6}$ $\theta = \dfrac{5\pi}{6}$

18. (a) (b)

$\theta = \dfrac{7\pi}{6}$ $\theta = -\dfrac{11\pi}{6}$

19. (a) $\theta = \dfrac{2\pi}{3}$ (b) $\theta = \dfrac{\pi}{12}$

20. (a) $\theta = -\dfrac{9\pi}{4}$ (b) $\theta = -\dfrac{2\pi}{15}$

In Exercises 21–24, find (if possible) the complement and supplement of each angle.

21. (a) $\dfrac{\pi}{3}$ (b) $\dfrac{3\pi}{4}$ **22.** (a) $\dfrac{\pi}{12}$ (b) $\dfrac{11\pi}{12}$

23. (a) 1 (b) 2 **24.** (a) 3 (b) 1.5

In Exercises 25–30, estimate the number of degrees in the angle.

25.

26.

27.

28.

29.

30.

In Exercises 31–34, determine the quadrant in which each angle lies.

31. (a) $130°$ (b) $285°$

32. (a) $8.3°$ (b) $257°\,30'$

33. (a) $-132°\,50'$ (b) $-336°$

34. (a) $-260°$ (b) $-3.4°$

In Exercises 35–38, sketch each angle in standard position.

35. (a) $30°$ (b) $150°$ **36.** (a) $-270°$ (b) $-120°$

37. (a) $405°$ (b) $480°$ **38.** (a) $-750°$ (b) $-600°$

In Exercises 39–42, determine two coterminal angles (one positive and one negative) for each angle. Give your answers in degrees.

39. (a)

(b)

$\theta = -36°$

40. (a)

$\theta = 120°$

(b)

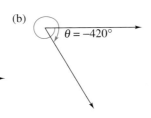

$\theta = -420°$

41. (a) $\theta = 240°$ (b) $\theta = -180°$

42. (a) $\theta = -420°$ (b) $\theta = 230°$

In Exercises 43–46, find (if possible) the complement and supplement of each angle.

43. (a) $18°$ (b) $115°$ **44.** (a) $3°$ (b) $64°$

45. (a) $79°$ (b) $150°$ **46.** (a) $130°$ (b) $170°$

In Exercises 47–50, rewrite each angle in radian measure as a multiple of π. (Do not use a calculator.)

47. (a) $30°$ (b) $150°$ **48.** (a) $315°$ (b) $120°$

49. (a) $-20°$ (b) $-240°$ **50.** (a) $-270°$ (b) $144°$

In Exercises 51–54, rewrite each angle in degree measure. (Do not use a calculator.)

51. (a) $\dfrac{3\pi}{2}$ (b) $\dfrac{7\pi}{6}$ **52.** (a) $-\dfrac{7\pi}{12}$ (b) $\dfrac{\pi}{9}$

53. (a) $\dfrac{7\pi}{3}$ (b) $-\dfrac{11\pi}{30}$ **54.** (a) $\dfrac{11\pi}{6}$ (b) $\dfrac{34\pi}{15}$

In Exercises 55–62, convert the angle measure from degrees to radians. Round to three decimal places.

55. $115°$ **56.** $87.4°$

57. $-216.35°$ **58.** $-48.27°$

59. $532°$ **60.** $345°$

61. $-0.83°$ **62.** $0.54°$

In Exercises 63–70, convert the angle measure from radians to degrees. Round to three decimal places.

63. $\dfrac{\pi}{7}$ **64.** $\dfrac{5\pi}{11}$

65. $\dfrac{15\pi}{8}$ **66.** $\dfrac{13\pi}{2}$

67. -4.2π **68.** 4.8π

69. -2 **70.** -0.57

In Exercises 71–74, convert each angle measure to decimal degree form.

71. (a) $54°\,45'$ (b) $-128°\,30'$

72. (a) $245°\,10'$ (b) $2°\,12'$

73. (a) $85°\,18'\,30''$ (b) $330°\,25''$

74. (a) $-135°\,36''$ (b) $-408°\,16'\,20''$

In Exercises 75–78, convert each angle measure to $D°\,M'\,S''$ form.

75. (a) $240.6°$ (b) $-145.8°$

76. (a) $-345.12°$ (b) $0.45°$

77. (a) $2.5°$ (b) $-3.58°$

78. (a) $-0.355°$ (b) $0.7865°$

In Exercises 79–82, find the angle in radians.

79.

80.

81.

82.

In Exercises 83–86, find the radian measure of the central angle of a circle of radius r that intercepts an arc of length s.

Radius r	Arc Length s
83. 27 inches	6 inches
84. 14 feet	8 feet
85. 14.5 centimeters	25 centimeters
86. 80 kilometers	160 kilometers

In Exercises 87–90, find the length of the arc on a circle of radius r intercepted by a central angle θ.

Radius r	Central Angle θ
87. 15 inches	180°
88. 9 feet	60°
89. 3 meters	1 radian
90. 20 centimeters	$\pi/4$ radian

In Exercises 91–94, find the area of the sector of the circle with radius r and central angle θ.

Radius r	Central Angle θ
91. 4 inches	$\dfrac{\pi}{3}$
92. 12 millimeters	$\dfrac{\pi}{4}$
93. 2.5 feet	225°
94. 1.4 miles	330°

Distance Between Cities **In Exercises 95 and 96, find the distance between the cities. Assume that Earth is a sphere of radius 4000 miles and that the cities are on the same longitude (one city is due north of the other).**

City	Latitude
95. Dallas, Texas	32° 47′ 39″ N
Omaha, Nebraska	41° 15′ 50″ N

City	Latitude
96. San Francisco, California	37° 47′ 36″ N
Seattle, Washington	47° 37′ 18″ N

97. ***Difference in Latitudes*** Assuming that Earth is a sphere of radius 6378 kilometers, what is the difference in the latitudes of Syracuse, New York and Annapolis, Maryland, where Syracuse is 450 kilometers due north of Annapolis?

98. ***Difference in Latitudes*** Assuming that Earth is a sphere of radius 6378 kilometers, what is the difference in the latitudes of Lynchburg, Virginia and Myrtle Beach, South Carolina, where Lynchburg is 400 kilometers due north of Myrtle Beach?

99. ***Instrumentation*** The pointer on a voltmeter is 6 centimeters in length (see figure). Find the angle through which the pointer rotates when it moves 2.5 centimeters on the scale.

FIGURE FOR 99

FIGURE FOR 100

100. ***Electric Hoist*** An electric hoist is being used to lift a beam (see figure). The diameter of the drum on the hoist is 10 inches, and the beam must be raised 2 feet. Find the number of degrees through which the drum must rotate.

101. ***Angular Speed*** A car is moving at a rate of 65 miles per hour, and the diameter of its wheels is 2.5 feet.

(a) Find the number of revolutions per minute the wheels are rotating.

(b) Find the angular speed of the wheels in radians per minute.

102. ***Angular Speed*** A two-inch-diameter pulley on an electric motor that runs at 1700 revolutions per minute is connected by a belt to a four-inch-diameter pulley on a saw arbor.

(a) Find the angular speed (in radians per minute) of each pulley.

(b) Find the revolutions per minute of the saw.

103. *Linear and Angular Speeds* A $7\frac{1}{4}$-inch circular power saw rotates at 5200 revolutions per minute.

(a) Find the angular speed of the saw blade in radians per minute.

(b) Find the linear speed (in feet per minute) of one of the 24 cutting teeth as they contact the wood being cut.

104. *Linear and Angular Speeds* A carousel with a 50-foot diameter makes 4 revolutions per minute.

(a) Find the angular speed of the carousel in radians per minute.

(b) Find the linear speed of the platform rim of the carousel.

105. *Linear and Angular Speeds* The diameter of a DVD is approximately 12 centimeters. The drive motor of the DVD player is controlled to rotate precisely between 200 and 500 revolutions per minute, depending on what track is being read.

(a) Find an interval for the angular speed of a DVD as it rotates.

(b) Find an interval for the linear speed of a point on the outermost track as the DVD rotates.

106. *Area* A car's rear windshield wiper rotates $125°$. The total length of the wiper mechanism is 25 inches and wipes the windshield over a distance of 14 inches. Find the area covered by the wiper.

107. *Area* A sprinkler system on a farm is set to spray water over a distance of 35 meters and to rotate through an angle of $140°$. Draw a diagram that shows the region that can be irrigated with the sprinkler. Find the area of the region.

Model It

108. *Speed of a Bicycle* The radii of the pedal sprocket, the wheel sprocket, and the wheel of the bicycle in the figure are 4 inches, 2 inches, and 14 inches, respectively. A cyclist is pedaling at a rate of 1 revolution per second.

14 in.

2 in.   4 in.

(a) Find the speed of the bicycle in feet per second and miles per hour.

(b) Use your result from part (a) to write a function for the distance d (in miles) a cyclist travels in terms of the number n of revolutions of the pedal sprocket.

Model It (continued)

(c) Write a function for the distance d (in miles) a cyclist travels in terms of the time t (in seconds). Compare this function with the function from part (b).

(d) Classify the types of functions you found in parts (b) and (c). Explain your reasoning.

Synthesis

True or False? In Exercises 109–111, determine whether the statement is true or false. Justify your answer.

109. A measurement of 4 radians corresponds to two complete revolutions from the initial side to the terminal side of an angle.

110. The difference between the measures of two coterminal angles is always a multiple of $360°$ if expressed in degrees and is always a multiple of 2π radians if expressed in radians.

111. An angle that measures $-1260°$ lies in Quadrant III.

112. *Writing* In your own words, explain the meanings of (a) an angle in standard position, (b) a negative angle, (c) coterminal angles, and (d) an obtuse angle.

113. *Think About It* A fan motor turns at a given angular speed. How does the speed of the tips of the blades change if a fan of greater diameter is installed on the motor? Explain.

114. *Think About It* Is a degree or a radian the larger unit of measure? Explain.

115. *Writing* If the radius of a circle is increasing and the magnitude of a central angle is held constant, how is the length of the intercepted arc changing? Explain your reasoning.

116. *Proof* Prove that the area of a circular sector of radius r with central angle θ is $A = \frac{1}{2}\theta r^2$, where θ is measured in radians.

Skills Review

In Exercises 117–120, simplify the radical expression.

117. $\dfrac{4}{4\sqrt{2}}$

118. $\dfrac{5\sqrt{5}}{2\sqrt{10}}$

119. $\sqrt{2^2 + 6^2}$

120. $\sqrt{17^2 - 9^2}$

In Exercises 121–124, sketch the graphs of $y = x^5$ and the specified transformation.

121. $f(x) = (x - 2)^5$

122. $f(x) = x^5 - 4$

123. $f(x) = 2 - x^5$

124. $f(x) = -(x + 3)^5$

4.2 Trigonometric Functions: The Unit Circle

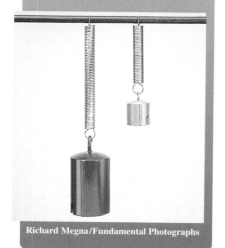

Richard Megna/Fundamental Photographs

The Unit Circle

The two historical perspectives of trigonometry incorporate different methods for introducing the trigonometric functions. Our first introduction to these functions is based on the unit circle.

Consider the **unit circle** given by

$$x^2 + y^2 = 1 \qquad \text{Unit circle}$$

as shown in Figure 4.20.

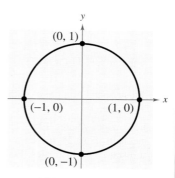

FIGURE **4.20**

Imagine that the real number line is wrapped around this circle, with positive numbers corresponding to a counterclockwise wrapping and negative numbers corresponding to a clockwise wrapping, as shown in Figure 4.21.

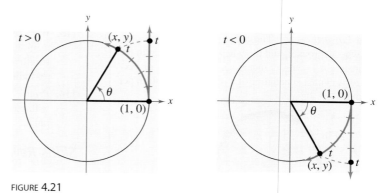

FIGURE **4.21**

As the real number line is wrapped around the unit circle, each real number t corresponds to a point (x, y) on the circle. For example, the real number 0 corresponds to the point $(1, 0)$. Moreover, because the unit circle has a circumference of 2π, the real number 2π also corresponds to the point $(1, 0)$.

In general, each real number t also corresponds to a central angle θ (in standard position) whose radian measure is t. With this interpretation of t, the arc length formula $s = r\theta$ (with $r = 1$) indicates that the real number t is the length of the arc intercepted by the angle θ, given in radians.

The Trigonometric Functions

From the preceding discussion, it follows that the coordinates x and y are two functions of the real variable t. You can use these coordinates to define the six trigonometric functions of t.

sine   cosecant   cosine   secant   tangent   cotangent

These six functions are normally abbreviated sin, csc, cos, sec, tan, and cot, respectively.

> ### Definitions of Trigonometric Functions
>
> Let t be a real number and let (x, y) be the point on the unit circle corresponding to t.
>
> $$\sin t = y \qquad\qquad \cos t = x \qquad\qquad \tan t = \frac{y}{x}, \quad x \neq 0$$
>
> $$\csc t = \frac{1}{y}, \quad y \neq 0 \qquad \sec t = \frac{1}{x}, \quad x \neq 0 \qquad \cot t = \frac{x}{y}, \quad y \neq 0$$

In the definitions of the trigonometric functions, note that the tangent and secant are not defined when $x = 0$. For instance, because $t = \pi/2$ corresponds to $(x, y) = (0, 1)$, it follows that $\tan(\pi/2)$ and $\sec(\pi/2)$ are *undefined*. Similarly, the cotangent and cosecant are not defined when $y = 0$. For instance, because $t = 0$ corresponds to $(x, y) = (1, 0)$, cot 0 and csc 0 are *undefined*.

In Figure 4.22, the unit circle has been divided into eight equal arcs, corresponding to t-values of

$$0, \frac{\pi}{4}, \frac{\pi}{2}, \frac{3\pi}{4}, \pi, \frac{5\pi}{4}, \frac{3\pi}{2}, \frac{7\pi}{4}, \text{ and } 2\pi.$$

Similarly, in Figure 4.23, the unit circle has been divided into 12 equal arcs, corresponding to t-values of

$$0, \frac{\pi}{6}, \frac{\pi}{3}, \frac{\pi}{2}, \frac{2\pi}{3}, \frac{5\pi}{6}, \pi, \frac{7\pi}{6}, \frac{4\pi}{3}, \frac{3\pi}{2}, \frac{5\pi}{3}, \frac{11\pi}{6}, \text{ and } 2\pi.$$

To verify the points on the unit circle in Figure 4.22, note that $\left(\frac{\sqrt{2}}{2}, \frac{\sqrt{2}}{2}\right)$ also lies on the line $y = x$. So, substituting x for y in the equation of the unit circle produces the following.

$$x^2 + x^2 = 1 \quad\Longrightarrow\quad 2x^2 = 1 \quad\Longrightarrow\quad x^2 = \frac{1}{2} \quad\Longrightarrow\quad x = \pm\frac{\sqrt{2}}{2}$$

Because the point is in the first quadrant, $x = \frac{\sqrt{2}}{2}$ and because $y = x$, you also have $y = \frac{\sqrt{2}}{2}$. You can use similar reasoning to verify the rest of the points in Figure 4.22 and the points in Figure 4.23.

Using the (x, y) coordinates in Figures 4.22 and 4.23, you can easily evaluate the trigonometric functions for common t-values. This procedure is demonstrated in Examples 1 and 2. You should study and learn these exact function values for common t-values because they will help you in later sections to perform calculations quickly and easily.

FIGURE **4.22**

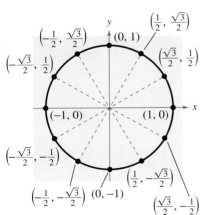

FIGURE **4.23**

Example 1   **Evaluating Trigonometric Functions**

Evaluate the six trigonometric functions at each real number.

a. $t = \dfrac{\pi}{6}$ **b.** $t = \dfrac{5\pi}{4}$ **c.** $t = 0$ **d.** $t = \pi$

Solution

For each t-value, begin by finding the corresponding point (x, y) on the unit circle. Then use the definitions of trigonometric functions listed on page 295.

a. $t = \dfrac{\pi}{6}$ corresponds to the point $(x, y) = \left(\dfrac{\sqrt{3}}{2}, \dfrac{1}{2}\right)$.

$$\sin \frac{\pi}{6} = y = \frac{1}{2} \qquad\qquad \csc \frac{\pi}{6} = \frac{1}{y} = \frac{1}{1/2} = 2$$

$$\cos \frac{\pi}{6} = x = \frac{\sqrt{3}}{2} \qquad\qquad \sec \frac{\pi}{6} = \frac{1}{x} = \frac{2}{\sqrt{3}} = \frac{2\sqrt{3}}{3}$$

$$\tan \frac{\pi}{6} = \frac{y}{x} = \frac{1/2}{\sqrt{3}/2} = \frac{1}{\sqrt{3}} = \frac{\sqrt{3}}{3} \qquad \cot \frac{\pi}{6} = \frac{x}{y} = \frac{\sqrt{3}/2}{1/2} = \sqrt{3}$$

b. $t = \dfrac{5\pi}{4}$ corresponds to the point $(x, y) = \left(-\dfrac{\sqrt{2}}{2}, -\dfrac{\sqrt{2}}{2}\right)$.

$$\sin \frac{5\pi}{4} = y = -\frac{\sqrt{2}}{2} \qquad\qquad \csc \frac{5\pi}{4} = \frac{1}{y} = -\frac{2}{\sqrt{2}} = -\sqrt{2}$$

$$\cos \frac{5\pi}{4} = x = -\frac{\sqrt{2}}{2} \qquad\qquad \sec \frac{5\pi}{4} = \frac{1}{x} = -\frac{2}{\sqrt{2}} = -\sqrt{2}$$

$$\tan \frac{5\pi}{4} = \frac{y}{x} = \frac{-\sqrt{2}/2}{-\sqrt{2}/2} = 1 \qquad \cot \frac{5\pi}{4} = \frac{x}{y} = \frac{-\sqrt{2}/2}{-\sqrt{2}/2} = 1$$

c. $t = 0$ corresponds to the point $(x, y) = (1, 0)$.

$$\sin 0 = y = 0 \qquad\qquad \csc 0 = \frac{1}{y} \text{ is undefined.}$$

$$\cos 0 = x = 1 \qquad\qquad \sec 0 = \frac{1}{x} = \frac{1}{1} = 1$$

$$\tan 0 = \frac{y}{x} = \frac{0}{1} = 0 \qquad\qquad \cot 0 = \frac{x}{y} \text{ is undefined.}$$

d. $t = \pi$ corresponds to the point $(x, y) = (-1, 0)$.

$$\sin \pi = y = 0 \qquad\qquad \csc \pi = \frac{1}{y} \text{ is undefined.}$$

$$\cos \pi = x = -1 \qquad\qquad \sec \pi = \frac{1}{x} = \frac{1}{-1} = -1$$

$$\tan \pi = \frac{y}{x} = \frac{0}{-1} = 0 \qquad\qquad \cot \pi = \frac{x}{y} \text{ is undefined.}$$

✓CHECKPOINT   Now try Exercise 23.

Exploration

With your graphing utility in *radian* and *parametric* modes, enter the equations

X1T = cos T   and   Y1T = sin T

and use the following settings.

Tmin = 0, Tmax = 6.3,
Tstep = 0.1
Xmin = -1.5, Xmax = 1.5,
Xscl = 1
Ymin = -1, Ymax = 1,
Yscl = 1

1. Graph the entered equations and describe the graph.

2. Use the *trace* feature to move the cursor around the graph. What do the *t*-values represent? What do the *x*- and *y*-values represent?

3. What are the least and greatest values of *x* and *y*?

Example 2   **Evaluating Trigonometric Functions**

Evaluate the six trigonometric functions at $t = -\dfrac{\pi}{3}$.

Solution

Moving *clockwise* around the unit circle, it follows that $t = -\pi/3$ corresponds to the point $(x, y) = \left(1/2, -\sqrt{3}/2\right)$.

$$\sin\left(-\frac{\pi}{3}\right) = -\frac{\sqrt{3}}{2} \qquad\qquad \csc\left(-\frac{\pi}{3}\right) = -\frac{2}{\sqrt{3}} = -\frac{2\sqrt{3}}{3}$$

$$\cos\left(-\frac{\pi}{3}\right) = \frac{1}{2} \qquad\qquad \sec\left(-\frac{\pi}{3}\right) = 2$$

$$\tan\left(-\frac{\pi}{3}\right) = \frac{-\sqrt{3}/2}{1/2} = -\sqrt{3} \quad \cot\left(-\frac{\pi}{3}\right) = \frac{1/2}{-\sqrt{3}/2} = -\frac{1}{\sqrt{3}} = -\frac{\sqrt{3}}{3}$$

✓**CHECKPOINT**   Now try Exercise 25.

Domain and Period of Sine and Cosine

The *domain* of the sine and cosine functions is the set of all real numbers. To determine the *range* of these two functions, consider the unit circle shown in Figure 4.24. Because $r = 1$, it follows that $\sin t = y$ and $\cos t = x$. Moreover, because (x, y) is on the unit circle, you know that $-1 \le y \le 1$ and $-1 \le x \le 1$. So, the values of sine and cosine also range between -1 and 1.

$$\begin{array}{ccc} -1 \le & y & \le 1 \\ -1 \le & \sin t & \le 1 \end{array} \quad \text{and} \quad \begin{array}{ccc} -1 \le & x & \le 1 \\ -1 \le & \cos t & \le 1 \end{array}$$

Adding 2π to each value of t in the interval $[0, 2\pi]$ completes a second revolution around the unit circle, as shown in Figure 4.25. The values of $\sin(t + 2\pi)$ and $\cos(t + 2\pi)$ correspond to those of $\sin t$ and $\cos t$. Similar results can be obtained for repeated revolutions (positive or negative) on the unit circle. This leads to the general result

$$\sin(t + 2\pi n) = \sin t$$

and

$$\cos(t + 2\pi n) = \cos t$$

for any integer n and real number t. Functions that behave in such a repetitive (or cyclic) manner are called **periodic.**

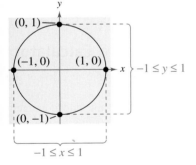

FIGURE **4.24**

$$t = \tfrac{\pi}{2}, \tfrac{\pi}{2} + 2\pi, \tfrac{\pi}{2} + 4\pi, \ldots$$

$$t = \tfrac{3\pi}{4}, \tfrac{3\pi}{4} + 2\pi, \ldots \quad t = \tfrac{\pi}{4}, \tfrac{\pi}{4} + 2\pi, \ldots$$

$$t = \pi, 3\pi, \ldots$$

$$t = 0, 2\pi, \ldots$$

$$t = \tfrac{5\pi}{4}, \tfrac{5\pi}{4} + 2\pi, \ldots$$

$$t = \tfrac{7\pi}{4}, \tfrac{7\pi}{4} + 2\pi, \tfrac{7\pi}{4} + 4\pi, \ldots$$

$$t = \tfrac{3\pi}{2}, \tfrac{3\pi}{2} + 2\pi, \tfrac{3\pi}{2} + 4\pi, \ldots$$

FIGURE **4.25**

Definition of Periodic Function

A function f is **periodic** if there exists a positive real number c such that

$$f(t + c) = f(t)$$

for all t in the domain of f. The smallest number c for which f is periodic is called the **period** of f.

Recall from Section 1.5 that a function f is *even* if $f(-t) = f(t)$, and is *odd* if $f(-t) = -f(t)$.

Even and Odd Trigonometric Functions

The cosine and secant functions are *even*.

$$\cos(-t) = \cos t \qquad \sec(-t) = \sec t$$

The sine, cosecant, tangent, and cotangent functions are *odd*.

$$\sin(-t) = -\sin t \qquad \csc(-t) = -\csc t$$

$$\tan(-t) = -\tan t \qquad \cot(-t) = -\cot t$$

STUDY TIP

From the definition of periodic function, it follows that the sine and cosine functions are periodic and have a period of 2π. The other four trigonometric functions are also periodic, and will be discussed further in Section 4.6.

Example 3   Using the Period to Evaluate the Sine and Cosine

a. Because $\dfrac{13\pi}{6} = 2\pi + \dfrac{\pi}{6}$, you have $\sin \dfrac{13\pi}{6} = \sin\left(2\pi + \dfrac{\pi}{6}\right) = \sin \dfrac{\pi}{6} = \dfrac{1}{2}$.

b. Because $-\dfrac{7\pi}{2} = -4\pi + \dfrac{\pi}{2}$, you have

$$\cos\left(-\dfrac{7\pi}{2}\right) = \cos\left(-4\pi + \dfrac{\pi}{2}\right) = \cos \dfrac{\pi}{2} = 0.$$

c. For $\sin t = \dfrac{4}{5}$, $\sin(-t) = -\dfrac{4}{5}$ because the sine function is odd.

✓**CHECKPOINT**   Now try Exercise 31.

Evaluating Trigonometric Functions with a Calculator

When evaluating a trigonometric function with a calculator, you need to set the calculator to the desired *mode* of measurement (*degree* or *radian*).

Most calculators do not have keys for the cosecant, secant, and cotangent functions. To evaluate these functions, you can use the $\boxed{x^{-1}}$ key with their respective reciprocal functions sine, cosine, and tangent. For example, to evaluate $\csc(\pi/8)$, use the fact that

$$\csc \dfrac{\pi}{8} = \dfrac{1}{\sin(\pi/8)}$$

and enter the following keystroke sequence in *radian* mode.

$\boxed{(}\ \boxed{\text{SIN}}\ \boxed{(}\ \boxed{\pi}\ \boxed{\div}\ 8\ \boxed{)}\ \boxed{)}\ \boxed{x^{-1}}\ \boxed{\text{ENTER}}$ Display 2.6131259

Technology

When evaluating trigonometric functions with a calculator, remember to enclose all fractional angle measures in parentheses. For instance, if you want to evaluate $\sin \theta$ for $\theta = \pi/6$, you should enter

$\boxed{\text{SIN}}\ \boxed{(}\ \boxed{\pi}\ \boxed{\div}\ 6\ \boxed{)}\ \boxed{\text{ENTER}}$.

These keystrokes yield the correct value of 0.5. Note that some calculators automatically place a left parenthesis after trigonometric functions. Check the user's guide for your calculator for specific keystrokes on how to evaluate trigonometric functions.

Example 4   Using a Calculator

Function	Mode	Calculator Keystrokes	Display
a. $\sin \dfrac{2\pi}{3}$	Radian	$\boxed{\text{SIN}}\ \boxed{(}\ 2\ \boxed{\pi}\ \boxed{\div}\ 3\ \boxed{)}\ \boxed{\text{ENTER}}$	0.8660254
b. $\cot 1.5$	Radian	$\boxed{(}\ \boxed{\text{TAN}}\ \boxed{(}\ 1.5\ \boxed{)}\ \boxed{)}\ \boxed{x^{-1}}\ \boxed{\text{ENTER}}$	0.0709148

✓**CHECKPOINT**   Now try Exercise 45.

4:2	**Exercises**

VOCABULARY CHECK: Fill in the blanks.

1. Each real number t corresponds to a point (x, y) on the _____ _____.

2. A function f is _____ if there exists a positive real number c such that $f(t + c) = f(t)$ for all t in the domain of f.

3. The smallest number c for which a function f is periodic is called the _____ of f.

4. A function f is _____ if $f(-t) = -f(t)$ and _____ if $f(-t) = f(t)$.

PREREQUISITE SKILLS REVIEW: Practice and review algebra skills needed for this section at **www.Eduspace.com**.

In Exercises 1–4, determine the exact values of the six trigonometric functions of the angle θ.

1.

2.

3.

4.

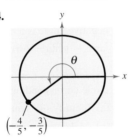

In Exercises 5–12, find the point (x, y) on the unit circle that corresponds to the real number t.

5. $t = \dfrac{\pi}{4}$

6. $t = \dfrac{\pi}{3}$

7. $t = \dfrac{7\pi}{6}$

8. $t = \dfrac{5\pi}{4}$

9. $t = \dfrac{4\pi}{3}$

10. $t = \dfrac{5\pi}{3}$

11. $t = \dfrac{3\pi}{2}$

12. $t = \pi$

In Exercises 13–22, evaluate (if possible) the sine, cosine, and tangent of the real number.

13. $t = \dfrac{\pi}{4}$

14. $t = \dfrac{\pi}{3}$

15. $t = -\dfrac{\pi}{6}$

16. $t = -\dfrac{\pi}{4}$

17. $t = -\dfrac{7\pi}{4}$

18. $t = -\dfrac{4\pi}{3}$

19. $t = \dfrac{11\pi}{6}$

20. $t = \dfrac{5\pi}{3}$

21. $t = -\dfrac{3\pi}{2}$

22. $t = -2\pi$

In Exercises 23–28, evaluate (if possible) the six trigonometric functions of the real number.

23. $t = \dfrac{3\pi}{4}$

24. $t = \dfrac{5\pi}{6}$

25. $t = -\dfrac{\pi}{2}$

26. $t = \dfrac{3\pi}{2}$

27. $t = \dfrac{4\pi}{3}$

28. $t = \dfrac{7\pi}{4}$

In Exercises 29–36, evaluate the trigonometric function using its period as an aid.

29. $\sin 5\pi$

30. $\cos 5\pi$

31. $\cos \dfrac{8\pi}{3}$

32. $\sin \dfrac{9\pi}{4}$

33. $\cos\left(-\dfrac{15\pi}{2}\right)$

34. $\sin \dfrac{19\pi}{6}$

35. $\sin\left(-\dfrac{9\pi}{4}\right)$

36. $\cos\left(-\dfrac{8\pi}{3}\right)$

In Exercises 37–42, use the value of the trigonometric function to evaluate the indicated functions.

37. $\sin t = \dfrac{1}{3}$
  (a) $\sin(-t)$
  (b) $\csc(-t)$

38. $\sin(-t) = \dfrac{3}{8}$
  (a) $\sin t$
  (b) $\csc t$

39. $\cos(-t) = -\dfrac{1}{5}$
  (a) $\cos t$
  (b) $\sec(-t)$

40. $\cos t = -\dfrac{3}{4}$
  (a) $\cos(-t)$
  (b) $\sec(-t)$

41. $\sin t = \dfrac{4}{5}$
  (a) $\sin(\pi - t)$
  (b) $\sin(t + \pi)$

42. $\cos t = \dfrac{4}{5}$
  (a) $\cos(\pi - t)$
  (b) $\cos(t + \pi)$

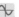 In Exercises 43–52, use a calculator to evaluate the trigonometric function. Round your answer to four decimal places. (Be sure the calculator is set in the correct angle mode.)

43. $\sin\dfrac{\pi}{4}$

44. $\tan\dfrac{\pi}{3}$

45. $\csc 1.3$

46. $\cot 1$

47. $\cos(-1.7)$

48. $\cos(-2.5)$

49. $\csc 0.8$

50. $\sec 1.8$

51. $\sec 22.8$

52. $\sin(-0.9)$

Estimation In Exercises 53 and 54, use the figure and a straightedge to approximate the value of each trigonometric function. To print an enlarged copy of the graph, go to the website *www.mathgraphs.com*.

53. (a) $\sin 5$ (b) $\cos 2$

54. (a) $\sin 0.75$ (b) $\cos 2.5$

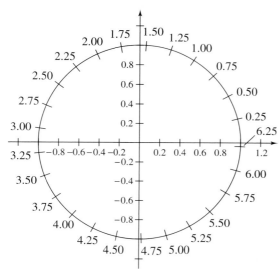

FIGURE FOR 53–56

Estimation In Exercises 55 and 56, use the figure and a straightedge to approximate the solution of each equation, where $0 \le t < 2\pi$. To print an enlarged copy of the graph, go to the website *www.mathgraphs.com*.

55. (a) $\sin t = 0.25$ (b) $\cos t = -0.25$

56. (a) $\sin t = -0.75$ (b) $\cos t = 0.75$

Model It

57. *Harmonic Motion* The displacement from equilibrium of an oscillating weight suspended by a spring and subject to the damping effect of friction is given by $y(t) = \frac{1}{4}e^{-t}\cos 6t$ where y is the displacement (in feet) and t is the time (in seconds).

Model It (continued)

(a) Complete the table.

t	0	$\frac{1}{4}$	$\frac{1}{2}$	$\frac{3}{4}$	1
y					

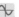 (b) Use the *table* feature of a graphing utility to approximate the time when the weight reaches equilibrium.

(c) What appears to happen to the displacement as t increases?

58. *Harmonic Motion* The displacement from equilibrium of an oscillating weight suspended by a spring is given by $y(t) = \frac{1}{4}\cos 6t$, where y is the displacement (in feet) and t is the time (in seconds). Find the displacement when (a) $t = 0$, (b) $t = \frac{1}{4}$, and (c) $t = \frac{1}{2}$.

Synthesis

True or False? In Exercises 59 and 60, determine whether the statement is true or false. Justify your answer.

59. Because $\sin(-t) = -\sin t$, it can be said that the sine of a negative angle is a negative number.

60. $\tan a = \tan(a - 6\pi)$

61. *Exploration* Let (x_1, y_1) and (x_2, y_2) be points on the unit circle corresponding to $t = t_1$ and $t = \pi - t_1$, respectively.

(a) Identify the symmetry of the points (x_1, y_1) and (x_2, y_2).

(b) Make a conjecture about any relationship between $\sin t_1$ and $\sin(\pi - t_1)$.

(c) Make a conjecture about any relationship between $\cos t_1$ and $\cos(\pi - t_1)$.

62. Use the unit circle to verify that the cosine and secant functions are even and that the sine, cosecant, tangent, and cotangent functions are odd.

Skills Review

In Exercises 63–66, find the inverse function f^{-1} of the one-to-one function f.

63. $f(x) = \frac{1}{2}(3x - 2)$

64. $f(x) = \frac{1}{4}x^3 + 1$

65. $f(x) = \sqrt{x^2 - 4}, \quad x \ge 2$

66. $f(x) = \dfrac{x + 2}{x - 4}$

In Exercises 67–70, sketch the graph of the rational function by hand. Show all asymptotes.

67. $f(x) = \dfrac{2x}{x - 3}$

68. $f(x) = \dfrac{5x}{x^2 + x - 6}$

69. $f(x) = \dfrac{x^2 + 3x - 10}{2x^2 - 8}$

70. $f(x) = \dfrac{x^3 - 6x^2 + x - 1}{2x^2 - 5x - 8}$

| 4.3 | **Right Triangle Trigonometry** |

What you should learn

- Evaluate trigonometric functions of acute angles.
- Use the fundamental trigonometric identities.
- Use a calculator to evaluate trigonometric functions.
- Use trigonometric functions to model and solve real-life problems.

Why you should learn it

Trigonometric functions are often used to analyze real-life situations. For instance, in Exercise 71 on page 311, you can use trigonometric functions to find the height of a helium-filled balloon.

Joseph Sohm; Chromosohm

The Six Trigonometric Functions

Our second look at the trigonometric functions is from a *right triangle* perspective. Consider a right triangle, with one acute angle labeled θ, as shown in Figure 4.26. Relative to the angle θ, the three sides of the triangle are the **hypotenuse,** the **opposite side** (the side opposite the angle θ), and the **adjacent side** (the side adjacent to the angle θ).

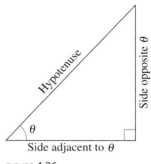

FIGURE 4.26

Using the lengths of these three sides, you can form six ratios that define the six trigonometric functions of the acute angle θ.

sine   cosecant   cosine   secant   tangent   cotangent

In the following definitions, it is important to see that $0° < \theta < 90°$ (θ lies in the first quadrant) and that for such angles the value of each trigonometric function is *positive*.

Right Triangle Definitions of Trigonometric Functions

Let θ be an *acute* angle of a right triangle. The six trigonometric functions of the angle θ are defined as follows. (Note that the functions in the second row are the *reciprocals* of the corresponding functions in the first row.)

$$\sin \theta = \frac{\text{opp}}{\text{hyp}} \qquad \cos \theta = \frac{\text{adj}}{\text{hyp}} \qquad \tan \theta = \frac{\text{opp}}{\text{adj}}$$

$$\csc \theta = \frac{\text{hyp}}{\text{opp}} \qquad \sec \theta = \frac{\text{hyp}}{\text{adj}} \qquad \cot \theta = \frac{\text{adj}}{\text{opp}}$$

The abbreviations opp, adj, and hyp represent the lengths of the three sides of a right triangle.

opp = the length of the side *opposite* θ

adj = the length of the side *adjacent to* θ

hyp = the length of the *hypotenuse*

FIGURE **4.27**

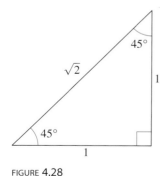

FIGURE **4.28**

Example 1   **Evaluating Trigonometric Functions**

Use the triangle in Figure 4.27 to find the values of the six trigonometric functions of θ.

Solution

By the Pythagorean Theorem, $(\text{hyp})^2 = (\text{opp})^2 + (\text{adj})^2$, it follows that

$$\text{hyp} = \sqrt{4^2 + 3^2}$$

$$= \sqrt{25}$$

$$= 5.$$

So, the six trigonometric functions of θ are

$$\sin \theta = \frac{\text{opp}}{\text{hyp}} = \frac{4}{5} \qquad \csc \theta = \frac{\text{hyp}}{\text{opp}} = \frac{5}{4}$$

$$\cos \theta = \frac{\text{adj}}{\text{hyp}} = \frac{3}{5} \qquad \sec \theta = \frac{\text{hyp}}{\text{adj}} = \frac{5}{3}$$

$$\tan \theta = \frac{\text{opp}}{\text{adj}} = \frac{4}{3} \qquad \cot \theta = \frac{\text{adj}}{\text{opp}} = \frac{3}{4}.$$

✓**CHECKPOINT**   Now try Exercise 3.

    In Example 1, you were given the lengths of two sides of the right triangle, but not the angle θ. Often, you will be asked to find the trigonometric functions of a *given* acute angle θ. To do this, construct a right triangle having θ as one of its angles.

Example 2   **Evaluating Trigonometric Functions of 45°**

Find the values of $\sin 45°$, $\cos 45°$, and $\tan 45°$.

Solution

Construct a right triangle having 45° as one of its acute angles, as shown in Figure 4.28. Choose the length of the adjacent side to be 1. From geometry, you know that the other acute angle is also 45°. So, the triangle is isosceles and the length of the opposite side is also 1. Using the Pythagorean Theorem, you find the length of the hypotenuse to be $\sqrt{2}$.

$$\sin 45° = \frac{\text{opp}}{\text{hyp}} = \frac{1}{\sqrt{2}} = \frac{\sqrt{2}}{2}$$

$$\cos 45° = \frac{\text{adj}}{\text{hyp}} = \frac{1}{\sqrt{2}} = \frac{\sqrt{2}}{2}$$

$$\tan 45° = \frac{\text{opp}}{\text{adj}} = \frac{1}{1} = 1$$

✓**CHECKPOINT**   Now try Exercise 17.

Example 3   **Evaluating Trigonometric Functions of 30° and 60°**

Use the equilateral triangle shown in Figure 4.29 to find the values of sin 60°, cos 60°, sin 30°, and cos 30°.

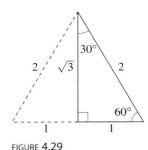

FIGURE 4.29

Solution

Use the Pythagorean Theorem and the equilateral triangle in Figure 4.29 to verify the lengths of the sides shown in the figure. For $\theta = 60°$, you have adj = 1, opp = $\sqrt{3}$, and hyp = 2. So,

$$\sin 60° = \frac{\text{opp}}{\text{hyp}} = \frac{\sqrt{3}}{2} \quad \text{and} \quad \cos 60° = \frac{\text{adj}}{\text{hyp}} = \frac{1}{2}.$$

For $\theta = 30°$, adj = $\sqrt{3}$, opp = 1, and hyp = 2. So,

$$\sin 30° = \frac{\text{opp}}{\text{hyp}} = \frac{1}{2} \quad \text{and} \quad \cos 30° = \frac{\text{adj}}{\text{hyp}} = \frac{\sqrt{3}}{2}.$$

✓CHECKPOINT   Now try Exercise 19.

Sines, Cosines, and Tangents of Special Angles

$$\sin 30° = \sin \frac{\pi}{6} = \frac{1}{2} \qquad \cos 30° = \cos \frac{\pi}{6} = \frac{\sqrt{3}}{2} \qquad \tan 30° = \tan \frac{\pi}{6} = \frac{\sqrt{3}}{3}$$

$$\sin 45° = \sin \frac{\pi}{4} = \frac{\sqrt{2}}{2} \qquad \cos 45° = \cos \frac{\pi}{4} = \frac{\sqrt{2}}{2} \qquad \tan 45° = \tan \frac{\pi}{4} = 1$$

$$\sin 60° = \sin \frac{\pi}{3} = \frac{\sqrt{3}}{2} \qquad \cos 60° = \cos \frac{\pi}{3} = \frac{1}{2} \qquad \tan 60° = \tan \frac{\pi}{3} = \sqrt{3}$$

In the box, note that $\sin 30° = \frac{1}{2} = \cos 60°$. This occurs because 30° and 60° are complementary angles. In general, it can be shown from the right triangle definitions that *cofunctions of complementary angles are equal*. That is, if θ is an acute angle, the following relationships are true.

$$\sin(90° - \theta) = \cos \theta \qquad\qquad \cos(90° - \theta) = \sin \theta$$

$$\tan(90° - \theta) = \cot \theta \qquad\qquad \cot(90° - \theta) = \tan \theta$$

$$\sec(90° - \theta) = \csc \theta \qquad\qquad \csc(90° - \theta) = \sec \theta$$

Trigonometric Identities

In trigonometry, a great deal of time is spent studying relationships between trigonometric functions (identities).

Fundamental Trigonometric Identities

Reciprocal Identities

$$\sin \theta = \frac{1}{\csc \theta} \qquad \cos \theta = \frac{1}{\sec \theta} \qquad \tan \theta = \frac{1}{\cot \theta}$$

$$\csc \theta = \frac{1}{\sin \theta} \qquad \sec \theta = \frac{1}{\cos \theta} \qquad \cot \theta = \frac{1}{\tan \theta}$$

Quotient Identities

$$\tan \theta = \frac{\sin \theta}{\cos \theta} \qquad \cot \theta = \frac{\cos \theta}{\sin \theta}$$

Pythagorean Identities

$$\sin^2 \theta + \cos^2 \theta = 1 \qquad 1 + \tan^2 \theta = \sec^2 \theta$$

$$1 + \cot^2 \theta = \csc^2 \theta$$

Note that $\sin^2 \theta$ represents $(\sin \theta)^2$, $\cos^2 \theta$ represents $(\cos \theta)^2$, and so on.

Example 4 Applying Trigonometric Identities

Let θ be an acute angle such that $\sin \theta = 0.6$. Find the values of (a) $\cos \theta$ and (b) $\tan \theta$ using trigonometric identities.

Solution

a. To find the value of $\cos \theta$, use the Pythagorean identity

$$\sin^2 \theta + \cos^2 \theta = 1.$$

So, you have

$$(0.6)^2 + \cos^2 \theta = 1 \qquad \text{Substitute 0.6 for } \sin \theta.$$
$$\cos^2 \theta = 1 - (0.6)^2 = 0.64 \qquad \text{Subtract } (0.6)^2 \text{ from each side.}$$
$$\cos \theta = \sqrt{0.64} = 0.8. \qquad \text{Extract the positive square root.}$$

b. Now, knowing the sine and cosine of θ, you can find the tangent of θ to be

$$\tan \theta = \frac{\sin \theta}{\cos \theta}$$
$$= \frac{0.6}{0.8}$$
$$= 0.75.$$

Use the definitions of $\cos \theta$ and $\tan \theta$, and the triangle shown in Figure 4.30, to check these results.

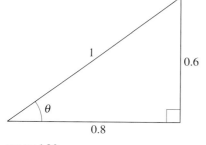

FIGURE **4.30**

✔CHECKPOINT Now try Exercise 29.

| Example 5 | **Applying Trigonometric Identities** |

Let θ be an acute angle such that $\tan\theta = 3$. Find the values of (a) $\cot\theta$ and (b) $\sec\theta$ using trigonometric identities.

Solution

a. $\cot\theta = \dfrac{1}{\tan\theta}$ Reciprocal identity

     $\cot\theta = \dfrac{1}{3}$

b. $\sec^2\theta = 1 + \tan^2\theta$ Pythagorean identity

     $\sec^2\theta = 1 + 3^2$

     $\sec^2\theta = 10$

     $\sec\theta = \sqrt{10}$

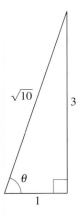

FIGURE **4.31**

Use the definitions of $\cot\theta$ and $\sec\theta$, and the triangle shown in Figure 4.31, to check these results.

✓CHECKPOINT   Now try Exercise 31.

Evaluating Trigonometric Functions with a Calculator

To use a calculator to evaluate trigonometric functions of angles measured in degrees, first set the calculator to *degree* mode and then proceed as demonstrated in Section 4.2. For instance, you can find values of $\cos 28°$ and $\sec 28°$ as follows.

Function	*Mode*	*Calculator Keystrokes*	*Display*
a. $\cos 28°$	Degree	COS 28 ENTER	0.8829476
b. $\sec 28°$	Degree	(COS (28)) x⁻¹ ENTER	1.1325701

     Throughout this text, angles are assumed to be measured in radians unless noted otherwise. For example, sin 1 means the sine of 1 radian and sin 1° means the sine of 1 degree.

| Example 6 | **Using a Calculator** |

Use a calculator to evaluate $\sec(5°\,40'\,12'')$.

Solution

Begin by converting to decimal degree form. [Recall that $1' = \frac{1}{60}(1°)$ and $1'' = \frac{1}{3600}(1°)$].

$$5°\,40'\,12'' = 5° + \left(\frac{40}{60}\right)^{\!\circ} + \left(\frac{12}{3600}\right)^{\!\circ} = 5.67°$$

Then, use a calculator to evaluate $\sec 5.67°$.

Function	*Calculator Keystrokes*	*Display*
$\sec(5°\,40'\,12'') = \sec 5.67°$	(COS (5.67)) x⁻¹ ENTER	1.0049166

✓CHECKPOINT   Now try Exercise 47.

FIGURE **4.32**

FIGURE **4.33**

Applications Involving Right Triangles

Many applications of trigonometry involve a process called **solving right triangles.** In this type of application, you are usually given one side of a right triangle and one of the acute angles and are asked to find one of the other sides, *or* you are given two sides and are asked to find one of the acute angles.

In Example 7, the angle you are given is the **angle of elevation,** which represents the angle from the horizontal upward to an object. For objects that lie below the horizontal, it is common to use the term **angle of depression,** as shown in Figure 4.32.

Example 7   Using Trigonometry to Solve a Right Triangle

A surveyor is standing 115 feet from the base of the Washington Monument, as shown in Figure 4.33. The surveyor measures the angle of elevation to the top of the monument as 78.3°. How tall is the Washington Monument?

Solution

From Figure 4.33, you can see that

$$\tan 78.3° = \frac{\text{opp}}{\text{adj}} = \frac{y}{x}$$

where $x = 115$ and y is the height of the monument. So, the height of the Washington Monument is

$$y = x \tan 78.3° \approx 115(4.82882) \approx 555 \text{ feet.}$$

✓*CHECKPOINT*   Now try Exercise 63.

Example 8   Using Trigonometry to Solve a Right Triangle

An historic lighthouse is 200 yards from a bike path along the edge of a lake. A walkway to the lighthouse is 400 yards long. Find the acute angle θ between the bike path and the walkway, as illustrated in Figure 4.34.

FIGURE **4.34**

Solution

From Figure 4.34, you can see that the sine of the angle θ is

$$\sin \theta = \frac{\text{opp}}{\text{hyp}} = \frac{200}{400} = \frac{1}{2}.$$

Now you should recognize that $\theta = 30°$.

✓*CHECKPOINT*   Now try Exercise 65.

By now you are able to recognize that $\theta = 30°$ is the acute angle that satisfies the equation $\sin \theta = \frac{1}{2}$. Suppose, however, that you were given the equation $\sin \theta = 0.6$ and were asked to find the acute angle θ. Because

$$\sin 30° = \frac{1}{2}$$

$$= 0.5000$$

and

$$\sin 45° = \frac{1}{\sqrt{2}}$$

$$\approx 0.7071$$

you might guess that θ lies somewhere between $30°$ and $45°$. In a later section, you will study a method by which a more precise value of θ can be determined.

Example 9 **Solving a Right Triangle**

Find the length c of the skateboard ramp shown in Figure 4.35.

FIGURE 4.35

Solution

From Figure 4.35, you can see that

$$\sin 18.4° = \frac{\text{opp}}{\text{hyp}}$$

$$= \frac{4}{c}.$$

So, the length of the skateboard ramp is

$$c = \frac{4}{\sin 18.4°}$$

$$\approx \frac{4}{0.3156}$$

$$\approx 12.7 \text{ feet.}$$

✓CHECKPOINT   Now try Exercise 67.

4.3 Exercises

VOCABULARY CHECK:

1. Match the trigonometric function with its right triangle definition.

(a) Sine   (b) Cosine   (c) Tangent   (d) Cosecant   (e) Secant   (f) Cotangent

(i) $\dfrac{\text{hypotenuse}}{\text{adjacent}}$ (ii) $\dfrac{\text{adjacent}}{\text{opposite}}$ (iii) $\dfrac{\text{hypotenuse}}{\text{opposite}}$ (iv) $\dfrac{\text{adjacent}}{\text{hypotenuse}}$ (v) $\dfrac{\text{opposite}}{\text{hypotenuse}}$ (vi) $\dfrac{\text{opposite}}{\text{adjacent}}$

In Exercises 2 and 3, fill in the blanks.

2. Relative to the angle θ, the three sides of a right triangle are the _____ side, the _____ side, and the _____.

3. An angle that measures from the horizontal upward to an object is called the angle of _____, whereas an angle that measures from the horizontal downward to an object is called the angle of _____.

PREREQUISITE SKILLS REVIEW: Practice and review algebra skills needed for this section at **www.Eduspace.com.**

In Exercises 1–4, find the exact values of the six trigonometric functions of the angle θ shown in the figure. (Use the Pythagorean Theorem to find the third side of the triangle.)

1.

2.

3.

4.

In Exercises 5–8, find the exact values of the six trigonometric functions of the angle θ for each of the two triangles. Explain why the function values are the same.

5.

6.

7.

8.

In Exercises 9–16, sketch a right triangle corresponding to the trigonometric function of the acute angle θ. Use the Pythagorean Theorem to determine the third side and then find the other five trigonometric functions of θ.

9. $\sin \theta = \frac{3}{4}$ **10.** $\cos \theta = \frac{5}{7}$

11. $\sec \theta = 2$ **12.** $\cot \theta = 5$

13. $\tan \theta = 3$ **14.** $\sec \theta = 6$

15. $\cot \theta = \frac{3}{2}$ **16.** $\csc \theta = \frac{17}{4}$

In Exercises 17–26, construct an appropriate triangle to complete the table. $(0 \le \theta \le 90°, 0 \le \theta \le \pi/2)$

	Function	θ (deg)	θ (rad)	Function Value
17.	sin	30°		
18.	cos	45°		
19.	tan		$\dfrac{\pi}{3}$	
20.	sec		$\dfrac{\pi}{4}$	
21.	cot			$\dfrac{\sqrt{3}}{3}$
22.	csc			$\sqrt{2}$
23.	cos		$\dfrac{\pi}{6}$	
24.	sin		$\dfrac{\pi}{4}$	
25.	cot			1
26.	tan			$\dfrac{\sqrt{3}}{3}$

In Exercises 27–32, use the given function value(s), and trigonometric identities (including the cofunction identities), to find the indicated trigonometric functions.

27. $\sin 60° = \dfrac{\sqrt{3}}{2}$, $\cos 60° = \dfrac{1}{2}$

    (a) $\tan 60°$ (b) $\sin 30°$

    (c) $\cos 30°$ (d) $\cot 60°$

28. $\sin 30° = \dfrac{1}{2}$, $\tan 30° = \dfrac{\sqrt{3}}{3}$

    (a) $\csc 30°$ (b) $\cot 60°$

    (c) $\cos 30°$ (d) $\cot 30°$

29. $\csc \theta = \dfrac{\sqrt{13}}{2}$, $\sec \theta = \dfrac{\sqrt{13}}{3}$

    (a) $\sin \theta$ (b) $\cos \theta$

    (c) $\tan \theta$ (d) $\sec(90° - \theta)$

30. $\sec \theta = 5$, $\tan \theta = 2\sqrt{6}$

    (a) $\cos \theta$ (b) $\cot \theta$

    (c) $\cot(90° - \theta)$ (d) $\sin \theta$

31. $\cos \alpha = \tfrac{1}{3}$

    (a) $\sec \alpha$ (b) $\sin \alpha$

    (c) $\cot \alpha$ (d) $\sin(90° - \alpha)$

32. $\tan \beta = 5$

    (a) $\cot \beta$ (b) $\cos \beta$

    (c) $\tan(90° - \beta)$ (d) $\csc \beta$

In Exercises 33–42, use trigonometric identities to transform the left side of the equation into the right side $(0 < \theta < \pi/2)$.

33. $\tan \theta \cot \theta = 1$

34. $\cos \theta \sec \theta = 1$

35. $\tan \alpha \cos \alpha = \sin \alpha$

36. $\cot \alpha \sin \alpha = \cos \alpha$

37. $(1 + \cos \theta)(1 - \cos \theta) = \sin^2 \theta$

38. $(1 + \sin \theta)(1 - \sin \theta) = \cos^2 \theta$

39. $(\sec \theta + \tan \theta)(\sec \theta - \tan \theta) = 1$

40. $\sin^2 \theta - \cos^2 \theta = 2 \sin^2 \theta - 1$

41. $\dfrac{\sin \theta}{\cos \theta} + \dfrac{\cos \theta}{\sin \theta} = \csc \theta \sec \theta$

42. $\dfrac{\tan \beta + \cot \beta}{\tan \beta} = \csc^2 \beta$

In Exercises 43–52, use a calculator to evaluate each function. Round your answers to four decimal places. (Be sure the calculator is in the correct angle mode.)

43. (a) $\sin 10°$ (b) $\cos 80°$

44. (a) $\tan 23.5°$ (b) $\cot 66.5°$

45. (a) $\sin 16.35°$ (b) $\csc 16.35°$

46. (a) $\cos 16° \, 18'$ (b) $\sin 73° \, 56'$

47. (a) $\sec 42° \, 12'$ (b) $\csc 48° \, 7'$

48. (a) $\cos 4° \, 50' \, 15''$ (b) $\sec 4° \, 50' \, 15''$

49. (a) $\cot 11° \, 15'$ (b) $\tan 11° \, 15'$

50. (a) $\sec 56° \, 8 \, 10''$ (b) $\cos 56° \, 8 \, 10''$

51. (a) $\csc 32° \, 40' \, 3''$ (b) $\tan 44° \, 28 \, 16''$

52. (a) $\sec\!\big(\tfrac{9}{5} \cdot 20 + 32\big)°$ (b) $\cot\!\big(\tfrac{9}{5} \cdot 30 + 32\big)°$

In Exercises 53–58, find the values of θ in degrees $(0° < \theta < 90°)$ and radians $(0 < \theta < \pi/2)$ without the aid of a calculator.

53. (a) $\sin \theta = \dfrac{1}{2}$ (b) $\csc \theta = 2$

54. (a) $\cos \theta = \dfrac{\sqrt{2}}{2}$ (b) $\tan \theta = 1$

55. (a) $\sec \theta = 2$ (b) $\cot \theta = 1$

56. (a) $\tan \theta = \sqrt{3}$ (b) $\cos \theta = \dfrac{1}{2}$

57. (a) $\csc \theta = \dfrac{2\sqrt{3}}{3}$ (b) $\sin \theta = \dfrac{\sqrt{2}}{2}$

58. (a) $\cot \theta = \dfrac{\sqrt{3}}{3}$ (b) $\sec \theta = \sqrt{2}$

In Exercises 59–62, solve for x, y, or r as indicated.

59. Solve for x.

60. Solve for y.

61. Solve for x.

62. Solve for r.

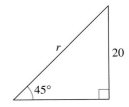

63. *Empire State Building*   You are standing 45 meters from the base of the Empire State Building. You estimate that the angle of elevation to the top of the 86th floor (the observatory) is 82°. If the total height of the building is another 123 meters above the 86th floor, what is the approximate height of the building? One of your friends is on the 86th floor. What is the distance between you and your friend?

64. *Height* A six-foot person walks from the base of a broadcasting tower directly toward the tip of the shadow cast by the tower. When the person is 132 feet from the tower and 3 feet from the tip of the shadow, the person's shadow starts to appear beyond the tower's shadow.

(a) Draw a right triangle that gives a visual representation of the problem. Show the known quantities of the triangle and use a variable to indicate the height of the tower.

(b) Use a trigonometric function to write an equation involving the unknown quantity.

(c) What is the height of the tower?

65. *Angle of Elevation* You are skiing down a mountain with a vertical height of 1500 feet. The distance from the top of the mountain to the base is 3000 feet. What is the angle of elevation from the base to the top of the mountain?

66. *Width of a River* A biologist wants to know the width w of a river so in order to properly set instruments for studying the pollutants in the water. From point A, the biologist walks downstream 100 feet and sights to point C (see figure). From this sighting, it is determined that $\theta = 54°$. How wide is the river?

67. *Length* A steel cable zip-line is being constructed for a competition on a reality television show. One end of the zip-line is attached to a platform on top of a 150-foot pole. The other end of the zip-line is attached to the top of a 5-foot stake. The angle of elevation to the platform is 23° (see figure).

(a) How long is the zip-line?

(b) How far is the stake from the pole?

(c) Contestants take an average of 6 seconds to reach the ground from the top of the zip-line. At what rate are contestants moving down the line? At what rate are they dropping vertically?

68. *Height of a Mountain* In traveling across flat land, you notice a mountain directly in front of you. Its angle of elevation (to the peak) is 3.5°. After you drive 13 miles closer to the mountain, the angle of elevation is 9°. Approximate the height of the mountain.

Not drawn to scale

69. *Machine Shop Calculations* A steel plate has the form of one-fourth of a circle with a radius of 60 centimeters. Two two-centimeter holes are to be drilled in the plate positioned as shown in the figure. Find the coordinates of the center of each hole.

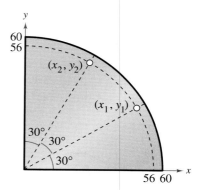

70. *Machine Shop Calculations* A tapered shaft has a diameter of 5 centimeters at the small end and is 15 centimeters long (see figure). The taper is 3°. Find the diameter d of the large end of the shaft.

Model It

71. Height A 20-meter line is used to tether a helium-filled balloon. Because of a breeze, the line makes an angle of approximately 85° with the ground.

(a) Draw a right triangle that gives a visual representation of the problem. Show the known quantities of the triangle and use a variable to indicate the height of the balloon.

(b) Use a trigonometric function to write an equation involving the unknown quantity.

(c) What is the height of the balloon?

(d) The breeze becomes stronger and the angle the balloon makes with the ground decreases. How does this affect the triangle you drew in part (a)?

(e) Complete the table, which shows the heights (in meters) of the balloon for decreasing angle measures θ.

Angle, θ	80°	70°	60°	50°
Height				

Angle, θ	40°	30°	20°	10°
Height				

(f) As the angle the balloon makes with the ground approaches 0°, how does this affect the height of the balloon? Draw a right triangle to explain your reasoning.

72. Geometry Use a compass to sketch a quarter of a circle of radius 10 centimeters. Using a protractor, construct an angle of 20° in standard position (see figure). Drop a perpendicular line from the point of intersection of the terminal side of the angle and the arc of the circle. By actual measurement, calculate the coordinates (x, y) of the point of intersection and use these measurements to approximate the six trigonometric functions of a 20° angle.

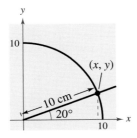

Synthesis

True or False?   **In Exercises 73–78, determine whether the statement is true or false. Justify your answer.**

73. $\sin 60° \csc 60° = 1$

74. $\sec 30° = \csc 60°$

75. $\sin 45° + \cos 45° = 1$

76. $\cot^2 10° - \csc^2 10° = -1$

77. $\dfrac{\sin 60°}{\sin 30°} = \sin 2°$

78. $\tan[(5°)^2] = \tan^2(5°)$

79. Writing In right triangle trigonometry, explain why $\sin 30° = \frac{1}{2}$ regardless of the size of the triangle.

80. Think About It You are given only the value $\tan \theta$. Is it possible to find the value of $\sec \theta$ without finding the measure of θ? Explain.

81. Exploration

(a) Complete the table.

θ	0.1	0.2	0.3	0.4	0.5
$\sin \theta$					

(b) Is θ or $\sin \theta$ greater for θ in the interval $(0, 0.5]$?

(c) As θ approaches 0, how do θ and $\sin \theta$ compare? Explain.

82. Exploration

(a) Complete the table.

θ	0°	18°	36°	54°	72°	90°
$\sin \theta$						
$\cos \theta$						

(b) Discuss the behavior of the sine function for θ in the range from 0° to 90°.

(c) Discuss the behavior of the cosine function for θ in the range from 0° to 90°.

(d) Use the definitions of the sine and cosine functions to explain the results of parts (b) and (c).

Skills Review

In Exercises 83–86, perform the operations and simplify.

83. $\dfrac{x^2 - 6x}{x^2 + 4x - 12} \cdot \dfrac{x^2 + 12x + 36}{x^2 - 36}$

84. $\dfrac{2t^2 + 5t - 12}{9 - 4t^2} \div \dfrac{t^2 - 16}{4t^2 + 12t + 9}$

85. $\dfrac{3}{x + 2} - \dfrac{2}{x - 2} + \dfrac{x}{x^2 + 4x + 4}$

86. $\dfrac{\left(\dfrac{3}{x} - \dfrac{1}{4}\right)}{\left(\dfrac{12}{x} - 1\right)}$

4.4 Trigonometric Functions of Any Angle

What you should learn

- Evaluate trigonometric functions of any angle.
- Use reference angles to evaluate trigonometric functions.
- Evaluate trigonometric functions of real numbers.

Why you should learn it

You can use trigonometric functions to model and solve real-life problems. For instance, in Exercise 87 on page 319, you can use trigonometric functions to model the monthly normal temperatures in New York City and Fairbanks, Alaska.

James Urbach/SuperStock

Introduction

In Section 4.3, the definitions of trigonometric functions were restricted to acute angles. In this section, the definitions are extended to cover *any* angle. If θ is an *acute* angle, these definitions coincide with those given in the preceding section.

Definitions of Trigonometric Functions of Any Angle

Let θ be an angle in standard position with (x, y) a point on the terminal side of θ and $r = \sqrt{x^2 + y^2} \neq 0$.

$$\sin \theta = \frac{y}{r} \qquad\qquad \cos \theta = \frac{x}{r}$$

$$\tan \theta = \frac{y}{x}, \quad x \neq 0 \qquad \cot \theta = \frac{x}{y}, \quad y \neq 0$$

$$\sec \theta = \frac{r}{x}, \quad x \neq 0 \qquad \csc \theta = \frac{r}{y}, \quad y \neq 0$$

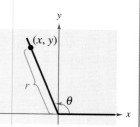

Because $r = \sqrt{x^2 + y^2}$ *cannot* be zero, it follows that the sine and cosine functions are defined for any real value of θ. However, if $x = 0$, the tangent and secant of θ are undefined. For example, the tangent of $90°$ is undefined. Similarly, if $y = 0$, the cotangent and cosecant of θ are undefined.

Example 1   Evaluating Trigonometric Functions

Let $(-3, 4)$ be a point on the terminal side of θ. Find the sine, cosine, and tangent of θ.

Solution

Referring to Figure 4.36, you can see that $x = -3$, $y = 4$, and

$$r = \sqrt{x^2 + y^2} = \sqrt{(-3)^2 + 4^2} = \sqrt{25} = 5.$$

So, you have the following.

$$\sin \theta = \frac{y}{r} = \frac{4}{5}$$

$$\cos \theta = \frac{x}{r} = -\frac{3}{5}$$

$$\tan \theta = \frac{y}{x} = -\frac{4}{3}$$

✓**CHECKPOINT**   Now try Exercise 1.

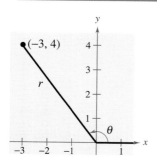

FIGURE 4.36

The *signs* of the trigonometric functions in the four quadrants can be determined easily from the definitions of the functions. For instance, because $\cos \theta = x/r$, it follows that $\cos \theta$ is positive wherever $x > 0$, which is in Quadrants I and IV. (Remember, r is always positive.) In a similar manner, you can verify the results shown in Figure 4.37.

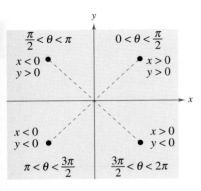

Example 2   **Evaluating Trigonometric Functions**

Given $\tan \theta = -\frac{5}{4}$ and $\cos \theta > 0$, find $\sin \theta$ and $\sec \theta$.

Solution

Note that θ lies in Quadrant IV because that is the only quadrant in which the tangent is negative and the cosine is positive. Moreover, using

$$\tan \theta = \frac{y}{x} = -\frac{5}{4}$$

and the fact that y is negative in Quadrant IV, you can let $y = -5$ and $x = 4$. So, $r = \sqrt{16 + 25} = \sqrt{41}$ and you have

$$\sin \theta = \frac{y}{r} = \frac{-5}{\sqrt{41}}$$

$$\approx -0.7809$$

$$\sec \theta = \frac{r}{x} = \frac{\sqrt{41}}{4}$$

$$\approx 1.6008.$$

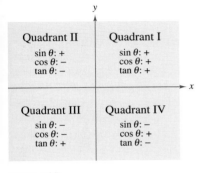

FIGURE 4.37

✓CHECKPOINT   Now try Exercise 17.

Example 3   **Trigonometric Functions of Quadrant Angles**

Evaluate the cosine and tangent functions at the four quadrant angles 0, $\dfrac{\pi}{2}$, π, and $\dfrac{3\pi}{2}$.

Solution

To begin, choose a point on the terminal side of each angle, as shown in Figure 4.38. For each of the four points, $r = 1$, and you have the following.

$$\cos 0 = \frac{x}{r} = \frac{1}{1} = 1 \qquad \tan 0 = \frac{y}{x} = \frac{0}{1} = 0 \qquad (x, y) = (1, 0)$$

$$\cos \frac{\pi}{2} = \frac{x}{r} = \frac{0}{1} = 0 \qquad \tan \frac{\pi}{2} = \frac{y}{x} = \frac{1}{0} \Longrightarrow \text{undefined} \qquad (x, y) = (0, 1)$$

$$\cos \pi = \frac{x}{r} = \frac{-1}{1} = -1 \quad \tan \pi = \frac{y}{x} = \frac{0}{-1} = 0 \qquad (x, y) = (-1, 0)$$

$$\cos \frac{3\pi}{2} = \frac{x}{r} = \frac{0}{1} = 0 \qquad \tan \frac{3\pi}{2} = \frac{y}{x} = \frac{-1}{0} \Longrightarrow \text{undefined} \quad (x, y) = (0, -1)$$

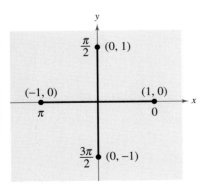

FIGURE 4.38

✓CHECKPOINT   Now try Exercise 29.

Reference Angles

The values of the trigonometric functions of angles greater than 90° (or less than 0°) can be determined from their values at corresponding acute angles called **reference angles.**

> **Definition of Reference Angle**
>
> Let θ be an angle in standard position. Its **reference angle** is the acute angle θ' formed by the terminal side of θ and the horizontal axis.

Figure 4.39 shows the reference angles for θ in Quadrants II, III, and IV.

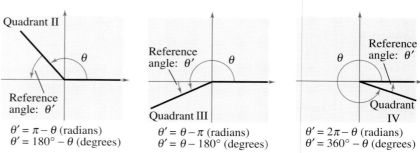

$\theta' = \pi - \theta$ (radians)
$\theta' = 180° - \theta$ (degrees)

$\theta' = \theta - \pi$ (radians)
$\theta' = \theta - 180°$ (degrees)

$\theta' = 2\pi - \theta$ (radians)
$\theta' = 360° - \theta$ (degrees)

FIGURE **4.39**

$\theta = 300°$
$\theta' = 60°$

FIGURE **4.40**

| **Example 4** | **Finding Reference Angles** |

Find the reference angle θ'.

a. $\theta = 300°$ **b.** $\theta = 2.3$ **c.** $\theta = -135°$

Solution

a. Because 300° lies in Quadrant IV, the angle it makes with the x-axis is

$$\theta' = 360° - 300°$$
$$= 60°. \qquad \text{Degrees}$$

Figure 4.40 shows the angle $\theta = 300°$ and its reference angle $\theta' = 60°$.

b. Because 2.3 lies between $\pi/2 \approx 1.5708$ and $\pi \approx 3.1416$, it follows that it is in Quadrant II and its reference angle is

$$\theta' = \pi - 2.3$$
$$\approx 0.8416. \qquad \text{Radians}$$

Figure 4.41 shows the angle $\theta = 2.3$ and its reference angle $\theta' = \pi - 2.3$.

c. First, determine that $-135°$ is coterminal with 225°, which lies in Quadrant III. So, the reference angle is

$$\theta' = 225° - 180°$$
$$= 45°. \qquad \text{Degrees}$$

Figure 4.42 shows the angle $\theta = -135°$ and its reference angle $\theta' = 45°$.

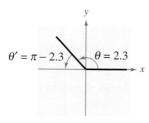

$\theta' = \pi - 2.3$
$\theta = 2.3$

FIGURE **4.41**

225° and −135° are coterminal.
225°
$\theta' = 45°$
$\theta = -135°$

FIGURE **4.42**

✓CHECKPOINT   Now try Exercise 37.

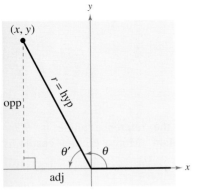

$$opp = |y|, adj = |x|$$

FIGURE **4.43**

Trigonometric Functions of Real Numbers

To see how a reference angle is used to evaluate a trigonometric function, consider the point (x, y) on the terminal side of θ, as shown in Figure 4.43. By definition, you know that

$$\sin \theta = \frac{y}{r} \qquad \text{and} \qquad \tan \theta = \frac{y}{x}.$$

For the right triangle with acute angle θ' and sides of lengths $|x|$ and $|y|$, you have

$$\sin \theta' = \frac{\text{opp}}{\text{hyp}} = \frac{|y|}{r}$$

and

$$\tan \theta' = \frac{\text{opp}}{\text{adj}} = \frac{|y|}{|x|}.$$

So, it follows that $\sin \theta$ and $\sin \theta'$ are equal, *except possibly in sign*. The same is true for $\tan \theta$ and $\tan \theta'$ *and* for the other four trigonometric functions. In all cases, the sign of the function value can be determined by the quadrant in which θ lies.

> ## Evaluating Trigonometric Functions of Any Angle
>
> To find the value of a trigonometric function of any angle θ:
>
> **1.** Determine the function value for the associated reference angle θ'.
>
> **2.** Depending on the quadrant in which θ lies, affix the appropriate sign to the function value.

By using reference angles and the special angles discussed in the preceding section, you can greatly extend the scope of *exact* trigonometric values. For instance, knowing the function values of 30° means that you know the function values of all angles for which 30° is a reference angle. For convenience, the table below shows the exact values of the trigonometric functions of special angles and quadrant angles.

Trigonometric Values of Common Angles

θ (degrees)	0°	30°	45°	60°	90°	180°	270°
θ (radians)	0	$\frac{\pi}{6}$	$\frac{\pi}{4}$	$\frac{\pi}{3}$	$\frac{\pi}{2}$	π	$\frac{3\pi}{2}$
$\sin \theta$	0	$\frac{1}{2}$	$\frac{\sqrt{2}}{2}$	$\frac{\sqrt{3}}{2}$	1	0	-1
$\cos \theta$	1	$\frac{\sqrt{3}}{2}$	$\frac{\sqrt{2}}{2}$	$\frac{1}{2}$	0	-1	0
$\tan \theta$	0	$\frac{\sqrt{3}}{3}$	1	$\sqrt{3}$	Undef.	0	Undef.

Example 5 **Using Reference Angles**

Evaluate each trigonometric function.

a. $\cos \dfrac{4\pi}{3}$ **b.** $\tan(-210°)$ **c.** $\csc \dfrac{11\pi}{4}$

Solution

a. Because $\theta = 4\pi/3$ lies in Quadrant III, the reference angle is $\theta' = (4\pi/3) - \pi = \pi/3$, as shown in Figure 4.44. Moreover, the cosine is negative in Quadrant III, so

$$\cos \frac{4\pi}{3} = (-) \cos \frac{\pi}{3}$$

$$= -\frac{1}{2}.$$

b. Because $-210° + 360° = 150°$, it follows that $-210°$ is coterminal with the second-quadrant angle $150°$. So, the reference angle is $\theta' = 180° - 150° = 30°$, as shown in Figure 4.45. Finally, because the tangent is negative in Quadrant II, you have

$$\tan(-210°) = (-) \tan 30°$$

$$= -\frac{\sqrt{3}}{3}.$$

c. Because $(11\pi/4) - 2\pi = 3\pi/4$, it follows that $11\pi/4$ is coterminal with the second-quadrant angle $3\pi/4$. So, the reference angle is $\theta' = \pi - (3\pi/4) = \pi/4$, as shown in Figure 4.46. Because the cosecant is positive in Quadrant II, you have

$$\csc \frac{11\pi}{4} = (+) \csc \frac{\pi}{4}$$

$$= \frac{1}{\sin(\pi/4)}$$

$$= \sqrt{2}.$$

FIGURE **4.44**

FIGURE **4.45**

FIGURE **4.46**

✓CHECKPOINT   Now try Exercise 51.

Example 6   **Using Trigonometric Identities**

Let θ be an angle in Quadrant II such that $\sin \theta = \frac{1}{3}$. Find (a) $\cos \theta$ and (b) $\tan \theta$ by using trigonometric identities.

Solution

a. Using the Pythagorean identity $\sin^2 \theta + \cos^2 \theta = 1$, you obtain

$$\left(\frac{1}{3}\right)^2 + \cos^2 \theta = 1 \qquad\qquad \text{Substitute } \tfrac{1}{3} \text{ for } \sin \theta.$$

$$\cos^2 \theta = 1 - \frac{1}{9} = \frac{8}{9}.$$

Because $\cos \theta < 0$ in Quadrant II, you can use the negative root to obtain

$$\cos \theta = -\frac{\sqrt{8}}{\sqrt{9}}$$

$$= -\frac{2\sqrt{2}}{3}.$$

b. Using the trigonometric identity $\tan \theta = \dfrac{\sin \theta}{\cos \theta}$, you obtain

$$\tan \theta = \frac{1/3}{-2\sqrt{2}/3} \qquad\qquad \text{Substitute for } \sin \theta \text{ and } \cos \theta.$$

$$= -\frac{1}{2\sqrt{2}}$$

$$= -\frac{\sqrt{2}}{4}.$$

✓**CHECKPOINT**   Now try Exercise 59.

You can use a calculator to evaluate trigonometric functions, as shown in the next example.

Example 7   **Using a Calculator**

Use a calculator to evaluate each trigonometric function.

a. $\cot 410°$ **b.** $\sin(-7)$ **c.** $\sec \dfrac{\pi}{9}$

Solution

Function	Mode	Calculator Keystrokes	Display
a. $\cot 410°$	Degree	(TAN (410)) x^{-1} ENTER	0.8390996
b. $\sin(-7)$	Radian	SIN ((−) 7) ENTER	−0.6569866
c. $\sec \dfrac{\pi}{9}$	Radian	(COS (π ÷ 9)) x^{-1} ENTER	1.0641778

✓**CHECKPOINT**   Now try Exercise 69.

4.4 Exercises

VOCABULARY CHECK:

In Exercises 1–6, let θ be an angle in standard position, with (x, y) a point on the terminal side of θ and $r\sqrt{x^2 + y^2} \neq 0$.

1. $\sin \theta =$ _____

2. $\dfrac{r}{y} =$ _____

3. $\tan \theta =$ _____

4. $\sec \theta =$ _____

5. $\dfrac{x}{r} =$ _____

6. $\dfrac{x}{y} =$ _____

7. The acute positive angle that is formed by the terminal side of the angle θ and the horizontal axis is called the _____ angle of θ and is denoted by θ'.

PREREQUISITE SKILLS REVIEW: Practice and review algebra skills needed for this section at **www.Eduspace.com.**

In Exercises 1–4, determine the exact values of the six trigonometric functions of the angle θ.

1. (a)   (b)

2. (a)   (b)

3. (a)   (b)

4. (a)   (b)

In Exercises 5–10, the point is on the terminal side of an angle in standard position. Determine the exact values of the six trigonometric functions of the angle.

5. $(7, 24)$

6. $(8, 15)$

7. $(-4, 10)$

8. $(-5, -2)$

9. $(-3.5, 6.8)$

10. $\left(3\frac{1}{2}, -7\frac{3}{4}\right)$

In Exercises 11–14, state the quadrant in which θ lies.

11. $\sin \theta < 0$ and $\cos \theta < 0$

12. $\sin \theta > 0$ and $\cos \theta > 0$

13. $\sin \theta > 0$ and $\tan \theta < 0$

14. $\sec \theta > 0$ and $\cot \theta < 0$

In Exercises 15–24, find the values of the six trigonometric functions of θ with the given constraint.

Function Value	Constraint
15. $\sin \theta = \frac{3}{5}$	θ lies in Quadrant II.
16. $\cos \theta = -\frac{4}{5}$	θ lies in Quadrant III.
17. $\tan \theta = -\frac{15}{8}$	$\sin \theta < 0$
18. $\cos \theta = \frac{8}{17}$	$\tan \theta < 0$
19. $\cot \theta = -3$	$\cos \theta > 0$
20. $\csc \theta = 4$	$\cot \theta < 0$
21. $\sec \theta = -2$	$\sin \theta > 0$
22. $\sin \theta = 0$	$\sec \theta = -1$
23. $\cot \theta$ is undefined.	$\pi/2 \leq \theta \leq 3\pi/2$
24. $\tan \theta$ is undefined.	$\pi \leq \theta \leq 2\pi$

In Exercises 25–28, the terminal side of θ lies on the given line in the specified quadrant. Find the values of the six trigonometric functions of θ by finding a point on the line.

Line	Quadrant
25. $y = -x$	II
26. $y = \frac{1}{3}x$	III
27. $2x - y = 0$	III
28. $4x + 3y = 0$	IV

In Exercises 29–36, evaluate the trigonometric function of the quadrant angle.

29. $\sin \pi$

30. $\csc \dfrac{3\pi}{2}$

31. $\sec \dfrac{3\pi}{2}$

32. $\sec \pi$

33. $\sin \dfrac{\pi}{2}$

34. $\cot \pi$

35. $\csc \pi$

36. $\cot \dfrac{\pi}{2}$

In Exercises 37–44, find the reference angle θ', and sketch θ and θ' in standard position.

37. $\theta = 203°$

38. $\theta = 309°$

39. $\theta = -245°$

40. $\theta = -145°$

41. $\theta = \dfrac{2\pi}{3}$

42. $\theta = \dfrac{7\pi}{4}$

43. $\theta = 3.5$

44. $\theta = \dfrac{11\pi}{3}$

In Exercises 45–58, evaluate the sine, cosine, and tangent of the angle without using a calculator.

45. $225°$

46. $300°$

47. $750°$

48. $-405°$

49. $-150°$

50. $-840°$

51. $\dfrac{4\pi}{3}$

52. $\dfrac{\pi}{4}$

53. $-\dfrac{\pi}{6}$

54. $-\dfrac{\pi}{2}$

55. $\dfrac{11\pi}{4}$

56. $\dfrac{10\pi}{3}$

57. $-\dfrac{3\pi}{2}$

58. $-\dfrac{25\pi}{4}$

In Exercises 59–64, find the indicated trigonometric value in the specified quadrant.

	Function	Quadrant	Trigonometric Value
59.	$\sin \theta = -\dfrac{3}{5}$	IV	$\cos \theta$
60.	$\cot \theta = -3$	II	$\sin \theta$
61.	$\tan \theta = \dfrac{3}{2}$	III	$\sec \theta$
62.	$\csc \theta = -2$	IV	$\cot \theta$
63.	$\cos \theta = \dfrac{5}{8}$	I	$\sec \theta$
64.	$\sec \theta = -\dfrac{9}{4}$	III	$\tan \theta$

In Exercises 65–80, use a calculator to evaluate the trigonometric function. Round your answer to four decimal places. (Be sure the calculator is set in the correct angle mode.)

65. $\sin 10°$

66. $\sec 225°$

67. $\cos(-110°)$

68. $\csc(-330°)$

69. $\tan 304°$

70. $\cot 178°$

71. $\sec 72°$

72. $\tan(-188°)$

73. $\tan 4.5$

74. $\cot 1.35$

75. $\tan \dfrac{\pi}{9}$

76. $\tan\left(-\dfrac{\pi}{9}\right)$

77. $\sin(-0.65)$

78. $\sec 0.29$

79. $\cot\left(-\dfrac{11\pi}{8}\right)$

80. $\csc\left(-\dfrac{15\pi}{14}\right)$

In Exercises 81–86, find two solutions of the equation. Give your answers in degrees ($0° \le \theta < 360°$) and in radians ($0 \le \theta < 2\pi$). Do not use a calculator.

81. (a) $\sin \theta = \dfrac{1}{2}$ (b) $\sin \theta = -\dfrac{1}{2}$

82. (a) $\cos \theta = \dfrac{\sqrt{2}}{2}$ (b) $\cos \theta = -\dfrac{\sqrt{2}}{2}$

83. (a) $\csc \theta = \dfrac{2\sqrt{3}}{3}$ (b) $\cot \theta = -1$

84. (a) $\sec \theta = 2$ (b) $\sec \theta = -2$

85. (a) $\tan \theta = 1$ (b) $\cot \theta = -\sqrt{3}$

86. (a) $\sin \theta = \dfrac{\sqrt{3}}{2}$ (b) $\sin \theta = -\dfrac{\sqrt{3}}{2}$

Model It

87. ***Data Analysis: Meteorology*** The table shows the monthly normal temperatures (in degrees Fahrenheit) for selected months for New York City (N) and Fairbanks, Alaska (F). (Source: National Climatic Data Center)

Month	New York City, N	Fairbanks, F
January	33	-10
April	52	32
July	77	62
October	58	24
December	38	-6

(a) Use the *regression* feature of a graphing utility to find a model of the form

$$y = a \sin(bt + c) + d$$

for each city. Let t represent the month, with $t = 1$ corresponding to January.

Model It (continued)

(b) Use the models from part (a) to find the monthly normal temperatures for the two cities in February, March, May, June, August, September, and November.

(c) Compare the models for the two cities.

88. Sales A company that produces snowboards, which are seasonal products, forecasts monthly sales over the next 2 years to be

$$S = 23.1 + 0.442t + 4.3 \cos \frac{\pi t}{6}$$

where S is measured in thousands of units and t is the time in months, with $t = 1$ representing January 2006. Predict sales for each of the following months.

(a) February 2006

(b) February 2007

(c) June 2006

(d) June 2007

89. Harmonic Motion The displacement from equilibrium of an oscillating weight suspended by a spring is given by

$$y(t) = 2 \cos 6t$$

where y is the displacement (in centimeters) and t is the time (in seconds). Find the displacement when (a) $t = 0$, (b) $t = \frac{1}{4}$, and (c) $t = \frac{1}{2}$.

90. Harmonic Motion The displacement from equilibrium of an oscillating weight suspended by a spring and subject to the damping effect of friction is given by

$$y(t) = 2e^{-t} \cos 6t$$

where y is the displacement (in centimeters) and t is the time (in seconds). Find the displacement when (a) $t = 0$, (b) $t = \frac{1}{4}$, and (c) $t = \frac{1}{2}$.

91. Electric Circuits The current I (in amperes) when 100 volts is applied to a circuit is given by

$$I = 5e^{-2t} \sin t$$

where t is the time (in seconds) after the voltage is applied. Approximate the current at $t = 0.7$ second after the voltage is applied.

92. Distance An airplane, flying at an altitude of 6 miles, is on a flight path that passes directly over an observer (see figure). If θ is the angle of elevation from the observer to the plane, find the distance d from the observer to the plane when (a) $\theta = 30°$, (b) $\theta = 90°$, and (c) $\theta = 120°$.

FIGURE FOR 92

Synthesis

True or False? In Exercises 93 and 94, determine whether the statement is true or false. Justify your answer.

93. In each of the four quadrants, the signs of the secant function and sine function will be the same.

94. To find the reference angle for an angle θ (given in degrees), find the integer n such that $0 \le 360°n - \theta \le 360°$. The difference $360°n - \theta$ is the reference angle.

95. Writing Consider an angle in standard position with $r = 12$ centimeters, as shown in the figure. Write a short paragraph describing the changes in the values of x, y, $\sin \theta$, $\cos \theta$, and $\tan \theta$ as θ increases continuously from $0°$ to $90°$.

96. Writing Explain how reference angles are used to find the trigonometric functions of obtuse angles.

Skills Review

In Exercises 97–106, graph the function. Identify the domain and any intercepts and asymptotes of the function.

97. $y = x^2 + 3x - 4$

98. $y = 2x^2 - 5x$

99. $f(x) = x^3 + 8$

100. $g(x) = x^4 + 2x^2 - 3$

101. $f(x) = \dfrac{x - 7}{x^2 + 4x + 4}$

102. $h(x) = \dfrac{x^2 - 1}{x + 5}$

103. $y = 2^{x-1}$

104. $y = 3^{x+1} + 2$

105. $y = \ln x^4$

106. $y = \log_{10}(x + 2)$

4.5 Graphs of Sine and Cosine Functions

What you should learn

- Sketch the graphs of basic sine and cosine functions.
- Use amplitude and period to help sketch the graphs of sine and cosine functions.
- Sketch translations of the graphs of sine and cosine functions.
- Use sine and cosine functions to model real-life data.

Why you should learn it

Sine and cosine functions are often used in scientific calculations. For instance, in Exercise 73 on page 330, you can use a trigonometric function to model the airflow of your respiratory cycle.

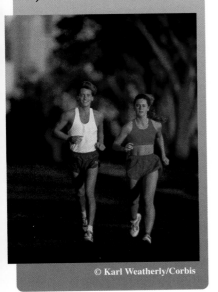

Basic Sine and Cosine Curves

In this section, you will study techniques for sketching the graphs of the sine and cosine functions. The graph of the sine function is a **sine curve.** In Figure 4.47, the black portion of the graph represents one period of the function and is called **one cycle** of the sine curve. The gray portion of the graph indicates that the basic sine curve repeats indefinitely in the positive and negative directions. The graph of the cosine function is shown in Figure 4.48.

Recall from Section 4.2 that the domain of the sine and cosine functions is the set of all real numbers. Moreover, the range of each function is the interval $[-1, 1]$, and each function has a period of 2π. Do you see how this information is consistent with the basic graphs shown in Figures 4.47 and 4.48?

FIGURE 4.47

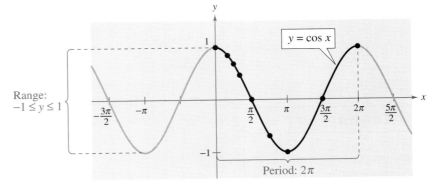

FIGURE 4.48

Note in Figures 4.47 and 4.48 that the sine curve is symmetric with respect to the *origin*, whereas the cosine curve is symmetric with respect to the *y-axis*. These properties of symmetry follow from the fact that the sine function is odd and the cosine function is even.

To sketch the graphs of the basic sine and cosine functions by hand, it helps to note five **key points** in one period of each graph: the *intercepts*, *maximum points*, and *minimum points* (see Figure 4.49).

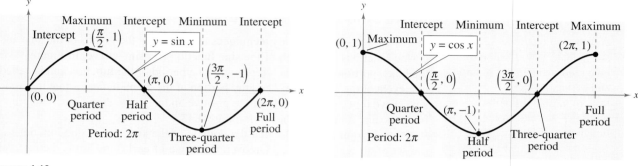

FIGURE 4.49

Example 1   Using Key Points to Sketch a Sine Curve

Sketch the graph of $y = 2 \sin x$ on the interval $[-\pi, 4\pi]$.

Solution

Note that

$$y = 2 \sin x = 2(\sin x)$$

indicates that the y-values for the key points will have twice the magnitude of those on the graph of $y = \sin x$. Divide the period 2π into four equal parts to get the key points for $y = 2 \sin x$.

Intercept	*Maximum*	*Intercept*	*Minimum*		*Intercept*
$(0, 0),$	$\left(\dfrac{\pi}{2}, 2\right),$	$(\pi, 0),$	$\left(\dfrac{3\pi}{2}, -2\right),$	and	$(2\pi, 0)$

By connecting these key points with a smooth curve and extending the curve in both directions over the interval $[-\pi, 4\pi]$, you obtain the graph shown in Figure 4.50.

Technology

When using a graphing utility to graph trigonometric functions, pay special attention to the viewing window you use. For instance, try graphing $y = [\sin(10x)]/10$ in the standard viewing window in *radian* mode. What do you observe? Use the *zoom* feature to find a viewing window that displays a good view of the graph.

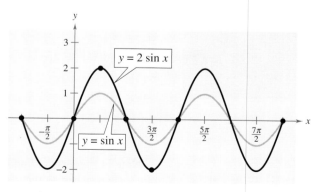

FIGURE 4.50

✓*CHECKPOINT*   Now try Exercise 35.

Amplitude and Period

In the remainder of this section you will study the graphic effect of each of the constants a, b, c, and d in equations of the forms

$$y = d + a \sin(bx - c)$$

and

$$y = d + a \cos(bx - c).$$

A quick review of the transformations you studied in Section 1.7 should help in this investigation.

The constant factor a in $y = a \sin x$ acts as a *scaling factor*—a *vertical stretch* or *vertical shrink* of the basic sine curve. If $|a| > 1$, the basic sine curve is stretched, and if $|a| < 1$, the basic sine curve is shrunk. The result is that the graph of $y = a \sin x$ ranges between $-a$ and a instead of between -1 and 1. The absolute value of a is the **amplitude** of the function $y = a \sin x$. The range of the function $y = a \sin x$ for $a > 0$ is $-a \le y \le a$.

Definition of Amplitude of Sine and Cosine Curves

The **amplitude** of $y = a \sin x$ and $y = a \cos x$ represents half the distance between the maximum and minimum values of the function and is given by

Amplitude $= |a|$.

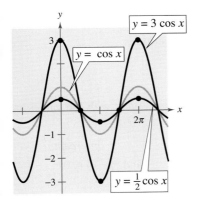

FIGURE **4.51**

Exploration

Sketch the graph of $y = \cos bx$ for $b = \frac{1}{2}$, 2, and 3. How does the value of b affect the graph? How many complete cycles occur between 0 and 2π for each value of b?

Example 2   **Scaling: Vertical Shrinking and Stretching**

On the same coordinate axes, sketch the graph of each function.

a. $y = \dfrac{1}{2} \cos x$ **b.** $y = 3 \cos x$

Solution

a. Because the amplitude of $y = \frac{1}{2} \cos x$ is $\frac{1}{2}$, the maximum value is $\frac{1}{2}$ and the minimum value is $-\frac{1}{2}$. Divide one cycle, $0 \le x \le 2\pi$, into four equal parts to get the key points

Maximum	Intercept	Minimum	Intercept		Maximum
$\left(0, \dfrac{1}{2}\right),$	$\left(\dfrac{\pi}{2}, 0\right),$	$\left(\pi, -\dfrac{1}{2}\right),$	$\left(\dfrac{3\pi}{2}, 0\right),$	and	$\left(2\pi, \dfrac{1}{2}\right).$

b. A similar analysis shows that the amplitude of $y = 3 \cos x$ is 3, and the key points are

Maximum	Intercept	Minimum	Intercept		Maximum
$(0, 3),$	$\left(\dfrac{\pi}{2}, 0\right),$	$(\pi, -3),$	$\left(\dfrac{3\pi}{2}, 0\right),$	and	$(2\pi, 3).$

The graphs of these two functions are shown in Figure 4.51. Notice that the graph of $y = \frac{1}{2} \cos x$ is a vertical *shrink* of the graph of $y = \cos x$ and the graph of $y = 3 \cos x$ is a vertical *stretch* of the graph of $y = \cos x$.

✓CHECKPOINT   Now try Exercise 37.

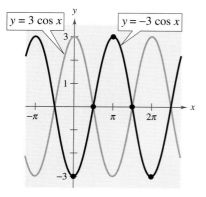

$y = 3 \cos x$ $y = -3 \cos x$

FIGURE 4.52

You know from Section 1.7 that the graph of $y = -f(x)$ is a **reflection** in the x-axis of the graph of $y = f(x)$. For instance, the graph of $y = -3 \cos x$ is a reflection of the graph of $y = 3 \cos x$, as shown in Figure 4.52.

Because $y = a \sin x$ completes one cycle from $x = 0$ to $x = 2\pi$, it follows that $y = a \sin bx$ completes one cycle from $x = 0$ to $x = 2\pi/b$.

Period of Sine and Cosine Functions

Let b be a positive real number. The **period** of $y = a \sin bx$ and $y = a \cos bx$ is given by

$$\text{Period} = \frac{2\pi}{b}.$$

Note that if $0 < b < 1$, the period of $y = a \sin bx$ is greater than 2π and represents a *horizontal stretching* of the graph of $y = a \sin x$. Similarly, if $b > 1$, the period of $y = a \sin bx$ is less than 2π and represents a *horizontal shrinking* of the graph of $y = a \sin x$. If b is negative, the identities $\sin(-x) = -\sin x$ and $\cos(-x) = \cos x$ are used to rewrite the function.

Exploration

Sketch the graph of

$$y = \sin(x - c)$$

where $c = -\pi/4, 0,$ and $\pi/4$. How does the value of c affect the graph?

Example 3   **Scaling: Horizontal Stretching**

Sketch the graph of $y = \sin \dfrac{x}{2}$.

Solution

The amplitude is 1. Moreover, because $b = \frac{1}{2}$, the period is

$$\frac{2\pi}{b} = \frac{2\pi}{\frac{1}{2}} = 4\pi. \qquad \text{Substitute for } b.$$

Now, divide the period-interval $[0, 4\pi]$ into four equal parts with the values π, 2π, and 3π to obtain the key points on the graph.

Intercept	Maximum	Intercept	Minimum		Intercept
$(0, 0),$	$(\pi, 1),$	$(2\pi, 0),$	$(3\pi, -1),$	and	$(4\pi, 0)$

The graph is shown in Figure 4.53.

STUDY TIP

In general, to divide a period-interval into four equal parts, successively add "period/4," starting with the left endpoint of the interval. For instance, for the period-interval $[-\pi/6, \pi/2]$ of length $2\pi/3$, you would successively add

$$\frac{2\pi/3}{4} = \frac{\pi}{6}$$

to get $-\pi/6, 0, \pi/6, \pi/3,$ and $\pi/2$ as the x-values for the key points on the graph.

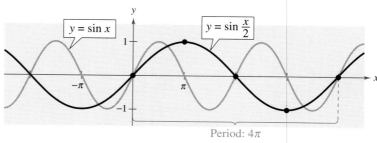

$y = \sin x$ $y = \sin \dfrac{x}{2}$

Period: 4π

FIGURE 4.53

✔CHECKPOINT   Now try Exercise 39.

Translations of Sine and Cosine Curves

The constant c in the general equations

$$y = a \sin(bx - c) \quad \text{and} \quad y = a \cos(bx - c)$$

creates a *horizontal translation* (shift) of the basic sine and cosine curves. Comparing $y = a \sin bx$ with $y = a \sin(bx - c)$, you find that the graph of $y = a \sin(bx - c)$ completes one cycle from $bx - c = 0$ to $bx - c = 2\pi$. By solving for x, you can find the interval for one cycle to be

Left endpoint Right endpoint

$$\dfrac{c}{b} \le x \le \dfrac{c}{b} + \dfrac{2\pi}{b}.$$

Period

This implies that the period of $y = a \sin(bx - c)$ is $2\pi/b$, and the graph of $y = a \sin bx$ is shifted by an amount c/b. The number c/b is the **phase shift.**

Graphs of Sine and Cosine Functions

The graphs of $y = a \sin(bx - c)$ and $y = a \cos(bx - c)$ have the following characteristics. (Assume $b > 0$.)

$$\text{Amplitude} = |a| \qquad \text{Period} = \dfrac{2\pi}{b}$$

The left and right endpoints of a one-cycle interval can be determined by solving the equations $bx - c = 0$ and $bx - c = 2\pi$.

Horizontal Translation

Example 4

Sketch the graph of $y = \dfrac{1}{2} \sin\left(x - \dfrac{\pi}{3}\right)$.

Solution

The amplitude is $\frac{1}{2}$ and the period is 2π. By solving the equations

$$x - \dfrac{\pi}{3} = 0 \quad \Longrightarrow \quad x = \dfrac{\pi}{3}$$

and

$$x - \dfrac{\pi}{3} = 2\pi \quad \Longrightarrow \quad x = \dfrac{7\pi}{3}$$

you see that the interval $[\pi/3, 7\pi/3]$ corresponds to one cycle of the graph. Dividing this interval into four equal parts produces the key points

Intercept	Maximum	Intercept	Minimum		Intercept
$\left(\dfrac{\pi}{3}, 0\right)$,	$\left(\dfrac{5\pi}{6}, \dfrac{1}{2}\right)$,	$\left(\dfrac{4\pi}{3}, 0\right)$,	$\left(\dfrac{11\pi}{6}, -\dfrac{1}{2}\right)$,	and	$\left(\dfrac{7\pi}{3}, 0\right)$.

The graph is shown in Figure 4.54.

✓CHECKPOINT   Now try Exercise 45.

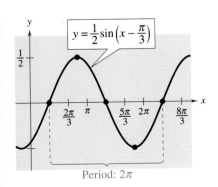

$y = \dfrac{1}{2} \sin\left(x - \dfrac{\pi}{3}\right)$

Period: 2π

FIGURE **4.54**

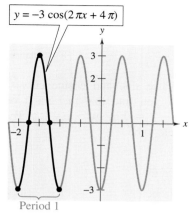

$y = -3 \cos(2\pi x + 4\pi)$

Period 1

FIGURE 4.55

Example 5 Horizontal Translation

Sketch the graph of

$$y = -3 \cos(2\pi x + 4\pi).$$

Solution

The amplitude is 3 and the period is $2\pi/2\pi = 1$. By solving the equations

$$2\pi x + 4\pi = 0$$
$$2\pi x = -4\pi$$
$$x = -2$$

and

$$2\pi x + 4\pi = 2\pi$$
$$2\pi x = -2\pi$$
$$x = -1$$

you see that the interval $[-2, -1]$ corresponds to one cycle of the graph. Dividing this interval into four equal parts produces the key points

Minimum	Intercept	Maximum	Intercept		Minimum
$(-2, -3)$,	$\left(-\frac{7}{4}, 0\right)$,	$\left(-\frac{3}{2}, 3\right)$,	$\left(-\frac{5}{4}, 0\right)$,	and	$(-1, -3)$.

The graph is shown in Figure 4.55.

✓CHECKPOINT   Now try Exercise 47.

The final type of transformation is the *vertical translation* caused by the constant d in the equations

$$y = d + a \sin(bx - c)$$

and

$$y = d + a \cos(bx - c).$$

The shift is d units upward for $d > 0$ and d units downward for $d < 0$. In other words, the graph oscillates about the horizontal line $y = d$ instead of about the x-axis.

Example 6 Vertical Translation

Sketch the graph of

$$y = 2 + 3 \cos 2x.$$

Solution

The amplitude is 3 and the period is π. The key points over the interval $[0, \pi]$ are

$(0, 5)$,	$\left(\frac{\pi}{4}, 2\right)$,	$\left(\frac{\pi}{2}, -1\right)$,	$\left(\frac{3\pi}{4}, 2\right)$,	and	$(\pi, 5)$.

The graph is shown in Figure 4.56. Compared with the graph of $f(x) = 3 \cos 2x$, the graph of $y - 2 + 3 \cos 2x$ is shifted upward two units.

✓CHECKPOINT   Now try Exercise 53.

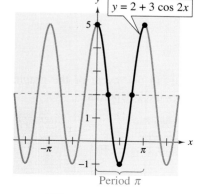

$y = 2 + 3 \cos 2x$

Period π

FIGURE 4.56

Mathematical Modeling

Sine and cosine functions can be used to model many real-life situations, including electric currents, musical tones, radio waves, tides, and weather patterns.

Example 7   **Finding a Trigonometric Model**

Throughout the day, the depth of water at the end of a dock in Bar Harbor, Maine varies with the tides. The table shows the depths (in feet) at various times during the morning.   (Source: Nautical Software, Inc.)

a. Use a trigonometric function to model the data.

b. Find the depths at 9 A.M. and 3 P.M.

c. A boat needs at least 10 feet of water to moor at the dock. During what times in the afternoon can it safely dock?

Time, t	Depth, y
Midnight	3.1
2 A.M.	7.8
4 A.M.	11.3
6 A.M.	10.9
8 A.M.	6.6
10 A.M.	1.7
Noon	0.9

Solution

a. Begin by graphing the data, as shown in Figure 4.57. You can use either a sine or cosine model. Suppose you use a cosine model of the form

$$y = a \cos(bt - c) + d.$$

The difference between the maximum height and the minimum height of the graph is twice the amplitude of the function. So, the amplitude is

$$a = \frac{1}{2}[(\text{maximum depth}) - (\text{minimum depth})] = \frac{1}{2}(11.3 - 0.1) = 5.6.$$

The cosine function completes one half of a cycle between the times at which the maximum and minimum depths occur. So, the period is

$$p = 2[(\text{time of min. depth}) - (\text{time of max. depth})] = 2(10 - 4) = 12$$

which implies that $b = 2\pi/p \approx 0.524$. Because high tide occurs 4 hours after midnight, consider the left endpoint to be $c/b = 4$, so $c \approx 2.094$. Moreover, because the average depth is $\frac{1}{2}(11.3 + 0.1) = 5.7$, it follows that $d = 5.7$. So, you can model the depth with the function given by

$$y = 5.6 \cos(0.524t - 2.094) + 5.7.$$

Changing Tides

FIGURE **4.57**

b. The depths at 9 A.M. and 3 P.M. are as follows.

$$y = 5.6 \cos(0.524 \cdot 9 - 2.094) + 5.7$$

$$\approx 0.84 \text{ foot} \qquad\qquad 9 \text{ A.M.}$$

$$y = 5.6 \cos(0.524 \cdot 15 - 2.094) + 5.7$$

$$\approx 10.57 \text{ feet} \qquad\qquad 3 \text{ P.M.}$$

c. To find out when the depth y is at least 10 feet, you can graph the model with the line $y = 10$ using a graphing utility, as shown in Figure 4.58. Using the *intersect* feature, you can determine that the depth is at least 10 feet between 2:42 P.M. ($t \approx 14.7$) and 5:18 P.M. ($t \approx 17.3$).

FIGURE **4.58**

✓CHECKPOINT   Now try Exercise 77.

4.5 | Exercises

VOCABULARY CHECK: Fill in the blanks.

1. One period of a sine or cosine function function is called one _____ of the sine curve or cosine curve.

2. The _____ of a sine or cosine curve represents half the distance between the maximum and minimum values of the function.

3. The period of a sine or cosine function is given by _____.

4. For the function given by $y = a \sin(bx - c)$, $\frac{c}{b}$ represents the _____ _____ of the graph of the function.

5. For the function given by $y = d + a \cos(bx - c)$, d represents a _____ _____ of the graph of the function.

PREREQUISITE SKILLS REVIEW: Practice and review algebra skills needed for this section at **www.Eduspace.com**.

In Exercises 1–14, find the period and amplitude.

1. $y = 3 \sin 2x$

2. $y = 2 \cos 3x$

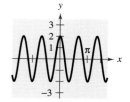

3. $y = \frac{5}{2} \cos \frac{x}{2}$

4. $y = -3 \sin \frac{x}{3}$

5. $y = \frac{1}{2} \sin \frac{\pi x}{3}$

6. $y = \frac{3}{2} \cos \frac{\pi x}{2}$

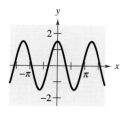

7. $y = -2 \sin x$

8. $y = -\cos \frac{2x}{3}$

9. $y = 3 \sin 10x$

10. $y = \frac{1}{3} \sin 8x$

11. $y = \frac{1}{2} \cos \frac{2x}{3}$

12. $y = \frac{5}{2} \cos \frac{x}{4}$

13. $y = \frac{1}{4} \sin 2\pi x$

14. $y = \frac{2}{3} \cos \frac{\pi x}{10}$

In Exercises 15–22, describe the relationship between the graphs of f and g. Consider amplitude, period, and shifts.

15. $f(x) = \sin x$
   $g(x) = \sin(x - \pi)$

16. $f(x) = \cos x$
   $g(x) = \cos(x + \pi)$

17. $f(x) = \cos 2x$
   $g(x) = -\cos 2x$

18. $f(x) = \sin 3x$
   $g(x) = \sin(-3x)$

19. $f(x) = \cos x$
   $g(x) = \cos 2x$

20. $f(x) = \sin x$
   $g(x) = \sin 3x$

21. $f(x) = \sin 2x$
   $g(x) = 3 + \sin 2x$

22. $f(x) = \cos 4x$
   $g(x) = -2 + \cos 4x$

In Exercises 23–26, describe the relationship between the graphs of f and g. Consider amplitude, period, and shifts.

23.

24.

25.

26.

In Exercises 27–34, graph f and g on the same set of coordinate axes. (Include two full periods.)

27. $f(x) = -2 \sin x$

$g(x) = 4 \sin x$

28. $f(x) = \sin x$

$g(x) = \sin \dfrac{x}{3}$

29. $f(x) = \cos x$

$g(x) = 1 + \cos x$

30. $f(x) = 2 \cos 2x$

$g(x) = -\cos 4x$

31. $f(x) = -\dfrac{1}{2} \sin \dfrac{x}{2}$

$g(x) = 3 - \dfrac{1}{2} \sin \dfrac{x}{2}$

32. $f(x) = 4 \sin \pi x$

$g(x) = 4 \sin \pi x - 3$

33. $f(x) = 2 \cos x$

$g(x) = 2 \cos(x + \pi)$

34. $f(x) = -\cos x$

$g(x) = -\cos(x - \pi)$

In Exercises 35–56, sketch the graph of the function. (Include two full periods.)

35. $y = 3 \sin x$

36. $y = \dfrac{1}{4} \sin x$

37. $y = \dfrac{1}{3} \cos x$

38. $y = 4 \cos x$

39. $y = \cos \dfrac{x}{2}$

40. $y = \sin 4x$

41. $y = \cos 2\pi x$

42. $y = \sin \dfrac{\pi x}{4}$

43. $y = -\sin \dfrac{2\pi x}{3}$

44. $y = -10 \cos \dfrac{\pi x}{6}$

45. $y = \sin\left(x - \dfrac{\pi}{4}\right)$

46. $y = \sin(x - \pi)$

47. $y = 3 \cos(x + \pi)$

48. $y = 4 \cos\left(x + \dfrac{\pi}{4}\right)$

49. $y = 2 - \sin \dfrac{2\pi x}{3}$

50. $y = -3 + 5 \cos \dfrac{\pi t}{12}$

51. $y = 2 + \dfrac{1}{10} \cos 60 \pi x$

52. $y = 2 \cos x - 3$

53. $y = 3 \cos(x + \pi) - 3$

54. $y = 4 \cos\left(x + \dfrac{\pi}{4}\right) + 4$

55. $y = \dfrac{2}{3} \cos\left(\dfrac{x}{2} - \dfrac{\pi}{4}\right)$

56. $y = -3 \cos(6x + \pi)$

In Exercises 57–62, use a graphing utility to graph the function. Include two full periods. Be sure to choose an appropriate viewing window.

57. $y = -2 \sin(4x + \pi)$

58. $y = -4 \sin\left(\dfrac{2}{3}x - \dfrac{\pi}{3}\right)$

59. $y = \cos\left(2\pi x - \dfrac{\pi}{2}\right) + 1$

60. $y = 3 \cos\left(\dfrac{\pi x}{2} + \dfrac{\pi}{2}\right) - 2$

61. $y = -0.1 \sin\left(\dfrac{\pi x}{10} + \pi\right)$

62. $y = \dfrac{1}{100} \sin 120\pi t$

Graphical Reasoning In Exercises 63–66, find a and d for the function $f(x) = a \cos x + d$ such that the graph of f matches the figure.

63.

64.

65.

66.
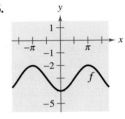

Graphical Reasoning In Exercises 67–70, find a, b, and c for the function $f(x) = a \sin(bx - c)$ such that the graph of f matches the figure.

67.

68.

69.

70.

In Exercises 71 and 72, use a graphing utility to graph y_1 and y_2 in the interval $[-2\pi, 2\pi]$. Use the graphs to find real numbers x such that $y_1 = y_2$.

71. $y_1 = \sin x$

$y_2 = -\dfrac{1}{2}$

72. $y_1 = \cos x$

$y_2 = -1$

73. *Respiratory Cycle*   For a person at rest, the velocity v (in liters per second) of air flow during a respiratory cycle (the time from the beginning of one breath to the beginning of the next) is given by $v = 0.85 \sin \dfrac{\pi t}{3}$, where t is the time (in seconds). (Inhalation occurs when $v > 0$, and exhalation occurs when $v < 0$.)

(a) Find the time for one full respiratory cycle.

(b) Find the number of cycles per minute.

(c) Sketch the graph of the velocity function.

74. *Respiratory Cycle*   After exercising for a few minutes, a person has a respiratory cycle for which the velocity of air flow is approximated by $v = 1.75 \sin \dfrac{\pi t}{2}$, where t is the time (in seconds). (Inhalation occurs when $v > 0$, and exhalation occurs when $v < 0$.)

(a) Find the time for one full respiratory cycle.

(b) Find the number of cycles per minute.

(c) Sketch the graph of the velocity function.

75. *Data Analysis: Meteorology*   The table shows the maximum daily high temperatures for Tallahassee T and Chicago C (in degrees Fahrenheit) for month t, with $t = 1$ corresponding to January. (Source: National Climatic Data Center)

Month, t	Tallahassee, T	Chicago, C
1	63.8	29.6
2	67.4	34.7
3	74.0	46.1
4	80.0	58.0
5	86.5	69.9
6	90.9	79.2
7	92.0	83.5
8	91.5	81.2
9	88.5	73.9
10	81.2	62.1
11	72.9	47.1
12	65.8	34.4

(a) A model for the temperature in Tallahassee is given by

$$T(t) = 77.90 + 14.10 \cos\left(\dfrac{\pi t}{6} - 3.67\right).$$

Find a trigonometric model for Chicago.

 (b) Use a graphing utility to graph the data points and the model for the temperatures in Tallahassee. How well does the model fit the data?

 (c) Use a graphing utility to graph the data points and the model for the temperatures in Chicago. How well does the model fit the data?

(d) Use the models to estimate the average maximum temperature in each city. Which term of the models did you use? Explain.

(e) What is the period of each model? Are the periods what you expected? Explain.

(f) Which city has the greater variability in temperature throughout the year? Which factor of the models determines this variability? Explain.

76. *Health*   The function given by $P = 100 - 20 \cos \dfrac{5\pi t}{3}$ approximates the blood pressure P (in millimeters) of mercury at time t (in seconds) for a person at rest.

(a) Find the period of the function.

(b) Find the number of heartbeats per minute.

77. *Piano Tuning*   When tuning a piano, a technician strikes a tuning fork for the A above middle C and sets up a wave motion that can be approximated by $y = 0.001 \sin 880\pi t$, where t is the time (in seconds).

(a) What is the period of the function?

(b) The frequency f is given by $f = 1/p$. What is the frequency of the note?

Model It

78. *Data Analysis: Astronomy*   The percent y of the moon's face that is illuminated on day x of the year 2007, where $x = 1$ represents January 1, is shown in the table. (Source: U.S. Naval Observatory)

x	y
3	1.0
11	0.5
19	0.0
26	0.5
32	1.0
40	0.5

(a) Create a scatter plot of the data.

(b) Find a trigonometric model that fits the data.

(c) Add the graph of your model in part (b) to the scatter plot. How well does the model fit the data?

(d) What is the period of the model?

(e) Estimate the moon's percent illumination for March 12, 2007.

79. *Fuel Consumption* The daily consumption C (in gallons) of diesel fuel on a farm is modeled by

$$C = 30.3 + 21.6 \sin\left(\frac{2\pi t}{365} + 10.9\right)$$

where t is the time (in days), with $t = 1$ corresponding to January 1.

(a) What is the period of the model? Is it what you expected? Explain.

(b) What is the average daily fuel consumption? Which term of the model did you use? Explain.

 (c) Use a graphing utility to graph the model. Use the graph to approximate the time of the year when consumption exceeds 40 gallons per day.

80. *Ferris Wheel* A Ferris wheel is built such that the height h (in feet) above ground of a seat on the wheel at time t (in seconds) can be modeled by

$$h(t) = 53 + 50 \sin\left(\frac{\pi}{10}t - \frac{\pi}{2}\right).$$

(a) Find the period of the model. What does the period tell you about the ride?

(b) Find the amplitude of the model. What does the amplitude tell you about the ride?

 (c) Use a graphing utility to graph one cycle of the model.

Synthesis

True or False? **In Exercises 81–83, determine whether the statement is true or false. Justify your answer.**

81. The graph of the function given by $f(x) = \sin(x + 2\pi)$ translates the graph of $f(x) = \sin x$ exactly one period to the right so that the two graphs look identical.

82. The function given by $y = \frac{1}{2}\cos 2x$ has an amplitude that is twice that of the function given by $y = \cos x$.

83. The graph of $y = -\cos x$ is a reflection of the graph of $y = \sin(x + \pi/2)$ in the x-axis.

84. *Writing* Use a graphing utility to graph the function given by $y = d + a \sin(bx - c)$, for several different values of a, b, c, and d. Write a paragraph describing the changes in the graph corresponding to changes in each constant.

Conjecture **In Exercises 85 and 86, graph f and g on the same set of coordinate axes. Include two full periods. Make a conjecture about the functions.**

85. $f(x) = \sin x, \quad g(x) = \cos\left(x - \frac{\pi}{2}\right)$

86. $f(x) = \sin x, \quad g(x) = -\cos\left(x + \frac{\pi}{2}\right)$

 87. *Exploration* Using calculus, it can be shown that the sine and cosine functions can be approximated by the polynomials

$$\sin x \approx x - \frac{x^3}{3!} + \frac{x^5}{5!} \quad \text{and} \quad \cos x \approx 1 - \frac{x^2}{2!} + \frac{x^4}{4!}$$

where x is in radians.

(a) Use a graphing utility to graph the sine function and its polynomial approximation in the same viewing window. How do the graphs compare?

(b) Use a graphing utility to graph the cosine function and its polynomial approximation in the same viewing window. How do the graphs compare?

(c) Study the patterns in the polynomial approximations of the sine and cosine functions and predict the next term in each. Then repeat parts (a) and (b). How did the accuracy of the approximations change when an additional term was added?

88. *Exploration* Use the polynomial approximations for the sine and cosine functions in Exercise 87 to approximate the following function values. Compare the results with those given by a calculator. Is the error in the approximation the same in each case? Explain.

(a) $\sin\dfrac{1}{2}$ (b) $\sin 1$ (c) $\sin\dfrac{\pi}{6}$

(d) $\cos(-0.5)$ (e) $\cos 1$ (f) $\cos\dfrac{\pi}{4}$

Skills Review

In Exercises 89–92, use the properties of logarithms to write the expression as a sum, difference, and/or constant multiple of a logarithm.

89. $\log_{10}\sqrt{x-2}$ **90.** $\log_2[x^2(x-3)]$

91. $\ln\dfrac{t^3}{t-1}$ **92.** $\ln\sqrt{\dfrac{z}{z^2+1}}$

In Exercises 93–96, write the expression as the logarithm of a single quantity.

93. $\frac{1}{2}(\log_{10} x + \log_{10} y)$ **94.** $2\log_2 x + \log_2(xy)$

95. $\ln 3x - 4 \ln y$

96. $\frac{1}{2}(\ln 2x - 2 \ln x) + 3 \ln x$

97. Make a Decision To work an extended application analyzing the normal daily maximum temperature and normal precipitation in Honolulu, Hawaii, visit this text's website at *college.hmco.com*. (*Data Source: NOAA*)

4.6   Graphs of Other Trigonometric Functions

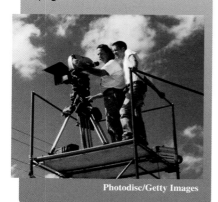

Photodisc/Getty Images

Graph of the Tangent Function

Recall that the tangent function is odd. That is, $\tan(-x) = -\tan x$. Consequently, the graph of $y = \tan x$ is symmetric with respect to the origin. You also know from the identity $\tan x = \sin x/\cos x$ that the tangent is undefined for values at which $\cos x = 0$. Two such values are $x = \pm\pi/2 \approx \pm 1.5708$.

x	$-\dfrac{\pi}{2}$	-1.57	-1.5	$-\dfrac{\pi}{4}$	0	$\dfrac{\pi}{4}$	1.5	1.57	$\dfrac{\pi}{2}$
$\tan x$	Undef.	-1255.8	-14.1	-1	0	1	14.1	1255.8	Undef.

As indicated in the table, $\tan x$ increases without bound as x approaches $\pi/2$ from the left, and decreases without bound as x approaches $-\pi/2$ from the right. So, the graph of $y = \tan x$ has *vertical asymptotes* at $x = \pi/2$ and $x = -\pi/2$, as shown in Figure 4.59. Moreover, because the period of the tangent function is π, vertical asymptotes also occur when $x = \pi/2 + n\pi$, where n is an integer. The domain of the tangent function is the set of all real numbers other than $x = \pi/2 + n\pi$, and the range is the set of all real numbers.

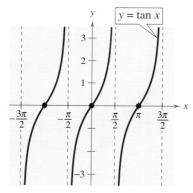

PERIOD: π
DOMAIN: ALL $x \neq \frac{\pi}{2} + n\pi$
RANGE: $(-\infty, \infty)$
VERTICAL ASYMPTOTES: $x = \frac{\pi}{2} + n\pi$

FIGURE 4.59

Sketching the graph of $y = a\tan(bx - c)$ is similar to sketching the graph of $y = a\sin(bx - c)$ in that you locate key points that identify the intercepts and asymptotes. Two consecutive vertical asymptotes can be found by solving the equations

$$bx - c = -\frac{\pi}{2} \quad \text{and} \quad bx - c = \frac{\pi}{2}.$$

The midpoint between two consecutive vertical asymptotes is an x-intercept of the graph. The period of the function $y = a\tan(bx - c)$ is the distance between two consecutive vertical asymptotes. The amplitude of a tangent function is not defined. After plotting the asymptotes and the x-intercept, plot a few additional points between the two asymptotes and sketch one cycle. Finally, sketch one or two additional cycles to the left and right.

Example 1   **Sketching the Graph of a Tangent Function**

Sketch the graph of $y = \tan \dfrac{x}{2}$.

Solution

By solving the equations

$$\dfrac{x}{2} = -\dfrac{\pi}{2} \quad \text{and} \quad \dfrac{x}{2} = \dfrac{\pi}{2}$$

$$x = -\pi \qquad\qquad x = \pi$$

you can see that two consecutive vertical asymptotes occur at $x = -\pi$ and $x = \pi$. Between these two asymptotes, plot a few points, including the x-intercept, as shown in the table. Three cycles of the graph are shown in Figure 4.60.

x	$-\pi$	$-\dfrac{\pi}{2}$	0	$\dfrac{\pi}{2}$	π
$\tan \dfrac{x}{2}$	Undef.	-1	0	1	Undef.

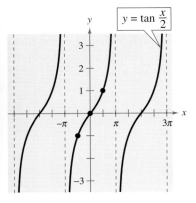

FIGURE **4.60**

✓**CHECKPOINT**   Now try Exercise 7.

Example 2   **Sketching the Graph of a Tangent Function**

Sketch the graph of $y = -3 \tan 2x$.

Solution

By solving the equations

$$2x = -\dfrac{\pi}{2} \quad \text{and} \quad 2x = \dfrac{\pi}{2}$$

$$x = -\dfrac{\pi}{4} \qquad\qquad x = \dfrac{\pi}{4}$$

you can see that two consecutive vertical asymptotes occur at $x = -\pi/4$ and $x = \pi/4$. Between these two asymptotes, plot a few points, including the x-intercept, as shown in the table. Three cycles of the graph are shown in Figure 4.61.

x	$-\dfrac{\pi}{4}$	$-\dfrac{\pi}{8}$	0	$\dfrac{\pi}{8}$	$\dfrac{\pi}{4}$
$-3 \tan 2x$	Undef.	3	0	-3	Undef.

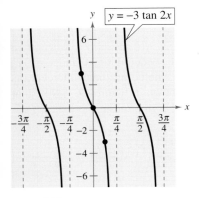

FIGURE **4.61**

✓**CHECKPOINT**   Now try Exercise 9.

By comparing the graphs in Examples 1 and 2, you can see that the graph of $y = a \tan(bx - c)$ increases between consecutive vertical asymptotes when $a > 0$, and decreases between consecutive vertical asymptotes when $a < 0$. In other words, the graph for $a < 0$ is a reflection in the x-axis of the graph for $a > 0$.

Graph of the Cotangent Function

The graph of the cotangent function is similar to the graph of the tangent function. It also has a period of π. However, from the identity

$$y = \cot x = \frac{\cos x}{\sin x}$$

you can see that the cotangent function has vertical asymptotes when $\sin x$ is zero, which occurs at $x = n\pi$, where n is an integer. The graph of the cotangent function is shown in Figure 4.62. Note that two consecutive vertical asymptotes of the graph of $y = a \cot(bx - c)$ can be found by solving the equations $bx - c = 0$ and $bx - c = \pi$.

Technology

Some graphing utilities have difficulty graphing trigonometric functions that have vertical asymptotes. Your graphing utility may connect parts of the graphs of tangent, cotangent, secant, and cosecant functions that are not supposed to be connected. To eliminate this problem, change the mode of the graphing utility to *dot* mode.

PERIOD: π
DOMAIN: ALL $x \neq n\pi$
RANGE: $(-\infty, \infty)$
VERTICAL ASYMPTOTES: $x = n\pi$

FIGURE 4.62

Example 3   Sketching the Graph of a Cotangent Function

Sketch the graph of $y = 2 \cot \dfrac{x}{3}$.

Solution

By solving the equations

$$\frac{x}{3} = 0 \qquad \text{and} \qquad \frac{x}{3} = \pi$$

$$x = 0 \qquad\qquad\qquad x = 3\pi$$

you can see that two consecutive vertical asymptotes occur at $x = 0$ and $x = 3\pi$. Between these two asymptotes, plot a few points, including the x-intercept, as shown in the table. Three cycles of the graph are shown in Figure 4.63. Note that the period is 3π, the distance between consecutive asymptotes.

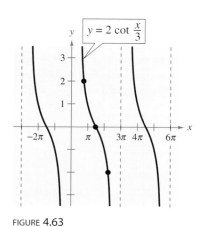

FIGURE 4.63

x	0	$\dfrac{3\pi}{4}$	$\dfrac{3\pi}{2}$	$\dfrac{9\pi}{4}$	3π
$2 \cot \dfrac{x}{3}$	Undef.	2	0	-2	Undef.

✔CHECKPOINT   Now try Exercise 19.

Graphs of the Reciprocal Functions

The graphs of the two remaining trigonometric functions can be obtained from the graphs of the sine and cosine functions using the reciprocal identities

$$\csc x = \frac{1}{\sin x} \quad \text{and} \quad \sec x = \frac{1}{\cos x}.$$

For instance, at a given value of x, the y-coordinate of sec x is the reciprocal of the y-coordinate of cos x. Of course, when cos $x = 0$, the reciprocal does not exist. Near such values of x, the behavior of the secant function is similar to that of the tangent function. In other words, the graphs of

$$\tan x = \frac{\sin x}{\cos x} \quad \text{and} \quad \sec x = \frac{1}{\cos x}$$

have vertical asymptotes at $x = \pi/2 + n\pi$, where n is an integer, and the cosine is zero at these x-values. Similarly,

$$\cot x = \frac{\cos x}{\sin x} \quad \text{and} \quad \csc x = \frac{1}{\sin x}$$

have vertical asymptotes where $\sin x = 0$—that is, at $x = n\pi$.

To sketch the graph of a secant or cosecant function, you should first make a sketch of its reciprocal function. For instance, to sketch the graph of $y = \csc x$, first sketch the graph of $y = \sin x$. Then take reciprocals of the y-coordinates to obtain points on the graph of $y = \csc x$. This procedure is used to obtain the graphs shown in Figure 4.64.

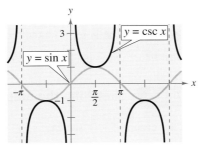

PERIOD: 2π
DOMAIN: ALL $x \neq n\pi$
RANGE: $(-\infty, -1] \cup [1, \infty)$
VERTICAL ASYMPTOTES: $x = n\pi$
SYMMETRY: ORIGIN
FIGURE 4.64

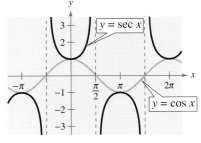

PERIOD: 2π
DOMAIN: ALL $x \neq \frac{\pi}{2} + n\pi$
RANGE: $(-\infty, -1] \cup [1, \infty)$
VERTICAL ASYMPTOTES: $x = \frac{\pi}{2} + n\pi$
SYMMETRY: y-AXIS

In comparing the graphs of the cosecant and secant functions with those of the sine and cosine functions, note that the "hills" and "valleys" are interchanged. For example, a hill (or maximum point) on the sine curve corresponds to a valley (a relative minimum) on the cosecant curve, and a valley (or minimum point) on the sine curve corresponds to a hill (a relative maximum) on the cosecant curve, as shown in Figure 4.65. Additionally, x-intercepts of the sine and cosine functions become vertical asymptotes of the cosecant and secant functions, respectively (see Figure 4.65).

FIGURE 4.65

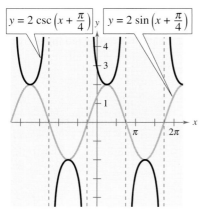

FIGURE 4.66

Example 4 **Sketching the Graph of a Cosecant Function**

Sketch the graph of $y = 2 \csc\left(x + \dfrac{\pi}{4}\right)$.

Solution

Begin by sketching the graph of

$$y = 2 \sin\left(x + \frac{\pi}{4}\right).$$

For this function, the amplitude is 2 and the period is 2π. By solving the equations

$$x + \frac{\pi}{4} = 0 \qquad \text{and} \qquad x + \frac{\pi}{4} = 2\pi$$

$$x = -\frac{\pi}{4} \qquad\qquad x = \frac{7\pi}{4}$$

you can see that one cycle of the sine function corresponds to the interval from $x = -\pi/4$ to $x = 7\pi/4$. The graph of this sine function is represented by the gray curve in Figure 4.66. Because the sine function is zero at the midpoint and endpoints of this interval, the corresponding cosecant function

$$y = 2 \csc\left(x + \frac{\pi}{4}\right)$$

$$= 2\left(\frac{1}{\sin[x + (\pi/4)]}\right)$$

has vertical asymptotes at $x = -\pi/4, x = 3\pi/4, x = 7\pi/4$, etc. The graph of the cosecant function is represented by the black curve in Figure 4.66.

✔**CHECKPOINT** Now try Exercise 25.

Example 5 **Sketching the Graph of a Secant Function**

Sketch the graph of $y = \sec 2x$.

Solution

Begin by sketching the graph of $y = \cos 2x$, as indicated by the gray curve in Figure 4.67. Then, form the graph of $y = \sec 2x$ as the black curve in the figure. Note that the x-intercepts of $y = \cos 2x$

$$\left(-\frac{\pi}{4}, 0\right), \qquad \left(\frac{\pi}{4}, 0\right), \qquad \left(\frac{3\pi}{4}, 0\right), \dots$$

correspond to the vertical asymptotes

$$x = -\frac{\pi}{4}, \qquad x = \frac{\pi}{4}, \qquad x = \frac{3\pi}{4}, \dots$$

of the graph of $y = \sec 2x$. Moreover, notice that the period of $y = \cos 2x$ and $y = \sec 2x$ is π.

✔**CHECKPOINT** Now try Exercise 27.

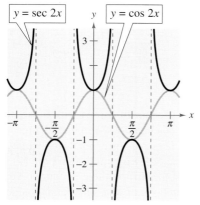

FIGURE 4.67

Damped Trigonometric Graphs

A *product* of two functions can be graphed using properties of the individual functions. For instance, consider the function

$$f(x) = x \sin x$$

as the product of the functions $y = x$ and $y = \sin x$. Using properties of absolute value and the fact that $|\sin x| \le 1$, you have $0 \le |x||\sin x| \le |x|$. Consequently,

$$-|x| \le x \sin x \le |x|$$

which means that the graph of $f(x) = x \sin x$ lies between the lines $y = -x$ and $y = x$. Furthermore, because

$$f(x) = x \sin x = \pm x \qquad \text{at} \qquad x = \frac{\pi}{2} + n\pi$$

and

$$f(x) = x \sin x = 0 \qquad \text{at} \qquad x = n\pi$$

the graph of f touches the line $y = -x$ or the line $y = x$ at $x = \pi/2 + n\pi$ and has x-intercepts at $x = n\pi$. A sketch of f is shown in Figure 4.68. In the function $f(x) = x \sin x$, the factor x is called the **damping factor.**

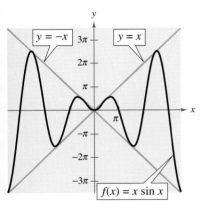

FIGURE 4.68

STUDY TIP

Do you see why the graph of $f(x) = x \sin x$ touches the lines $y = \pm x$ at $x = \pi/2 + n\pi$ and why the graph has x-intercepts at $x = n\pi$? Recall that the sine function is equal to 1 at $\pi/2$, $3\pi/2$, $5\pi/2$, . . . (odd multiples of $\pi/2$) and is equal to 0 at π, 2π, 3π, . . . (multiples of π).

Example 6   Damped Sine Wave

Sketch the graph of

$$f(x) = e^{-x} \sin 3x.$$

Solution

Consider $f(x)$ as the product of the two functions

$$y = e^{-x} \qquad \text{and} \qquad y = \sin 3x$$

each of which has the set of real numbers as its domain. For any real number x, you know that $e^{-x} \ge 0$ and $|\sin 3x| \le 1$. So, $e^{-x}|\sin 3x| \le e^{-x}$, which means that

$$-e^{-x} \le e^{-x} \sin 3x \le e^{-x}.$$

Furthermore, because

$$f(x) = e^{-x} \sin 3x = \pm e^{-x} \qquad \text{at} \qquad x = \frac{\pi}{6} + \frac{n\pi}{3}$$

and

$$f(x) = e^{-x} \sin 3x = 0 \qquad \text{at} \qquad x = \frac{n\pi}{3}$$

the graph of f touches the curves $y = -e^{-x}$ and $y = e^{-x}$ at $x = \pi/6 + n\pi/3$ and has intercepts at $x = n\pi/3$. A sketch is shown in Figure 4.69.

 ✓CHECKPOINT   Now try Exercise 65.

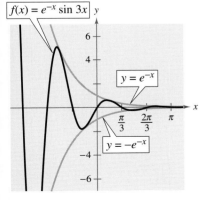

FIGURE 4.69

Figure 4.70 summarizes the characteristics of the six basic trigonometric functions.

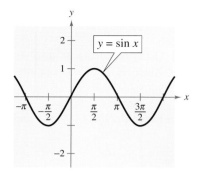

DOMAIN: ALL REALS
RANGE: $[-1, 1]$
PERIOD: 2π

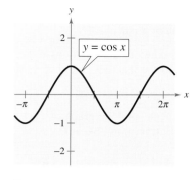

DOMAIN: ALL REALS
RANGE: $[-1, 1]$
PERIOD: 2π

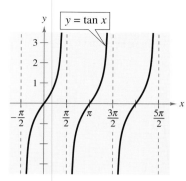

DOMAIN: ALL $x \neq \frac{\pi}{2} + n\pi$
RANGE: $(-\infty, \infty)$
PERIOD: π

DOMAIN: ALL $x \neq n\pi$
RANGE: $(-\infty, -1] \cup [1, \infty)$
PERIOD: 2π
FIGURE 4.70

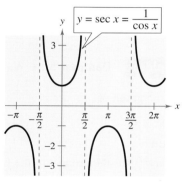

DOMAIN: ALL $x \neq \frac{\pi}{2} + n\pi$
RANGE: $(-\infty, -1] \cup [1, \infty)$
PERIOD: 2π

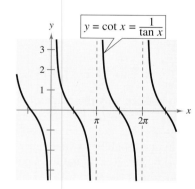

DOMAIN: ALL $x \neq n\pi$
RANGE: $(-\infty, \infty)$
PERIOD: π

*W*RITING ABOUT *M*ATHEMATICS

Combining Trigonometric Functions Recall from Section 1.8 that functions can be combined arithmetically. This also applies to trigonometric functions. For each of the functions

$$h(x) = x + \sin x \quad \text{and} \quad h(x) = \cos x - \sin 3x$$

(a) identify two simpler functions f and g that comprise the combination, (b) use a table to show how to obtain the numerical values of $h(x)$ from the numerical values of $f(x)$ and $g(x)$, and (c) use graphs of f and g to show how h may be formed.

Can you find functions

$$f(x) = d + a\sin(bx + c) \quad \text{and} \quad g(x) = d + a\cos(bx + c)$$

such that $f(x) + g(x) = 0$ for all x?

4.6 | Exercises

VOCABULARY CHECK: Fill in the blanks.

1. The graphs of the tangent, cotangent, secant, and cosecant functions all have _____ asymptotes.
2. To sketch the graph of a secant or cosecant function, first make a sketch of its corresponding _____ function.
3. For the functions given by $f(x) = g(x) \cdot \sin x$, $g(x)$ is called the _____ factor of the function $f(x)$.
4. The period of $y = \tan x$ is _____.
5. The domain of $y = \cot x$ is all real numbers such that _____.
6. The range of $y = \sec x$ is _____.
7. The period of $y = \csc x$ is _____.

PREREQUISITE SKILLS REVIEW: Practice and review algebra skills needed for this section at **www.Eduspace.com.**

In Exercises 1–6, match the function with its graph. State the period of the function. [The graphs are labeled (a), (b), (c), (d), (e), and (f).]

(a)

(b)

(c)

(d)

(e)

(f)

1. $y = \sec 2x$
2. $y = \tan \dfrac{x}{2}$
3. $y = \dfrac{1}{2} \cot \pi x$
4. $y = -\csc x$
5. $y = \dfrac{1}{2} \sec \dfrac{\pi x}{2}$
6. $y = -2 \sec \dfrac{\pi x}{2}$

In Exercises 7–30, sketch the graph of the function. Include two full periods.

7. $y = \dfrac{1}{3} \tan x$
8. $y = \dfrac{1}{4} \tan x$
9. $y = \tan 3x$
10. $y = -3 \tan \pi x$
11. $y = -\dfrac{1}{2} \sec x$
12. $y = \dfrac{1}{4} \sec x$
13. $y = \csc \pi x$
14. $y = 3 \csc 4x$
15. $y = \sec \pi x - 1$
16. $y = -2 \sec 4x + 2$
17. $y = \csc \dfrac{x}{2}$
18. $y = \csc \dfrac{x}{3}$
19. $y = \cot \dfrac{x}{2}$
20. $y = 3 \cot \dfrac{\pi x}{2}$
21. $y = \dfrac{1}{2} \sec 2x$
22. $y = -\dfrac{1}{2} \tan x$
23. $y = \tan \dfrac{\pi x}{4}$
24. $y = \tan(x + \pi)$
25. $y = \csc(\pi - x)$
26. $y = \csc(2x - \pi)$
27. $y = 2 \sec(x + \pi)$
28. $y = -\sec \pi x + 1$
29. $y = \dfrac{1}{4} \csc\left(x + \dfrac{\pi}{4}\right)$
30. $y = 2 \cot\left(x + \dfrac{\pi}{2}\right)$

In Exercises 31–40, use a graphing utility to graph the function. Include two full periods.

31. $y = \tan \dfrac{x}{3}$
32. $y = -\tan 2x$
33. $y = -2 \sec 4x$
34. $y = \sec \pi x$
35. $y = \tan\left(x - \dfrac{\pi}{4}\right)$
36. $y = \dfrac{1}{4} \cot\left(x - \dfrac{\pi}{2}\right)$
37. $y = -\csc(4x - \pi)$
38. $y = 2 \sec(2x - \pi)$
39. $y = 0.1 \tan\left(\dfrac{\pi x}{4} + \dfrac{\pi}{4}\right)$
40. $y = \dfrac{1}{3} \sec\left(\dfrac{\pi x}{2} + \dfrac{\pi}{2}\right)$

In Exercises 41–48, use a graph to solve the equation on the interval $[-2\pi, 2\pi]$.

41. $\tan x = 1$

42. $\tan x = \sqrt{3}$

43. $\cot x = -\dfrac{\sqrt{3}}{3}$

44. $\cot x = 1$

45. $\sec x = -2$

46. $\sec x = 2$

47. $\csc x = \sqrt{2}$

48. $\csc x = -\dfrac{2\sqrt{3}}{3}$

In Exercises 49 and 50, use the graph of the function to determine whether the function is even, odd, or neither.

49. $f(x) = \sec x$ **50.** $f(x) = \tan x$

51. *Graphical Reasoning*   Consider the functions given by

$$f(x) = 2 \sin x \quad \text{and} \quad g(x) = \frac{1}{2} \csc x$$

on the interval $(0, \pi)$.

(a) Graph f and g in the same coordinate plane.

(b) Approximate the interval in which $f > g$.

(c) Describe the behavior of each of the functions as x approaches π. How is the behavior of g related to the behavior of f as x approaches π?

 52. *Graphical Reasoning*   Consider the functions given by

$$f(x) = \tan \frac{\pi x}{2} \quad \text{and} \quad g(x) = \frac{1}{2} \sec \frac{\pi x}{2}$$

on the interval $(-1, 1)$.

(a) Use a graphing utility to graph f and g in the same viewing window.

(b) Approximate the interval in which $f < g$.

(c) Approximate the interval in which $2f < 2g$. How does the result compare with that of part (b)? Explain.

 In Exercises 53–56, use a graphing utility to graph the two equations in the same viewing window. Use the graphs to determine whether the expressions are equivalent. Verify the results algebraically.

53. $y_1 = \sin x \csc x, \quad y_2 = 1$

54. $y_1 = \sin x \sec x, \quad y_2 = \tan x$

55. $y_1 = \dfrac{\cos x}{\sin x}, \quad y_2 = \cot x$

56. $y_1 = \sec^2 x - 1, \quad y_2 = \tan^2 x$

In Exercises 57–60, match the function with its graph. Describe the behavior of the function as x approaches zero. [The graphs are labeled (a), (b), (c), and (d).]

(a)

(b)

(c)

(d)

57. $f(x) = |x \cos x|$

58. $f(x) = x \sin x$

59. $g(x) = |x| \sin x$

60. $g(x) = |x| \cos x$

Conjecture   In Exercises 61–64, graph the functions f and g. Use the graphs to make a conjecture about the relationship between the functions.

61. $f(x) = \sin x + \cos\left(x + \dfrac{\pi}{2}\right), \quad g(x) = 0$

62. $f(x) = \sin x - \cos\left(x + \dfrac{\pi}{2}\right), \quad g(x) = 2 \sin x$

63. $f(x) = \sin^2 x, \quad g(x) = \frac{1}{2}(1 - \cos 2x)$

64. $f(x) = \cos^2 \dfrac{\pi x}{2}, \quad g(x) = \frac{1}{2}(1 + \cos \pi x)$

 In Exercises 65–68, use a graphing utility to graph the function and the damping factor of the function in the same viewing window. Describe the behavior of the function as x increases without bound.

65. $g(x) = e^{-x^2/2} \sin x$ **66.** $f(x) = e^{-x} \cos x$

67. $f(x) = 2^{-x/4} \cos \pi x$ **68.** $h(x) = 2^{-x^2/4} \sin x$

 Exploration   In Exercises 69–74, use a graphing utility to graph the function. Describe the behavior of the function as x approaches zero.

69. $y = \dfrac{6}{x} + \cos x, \quad x > 0$ **70.** $y = \dfrac{4}{x} + \sin 2x, \quad x > 0$

71. $g(x) = \dfrac{\sin x}{x}$

72. $f(x) = \dfrac{1 - \cos x}{x}$

73. $f(x) = \sin \dfrac{1}{x}$

74. $h(x) = x \sin \dfrac{1}{x}$

75. *Distance*   A plane flying at an altitude of 7 miles above a radar antenna will pass directly over the radar antenna (see figure). Let d be the ground distance from the antenna to the point directly under the plane and let x be the angle of elevation to the plane from the antenna. (d is positive as the plane approaches the antenna.) Write d as a function of x and graph the function over the interval $0 < x < \pi$.

7 mi

Not drawn to scale

76. *Television Coverage*   A television camera is on a reviewing platform 27 meters from the street on which a parade will be passing from left to right (see figure). Write the distance d from the camera to a particular unit in the parade as a function of the angle x, and graph the function over the interval $-\pi/2 < x < \pi/2$. (Consider x as negative when a unit in the parade approaches from the left.)

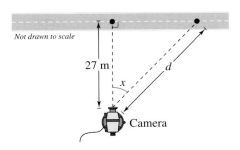

Not drawn to scale

27 m

x

d

Camera

Model It

77. *Predator-Prey Model*   The population C of coyotes (a predator) at time t (in months) in a region is estimated to be

$$C = 5000 + 2000 \sin \frac{\pi t}{12}$$

and the population R of rabbits (its prey) is estimated to be

Model It (continued)

$$R = 25{,}000 + 15{,}000 \cos \frac{\pi t}{12}.$$

(a) Use a graphing utility to graph both models in the same viewing window. Use the window setting $0 \le t \le 100$.

(b) Use the graphs of the models in part (a) to explain the oscillations in the size of each population.

(c) The cycles of each population follow a periodic pattern. Find the period of each model and describe several factors that could be contributing to the cyclical patterns.

78. *Sales*   The projected monthly sales S (in thousands of units) of lawn mowers (a seasonal product) are modeled by $S = 74 + 3t - 40 \cos(\pi t/6)$, where t is the time (in months), with $t = 1$ corresponding to January. Graph the sales function over 1 year.

79. *Meterology*   The normal monthly high temperatures H (in degrees Fahrenheit) for Erie, Pennsylvania are approximated by

$$H(t) = 54.33 - 20.38 \cos \frac{\pi t}{6} - 15.69 \sin \frac{\pi t}{6}$$

and the normal monthly low temperatures L are approximated by

$$L(t) = 39.36 - 15.70 \cos \frac{\pi t}{6} - 14.16 \sin \frac{\pi t}{6}$$

where t is the time (in months), with $t = 1$ corresponding to January (see figure). (Source: National Oceanic and Atmospheric Administration)

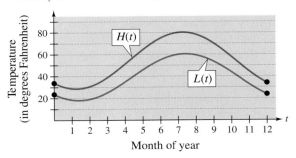

Month of year

(a) What is the period of each function?

(b) During what part of the year is the difference between the normal high and normal low temperatures greatest? When is it smallest?

(c) The sun is northernmost in the sky around June 21, but the graph shows the warmest temperatures at a later date. Approximate the lag time of the temperatures relative to the position of the sun.

80. *Harmonic Motion* An object weighing W pounds is suspended from the ceiling by a steel spring (see figure). The weight is pulled downward (positive direction) from its equilibrium position and released. The resulting motion of the weight is described by the function

$$y = \frac{1}{2}e^{-t/4}\cos 4t, \quad t > 0$$

where y is the distance (in feet) and t is the time (in seconds).

Equilibrium

y

 (a) Use a graphing utility to graph the function.

(b) Describe the behavior of the displacement function for increasing values of time t.

Synthesis

True or False? **In Exercises 81 and 82, determine whether the statement is true or false. Justify your answer.**

81. The graph of $y = \csc x$ can be obtained on a calculator by graphing the reciprocal of $y = \sin x$.

82. The graph of $y = \sec x$ can be obtained on a calculator by graphing a translation of the reciprocal of $y = \sin x$.

83. *Writing* Describe the behavior of $f(x) = \tan x$ as x approaches $\pi/2$ from the left and from the right.

84. *Writing* Describe the behavior of $f(x) = \csc x$ as x approaches π from the left and from the right.

85. *Exploration* Consider the function given by

$$f(x) = x - \cos x.$$

 (a) Use a graphing utility to graph the function and verify that there exists a zero between 0 and 1. Use the graph to approximate the zero.

(b) Starting with $x_0 = 1$, generate a sequence $x_1, x_2, x_3, \ldots$, where $x_n = \cos(x_{n-1})$. For example,

$x_0 = 1$

$x_1 = \cos(x_0)$

$x_2 = \cos(x_1)$

$x_3 = \cos(x_2)$

$\vdots$

What value does the sequence approach?

86. *Approximation* Using calculus, it can be shown that the tangent function can be approximated by the polynomial

$$\tan x \approx x + \frac{2x^3}{3!} + \frac{16x^5}{5!}$$

where x is in radians. Use a graphing utility to graph the tangent function and its polynomial approximation in the same viewing window. How do the graphs compare?

87. *Approximation* Using calculus, it can be shown that the secant function can be approximated by the polynomial

$$\sec x \approx 1 + \frac{x^2}{2!} + \frac{5x^4}{4!}$$

where x is in radians. Use a graphing utility to graph the secant function and its polynomial approximation in the same viewing window. How do the graphs compare?

88. *Pattern Recognition*

 (a) Use a graphing utility to graph each function.

$$y_1 = \frac{4}{\pi}\left(\sin \pi x + \frac{1}{3}\sin 3\pi x\right)$$

$$y_2 = \frac{4}{\pi}\left(\sin \pi x + \frac{1}{3}\sin 3\pi x + \frac{1}{5}\sin 5\pi x\right)$$

 (b) Identify the pattern started in part (a) and find a function y_3 that continues the pattern one more term. Use a graphing utility to graph y_3.

(c) The graphs in parts (a) and (b) approximate the periodic function in the figure. Find a function y_4 that is a better approximation.

Skills Review

In Exercises 89–92, solve the exponential equation. Round your answer to three decimal places.

89. $e^{2x} = 54$

90. $8^{3x} = 98$

91. $\dfrac{300}{1 + e^{-x}} = 100$

92. $\left(1 + \dfrac{0.15}{365}\right)^{365t} = 5$

In Exercises 93–98, solve the logarithmic equation. Round your answer to three decimal places.

93. $\ln(3x - 2) = 73$

94. $\ln(14 - 2x) = 68$

95. $\ln(x^2 + 1) = 3.2$

96. $\ln \sqrt{x + 4} = 5$

97. $\log_8 x + \log_8(x - 1) = \frac{1}{3}$

98. $\log_6 x + \log_6(x^2 - 1) = \log_6 64x$

What you should learn

- Evaluate and graph the inverse sine function.
- Evaluate and graph the other inverse trigonometric functions.
- Evaluate and graph the compositions of trigonometric functions.

Why you should learn it

You can use inverse trigonometric functions to model and solve real-life problems. For instance, in Exercise 92 on page 351, an inverse trigonometric function can be used to model the angle of elevation from a television camera to a space shuttle launch.

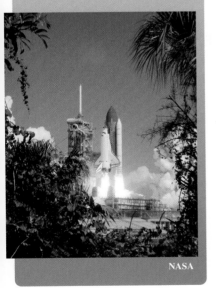

NASA

Inverse Sine Function

Recall from Section 1.9 that, for a function to have an inverse function, it must be one-to-one—that is, it must pass the Horizontal Line Test. From Figure 4.71, you can see that $y = \sin x$ does not pass the test because different values of x yield the same y-value.

$\sin x$ has an inverse function on this interval.

FIGURE 4.71

However, if you restrict the domain to the interval $-\pi/2 \le x \le \pi/2$ (corresponding to the black portion of the graph in Figure 4.71), the following properties hold.

1. On the interval $[-\pi/2, \pi/2]$, the function $y = \sin x$ is increasing.
2. On the interval $[-\pi/2, \pi/2]$, $y = \sin x$ takes on its full range of values, $-1 \le \sin x \le 1$.
3. On the interval $[-\pi/2, \pi/2]$, $y = \sin x$ is one-to-one.

So, on the restricted domain $-\pi/2 \le x \le \pi/2$, $y = \sin x$ has a unique inverse function called the **inverse sine function.** It is denoted by

$$y = \arcsin x \qquad \text{or} \qquad y = \sin^{-1} x.$$

The notation $\sin^{-1} x$ is consistent with the inverse function notation $f^{-1}(x)$. The arcsin x notation (read as "the arcsine of x") comes from the association of a central angle with its intercepted *arc length* on a unit circle. So, arcsin x means the angle (or arc) whose sine is x. Both notations, arcsin x and $\sin^{-1} x$, are commonly used in mathematics, so remember that $\sin^{-1} x$ denotes the *inverse* sine function rather than $1/\sin x$. The values of arcsin x lie in the interval $-\pi/2 \le \arcsin x \le \pi/2$. The graph of $y = \arcsin x$ is shown in Example 2.

Definition of Inverse Sine Function

The **inverse sine function** is defined by

$$y = \arcsin x \qquad \text{if and only if} \qquad \sin y = x$$

where $-1 \le x \le 1$ and $-\pi/2 \le y \le \pi/2$. The domain of $y = \arcsin x$ is $[-1, 1]$, and the range is $[-\pi/2, \pi/2]$.

STUDY TIP

When evaluating the inverse sine function, it helps to remember the phrase "the arcsine of x is the angle (or number) whose sine is x."

Example 1 **Evaluating the Inverse Sine Function**

If possible, find the exact value.

a. $\arcsin\left(-\dfrac{1}{2}\right)$ **b.** $\sin^{-1}\dfrac{\sqrt{3}}{2}$ **c.** $\sin^{-1}2$

Solution

a. Because $\sin\left(-\dfrac{\pi}{6}\right) = -\dfrac{1}{2}$ for $-\dfrac{\pi}{2} \le y \le \dfrac{\pi}{2}$, it follows that

$$\arcsin\left(-\dfrac{1}{2}\right) = -\dfrac{\pi}{6}. \qquad \text{Angle whose sine is } -\tfrac{1}{2}$$

b. Because $\sin\dfrac{\pi}{3} = \dfrac{\sqrt{3}}{2}$ for $-\dfrac{\pi}{2} \le y \le \dfrac{\pi}{2}$, it follows that

$$\sin^{-1}\dfrac{\sqrt{3}}{2} = \dfrac{\pi}{3}. \qquad \text{Angle whose sine is } \sqrt{3}/2$$

c. It is not possible to evaluate $y = \sin^{-1}x$ when $x = 2$ because there is no angle whose sine is 2. Remember that the domain of the inverse sine function is $[-1, 1]$.

✓CHECKPOINT   Now try Exercise 1.

Example 2 **Graphing the Arcsine Function**

Sketch a graph of

$$y = \arcsin x.$$

Solution

By definition, the equations $y = \arcsin x$ and $\sin y = x$ are equivalent for $-\pi/2 \le y \le \pi/2$. So, their graphs are the same. From the interval $[-\pi/2, \pi/2]$, you can assign values to y in the second equation to make a table of values. Then plot the points and draw a smooth curve through the points.

y	$-\dfrac{\pi}{2}$	$-\dfrac{\pi}{4}$	$-\dfrac{\pi}{6}$	0	$\dfrac{\pi}{6}$	$\dfrac{\pi}{4}$	$\dfrac{\pi}{2}$
$x = \sin y$	-1	$-\dfrac{\sqrt{2}}{2}$	$-\dfrac{1}{2}$	0	$\dfrac{1}{2}$	$\dfrac{\sqrt{2}}{2}$	1

The resulting graph for $y = \arcsin x$ is shown in Figure 4.72. Note that it is the reflection (in the line $y = x$) of the black portion of the graph in Figure 4.71. Be sure you see that Figure 4.72 shows the *entire* graph of the inverse sine function. Remember that the domain of $y = \arcsin x$ is the closed interval $[-1, 1]$ and the range is the closed interval $[-\pi/2, \pi/2]$.

✓CHECKPOINT   Now try Exercise 17.

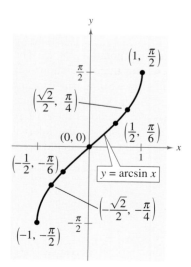

FIGURE **4.72**

Other Inverse Trigonometric Functions

The cosine function is decreasing and one-to-one on the interval $0 \leq x \leq \pi$, as shown in Figure 4.73.

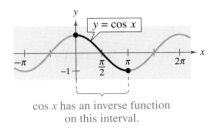

cos x has an inverse function on this interval.

FIGURE **4.73**

Consequently, on this interval the cosine function has an inverse function—the **inverse cosine function**—denoted by

$$y = \arccos x \qquad \text{or} \qquad y = \cos^{-1} x.$$

Similarly, you can define an **inverse tangent function** by restricting the domain of $y = \tan x$ to the interval $(-\pi/2, \pi/2)$. The following list summarizes the definitions of the three most common inverse trigonometric functions. The remaining three are defined in Exercises 101–103.

> **Definitions of the Inverse Trigonometric Functions**
>
> | *Function* | *Domain* | *Range* |
> |---|---|---|
> | $y = \arcsin x$ if and only if $\sin y = x$ | $-1 \leq x \leq 1$ | $-\dfrac{\pi}{2} \leq y \leq \dfrac{\pi}{2}$ |
> | $y = \arccos x$ if and only if $\cos y = x$ | $-1 \leq x \leq 1$ | $0 \leq y \leq \pi$ |
> | $y = \arctan x$ if and only if $\tan y = x$ | $-\infty < x < \infty$ | $-\dfrac{\pi}{2} < y < \dfrac{\pi}{2}$ |

The graphs of these three inverse trigonometric functions are shown in Figure 4.74.

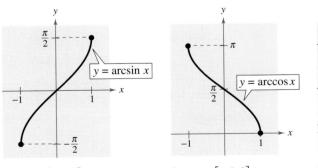

DOMAIN: $[-1, 1]$
RANGE: $\left[-\frac{\pi}{2}, \frac{\pi}{2}\right]$

DOMAIN: $[-1, 1]$
RANGE: $[0, \pi]$

DOMAIN: $(-\infty, \infty)$
RANGE: $\left(-\frac{\pi}{2}, \frac{\pi}{2}\right)$

FIGURE **4.74**

Example 3 **Evaluating Inverse Trigonometric Functions**

Find the exact value.

a. $\arccos \dfrac{\sqrt{2}}{2}$
b. $\cos^{-1}(-1)$

c. $\arctan 0$
d. $\tan^{-1}(-1)$

Solution

a. Because $\cos(\pi/4) = \sqrt{2}/2$, and $\pi/4$ lies in $[0, \pi]$, it follows that

$$\arccos \dfrac{\sqrt{2}}{2} = \dfrac{\pi}{4}.$$ Angle whose cosine is $\sqrt{2}/2$

b. Because $\cos \pi = -1$, and π lies in $[0, \pi]$, it follows that

$$\cos^{-1}(-1) = \pi.$$ Angle whose cosine is -1

c. Because $\tan 0 = 0$, and 0 lies in $(-\pi/2, \pi/2)$, it follows that

$$\arctan 0 = 0.$$ Angle whose tangent is 0

d. Because $\tan(-\pi/4) = -1$, and $-\pi/4$ lies in $(-\pi/2, \pi/2)$, it follows that

$$\tan^{-1}(-1) = -\dfrac{\pi}{4}.$$ Angle whose tangent is -1

✓**CHECKPOINT**   Now try Exercise 11.

Example 4 **Calculators and Inverse Trigonometric Functions**

Use a calculator to approximate the value (if possible).

a. $\arctan(-8.45)$

b. $\sin^{-1} 0.2447$

c. $\arccos 2$

Solution

Function	Mode	Calculator Keystrokes
a. $\arctan(-8.45)$	Radian	TAN⁻¹ ((–) 8.45) ENTER

From the display, it follows that $\arctan(-8.45) \approx -1.453001$.

| b. $\sin^{-1} 0.2447$ | Radian | SIN⁻¹ (0.2447) ENTER |

From the display, it follows that $\sin^{-1} 0.2447 \approx 0.2472103$.

| c. $\arccos 2$ | Radian | COS⁻¹ (2) ENTER |

In *real number* mode, the calculator should display an *error message* because the domain of the inverse cosine function is $[-1, 1]$.

✓**CHECKPOINT**   Now try Exercise 25.

STUDY TIP

It is important to remember that the domain of the inverse sine function and the inverse cosine function is $[-1, 1]$, as indicated in Example 4(c).

In Example 4, if you had set the calculator to *degree* mode, the displays would have been in degrees rather than radians. This convention is peculiar to calculators. By definition, the values of inverse trigonometric functions are *always in radians*.

Compositions of Functions

Recall from Section 1.9 that for all x in the domains of f and f^{-1}, inverse functions have the properties

$$f(f^{-1}(x)) = x \quad \text{and} \quad f^{-1}(f(x)) = x.$$

Inverse Properties of Trigonometric Functions

If $-1 \le x \le 1$ and $-\pi/2 \le y \le \pi/2$, then

$$\sin(\arcsin x) = x \quad \text{and} \quad \arcsin(\sin y) = y.$$

If $-1 \le x \le 1$ and $0 \le y \le \pi$, then

$$\cos(\arccos x) = x \quad \text{and} \quad \arccos(\cos y) = y.$$

If x is a real number and $-\pi/2 < y < \pi/2$, then

$$\tan(\arctan x) = x \quad \text{and} \quad \arctan(\tan y) = y.$$

Keep in mind that these inverse properties do not apply for arbitrary values of x and y. For instance,

$$\arcsin\left(\sin \frac{3\pi}{2}\right) = \arcsin(-1) = -\frac{\pi}{2} \ne \frac{3\pi}{2}.$$

In other words, the property

$$\arcsin(\sin y) = y$$

is not valid for values of y outside the interval $[-\pi/2,\ \pi/2]$.

Example 5   Using Inverse Properties

If possible, find the exact value.

a. $\tan[\arctan(-5)]$ **b.** $\arcsin\left(\sin \dfrac{5\pi}{3}\right)$ **c.** $\cos(\cos^{-1} \pi)$

Solution

a. Because -5 lies in the domain of the arctan function, the inverse property applies, and you have

$$\tan[\arctan(-5)] = -5.$$

b. In this case, $5\pi/3$ does not lie within the range of the arcsine function, $-\pi/2 \le y \le \pi/2$. However, $5\pi/3$ is coterminal with

$$\frac{5\pi}{3} - 2\pi = -\frac{\pi}{3}$$

which does lie in the range of the arcsine function, and you have

$$\arcsin\left(\sin \frac{5\pi}{3}\right) = \arcsin\left[\sin\left(-\frac{\pi}{3}\right)\right] = -\frac{\pi}{3}.$$

c. The expression $\cos(\cos^{-1} \pi)$ is not defined because $\cos^{-1} \pi$ is not defined. Remember that the domain of the inverse cosine function is $[-1, 1]$.

✓CHECKPOINT   Now try Exercise 43.

Angle whose cosine is $\frac{2}{3}$

FIGURE **4.75**

Angle whose sine is $-\frac{3}{5}$

FIGURE **4.76**

Example 6 shows how to use right triangles to find exact values of compositions of inverse functions. Then, Example 7 shows how to use right triangles to convert a trigonometric expression into an algebraic expression. This conversion technique is used frequently in calculus.

Example 6   Evaluating Compositions of Functions

Find the exact value.

a. $\tan\left(\arccos\frac{2}{3}\right)$ **b.** $\cos\left[\arcsin\left(-\frac{3}{5}\right)\right]$

Solution

a. If you let $u = \arccos\frac{2}{3}$, then $\cos u = \frac{2}{3}$. Because $\cos u$ is positive, u is a *first*-quadrant angle. You can sketch and label angle u as shown in Figure 4.75. Consequently,

$$\tan\left(\arccos\frac{2}{3}\right) = \tan u = \frac{\text{opp}}{\text{adj}} = \frac{\sqrt{5}}{2}.$$

b. If you let $u = \arcsin\left(-\frac{3}{5}\right)$, then $\sin u = -\frac{3}{5}$. Because $\sin u$ is negative, u is a *fourth*-quadrant angle. You can sketch and label angle u as shown in Figure 4.76. Consequently,

$$\cos\left[\arcsin\left(-\frac{3}{5}\right)\right] = \cos u = \frac{\text{adj}}{\text{hyp}} = \frac{4}{5}.$$

✔CHECKPOINT   Now try Exercise 51.

Example 7   Some Problems from Calculus

Write each of the following as an algebraic expression in x.

a. $\sin(\arccos 3x), \quad 0 \le x \le \frac{1}{3}$ **b.** $\cot(\arccos 3x), \quad 0 \le x < \frac{1}{3}$

Solution

If you let $u = \arccos 3x$, then $\cos u = 3x$, where $-1 \le 3x \le 1$. Because

$$\cos u = \frac{\text{adj}}{\text{hyp}} = \frac{3x}{1}$$

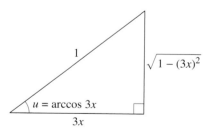

Angle whose cosine is $3x$

FIGURE **4.77**

you can sketch a right triangle with acute angle u, as shown in Figure 4.77. From this triangle, you can easily convert each expression to algebraic form.

a. $\sin(\arccos 3x) = \sin u = \dfrac{\text{opp}}{\text{hyp}} = \sqrt{1 - 9x^2}, \quad 0 \le x \le \dfrac{1}{3}$

b. $\cot(\arccos 3x) = \cot u = \dfrac{\text{adj}}{\text{opp}} = \dfrac{3x}{\sqrt{1 - 9x^2}}, \quad 0 \le x < \dfrac{1}{3}$

✔CHECKPOINT   Now try Exercise 59.

In Example 7, similar arguments can be made for x-values lying in the interval $\left[-\frac{1}{3}, 0\right]$.

VOCABULARY CHECK: Fill in the blanks.

Function	Alternative Notation	Domain	Range
1. $y = \arcsin x$	_____	_____	$-\dfrac{\pi}{2} \le y \le \dfrac{\pi}{2}$
2. _____	$y = \cos^{-1} x$	$-1 \le x \le 1$	_____
3. $y = \arctan x$	_____	_____	_____

PREREQUISITE SKILLS REVIEW: Practice and review algebra skills needed for this section at **www.Eduspace.com.**

In Exercises 1–16, evaluate the expression without using a calculator.

1. $\arcsin \dfrac{1}{2}$ **2.** $\arcsin 0$

3. $\arccos \dfrac{1}{2}$ **4.** $\arccos 0$

5. $\arctan \dfrac{\sqrt{3}}{3}$ **6.** $\arctan(-1)$

7. $\cos^{-1}\left(-\dfrac{\sqrt{3}}{2}\right)$ **8.** $\sin^{-1}\left(-\dfrac{\sqrt{2}}{2}\right)$

9. $\arctan(-\sqrt{3})$ **10.** $\arctan \sqrt{3}$

11. $\arccos\left(-\dfrac{1}{2}\right)$ **12.** $\arcsin \dfrac{\sqrt{2}}{2}$

13. $\sin^{-1} \dfrac{\sqrt{3}}{2}$ **14.** $\tan^{-1}\left(-\dfrac{\sqrt{3}}{3}\right)$

15. $\tan^{-1} 0$ **16.** $\cos^{-1} 1$

In Exercises 17 and 18, use a graphing utility to graph f, g, and $y = x$ in the same viewing window to verify geometrically that g is the inverse function of f. (Be sure to restrict the domain of f properly.)

17. $f(x) = \sin x, \quad g(x) = \arcsin x$

18. $f(x) = \tan x, \quad g(x) = \arctan x$

In Exercises 19–34, use a calculator to evaluate the expression. Round your result to two decimal places.

19. $\arccos 0.28$ **20.** $\arcsin 0.45$

21. $\arcsin(-0.75)$ **22.** $\arccos(-0.7)$

23. $\arctan(-3)$ **24.** $\arctan 15$

25. $\sin^{-1} 0.31$ **26.** $\cos^{-1} 0.26$

27. $\arccos(-0.41)$ **28.** $\arcsin(-0.125)$

29. $\arctan 0.92$ **30.** $\arctan 2.8$

31. $\arcsin \dfrac{3}{4}$ **32.** $\arccos\left(-\dfrac{1}{3}\right)$

33. $\tan^{-1} \dfrac{7}{2}$ **34.** $\tan^{-1}\left(-\dfrac{95}{7}\right)$

In Exercises 35 and 36, determine the missing coordinates of the points on the graph of the function.

35.

36.

In Exercises 37–42, use an inverse trigonometric function to write θ as a function of x.

37.

38.

39.

40.

41.

42.

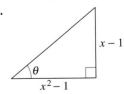

In Exercises 43–48, use the properties of inverse trigonometric functions to evaluate the expression.

43. $\sin(\arcsin 0.3)$ **44.** $\tan(\arctan 25)$

45. $\cos[\arccos(-0.1)]$ **46.** $\sin[\arcsin(-0.2)]$

47. $\arcsin(\sin 3\pi)$ **48.** $\arccos\left(\cos \dfrac{7\pi}{2}\right)$

In Exercises 49–58, find the exact value of the expression. (*Hint:* Sketch a right triangle.)

49. $\sin\left(\arctan\frac{3}{4}\right)$

50. $\sec\left(\arcsin\frac{4}{5}\right)$

51. $\cos(\tan^{-1}2)$

52. $\sin\left(\cos^{-1}\frac{\sqrt{5}}{5}\right)$

53. $\cos\left(\arcsin\frac{5}{13}\right)$

54. $\csc\left[\arctan\left(-\frac{5}{12}\right)\right]$

55. $\sec\left[\arctan\left(-\frac{3}{5}\right)\right]$

56. $\tan\left[\arcsin\left(-\frac{3}{4}\right)\right]$

57. $\sin\left[\arccos\left(-\frac{2}{3}\right)\right]$

58. $\cot\left(\arctan\frac{5}{8}\right)$

 In Exercises 59–68, write an algebraic expression that is equivalent to the expression. (*Hint:* Sketch a right triangle, as demonstrated in Example 7.)

59. $\cot(\arctan x)$

60. $\sin(\arctan x)$

61. $\cos(\arcsin 2x)$

62. $\sec(\arctan 3x)$

63. $\sin(\arccos x)$

64. $\sec[\arcsin(x-1)]$

65. $\tan\left(\arccos\frac{x}{3}\right)$

66. $\cot\left(\arctan\frac{1}{x}\right)$

67. $\csc\left(\arctan\frac{x}{\sqrt{2}}\right)$

68. $\cos\left(\arcsin\frac{x-h}{r}\right)$

 In Exercises 69 and 70, use a graphing utility to graph f and g in the same viewing window to verify that the two functions are equal. Explain why they are equal. Identify any asymptotes of the graphs.

69. $f(x)=\sin(\arctan 2x),\quad g(x)=\dfrac{2x}{\sqrt{1+4x^2}}$

70. $f(x)=\tan\left(\arccos\dfrac{x}{2}\right),\quad g(x)=\dfrac{\sqrt{4-x^2}}{x}$

In Exercises 71–74, fill in the blank.

71. $\arctan\dfrac{9}{x}=\arcsin(\quad),\quad x\neq 0$

72. $\arcsin\dfrac{\sqrt{36-x^2}}{6}=\arccos(\quad),\quad 0\le x\le 6$

73. $\arccos\dfrac{3}{\sqrt{x^2-2x+10}}=\arcsin(\quad)$

74. $\arccos\dfrac{x-2}{2}=\arctan(\quad),\quad |x-2|\le 2$

In Exercises 75 and 76, sketch a graph of the function and compare the graph of g with the graph of $f(x)=\arcsin x$.

75. $g(x)=\arcsin(x-1)$

76. $g(x)=\arcsin\dfrac{x}{2}$

In Exercises 77–82, sketch a graph of the function.

77. $y=2\arccos x$

78. $g(t)=\arccos(t+2)$

79. $f(x)=\arctan 2x$

80. $f(x)=\dfrac{\pi}{2}+\arctan x$

81. $h(v)=\tan(\arccos v)$

82. $f(x)=\arccos\dfrac{x}{4}$

 In Exercises 83–88, use a graphing utility to graph the function.

83. $f(x)=2\arccos(2x)$

84. $f(x)=\pi\arcsin(4x)$

85. $f(x)=\arctan(2x-3)$

86. $f(x)=-3+\arctan(\pi x)$

87. $f(x)=\pi-\sin^{-1}\left(\dfrac{2}{3}\right)$

88. $f(x)=\dfrac{\pi}{2}+\cos^{-1}\left(\dfrac{1}{\pi}\right)$

In Exercises 89 and 90, write the function in terms of the sine function by using the identity

$$A\cos\omega t+B\sin\omega t=\sqrt{A^2+B^2}\sin\left(\omega t+\arctan\frac{A}{B}\right).$$

Use a graphing utility to graph both forms of the function. What does the graph imply?

89. $f(t)=3\cos 2t+3\sin 2t$

90. $f(t)=4\cos\pi t+3\sin\pi t$

91. *Docking a Boat*   A boat is pulled in by means of a winch located on a dock 5 feet above the deck of the boat (see figure). Let θ be the angle of elevation from the boat to the winch and let s be the length of the rope from the winch to the boat.

(a) Write θ as a function of s.

(b) Find θ when $s=40$ feet and $s=20$ feet.

92. Photography A television camera at ground level is filming the lift-off of a space shuttle at a point 750 meters from the launch pad (see figure). Let θ be the angle of elevation to the shuttle and let s be the height of the shuttle.

Not drawn to scale

(a) Write θ as a function of s.

(b) Find θ when $s = 300$ meters and $s = 1200$ meters.

Model It

93. Photography A photographer is taking a picture of a three-foot-tall painting hung in an art gallery. The camera lens is 1 foot below the lower edge of the painting (see figure). The angle β subtended by the camera lens x feet from the painting is

$$\beta = \arctan \frac{3x}{x^2 + 4}, \quad x > 0.$$

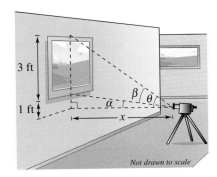

Not drawn to scale

(a) Use a graphing utility to graph β as a function of x.

(b) Move the cursor along the graph to approximate the distance from the picture when β is maximum.

(c) Identify the asymptote of the graph and discuss its meaning in the context of the problem.

94. Granular Angle of Repose Different types of granular substances naturally settle at different angles when stored in cone-shaped piles. This angle θ is called the *angle of repose* (see figure). When rock salt is stored in a cone-shaped pile 11 feet high, the diameter of the pile's base is about 34 feet. (Source: Bulk-Store Structures, Inc.)

(a) Find the angle of repose for rock salt.

(b) How tall is a pile of rock salt that has a base diameter of 40 feet?

95. Granular Angle of Repose When whole corn is stored in a cone-shaped pile 20 feet high, the diameter of the pile's base is about 82 feet.

(a) Find the angle of repose for whole corn.

(b) How tall is a pile of corn that has a base diameter of 100 feet?

96. Angle of Elevation An airplane flies at an altitude of 6 miles toward a point directly over an observer. Consider θ and x as shown in the figure.

Not drawn to scale

(a) Write θ as a function of x.

(b) Find θ when $x = 7$ miles and $x = 1$ mile.

97. Security Patrol A security car with its spotlight on is parked 20 meters from a warehouse. Consider θ and x as shown in the figure.

Not drawn to scale

(a) Write θ as a function of x.

(b) Find θ when $x = 5$ meters and $x = 12$ meters.

Synthesis

True or False?   In Exercises 98–100, determine whether the statement is true or false. Justify your answer.

98. $\sin \dfrac{5\pi}{6} = \dfrac{1}{2}$ ⟹ $\arcsin \dfrac{1}{2} = \dfrac{5\pi}{6}$

99. $\tan \dfrac{5\pi}{4} = 1$ ⟹ $\arctan 1 = \dfrac{5\pi}{4}$

100. $\arctan x = \dfrac{\arcsin x}{\arccos x}$

101. Define the inverse cotangent function by restricting the domain of the cotangent function to the interval $(0, \pi)$, and sketch its graph.

102. Define the inverse secant function by restricting the domain of the secant function to the intervals $[0, \pi/2)$ and $(\pi/2, \pi]$, and sketch its graph.

103. Define the inverse cosecant function by restricting the domain of the cosecant function to the intervals $[-\pi/2, 0)$ and $(0, \pi/2]$, and sketch its graph.

104. Use the results of Exercises 101–103 to evaluate each expression without using a calculator.

(a) $\operatorname{arcsec} \sqrt{2}$ (b) $\operatorname{arcsec} 1$

(c) $\operatorname{arccot}\left(-\sqrt{3}\right)$ (d) $\operatorname{arccsc} 2$

105. Area   In calculus, it is shown that the area of the region bounded by the graphs of $y = 0$, $y = 1/(x^2 + 1)$, $x = a$, and $x = b$ is given by

Area $= \arctan b - \arctan a$

(see figure). Find the area for the following values of a and b.

(a) $a = 0, b = 1$ (b) $a = -1, b = 1$

(c) $a = 0, b = 3$ (d) $a = -1, b = 3$

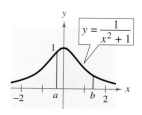

106. Think About It   Use a graphing utility to graph the functions

$f(x) = \sqrt{x}$ and $g(x) = 6 \arctan x$.

For $x > 0$, it appears that $g > f$. Explain why you know that there exists a positive real number a such that $g < f$ for $x > a$. Approximate the number a.

107. Think About It   Consider the functions given by

$f(x) = \sin x$ and $f^{-1}(x) = \arcsin x$.

(a) Use a graphing utility to graph the composite functions $f \circ f^{-1}$ and $f^{-1} \circ f$.

(b) Explain why the graphs in part (a) are not the graph of the line $y = x$. Why do the graphs of $f \circ f^{-1}$ and $f^{-1} \circ f$ differ?

108. Proof   Prove each identity.

(a) $\arcsin(-x) = -\arcsin x$

(b) $\arctan(-x) = -\arctan x$

(c) $\arctan x + \arctan \dfrac{1}{x} = \dfrac{\pi}{2}$, $x > 0$

(d) $\arcsin x + \arccos x = \dfrac{\pi}{2}$

(e) $\arcsin x = \arctan \dfrac{x}{\sqrt{1 - x^2}}$

Skills Review

In Exercises 109–112, evaluate the expression. Round your result to three decimal places.

109. $(8.2)^{3.4}$ **110.** $10(14)^{-2}$

111. $(1.1)^{50}$ **112.** $16^{-2\pi}$

In Exercises 113–116, sketch a right triangle corresponding to the trigonometric function of the acute angle θ. Use the Pythagorean Theorem to determine the third side. Then find the other five trigonometric functions of θ.

113. $\sin \theta = \frac{3}{4}$ **114.** $\tan \theta = 2$

115. $\cos \theta = \frac{5}{6}$ **116.** $\sec \theta = 3$

117. Partnership Costs   A group of people agree to share equally in the cost of a $250,000 endowment to a college. If they could find two more people to join the group, each person's share of the cost would decrease by $6250. How many people are presently in the group?

118. Speed   A boat travels at a speed of 18 miles per hour in still water. It travels 35 miles upstream and then returns to the starting point in a total of 4 hours. Find the speed of the current.

119. Compound Interest   A total of $15,000 is invested in an account that pays an annual interest rate of 3.5%. Find the balance in the account after 10 years, if interest is compounded (a) quarterly, (b) monthly, (c) daily, and (d) continuously.

120. Profit   Because of a slump in the economy, a department store finds that its annual profits have dropped from $742,000 in 2002 to $632,000 in 2004. The profit follows an exponential pattern of decline. What is the expected profit for 2008? (Let $t = 2$ represent 2002.)

4.8   Applications and Models

What you should learn

- Solve real-life problems involving right triangles.
- Solve real-life problems involving directional bearings.
- Solve real-life problems involving harmonic motion.

Why you should learn it

Right triangles often occur in real-life situations. For instance, in Exercise 62 on page 362, right triangles are used to determine the shortest grain elevator for a grain storage bin on a farm.

Applications Involving Right Triangles

In this section, the three angles of a right triangle are denoted by the letters A, B, and C (where C is the right angle), and the lengths of the sides opposite these angles by the letters a, b, and c (where c is the hypotenuse).

Example 1   Solving a Right Triangle

Solve the right triangle shown in Figure 4.78 for all unknown sides and angles.

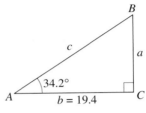

FIGURE 4.78

Solution

Because $C = 90°$, it follows that $A + B = 90°$ and $B = 90° - 34.2° = 55.8°$. To solve for a, use the fact that

$$\tan A = \frac{\text{opp}}{\text{adj}} = \frac{a}{b} \quad \Longrightarrow \quad a = b \tan A.$$

So, $a = 19.4 \tan 34.2° \approx 13.18$. Similarly, to solve for c, use the fact that

$$\cos A = \frac{\text{adj}}{\text{hyp}} = \frac{b}{c} \quad \Longrightarrow \quad c = \frac{b}{\cos A}.$$

So, $c = \dfrac{19.4}{\cos 34.2°} \approx 23.46$.

✓CHECKPOINT   Now try Exercise 1.

Example 2   Finding a Side of a Right Triangle

A safety regulation states that the maximum angle of elevation for a rescue ladder is 72°. A fire department's longest ladder is 110 feet. What is the maximum safe rescue height?

Solution

A sketch is shown in Figure 4.79. From the equation $\sin A = a/c$, it follows that

$$a = c \sin A = 110 \sin 72° \approx 104.6.$$

So, the maximum safe rescue height is about 104.6 feet above the height of the fire truck.

✓CHECKPOINT   Now try Exercise 15.

FIGURE 4.79

FIGURE **4.80**

Example 3 Finding a Side of a Right Triangle

At a point 200 feet from the base of a building, the angle of elevation to the *bottom* of a smokestack is 35°, whereas the angle of elevation to the *top* is 53°, as shown in Figure 4.80. Find the height s of the smokestack alone.

Solution

Note from Figure 4.80 that this problem involves two right triangles. For the smaller right triangle, use the fact that

$$\tan 35° = \frac{a}{200}$$

to conclude that the height of the building is

$$a = 200 \tan 35°.$$

For the larger right triangle, use the equation

$$\tan 53° = \frac{a + s}{200}$$

to conclude that $a + s = 200 \tan 53°$. So, the height of the smokestack is

$$s = 200 \tan 53° - a$$

$$= 200 \tan 53° - 200 \tan 35°$$

$$\approx 125.4 \text{ feet.}$$

✓*CHECKPOINT*   Now try Exercise 19.

Example 4 Finding an Acute Angle of a Right Triangle

FIGURE **4.81**

A swimming pool is 20 meters long and 12 meters wide. The bottom of the pool is slanted so that the water depth is 1.3 meters at the shallow end and 4 meters at the deep end, as shown in Figure 4.81. Find the angle of depression of the bottom of the pool.

Solution

Using the tangent function, you can see that

$$\tan A = \frac{\text{opp}}{\text{adj}}$$

$$= \frac{2.7}{20}$$

$$= 0.135.$$

So, the angle of depression is

$$A = \arctan 0.135$$

$$\approx 0.13419 \text{ radian}$$

$$\approx 7.69°.$$

✓*CHECKPOINT*   Now try Exercise 25.

Trigonometry and Bearings

In surveying and navigation, directions are generally given in terms of **bearings.** A bearing measures the acute angle that a path or line of sight makes with a fixed north-south line, as shown in Figure 4.82. For instance, the bearing S 35° E in Figure 4.82 means 35 degrees east of south.

FIGURE **4.82**

Example 5   Finding Directions in Terms of Bearings

A ship leaves port at noon and heads due west at 20 knots, or 20 nautical miles (nm) per hour. At 2 P.M. the ship changes course to N 54° W, as shown in Figure 4.83. Find the ship's bearing and distance from the port of departure at 3 P.M.

FIGURE **4.83**

Solution

For triangle BCD, you have $B = 90° - 54° = 36°$. The two sides of this triangle can be determined to be

$$b = 20 \sin 36° \quad \text{and} \quad d = 20 \cos 36°.$$

For triangle ACD, you can find angle A as follows.

$$\tan A = \frac{b}{d + 40} = \frac{20 \sin 36°}{20 \cos 36° + 40} \approx 0.2092494$$

$$A \approx \arctan 0.2092494 \approx 0.2062732 \text{ radian} \approx 11.82°$$

The angle with the north-south line is $90° - 11.82° = 78.18°$. So, the bearing of the ship is N 78.18° W. Finally, from triangle ACD, you have $\sin A = b/c$, which yields

$$c = \frac{b}{\sin A} = \frac{20 \sin 36°}{\sin 11.82°}$$

$$\approx 57.4 \text{ nautical miles.} \qquad \text{Distance from port}$$

✓CHECKPOINT   Now try Exercise 31.

STUDY TIP

In *air navigation*, bearings are measured in degrees *clockwise* from north. Examples of air navigation bearings are shown below.

Harmonic Motion

The periodic nature of the trigonometric functions is useful for describing the motion of a point on an object that vibrates, oscillates, rotates, or is moved by wave motion.

For example, consider a ball that is bobbing up and down on the end of a spring, as shown in Figure 4.84. Suppose that 10 centimeters is the maximum distance the ball moves vertically upward or downward from its equilibrium (at rest) position. Suppose further that the time it takes for the ball to move from its maximum displacement above zero to its maximum displacement below zero and back again is $t = 4$ seconds. Assuming the ideal conditions of perfect elasticity and no friction or air resistance, the ball would continue to move up and down in a uniform and regular manner.

Equilibrium

Maximum negative
displacement

Maximum positive
displacement

FIGURE 4.84

From this spring you can conclude that the period (time for one complete cycle) of the motion is

Period = 4 seconds

its amplitude (maximum displacement from equilibrium) is

Amplitude = 10 centimeters

and its **frequency** (number of cycles per second) is

Frequency = $\dfrac{1}{4}$ cycle per second.

Motion of this nature can be described by a sine or cosine function, and is called **simple harmonic motion.**

> ## Definition of Simple Harmonic Motion
>
> A point that moves on a coordinate line is said to be in **simple harmonic motion** if its distance d from the origin at time t is given by either
>
> $$d = a \sin \omega t \qquad \text{or} \qquad d = a \cos \omega t$$
>
> where a and ω are real numbers such that $\omega > 0$. The motion has amplitude $|a|$, period $2\pi/\omega$, and frequency $\omega/(2\pi)$.

Example 6   Simple Harmonic Motion

Write the equation for the simple harmonic motion of the ball described in Figure 4.84, where the period is 4 seconds. What is the frequency of this harmonic motion?

Solution

Because the spring is at equilibrium ($d = 0$) when $t = 0$, you use the equation

$$d = a \sin \omega t.$$

Moreover, because the maximum displacement from zero is 10 and the period is 4, you have

$$\text{Amplitude} = |a| = 10$$

$$\text{Period} = \frac{2\pi}{\omega} = 4 \quad \Longrightarrow \quad \omega = \frac{\pi}{2}.$$

Consequently, the equation of motion is

$$d = 10 \sin \frac{\pi}{2} t.$$

Note that the choice of $a = 10$ or $a = -10$ depends on whether the ball initially moves up or down. The frequency is

$$\text{Frequency} = \frac{\omega}{2\pi}$$

$$= \frac{\pi/2}{2\pi}$$

$$= \frac{1}{4} \text{ cycle per second.}$$

✓CHECKPOINT   Now try Exercise 51.

FIGURE 4.85

One illustration of the relationship between sine waves and harmonic motion can be seen in the wave motion resulting when a stone is dropped into a calm pool of water. The waves move outward in roughly the shape of sine (or cosine) waves, as shown in Figure 4.85. As an example, suppose you are fishing and your fishing bob is attached so that it does not move horizontally. As the waves move outward from the dropped stone, your fishing bob will move up and down in simple harmonic motion, as shown in Figure 4.86.

FIGURE 4.86

Example 7 **Simple Harmonic Motion**

Given the equation for simple harmonic motion

$$d = 6 \cos \frac{3\pi}{4} t$$

find (a) the maximum displacement, (b) the frequency, (c) the value of d when $t = 4$, and (d) the least positive value of t for which $d = 0$.

Algebraic Solution

The given equation has the form $d = a \cos \omega t$, with $a = 6$ and $\omega = 3\pi/4$.

a. The maximum displacement (from the point of equilibrium) is given by the amplitude. So, the maximum displacement is 6.

b. Frequency $= \dfrac{\omega}{2\pi}$

$$= \frac{3\pi/4}{2\pi} = \frac{3}{8} \text{ cycle per unit of time}$$

c. $d = 6 \cos \left[\dfrac{3\pi}{4} (4) \right]$

$$= 6 \cos 3\pi$$

$$= 6(-1)$$

$$= -6$$

d. To find the least positive value of t for which $d = 0$, solve the equation

$$d = 6 \cos \frac{3\pi}{4} t = 0.$$

First divide each side by 6 to obtain

$$\cos \frac{3\pi}{4} t = 0.$$

This equation is satisfied when

$$\frac{3\pi}{4} t = \frac{\pi}{2}, \frac{3\pi}{2}, \frac{5\pi}{2}, \ldots$$

Multiply these values by $4/(3\pi)$ to obtain

$$t = \frac{2}{3}, 2, \frac{10}{3}, \ldots$$

So, the least positive value of t is $t = \frac{2}{3}$.

✓CHECKPOINT   Now try Exercise 55.

Graphical Solution

Use a graphing utility set in *radian* mode to graph

$$y = 6 \cos \frac{3\pi}{4} x.$$

a. Use the *maximum* feature of the graphing utility to estimate that the maximum displacement from the point of equilibrium $y = 0$ is 6, as shown in Figure 4.87.

FIGURE **4.87**

b. The period is the time for the graph to complete one cycle, which is $x \approx 2.667$. You can estimate the frequency as follows.

$$\text{Frequency} \approx \frac{1}{2.667} \approx 0.375 \text{ cycle per unit of time}$$

c. Use the *trace* feature to estimate that the value of y when $x = 4$ is $y = -6$, as shown in Figure 4.88.

d. Use the *zero* or *root* feature to estimate that the least positive value of x for which $y = 0$ is $x \approx 0.6667$, as shown in Figure 4.89.

FIGURE **4.88**

FIGURE **4.89**

4.8 | Exercises

VOCABULARY CHECK: Fill in the blanks.

1. An angle that measures from the horizontal upward to an object is called the angle of _____,
   whereas an angle that measures from the horizontal downward to an object is called the angle of _____.

2. A _____ measures the acute angle a path or line of sight makes with a fixed north-south line.

3. A point that moves on a coordinate line is said to be in simple _____ _____ if its distance d
   from the origin at time t is given by either $d = a \sin \omega t$ or $d = a \cos \omega t$.

PREREQUISITE SKILLS REVIEW: Practice and review algebra skills needed for this section at **www.Eduspace.com.**

In Exercises 1–10, solve the right triangle shown in the figure. Round your answers to two decimal places.

1. $A = 20°$, $b = 10$
2. $B = 54°$, $c = 15$
3. $B = 71°$, $b = 24$
4. $A = 8.4°$, $a = 40.5$
5. $a = 6$, $b = 10$
6. $a = 25$, $c = 35$
7. $b = 16$, $c = 52$
8. $b = 1.32$, $c = 9.45$
9. $A = 12°15'$, $c = 430.5$
10. $B = 65°12'$, $a = 14.2$

FIGURE FOR 1–10

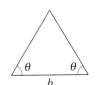

FIGURE FOR 11–14

In Exercises 11–14, find the altitude of the isosceles triangle shown in the figure. Round your answers to two decimal places.

11. $\theta = 52°$, $b = 4$ inches
12. $\theta = 18°$, $b = 10$ meters
13. $\theta = 41°$, $b = 46$ inches
14. $\theta = 27°$, $b = 11$ feet

15. **Length**   The sun is 25° above the horizon. Find the length of a shadow cast by a silo that is 50 feet tall (see figure).

16. **Length**   The sun is 20° above the horizon. Find the length of a shadow cast by a building that is 600 feet tall.

17. **Height**   A ladder 20 feet long leans against the side of a house. Find the height from the top of the ladder to the ground if the angle of elevation of the ladder is 80°.

18. **Height**   The length of a shadow of a tree is 125 feet when the angle of elevation of the sun is 33°. Approximate the height of the tree.

19. **Height**   From a point 50 feet in front of a church, the angles of elevation to the base of the steeple and the top of the steeple are 35° and 47° 40′, respectively.

    (a) Draw right triangles that give a visual representation of the problem. Label the known and unknown quantities.

    (b) Use a trigonometric function to write an equation involving the unknown quantity.

    (c) Find the height of the steeple.

20. **Height**   You are standing 100 feet from the base of a platform from which people are bungee jumping. The angle of elevation from your position to the top of the platform from which they jump is 51°. From what height are the people jumping?

21. **Depth**   The sonar of a navy cruiser detects a submarine that is 4000 feet from the cruiser. The angle between the water line and the submarine is 34° (see figure). How deep is the submarine?

34°

4000 ft

Not drawn to scale

22. **Angle of Elevation**   An engineer erects a 75-foot cellular telephone tower. Find the angle of elevation to the top of the tower at a point on level ground 50 feet from its base.

23. *Angle of Elevation* The height of an outdoor basketball backboard is $12\frac{1}{2}$ feet, and the backboard casts a shadow $17\frac{1}{3}$ feet long.

(a) Draw a right triangle that gives a visual representation of the problem. Label the known and unknown quantities.

(b) Use a trigonometric function to write an equation involving the unknown quantity.

(c) Find the angle of elevation of the sun.

24. *Angle of Depression* A Global Positioning System satellite orbits 12,500 miles above Earth's surface (see figure). Find the angle of depression from the satellite to the horizon. Assume the radius of Earth is 4000 miles.

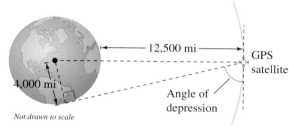

Not drawn to scale

25. *Angle of Depression* A cellular telephone tower that is 150 feet tall is placed on top of a mountain that is 1200 feet above sea level. What is the angle of depression from the top of the tower to a cell phone user who is 5 horizontal miles away and 400 feet above sea level?

26. *Airplane Ascent* During takeoff, an airplane's angle of ascent is 18° and its speed is 275 feet per second.

(a) Find the plane's altitude after 1 minute.

(b) How long will it take the plane to climb to an altitude of 10,000 feet?

27. *Mountain Descent* A sign on a roadway at the top of a mountain indicates that for the next 4 miles the grade is 10.5° (see figure). Find the change in elevation over that distance for a car descending the mountain.

Not drawn to scale

28. *Mountain Descent* A roadway sign at the top of a mountain indicates that for the next 4 miles the grade is 12%. Find the angle of the grade and the change in elevation over the 4 miles for a car descending the mountain.

29. *Navigation* An airplane flying at 600 miles per hour has a bearing of 52°. After flying for 1.5 hours, how far north and how far east will the plane have traveled from its point of departure?

30. *Navigation* A jet leaves Reno, Nevada and is headed toward Miami, Florida at a bearing of 100°. The distance between the two cities is approximately 2472 miles.

(a) How far north and how far west is Reno relative to Miami?

(b) If the jet is to return directly to Reno from Miami, at what bearing should it travel?

31. *Navigation* A ship leaves port at noon and has a bearing of S 29° W. The ship sails at 20 knots.

(a) How many nautical miles south and how many nautical miles west will the ship have traveled by 6:00 P.M.?

(b) At 6:00 P.M., the ship changes course to due west. Find the ship's bearing and distance from the port of departure at 7:00 P.M.

32. *Navigation* A privately owned yacht leaves a dock in Myrtle Beach, South Carolina and heads toward Freeport in the Bahamas at a bearing of S 1.4° E. The yacht averages a speed of 20 knots over the 428 nautical-mile trip.

(a) How long will it take the yacht to make the trip?

(b) How far east and south is the yacht after 12 hours?

(c) If a plane leaves Myrtle Beach to fly to Freeport, what bearing should be taken?

33. *Surveying* A surveyor wants to find the distance across a swamp (see figure). The bearing from A to B is N 32° W. The surveyor walks 50 meters from A, and at the point C the bearing to B is N 68° W. Find (a) the bearing from A to C and (b) the distance from A to B.

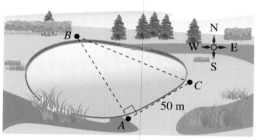

34. *Location of a Fire* Two fire towers are 30 kilometers apart, where tower A is due west of tower B. A fire is spotted from the towers, and the bearings from A and B are N 76° E and N 56° W, respectively (see figure). Find the distance d of the fire from the line segment AB.

Not drawn to scale

35. *Navigation*   A ship is 45 miles east and 30 miles south of port. The captain wants to sail directly to port. What bearing should be taken?

36. *Navigation*   An airplane is 160 miles north and 85 miles east of an airport. The pilot wants to fly directly to the airport. What bearing should be taken?

37. *Distance*   An observer in a lighthouse 350 feet above sea level observes two ships directly offshore. The angles of depression to the ships are 4° and 6.5° (see figure). How far apart are the ships?

Not drawn to scale

38. *Distance*   A passenger in an airplane at an altitude of 10 kilometers sees two towns directly to the east of the plane. The angles of depression to the towns are 28° and 55° (see figure). How far apart are the towns?

Not drawn to scale

39. *Altitude*   A plane is observed approaching your home and you assume that its speed is 550 miles per hour. The angle of elevation of the plane is 16° at one time and 57° one minute later. Approximate the altitude of the plane.

40. *Height*   While traveling across flat land, you notice a mountain directly in front of you. The angle of elevation to the peak is 2.5°. After you drive 17 miles closer to the mountain, the angle of elevation is 9°. Approximate the height of the mountain.

Geometry   **In Exercises 41 and 42, find the angle α between two nonvertical lines L_1 and L_2. The angle α satisfies the equation**

$$\tan \alpha = \left| \frac{m_2 - m_1}{1 + m_2 m_1} \right|$$

where m_1 and m_2 are the slopes of L_1 and L_2, respectively. (Assume that $m_1 m_2 \neq -1$.)

41. L_1: $3x - 2y = 5$
      L_2: $x + y = 1$

42. L_1: $2x - y = 8$
      L_2: $x - 5y = -4$

43. *Geometry*   Determine the angle between the diagonal of a cube and the diagonal of its base, as shown in the figure.

   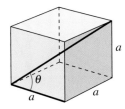

FIGURE FOR **43**   FIGURE FOR **44**

44. *Geometry*   Determine the angle between the diagonal of a cube and its edge, as shown in the figure.

45. *Geometry*   Find the length of the sides of a regular pentagon inscribed in a circle of radius 25 inches.

46. *Geometry*   Find the length of the sides of a regular hexagon inscribed in a circle of radius 25 inches.

47. *Hardware*   Write the distance y across the flat sides of a hexagonal nut as a function of r, as shown in the figure.

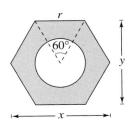

48. *Bolt Holes*   The figure shows a circular piece of sheet metal that has a diameter of 40 centimeters and contains 12 equally spaced bolt holes. Determine the straight-line distance between the centers of consecutive bolt holes.

Trusses   In Exercises 49 and 50, find the lengths of all the unknown members of the truss.

49.

50.

Harmonic Motion   In Exercises 51–54, find a model for simple harmonic motion satisfying the specified conditions.

Displacement $(t = 0)$	Amplitude	Period
51. 0	4 centimeters	2 seconds
52. 0	3 meters	6 seconds
53. 3 inches	3 inches	1.5 seconds
54. 2 feet	2 feet	10 seconds

Harmonic Motion   In Exercises 55–58, for the simple harmonic motion described by the trigonometric function, find (a) the maximum displacement, (b) the frequency, (c) the value of d when t = 5, and (d) the least positive value of t for which d = 0. Use a graphing utility to verify your results.

55. $d = 4 \cos 8\pi t$

56. $d = \frac{1}{2} \cos 20\pi t$

57. $d = \frac{1}{16} \sin 120\pi t$

58. $d = \frac{1}{64} \sin 792\pi t$

59. *Tuning Fork*   A point on the end of a tuning fork moves in simple harmonic motion described by $d = a \sin \omega t$. Find ω given that the tuning fork for middle C has a frequency of 264 vibrations per second.

60. *Wave Motion*   A buoy oscillates in simple harmonic motion as waves go past. It is noted that the buoy moves a total of 3.5 feet from its low point to its high point (see figure), and that it returns to its high point every 10 seconds. Write an equation that describes the motion of the buoy if its high point is at $t = 0$.

FIGURE FOR **60**

61. *Oscillation of a Spring*   A ball that is bobbing up and down on the end of a spring has a maximum displacement of 3 inches. Its motion (in ideal conditions) is modeled by $y = \frac{1}{4} \cos 16t$ $(t > 0)$, where y is measured in feet and t is the time in seconds.

(a) Graph the function.

(b) What is the period of the oscillations?

(c) Determine the first time the weight passes the point of equilibrium $(y = 0)$.

Model It

62. *Numerical and Graphical Analysis*   A two-meter-high fence is 3 meters from the side of a grain storage bin. A grain elevator must reach from ground level outside the fence to the storage bin (see figure). The objective is to determine the shortest elevator that meets the constraints.

(a) Complete four rows of the table.

θ	L_1	L_2	$L_1 + L_2$
0.1	$\dfrac{2}{\sin 0.1}$	$\dfrac{3}{\cos 0.1}$	23.0
0.2	$\dfrac{2}{\sin 0.2}$	$\dfrac{3}{\cos 0.2}$	13.1

Model It (continued)

 (b) Use a graphing utility to generate additional rows of the table. Use the table to estimate the minimum length of the elevator.

(c) Write the length $L_1 + L_2$ as a function of θ.

 (d) Use a graphing utility to graph the function. Use the graph to estimate the minimum length. How does your estimate compare with that of part (b)?

63. *Numerical and Graphical Analysis*   The cross section of an irrigation canal is an isosceles trapezoid of which three of the sides are 8 feet long (see figure). The objective is to find the angle θ that maximizes the area of the cross section. [*Hint:* The area of a trapezoid is $(h/2)(b_1 + b_2)$.]

(a) Complete seven additional rows of the table.

Base 1	Base 2	Altitude	Area
8	$8 + 16 \cos 10°$	$8 \sin 10°$	22.1
8	$8 + 16 \cos 20°$	$8 \sin 20°$	42.5

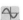 (b) Use a graphing utility to generate additional rows of the table. Use the table to estimate the maximum cross-sectional area.

(c) Write the area A as a function of θ.

 (d) Use a graphing utility to graph the function. Use the graph to estimate the maximum cross-sectional area. How does your estimate compare with that of part (b)?

64. *Data Analysis*   The table shows the average sales S (in millions of dollars) of an outerwear manufacturer for each month t, where $t = 1$ represents January.

Time, t	1	2	3	4	5	6
Sales, s	13.46	11.15	8.00	4.85	2.54	1.70

Time, t	7	8	9	10	11	12
Sales, s	2.54	4.85	8.00	11.15	13.46	14.3

(a) Create a scatter plot of the data.

(b) Find a trigonometric model that fits the data. Graph the model with your scatter plot. How well does the model fit the data?

(c) What is the period of the model? Do you think it is reasonable given the context? Explain your reasoning.

(d) Interpret the meaning of the model's amplitude in the context of the problem.

Synthesis

True or False?   In Exercises 65 and 66, determine whether the statement is true or false. Justify your answer.

65. The Leaning Tower of Pisa is not vertical, but if you know the exact angle of elevation θ to the 191-foot tower when you stand near it, then you can determine the exact distance to the tower d by using the formula

$$\tan \theta = \frac{191}{d}.$$

66. For the harmonic motion of a ball bobbing up and down on the end of a spring, one period can be described as the length of one coil of the spring.

67. *Writing*   Is it true that N 24° E means 24 degrees north of east? Explain.

68. *Writing*   Explain the difference between bearings used in nautical navigation and bearings used in air navigation.

Skills Review

In Exercises 69–72, write the slope-intercept form of the equation of the line with the specified characteristics. Then sketch the line.

69. $m = 4$, passes through $(-1, 2)$

70. $m = -\frac{1}{2}$, passes through $\left(\frac{1}{3}, 0\right)$

71. Passes through $(-2, 6)$ and $(3, 2)$

72. Passes through $\left(\frac{1}{4}, -\frac{2}{3}\right)$ and $\left(-\frac{1}{2}, \frac{1}{3}\right)$

4 Chapter Summary

What did you learn?

<table>
<tr><td>**4**</td><td>**Review Exercises**</td></tr>
</table>

4.1 In Exercises 1 and 2, estimate the angle to the nearest one-half radian.

1.

2.

In Exercises 3–10, (a) sketch the angle in standard position, (b) determine the quadrant in which the angle lies, and (c) determine one positive and one negative coterminal angle.

3. $\dfrac{11\pi}{4}$

4. $\dfrac{2\pi}{9}$

5. $-\dfrac{4\pi}{3}$

6. $-\dfrac{23\pi}{3}$

7. $70°$

8. $280°$

9. $-110°$

10. $-405°$

In Exercises 11–14, convert the angle measure from degrees to radians. Round your answer to three decimal places.

11. $480°$

12. $-127.5°$

13. $-33°\,45'$

14. $196°\,77'$

In Exercises 15–18, convert the angle measure from radians to degrees. Round your answer to three decimal places.

15. $\dfrac{5\pi}{7}$

16. $-\dfrac{11\pi}{6}$

17. -3.5

18. 5.7

19. *Arc Length* Find the length of the arc on a circle with a radius of 20 inches intercepted by a central angle of $138°$.

20. *Arc Length* Find the length of the arc on a circle with a radius of 11 meters intercepted by a central angle of $60°$.

21. *Phonograph* Compact discs have all but replaced phonograph records. Phonograph records are vinyl discs that rotate on a turntable. A typical record album is 12 inches in diameter and plays at $33\frac{1}{3}$ revolutions per minute.

(a) What is the angular speed of a record album?

(b) What is the linear speed of the outer edge of a record album?

22. *Bicycle* At what speed is a bicyclist traveling when his 27-inch-diameter tires are rotating at an angular speed of 5π radians per second?

23. *Circular Sector* Find the area of the sector of a circle with a radius of 18 inches and central angle $\theta = 120°$.

24. *Circular Sector* Find the area of the sector of a circle with a radius of 6.5 millimeters and central angle $\theta = 5\pi/6$.

4.2 In Exercises 25–28, find the point (x, y) on the unit circle that corresponds to the real number t.

25. $t = \dfrac{2\pi}{3}$

26. $t = \dfrac{3\pi}{4}$

27. $t = \dfrac{5\pi}{6}$

28. $t = -\dfrac{4\pi}{3}$

In Exercises 29–32, evaluate (if possible) the six trigonometric functions of the real number.

29. $t = \dfrac{7\pi}{6}$

30. $t = \dfrac{\pi}{4}$

31. $t = -\dfrac{2\pi}{3}$

32. $t = 2\pi$

In Exercises 33–36, evaluate the trigonometric function using its period as an aid.

33. $\sin \dfrac{11\pi}{4}$

34. $\cos 4\pi$

35. $\sin\left(-\dfrac{17\pi}{6}\right)$

36. $\cos\left(-\dfrac{13\pi}{3}\right)$

In Exercises 37–40, use a calculator to evaluate the trigonometric function. Round your answer to four decimal places.

37. $\tan 33$

38. $\csc 10.5$

39. $\sec \dfrac{12\pi}{5}$

40. $\sin\left(-\dfrac{\pi}{9}\right)$

4.3 In Exercises 41–44, find the exact values of the six trigonometric functions of the angle θ shown in the figure.

41.

42.

43.

44.

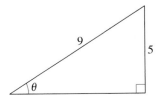

In Exercises 45–48, use the given function value and trigonometric identities (including the cofunction identities) to find the indicated trigonometric functions.

45. $\sin \theta = \frac{1}{3}$ (a) $\csc \theta$ (b) $\cos \theta$
              (c) $\sec \theta$ (d) $\tan \theta$

46. $\tan \theta = 4$ (a) $\cot \theta$ (b) $\sec \theta$
              (c) $\cos \theta$ (d) $\csc \theta$

47. $\csc \theta = 4$ (a) $\sin \theta$ (b) $\cos \theta$
              (c) $\sec \theta$ (d) $\tan \theta$

48. $\csc \theta = 5$ (a) $\sin \theta$ (b) $\cot \theta$
              (c) $\tan \theta$ (d) $\sec(90° - \theta)$

In Exercises 49–54, use a calculator to evaluate the trigonometric function. Round your answer to four decimal places.

49. $\tan 33°$

50. $\csc 11°$

51. $\sin 34.2°$

52. $\sec 79.3°$

53. $\cot 15° 14'$

54. $\cos 78° 11' 58''$

55. *Railroad Grade* A train travels 3.5 kilometers on a straight track with a grade of $1° 10'$ (see figure). What is the vertical rise of the train in that distance?

3.5 km   1°10'

Not drawn to scale

56. *Guy Wire* A guy wire runs from the ground to the top of a 25-foot telephone pole. The angle formed between the wire and the ground is $52°$. How far from the base of the pole is the wire attached to the ground?

4.4 In Exercises 57–64, the point is on the terminal side of an angle θ in standard position. Determine the exact values of the six trigonometric functions of the angle θ.

57. $(12, 16)$

58. $(3, -4)$

59. $\left(\frac{2}{3}, \frac{5}{2}\right)$

60. $\left(-\frac{10}{3}, -\frac{2}{3}\right)$

61. $(-0.5, 4.5)$

62. $(0.3, 0.4)$

63. $(x, 4x), \; x > 0$

64. $(-2x, -3x), \; x > 0$

In Exercises 65–70, find the values of the six trigonometric functions of θ.

Function Value	*Constraint*
65. $\sec \theta = \frac{6}{5}$	$\tan \theta < 0$
66. $\csc \theta = \frac{3}{2}$	$\cos \theta < 0$
67. $\sin \theta = \frac{3}{8}$	$\cos \theta < 0$
68. $\tan \theta = \frac{5}{4}$	$\cos \theta < 0$
69. $\cos \theta = -\frac{2}{5}$	$\sin \theta > 0$
70. $\sin \theta = -\frac{2}{4}$	$\cos \theta > 0$

In Exercises 71–74, find the reference angle θ', and sketch θ and θ' in standard position.

71. $\theta = 264°$ **72.** $\theta = 635°$

73. $\theta = -\dfrac{6\pi}{5}$ **74.** $\theta = \dfrac{17\pi}{3}$

In Exercises 75–82, evaluate the sine, cosine, and tangent of the angle without using a calculator.

75. $\dfrac{\pi}{3}$ **76.** $\dfrac{\pi}{4}$

77. $-\dfrac{7\pi}{3}$ **78.** $-\dfrac{5\pi}{4}$

79. $495°$ **80.** $-150°$

81. $-240°$ **82.** $315°$

In Exercises 83–88, use a calculator to evaluate the trigonometric function. Round your answer to four decimal places.

83. $\sin 4$ **84.** $\tan 3$

85. $\sin(-3.2)$ **86.** $\cot(-4.8)$

85. $\sin \dfrac{12\pi}{5}$ **88.** $\tan\left(-\dfrac{25\pi}{7}\right)$

4.5 In Exercises 89–96, sketch the graph of the function. Include two full periods.

89. $y = \sin x$ **90.** $y = \cos x$

91. $f(x) = 5 \sin \dfrac{2x}{5}$ **92.** $f(x) = 8 \cos\left(-\dfrac{x}{4}\right)$

93. $y = 2 + \sin x$ **94.** $y = -4 - \cos \pi x$

95. $g(t) = \frac{5}{2} \sin(t - \pi)$ **96.** $g(t) = 3 \cos(t + \pi)$

97. *Sound Waves* Sound waves can be modeled by sine functions of the form $y = a \sin bx$, where x is measured in seconds.

     (a) Write an equation of a sound wave whose amplitude is 2 and whose period is $\frac{1}{264}$ second.

     (b) What is the frequency of the sound wave described in part (a)?

98. *Data Analysis: Meteorology* The times S of sunset (Greenwich Mean Time) at 40° north latitude on the 15th of each month are: 1(16:59), 2(17:35), 3(18:06), 4(18:38), 5(19:08), 6(19:30), 7(19:28), 8(18:57), 9(18:09), 10(17:21), 11(16:44), 12(16:36). The month is represented by t, with $t = 1$ corresponding to January. A model (in which minutes have been converted to the decimal parts of an hour) for the data is

$$S(t) = 18.09 + 1.41 \sin\left(\frac{\pi t}{6} + 4.60\right).$$

 (a) Use a graphing utility to graph the data points and the model in the same viewing window.

(b) What is the period of the model? Is it what you expected? Explain.

(c) What is the amplitude of the model? What does it represent in the model? Explain.

4.6 In Exercises 99–106, sketch a graph of the function. Include two full periods.

99. $f(x) = \tan x$

100. $f(t) = \tan\left(t - \frac{\pi}{4}\right)$

101. $f(x) = \cot x$

102. $g(t) = 2 \cot 2t$

103. $f(x) = \sec x$

104. $h(t) = \sec\left(t - \frac{\pi}{4}\right)$

105. $f(x) = \csc x$

106. $f(t) = 3 \csc\left(2t + \frac{\pi}{4}\right)$

In Exercises 107 and 108, use a graphing utility to graph the function and the damping factor of the function in the same viewing window. Describe the behavior of the function as x increases without bound.

107. $f(x) = x \cos x$

108. $g(x) = x^4 \cos x$

4.7 In Exercises 109–114, evaluate the expression. If necessary, round your answer to two decimal places.

109. $\arcsin\left(-\frac{1}{2}\right)$

110. $\arcsin(-1)$

111. $\arcsin 0.4$

112. $\arcsin 0.213$

113. $\sin^{-1}(-0.44)$

114. $\sin^{-1} 0.89$

In Exercises 115–118, evaluate the expression without the aid of a calculator.

115. $\arccos \dfrac{\sqrt{3}}{2}$

116. $\arccos \dfrac{\sqrt{2}}{2}$

117. $\cos^{-1}(-1)$

118. $\cos^{-1} \dfrac{\sqrt{3}}{2}$

In Exercises 119–122, use a calculator to evaluate the expression. Round your answer to two decimal places.

119. $\arccos 0.324$

120. $\arccos(-0.888)$

121. $\tan^{-1}(-1.5)$

122. $\tan^{-1} 8.2$

In Exercises 123–126, use a graphing utility to graph the function.

123. $f(x) = 2 \arcsin x$

124. $f(x) = 3 \arccos x$

125. $f(x) = \arctan \dfrac{x}{2}$

126. $f(x) = -\arcsin 2x$

In Exercises 127–130, find the exact value of the expression.

127. $\cos\left(\arctan \frac{3}{4}\right)$

128. $\tan\left(\arccos \frac{3}{5}\right)$

129. $\sec\left(\arctan \frac{12}{5}\right)$

130. $\cot\left[\arcsin\left(-\frac{12}{13}\right)\right]$

In Exercises 131 and 132, write an algebraic expression that is equivalent to the expression.

131. $\tan\left(\arccos \dfrac{x}{2}\right)$

132. $\sec[\arcsin(x - 1)]$

4.8 **133.** *Angle of Elevation* The height of a radio transmission tower is 70 meters, and it casts a shadow of length 30 meters (see figure). Find the angle of elevation of the sun.

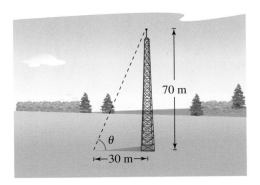

134. *Height* Your football has landed at the edge of the roof of your school building. When you are 25 feet from the base of the building, the angle of elevation to your football is 21°. How high off the ground is your football?

135. *Distance* From city A to city B, a plane flies 650 miles at a bearing of 48°. From city B to city C, the plane flies 810 miles at a bearing of 115°. Find the distance from city A to city C and the bearing from city A to city C.

136. *Wave Motion* Your fishing bobber oscillates in simple harmonic motion from the waves in the lake where you fish. Your bobber moves a total of 1.5 inches from its high point to its low point and returns to its high point every 3 seconds. Write an equation modeling the motion of your bobber if it is at its high point at time $t = 0$.

Synthesis

True or False? **In Exercises 137–140, determine whether the statement is true or false. Justify your answer.**

137. The tangent function is often useful for modeling simple harmonic motion.

138. The inverse sine function $y = \arcsin x$ cannot be defined as a function over any interval that is greater than the interval defined as $-\pi/2 \le y \le \pi/2$.

139. $y = \sin \theta$ is not a function because $\sin 30° = \sin 150°$.

140. Because $\tan 3\pi/4 = -1$, $\arctan(-1) = 3\pi/4$.

In Exercises 141–144, match the function $y = a \sin bx$ with its graph. Base your selection solely on your interpretation of the constants a and b. Explain your reasoning. [The graphs are labeled (a), (b), (c), and (d).]

(a)

(b)

(c)

(d)

141. $y = 3 \sin x$

142. $y = -3 \sin x$

143. $y = 2 \sin \pi x$

144. $y = 2 \sin \dfrac{x}{2}$

145. *Writing* Describe the behavior of $f(\theta) = \sec \theta$ at the zeros of $g(\theta) = \cos \theta$. Explain your reasoning.

146. *Conjecture*

(a) Use a graphing utility to complete the table.

θ	0.1	0.4	0.7	1.0	1.3
$\tan\left(\theta - \dfrac{\pi}{2}\right)$					
$-\cot \theta$					

(b) Make a conjecture about the relationship between $\tan\left(\theta - \dfrac{\pi}{2}\right)$ and $-\cot \theta$.

147. *Writing* When graphing the sine and cosine functions, determining the amplitude is part of the analysis. Explain why this is not true for the other four trigonometric functions.

148. *Oscillation of a Spring* A weight is suspended from a ceiling by a steel spring. The weight is lifted (positive direction) from the equilibrium position and released. The resulting motion of the weight is modeled by

$$y = Ae^{-kt} \cos bt = \tfrac{1}{5}e^{-t/10} \cos 6t$$

where y is the distance in feet from equilibrium and t is the time in seconds. The graph of the function is shown in the figure. For each of the following, describe the change in the system without graphing the resulting function.

(a) A is changed from $\frac{1}{5}$ to $\frac{1}{3}$.

(b) k is changed from $\frac{1}{10}$ to $\frac{1}{3}$.

(c) b is changed from 6 to 9.

149. *Graphical Reasoning* The formulas for the area of a circular sector and arc length are $A = \frac{1}{2}r^2\theta$ and $s = r\theta$, respectively. (r is the radius and θ is the angle measured in radians.)

(a) For $\theta = 0.8$, write the area and arc length as functions of r. What is the domain of each function? Use a graphing utility to graph the functions. Use the graphs to determine which function changes more rapidly as r increases. Explain.

(b) For $r = 10$ centimeters, write the area and arc length as functions of θ. What is the domain of each function? Use a graphing utility to graph and identify the functions.

150. *Writing* Describe a real-life application that can be represented by a simple harmonic motion model and is different from any that you've seen in this chapter. Explain which function you would use to model your application and why. Explain how you would determine the amplitude, period, and frequency of the model for your application.

4 Chapter Test

Take this test as you would take a test in class. When you are finished, check your work against the answers given in the back of the book.

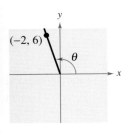

$(-2, 6)$

θ

FIGURE FOR **4**

1. Consider an angle that measures $\dfrac{5\pi}{4}$ radians.
   (a) Sketch the angle in standard position.
   (b) Determine two coterminal angles (one positive and one negative).
   (c) Convert the angle to degree measure.

2. A truck is moving at a rate of 90 kilometers per hour, and the diameter of its wheels is 1 meter. Find the angular speed of the wheels in radians per minute.

3. A water sprinkler sprays water on a lawn over a distance of 25 feet and rotates through an angle of 130°. Find the area of the lawn watered by the sprinkler.

4. Find the exact values of the six trigonometric functions of the angle θ shown in the figure.

5. Given that $\tan \theta = \frac{3}{2}$, find the other five trigonometric functions of θ.

6. Determine the reference angle θ' of the angle $\theta = 290°$ and sketch θ and θ' in standard position.

7. Determine the quadrant in which θ lies if $\sec \theta < 0$ and $\tan \theta > 0$.

8. Find two exact values of θ in degrees $(0 \le \theta < 360°)$ if $\cos \theta = -\sqrt{3}/2$. (Do not use a calculator.)

9. Use a calculator to approximate two values of θ in radians $(0 \le \theta < 2\pi)$ if $\csc \theta = 1.030$. Round the results to two decimal places.

In Exercises 10 and 11, find the remaining five trigonometric functions of θ satisfying the conditions.

10. $\cos \theta = \frac{3}{5}, \quad \tan \theta < 0$

11. $\sec \theta = -\frac{17}{8}, \quad \sin \theta > 0$

In Exercises 12 and 13, sketch the graph of the function. (Include two full periods.)

12. $g(x) = -2 \sin\left(x - \dfrac{\pi}{4}\right)$

13. $f(\alpha) = \dfrac{1}{2} \tan 2\alpha$

In Exercises 14 and 15, use a graphing utility to graph the function. If the function is periodic, find its period.

14. $y = \sin 2\pi x + 2 \cos \pi x$

15. $y = 6e^{-0.12t} \cos(0.25t), \quad 0 \le t \le 32$

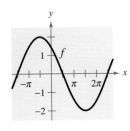

FIGURE FOR **16**

16. Find a, b, and c for the function $f(x) = a \sin(bx + c)$ such that the graph of f matches the figure.

17. Find the exact value of $\tan\left(\arccos \frac{2}{3}\right)$ without the aid of a calculator.

18. Graph the function $f(x) = 2 \arcsin\left(\frac{1}{2}x\right)$.

19. A plane is 80 miles south and 95 miles east of Cleveland Hopkins International Airport. What bearing should be taken to fly directly to the airport?

20. Write the equation for the simple harmonic motion of a ball on a spring that starts at its lowest point of 6 inches below equilibrium, bounces to its maximum height of 6 inches above equilibrium, and returns to its lowest point in a total of 2 seconds.

Proofs in Mathematics

The Pythagorean Theorem

The Pythagorean Theorem is one of the most famous theorems in mathematics. More than 100 different proofs now exist. James A. Garfield, the twentieth president of the United States, developed a proof of the Pythagorean Theorem in 1876. His proof, shown below, involved the fact that a trapezoid can be formed from two congruent right triangles and an isosceles right triangle.

The Pythagorean Theorem

In a right triangle, the sum of the squares of the lengths of the legs is equal to the square of the length of the hypotenuse, where a and b are the legs and c is the hypotenuse.

$$a^2 + b^2 = c^2$$

Proof

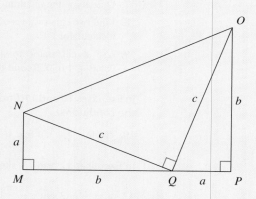

$$\frac{\text{Area of}}{\text{trapezoid } MNOP} = \frac{\text{Area of}}{\triangle MNQ} + \frac{\text{Area of}}{\triangle PQO} + \frac{\text{Area of}}{\triangle NOQ}$$

$$\frac{1}{2}(a + b)(a + b) = \frac{1}{2}ab + \frac{1}{2}ab + \frac{1}{2}c^2$$

$$\frac{1}{2}(a + b)(a + b) = ab + \frac{1}{2}c^2$$

$$(a + b)(a + b) = 2ab + c^2$$

$$a^2 + 2ab + b^2 = 2ab + c^2$$

$$a^2 + b^2 = c^2$$

This collection of thought-provoking and challenging exercises further explores and expands upon concepts learned in this chapter.

1. The restaurant at the top of the Space Needle in Seattle, Washington is circular and has a radius of 47.25 feet. The dining part of the restaurant revolves, making about one complete revolution every 48 minutes. A dinner party was seated at the edge of the revolving restaurant at 6:45 P.M. and was finished at 8:57 P.M.

(a) Find the angle through which the dinner party rotated.

(b) Find the distance the party traveled during dinner.

2. A bicycle's gear ratio is the number of times the freewheel turns for every one turn of the chainwheel (see figure). The table shows the numbers of teeth in the freewheel and chainwheel for the first five gears of an 18-speed touring bicycle. The chainwheel completes one rotation for each gear. Find the angle through which the freewheel turns for each gear. Give your answers in both degrees and radians.

Gear number	Number of teeth in freewheel	Number of teeth in chainwheel
1	32	24
2	26	24
3	22	24
4	32	40
5	19	24

Freewheel

Chainwheel

3. A surveyor in a helicopter is trying to determine the width of an island, as shown in the figure.

3000 ft

d

x

w

Not drawn to scale

(a) What is the shortest distance d the helicopter would have to travel to land on the island?

(b) What is the horizontal distance x that the helicopter would have to travel before it would be directly over the nearer end of the island?

(c) Find the width w of the island. Explain how you obtained your answer.

4. Use the figure below.

(a) Explain why $\triangle ABC$, $\triangle ADE$, and $\triangle AFG$ are similar triangles.

(b) What does similarity imply about the ratios

$$\frac{BC}{AB}, \frac{DE}{AD}, \text{ and } \frac{FG}{AF}?$$

(c) Does the value of sin A depend on which triangle from part (a) is used to calculate it? Would the value of sin A change if it were found using a different right triangle that was similar to the three given triangles?

(d) Do your conclusions from part (c) apply to the other five trigonometric functions? Explain.

 5. Use a graphing utility to graph h, and use the graph to decide whether h is even, odd, or neither.

(a) $h(x) = \cos^2 x$

(b) $h(x) = \sin^2 x$

6. If f is an even function and g is an odd function, use the results of Exercise 5 to make a conjecture about h, where

(a) $h(x) = [f(x)]^2$

(b) $h(x) = [g(x)]^2$.

7. The model for the height h (in feet) of a Ferris wheel car is

$$h = 50 + 50 \sin 8\pi t$$

where t is the time (in minutes). (The Ferris wheel has a radius of 50 feet.) This model yields a height of 50 feet when $t = 0$. Alter the model so that the height of the car is 1 foot when $t = 0$.

8. The pressure P (in millimeters of mercury) against the walls of the blood vessels of a patient is modeled by

$$P = 100 - 20 \cos\left(\frac{8\pi}{3}t\right)$$

where t is time (in seconds).

 (a) Use a graphing utility to graph the model.

(b) What is the period of the model? What does the period tell you about this situation?

(c) What is the amplitude of the model? What does it tell you about this situation?

(d) If one cycle of this model is equivalent to one heartbeat, what is the pulse of this patient?

(e) If a physician wants this patient's pulse rate to be 64 beats per minute or less, what should the period be? What should the coefficient of t be?

9. A popular theory that attempts to explain the ups and downs of everyday life states that each of us has three cycles, called biorhythms, which begin at birth. These three cycles can be modeled by sine waves.

Physical (23 days): $\quad P = \sin\dfrac{2\pi t}{23}, \quad t \geq 0$

Emotional (28 days): $\quad E = \sin\dfrac{2\pi t}{28}, \quad t \geq 0$

Intellectual (33 days): $\quad I = \sin\dfrac{2\pi t}{33}, \quad t \geq 0$

where t is the number of days since birth. Consider a person who was born on July 20, 1986.

 (a) Use a graphing utility to graph the three models in the same viewing window for $7300 \leq t \leq 7380$.

(b) Describe the person's biorhythms during the month of September 2006.

(c) Calculate the person's three energy levels on September 22, 2006.

 10. (a) Use a graphing utility to graph the functions given by

$$f(x) = 2\cos 2x + 3\sin 3x$$

and

$$g(x) = 2\cos 2x + 3\sin 4x.$$

(b) Use the graphs from part (a) to find the period of each function.

(c) If α and β are positive integers, is the function given by

$$h(x) = A\cos \alpha x + B\sin \beta x$$

periodic? Explain your reasoning.

11. Two trigonometric functions f and g have periods of 2, and their graphs intersect at $x = 5.35$.

(a) Give one smaller and one larger positive value of x at which the functions have the same value.

(b) Determine one negative value of x at which the graphs intersect.

(c) Is it true that $f(13.35) = g(-4.65)$? Explain your reasoning.

12. The function f is periodic, with period c. So, $f(t + c) = f(t)$. Are the following equal? Explain.

(a) $f(t - 2c) = f(t)$ (b) $f\left(t + \frac{1}{2}c\right) = f\left(\frac{1}{2}t\right)$

(c) $f\left(\frac{1}{2}(t + c)\right) = f\left(\frac{1}{2}t\right)$

13. If you stand in shallow water and look at an object below the surface of the water, the object will look farther away from you than it really is. This is because when light rays pass between air and water, the water refracts, or bends, the light rays. The index of refraction for water is 1.333. This is the ratio of the sine of θ_1 and the sine of θ_2 (see figure).

(a) You are standing in water that is 2 feet deep and are looking at a rock at angle $\theta_1 = 60°$ (measured from a line perpendicular to the surface of the water). Find θ_2.

(b) Find the distances x and y.

(c) Find the distance d between where the rock is and where it appears to be.

(d) What happens to d as you move closer to the rock? Explain your reasoning.

 14. In calculus, it can be shown that the arctangent function can be approximated by the polynomial

$$\arctan x \approx x - \frac{x^3}{3} + \frac{x^5}{5} - \frac{x^7}{7}$$

where x is in radians.

(a) Use a graphing utility to graph the arctangent function and its polynomial approximation in the same viewing window. How do the graphs compare?

(b) Study the pattern in the polynomial approximation of the arctangent function and guess the next term. Then repeat part (a). How does the accuracy of the approximation change when additional terms are added?

Analytic Trigonometry

5

Concepts of trigonometry can be used to model the height above ground of a seat on a Ferris wheel.

© Patrick Ward/Corbis

SELECTED APPLICATIONS

Trigonometric equations and identities have many real-life applications. The applications listed below represent a small sample of the applications in this chapter.

5.1 Using Fundamental Identities

What you should learn

• Recognize and write the fundamental trigonometric identities.

• Use the fundamental trigonometric identities to evaluate trigonometric functions, simplify trigonometric expressions, and rewrite trigonometric expressions.

Why you should learn it

Fundamental trigonometric identities can be used to simplify trigonometric expressions. For instance, in Exercise 99 on page 381, you can use trigonometric identities to simplify an expression for the coefficient of friction.

Introduction

In Chapter 4, you studied the basic definitions, properties, graphs, and applications of the individual trigonometric functions. In this chapter, you will learn how to use the fundamental identities to do the following.

1. Evaluate trigonometric functions.

2. Simplify trigonometric expressions.

3. Develop additional trigonometric identities.

4. Solve trigonometric equations.

Fundamental Trigonometric Identities

Reciprocal Identities

$$\sin u = \frac{1}{\csc u} \qquad \cos u = \frac{1}{\sec u} \qquad \tan u = \frac{1}{\cot u}$$

$$\csc u = \frac{1}{\sin u} \qquad \sec u = \frac{1}{\cos u} \qquad \cot u = \frac{1}{\tan u}$$

Quotient Identities

$$\tan u = \frac{\sin u}{\cos u} \qquad \cot u = \frac{\cos u}{\sin u}$$

Pythagorean Identities

$$\sin^2 u + \cos^2 u = 1 \qquad 1 + \tan^2 u = \sec^2 u \qquad 1 + \cot^2 u = \csc^2 u$$

Cofunction Identities

$$\sin\left(\frac{\pi}{2} - u\right) = \cos u \qquad \cos\left(\frac{\pi}{2} - u\right) = \sin u$$

$$\tan\left(\frac{\pi}{2} - u\right) = \cot u \qquad \cot\left(\frac{\pi}{2} - u\right) = \tan u$$

$$\sec\left(\frac{\pi}{2} - u\right) = \csc u \qquad \csc\left(\frac{\pi}{2} - u\right) = \sec u$$

Even/Odd Identities

$$\sin(-u) = -\sin u \qquad \cos(-u) = \cos u \qquad \tan(-u) = -\tan u$$

$$\csc(-u) = -\csc u \qquad \sec(-u) = \sec u \qquad \cot(-u) = -\cot u$$

Pythagorean identities are sometimes used in radical form such as

$$\sin u = \pm\sqrt{1 - \cos^2 u}$$

or

$$\tan u = \pm\sqrt{\sec^2 u - 1}$$

where the sign depends on the choice of u.

The *HM mathSpace*® CD-ROM and *Eduspace*® for this text contain additional resources related to the concepts discussed in this chapter.

Using the Fundamental Identities

One common use of trigonometric identities is to use given values of trigonometric functions to evaluate other trigonometric functions.

Example 1   Using Identities to Evaluate a Function

Use the values $\sec u = -\frac{3}{2}$ and $\tan u > 0$ to find the values of all six trigonometric functions.

Solution

Using a reciprocal identity, you have

$$\cos u = \frac{1}{\sec u} = \frac{1}{-3/2} = -\frac{2}{3}.$$

Using a Pythagorean identity, you have

$$\sin^2 u = 1 - \cos^2 u \qquad \text{Pythagorean identity}$$

$$= 1 - \left(-\frac{2}{3}\right)^2 \qquad \text{Substitute } -\frac{2}{3} \text{ for } \cos u.$$

$$= 1 - \frac{4}{9} = \frac{5}{9}. \qquad \text{Simplify.}$$

Because $\sec u < 0$ and $\tan u > 0$, it follows that u lies in Quadrant III. Moreover, because $\sin u$ is negative when u is in Quadrant III, you can choose the negative root and obtain $\sin u = -\sqrt{5}/3$. Now, knowing the values of the sine and cosine, you can find the values of all six trigonometric functions.

$$\sin u = -\frac{\sqrt{5}}{3} \qquad\qquad \csc u = \frac{1}{\sin u} = -\frac{3}{\sqrt{5}} = -\frac{3\sqrt{5}}{5}$$

$$\cos u = -\frac{2}{3} \qquad\qquad \sec u = \frac{1}{\cos u} = -\frac{3}{2}$$

$$\tan u = \frac{\sin u}{\cos u} = \frac{-\sqrt{5}/3}{-2/3} = \frac{\sqrt{5}}{2} \qquad\qquad \cot u = \frac{1}{\tan u} = \frac{2}{\sqrt{5}} = \frac{2\sqrt{5}}{5}$$

✓CHECKPOINT   Now try Exercise 11.

Example 2   Simplifying a Trigonometric Expression

Simplify $\sin x \cos^2 x - \sin x$.

Solution

First factor out a common monomial factor and then use a fundamental identity.

$$\sin x \cos^2 x - \sin x = \sin x(\cos^2 x - 1) \qquad \text{Factor out common monomial factor.}$$

$$= -\sin x(1 - \cos^2 x) \qquad \text{Factor out } -1.$$

$$= -\sin x(\sin^2 x) \qquad \text{Pythagorean identity}$$

$$= -\sin^3 x \qquad \text{Multiply.}$$

✓CHECKPOINT   Now try Exercise 45.

When factoring trigonometric expressions, it is helpful to find a special polynomial factoring form that fits the expression, as shown in Example 3.

Example 3 Factoring Trigonometric Expressions

Factor each expression.

a. $\sec^2 \theta - 1$ **b.** $4 \tan^2 \theta + \tan \theta - 3$

Solution

a. Here you have the difference of two squares, which factors as

$$\sec^2 \theta - 1 = (\sec \theta - 1)(\sec \theta + 1).$$

b. This expression has the polynomial form $ax^2 + bx + c$, and it factors as

$$4 \tan^2 \theta + \tan \theta - 3 = (4 \tan \theta - 3)(\tan \theta + 1).$$

✓CHECKPOINT   Now try Exercise 47.

On occasion, factoring or simplifying can best be done by first rewriting the expression in terms of just *one* trigonometric function or in terms of *sine and cosine only*. These strategies are illustrated in Examples 4 and 5, respectively.

Example 4 Factoring a Trigonometric Expression

Factor $\csc^2 x - \cot x - 3$.

Solution

Use the identity $\csc^2 x = 1 + \cot^2 x$ to rewrite the expression in terms of the cotangent.

$$\csc^2 x - \cot x - 3 = (1 + \cot^2 x) - \cot x - 3 \qquad \text{Pythagorean identity}$$
$$= \cot^2 x - \cot x - 2 \qquad \text{Combine like terms.}$$
$$= (\cot x - 2)(\cot x + 1) \qquad \text{Factor.}$$

✓CHECKPOINT   Now try Exercise 51.

Example 5 Simplifying a Trigonometric Expression

Simplify $\sin t + \cot t \cos t$.

Solution

Begin by rewriting $\cot t$ in terms of sine and cosine.

$$\sin t + \cot t \cos t = \sin t + \left(\frac{\cos t}{\sin t} \right) \cos t \qquad \text{Quotient identity}$$
$$= \frac{\sin^2 t + \cos^2 t}{\sin t} \qquad \text{Add fractions.}$$
$$= \frac{1}{\sin t} \qquad \text{Pythagorean identity}$$
$$= \csc t \qquad \text{Reciprocal identity}$$

✓CHECKPOINT   Now try Exercise 57.

STUDY TIP

Remember that when adding rational expressions, you must first find the least common denominator (LCD). In Example 5, the LCD is $\sin t$.

Example 6   **Adding Trigonometric Expressions**

Perform the addition and simplify.

$$\frac{\sin \theta}{1 + \cos \theta} + \frac{\cos \theta}{\sin \theta}$$

Solution

$$\frac{\sin \theta}{1 + \cos \theta} + \frac{\cos \theta}{\sin \theta} = \frac{(\sin \theta)(\sin \theta) + (\cos \theta)(1 + \cos \theta)}{(1 + \cos \theta)(\sin \theta)}$$

$$= \frac{\sin^2 \theta + \cos^2 \theta + \cos \theta}{(1 + \cos \theta)(\sin \theta)} \qquad \text{Multiply.}$$

$$= \frac{1 + \cos \theta}{(1 + \cos \theta)(\sin \theta)} \qquad \begin{array}{l}\text{Pythagorean identity:} \\ \sin^2 \theta + \cos^2 \theta = 1\end{array}$$

$$= \frac{1}{\sin \theta} \qquad \text{Divide out common factor.}$$

$$= \csc \theta \qquad \text{Reciprocal identity}$$

✓*CHECKPOINT*   Now try Exercise 61.

The last two examples in this section involve techniques for rewriting expressions in forms that are used in calculus.

Example 7   **Rewriting a Trigonometric Expression**

Rewrite $\dfrac{1}{1 + \sin x}$ so that it is *not* in fractional form.

Solution

From the Pythagorean identity $\cos^2 x = 1 - \sin^2 x = (1 - \sin x)(1 + \sin x)$, you can see that multiplying both the numerator and the denominator by $(1 - \sin x)$ will produce a monomial denominator.

$$\frac{1}{1 + \sin x} = \frac{1}{1 + \sin x} \cdot \frac{1 - \sin x}{1 - \sin x} \qquad \begin{array}{l}\text{Multiply numerator and} \\ \text{denominator by } (1 - \sin x).\end{array}$$

$$= \frac{1 - \sin x}{1 - \sin^2 x} \qquad \text{Multiply.}$$

$$= \frac{1 - \sin x}{\cos^2 x} \qquad \text{Pythagorean identity}$$

$$= \frac{1}{\cos^2 x} - \frac{\sin x}{\cos^2 x} \qquad \text{Write as separate fractions.}$$

$$= \frac{1}{\cos^2 x} - \frac{\sin x}{\cos x} \cdot \frac{1}{\cos x} \qquad \text{Product of fractions}$$

$$= \sec^2 x - \tan x \sec x \qquad \text{Reciprocal and quotient identities}$$

✓*CHECKPOINT*   Now try Exercise 65.

Example 8 Trigonometric Substitution

Use the substitution $x = 2 \tan \theta$, $0 < \theta < \pi/2$, to write

$$\sqrt{4 + x^2}$$

as a trigonometric function of θ.

Solution

Begin by letting $x = 2 \tan \theta$. Then, you can obtain

$$\sqrt{4 + x^2} = \sqrt{4 + (2 \tan \theta)^2} \qquad \text{Substitute } 2 \tan \theta \text{ for } x.$$

$$= \sqrt{4 + 4 \tan^2 \theta} \qquad \text{Rule of exponents}$$

$$= \sqrt{4(1 + \tan^2 \theta)} \qquad \text{Factor.}$$

$$= \sqrt{4 \sec^2 \theta} \qquad \text{Pythagorean identity}$$

$$= 2 \sec \theta. \qquad \sec \theta > 0 \text{ for } 0 < \theta < \pi/2$$

✔CHECKPOINT   Now try Exercise 77.

Figure 5.1 shows the right triangle illustration of the trigonometric substitution $x = 2 \tan \theta$ in Example 8. You can use this triangle to check the solution of Example 8. For $0 < \theta < \pi/2$, you have

$$\text{opp} = x, \quad \text{adj} = 2, \quad \text{and} \quad \text{hyp} = \sqrt{4 + x^2}.$$

With these expressions, you can write the following.

$$\sec \theta = \frac{\text{hyp}}{\text{adj}}$$

$$\sec \theta = \frac{\sqrt{4 + x^2}}{2}$$

$$2 \sec \theta = \sqrt{4 + x^2}$$

So, the solution checks.

Angle whose tangent is $\dfrac{x}{2}$.

FIGURE 5.1

Example 9 Rewriting a Logarithmic Expression

Rewrite $\ln|\csc \theta| + \ln|\tan \theta|$ as a single logarithm and simplify the result.

Solution

$$\ln|\csc \theta| + \ln|\tan \theta| = \ln|\csc \theta \tan \theta| \qquad \text{Product Property of Logarithms}$$

$$= \ln\left|\frac{1}{\sin \theta} \cdot \frac{\sin \theta}{\cos \theta}\right| \qquad \text{Reciprocal and quotient identities}$$

$$= \ln\left|\frac{1}{\cos \theta}\right| \qquad \text{Simplify.}$$

$$= \ln|\sec \theta| \qquad \text{Reciprocal identity}$$

✔CHECKPOINT   Now try Exercise 91.

5.1	**Exercises**	The *HM mathSpace*® CD-ROM and *Eduspace*® for this text contain step-by-step solutions to all odd-numbered exercises. They also provide Tutorial Exercises for additional help.

VOCABULARY CHECK: Fill in the blank to complete the trigonometric identity.

1. $\dfrac{\sin u}{\cos u} = $ _____

2. $\dfrac{1}{\sec u} = $ _____

3. $\dfrac{1}{\tan u} = $ _____

4. $\dfrac{1}{\sin u} = $ _____

5. $1 + $ _____ $= \csc^2 u$

6. $1 + \tan^2 u = $ _____

7. $\sin\left(\dfrac{\pi}{2} - u\right) = $ _____

8. $\sec\left(\dfrac{\pi}{2} - u\right) = $ _____

9. $\cos(-u) = $ _____

10. $\tan(-u) = $ _____

PREREQUISITE SKILLS REVIEW: Practice and review algebra skills needed for this section at **www.Eduspace.com.**

In Exercises 1–14, use the given values to evaluate (if possible) all six trigonometric functions.

1. $\sin x = \dfrac{\sqrt{3}}{2}, \quad \cos x = -\dfrac{1}{2}$

2. $\tan x = \dfrac{\sqrt{3}}{3}, \quad \cos x = -\dfrac{\sqrt{3}}{2}$

3. $\sec \theta = \sqrt{2}, \quad \sin \theta = -\dfrac{\sqrt{2}}{2}$

4. $\csc \theta = \dfrac{5}{3}, \quad \tan \theta = \dfrac{3}{4}$

5. $\tan x = \dfrac{5}{12}, \quad \sec x = -\dfrac{13}{12}$

6. $\cot \phi = -3, \quad \sin \phi = \dfrac{\sqrt{10}}{10}$

7. $\sec \phi = \dfrac{3}{2}, \quad \csc \phi = -\dfrac{3\sqrt{5}}{5}$

8. $\cos\left(\dfrac{\pi}{2} - x\right) = \dfrac{3}{5}, \quad \cos x = \dfrac{4}{5}$

9. $\sin(-x) = -\dfrac{1}{3}, \quad \tan x = -\dfrac{\sqrt{2}}{4}$

10. $\sec x = 4, \quad \sin x > 0$

11. $\tan \theta = 2, \quad \sin \theta < 0$

12. $\csc \theta = -5, \quad \cos \theta < 0$

13. $\sin \theta = -1, \quad \cot \theta = 0$

14. $\tan \theta$ is undefined, $\quad \sin \theta > 0$

In Exercises 15–20, match the trigonometric expression with one of the following.

(a) $\sec x$ (b) -1 (c) $\cot x$

(d) 1 (e) $-\tan x$ (f) $\sin x$

15. $\sec x \cos x$

16. $\tan x \csc x$

17. $\cot^2 x - \csc^2 x$

18. $(1 - \cos^2 x)(\csc x)$

19. $\dfrac{\sin(-x)}{\cos(-x)}$

20. $\dfrac{\sin[(\pi/2) - x]}{\cos[(\pi/2) - x]}$

In Exercises 21–26, match the trigonometric expression with one of the following.

(a) $\csc x$ (b) $\tan x$ (c) $\sin^2 x$

(d) $\sin x \tan x$ (e) $\sec^2 x$ (f) $\sec^2 x + \tan^2 x$

21. $\sin x \sec x$

22. $\cos^2 x(\sec^2 x - 1)$

23. $\sec^4 x - \tan^4 x$

24. $\cot x \sec x$

25. $\dfrac{\sec^2 x - 1}{\sin^2 x}$

26. $\dfrac{\cos^2[(\pi/2) - x]}{\cos x}$

In Exercises 27–44, use the fundamental identities to simplify the expression. There is more than one correct form of each answer.

27. $\cot \theta \sec \theta$

28. $\cos \beta \tan \beta$

29. $\sin \phi(\csc \phi - \sin \phi)$

30. $\sec^2 x(1 - \sin^2 x)$

31. $\dfrac{\cot x}{\csc x}$

32. $\dfrac{\csc \theta}{\sec \theta}$

33. $\dfrac{1 - \sin^2 x}{\csc^2 x - 1}$

34. $\dfrac{1}{\tan^2 x + 1}$

35. $\sec \alpha \cdot \dfrac{\sin \alpha}{\tan \alpha}$

36. $\dfrac{\tan^2 \theta}{\sec^2 \theta}$

37. $\cos\left(\dfrac{\pi}{2} - x\right)\sec x$

38. $\cot\left(\dfrac{\pi}{2} - x\right)\cos x$

39. $\dfrac{\cos^2 y}{1 - \sin y}$

40. $\cos t(1 + \tan^2 t)$

41. $\sin \beta \tan \beta + \cos \beta$

42. $\csc \phi \tan \phi + \sec \phi$

43. $\cot u \sin u + \tan u \cos u$

44. $\sin \theta \sec \theta + \cos \theta \csc \theta$

In Exercises 45–56, factor the expression and use the fundamental identities to simplify. There is more than one correct form of each answer.

45. $\tan^2 x - \tan^2 x \sin^2 x$

46. $\sin^2 x \csc^2 x - \sin^2 x$

47. $\sin^2 x \sec^2 x - \sin^2 x$

48. $\cos^2 x + \cos^2 x \tan^2 x$

49. $\dfrac{\sec^2 x - 1}{\sec x - 1}$

50. $\dfrac{\cos^2 x - 4}{\cos x - 2}$

51. $\tan^4 x + 2 \tan^2 x + 1$

52. $1 - 2 \cos^2 x + \cos^4 x$

53. $\sin^4 x - \cos^4 x$

54. $\sec^4 x - \tan^4 x$

55. $\csc^3 x - \csc^2 x - \csc x + 1$

56. $\sec^3 x - \sec^2 x - \sec x + 1$

In Exercises 57–60, perform the multiplication and use the fundamental identities to simplify. There is more than one correct form of each answer.

57. $(\sin x + \cos x)^2$

58. $(\cot x + \csc x)(\cot x - \csc x)$

59. $(2 \csc x + 2)(2 \csc x - 2)$

60. $(3 - 3 \sin x)(3 + 3 \sin x)$

In Exercises 61–64, perform the addition or subtraction and use the fundamental identities to simplify. There is more than one correct form of each answer.

61. $\dfrac{1}{1 + \cos x} + \dfrac{1}{1 - \cos x}$

62. $\dfrac{1}{\sec x + 1} - \dfrac{1}{\sec x - 1}$

63. $\dfrac{\cos x}{1 + \sin x} + \dfrac{1 + \sin x}{\cos x}$

64. $\tan x - \dfrac{\sec^2 x}{\tan x}$

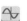 In Exercises 65–68, rewrite the expression so that it is not in fractional form. There is more than one correct form of each answer.

65. $\dfrac{\sin^2 y}{1 - \cos y}$

66. $\dfrac{5}{\tan x + \sec x}$

67. $\dfrac{3}{\sec x - \tan x}$

68. $\dfrac{\tan^2 x}{\csc x + 1}$

 Numerical and Graphical Analysis In Exercises 69–72, use a graphing utility to complete the table and graph the functions. Make a conjecture about y_1 and y_2.

x	0.2	0.4	0.6	0.8	1.0	1.2	1.4
y_1							
y_2							

69. $y_1 = \cos\left(\dfrac{\pi}{2} - x\right)$, $y_2 = \sin x$

70. $y_1 = \sec x - \cos x$, $y_2 = \sin x \tan x$

71. $y_1 = \dfrac{\cos x}{1 - \sin x}$, $y_2 = \dfrac{1 + \sin x}{\cos x}$

72. $y_1 = \sec^4 x - \sec^2 x$, $y_2 = \tan^2 x + \tan^4 x$

 In Exercises 73–76, use a graphing utility to determine which of the six trigonometric functions is equal to the expression. Verify your answer algebraically.

73. $\cos x \cot x + \sin x$

74. $\sec x \csc x - \tan x$

75. $\dfrac{1}{\sin x}\left(\dfrac{1}{\cos x} - \cos x\right)$

76. $\dfrac{1}{2}\left(\dfrac{1 + \sin \theta}{\cos \theta} + \dfrac{\cos \theta}{1 + \sin \theta}\right)$

In Exercises 77–82, use the trigonometric substitution to write the algebraic expression as a trigonometric function of θ, where $0 < \theta < \pi/2$.

77. $\sqrt{9 - x^2}$, $x = 3 \cos \theta$

78. $\sqrt{64 - 16x^2}$, $x = 2 \cos \theta$

79. $\sqrt{x^2 - 9}$, $x = 3 \sec \theta$

80. $\sqrt{x^2 - 4}$, $x = 2 \sec \theta$

81. $\sqrt{x^2 + 25}$, $x = 5 \tan \theta$

82. $\sqrt{x^2 + 100}$, $x = 10 \tan \theta$

In Exercises 83–86, use the trigonometric substitution to write the algebraic equation as a trigonometric equation of θ, where $-\pi/2 < \theta < \pi/2$. Then find $\sin \theta$ and $\cos \theta$.

83. $3 = \sqrt{9 - x^2}$, $x = 3 \sin \theta$

84. $3 = \sqrt{36 - x^2}$, $x = 6 \sin \theta$

85. $2\sqrt{2} = \sqrt{16 - 4x^2}$, $x = 2 \cos \theta$

86. $-5\sqrt{3} = \sqrt{100 - x^2}$, $x = 10 \cos \theta$

In Exercises 87–90, use a graphing utility to solve the equation for θ, where $0 \le \theta < 2\pi$.

87. $\sin \theta = \sqrt{1 - \cos^2 \theta}$

88. $\cos \theta = -\sqrt{1 - \sin^2 \theta}$

89. $\sec \theta = \sqrt{1 + \tan^2 \theta}$

90. $\csc \theta = \sqrt{1 + \cot^2 \theta}$

In Exercises 91–94, rewrite the expression as a single logarithm and simplify the result.

91. $\ln|\cos x| - \ln|\sin x|$

92. $\ln|\sec x| + \ln|\sin x|$

93. $\ln|\cot t| + \ln(1 + \tan^2 t)$

94. $\ln(\cos^2 t) + \ln(1 + \tan^2 t)$

In Exercises 95–98, use a calculator to demonstrate the identity for each value of θ.

95. $\csc^2 \theta - \cot^2 \theta = 1$

   (a) $\theta = 132°$,   (b) $\theta = \dfrac{2\pi}{7}$

96. $\tan^2 \theta + 1 = \sec^2 \theta$

   (a) $\theta = 346°$,   (b) $\theta = 3.1$

97. $\cos\left(\dfrac{\pi}{2} - \theta\right) = \sin \theta$

   (a) $\theta = 80°$,   (b) $\theta = 0.8$

98. $\sin(-\theta) = -\sin \theta$

   (a) $\theta = 250°$,   (b) $\theta = \frac{1}{2}$

99. *Friction*   The forces acting on an object weighing W units on an inclined plane positioned at an angle of θ with the horizontal (see figure) are modeled by

$$\mu W \cos \theta = W \sin \theta$$

where μ is the coefficient of friction. Solve the equation for μ and simplify the result.

100. *Rate of Change*   The rate of change of the function

$$f(x) = -\csc x - \sin x$$

is given by the expression

$$\csc x \cot x - \cos x.$$

Show that this expression can also be written as $\cos x \cot^2 x.$

Synthesis

True or False?   **In Exercises 101 and 102, determine whether the statement is true or false. Justify your answer.**

101. The even and odd trigonometric identities are helpful for determining whether the value of a trigonometric function is positive or negative.

102. A cofunction identity can be used to transform a tangent function so that it can be represented by a cosecant function.

In Exercises 103–106, fill in the blanks. (*Note:* The notation $x \to c^+$ indicates that x approaches c from the right and $x \to c^-$ indicates that x approaches c from the left.)

103. As $x \to \dfrac{\pi}{2}^-$, $\sin x \to$ ▢ and $\csc x \to$ ▢ .

104. As $x \to 0^+$, $\cos x \to$ ▢ and $\sec x \to$ ▢ .

105. As $x \to \dfrac{\pi}{2}^-$, $\tan x \to$ ▢ and $\cot x \to$ ▢ .

106. As $x \to \pi^+$, $\sin x \to$ ▢ and $\csc x \to$ ▢ .

In Exercises 107–112, determine whether or not the equation is an identity, and give a reason for your answer.

107. $\cos \theta = \sqrt{1 - \sin^2 \theta}$ **108.** $\cot \theta = \sqrt{\csc^2 \theta + 1}$

109. $\dfrac{(\sin k\theta)}{(\cos k\theta)} = \tan \theta,$ k is a constant.

110. $\dfrac{1}{(5 \cos \theta)} = 5 \sec \theta$

111. $\sin \theta \csc \theta = 1$ **112.** $\csc^2 \theta = 1$

113. Use the definitions of sine and cosine to derive the Pythagorean identity $\sin^2 \theta + \cos^2 \theta = 1$.

114. *Writing*   Use the Pythagorean identity

$$\sin^2 \theta + \cos^2 \theta = 1$$

to derive the other Pythagorean identities, $1 + \tan^2 \theta = \sec^2 \theta$ and $1 + \cot^2 \theta = \csc^2 \theta$. Discuss how to remember these identities and other fundamental identities.

Skills Review

In Exercises 115 and 116, perform the operation and simplify.

115. $\left(\sqrt{x} + 5\right)\left(\sqrt{x} - 5\right)$ **116.** $\left(2\sqrt{z} + 3\right)^2$

In Exercises 117–120, perform the addition or subtraction and simplify.

117. $\dfrac{1}{x + 5} + \dfrac{x}{x - 8}$ **118.** $\dfrac{6x}{x - 4} - \dfrac{3}{4 - x}$

119. $\dfrac{2x}{x^2 - 4} - \dfrac{7}{x + 4}$ **120.** $\dfrac{x}{x^2 - 25} + \dfrac{x^2}{x - 5}$

In Exercises 121–124, sketch the graph of the function. (Include two full periods.)

121. $f(x) = \dfrac{1}{2} \sin \pi x$ **122.** $f(x) = -2 \tan \dfrac{\pi x}{2}$

123. $f(x) = \dfrac{1}{2} \sec\left(x + \dfrac{\pi}{4}\right)$ **124.** $f(x) = \dfrac{3}{2} \cos(x - \pi) + 3$

5.2 Verifying Trigonometric Identities

What you should learn

• Verify trigonometric identities.

Why you should learn it

You can use trigonometric identities to rewrite trigonometric equations that model real-life situations. For instance, in Exercise 56 on page 388, you can use trigonometric identities to simplify the equation that models the length of a shadow cast by a gnomon (a device used to tell time).

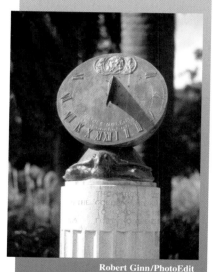

Robert Ginn/PhotoEdit

Introduction

In this section, you will study techniques for verifying trigonometric identities. In the next section, you will study techniques for solving trigonometric equations. The key to verifying identities *and* solving equations is the ability to use the fundamental identities and the rules of algebra to rewrite trigonometric expressions.

Remember that a *conditional equation* is an equation that is true for only some of the values in its domain. For example, the conditional equation

$$\sin x = 0 \qquad \text{Conditional equation}$$

is true only for $x = n\pi$, where n is an integer. When you find these values, you are *solving* the equation.

On the other hand, an equation that is true for all real values in the domain of the variable is an *identity*. For example, the familiar equation

$$\sin^2 x = 1 - \cos^2 x \qquad \text{Identity}$$

is true for all real numbers x. So, it is an identity.

Verifying Trigonometric Identities

Although there are similarities, verifying that a trigonometric equation is an identity is quite different from solving an equation. There is no well-defined set of rules to follow in verifying trigonometric identities, and the process is best learned by practice.

Guidelines for Verifying Trigonometric Identities

1. Work with one side of the equation at a time. It is often better to work with the more complicated side first.

2. Look for opportunities to factor an expression, add fractions, square a binomial, or create a monomial denominator.

3. Look for opportunities to use the fundamental identities. Note which functions are in the final expression you want. Sines and cosines pair up well, as do secants and tangents, and cosecants and cotangents.

4. If the preceding guidelines do not help, try converting all terms to sines and cosines.

5. Always try *something*. Even paths that lead to dead ends provide insights.

Verifying trigonometric identities is a useful process if you need to convert a trigonometric expression into a form that is more useful algebraically. When you verify an identity, you cannot *assume* that the two sides of the equation are equal because you are trying to verify that they *are* equal. As a result, when verifying identities, you cannot use operations such as adding the same quantity to each side of the equation or cross multiplication.

Example 1 **Verifying a Trigonometric Identity**

Verify the identity $\dfrac{\sec^2 \theta - 1}{\sec^2 \theta} = \sin^2 \theta.$

Solution

Because the left side is more complicated, start with it.

$$\dfrac{\sec^2 \theta - 1}{\sec^2 \theta} = \dfrac{(\tan^2 \theta + 1) - 1}{\sec^2 \theta} \qquad \text{Pythagorean identity}$$

$$= \dfrac{\tan^2 \theta}{\sec^2 \theta} \qquad \text{Simplify.}$$

$$= \tan^2 \theta (\cos^2 \theta) \qquad \text{Reciprocal identity}$$

$$= \dfrac{\sin^2 \theta}{(\cos^2 \theta)} (\cos^2 \theta) \qquad \text{Quotient identity}$$

$$= \sin^2 \theta \qquad \text{Simplify.}$$

Notice how the identity is verified. You start with the left side of the equation (the more complicated side) and use the fundamental trigonometric identities to simplify it until you obtain the right side.

✓ CHECKPOINT   Now try Exercise 5.

There is more than one way to verify an identity. Here is another way to verify the identity in Example 1.

$$\dfrac{\sec^2 \theta - 1}{\sec^2 \theta} = \dfrac{\sec^2 \theta}{\sec^2 \theta} - \dfrac{1}{\sec^2 \theta} \qquad \text{Rewrite as the difference of fractions.}$$

$$= 1 - \cos^2 \theta \qquad \text{Reciprocal identity}$$

$$= \sin^2 \theta \qquad \text{Pythagorean identity}$$

Example 2 **Combining Fractions Before Using Identities**

Verify the identity $\dfrac{1}{1 - \sin \alpha} + \dfrac{1}{1 + \sin \alpha} = 2 \sec^2 \alpha.$

Solution

$$\dfrac{1}{1 - \sin \alpha} + \dfrac{1}{1 + \sin \alpha} = \dfrac{1 + \sin \alpha + 1 - \sin \alpha}{(1 - \sin \alpha)(1 + \sin \alpha)} \qquad \text{Add fractions.}$$

$$= \dfrac{2}{1 - \sin^2 \alpha} \qquad \text{Simplify.}$$

$$= \dfrac{2}{\cos^2 \alpha} \qquad \text{Pythagorean identity}$$

$$= 2 \sec^2 \alpha \qquad \text{Reciprocal identity}$$

✓ CHECKPOINT   Now try Exercise 19.

STUDY TIP

Remember that an identity is only true for all real values in the domain of the variable. For instance, in Example 1 the identity is not true when $\theta = \pi/2$ because $\sec^2 \theta$ is not defined when $\theta = \pi/2$.

Example 3 Verifying Trigonometric Identity

Verify the identity $(\tan^2 x + 1)(\cos^2 x - 1) = -\tan^2 x$.

Algebraic Solution

By applying identities before multiplying, you obtain the following.

$$(\tan^2 x + 1)(\cos^2 x - 1) = (\sec^2 x)(-\sin^2 x) \qquad \text{Pythagorean identities}$$

$$= -\frac{\sin^2 x}{\cos^2 x} \qquad \text{Reciprocal identity}$$

$$= -\left(\frac{\sin x}{\cos x}\right)^2 \qquad \text{Rule of exponents}$$

$$= -\tan^2 x \qquad \text{Quotient identity}$$

✔CHECKPOINT   Now try Exercise 39.

Numerical Solution

Use the *table* feature of a graphing utility set in *radian* mode to create a table that shows the values of $y_1 = (\tan^2 x + 1)(\cos^2 x - 1)$ and $y_2 = -\tan^2 x$ for different values of x, as shown in Figure 5.2. From the table you can see that the values of y_1 and y_2 appear to be identical, so $(\tan^2 x + 1)(\cos^2 x - 1) = -\tan^2 x$ appears to be an identity.

X	Y₁	Y₂
-.5	-.2984	-.2984
-.25	-.0652	-.0652
0	0	0
.25	-.0652	-.0652
.5	-.2984	-.2984
.75	-.8679	-.8679
1	-2.426	-2.426

X=-.5

FIGURE 5.2

Example 4 Converting to Sines and Cosines

Verify the identity $\tan x + \cot x = \sec x \csc x$.

Solution

Try converting the left side into sines and cosines.

$$\tan x + \cot x = \frac{\sin x}{\cos x} + \frac{\cos x}{\sin x} \qquad \text{Quotient identities}$$

$$= \frac{\sin^2 x + \cos^2 x}{\cos x \sin x} \qquad \text{Add fractions.}$$

$$= \frac{1}{\cos x \sin x} \qquad \text{Pythagorean identity}$$

$$= \frac{1}{\cos x} \cdot \frac{1}{\sin x} = \sec x \csc x \qquad \text{Reciprocal identities}$$

✔CHECKPOINT   Now try Exercise 29.

> **STUDY TIP**
>
> Although a graphing utility can be useful in helping to verify an identity, you must use algebraic techniques to produce a *valid* proof.

> **STUDY TIP**
>
> As shown at the right, $\csc^2 x(1 + \cos x)$ is considered a simplified form of $1/(1 - \cos x)$ because the expression does not contain any fractions.

Recall from algebra that *rationalizing the denominator* using conjugates is, on occasion, a powerful simplification technique. A related form of this technique, shown below, works for simplifying trigonometric expressions as well.

$$\frac{1}{1 - \cos x} = \frac{1}{1 - \cos x}\left(\frac{1 + \cos x}{1 + \cos x}\right) = \frac{1 + \cos x}{1 - \cos^2 x} = \frac{1 + \cos x}{\sin^2 x}$$

$$= \csc^2 x(1 + \cos x)$$

This technique is demonstrated in the next example.

Example 5   **Verifying Trigonometric Identities**

Verify the identity $\sec y + \tan y = \dfrac{\cos y}{1 - \sin y}$.

Solution

Begin with the *right* side, because you can create a monomial denominator by multiplying the numerator and denominator by $1 + \sin y$.

$$\frac{\cos y}{1 - \sin y} = \frac{\cos y}{1 - \sin y}\left(\frac{1 + \sin y}{1 + \sin y}\right) \qquad \text{Multiply numerator and denominator by } 1 + \sin y.$$

$$= \frac{\cos y + \cos y \sin y}{1 - \sin^2 y} \qquad \text{Multiply.}$$

$$= \frac{\cos y + \cos y \sin y}{\cos^2 y} \qquad \text{Pythagorean identity}$$

$$= \frac{\cos y}{\cos^2 y} + \frac{\cos y \sin y}{\cos^2 y} \qquad \text{Write as separate fractions.}$$

$$= \frac{1}{\cos y} + \frac{\sin y}{\cos y} \qquad \text{Simplify.}$$

$$= \sec y + \tan y \qquad \text{Identities}$$

✔CHECKPOINT   Now try Exercise 33.

   In Examples 1 through 5, you have been verifying trigonometric identities by working with one side of the equation and converting to the form given on the other side. On occasion, it is practical to work with each side *separately*, to obtain one common form equivalent to both sides. This is illustrated in Example 6.

Example 6   **Working with Each Side Separately**

Verify the identity $\dfrac{\cot^2 \theta}{1 + \csc \theta} = \dfrac{1 - \sin \theta}{\sin \theta}$.

Solution

Working with the left side, you have

$$\frac{\cot^2 \theta}{1 + \csc \theta} = \frac{\csc^2 \theta - 1}{1 + \csc \theta} \qquad \text{Pythagorean identity}$$

$$= \frac{(\csc \theta - 1)(\csc \theta + 1)}{1 + \csc \theta} \qquad \text{Factor.}$$

$$= \csc \theta - 1. \qquad \text{Simplify.}$$

Now, simplifying the right side, you have

$$\frac{1 - \sin \theta}{\sin \theta} = \frac{1}{\sin \theta} - \frac{\sin \theta}{\sin \theta} \qquad \text{Write as separate fractions.}$$

$$= \csc \theta - 1. \qquad \text{Reciprocal identity}$$

The identity is verified because both sides are equal to $\csc \theta - 1$.

✔CHECKPOINT   Now try Exercise 47.

In Example 7, powers of trigonometric functions are rewritten as more complicated sums of products of trigonometric functions. This is a common procedure used in calculus.

Example 7 Three Examples from Calculus

Verify each identity.

a. $\tan^4 x = \tan^2 x \sec^2 x - \tan^2 x$

b. $\sin^3 x \cos^4 x = (\cos^4 x - \cos^6 x) \sin x$

c. $\csc^4 x \cot x = \csc^2 x (\cot x + \cot^3 x)$

Solution

a.
$$\tan^4 x = (\tan^2 x)(\tan^2 x) \qquad \text{Write as separate factors.}$$
$$= \tan^2 x (\sec^2 x - 1) \qquad \text{Pythagorean identity}$$
$$= \tan^2 x \sec^2 x - \tan^2 x \qquad \text{Multiply.}$$

b.
$$\sin^3 x \cos^4 x = \sin^2 x \cos^4 x \sin x \qquad \text{Write as separate factors.}$$
$$= (1 - \cos^2 x)\cos^4 x \sin x \qquad \text{Pythagorean identity}$$
$$= (\cos^4 x - \cos^6 x) \sin x \qquad \text{Multiply.}$$

c.
$$\csc^4 x \cot x = \csc^2 x \csc^2 x \cot x \qquad \text{Write as separate factors.}$$
$$= \csc^2 x (1 + \cot^2 x) \cot x \qquad \text{Pythagorean identity}$$
$$= \csc^2 x (\cot x + \cot^3 x) \qquad \text{Multiply.}$$

✓*CHECKPOINT* Now try Exercise 49.

---

*W*RITING ABOUT *M*ATHEMATICS

Error Analysis You are tutoring a student in trigonometry. One of the homework problems your student encounters asks whether the following statement is an identity.

$$\tan^2 x \sin^2 x \overset{?}{=} \frac{5}{6} \tan^2 x$$

Your student does not attempt to verify the equivalence algebraically, but mistakenly uses only a graphical approach. Using range settings of

$$\text{Xmin} = -3\pi \qquad\qquad \text{Ymin} = -20$$
$$\text{Xmax} = 3\pi \qquad\qquad \text{Ymax} = 20$$
$$\text{Xscl} = \pi/2 \qquad\qquad \text{Yscl} = 1$$

your student graphs both sides of the expression on a graphing utility and concludes that the statement is an identity.

What is wrong with your student's reasoning? Explain. Discuss the limitations of verifying identities graphically.

5.2 Exercises

VOCABULARY CHECK:

In Exercises 1 and 2, fill in the blanks.

1. An equation that is true for all real values in its domain is called an _____.

2. An equation that is true for only some values in its domain is called a _____ _____.

In Exercises 3–8, fill in the blank to complete the trigonometric identity.

3. $\dfrac{1}{\cot u} = $ _____

4. $\dfrac{\cos u}{\sin u} = $ _____

5. $\sin^2 u + $ _____ $= 1$

6. $\cos\left(\dfrac{\pi}{2} - u\right) = $ _____

7. $\csc(-u) = $ _____

8. $\sec(-u) = $ _____

PREREQUISITE SKILLS REVIEW: Practice and review algebra skills needed for this section at **www.Eduspace.com.**

In Exercises 1–38, verify the identity.

1. $\sin t \csc t = 1$

2. $\sec y \cos y = 1$

3. $(1 + \sin \alpha)(1 - \sin \alpha) = \cos^2 \alpha$

4. $\cot^2 y(\sec^2 y - 1) = 1$

5. $\cos^2 \beta - \sin^2 \beta = 1 - 2\sin^2 \beta$

6. $\cos^2 \beta - \sin^2 \beta = 2\cos^2 \beta - 1$

7. $\sin^2 \alpha - \sin^4 \alpha = \cos^2 \alpha - \cos^4 \alpha$

8. $\cos x + \sin x \tan x = \sec x$

9. $\dfrac{\csc^2 \theta}{\cot \theta} = \csc \theta \sec \theta$

10. $\dfrac{\cot^3 t}{\csc t} = \cos t(\csc^2 t - 1)$

11. $\dfrac{\cot^2 t}{\csc t} = \csc t - \sin t$

12. $\dfrac{1}{\tan \beta} + \tan \beta = \dfrac{\sec^2 \beta}{\tan \beta}$

13. $\sin^{1/2} x \cos x - \sin^{5/2} x \cos x = \cos^3 x \sqrt{\sin x}$

14. $\sec^6 x(\sec x \tan x) - \sec^4 x(\sec x \tan x) = \sec^5 x \tan^3 x$

15. $\dfrac{1}{\sec x \tan x} = \csc x - \sin x$

16. $\dfrac{\sec \theta - 1}{1 - \cos \theta} = \sec \theta$

17. $\csc x - \sin x = \cos x \cot x$

18. $\sec x - \cos x = \sin x \tan x$

19. $\dfrac{1}{\tan x} + \dfrac{1}{\cot x} = \tan x + \cot x$

20. $\dfrac{1}{\sin x} - \dfrac{1}{\csc x} = \csc x - \sin x$

21. $\dfrac{\cos \theta \cot \theta}{1 - \sin \theta} - 1 = \csc \theta$

22. $\dfrac{1 + \sin \theta}{\cos \theta} + \dfrac{\cos \theta}{1 + \sin \theta} = 2\sec \theta$

23. $\dfrac{1}{\sin x + 1} + \dfrac{1}{\csc x + 1} = 1$

24. $\cos x - \dfrac{\cos x}{1 - \tan x} = \dfrac{\sin x \cos x}{\sin x - \cos x}$

25. $\tan\left(\dfrac{\pi}{2} - \theta\right)\tan \theta = 1$

26. $\dfrac{\cos[(\pi/2) - x]}{\sin[(\pi/2) - x]} = \tan x$

27. $\dfrac{\csc(-x)}{\sec(-x)} = -\cot x$

28. $(1 + \sin y)[1 + \sin(-y)] = \cos^2 y$

29. $\dfrac{\tan x \cot x}{\cos x} = \sec x$

30. $\dfrac{\tan x + \tan y}{1 - \tan x \tan y} = \dfrac{\cot x + \cot y}{\cot x \cot y - 1}$

31. $\dfrac{\tan x + \cot y}{\tan x \cot y} = \tan y + \cot x$

32. $\dfrac{\cos x - \cos y}{\sin x + \sin y} + \dfrac{\sin x - \sin y}{\cos x + \cos y} = 0$

33. $\sqrt{\dfrac{1 + \sin \theta}{1 - \sin \theta}} = \dfrac{1 + \sin \theta}{|\cos \theta|}$

34. $\sqrt{\dfrac{1 - \cos \theta}{1 + \cos \theta}} = \dfrac{1 - \cos \theta}{|\sin \theta|}$

35. $\cos^2 \beta + \cos^2\left(\dfrac{\pi}{2} - \beta\right) = 1$

36. $\sec^2 y - \cot^2\left(\dfrac{\pi}{2} - y\right) = 1$

37. $\sin t \csc\left(\dfrac{\pi}{2} - t\right) = \tan t$

38. $\sec^2\left(\dfrac{\pi}{2} - x\right) - 1 = \cot^2 x$

In Exercises 39–46, (a) use a graphing utility to graph each side of the equation to determine whether the equation is an identity, (b) use the *table* feature of a graphing utility to determine whether the equation is an identity, and (c) confirm the results of parts (a) and (b) algebraically.

39. $2 \sec^2 x - 2 \sec^2 x \sin^2 x - \sin^2 x - \cos^2 x = 1$

40. $\csc x(\csc x - \sin x) + \dfrac{\sin x - \cos x}{\sin x} + \cot x = \csc^2 x$

41. $2 + \cos^2 x - 3 \cos^4 x = \sin^2 x(3 + 2 \cos^2 x)$

42. $\tan^4 x + \tan^2 x - 3 = \sec^2 x(4 \tan^2 x - 3)$

43. $\csc^4 x - 2 \csc^2 x + 1 = \cot^4 x$

44. $(\sin^4 \beta - 2 \sin^2 \beta + 1) \cos \beta = \cos^5 \beta$

45. $\dfrac{\cos x}{1 - \sin x} = \dfrac{1 - \sin x}{\cos x}$ **46.** $\dfrac{\cot \alpha}{\csc \alpha + 1} = \dfrac{\csc \alpha + 1}{\cot \alpha}$

In Exercises 47–50, verify the identity.

47. $\tan^5 x = \tan^3 x \sec^2 x - \tan^3 x$

48. $\sec^4 x \tan^2 x = (\tan^2 x + \tan^4 x) \sec^2 x$

49. $\cos^3 x \sin^2 x = (\sin^2 x - \sin^4 x) \cos x$

50. $\sin^4 x + \cos^4 x = 1 - 2 \cos^2 x + 2 \cos^4 x$

In Exercises 51–54, use the cofunction identities to evaluate the expression without the aid of a calculator.

51. $\sin^2 25° + \sin^2 65°$ **52.** $\cos^2 55° + \cos^2 35°$

53. $\cos^2 20° + \cos^2 52° + \cos^2 38° + \cos^2 70°$

54. $\sin^2 12° + \sin^2 40° + \sin^2 50° + \sin^2 78°$

55. *Rate of Change*   The rate of change of the function $f(x) = \sin x + \csc x$ with respect to change in the variable x is given by the expression $\cos x - \csc x \cot x$. Show that the expression for the rate of change can also be $-\cos x \cot^2 x$.

Model It

56. *Shadow Length*   The length s of a shadow cast by a vertical gnomon (a device used to tell time) of height h when the angle of the sun above the horizon is θ (see figure) can be modeled by the equation

$$s = \dfrac{h \sin(90° - \theta)}{\sin \theta}.$$

Model It (continued)

(a) Verify that the equation for s is equal to $h \cot \theta$.

 (b) Use a graphing utility to complete the table. Let $h = 5$ feet.

θ	10°	20°	30°	40°	50°
s					

θ	60°	70°	80°	90°
s				

(c) Use your table from part (b) to determine the angles of the sun for which the length of the shadow is the greatest and the least.

(d) Based on your results from part (c), what time of day do you think it is when the angle of the sun above the horizon is 90°?

Synthesis

True or False?   **In Exercises 57 and 58, determine whether the statement is true or false. Justify your answer.**

57. The equation $\sin^2 \theta + \cos^2 \theta = 1 + \tan^2 \theta$ is an identity, because $\sin^2(0) + \cos^2(0) = 1$ and $1 + \tan^2(0) = 1$.

58. The equation $1 + \tan^2 \theta = 1 + \cot^2 \theta$ is *not* an identity, because it is true that $1 + \tan^2(\pi/6) = 1\frac{1}{3}$, and $1 + \cot^2(\pi/6) = 4$.

Think About It   **In Exercises 59 and 60, explain why the equation is not an identity and find one value of the variable for which the equation is not true.**

59. $\sin \theta = \sqrt{1 - \cos^2 \theta}$

60. $\tan \theta = \sqrt{\sec^2 \theta - 1}$

Skills Review

In Exercises 61–64, perform the operation and simplify.

61. $(2 + 3i) - \sqrt{-26}$ **62.** $(2 - 5i)^2$

63. $\sqrt{-16}\left(1 + \sqrt{-4}\right)$ **64.** $(3 + 2i)^3$

In Exercises 65–68, use the Quadratic Formula to solve the quadratic equation.

65. $x^2 + 6x - 12 = 0$ **66.** $x^2 + 5x - 7 = 0$

67. $3x^2 - 6x - 12 = 0$ **68.** $8x^2 - 4x - 3 = 0$

5.3   Solving Trigonometric Equations

Why you should learn it

You can use trigonometric equations to solve a variety of real-life problems. For instance, in Exercise 72 on page 398, you can solve a trigonometric equation to help answer questions about monthly sales of skiing equipment.

Tom Stillo/Index Stock Imagery

Introduction

To solve a trigonometric equation, use standard algebraic techniques such as collecting like terms and factoring. Your preliminary goal in solving a trigonometric equation is to *isolate* the trigonometric function involved in the equation. For example, to solve the equation $2 \sin x = 1$, divide each side by 2 to obtain

$$\sin x = \frac{1}{2}.$$

To solve for x, note in Figure 5.3 that the equation $\sin x = \frac{1}{2}$ has solutions $x = \pi/6$ and $x = 5\pi/6$ in the interval $[0, 2\pi)$. Moreover, because $\sin x$ has a period of 2π, there are infinitely many other solutions, which can be written as

$$x = \frac{\pi}{6} + 2n\pi \qquad \text{and} \qquad x = \frac{5\pi}{6} + 2n\pi \qquad \text{General solution}$$

where n is an integer, as shown in Figure 5.3.

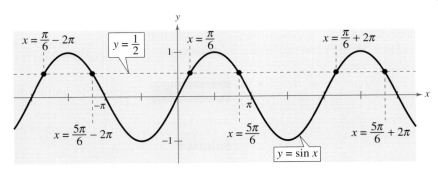

FIGURE 5.3

Another way to show that the equation $\sin x = \frac{1}{2}$ has infinitely many solutions is indicated in Figure 5.4. Any angles that are coterminal with $\pi/6$ or $5\pi/6$ will also be solutions of the equation.

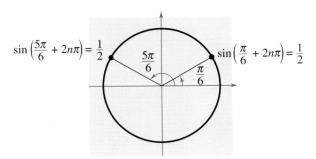

FIGURE 5.4

When solving trigonometric equations, you should write your answer(s) using exact values rather than decimal approximations.

Example 1 **Collecting Like Terms**

Solve $\sin x + \sqrt{2} = -\sin x$.

Solution

Begin by rewriting the equation so that $\sin x$ is isolated on one side of the equation.

$$\sin x + \sqrt{2} = -\sin x \qquad\qquad \text{Write original equation.}$$

$$\sin x + \sin x + \sqrt{2} = 0 \qquad\qquad \text{Add } \sin x \text{ to each side.}$$

$$\sin x + \sin x = -\sqrt{2} \qquad\qquad \text{Subtract } \sqrt{2} \text{ from each side.}$$

$$2 \sin x = -\sqrt{2} \qquad\qquad \text{Combine like terms.}$$

$$\sin x = -\frac{\sqrt{2}}{2} \qquad\qquad \text{Divide each side by 2.}$$

Because $\sin x$ has a period of 2π, first find all solutions in the interval $[0, 2\pi)$. These solutions are $x = 5\pi/4$ and $x = 7\pi/4$. Finally, add multiples of 2π to each of these solutions to get the general form

$$x = \frac{5\pi}{4} + 2n\pi \qquad \text{and} \qquad x = \frac{7\pi}{4} + 2n\pi \qquad \text{General solution}$$

where n is an integer.

✓CHECKPOINT   Now try Exercise 7.

Example 2 **Extracting Square Roots**

Solve $3 \tan^2 x - 1 = 0$.

Solution

Begin by rewriting the equation so that $\tan x$ is isolated on one side of the equation.

$$3 \tan^2 x - 1 = 0 \qquad\qquad \text{Write original equation.}$$

$$3 \tan^2 x = 1 \qquad\qquad \text{Add 1 to each side.}$$

$$\tan^2 x = \frac{1}{3} \qquad\qquad \text{Divide each side by 3.}$$

$$\tan x = \pm\frac{1}{\sqrt{3}} = \pm\frac{\sqrt{3}}{3} \qquad\qquad \text{Extract square roots.}$$

Because $\tan x$ has a period of π, first find all solutions in the interval $[0, \pi)$. These solutions are $x = \pi/6$ and $x = 5\pi/6$. Finally, add multiples of π to each of these solutions to get the general form

$$x = \frac{\pi}{6} + n\pi \qquad \text{and} \qquad x = \frac{5\pi}{6} + n\pi \qquad \text{General solution}$$

where n is an integer.

✓CHECKPOINT   Now try Exercise 11.

The equations in Examples 1 and 2 involved only one trigonometric function. When two or more functions occur in the same equation, collect all terms on one side and try to separate the functions by factoring or by using appropriate identities. This may produce factors that yield no solutions, as illustrated in Example 3.

Exploration

Using the equation from Example 3, explain what would happen if you divided each side of the equation by $\cot x$. Is this a correct method to use when solving equations?

Example 3   Factoring

Solve $\cot x \cos^2 x = 2 \cot x$.

Solution

Begin by rewriting the equation so that all terms are collected on one side of the equation.

$$\cot x \cos^2 x = 2 \cot x \qquad \text{Write original equation.}$$

$$\cot x \cos^2 x - 2 \cot x = 0 \qquad \text{Subtract } 2 \cot x \text{ from each side.}$$

$$\cot x(\cos^2 x - 2) = 0 \qquad \text{Factor.}$$

By setting each of these factors equal to zero, you obtain

$$\cot x = 0 \qquad \text{and} \qquad \cos^2 x - 2 = 0$$

$$x = \frac{\pi}{2} \qquad\qquad\qquad \cos^2 x = 2$$

$$\cos x = \pm\sqrt{2}.$$

The equation $\cot x = 0$ has the solution $x = \pi/2$ [in the interval $(0, \pi)$]. No solution is obtained for $\cos x = \pm\sqrt{2}$ because $\pm\sqrt{2}$ are outside the range of the cosine function. Because $\cot x$ has a period of π, the general form of the solution is obtained by adding multiples of π to $x = \pi/2$, to get

$$x = \frac{\pi}{2} + n\pi \qquad \text{General solution}$$

where n is an integer. You can confirm this graphically by sketching the graph of $y = \cot x \cos^2 x - 2 \cot x$, as shown in Figure 5.5. From the graph you can see that the x-intercepts occur at $-3\pi/2$, $-\pi/2$, $\pi/2$, $3\pi/2$, and so on. These x-intercepts correspond to the solutions of $\cot x \cos^2 x - 2 \cot x = 0$.

$$y = \cot x \cos^2 x - 2 \cot x$$

FIGURE 5.5

✓CHECKPOINT   Now try Exercise 15.

Equations of Quadratic Type

Many trigonometric equations are of quadratic type $ax^2 + bx + c = 0$. Here are a couple of examples.

Quadratic in sin x	*Quadratic in sec x*
$2 \sin^2 x - \sin x - 1 = 0$	$\sec^2 x - 3 \sec x - 2 = 0$
$2(\sin x)^2 - \sin x - 1 = 0$	$(\sec x)^2 - 3(\sec x) - 2 = 0$

To solve equations of this type, factor the quadratic or, if this is not possible, use the Quadratic Formula.

Example 4   Factoring an Equation of Quadratic Type

Find all solutions of $2 \sin^2 x - \sin x - 1 = 0$ in the interval $[0, 2\pi)$.

Algebraic Solution

Begin by treating the equation as a quadratic in $\sin x$ and factoring.

$$2 \sin^2 x - \sin x - 1 = 0 \quad \text{Write original equation.}$$

$$(2 \sin x + 1)(\sin x - 1) = 0 \quad \text{Factor.}$$

Setting each factor equal to zero, you obtain the following solutions in the interval $[0, 2\pi)$.

$$2 \sin x + 1 = 0 \qquad \text{and} \quad \sin x - 1 = 0$$

$$\sin x = -\frac{1}{2} \qquad\qquad \sin x = 1$$

$$x = \frac{7\pi}{6}, \frac{11\pi}{6} \qquad\qquad x = \frac{\pi}{2}$$

✓CHECKPOINT   Now try Exercise 29.

Graphical Solution

Use a graphing utility set in *radian* mode to graph $y = 2 \sin^2 x - \sin x - 1$ for $0 \le x < 2\pi$, as shown in Figure 5.6. Use the *zero* or *root* feature or the *zoom* and *trace* features to approximate the x-intercepts to be

$$x \approx 1.571 \approx \frac{\pi}{2}, x \approx 3.665 \approx \frac{7\pi}{6}, \text{ and } x \approx 5.760 \approx \frac{11\pi}{6}.$$

These values are the approximate solutions of $2 \sin^2 x - \sin x - 1 = 0$ in the interval $[0, 2\pi)$.

FIGURE 5.6

Example 5   Rewriting with a Single Trigonometric Function

Solve $2 \sin^2 x + 3 \cos x - 3 = 0$.

Solution

This equation contains both sine and cosine functions. You can rewrite the equation so that it has only cosine functions by using the identity $\sin^2 x = 1 - \cos^2 x$.

$$2 \sin^2 x + 3 \cos x - 3 = 0 \qquad \text{Write original equation.}$$

$$2(1 - \cos^2 x) + 3 \cos x - 3 = 0 \qquad \text{Pythagorean identity}$$

$$2 \cos^2 x - 3 \cos x + 1 = 0 \qquad \text{Multiply each side by } -1.$$

$$(2 \cos x - 1)(\cos x - 1) = 0 \qquad \text{Factor.}$$

Set each factor equal to zero to find the solutions in the interval $[0, 2\pi)$.

$$2 \cos x - 1 = 0 \implies \cos x = \frac{1}{2} \implies x = \frac{\pi}{3}, \frac{5\pi}{3}$$

$$\cos x - 1 = 0 \implies \cos x = 1 \implies x = 0$$

Because $\cos x$ has a period of 2π, the general form of the solution is obtained by adding multiples of 2π to get

$$x = 2n\pi, \quad x = \frac{\pi}{3} + 2n\pi, \quad x = \frac{5\pi}{3} + 2n\pi \qquad \text{General solution}$$

where n is an integer.

✓CHECKPOINT   Now try Exercise 31.

Sometimes you must square each side of an equation to obtain a quadratic, as demonstrated in the next example. Because this procedure can introduce extraneous solutions, you should check any solutions in the original equation to see whether they are valid or extraneous.

| **Example 6** | **Squaring and Converting to Quadratic Type** |

Find all solutions of $\cos x + 1 = \sin x$ in the interval $[0, 2\pi)$.

Solution

It is not clear how to rewrite this equation in terms of a single trigonometric function. Notice what happens when you square each side of the equation.

$$\cos x + 1 = \sin x \qquad \text{Write original equation.}$$

$$\cos^2 x + 2\cos x + 1 = \sin^2 x \qquad \text{Square each side.}$$

$$\cos^2 x + 2\cos x + 1 = 1 - \cos^2 x \qquad \text{Pythagorean identity}$$

$$\cos^2 x + \cos^2 x + 2\cos x + 1 - 1 = 0 \qquad \text{Rewrite equation.}$$

$$2\cos^2 x + 2\cos x = 0 \qquad \text{Combine like terms.}$$

$$2\cos x(\cos x + 1) = 0 \qquad \text{Factor.}$$

Setting each factor equal to zero produces

$$2\cos x = 0 \qquad \text{and} \qquad \cos x + 1 = 0$$

$$\cos x = 0 \qquad\qquad\qquad \cos x = -1$$

$$x = \frac{\pi}{2}, \frac{3\pi}{2} \qquad\qquad\qquad x = \pi.$$

Because you squared the original equation, check for extraneous solutions.

Check x = π/2

$$\cos \frac{\pi}{2} + 1 \overset{?}{=} \sin \frac{\pi}{2} \qquad \text{Substitute } \pi/2 \text{ for } x.$$

$$0 + 1 = 1 \qquad \text{Solution checks.} \checkmark$$

Check x = 3π/2

$$\cos \frac{3\pi}{2} + 1 \overset{?}{=} \sin \frac{3\pi}{2} \qquad \text{Substitute } 3\pi/2 \text{ for } x.$$

$$0 + 1 \neq -1 \qquad \text{Solution does not check.}$$

Check x = π

$$\cos \pi + 1 \overset{?}{=} \sin \pi \qquad \text{Substitute } \pi \text{ for } x.$$

$$-1 + 1 = 0 \qquad \text{Solution checks.} \checkmark$$

Of the three possible solutions, $x = 3\pi/2$ is extraneous. So, in the interval $[0, 2\pi)$, the only two solutions are $x = \pi/2$ and $x = \pi$.

✓CHECKPOINT   Now try Exercise 33.

STUDY TIP

You square each side of the equation in Example 6 because the squares of the sine and cosine functions are related by a Pythagorean identity. The same is true for the squares of the secant and tangent functions and the cosecant and cotangent functions.

Exploration

Use a graphing utility to confirm the solutions found in Example 6 in two different ways. Do both methods produce the same x-values? Which method do you prefer? Why?

1. Graph both sides of the equation and find the x-coordinates of the points at which the graphs intersect.

   Left side: $y = \cos x + 1$

   Right side: $y = \sin x$

2. Graph the equation

   $$y = \cos x + 1 - \sin x$$

   and find the x-intercepts of the graph.

Functions Involving Multiple Angles

The next two examples involve trigonometric functions of multiple angles of the forms $\sin ku$ and $\cos ku$. To solve equations of these forms, first solve the equation for ku, then divide your result by k.

Example 7 Functions of Multiple Angles

Solve $2 \cos 3t - 1 = 0$.

Solution

$$2 \cos 3t - 1 = 0 \qquad \text{Write original equation.}$$
$$2 \cos 3t = 1 \qquad \text{Add 1 to each side.}$$
$$\cos 3t = \frac{1}{2} \qquad \text{Divide each side by 2.}$$

In the interval $[0, 2\pi)$, you know that $3t = \pi/3$ and $3t = 5\pi/3$ are the only solutions, so, in general, you have

$$3t = \frac{\pi}{3} + 2n\pi \qquad \text{and} \qquad 3t = \frac{5\pi}{3} + 2n\pi.$$

Dividing these results by 3, you obtain the general solution

$$t = \frac{\pi}{9} + \frac{2n\pi}{3} \qquad \text{and} \qquad t = \frac{5\pi}{9} + \frac{2n\pi}{3} \qquad \text{General solution}$$

where n is an integer.

✓CHECKPOINT Now try Exercise 35.

Example 8 Functions of Multiple Angles

Solve $3 \tan \dfrac{x}{2} + 3 = 0$.

Solution

$$3 \tan \frac{x}{2} + 3 = 0 \qquad \text{Write original equation.}$$
$$3 \tan \frac{x}{2} = -3 \qquad \text{Subtract 3 from each side.}$$
$$\tan \frac{x}{2} = -1 \qquad \text{Divide each side by 3.}$$

In the interval $[0, \pi)$, you know that $x/2 = 3\pi/4$ is the only solution, so, in general, you have

$$\frac{x}{2} = \frac{3\pi}{4} + n\pi.$$

Multiplying this result by 2, you obtain the general solution

$$x = \frac{3\pi}{2} + 2n\pi \qquad \text{General solution}$$

where n is an integer.

✓CHECKPOINT Now try Exercise 39.

Using Inverse Functions

In the next example, you will see how inverse trigonometric functions can be used to solve an equation.

Example 9   Using Inverse Functions

Solve $\sec^2 x - 2 \tan x = 4$.

Solution

$$\sec^2 x - 2 \tan x = 4 \qquad \text{Write original equation.}$$

$$1 + \tan^2 x - 2 \tan x - 4 = 0 \qquad \text{Pythagorean identity}$$

$$\tan^2 x - 2 \tan x - 3 = 0 \qquad \text{Combine like terms.}$$

$$(\tan x - 3)(\tan x + 1) = 0 \qquad \text{Factor.}$$

Setting each factor equal to zero, you obtain two solutions in the interval $(-\pi/2, \pi/2)$. [Recall that the range of the inverse tangent function is $(-\pi/2, \pi/2)$.]

$$\tan x - 3 = 0 \qquad \text{and} \qquad \tan x + 1 = 0$$

$$\tan x = 3 \qquad\qquad\qquad \tan x = -1$$

$$x = \arctan 3 \qquad\qquad\qquad x = -\frac{\pi}{4}$$

Finally, because $\tan x$ has a period of π, you obtain the general solution by adding multiples of π

$$x = \arctan 3 + n\pi \qquad \text{and} \qquad x = -\frac{\pi}{4} + n\pi \qquad \text{General solution}$$

where n is an integer. You can use a calculator to approximate the value of arctan 3.

✓CHECKPOINT   Now try Exercise 59.

---

*W*RITING ABOUT *M*ATHEMATICS

Equations with No Solutions   One of the following equations has solutions and the other two do not. Which two equations do not have solutions?

a. $\sin^2 x - 5 \sin x + 6 = 0$

b. $\sin^2 x - 4 \sin x + 6 = 0$

c. $\sin^2 x - 5 \sin x - 6 = 0$

Find conditions involving the constants b and c that will guarantee that the equation

$$\sin^2 x + b \sin x + c = 0$$

has at least one solution on some interval of length 2π.

5.3 | Exercises

VOCABULARY CHECK: Fill in the blanks.

1. The equation $2 \sin \theta + 1 = 0$ has the solutions $\theta = \dfrac{7\pi}{6} + 2n\pi$ and $\theta = \dfrac{11\pi}{6} + 2n\pi$, which are called _____ solutions.

2. The equation $2 \tan^2 x - 3 \tan x + 1 = 0$ is a trigonometric equation that is of _____ type.

3. A solution to an equation that does not satisfy the original equation is called an _____ solution.

PREREQUISITE SKILLS REVIEW: Practice and review algebra skills needed for this section at **www.Eduspace.com.**

In Exercises 1–6, verify that the x-values are solutions of the equation.

1. $2 \cos x - 1 = 0$

   (a) $x = \dfrac{\pi}{3}$ (b) $x = \dfrac{5\pi}{3}$

2. $\sec x - 2 = 0$

   (a) $x = \dfrac{\pi}{3}$ (b) $x = \dfrac{5\pi}{3}$

3. $3 \tan^2 2x - 1 = 0$

   (a) $x = \dfrac{\pi}{12}$ (b) $x = \dfrac{5\pi}{12}$

4. $2 \cos^2 4x - 1 = 0$

   (a) $x = \dfrac{\pi}{16}$ (b) $x = \dfrac{3\pi}{16}$

5. $2 \sin^2 x - \sin x - 1 = 0$

   (a) $x = \dfrac{\pi}{2}$ (b) $x = \dfrac{7\pi}{6}$

6. $\csc^4 x - 4 \csc^2 x = 0$

   (a) $x = \dfrac{\pi}{6}$ (b) $x = \dfrac{5\pi}{6}$

In Exercises 7–20, solve the equation.

7. $2 \cos x + 1 = 0$ 8. $2 \sin x + 1 = 0$

9. $\sqrt{3} \csc x - 2 = 0$ 10. $\tan x + \sqrt{3} = 0$

11. $3 \sec^2 x - 4 = 0$ 12. $3 \cot^2 x - 1 = 0$

13. $\sin x(\sin x + 1) = 0$

14. $(3 \tan^2 x - 1)(\tan^2 x - 3) = 0$

15. $4 \cos^2 x - 1 = 0$ 16. $\sin^2 x = 3 \cos^2 x$

17. $2 \sin^2 2x = 1$ 18. $\tan^2 3x = 3$

19. $\tan 3x(\tan x - 1) = 0$ 20. $\cos 2x(2 \cos x + 1) = 0$

In Exercises 21–34, find all solutions of the equation in the interval $[0, 2\pi)$.

21. $\cos^3 x = \cos x$ 22. $\sec^2 x - 1 = 0$

23. $3 \tan^3 x = \tan x$ 24. $2 \sin^2 x = 2 + \cos x$

25. $\sec^2 x - \sec x = 2$ 26. $\sec x \csc x = 2 \csc x$

27. $2 \sin x + \csc x = 0$ 28. $\sec x + \tan x = 1$

29. $2 \cos^2 x + \cos x - 1 = 0$

30. $2 \sin^2 x + 3 \sin x + 1 = 0$

31. $2 \sec^2 x + \tan^2 x - 3 = 0$

32. $\cos x + \sin x \tan x = 2$

33. $\csc x + \cot x = 1$

34. $\sin x - 2 = \cos x - 2$

In Exercises 35–40, solve the multiple-angle equation.

35. $\cos 2x = \dfrac{1}{2}$ 36. $\sin 2x = -\dfrac{\sqrt{3}}{2}$

37. $\tan 3x = 1$ 38. $\sec 4x = 2$

39. $\cos \dfrac{x}{2} = \dfrac{\sqrt{2}}{2}$ 40. $\sin \dfrac{x}{2} = -\dfrac{\sqrt{3}}{2}$

In Exercises 41–44, find the x-intercepts of the graph.

41. $y = \sin \dfrac{\pi x}{2} + 1$ 42. $y = \sin \pi x + \cos \pi x$

43. $y = \tan^2\left(\dfrac{\pi x}{6}\right) - 3$ 44. $y = \sec^4\left(\dfrac{\pi x}{8}\right) - 4$

        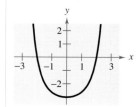

In Exercises 45–54, use a graphing utility to approximate the solutions (to three decimal places) of the equation in the interval $[0, 2\pi)$.

45. $2 \sin x + \cos x = 0$

46. $4 \sin^3 x + 2 \sin^2 x - 2 \sin x - 1 = 0$

47. $\dfrac{1 + \sin x}{\cos x} + \dfrac{\cos x}{1 + \sin x} = 4$

48. $\dfrac{\cos x \cot x}{1 - \sin x} = 3$

49. $x \tan x - 1 = 0$ **50.** $x \cos x - 1 = 0$

51. $\sec^2 x + 0.5 \tan x - 1 = 0$

52. $\csc^2 x + 0.5 \cot x - 5 = 0$

53. $2 \tan^2 x + 7 \tan x - 15 = 0$

54. $6 \sin^2 x - 7 \sin x + 2 = 0$

In Exercises 55–58, use the Quadratic Formula to solve the equation in the interval $[0, 2\pi)$. Then use a graphing utility to approximate the angle x.

55. $12 \sin^2 x - 13 \sin x + 3 = 0$

56. $3 \tan^2 x + 4 \tan x - 4 = 0$

57. $\tan^2 x + 3 \tan x + 1 = 0$

58. $4 \cos^2 x - 4 \cos x - 1 = 0$

In Exercises 59–62, use inverse functions where needed to find all solutions of the equation in the interval $[0, 2\pi)$.

59. $\tan^2 x - 6 \tan x + 5 = 0$

60. $\sec^2 x + \tan x - 3 = 0$

61. $2 \cos^2 x - 5 \cos x + 2 = 0$

62. $2 \sin^2 x - 7 \sin x + 3 = 0$

In Exercises 63 and 64, (a) use a graphing utility to graph the function and approximate the maximum and minimum points on the graph in the interval $[0, 2\pi)$, and (b) solve the trigonometric equation and demonstrate that its solutions are the x-coordinates of the maximum and minimum points of f. (Calculus is required to find the trigonometric equation.)

Function	Trigonometric Equation
63. $f(x) = \sin x + \cos x$	$\cos x - \sin x = 0$
64. $f(x) = 2 \sin x + \cos 2x$	$2 \cos x - 4 \sin x \cos x = 0$

Fixed Point In Exercises 65 and 66, find the smallest positive fixed point of the function f. [A *fixed point* of a function f is a real number c such that $f(c) = c$.]

65. $f(x) = \tan \dfrac{\pi x}{4}$ **66.** $f(x) = \cos x$

67. *Graphical Reasoning*   Consider the function given by

$$f(x) = \cos \frac{1}{x}$$

and its graph shown in the figure.

(a) What is the domain of the function?

(b) Identify any symmetry and any asymptotes of the graph.

(c) Describe the behavior of the function as $x \to 0$.

(d) How many solutions does the equation

$$\cos \frac{1}{x} = 0$$

have in the interval $[-1, 1]$? Find the solutions.

(e) Does the equation $\cos(1/x) = 0$ have a greatest solution? If so, approximate the solution. If not, explain why.

68. *Graphical Reasoning*   Consider the function given by

$$f(x) = \frac{\sin x}{x}$$

and its graph shown in the figure.

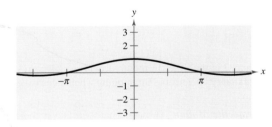

(a) What is the domain of the function?

(b) Identify any symmetry and any asymptotes of the graph.

(c) Describe the behavior of the function as $x \to 0$.

(d) How many solutions does the equation

$$\frac{\sin x}{x} = 0$$

have in the interval $[-8, 8]$? Find the solutions.

69. *Harmonic Motion* A weight is oscillating on the end of a spring (see figure). The position of the weight relative to the point of equilibrium is given by $y = \frac{1}{12}(\cos 8t - 3 \sin 8t)$, where y is the displacement (in meters) and t is the time (in seconds). Find the times when the weight is at the point of equilibrium ($y = 0$) for $0 \le t \le 1$.

70. *Damped Harmonic Motion* The displacement from equilibrium of a weight oscillating on the end of a spring is given by $y = 1.56e^{-0.22t}\cos 4.9t$, where y is the displacement (in feet) and t is the time (in seconds). Use a graphing utility to graph the displacement function for $0 \le t \le 10$. Find the time beyond which the displacement does not exceed 1 foot from equilibrium.

71. *Sales* The monthly sales S (in thousands of units) of a seasonal product are approximated by

$$S = 74.50 + 43.75 \sin \frac{\pi t}{6}$$

where t is the time (in months), with $t = 1$ corresponding to January. Determine the months when sales exceed 100,000 units.

72. *Sales* The monthly sales S (in hundreds of units) of skiing equipment at a sports store are approximated by

$$S = 58.3 + 32.5 \cos \frac{\pi t}{6}$$

where t is the time (in months), with $t = 1$ corresponding to January. Determine the months when sales exceed 7500 units.

73. *Projectile Motion* A batted baseball leaves the bat at an angle of θ with the horizontal and an initial velocity of $v_0 = 100$ feet per second. The ball is caught by an outfielder 300 feet from home plate (see figure). Find θ if the range r of a projectile is given by $r = \frac{1}{32}v_0{}^2 \sin 2\theta$.

Not drawn to scale

74. *Projectile Motion* A sharpshooter intends to hit a target at a distance of 1000 yards with a gun that has a muzzle velocity of 1200 feet per second (see figure). Neglecting air resistance, determine the gun's minimum angle of elevation θ if the range r is given by

$$r = \frac{1}{32}v_0{}^2 \sin 2\theta.$$

Not drawn to scale

75. *Ferris Wheel* A Ferris wheel is built such that the height h (in feet) above ground of a seat on the wheel at time t (in minutes) can be modeled by

$$h(t) = 53 + 50 \sin\left(\frac{\pi}{16}t - \frac{\pi}{2}\right).$$

The wheel makes one revolution every 32 seconds. The ride begins when $t = 0$.

(a) During the first 32 seconds of the ride, when will a person on the Ferris wheel be 53 feet above ground?

(b) When will a person be at the top of the Ferris wheel for the first time during the ride? If the ride lasts 160 seconds, how many times will a person be at the top of the ride, and at what times?

Model It

76. *Data Analysis: Unemployment Rate* The table shows the unemployment rates r in the United States for selected years from 1990 through 2004. The time t is measured in years, with $t = 0$ corresponding to 1990. (Source: U.S. Bureau of Labor Statistics)

Time, t	Rate, r	Time, t	Rate, r
0	5.6	8	4.5
2	7.5	10	4.0
4	6.1	12	5.8
6	5.4	14	5.5

(a) Create a scatter plot of the data.

Model It (continued)

(b) Which of the following models best represents the data? Explain your reasoning.

(1) $r = 1.24 \sin(0.47t + 0.40) + 5.45$

(2) $r = 1.24 \sin(0.47t - 0.01) + 5.45$

(3) $r = \sin(0.10t + 5.61) + 4.80$

(4) $r = 896 \sin(0.57t - 2.05) + 6.48$

(c) What term in the model gives the average unemployment rate? What is the rate?

(d) Economists study the lengths of business cycles such as unemployment rates. Based on this short span of time, use the model to find the length of this cycle.

(e) Use the model to estimate the next time the unemployment rate will be 5% or less.

---

77. Geometry   The area of a rectangle (see figure) inscribed in one arc of the graph of $y = \cos x$ is given by

$$A = 2x \cos x, \quad 0 < x < \frac{\pi}{2}.$$

 (a) Use a graphing utility to graph the area function, and approximate the area of the largest inscribed rectangle.

(b) Determine the values of x for which $A \geq 1$.

78. Quadratic Approximation   Consider the function given by $f(x) = 3 \sin(0.6x - 2)$.

(a) Approximate the zero of the function in the interval $[0, 6]$.

 (b) A quadratic approximation agreeing with f at $x = 5$ is $g(x) = -0.45x^2 + 5.52x - 13.70$. Use a graphing utility to graph f and g in the same viewing window. Describe the result.

(c) Use the Quadratic Formula to find the zeros of g. Compare the zero in the interval $[0, 6]$ with the result of part (a).

Synthesis

True or False?   **In Exercises 79 and 80, determine whether the statement is true or false. Justify your answer.**

79. The equation $2 \sin 4t - 1 = 0$ has four times the number of solutions in the interval $[0, 2\pi)$ as the equation $2 \sin t - 1 = 0$.

80. If you correctly solve a trigonometric equation to the statement $\sin x = 3.4$, then you can finish solving the equation by using an inverse function.

In Exercises 81 and 82, use the graph to approximate the number of points of intersection of the graphs of y_1 and y_2.

81. $y_1 = 2 \sin x$
$y_2 = 3x + 1$

82. $y_1 = 2 \sin x$
$y_2 = \frac{1}{2}x + 1$

Skills Review

In Exercises 83 and 84, solve triangle ABC by finding all missing angle measures and side lengths.

83.

84.

In Exercises 85–88, use reference angles to find the exact values of the sine, cosine, and tangent of the angle with the given measure.

85. $390°$

86. $600°$

87. $-1845°$

88. $-1410°$

89. Angle of Depression   Find the angle of depression from the top of a lighthouse 250 feet above water level to the water line of a ship 2 miles offshore.

90. Height   From a point 100 feet in front of a public library, the angles of elevation to the base of the flagpole and the top of the pole are $28°$ and $39° \, 45'$, respectively. The flagpole is mounted on the front of the library's roof. Find the height of the flagpole.

---

91. Make a Decision   To work an extended application analyzing the normal daily high temperatures in Phoenix and in Seattle, visit this text's website at *college.hmco.com*. *(Data Source: NOAA)*

5.4 Sum and Difference Formulas

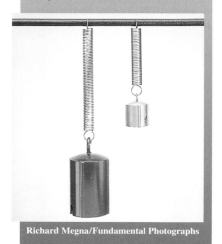

Richard Megna/Fundamental Photographs

Using Sum and Difference Formulas

In this and the following section, you will study the uses of several trigonometric identities and formulas.

Sum and Difference Formulas

$$\sin(u + v) = \sin u \cos v + \cos u \sin v$$

$$\sin(u - v) = \sin u \cos v - \cos u \sin v$$

$$\cos(u + v) = \cos u \cos v - \sin u \sin v$$

$$\cos(u - v) = \cos u \cos v + \sin u \sin v$$

$$\tan(u + v) = \frac{\tan u + \tan v}{1 - \tan u \tan v}$$

$$\tan(u - v) = \frac{\tan u - \tan v}{1 + \tan u \tan v}$$

For a proof of the sum and difference formulas, see Proofs in Mathematics on page 442.

Exploration

Use a graphing utility to graph $y_1 = \cos(x + 2)$ and $y_2 = \cos x + \cos 2$ in the same viewing window. What can you conclude about the graphs? Is it true that $\cos(x + 2) = \cos x + \cos 2$?

Use a graphing utility to graph $y_1 = \sin(x + 4)$ and $y_2 = \sin x + \sin 4$ in the same viewing window. What can you conclude about the graphs? Is it true that $\sin(x + 4) = \sin x + \sin 4$?

Examples 1 and 2 show how **sum and difference formulas** can be used to find exact values of trigonometric functions involving sums or differences of special angles.

Example 1 Evaluating a Trigonometric Function

Find the exact value of $\cos 75°$.

Solution

To find the *exact* value of $\cos 75°$, use the fact that $75° = 30° + 45°$. Consequently, the formula for $\cos(u + v)$ yields

$$\cos 75° = \cos(30° + 45°)$$

$$= \cos 30° \cos 45° - \sin 30° \sin 45°$$

$$= \frac{\sqrt{3}}{2}\left(\frac{\sqrt{2}}{2}\right) - \frac{1}{2}\left(\frac{\sqrt{2}}{2}\right) = \frac{\sqrt{6} - \sqrt{2}}{4}.$$

Try checking this result on your calculator. You will find that $\cos 75° \approx 0.259$.

✓CHECKPOINT Now try Exercise 1.

The Granger Collection, New York

Historical Note

Hipparchus, considered the most eminent of Greek astronomers, was born about 160 B.C. in Nicaea. He was credited with the invention of trigonometry. He also derived the sum and difference formulas for $\sin(A \pm B)$ and $\cos(A \pm B)$.

Example 2   Evaluating a Trigonometric Expression

Find the exact value of $\sin \dfrac{\pi}{12}$.

Solution

Using the fact that

$$\frac{\pi}{12} = \frac{\pi}{3} - \frac{\pi}{4}$$

together with the formula for $\sin(u - v)$, you obtain

$$\sin \frac{\pi}{12} = \sin\left(\frac{\pi}{3} - \frac{\pi}{4}\right)$$

$$= \sin \frac{\pi}{3} \cos \frac{\pi}{4} - \cos \frac{\pi}{3} \sin \frac{\pi}{4}$$

$$= \frac{\sqrt{3}}{2}\left(\frac{\sqrt{2}}{2}\right) - \frac{1}{2}\left(\frac{\sqrt{2}}{2}\right)$$

$$= \frac{\sqrt{6} - \sqrt{2}}{4}.$$

✓CHECKPOINT   Now try Exercise 3.

Example 3   Evaluating a Trigonometric Expression

Find the exact value of $\sin 42° \cos 12° - \cos 42° \sin 12°$.

Solution

Recognizing that this expression fits the formula for $\sin(u - v)$, you can write

$$\sin 42° \cos 12° - \cos 42° \sin 12° = \sin(42° - 12°)$$

$$= \sin 30°$$

$$= \tfrac{1}{2}.$$

✓CHECKPOINT   Now try Exercise 31.

Example 4   An Application of a Sum Formula

Write $\cos(\arctan 1 + \arccos x)$ as an algebraic expression.

Solution

This expression fits the formula for $\cos(u + v)$. Angles $u = \arctan 1$ and $v = \arccos x$ are shown in Figure 5.7. So

$$\cos(u + v) = \cos(\arctan 1) \cos(\arccos x) - \sin(\arctan 1) \sin(\arccos x)$$

$$= \frac{1}{\sqrt{2}} \cdot x - \frac{1}{\sqrt{2}} \cdot \sqrt{1 - x^2}$$

$$= \frac{x - \sqrt{1 - x^2}}{\sqrt{2}}.$$

✓CHECKPOINT   Now try Exercise 51.

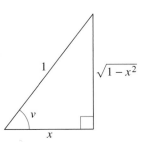

FIGURE **5.7**

Example 5 shows how to use a difference formula to prove the cofunction identity

$$\cos\left(\frac{\pi}{2} - x\right) = \sin x.$$

Example 5 Proving a Cofunction Identity

Prove the cofunction identity $\cos\left(\frac{\pi}{2} - x\right) = \sin x$.

Solution
Using the formula for $\cos(u - v)$, you have

$$\cos\left(\frac{\pi}{2} - x\right) = \cos\frac{\pi}{2}\cos x + \sin\frac{\pi}{2}\sin x$$

$$= (0)(\cos x) + (1)(\sin x) = \sin x.$$

✓CHECKPOINT   Now try Exercise 55.

Sum and difference formulas can be used to rewrite expressions such as

$$\sin\left(\theta + \frac{n\pi}{2}\right) \quad \text{and} \quad \cos\left(\theta + \frac{n\pi}{2}\right), \quad \text{where } n \text{ is an integer}$$

as expressions involving only $\sin\theta$ or $\cos\theta$. The resulting formulas are called **reduction formulas.**

Example 6 Deriving Reduction Formulas

Simplify each expression.

a. $\cos\left(\theta - \frac{3\pi}{2}\right)$ **b.** $\tan(\theta + 3\pi)$

Solution
a. Using the formula for $\cos(u - v)$, you have

$$\cos\left(\theta - \frac{3\pi}{2}\right) = \cos\theta\cos\frac{3\pi}{2} + \sin\theta\sin\frac{3\pi}{2}$$

$$= (\cos\theta)(0) + (\sin\theta)(-1)$$

$$= -\sin\theta.$$

b. Using the formula for $\tan(u + v)$, you have

$$\tan(\theta + 3\pi) = \frac{\tan\theta + \tan 3\pi}{1 - \tan\theta\tan 3\pi}$$

$$= \frac{\tan\theta + 0}{1 - (\tan\theta)(0)}$$

$$= \tan\theta.$$

✓CHECKPOINT   Now try Exercise 65.

Example 7   **Solving a Trigonometric Equation**

Find all solutions of $\sin\left(x + \dfrac{\pi}{4}\right) + \sin\left(x - \dfrac{\pi}{4}\right) = -1$ in the interval $[0, 2\pi)$.

Solution

Using sum and difference formulas, rewrite the equation as

$$\sin x \cos \frac{\pi}{4} + \cos x \sin \frac{\pi}{4} + \sin x \cos \frac{\pi}{4} - \cos x \sin \frac{\pi}{4} = -1$$

$$2 \sin x \cos \frac{\pi}{4} = -1$$

$$2(\sin x)\left(\frac{\sqrt{2}}{2}\right) = -1$$

$$\sin x = -\frac{1}{\sqrt{2}}$$

$$\sin x = -\frac{\sqrt{2}}{2}.$$

So, the only solutions in the interval $[0, 2\pi)$ are

$$x = \frac{5\pi}{4} \qquad \text{and} \qquad x = \frac{7\pi}{4}.$$

You can confirm this graphically by sketching the graph of

$$y = \sin\left(x + \frac{\pi}{4}\right) + \sin\left(x - \frac{\pi}{4}\right) + 1 \text{ for } 0 \le x < 2\pi,$$

as shown in Figure 5.8. From the graph you can see that the x-intercepts are $5\pi/4$ and $7\pi/4$.

✓CHECKPOINT   Now try Exercise 69.

The next example was taken from calculus. It is used to derive the derivative of the sine function.

Example 8   **An Application from Calculus**   ∫

Verify that

$$\frac{\sin(x + h) - \sin x}{h} = (\cos x)\left(\frac{\sin h}{h}\right) - (\sin x)\left(\frac{1 - \cos h}{h}\right)$$

where $h \ne 0$.

Solution

Using the formula for $\sin(u + v)$, you have

$$\frac{\sin(x + h) - \sin x}{h} = \frac{\sin x \cos h + \cos x \sin h - \sin x}{h}$$

$$= \frac{\cos x \sin h - \sin x(1 - \cos h)}{h}$$

$$= (\cos x)\left(\frac{\sin h}{h}\right) - (\sin x)\left(\frac{1 - \cos h}{h}\right).$$

✓CHECKPOINT   Now try Exercise 91.

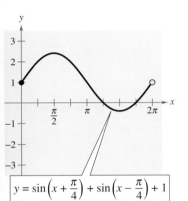

$y = \sin\left(x + \dfrac{\pi}{4}\right) + \sin\left(x - \dfrac{\pi}{4}\right) + 1$

FIGURE 5.8

5.4 | Exercises

VOCABULARY CHECK: Fill in the blank to complete the trigonometric identity.

1. $\sin(u - v) = $ _____
2. $\cos(u + v) = $ _____
3. $\tan(u + v) = $ _____
4. $\sin(u + v) = $ _____
5. $\cos(u - v) = $ _____
6. $\tan(u - v) = $ _____

PREREQUISITE SKILLS REVIEW: Practice and review algebra skills needed for this section at **www.Eduspace.com.**

In Exercises 1–6, find the exact value of each expression.

1. (a) $\cos(120° + 45°)$ (b) $\cos 120° + \cos 45°$
2. (a) $\sin(135° - 30°)$ (b) $\sin 135° - \cos 30°$
3. (a) $\cos\left(\dfrac{\pi}{4} + \dfrac{\pi}{3}\right)$ (b) $\cos\dfrac{\pi}{4} + \cos\dfrac{\pi}{3}$
4. (a) $\sin\left(\dfrac{3\pi}{4} + \dfrac{5\pi}{6}\right)$ (b) $\sin\dfrac{3\pi}{4} + \sin\dfrac{5\pi}{6}$
5. (a) $\sin\left(\dfrac{7\pi}{6} - \dfrac{\pi}{3}\right)$ (b) $\sin\dfrac{7\pi}{6} - \sin\dfrac{\pi}{3}$
6. (a) $\sin(315° - 60°)$ (b) $\sin 315° - \sin 60°$

In Exercises 7–22, find the exact values of the sine, cosine, and tangent of the angle by using a sum or difference formula.

7. $105° = 60° + 45°$
8. $165° = 135° + 30°$
9. $195° = 225° - 30°$
10. $255° = 300° - 45°$
11. $\dfrac{11\pi}{12} = \dfrac{3\pi}{4} + \dfrac{\pi}{6}$
12. $\dfrac{7\pi}{12} = \dfrac{\pi}{3} + \dfrac{\pi}{4}$
13. $\dfrac{17\pi}{12} = \dfrac{9\pi}{4} - \dfrac{5\pi}{6}$
14. $-\dfrac{\pi}{12} = \dfrac{\pi}{6} - \dfrac{\pi}{4}$
15. $285°$
16. $-105°$
17. $-165°$
18. $15°$
19. $\dfrac{13\pi}{12}$
20. $-\dfrac{7\pi}{12}$
21. $-\dfrac{13\pi}{12}$
22. $\dfrac{5\pi}{12}$

In Exercises 23–30, write the expression as the sine, cosine, or tangent of an angle.

23. $\cos 25° \cos 15° - \sin 25° \sin 15°$
24. $\sin 140° \cos 50° + \cos 140° \sin 50°$
25. $\dfrac{\tan 325° - \tan 86°}{1 + \tan 325° \tan 86°}$
26. $\dfrac{\tan 140° - \tan 60°}{1 + \tan 140° \tan 60°}$

27. $\sin 3 \cos 1.2 - \cos 3 \sin 1.2$
28. $\cos\dfrac{\pi}{7}\cos\dfrac{\pi}{5} - \sin\dfrac{\pi}{7}\sin\dfrac{\pi}{5}$
29. $\dfrac{\tan 2x + \tan x}{1 - \tan 2x \tan x}$
30. $\cos 3x \cos 2y + \sin 3x \sin 2y$

In Exercises 31–36, find the exact value of the expression.

31. $\sin 330° \cos 30° - \cos 330° \sin 30°$
32. $\cos 15° \cos 60° + \sin 15° \sin 60°$
33. $\sin\dfrac{\pi}{12}\cos\dfrac{\pi}{4} + \cos\dfrac{\pi}{12}\sin\dfrac{\pi}{4}$
34. $\cos\dfrac{\pi}{16}\cos\dfrac{3\pi}{16} - \sin\dfrac{\pi}{16}\sin\dfrac{3\pi}{16}$
35. $\dfrac{\tan 25° + \tan 110°}{1 - \tan 25° \tan 110°}$
36. $\dfrac{\tan(5\pi/4) - \tan(\pi/12)}{1 + \tan(5\pi/4)\tan(\pi/12)}$

In Exercises 37–44, find the exact value of the trigonometric function given that $\sin u = \frac{5}{13}$ and $\cos v = -\frac{3}{5}$. (Both u and v are in Quadrant II.)

37. $\sin(u + v)$ **38.** $\cos(u - v)$
39. $\cos(u + v)$ **40.** $\sin(v - u)$
41. $\tan(u + v)$ **42.** $\csc(u - v)$
43. $\sec(v - u)$ **44.** $\cot(u + v)$

In Exercises 45–50, find the exact value of the trigonometric function given that $\sin u = -\frac{7}{25}$ and $\cos v = -\frac{4}{5}$. (Both u and v are in Quadrant III.)

45. $\cos(u + v)$ **46.** $\sin(u + v)$
47. $\tan(u - v)$ **48.** $\cot(v - u)$
49. $\sec(u + v)$ **50.** $\cos(u - v)$

In Exercises 51–54, write the trigonometric expression as an algebraic expression.

51. $\sin(\arcsin x + \arccos x)$ **52.** $\sin(\arctan 2x - \arccos x)$

53. $\cos(\arccos x + \arcsin x)$

54. $\cos(\arccos x - \arctan x)$

In Exercises 55–64, verify the identity.

55. $\sin(3\pi - x) = \sin x$ **56.** $\sin\left(\dfrac{\pi}{2} + x\right) = \cos x$

57. $\sin\left(\dfrac{\pi}{6} + x\right) = \dfrac{1}{2}(\cos x + \sqrt{3}\sin x)$

58. $\cos\left(\dfrac{5\pi}{4} - x\right) = -\dfrac{\sqrt{2}}{2}(\cos x + \sin x)$

59. $\cos(\pi - \theta) + \sin\left(\dfrac{\pi}{2} + \theta\right) = 0$

60. $\tan\left(\dfrac{\pi}{4} - \theta\right) = \dfrac{1 - \tan\theta}{1 + \tan\theta}$

61. $\cos(x + y)\cos(x - y) = \cos^2 x - \sin^2 y$

62. $\sin(x + y)\sin(x - y) = \sin^2 x - \sin^2 y$

63. $\sin(x + y) + \sin(x - y) = 2\sin x \cos y$

64. $\cos(x + y) + \cos(x - y) = 2\cos x \cos y$

In Exercises 65–68, simplify the expression algebraically and use a graphing utility to confirm your answer graphically.

65. $\cos\left(\dfrac{3\pi}{2} - x\right)$ **66.** $\cos(\pi + x)$

67. $\sin\left(\dfrac{3\pi}{2} + \theta\right)$ **68.** $\tan(\pi + \theta)$

In Exercises 69–72, find all solutions of the equation in the interval $[0, 2\pi)$.

69. $\sin\left(x + \dfrac{\pi}{3}\right) + \sin\left(x - \dfrac{\pi}{3}\right) = 1$

70. $\sin\left(x + \dfrac{\pi}{6}\right) - \sin\left(x - \dfrac{\pi}{6}\right) = \dfrac{1}{2}$

71. $\cos\left(x + \dfrac{\pi}{4}\right) - \cos\left(x - \dfrac{\pi}{4}\right) = 1$

72. $\tan(x + \pi) + 2\sin(x + \pi) = 0$

In Exercises 73 and 74, use a graphing utility to approximate the solutions in the interval $[0, 2\pi)$.

73. $\cos\left(x + \dfrac{\pi}{4}\right) + \cos\left(x - \dfrac{\pi}{4}\right) = 1$

74. $\tan(x + \pi) - \cos\left(x + \dfrac{\pi}{2}\right) = 0$

Model It

75. *Harmonic Motion*   A weight is attached to a spring suspended vertically from a ceiling. When a driving force is applied to the system, the weight moves vertically from its equilibrium position, and this motion is modeled by

$$y = \dfrac{1}{3}\sin 2t + \dfrac{1}{4}\cos 2t$$

where y is the distance from equilibrium (in feet) and t is the time (in seconds).

(a) Use the identity

$$a\sin B\theta + b\cos B\theta = \sqrt{a^2 + b^2}\sin(B\theta + C)$$

where $C = \arctan(b/a)$, $a > 0$, to write the model in the form

$$y = \sqrt{a^2 + b^2}\sin(Bt + C).$$

(b) Find the amplitude of the oscillations of the weight.

(c) Find the frequency of the oscillations of the weight.

76. *Standing Waves*   The equation of a standing wave is obtained by adding the displacements of two waves traveling in opposite directions (see figure). Assume that each of the waves has amplitude A, period T, and wavelength λ. If the models for these waves are

$$y_1 = A\cos 2\pi\left(\dfrac{t}{T} - \dfrac{x}{\lambda}\right) \quad \text{and} \quad y_2 = A\cos 2\pi\left(\dfrac{t}{T} + \dfrac{x}{\lambda}\right)$$

show that

$$y_1 + y_2 = 2A\cos\dfrac{2\pi t}{T}\cos\dfrac{2\pi x}{\lambda}.$$

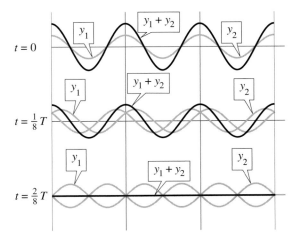

Synthesis

True or False? **In Exercises 77–80, determine whether the statement is true or false. Justify your answer.**

77. $\sin(u \pm v) = \sin u \pm \sin v$

78. $\cos(u \pm v) = \cos u \pm \cos v$

79. $\cos\left(x - \dfrac{\pi}{2}\right) = -\sin x$

80. $\sin\left(x - \dfrac{\pi}{2}\right) = -\cos x$

In Exercises 81–84, verify the identity.

81. $\cos(n\pi + \theta) = (-1)^n \cos\theta,\quad n$ is an integer

82. $\sin(n\pi + \theta) = (-1)^n \sin\theta,\quad n$ is an integer

83. $a \sin B\theta + b \cos B\theta = \sqrt{a^2 + b^2}\,\sin(B\theta + C),$
where $C = \arctan(b/a)$ and $a > 0$

84. $a \sin B\theta + b \cos B\theta = \sqrt{a^2 + b^2}\,\cos(B\theta - C),$
where $C = \arctan(a/b)$ and $b > 0$

In Exercises 85–88, use the formulas given in Exercises 83 and 84 to write the trigonometric expression in the following forms.

(a) $\sqrt{a^2 + b^2}\,\sin(B\theta + C)$ (b) $\sqrt{a^2 + b^2}\,\cos(B\theta - C)$

85. $\sin\theta + \cos\theta$

86. $3 \sin 2\theta + 4 \cos 2\theta$

87. $12 \sin 3\theta + 5 \cos 3\theta$

88. $\sin 2\theta - \cos 2\theta$

In Exercises 89 and 90, use the formulas given in Exercises 83 and 84 to write the trigonometric expression in the form $a \sin B\theta + b \cos B\theta$.

89. $2 \sin\left(\theta + \dfrac{\pi}{2}\right)$

90. $5 \cos\left(\theta + \dfrac{\pi}{4}\right)$

91. Verify the following identity used in calculus.
$$\frac{\cos(x + h) - \cos x}{h}$$
$$= \frac{\cos x(\cos h - 1)}{h} - \frac{\sin x \sin h}{h}$$

92. *Exploration* Let $x = \pi/6$ in the identity in Exercise 91 and define the functions f and g as follows.
$$f(h) = \frac{\cos(\pi/6 + h) - \cos(\pi/6)}{h}$$
$$g(h) = \cos\frac{\pi}{6}\left(\frac{\cos h - 1}{h}\right) - \sin\frac{\pi}{6}\left(\frac{\sin h}{h}\right)$$

(a) What are the domains of the functions f and g?

 (b) Use a graphing utility to complete the table.

h	0.01	0.02	0.05	0.1	0.2	0.5
$f(h)$						
$g(h)$						

 (c) Use a graphing utility to graph the functions f and g.

 (d) Use the table and the graphs to make a conjecture about the values of the functions f and g as $h \to 0$.

In Exercises 93 and 94, use the figure, which shows two lines whose equations are
$$y_1 = m_1 x + b_1 \quad \text{and} \quad y_2 = m_2 x + b_2.$$

Assume that both lines have positive slopes. Derive a formula for the angle between the two lines. Then use your formula to find the angle between the given pair of lines.

93. $y = x$ and $y = \sqrt{3}x$

94. $y = x$ and $y = \dfrac{1}{\sqrt{3}}x$

 95. *Conjecture* Consider the function given by
$$f(\theta) = \sin^2\left(\theta + \frac{\pi}{4}\right) + \sin^2\left(\theta - \frac{\pi}{4}\right).$$
Use a graphing utility to graph the function and use the graph to create an identity. Prove your conjecture.

96. *Proof*

(a) Write a proof of the formula for $\sin(u + v)$.

(b) Write a proof of the formula for $\sin(u - v)$.

Skills Review

In Exercises 97–100, find the inverse function of f. Verify that $f(f^{-1}(x)) = x$ and $f^{-1}(f(x)) = x$.

97. $f(x) = 5(x - 3)$

98. $f(x) = \dfrac{7 - x}{8}$

99. $f(x) = x^2 - 8$

100. $f(x) = \sqrt{x - 16}$

In Exercises 101–104, apply the inverse properties of $\ln x$ and e^x to simplify the expression.

101. $\log_3 3^{4x-3}$

102. $\log_8 8^{3x^2}$

103. $e^{\ln(6x-3)}$

104. $12x + e^{\ln x(x-2)}$

5.5   Multiple Angle and Product-to-Sum Formulas

Multiple-Angle Formulas

In this section, you will study four other categories of trigonometric identities.

1. The first category involves *functions of multiple angles* such as $\sin ku$ and $\cos ku$.

2. The second category involves *squares of trigonometric functions* such as $\sin^2 u$.

3. The third category involves *functions of half-angles* such as $\sin(u/2)$.

4. The fourth category involves *products of trigonometric functions* such as $\sin u \cos v$.

You should learn the **double-angle formulas** because they are used often in trigonometry and calculus. For proofs of the formulas, see Proofs in Mathematics on page 443.

Double-Angle Formulas

$$\sin 2u = 2 \sin u \cos u \qquad \cos 2u = \cos^2 u - \sin^2 u$$

$$\tan 2u = \frac{2 \tan u}{1 - \tan^2 u} \qquad\qquad = 2 \cos^2 u - 1$$

$$= 1 - 2 \sin^2 u$$

Example 1   Solving a Multiple-Angle Equation

Solve $2 \cos x + \sin 2x = 0$.

Solution

Begin by rewriting the equation so that it involves functions of x (rather than $2x$). Then factor and solve as usual.

$2 \cos x + \sin 2x = 0$	Write original equation.
$2 \cos x + 2 \sin x \cos x = 0$	Double-angle formula
$2 \cos x(1 + \sin x) = 0$	Factor.
$2 \cos x = 0$ and $1 + \sin x = 0$	Set factors equal to zero.
$x = \dfrac{\pi}{2}, \dfrac{3\pi}{2} \qquad\qquad x = \dfrac{3\pi}{2}$	Solutions in $[0, 2\pi)$

So, the general solution is

$$x = \frac{\pi}{2} + 2n\pi \qquad \text{and} \qquad x = \frac{3\pi}{2} + 2n\pi$$

where n is an integer. Try verifying these solutions graphically.

✓CHECKPOINT   Now try Exercise 9.

Example 2   Using Double-Angle Formulas to Analyze Graphs

Use a double-angle formula to rewrite the equation

$$y = 4 \cos^2 x - 2.$$

Then sketch the graph of the equation over the interval $[0, 2\pi]$.

Solution

Using the double-angle formula for $\cos 2u$, you can rewrite the original equation as

$$y = 4 \cos^2 x - 2 \qquad \text{Write original equation.}$$

$$= 2(2 \cos^2 x - 1) \qquad \text{Factor.}$$

$$= 2 \cos 2x. \qquad \text{Use double-angle formula.}$$

Using the techniques discussed in Section 4.5, you can recognize that the graph of this function has an amplitude of 2 and a period of π. The key points in the interval $[0, \pi]$ are as follows.

Maximum	Intercept	Minimum	Intercept	Maximum
$(0, 2)$	$\left(\dfrac{\pi}{4}, 0\right)$	$\left(\dfrac{\pi}{2}, -2\right)$	$\left(\dfrac{3\pi}{4}, 0\right)$	$(\pi, 2)$

FIGURE 5.9

Two cycles of the graph are shown in Figure 5.9.

✔CHECKPOINT   Now try Exercise 21.

Example 3   Evaluating Functions Involving Double Angles

Use the following to find $\sin 2\theta$, $\cos 2\theta$, and $\tan 2\theta$.

$$\cos \theta = \frac{5}{13}, \qquad \frac{3\pi}{2} < \theta < 2\pi$$

Solution

From Figure 5.10, you can see that $\sin \theta = y/r = -12/13$. Consequently, using each of the double-angle formulas, you can write

$$\sin 2\theta = 2 \sin \theta \cos \theta = 2\left(-\frac{12}{13}\right)\left(\frac{5}{13}\right) = -\frac{120}{169}$$

$$\cos 2\theta = 2 \cos^2 \theta - 1 = 2\left(\frac{25}{169}\right) - 1 = -\frac{119}{169}$$

$$\tan 2\theta = \frac{\sin 2\theta}{\cos 2\theta} = \frac{120}{119}.$$

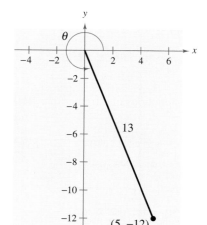

FIGURE 5.10

✔CHECKPOINT   Now try Exercise 23.

The double-angle formulas are not restricted to angles 2θ and θ. Other *double* combinations, such as 4θ and 2θ or 6θ and 3θ, are also valid. Here are two examples.

$$\sin 4\theta = 2 \sin 2\theta \cos 2\theta \qquad \text{and} \qquad \cos 6\theta = \cos^2 3\theta - \sin^2 3\theta$$

By using double-angle formulas together with the sum formulas given in the preceding section, you can form other multiple-angle formulas.

Example 4   **Deriving a Triple-Angle Formula**

$$\sin 3x = \sin(2x + x)$$
$$= \sin 2x \cos x + \cos 2x \sin x$$
$$= 2 \sin x \cos x \cos x + (1 - 2 \sin^2 x)\sin x$$
$$= 2 \sin x \cos^2 x + \sin x - 2 \sin^3 x$$
$$= 2 \sin x(1 - \sin^2 x) + \sin x - 2 \sin^3 x$$
$$= 2 \sin x - 2 \sin^3 x + \sin x - 2 \sin^3 x$$
$$= 3 \sin x - 4 \sin^3 x$$

✓CHECKPOINT   Now try Exercise 97.

Power-Reducing Formulas

The double-angle formulas can be used to obtain the following **power-reducing formulas.** Example 5 shows a typical power reduction that is used in calculus.

Power-Reducing Formulas

$$\sin^2 u = \frac{1 - \cos 2u}{2} \qquad \cos^2 u = \frac{1 + \cos 2u}{2} \qquad \tan^2 u = \frac{1 - \cos 2u}{1 + \cos 2u}$$

For a proof of the power-reducing formulas, see Proofs in Mathematics on page 443.

Example 5   **Reducing a Power**

Rewrite $\sin^4 x$ as a sum of first powers of the cosines of multiple angles.

Solution

Note the repeated use of power-reducing formulas.

$$\sin^4 x = (\sin^2 x)^2 \qquad\qquad\qquad \text{Property of exponents}$$

$$= \left(\frac{1 - \cos 2x}{2}\right)^2 \qquad\qquad \text{Power-reducing formula}$$

$$= \frac{1}{4}(1 - 2 \cos 2x + \cos^2 2x) \qquad \text{Expand.}$$

$$= \frac{1}{4}\left(1 - 2 \cos 2x + \frac{1 + \cos 4x}{2}\right) \qquad \text{Power-reducing formula}$$

$$= \frac{1}{4} - \frac{1}{2} \cos 2x + \frac{1}{8} + \frac{1}{8} \cos 4x \qquad \text{Distributive Property}$$

$$= \frac{1}{8}(3 - 4 \cos 2x + \cos 4x) \qquad \text{Factor out common factor.}$$

✓CHECKPOINT   Now try Exercise 29.

Half-Angle Formulas

You can derive some useful alternative forms of the power-reducing formulas by replacing u with $u/2$. The results are called **half-angle formulas.**

Half-Angle Formulas

$$\sin \frac{u}{2} = \pm \sqrt{\frac{1 - \cos u}{2}}$$

$$\cos \frac{u}{2} = \pm \sqrt{\frac{1 + \cos u}{2}}$$

$$\tan \frac{u}{2} = \frac{1 - \cos u}{\sin u} = \frac{\sin u}{1 + \cos u}$$

The signs of $\sin \dfrac{u}{2}$ and $\cos \dfrac{u}{2}$ depend on the quadrant in which $\dfrac{u}{2}$ lies.

Example 6 **Using a Half-Angle Formula**

Find the exact value of $\sin 105°$.

Solution

Begin by noting that $105°$ is half of $210°$. Then, using the half-angle formula for $\sin(u/2)$ and the fact that $105°$ lies in Quadrant II, you have

$$\sin 105° = \sqrt{\frac{1 - \cos 210°}{2}}$$

$$= \sqrt{\frac{1 - (-\cos 30°)}{2}}$$

$$= \sqrt{\frac{1 + \left(\sqrt{3}/2\right)}{2}}$$

$$= \frac{\sqrt{2 + \sqrt{3}}}{2}.$$

The positive square root is chosen because $\sin \theta$ is positive in Quadrant II.

✓**CHECKPOINT** Now try Exercise 41.

Use your calculator to verify the result obtained in Example 6. That is, evaluate $\sin 105°$ and $\left(\sqrt{2 + \sqrt{3}}\right)/2$.

$$\sin 105° \approx 0.9659258$$

$$\frac{\sqrt{2 + \sqrt{3}}}{2} \approx 0.9659258$$

You can see that both values are approximately 0.9659258.

STUDY TIP

To find the exact value of a trigonometric function with an angle measure in D°M′S″ form using a half-angle formula, first convert the angle measure to decimal degree form. Then multiply the resulting angle measure by 2.

Example 7   **Solving a Trigonometric Equation**

Find all solutions of $2 - \sin^2 x = 2 \cos^2 \dfrac{x}{2}$ in the interval $[0, 2\pi)$.

Algebraic Solution

$$2 - \sin^2 x = 2 \cos^2 \frac{x}{2} \qquad \text{Write original equation.}$$

$$2 - \sin^2 x = 2 \left(\pm \sqrt{\frac{1 + \cos x}{2}} \right)^2 \qquad \text{Half-angle formula}$$

$$2 - \sin^2 x = 2 \left(\frac{1 + \cos x}{2} \right) \qquad \text{Simplify.}$$

$$2 - \sin^2 x = 1 + \cos x \qquad \text{Simplify.}$$

$$2 - (1 - \cos^2 x) = 1 + \cos x \qquad \text{Pythagorean identity}$$

$$\cos^2 x - \cos x = 0 \qquad \text{Simplify.}$$

$$\cos x (\cos x - 1) = 0 \qquad \text{Factor.}$$

By setting the factors $\cos x$ and $\cos x - 1$ equal to zero, you find that the solutions in the interval $[0, 2\pi)$ are

$$x = \frac{\pi}{2}, \qquad x = \frac{3\pi}{2}, \qquad \text{and} \qquad x = 0.$$

✔CHECKPOINT   Now try Exercise 59.

Graphical Solution

Use a graphing utility set in *radian* mode to graph $y = 2 - \sin^2 x - 2 \cos^2(x/2)$, as shown in Figure 5.11. Use the *zero* or *root* feature or the *zoom* and *trace* features to approximate the x-intercepts in the interval $[0, 2\pi)$ to be

$$x = 0, \, x \approx 1.571 \approx \frac{\pi}{2}, \text{ and } x \approx 4.712 \approx \frac{3\pi}{2}.$$

These values are the approximate solutions of $2 - \sin^2 x - 2 \cos^2(x/2) = 0$ in the interval $[0, 2\pi)$.

FIGURE 5.11

Product-to-Sum Formulas

Each of the following **product-to-sum formulas** is easily verified using the sum and difference formulas discussed in the preceding section.

> **Product-to-Sum Formulas**
>
> $$\sin u \sin v = \frac{1}{2} [\cos(u - v) - \cos(u + v)]$$
>
> $$\cos u \cos v = \frac{1}{2} [\cos(u - v) + \cos(u + v)]$$
>
> $$\sin u \cos v = \frac{1}{2} [\sin(u + v) + \sin(u - v)]$$
>
> $$\cos u \sin v = \frac{1}{2} [\sin(u + v) - \sin(u - v)]$$

Product-to-sum formulas are used in calculus to evaluate integrals involving the products of sines and cosines of two different angles.

Example 8   Writing Products as Sums

Rewrite the product $\cos 5x \sin 4x$ as a sum or difference.

Solution

Using the appropriate product-to-sum formula, you obtain

$$\cos 5x \sin 4x = \tfrac{1}{2}[\sin(5x + 4x) - \sin(5x - 4x)]$$

$$= \tfrac{1}{2} \sin 9x - \tfrac{1}{2} \sin x.$$

✓CHECKPOINT   Now try Exercise 67.

     Occasionally, it is useful to reverse the procedure and write a sum of trigonometric functions as a product. This can be accomplished with the following **sum-to-product formulas.**

Sum-to-Product Formulas

$$\sin u + \sin v = 2 \sin\!\left(\frac{u + v}{2}\right) \cos\!\left(\frac{u - v}{2}\right)$$

$$\sin u - \sin v = 2 \cos\!\left(\frac{u + v}{2}\right) \sin\!\left(\frac{u - v}{2}\right)$$

$$\cos u + \cos v = 2 \cos\!\left(\frac{u + v}{2}\right) \cos\!\left(\frac{u - v}{2}\right)$$

$$\cos u - \cos v = -2 \sin\!\left(\frac{u + v}{2}\right) \sin\!\left(\frac{u - v}{2}\right)$$

For a proof of the sum-to-product formulas, see Proofs in Mathematics on page 444.

Example 9   Using a Sum-to-Product Formula

Find the exact value of $\cos 195° + \cos 105°$.

Solution

Using the appropriate sum-to-product formula, you obtain

$$\cos 195° + \cos 105° = 2 \cos\!\left(\frac{195° + 105°}{2}\right) \cos\!\left(\frac{195° - 105°}{2}\right)$$

$$= 2 \cos 150° \cos 45°$$

$$= 2\!\left(-\frac{\sqrt{3}}{2}\right)\!\left(\frac{\sqrt{2}}{2}\right)$$

$$= -\frac{\sqrt{6}}{2}.$$

✓CHECKPOINT   Now try Exercise 83.

Example 10   **Solving a Trigonometric Equation**

Solve $\sin 5x + \sin 3x = 0$.

Solution

$$\sin 5x + \sin 3x = 0 \qquad \text{Write original equation.}$$

$$2 \sin\left(\frac{5x + 3x}{2}\right) \cos\left(\frac{5x - 3x}{2}\right) = 0 \qquad \text{Sum-to-product formula}$$

$$2 \sin 4x \cos x = 0 \qquad \text{Simplify.}$$

By setting the factor $2 \sin 4x$ equal to zero, you can find that the solutions in the interval $[0, 2\pi)$ are

$$x = 0, \frac{\pi}{4}, \frac{\pi}{2}, \frac{3\pi}{4}, \pi, \frac{5\pi}{4}, \frac{3\pi}{2}, \frac{7\pi}{4}.$$

The equation $\cos x = 0$ yields no additional solutions, and you can conclude that the solutions are of the form

$$x = \frac{n\pi}{4}$$

where n is an integer. You can confirm this graphically by sketching the graph of $y = \sin 5x + \sin 3x$, as shown in Figure 5.12. From the graph you can see that the x-intercepts occur at multiples of $\pi/4$.

✓*CHECKPOINT*   Now try Exercise 87.

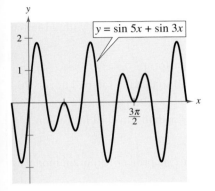

$y = \sin 5x + \sin 3x$

FIGURE **5.12**

Example 11   **Verifying a Trigonometric Identity**

Verify the identity

$$\frac{\sin t + \sin 3t}{\cos t + \cos 3t} = \tan 2t.$$

Solution

Using appropriate sum-to-product formulas, you have

$$\frac{\sin t + \sin 3t}{\cos t + \cos 3t} = \frac{2 \sin\left(\dfrac{t + 3t}{2}\right) \cos\left(\dfrac{t - 3t}{2}\right)}{2 \cos\left(\dfrac{t + 3t}{2}\right) \cos\left(\dfrac{t - 3t}{2}\right)}$$

$$= \frac{2 \sin(2t)\cos(-t)}{2 \cos(2t)\cos(-t)}$$

$$= \frac{\sin 2t}{\cos 2t}$$

$$= \tan 2t.$$

✓*CHECKPOINT*   Now try Exercise 105.

Application

Example 12 **Projectile Motion**

Ignoring air resistance, the range of a projectile fired at an angle θ with the horizontal and with an initial velocity of v_0 feet per second is given by

$$r = \frac{1}{16} v_0{}^2 \sin \theta \cos \theta$$

where r is the horizontal distance (in feet) that the projectile will travel. A place kicker for a football team can kick a football from ground level with an initial velocity of 80 feet per second (see Figure 5.13).

Not drawn to scale

FIGURE **5.13**

a. Write the projectile motion model in a simpler form.

b. At what angle must the player kick the football so that the football travels 200 feet?

c. For what angle is the horizontal distance the football travels a maximum?

Solution

a. You can use a double-angle formula to rewrite the projectile motion model as

$$r = \frac{1}{32} v_0{}^2 (2 \sin \theta \cos \theta) \qquad \text{Rewrite original projectile motion model.}$$

$$= \frac{1}{32} v_0{}^2 \sin 2\theta. \qquad \text{Rewrite model using a double-angle formula.}$$

b. $\quad r = \dfrac{1}{32} v_0{}^2 \sin 2\theta \qquad$ Write projectile motion model.

$$200 = \frac{1}{32}(80)^2 \sin 2\theta \qquad \text{Substitute 200 for } r \text{ and 80 for } v_0.$$

$$200 = 200 \sin 2\theta \qquad \text{Simplify.}$$

$$1 = \sin 2\theta \qquad \text{Divide each side by 200.}$$

You know that $2\theta = \pi/2$, so dividing this result by 2 produces $\theta = \pi/4$. Because $\pi/4 = 45°$, you can conclude that the player must kick the football at an angle of $45°$ so that the football will travel 200 feet.

c. From the model $r = 200 \sin 2\theta$ you can see that the amplitude is 200. So the maximum range is $r = 200$ feet. From part (b), you know that this corresponds to an angle of $45°$. Therefore, kicking the football at an angle of $45°$ will produce a maximum horizontal distance of 200 feet.

✓CHECKPOINT   Now try Exercise 119.

WRITING ABOUT **M**ATHEMATICS

Deriving an Area Formula   Describe how you can use a double-angle formula or a half-angle formula to derive a formula for the area of an isosceles triangle. Use a labeled sketch to illustrate your derivation. Then write two examples that show how your formula can be used.

5.5 | Exercises

VOCABULARY CHECK: Fill in the blank to complete the trigonometric formula.

1. $\sin 2u =$ _____

2. $\dfrac{1 + \cos 2u}{2} =$ _____

3. $\cos 2u =$ _____

4. $\dfrac{1 - \cos 2u}{1 + \cos 2u} =$ _____

5. $\sin \dfrac{u}{2} =$ _____

6. $\tan \dfrac{u}{2} =$ _____

7. $\cos u \cos v =$ _____

8. $\sin u \cos v =$ _____

9. $\sin u + \sin v =$ _____

10. $\cos u - \cos v =$ _____

PREREQUISITE SKILLS REVIEW: Practice and review algebra skills needed for this section at **www.Eduspace.com.**

In Exercises 1–8, use the figure to find the exact value of the trigonometric function.

1. $\sin \theta$

2. $\tan \theta$

3. $\cos 2\theta$

4. $\sin 2\theta$

5. $\tan 2\theta$

6. $\sec 2\theta$

7. $\csc 2\theta$

8. $\cot 2\theta$

In Exercises 9–18, find the exact solutions of the equation in the interval $[0, 2\pi)$.

9. $\sin 2x - \sin x = 0$

10. $\sin 2x + \cos x = 0$

11. $4 \sin x \cos x = 1$

12. $\sin 2x \sin x = \cos x$

13. $\cos 2x - \cos x = 0$

14. $\cos 2x + \sin x = 0$

15. $\tan 2x - \cot x = 0$

16. $\tan 2x - 2 \cos x = 0$

17. $\sin 4x = -2 \sin 2x$

18. $(\sin 2x + \cos 2x)^2 = 1$

In Exercises 19–22, use a double-angle formula to rewrite the expression.

19. $6 \sin x \cos x$

20. $6 \cos^2 x - 3$

21. $4 - 8 \sin^2 x$

22. $(\cos x + \sin x)(\cos x - \sin x)$

In Exercises 23–28, find the exact values of sin 2u, cos 2u, and tan 2u using the double-angle formulas.

23. $\sin u = -\dfrac{4}{5}, \quad \pi < u < \dfrac{3\pi}{2}$

24. $\cos u = -\dfrac{2}{3}, \quad \dfrac{\pi}{2} < u < \pi$

25. $\tan u = \dfrac{3}{4}, \quad 0 < u < \dfrac{\pi}{2}$

26. $\cot u = -4, \quad \dfrac{3\pi}{2} < u < 2\pi$

27. $\sec u = -\dfrac{5}{2}, \quad \dfrac{\pi}{2} < u < \pi$

28. $\csc u = 3, \quad \dfrac{\pi}{2} < u < \pi$

In Exercises 29–34, use the power-reducing formulas to rewrite the expression in terms of the first power of the cosine.

29. $\cos^4 x$

30. $\sin^8 x$

31. $\sin^2 x \cos^2 x$

32. $\sin^4 x \cos^4 x$

33. $\sin^2 x \cos^4 x$

34. $\sin^4 x \cos^2 x$

In Exercises 35–40, use the figure to find the exact value of the trigonometric function.

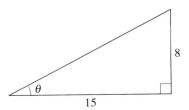

35. $\cos \dfrac{\theta}{2}$

36. $\sin \dfrac{\theta}{2}$

37. $\tan \dfrac{\theta}{2}$

38. $\sec \dfrac{\theta}{2}$

39. $\csc \dfrac{\theta}{2}$

40. $\cot \dfrac{\theta}{2}$

In Exercises 41–48, use the half-angle formulas to determine the exact values of the sine, cosine, and tangent of the angle.

41. $75°$

42. $165°$

43. $112° \, 30'$

44. $67° \, 30'$

45. $\dfrac{\pi}{8}$

46. $\dfrac{\pi}{12}$

47. $\dfrac{3\pi}{8}$

48. $\dfrac{7\pi}{12}$

In Exercises 49–54, find the exact values of $\sin(u/2)$, $\cos(u/2)$, and $\tan(u/2)$ using the half-angle formulas.

49. $\sin u = \dfrac{5}{13}, \quad \dfrac{\pi}{2} < u < \pi$

50. $\cos u = \dfrac{3}{5}, \quad 0 < u < \dfrac{\pi}{2}$

51. $\tan u = -\dfrac{5}{8}, \quad \dfrac{3\pi}{2} < u < 2\pi$

52. $\cot u = 3, \quad \pi < u < \dfrac{3\pi}{2}$

53. $\csc u = -\dfrac{5}{3}, \quad \pi < u < \dfrac{3\pi}{2}$

54. $\sec u = -\dfrac{7}{2}, \quad \dfrac{\pi}{2} < u < \pi$

In Exercises 55–58, use the half-angle formulas to simplify the expression.

55. $\sqrt{\dfrac{1 - \cos 6x}{2}}$

56. $\sqrt{\dfrac{1 + \cos 4x}{2}}$

57. $-\sqrt{\dfrac{1 - \cos 8x}{1 + \cos 8x}}$

58. $-\sqrt{\dfrac{1 - \cos(x - 1)}{2}}$

 In Exercises 59–62, find all solutions of the equation in the interval $[0, 2\pi)$. Use a graphing utility to graph the equation and verify the solutions.

59. $\sin \dfrac{x}{2} + \cos x = 0$

60. $\sin \dfrac{x}{2} + \cos x - 1 = 0$

61. $\cos \dfrac{x}{2} - \sin x = 0$

62. $\tan \dfrac{x}{2} - \sin x = 0$

In Exercises 63–74, use the product-to-sum formulas to write the product as a sum or difference.

63. $6 \sin \dfrac{\pi}{4} \cos \dfrac{\pi}{4}$

64. $4 \cos \dfrac{\pi}{3} \sin \dfrac{5\pi}{6}$

65. $10 \cos 75° \cos 15°$

66. $6 \sin 45° \cos 15°$

67. $\cos 4\theta \sin 6\theta$

68. $3 \sin 2\alpha \sin 3\alpha$

69. $5 \cos(-5\beta) \cos 3\beta$

70. $\cos 2\theta \cos 4\theta$

71. $\sin(x + y) \sin(x - y)$

72. $\sin(x + y) \cos(x - y)$

73. $\cos(\theta - \pi) \sin(\theta + \pi)$

74. $\sin(\theta + \pi) \sin(\theta - \pi)$

In Exercises 75–82, use the sum-to-product formulas to write the sum or difference as a product.

75. $\sin 5\theta - \sin 3\theta$

76. $\sin 3\theta + \sin \theta$

77. $\cos 6x + \cos 2x$

78. $\sin x + \sin 5x$

79. $\sin(\alpha + \beta) - \sin(\alpha - \beta)$

80. $\cos(\phi + 2\pi) + \cos \phi$

81. $\cos\left(\theta + \dfrac{\pi}{2}\right) - \cos\left(\theta - \dfrac{\pi}{2}\right)$

82. $\sin\left(x + \dfrac{\pi}{2}\right) + \sin\left(x - \dfrac{\pi}{2}\right)$

In Exercises 83–86, use the sum-to-product formulas to find the exact value of the expression.

83. $\sin 60° + \sin 30°$

84. $\cos 120° + \cos 30°$

85. $\cos \dfrac{3\pi}{4} - \cos \dfrac{\pi}{4}$

86. $\sin \dfrac{5\pi}{4} - \sin \dfrac{3\pi}{4}$

In Exercises 87–90, find all solutions of the equation in the interval $[0, 2\pi)$. Use a graphing utility to graph the equation and verify the solutions.

87. $\sin 6x + \sin 2x = 0$

88. $\cos 2x - \cos 6x = 0$

89. $\dfrac{\cos 2x}{\sin 3x - \sin x} - 1 = 0$

90. $\sin^2 3x - \sin^2 x = 0$

In Exercises 91–94, use the figure and trigonometric identities to find the exact value of the trigonometric function in two ways.

91. $\sin^2 \alpha$

92. $\cos^2 \alpha$

93. $\sin \alpha \cos \beta$

94. $\cos \alpha \sin \beta$

In Exercises 95–110, verify the identity.

95. $\csc 2\theta = \dfrac{\csc \theta}{2 \cos \theta}$

96. $\sec 2\theta = \dfrac{\sec^2 \theta}{2 - \sec^2 \theta}$

97. $\cos^2 2\alpha - \sin^2 2\alpha = \cos 4\alpha$

98. $\cos^4 x - \sin^4 x = \cos 2x$

99. $(\sin x + \cos x)^2 = 1 + \sin 2x$

100. $\sin\dfrac{\alpha}{3}\cos\dfrac{\alpha}{3} = \dfrac{1}{2}\sin\dfrac{2\alpha}{3}$

101. $1 + \cos 10y = 2\cos^2 5y$

102. $\dfrac{\cos 3\beta}{\cos \beta} = 1 - 4\sin^2 \beta$

103. $\sec\dfrac{u}{2} = \pm\sqrt{\dfrac{2\tan u}{\tan u + \sin u}}$

104. $\tan\dfrac{u}{2} = \csc u - \cot u$

105. $\dfrac{\sin x \pm \sin y}{\cos x + \cos y} = \tan\dfrac{x \pm y}{2}$

106. $\dfrac{\sin x + \sin y}{\cos x - \cos y} = -\cot\dfrac{x - y}{2}$

107. $\dfrac{\cos 4x + \cos 2x}{\sin 4x + \sin 2x} = \cot 3x$

108. $\dfrac{\cos t + \cos 3t}{\sin 3t - \sin t} = \cot t$

109. $\sin\left(\dfrac{\pi}{6} + x\right) + \sin\left(\dfrac{\pi}{6} - x\right) = \cos x$

110. $\cos\left(\dfrac{\pi}{3} + x\right) + \cos\left(\dfrac{\pi}{3} - x\right) = \cos x$

In Exercises 111–114, use a graphing utility to verify the identity. Confirm that it is an identity algebraically.

111. $\cos 3\beta = \cos^3 \beta - 3\sin^2 \beta \cos \beta$

112. $\sin 4\beta = 4\sin \beta \cos \beta(1 - 2\sin^2 \beta)$

113. $(\cos 4x - \cos 2x)/(2\sin 3x) = -\sin x$

114. $(\cos 3x - \cos x)/(\sin 3x - \sin x) = -\tan 2x$

In Exercises 115 and 116, graph the function by hand in the interval $[0, 2\pi]$ by using the power-reducing formulas.

115. $f(x) = \sin^2 x$ **116.** $f(x) = \cos^2 x$

In Exercises 117 and 118, write the trigonometric expression as an algebraic expression.

117. $\sin(2 \arcsin x)$ **118.** $\cos(2 \arccos x)$

119. *Projectile Motion* The range of a projectile fired at an angle θ with the horizontal and with an initial velocity of v_0 feet per second is

$$r = \dfrac{1}{32}v_0^2 \sin 2\theta$$

where r is measured in feet. An athlete throws a javelin at 75 feet per second. At what angle must the athlete throw the javelin so that the javelin travels 130 feet?

120. *Geometry* The length of each of the two equal sides of an isosceles triangle is 10 meters (see figure). The angle between the two sides is θ.

(a) Write the area of the triangle as a function of $\theta/2$.

(b) Write the area of the triangle as a function of θ. Determine the value of θ such that the area is a maximum.

Model It

121. *Mach Number* The mach number M of an airplane is the ratio of its speed to the speed of sound. When an airplane travels faster than the speed of sound, the sound waves form a cone behind the airplane (see figure). The mach number is related to the apex angle θ of the cone by

$$\sin\dfrac{\theta}{2} = \dfrac{1}{M}.$$

(a) Find the angle θ that corresponds to a mach number of 1.

(b) Find the angle θ that corresponds to a mach number of 4.5.

(c) The speed of sound is about 760 miles per hour. Determine the speed of an object with the mach numbers from parts (a) and (b).

(d) Rewrite the equation in terms of θ.

122. **Railroad Track** When two railroad tracks merge, the overlapping portions of the tracks are in the shapes of circular arcs (see figure). The radius of each arc r (in feet) and the angle θ are related by

$$\frac{x}{2} = 2r \sin^2 \frac{\theta}{2}.$$

Write a formula for x in terms of $\cos \theta$.

Synthesis

True or False? In Exercises 123 and 124, determine whether the statement is true or false. Justify your answer.

123. Because the sine function is an odd function, for a negative number u, $\sin 2u = -2 \sin u \cos u$.

124. $\sin \dfrac{u}{2} = -\sqrt{\dfrac{1 - \cos u}{2}}$ when u is in the second quadrant.

 In Exercises 125 and 126, (a) use a graphing utility to graph the function and approximate the maximum and minimum points on the graph in the interval $[0, 2\pi)$ and (b) solve the trigonometric equation and verify that its solutions are the x-coordinates of the maximum and minimum points of f. (Calculus is required to find the trigonometric equation.)

Function	*Trigonometric Equation*
125. $f(x) = 4 \sin \dfrac{x}{2} + \cos x$	$2 \cos \dfrac{x}{2} - \sin x = 0$
126. $f(x) = \cos 2x - 2 \sin x$	$-2 \cos x(2 \sin x + 1) = 0$

127. **Exploration** Consider the function given by

$$f(x) = \sin^4 x + \cos^4 x.$$

(a) Use the power-reducing formulas to write the function in terms of cosine to the first power.

 (b) Determine another way of rewriting the function. Use a graphing utility to rule out incorrectly rewritten functions.

 (c) Add a trigonometric term to the function so that it becomes a perfect square trinomial. Rewrite the function as a perfect square trinomial minus the term that you added. Use a graphing utility to rule out incorrectly rewritten functions.

 (d) Rewrite the result of part (c) in terms of the sine of a double angle. Use a graphing utility to rule out incorrectly rewritten functions.

(e) When you rewrite a trigonometric expression, the result may not be the same as a friend's. Does this mean that one of you is wrong? Explain.

128. **Conjecture** Consider the function given by

$$f(x) = 2 \sin x \left(2 \cos^2 \frac{x}{2} - 1 \right).$$

 (a) Use a graphing utility to graph the function.

(b) Make a conjecture about the function that is an identity with f.

(c) Verify your conjecture analytically.

Skills Review

In Exercises 129–132, (a) plot the points, (b) find the distance between the points, and (c) find the midpoint of the line segment connecting the points.

129. $(5, 2), (-1, 4)$

130. $(-4, -3), (6, 10)$

131. $\left(0, \frac{1}{2}\right), \left(\frac{4}{3}, \frac{5}{2}\right)$

132. $\left(\frac{1}{3}, \frac{2}{3}\right), \left(-1, -\frac{3}{2}\right)$

In Exercises 133–136, find (if possible) the complement and supplement of each angle.

133. (a) $55°$ (b) $162°$

134. (a) $109°$ (b) $78°$

135. (a) $\dfrac{\pi}{18}$ (b) $\dfrac{9\pi}{20}$

136. (a) 0.95 (b) 2.76

137. **Profit** The total profit for a car manufacturer in October was 16% higher than it was in September. The total profit for the 2 months was $507,600. Find the profit for each month.

138. **Mixture Problem** A 55-gallon barrel contains a mixture with a concentration of 30%. How much of this mixture must be withdrawn and replaced by 100% concentrate to bring the mixture up to 50% concentration?

139. **Distance** A baseball diamond has the shape of a square in which the distance between each of the consecutive bases is 90 feet. Approximate the straight-line distance from home plate to second base.

5.6 Law of Sines

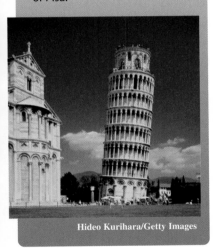

Hideo Kurihara/Getty Images

Introduction

In Chapter 4, you studied techniques for solving right triangles. In this section and the next, you will solve **oblique triangles**—triangles that have no right angles. As standard notation, the angles of a triangle are labeled A, B, and C, and their opposite sides are labeled a, b, and c, as shown in Figure 5.14.

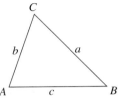

FIGURE 5.14

To solve an oblique triangle, you need to know the measure of at least one side and any two other parts of the triangle—either two sides, two angles, or one angle and one side. This breaks down into the following four cases.

1. Two angles and any side (AAS or ASA)
2. Two sides and an angle opposite one of them (SSA)
3. Three sides (SSS)
4. Two sides and their included angle (SAS)

The first two cases can be solved using the **Law of Sines,** whereas the last two cases require the Law of Cosines (see Section 5.7).

Law of Sines

If ABC is a triangle with sides a, b, and c, then

$$\frac{a}{\sin A} = \frac{b}{\sin B} = \frac{c}{\sin C}.$$

A is acute.

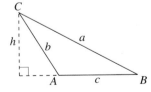

A is obtuse.

The Law of Sines can also be written in the reciprocal form

$$\frac{\sin A}{a} = \frac{\sin B}{b} = \frac{\sin C}{c}.$$

For a proof of the Law of Sines, see Proofs in Mathematics on page 444.

The HM mathSpace® CD-ROM and Eduspace® for this text contain additional resources related to the concepts discussed in this chapter.

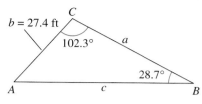

FIGURE **5.15**

Example 1   **Given Two Angles and One Side—AAS**

For the triangle in Figure 5.15, $C = 102.3°$, $B = 28.7°$, and $b = 27.4$ feet. Find the remaining angle and sides.

Solution

The third angle of the triangle is

$$A = 180° - B - C$$
$$= 180° - 28.7° - 102.3°$$
$$= 49.0°.$$

By the Law of Sines, you have

$$\frac{a}{\sin A} = \frac{b}{\sin B} = \frac{c}{\sin C}.$$

Using $b = 27.4$ produces

$$a = \frac{b}{\sin B}(\sin A) = \frac{27.4}{\sin 28.7°}(\sin 49.0°) \approx 43.06 \text{ feet}$$

and

$$c = \frac{b}{\sin B}(\sin C) = \frac{27.4}{\sin 28.7°}(\sin 102.3°) \approx 55.75 \text{ feet}.$$

✓CHECKPOINT   Now try Exercise 1.

Example 2   **Given Two Angles and One Side—ASA**

A pole tilts *toward* the sun at an 8° angle from the vertical, and it casts a 22-foot shadow. The angle of elevation from the tip of the shadow to the top of the pole is 43°. How tall is the pole?

Solution

From Figure 5.16, note that $A = 43°$ and $B = 90° + 8° = 98°$. So, the third angle is

$$C = 180° - A - B$$
$$= 180° - 43° - 98°$$
$$= 39°.$$

By the Law of Sines, you have

$$\frac{a}{\sin A} = \frac{c}{\sin C}.$$

Because $c = 22$ feet, the length of the pole is

$$a = \frac{c}{\sin C}(\sin A) = \frac{22}{\sin 39°}(\sin 43°) \approx 23.84 \text{ feet}.$$

✓CHECKPOINT   Now try Exercise 35.

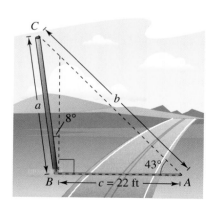

FIGURE **5.16**

For practice, try reworking Example 2 for a pole that tilts *away from* the sun under the same conditions.

The Ambiguous Case (SSA)

In Examples 1 and 2 you saw that two angles and one side determine a unique triangle. However, if two sides and one opposite angle are given, three possible situations can occur: (1) no such triangle exists, (2) one such triangle exists, or (3) two distinct triangles may satisfy the conditions.

The Ambiguous Case (SSA)

Consider a triangle in which you are given a, b, and A. $(h = b \sin A)$

	A is acute.	A is acute.	A is acute.	A is acute.	A is obtuse.	A is obtuse.
Sketch						
Necessary condition	$a < h$	$a = h$	$a \geq b$	$h < a < b$	$a \leq b$	$a > b$
Triangles possible	None	One	One	Two	None	One

Example 3   Single-Solution Case—SSA

For the triangle in Figure 5.17, $a = 22$ inches, $b = 12$ inches, and $A = 42°$. Find the remaining side and angles.

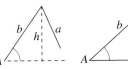

$b = 12$ in. $a = 22$ in.

One solution: $a > b$

FIGURE **5.17**

Solution

By the Law of Sines, you have

$$\frac{\sin B}{b} = \frac{\sin A}{a} \qquad \text{Reciprocal form}$$

$$\sin B = b\left(\frac{\sin A}{a}\right) \qquad \text{Multiply each side by } b.$$

$$\sin B = 12\left(\frac{\sin 42°}{22}\right) \qquad \text{Substitute for } A, a, \text{ and } b.$$

$$B \approx 21.41°. \qquad B \text{ is acute.}$$

Now, you can determine that

$$C \approx 180° - 42° - 21.41° = 116.59°.$$

Then, the remaining side is

$$\frac{c}{\sin C} = \frac{a}{\sin A}$$

$$c = \frac{a}{\sin A}(\sin C) = \frac{22}{\sin 42°}(\sin 116.59°) \approx 29.40 \text{ inches.}$$

✓CHECKPOINT   Now try Exercise 19.

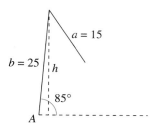

No solution: $a < h$

FIGURE 5.18

Example 4   **No-Solution Case—SSA**

Show that there is no triangle for which $a = 15$, $b = 25$, and $A = 85°$.

Solution

Begin by making the sketch shown in Figure 5.18. From this figure it appears that no triangle is formed. You can verify this using the Law of Sines.

$$\frac{\sin B}{b} = \frac{\sin A}{a} \qquad \text{Reciprocal form}$$

$$\sin B = b\left(\frac{\sin A}{a}\right) \qquad \text{Multiply each side by } b.$$

$$\sin B = 25\left(\frac{\sin 85°}{15}\right) \approx 1.660 > 1$$

This contradicts the fact that $|\sin B| \leq 1$. So, no triangle can be formed having sides $a = 15$ and $b = 25$ and an angle of $A = 85°$.

✓**CHECKPOINT**   Now try Exercise 21.

Example 5   **Two-Solution Case—SSA**

Find two triangles for which $a = 12$ meters, $b = 31$ meters, and $A = 20.5°$.

Solution

By the Law of Sines, you have

$$\frac{\sin B}{b} = \frac{\sin A}{a} \qquad \text{Reciprocal form}$$

$$\sin B = b\left(\frac{\sin A}{a}\right) = 31\left(\frac{\sin 20.5°}{12}\right) \approx 0.9047.$$

There are two angles $B_1 \approx 64.8°$ and $B_2 \approx 180° - 64.8° = 115.2°$ between $0°$ and $180°$ whose sine is 0.9047. For $B_1 \approx 64.8°$, you obtain

$$C \approx 180° - 20.5° - 64.8° = 94.7°$$

$$c = \frac{a}{\sin A}(\sin C) = \frac{12}{\sin 20.5°}(\sin 94.7°) \approx 34.15 \text{ meters.}$$

For $B_2 \approx 115.2°$, you obtain

$$C \approx 180° - 20.5° - 115.2° = 44.3°$$

$$c = \frac{a}{\sin A}(\sin C) = \frac{12}{\sin 20.5°}(\sin 44.3°) \approx 23.93 \text{ meters.}$$

The resulting triangles are shown in Figure 5.19.

FIGURE 5.19

✓**CHECKPOINT**   Now try Exercise 23.

Area of an Oblique Triangle

The procedure used to prove the Law of Sines leads to a simple formula for the area of an oblique triangle. Referring to Figure 5.20, note that each triangle has a height of $h = b \sin A$. Consequently, the area of each triangle is

$$\text{Area} = \frac{1}{2}(\text{base})(\text{height}) = \frac{1}{2}(c)(b \sin A) = \frac{1}{2}bc \sin A.$$

By similar arguments, you can develop the formulas

$$\text{Area} = \frac{1}{2}ab \sin C = \frac{1}{2}ac \sin B.$$

A is acute

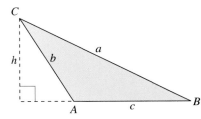

A is obtuse

FIGURE 5.20

> ## Area of an Oblique Triangle
>
> The area of any triangle is one-half the product of the lengths of two sides times the sine of their included angle. That is,
>
> $$\text{Area} = \frac{1}{2}bc \sin A = \frac{1}{2}ab \sin C = \frac{1}{2}ac \sin B.$$

Note that if angle A is 90°, the formula gives the area for a right triangle:

$$\text{Area} = \frac{1}{2}bc(\sin 90°) = \frac{1}{2}bc = \frac{1}{2}(\text{base})(\text{height}). \qquad \text{sin 90° = 1}$$

Similar results are obtained for angles C and B equal to 90°.

Example 6   Finding the Area of a Triangular Lot

Find the area of a triangular lot having two sides of lengths 90 meters and 52 meters and an included angle of 102°.

Solution

Consider $a = 90$ meters, $b = 52$ meters, and angle $C = 102°$, as shown in Figure 5.21. Then, the area of the triangle is

$$\text{Area} = \frac{1}{2}ab \sin C = \frac{1}{2}(90)(52)(\sin 102°) \approx 2289 \text{ square meters.}$$

✓CHECKPOINT   Now try Exercise 29.

FIGURE 5.21

FIGURE **5.22**

FIGURE **5.23**

Application

Example 7   **An Application of the Law of Sines**

The course for a boat race starts at point A in Figure 5.22 and proceeds in the direction S 52° W to point B, then in the direction S 40° E to point C, and finally back to A. Point C lies 8 kilometers directly south of point A. Approximate the total distance of the race course.

Solution

Because lines BD and AC are parallel, it follows that $\angle BCA \cong \angle DBC$. Consequently, triangle ABC has the measures shown in Figure 5.23. For angle B, you have $B = 180° - 52° - 40° = 88°$. Using the Law of Sines

$$\frac{a}{\sin 52°} = \frac{b}{\sin 88°} = \frac{c}{\sin 40°}$$

you can let $b = 8$ and obtain

$$a = \frac{8}{\sin 88°}(\sin 52°) \approx 6.308$$

and

$$c = \frac{8}{\sin 88°}(\sin 40°) \approx 5.145.$$

The total length of the course is approximately

$$\text{Length} \approx 8 + 6.308 + 5.145$$

$$= 19.453 \text{ kilometers.}$$

✓**CHECKPOINT**   Now try Exercise 39.

***W**RITING ABOUT **M**ATHEMATICS*

Using the Law of Sines   In this section, you have been using the Law of Sines to solve *oblique* triangles. Can the Law of Sines also be used to solve a right triangle? If so, write a short paragraph explaining how to use the Law of Sines to solve each triangle. Is there an easier way to solve these triangles?

a. (AAS)

b. (ASA)

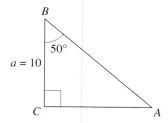

5.6 | Exercises

VOCABULARY CHECK: Fill in the blanks.

1. An _____ triangle is a triangle that has no right angle.

2. For triangle ABC, the Law of Sines is given by $\dfrac{a}{\sin A} =$ _____ $= \dfrac{c}{\sin C}$.

3. The area of an oblique triangle is given by $\frac{1}{2}bc \sin A = \frac{1}{2}ab \sin C =$ _____ .

PREREQUISITE SKILLS REVIEW: Practice and review algebra skills needed for this section at **www.Eduspace.com.**

In Exercises 1–18, use the Law of Sines to solve the triangle. Round your answers to two decimal places.

1.

2.

3.

4.

5. $A = 36°, \quad a = 8, \quad b = 5$

6. $A = 60°, \quad a = 9, \quad c = 10$

7. $A = 102.4°, \quad C = 16.7°, \quad a = 21.6$

8. $A = 24.3°, \quad C = 54.6°, \quad c = 2.68$

9. $A = 83° \, 20', \quad C = 54.6°, \quad c = 18.1$

10. $A = 5° \, 40', \quad B = 8° \, 15', \quad b = 4.8$

11. $B = 15° \, 30', \quad a = 4.5, \quad b = 6.8$

12. $B = 2° \, 45', \quad b = 6.2, \quad c = 5.8$

13. $C = 145°, \quad b = 4, \quad c = 14$

14. $A = 100°, \quad a = 125, \quad c = 10$

15. $A = 110° \, 15', \quad a = 48, \quad b = 16$

16. $C = 85° \, 20', \quad a = 35, \quad c = 50$

17. $A = 55°, \quad B = 42°, \quad c = \frac{3}{4}$

18. $B = 28°, \quad C = 104°, \quad a = 3\frac{5}{8}$

In Exercises 19–24, use the Law of Sines to solve (if possible) the triangle. If two solutions exist, find both. Round your answers to two decimal places.

19. $A = 110°, \quad a = 125, \quad b = 100$

20. $A = 110°, \quad a = 125, \quad b = 200$

21. $A = 76°, \quad a = 18, \quad b = 20$

22. $A = 76°, \quad a = 34, \quad b = 21$

23. $A = 58°, \quad a = 11.4, \quad b = 12.8$

24. $A = 58°, \quad a = 4.5, \quad b = 12.8$

In Exercises 25–28, find values for b such that the triangle has (a) one solution, (b) two solutions, and (c) no solution.

25. $A = 36°, \quad a = 5$

26. $A = 60°, \quad a = 10$

27. $A = 10°, \quad a = 10.8$

28. $A = 88°, \quad a = 315.6$

In Exercises 29–34, find the area of the triangle having the indicated angle and sides.

29. $C = 120°, \quad a = 4, \quad b = 6$

30. $B = 130°, \quad a = 62, \quad c = 20$

31. $A = 43° \, 45', \quad b = 57, \quad c = 85$

32. $A = 5° \, 15', \quad b = 4.5, \quad c = 22$

33. $B = 72° \, 30', \quad a = 105, \quad c = 64$

34. $C = 84° \, 30', \quad a = 16, \quad b = 20$

35. *Height* Because of prevailing winds, a tree grew so that it was leaning 4° from the vertical. At a point 35 meters from the tree, the angle of elevation to the top of the tree is 23° (see figure). Find the height h of the tree.

36. *Height* A flagpole at a right angle to the horizontal is located on a slope that makes an angle of 12° with the horizontal. The flagpole's shadow is 16 meters long and points directly up the slope. The angle of elevation from the tip of the shadow to the sun is 20°.

(a) Draw a triangle that represents the problem. Show the known quantities on the triangle and use a variable to indicate the height of the flagpole.

(b) Write an equation involving the unknown quantity.

(c) Find the height of the flagpole.

37. *Angle of Elevation* A 10-meter telephone pole casts a 17-meter shadow directly down a slope when the angle of elevation of the sun is 42° (see figure). Find θ, the angle of elevation of the ground.

38. *Flight Path* A plane flies 500 kilometers with a bearing of 316° from Naples to Elgin (see figure). The plane then flies 720 kilometers from Elgin to Canton (Canton is due west of Naples). Find the bearing of the flight from Elgin to Canton.

39. *Bridge Design* A bridge is to be built across a small lake from a gazebo to a dock (see figure). The bearing from the gazebo to the dock is S 41° W. From a tree 100 meters from the gazebo, the bearings to the gazebo and the dock are S 74° E and S 28° E, respectively. Find the distance from the gazebo to the dock.

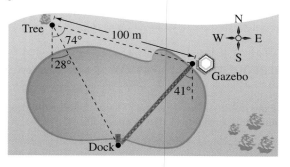

40. *Railroad Track Design* The circular arc of a railroad curve has a chord of length 3000 feet and a central angle of 40°.

(a) Draw a diagram that visually represents the problem. Show the known quantities on the diagram and use the variables r and s to represent the radius of the arc and the length of the arc, respectively.

(b) Find the radius r of the circular arc.

(c) Find the length s of the circular arc.

41. *Glide Path* A pilot has just started on the glide path for landing at an airport with a runway of length 9000 feet. The angles of depression from the plane to the ends of the runway are 17.5° and 18.8°.

(a) Draw a diagram that visually represents the problem.

(b) Find the air distance the plane must travel until touching down on the near end of the runway.

(c) Find the ground distance the plane must travel until touching down.

(d) Find the altitude of the plane when the pilot begins the descent.

42. *Locating a Fire* The bearing from the Pine Knob fire tower to the Colt Station fire tower is N 65° E, and the two towers are 30 kilometers apart. A fire spotted by rangers in each tower has a bearing of N 80° E from Pine Knob and S 70° E from Colt Station (see figure). Find the distance of the fire from each tower.

43. *Distance* A boat is sailing due east parallel to the shoreline at a speed of 10 miles per hour. At a given time, the bearing to the lighthouse is S 70° E, and 15 minutes later the bearing is S 63° E (see figure). The lighthouse is located at the shoreline. What is the distance from the boat to the shoreline?

Model It

44. *Shadow Length* The Leaning Tower of Pisa in Italy is characterized by its tilt. The tower leans because it was built on a layer of unstable soil—clay, sand, and water. The tower is approximately 58.36 meters tall from its foundation (see figure). The top of the tower leans about 5.45 meters off center.

(a) Find the angle of lean α of the tower.

(b) Write β as a function of d and θ, where θ is the angle of elevation to the sun.

(c) Use the Law of Sines to write an equation for the length d of the shadow cast by the tower.

(d) Use a graphing utility to complete the table.

θ	10°	20°	30°	40°	50°	60°
d						

Synthesis

True or False? **In Exercises 45 and 46, determine whether the statement is true or false. Justify your answer.**

45. If a triangle contains an obtuse angle, then it must be oblique.

46. Two angles and one side of a triangle do not necessarily determine a unique triangle.

47. *Graphical and Numerical Analysis* In the figure, α and β are positive angles.

(a) Write α as a function of β.

(b) Use a graphing utility to graph the function. Determine its domain and range.

(c) Use the result of part (a) to write c as a function of β.

(d) Use a graphing utility to graph the function in part (c). Determine its domain and range.

(e) Complete the table. What can you infer?

β	0.4	0.8	1.2	1.6	2.0	2.4	2.8
α							
c							

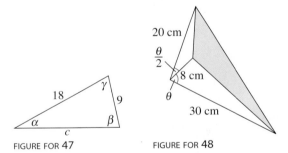

FIGURE FOR 47   FIGURE FOR 48

48. *Graphical Analysis*

(a) Write the area A of the shaded region in the figure as a function of θ.

(b) Use a graphing utility to graph the area function.

(c) Determine the domain of the area function. Explain how the area of the region and the domain of the function would change if the eight-centimeter line segment were decreased in length.

Skills Review

In Exercises 49–52, use the fundamental trigonometric identities to simplify the expression.

49. $\sin x \cot x$

50. $\tan x \cos x \sec x$

51. $1 - \sin^2\left(\dfrac{\pi}{2} - x\right)$

52. $1 + \cot^2\left(\dfrac{\pi}{2} - x\right)$

5.7 Law of Cosines

What you should learn

- Use the Law of Cosines to solve oblique triangles (SSS or SAS).
- Use the Law of Cosines to model and solve real-life problems.
- Use Heron's Area Formula to find the area of a triangle.

Why you should learn it

You can use the Law of Cosines to solve real-life problems involving oblique triangles. For instance, in Exercise 31 on page 433, you can use the Law of Cosines to approximate the length of a marsh.

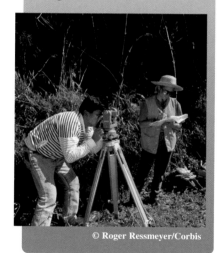

© Roger Ressmeyer/Corbis

Introduction

Two cases remain in the list of conditions needed to solve an oblique triangle—SSS and SAS. If you are given three sides (SSS), or two sides and their included angle (SAS), none of the ratios in the Law of Sines would be complete. In such cases, you can use the **Law of Cosines.**

Law of Cosines

Standard Form	Alternative Form
$a^2 = b^2 + c^2 - 2bc \cos A$	$\cos A = \dfrac{b^2 + c^2 - a^2}{2bc}$
$b^2 = a^2 + c^2 - 2ac \cos B$	$\cos B = \dfrac{a^2 + c^2 - b^2}{2ac}$
$c^2 = a^2 + b^2 - 2ab \cos C$	$\cos C = \dfrac{a^2 + b^2 - c^2}{2ab}$

For a proof of the Law of Cosines, see Proofs in Mathematics on page 445.

Example 1 Three Sides of a Triangle—SSS

Find the three angles of the triangle in Figure 5.24.

FIGURE 5.24

Solution

It is a good idea first to find the angle opposite the longest side—side b in this case. Using the alternative form of the Law of Cosines, you find that

$$\cos B = \frac{a^2 + c^2 - b^2}{2ac} = \frac{8^2 + 14^2 - 19^2}{2(8)(14)} \approx -0.45089.$$

Because $\cos B$ is negative, you know that B is an *obtuse* angle given by $B \approx 116.80°$. At this point, it is simpler to use the Law of Sines to determine A.

$$\sin A = a\left(\frac{\sin B}{b}\right) \approx 8\left(\frac{\sin 116.80°}{19}\right) \approx 0.37583$$

Because B is obtuse, A must be acute, because a triangle can have, at most, one obtuse angle. So, $A \approx 22.08°$ and $C \approx 180° - 22.08° - 116.80° = 41.12°$.

✓CHECKPOINT   Now try Exercise 1.

Do you see why it was wise to find the largest angle *first* in Example 1? Knowing the cosine of an angle, you can determine whether the angle is acute or obtuse. That is,

Do you see why it was wise to find the largest angle *first* in Example 1? Knowing the cosine of an angle, you can determine whether the angle is acute or obtuse. That is,

$\cos\theta > 0$ for $0° < \theta < 90°$ Acute

$\cos\theta < 0$ for $90° < \theta < 180°$.   Obtuse

So, in Example 1, once you found that angle B was obtuse, you knew that angles A and C were both acute. If the largest angle is acute, the remaining two angles are acute also.

Exploration

What familiar formula do you obtain when you use the third form of the Law of Cosines

$$c^2 = a^2 + b^2 - 2ab\cos C$$

and you let $C = 90°$? What is the relationship between the Law of Cosines and this formula?

Example 2   Two Sides and the Included Angle—SAS

Find the remaining angles and side of the triangle in Figure 5.25.

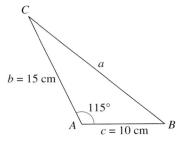

FIGURE **5.25**

Solution

Use the Law of Cosines to find the unknown side a in the figure.

$$a^2 = b^2 + c^2 - 2bc\cos A$$

$$a^2 = 15^2 + 10^2 - 2(15)(10)\cos 115°$$

$$a^2 \approx 451.79$$

$$a \approx 21.26$$

Because $a \approx 21.26$ centimeters, you now know the ratio $\sin A/a$ and you can use the reciprocal form of the Law of Sines to solve for B.

$$\frac{\sin B}{b} = \frac{\sin A}{a}$$

$$\sin B = b\left(\frac{\sin A}{a}\right)$$

$$= 15\left(\frac{\sin 115°}{21.26}\right)$$

$$\approx 0.63945$$

So, $B = \arcsin 0.63945 \approx 39.75°$ and $C \approx 180° - 115° - 39.75° = 25.25°$.

✓CHECKPOINT   Now try Exercise 3.

STUDY TIP

When solving an oblique triangle given three sides, you use the alternative form of the Law of Cosines to solve for an angle. When solving an oblique triangle given two sides and their included angle, you use the standard form of the Law of Cosines to solve for an unknown.

Applications

Example 3 **An Application of the Law of Cosines**

The pitcher's mound on a women's softball field is 43 feet from home plate and the distance between the bases is 60 feet, as shown in Figure 5.26. (The pitcher's mound is not halfway between home plate and second base.) How far is the pitcher's mound from first base?

Solution

In triangle HPF, $H = 45°$ (line HP bisects the right angle at H), $f = 43$, and $p = 60$. Using the Law of Cosines for this SAS case, you have

$$h^2 = f^2 + p^2 - 2fp \cos H$$

$$= 43^2 + 60^2 - 2(43)(60) \cos 45° \approx 1800.3$$

So, the approximate distance from the pitcher's mound to first base is

$$h \approx \sqrt{1800.3} \approx 42.43 \text{ feet.}$$

✔CHECKPOINT   Now try Exercise 31.

FIGURE **5.26**

Example 4 **An Application of the Law of Cosines**

A ship travels 60 miles due east, then adjusts its course northward, as shown in Figure 5.27. After traveling 80 miles in that direction, the ship is 139 miles from its point of departure. Describe the bearing from point B to point C.

FIGURE **5.27**

Solution

You have $a = 80$, $b = 139$, and $c = 60$; so, using the alternative form of the Law of Cosines, you have

$$\cos B = \frac{a^2 + c^2 - b^2}{2ac}$$

$$= \frac{80^2 + 60^2 - 139^2}{2(80)(60)}$$

$$\approx -0.97094.$$

So, $B \approx \arccos(-0.97094) \approx 166.15°$, and thus the bearing measured from due north from point B to point C is $166.15° - 90° = 76.15°$, or N $76.15°$ E.

✔CHECKPOINT   Now try Exercise 37.

Historical Note
Heron of Alexandria (c. 100 B.C.) was a Greek geometer and inventor. His works describe how to find the areas of triangles, quadrilaterals, regular polygons having 3 to 12 sides, and circles as well as the surface areas and volumes of three-dimensional objects.

Heron's Area Formula

The Law of Cosines can be used to establish the following formula for the area of a triangle. This formula is called **Heron's Area Formula** after the Greek mathematician Heron (c. 100 B.C.).

> ### Heron's Area Formula
>
> Given any triangle with sides of lengths a, b, and c, the area of the triangle is
>
> $$\text{Area} = \sqrt{s(s-a)(s-b)(s-c)}$$
>
> where $s = (a+b+c)/2$.

For a proof of Heron's Area Formula, see Proofs in Mathematics on page 446.

Example 5   Using Heron's Area Formula

Find the area of a triangle having sides of lengths $a = 43$ meters, $b = 53$ meters, and $c = 72$ meters.

Solution

Because $s = (a+b+c)/2 = 168/2 = 84$, Heron's Area Formula yields

$$\text{Area} = \sqrt{s(s-a)(s-b)(s-c)}$$

$$= \sqrt{84(41)(31)(12)} \approx 1131.89 \text{ square meters.}$$

✓CHECKPOINT   Now try Exercise 47.

You have now studied three different formulas for the area of a triangle.

Standard Formula	$\text{Area} = \frac{1}{2}bh$
Oblique Triangle	$\text{Area} = \frac{1}{2}bc\sin A = \frac{1}{2}ab\sin C = \frac{1}{2}ac\sin B$
Heron's Area Formula	$\text{Area} = \sqrt{s(s-a)(s-b)(s-c)}$

> ## 𝒲RITING ABOUT 𝓜ATHEMATICS
>
> **The Area of a Triangle** Use the most appropriate formula to find the area of each triangle below. Show your work and give your reasons for choosing each formula.
>
> **a.**
>
>
>
> **b.**
>
>
>
> **c.**
>
>
>
> **d.**
>
>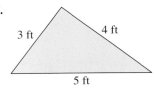

5.7 | Exercises

VOCABULARY CHECK: Fill in the blanks.

1. If you are given three sides of a triangle, you would use the Law of _____ to find the three angles of the triangle.

2. The standard form of the Law of Cosines for $\cos B = \dfrac{a^2 + c^2 - b^2}{2ac}$ is _____ .

3. The Law of Cosines can be used to establish a formula for finding the area of a triangle called _____ _____ Formula.

PREREQUISITE SKILLS REVIEW: Practice and review algebra skills needed for this section at **www.Eduspace.com.**

In Exercises 1–16, use the Law of Cosines to solve the triangle. Round your answers to two decimal places.

1.

2.

3.

4.

5. $a = 11$, $b = 14$, $c = 20$
6. $a = 55$, $b = 25$, $c = 72$
7. $a = 75.4$, $b = 52$, $c = 52$
8. $a = 1.42$, $b = 0.75$, $c = 1.25$
9. $A = 135°$, $b = 4$, $c = 9$
10. $A = 55°$, $b = 3$, $c = 10$
11. $B = 10° 35'$, $a = 40$, $c = 30$
12. $B = 75° 20'$, $a = 6.2$, $c = 9.5$
13. $B = 125° 40'$, $a = 32$, $c = 32$
14. $C = 15° 15'$, $a = 6.25$, $b = 2.15$
15. $C = 43°$, $a = \frac{4}{9}$, $b = \frac{7}{9}$
16. $C = 103°$, $a = \frac{3}{8}$, $b = \frac{3}{4}$

In Exercises 17–22, complete the table by solving the parallelogram shown in the figure. (The lengths of the diagonals are given by c and d.)

	a	b	c	d	θ	ϕ
17.	5	8			45°	
18.	25	35				120°
19.	10	14	20			
20.	40	60		80		
21.	15		25	20		
22.		25	50	35		

In Exercises 23–28, use Heron's Area Formula to find the area of the triangle.

23. $a = 5$, $b = 7$, $c = 10$
24. $a = 12$, $b = 15$, $c = 9$
25. $a = 2.5$, $b = 10.2$, $c = 9$
26. $a = 75.4$, $b = 52$, $c = 52$
27. $a = 12.32$, $b = 8.46$, $c = 15.05$
28. $a = 3.05$, $b = 0.75$, $c = 2.45$

29. *Navigation* A boat race runs along a triangular course marked by buoys A, B, and C. The race starts with the boats headed west for 3700 meters. The other two sides of the course lie to the north of the first side, and their lengths are 1700 meters and 3000 meters. Draw a figure that gives a visual representation of the problem, and find the bearings for the last two legs of the race.

30. *Navigation* A plane flies 810 miles from Franklin to Centerville with a bearing of 75°. Then it flies 648 miles from Centerville to Rosemount with a bearing of 32°. Draw a figure that visually represents the problem, and find the straight-line distance and bearing from Franklin to Rosemount.

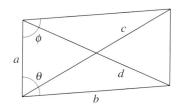

31. Surveying   To approximate the length of a marsh, a surveyor walks 250 meters from point A to point B, then turns $75°$ and walks 220 meters to point C (see figure). Approximate the length AC of the marsh.

32. Surveying   A triangular parcel of land has 115 meters of frontage, and the other boundaries have lengths of 76 meters and 92 meters. What angles does the frontage make with the two other boundaries?

33. Surveying   A triangular parcel of ground has sides of lengths 725 feet, 650 feet, and 575 feet. Find the measure of the largest angle.

34. Streetlight Design   Determine the angle θ in the design of the streetlight shown in the figure.

35. Distance   Two ships leave a port at 9 A.M. One travels at a bearing of N $53°$ W at 12 miles per hour, and the other travels at a bearing of S $67°$ W at 16 miles per hour. Approximate how far apart they are at noon that day.

36. Length   A 100-foot vertical tower is to be erected on the side of a hill that makes a $6°$ angle with the horizontal (see figure). Find the length of each of the two guy wires that will be anchored 75 feet uphill and downhill from the base of the tower.

37. Navigation   On a map, Orlando is 178 millimeters due south of Niagara Falls, Denver is 273 millimeters from Orlando, and Denver is 235 millimeters from Niagara Falls (see figure).

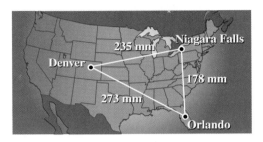

(a) Find the bearing of Denver from Orlando.

(b) Find the bearing of Denver from Niagara Falls.

38. Navigation   On a map, Minneapolis is 165 millimeters due west of Albany, Phoenix is 216 millimeters from Minneapolis, and Phoenix is 368 millimeters from Albany (see figure).

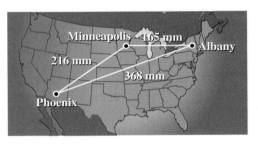

(a) Find the bearing of Minneapolis from Phoenix.

(b) Find the bearing of Albany from Phoenix.

39. Baseball   On a baseball diamond with 90-foot sides, the pitcher's mound is 60.5 feet from home plate. How far is it from the pitcher's mound to third base?

40. Baseball   The baseball player in center field is playing approximately 330 feet from the television camera that is behind home plate. A batter hits a fly ball that goes to the wall 420 feet from the camera (see figure). The camera turns $8°$ to follow the play. Approximately how far does the center fielder have to run to make the catch?

41. *Aircraft Tracking* To determine the distance between two aircraft, a tracking station continuously determines the distance to each aircraft and the angle A between them (see figure). Determine the distance a between the planes when $A = 42°$, $b = 35$ miles, and $c = 20$ miles.

FIGURE FOR 41

42. *Aircraft Tracking* Use the figure for Exercise 41 to determine the distance a between the planes when $A = 11°$, $b = 20$ miles, and $c = 20$ miles.

43. *Trusses* Q is the midpoint of the line segment $\overline{PR}$ in the truss rafter shown in the figure. What are the lengths of the line segments $\overline{PQ}$, $\overline{QS}$, and $\overline{RS}$?

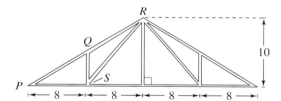

Model It

44. *Engine Design* An engine has a seven-inch connecting rod fastened to a crank (see figure).

(a) Use the Law of Cosines to write an equation giving the relationship between x and θ.

(b) Write x as a function of θ. (Select the sign that yields positive values of x.)

 (c) Use a graphing utility to graph the function in part (b).

 (d) Use the graph in part (c) to determine the maximum distance the piston moves in one cycle.

45. *Paper Manufacturing* In a process with continuous paper, the paper passes across three rollers of radii 3 inches, 4 inches, and 6 inches (see figure). The centers of the three-inch and six-inch rollers are d inches apart, and the length of the arc in contact with the paper on the four-inch roller is s inches. Complete the table.

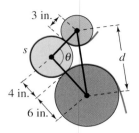

d (inches)	9	10	12	13	14	15	16
θ (degrees)							
s (inches)							

46. *Awning Design* A retractable awning above a patio door lowers at an angle of $50°$ from the exterior wall at a height of 10 feet above the ground (see figure). No direct sunlight is to enter the door when the angle of elevation of the sun is greater than $70°$. What is the length x of the awning?

47. *Geometry* The lengths of the sides of a triangular parcel of land are approximately 200 feet, 500 feet, and 600 feet. Approximate the area of the parcel.

48. *Geometry* A parking lot has the shape of a parallelogram (see figure). The lengths of two adjacent sides are 70 meters and 100 meters. The angle between the two sides is $70°$. What is the area of the parking lot?

49. *Geometry* You want to buy a triangular lot measuring 510 yards by 840 yards by 1120 yards. The price of the land is $2000 per acre. How much does the land cost? (*Hint:* 1 acre = 4840 square yards)

50. *Geometry* You want to buy a triangular lot measuring 1350 feet by 1860 feet by 2490 feet. The price of the land is $2200 per acre. How much does the land cost? (*Hint:* 1 acre = 43,560 square feet)

Synthesis

True or False? **In Exercises 51–53, determine whether the statement is true or false. Justify your answer.**

51. In Heron's Area Formula, s is the average of the lengths of the three sides of the triangle.

52. In addition to SSS and SAS, the Law of Cosines can be used to solve triangles with SSA conditions.

53. A triangle with side lengths of 10 centimeters, 16 centimeters, and 5 centimeters can be solved using the Law of Cosines.

54. *Circumscribed and Inscribed Circles* Let R and r be the radii of the circumscribed and inscribed circles of a triangle ABC, respectively (see figure), and let

$$s = \frac{a + b + c}{2}.$$

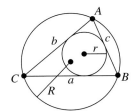

(a) Prove that $2R = \dfrac{a}{\sin A} = \dfrac{b}{\sin B} = \dfrac{c}{\sin C}.$

(b) Prove that $r = \sqrt{\dfrac{(s - a)(s - b)(s - c)}{s}}.$

Circumscribed and Inscribed Circles **In Exercises 55 and 56, use the results of Exercise 54.**

55. Given a triangle with

$a = 25, b = 55,$ and $c = 72$

find the areas of (a) the triangle, (b) the circumscribed circle, and (c) the inscribed circle.

56. Find the length of the largest circular running track that can be built on a triangular piece of property with sides of lengths 200 feet, 250 feet, and 325 feet.

57. *Proof* Use the Law of Cosines to prove that

$$\frac{1}{2} bc\,(1 + \cos A) = \frac{a + b + c}{2} \cdot \frac{-a + b + c}{2}.$$

58. *Proof* Use the Law of Cosines to prove that

$$\frac{1}{2} bc\,(1 - \cos A) = \frac{a - b + c}{2} \cdot \frac{a + b - c}{2}.$$

Skills Review

In Exercises 59–64, evaluate the expression without using a calculator.

59. $\arcsin(-1)$

60. $\arccos 0$

61. $\arctan \sqrt{3}$

62. $\arctan\left(-\sqrt{3}\right)$

63. $\arcsin\left(-\dfrac{\sqrt{3}}{2}\right)$

64. $\arccos\left(-\dfrac{\sqrt{3}}{2}\right)$

In Exercises 65–68, write an algebraic expression that is equivalent to the expression.

65. $\sec(\arcsin 2x)$

66. $\tan(\arccos 3x)$

67. $\cot[\arctan(x - 2)]$

68. $\cos\left(\arcsin \dfrac{x - 1}{2}\right)$

In Exercises 69–72, use trigonometric substitution to write the algebraic equation as a trigonometric function of θ, where $-\pi/2 < \theta < \pi/2$. Then find $\sec \theta$ and $\csc \theta$.

69. $5 = \sqrt{25 - x^2}, \quad x = 5 \sin \theta$

70. $-\sqrt{2} = \sqrt{4 - x^2}, \quad x = 2 \cos \theta$

71. $-\sqrt{3} = \sqrt{x^2 - 9}, \quad x = 3 \sec \theta$

72. $12 = \sqrt{36 + x^2}, \quad x = 6 \tan \theta$

In Exercises 73 and 74, write the sum or difference as a product.

73. $\cos \dfrac{5\pi}{6} - \cos \dfrac{\pi}{3}$

74. $\sin\left(x - \dfrac{\pi}{2}\right) - \sin\left(x + \dfrac{\pi}{2}\right)$

5 Chapter Summary

What did you learn?

5 Review Exercises

In Exercises 1–6, name the trigonometric function that is equivalent to the expression.

1. $\dfrac{1}{\cos x}$

2. $\dfrac{1}{\sin x}$

3. $\dfrac{1}{\sec x}$

4. $\dfrac{1}{\tan x}$

5. $\dfrac{\cos x}{\sin x}$

6. $\sqrt{1 + \tan^2 x}$

In Exercises 7–10, use the given values and trigonometric identities to evaluate (if possible) all six trigonometric functions.

7. $\sin x = \frac{3}{5}, \quad \cos x = \frac{4}{5}$

8. $\tan \theta = \dfrac{2}{3}, \quad \sec \theta = \dfrac{\sqrt{13}}{3}$

9. $\sin\left(\dfrac{\pi}{2} - x\right) = \dfrac{\sqrt{2}}{2}, \quad \sin x = -\dfrac{\sqrt{2}}{2}$

10. $\csc\left(\dfrac{\pi}{2} - \theta\right) = 9, \quad \sin \theta = \dfrac{4\sqrt{5}}{9}$

In Exercises 11–22, use the fundamental trigonometric identities to simplify the expression.

11. $\dfrac{1}{\cot^2 x + 1}$

12. $\dfrac{\tan \theta}{1 - \cos^2 \theta}$

13. $\tan^2 x(\csc^2 x - 1)$

14. $\cot^2 x(\sin^2 x)$

15. $\dfrac{\sin\left(\dfrac{\pi}{2} - \theta\right)}{\sin \theta}$

16. $\dfrac{\cot\left(\dfrac{\pi}{2} - u\right)}{\cos u}$

17. $\cos^2 x + \cos^2 x \cot^2 x$

18. $\tan^2 \theta \csc^2 \theta - \tan^2 \theta$

19. $(\tan x + 1)^2 \cos x$

20. $(\sec x - \tan x)^2$

21. $\dfrac{1}{\csc \theta + 1} - \dfrac{1}{\csc \theta - 1}$

22. $\dfrac{\cos^2 x}{1 - \sin x}$

23. *Rate of Change* The rate of change of the function $f(x) = \csc x - \cot x$ is given by the expression $\csc^2 x - \csc x \cot x$. Show that this expression can also be written as

$$\dfrac{1 - \cos x}{\sin^2 x}.$$

24. *Rate of Change* The rate of change of the function $f(x) = 2\sqrt{\sin x}$ is given by the expression $\sin^{-1/2} x \cos x$. Show that this expression can also be written as $\cot x\sqrt{\sin x}$.

In Exercises 25–32, verify the identity.

25. $\cos x(\tan^2 x + 1) = \sec x$

26. $\sec^2 x \cot x - \cot x = \tan x$

27. $\cos\left(x + \dfrac{\pi}{2}\right) = -\sin x$

28. $\cot\left(\dfrac{\pi}{2} - x\right) = \tan x$

29. $\dfrac{1}{\tan \theta \csc \theta} = \cos \theta$

30. $\dfrac{1}{\tan x \csc x \sin x} = \cot x$

31. $\sin^5 x \cos^2 x = (\cos^2 x - 2\cos^4 x + \cos^6 x)\sin x$

32. $\cos^3 x \sin^2 x = (\sin^2 x - \sin^4 x)\cos x$

In Exercises 33–38, solve the equation.

33. $\sin x = \sqrt{3} - \sin x$

34. $4\cos \theta = 1 + 2\cos \theta$

35. $3\sqrt{3} \tan u = 3$

36. $\frac{1}{2}\sec x - 1 = 0$

37. $3\csc^2 x = 4$

38. $4\tan^2 u - 1 = \tan^2 u$

In Exercises 39–46, find all solutions of the equation in the interval $[0, 2\pi)$.

39. $2\cos^2 x - \cos x = 1$

40. $2\sin^2 x - 3\sin x = -1$

41. $\cos^2 x + \sin x = 1$

42. $\sin^2 x + 2\cos x = 2$

43. $2\sin 2x - \sqrt{2} = 0$

44. $\sqrt{3} \tan 3x = 0$

45. $\cos 4x(\cos x - 1) = 0$

46. $3\csc^2 5x = -4$

In Exercises 47–50, use inverse functions where needed to find all solutions of the equation in the interval $[0, 2\pi)$.

47. $\sin^2 x - 2\sin x = 0$

48. $2\cos^2 x + 3\cos x = 0$

49. $\tan^2 \theta + \tan \theta - 12 = 0$

50. $\sec^2 x + 6\tan x + 4 = 0$

In Exercises 51–54, find the exact values of the sine, cosine, and tangent of the angle by using a sum or difference formula.

51. $285° = 315° - 30°$

52. $345° = 300° + 45°$

53. $\dfrac{25\pi}{12} = \dfrac{11\pi}{6} + \dfrac{\pi}{4}$

54. $\dfrac{19\pi}{12} = \dfrac{11\pi}{6} - \dfrac{\pi}{4}$

In Exercises 55–58, write the expression as the sine, cosine, or tangent of an angle.

55. $\sin 60° \cos 45° - \cos 60° \sin 45°$

56. $\cos 45° \cos 120° - \sin 45° \sin 120°$

57. $\dfrac{\tan 25° + \tan 10°}{1 - \tan 25° \tan 10°}$

58. $\dfrac{\tan 68° - \tan 115°}{1 + \tan 68° \tan 115°}$

In Exercises 59–64, find the exact value of the trigonometric function given that $\sin u = \frac{3}{4}$ and $\cos v = -\frac{5}{13}$. (Both u and v are in Quadrant II.)

59. $\sin(u + v)$

60. $\tan(u + v)$

61. $\cos(u - v)$

62. $\sin(u - v)$

63. $\cos(u + v)$

64. $\tan(u - v)$

In Exercises 65–70, verify the identity.

65. $\cos\left(x + \dfrac{\pi}{2}\right) = -\sin x$

66. $\sin\left(x - \dfrac{3\pi}{2}\right) = \cos x$

67. $\cot\left(\dfrac{\pi}{2} - x\right) = \tan x$

68. $\sin(\pi - x) = \sin x$

69. $\cos 3x = 4\cos^3 x - 3\cos x$

70. $\dfrac{\sin(\alpha + \beta)}{\cos \alpha \cos \beta} = \tan \alpha + \tan\beta$

In Exercises 71–74, find all solutions of the equation in the interval $[0, 2\pi)$.

71. $\sin\left(x + \dfrac{\pi}{4}\right) - \sin\left(x - \dfrac{\pi}{4}\right) = 1$

72. $\cos\left(x + \dfrac{\pi}{6}\right) - \cos\left(x - \dfrac{\pi}{6}\right) = 1$

73. $\sin\left(x + \dfrac{\pi}{2}\right) - \sin\left(x - \dfrac{\pi}{2}\right) = \sqrt{3}$

74. $\cos\left(x + \dfrac{3\pi}{4}\right) - \cos\left(x - \dfrac{3\pi}{4}\right) = 0$

5.5 **In Exercises 75 and 76, find the exact values of $\sin 2u$, $\cos 2u$, and $\tan 2u$ using the double-angle formulas.**

75. $\sin u = -\dfrac{4}{5}, \quad \pi < u < \dfrac{3\pi}{2}$

76. $\cos u = -\dfrac{2}{\sqrt{5}}, \quad \dfrac{\pi}{2} < u < \pi$

In Exercises 77 and 78, use double-angle formulas to verify the identity algebraically and use a graphing utility to confirm your result graphically.

77. $\sin 4x = 8\cos^3 x \sin x - 4\cos x \sin x$

78. $\tan^2 x = \dfrac{1 - \cos 2x}{1 + \cos 2x}$

In Exercises 79–82, use the power-reducing formulas to rewrite the expression in terms of the first power of the cosine.

79. $\tan^2 2x$

80. $\cos^2 3x$

81. $\sin^2 x \tan^2 x$

82. $\cos^2 x \tan^2 x$

In Exercises 83–86, use the half-angle formulas to determine the exact values of the sine, cosine, and tangent of the angle.

83. $-75°$

84. $15°$

85. $\dfrac{19\pi}{12}$

86. $-\dfrac{17\pi}{12}$

In Exercises 87–90, find the exact values of $\sin(u/2)$, $\cos(u/2)$, and $\tan(u/2)$ using the half-angle formulas.

87. $\sin u = \frac{3}{5}, \ 0 < u < \pi/2$

88. $\tan u = \frac{5}{8}, \ \pi < u < 3\pi/2$

89. $\cos u = -\frac{2}{7}, \ \pi/2 < u < \pi$

90. $\sec u = -6, \ \pi/2 < u < \pi$

In Exercises 91 and 92, use the half-angle formulas to simplify the expression.

91. $-\sqrt{\dfrac{1 + \cos 10x}{2}}$

92. $\dfrac{\sin 6x}{1 + \cos 6x}$

In Exercises 93–96, use the product-to-sum formulas to write the product as a sum or difference.

93. $\cos \dfrac{\pi}{6} \sin \dfrac{\pi}{6}$

94. $6 \sin 15° \sin 45°$

95. $\cos 5\theta \cos 3\theta$

96. $4 \sin 3\alpha \cos 2\alpha$

In Exercises 97–100, use the sum-to-product formulas to write the sum or difference as a product.

97. $\sin 4\theta - \sin 2\theta$

98. $\cos 3\theta + \cos 2\theta$

99. $\cos\left(x + \dfrac{\pi}{6}\right) - \cos\left(x - \dfrac{\pi}{6}\right)$

100. $\sin\left(x + \dfrac{\pi}{4}\right) - \sin\left(x - \dfrac{\pi}{4}\right)$

101. *Projectile Motion* A baseball leaves the hand of the person at first base at an angle of θ with the horizontal and at an initial velocity of $v_0 = 80$ feet per second. The ball is caught by the person at second base 100 feet away. Find θ if the range r of a projectile is

$$r = \dfrac{1}{32} v_0{}^2 \sin 2\theta.$$

102. *Geometry* A trough for feeding cattle is 4 meters long and its cross sections are isosceles triangles with the two equal sides being $\frac{1}{2}$ meter (see figure). The angle between the two sides is θ.

(a) Write the trough's volume as a function of $\frac{\theta}{2}$.

(b) Write the volume of the trough as a function of θ and determine the value of θ such that the volume is maximum.

Harmonic Motion **In Exercises 103–106, use the following information. A weight is attached to a spring suspended vertically from a ceiling. When a driving force is applied to the system, the weight moves vertically from its equilibrium position, and this motion is described by the model**

$$y = 1.5 \sin 8t - 0.5 \cos 8t$$

where y is the distance from equilibrium (in feet) and t is the time (in seconds).

103. Use a graphing utility to graph the model.

104. Write the model in the form

$$y = \sqrt{a^2 + b^2} \sin(Bt + C).$$

105. Find the amplitude of the oscillations of the weight.

106. Find the frequency of the oscillations of the weight.

5.6 **In Exercises 107–116, use the Law of Sines to solve (if possible) the triangle. If two solutions exist, find both. Round your answers to two decimal places.**

107. $B = 72°$, $C = 82°$, $b = 54$

108. $B = 10°$, $C = 20°$, $c = 33$

109. $A = 16°$, $B = 98°$, $c = 8.4$

110. $A = 95°$, $B = 45°$, $c = 104.8$

111. $A = 24°$, $C = 48°$, $b = 27.5$

112. $B = 64°$, $C = 36°$, $a = 367$

113. $B = 150°$, $b = 30$, $c = 10$

114. $B = 150°$, $a = 10$, $b = 3$

115. $A = 75°$, $a = 51.2$, $b = 33.7$

116. $B = 25°$, $a = 6.2$, $b = 4$

In Exercises 117–120, find the area of the triangle having the indicated angle and sides.

117. $A = 27°$, $b = 5$, $c = 7$

118. $B = 80°$, $a = 4$, $c = 8$

119. $C = 123°$, $a = 16$, $b = 5$

120. $A = 11°$, $b = 22$, $c = 21$

121. *Height* From a certain distance, the angle of elevation to the top of a building is $17°$. At a point 50 meters closer to the building, the angle of elevation is $31°$. Approximate the height of the building.

122. *Geometry* Find the length of the side w of the parallelogram.

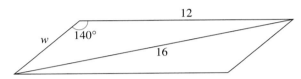

123. *Height* A tree stands on a hillside of slope $28°$ from the horizontal. From a point 75 feet down the hill, the angle of elevation to the top of the tree is $45°$ (see figure). Find the height of the tree.

124. *River Width* A surveyor finds that a tree on the opposite bank of a river, flowing due east, has a bearing of N $22°$ $30'$ E from a certain point and a bearing of N $15°$ W from a point 400 feet downstream. Find the width of the river.

5.7 **In Exercises 125–132, use the Law of Cosines to solve the triangle. Round your answers to two decimal places.**

125. $a = 5$, $b = 8$, $c = 10$

126. $a = 80$, $b = 60$, $c = 100$

127. $a = 2.5$, $b = 5.0$, $c = 4.5$

128. $a = 16.4$, $b = 8.8$, $c = 12.2$

129. $B = 110°$, $a = 4$, $c = 4$

130. $B = 150°$, $a = 10$, $c = 20$

131. $C = 43°$, $a = 22.5$, $b = 31.4$

132. $A = 62°$, $b = 11.34$, $c = 19.52$

133. *Surveying* To approximate the length of a marsh, a surveyor walks 425 meters from point A to point B. Then the surveyor turns 65° and walks 300 meters to point C (see figure). Approximate the length AC of the marsh.

134. *Navigation* Two planes leave Raleigh-Durham Airport at approximately the same time. One is flying 425 miles per hour at a bearing of 355°, and the other is flying 530 miles per hour at a bearing of 67°. Draw a figure that gives a visual representation of the problem and determine the distance between the planes after they have flown for 2 hours.

In Exercises 135–138, use Heron's Area Formula to find the area of the triangle.

135. $a = 4$, $b = 5$, $c = 7$

136. $a = 15$, $b = 8$, $c = 10$

137. $a = 12.3$, $b = 15.8$, $c = 3.7$

138. $a = 38.1$, $b = 26.7$, $c = 19.4$

Synthesis

True or False? **In Exercises 139–144, determine whether the statement is true or false. Justify your answer.**

139. If $\dfrac{\pi}{2} < \theta < \pi$, then $\cos\dfrac{\theta}{2} < 0$.

140. $\sin(x + y) = \sin x + \sin y$

141. $4\sin(-x)\cos(-x) = -2\sin 2x$

142. $4\sin 45° \cos 15° = 1 + \sqrt{3}$

143. The Law of Sines is true if one of the angles in the triangle is a right angle.

144. When the Law of Sines is used, the solution is always unique.

145. List the reciprocal identities, quotient identities, and Pythagorean identities from memory.

146. *Think About It* If a trigonometric equation has an infinite number of solutions, is it true that the equation is an identity? Explain.

147. *Think About It* Explain why you know from observation that the equation $a\sin x - b = 0$ has no solution if $|a| < |b|$.

148. *Surface Area* The surface area of a honeycomb is given by the equation

$$S = 6hs + \frac{3}{2}s^2\left(\frac{\sqrt{3} - \cos\theta}{\sin\theta}\right), \quad 0 < \theta \le 90°$$

where $h = 2.4$ inches, $s = 0.75$ inch, and θ is the angle shown in the figure.

(a) For what value(s) of θ is the surface area 12 square inches?

(b) What value of θ gives the minimum surface area?

In Exercises 149 and 150, use the graphs of y_1 and y_2 to determine how to change one function to form the identity $y_1 = y_2$.

149. $y_1 = \sec^2\left(\dfrac{\pi}{2} - x\right)$

$y_2 = \cot^2 x$

150. $y_1 = \dfrac{\cos 3x}{\cos x}$

$y_2 = (2\sin x)^2$

In Exercises 151 and 152, use the *zero* or *root* feature of a graphing utility to approximate the solutions of the equation.

151. $y = \sqrt{x + 3} + 4\cos x$

152. $y = 2 - \dfrac{1}{2}x^2 + 3\sin\dfrac{\pi x}{2}$

5 Chapter Test

Take this test as you would take a test in class. When you are finished, check your work against the answers given in the back of the book.

1. If $\tan \theta = \frac{3}{2}$ and $\cos \theta < 0$, use the fundamental identities to evaluate the other five trigonometric functions of θ.

2. Use the fundamental identities to simplify $\csc^2 \beta(1 - \cos^2 \beta)$.

3. Factor and simplify $\dfrac{\sec^4 x - \tan^4 x}{\sec^2 x + \tan^2 x}$.

4. Add and simplify $\dfrac{\cos \theta}{\sin \theta} + \dfrac{\sin \theta}{\cos \theta}$.

In Exercises 5–10, verify the identity.

5. $\sin \theta \sec \theta = \tan \theta$

6. $\sec^2 x \tan^2 x + \sec^2 x = \sec^4 x$

7. $\dfrac{\csc \alpha + \sec \alpha}{\sin \alpha + \cos \alpha} = \cot \alpha + \tan \alpha$

8. $\cos\left(x + \dfrac{\pi}{2}\right) = -\sin x$

9. $\sin(n\pi + \theta) = (-1)^n \sin \theta$, n is an integer.

10. $(\sin x + \cos x)^2 = 1 + \sin 2x$

11. Rewrite $\sin^4 x \tan^2 x$ in terms of the first power of the cosine.

12. Use a half-angle formula to simplify the expression $\dfrac{\sin 4\theta}{1 + \cos 4\theta}$.

13. Write $4 \cos 2\theta \sin 4\theta$ as a sum or difference.

14. Write $\sin 3\theta - \sin 4\theta$ as a product.

In Exercises 15–18, find all solutions of the equation in the interval $[0, 2\pi)$.

15. $\tan^2 x + \tan x = 0$

16. $\sin 2\alpha - \cos \alpha = 0$

17. $4 \cos^2 x - 3 = 0$

18. $\csc^2 x - \csc x - 2 = 0$

19. Find the exact value of $\cos 105°$ using the fact that $105° = 135° - 30°$.

20. Use the figure to find the exact values of $\sin 2u$, $\cos 2u$, and $\tan 2u$.

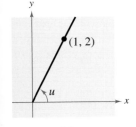

FIGURE FOR 20

In Exercises 21–26, use the information to solve the triangle. If two solutions exist, find both solutions. Round your answers to two decimal places.

21. $A = 24°$, $B = 68°$, $a = 12.2$

22. $B = 104°$, $C = 33°$, $a = 18.1$

23. $A = 24°$, $a = 11.2$, $b = 13.4$

24. $a = 4.0$, $b = 7.3$, $c = 12.4$

25. $B = 100°$, $a = 15$, $b = 23$

26. $C = 123°$, $a = 41$, $b = 57$

27. Cheyenne, Wyoming has a latitude of 41°N. At this latitude, the position of the sun at sunrise can be modeled by

$$D = 31 \sin\left(\frac{2\pi}{365}t - 1.4\right)$$

where t is the time (in days) and $t = 1$ represents January 1. In this model, D represents the number of degrees north or south of due east that the sun rises. Use a graphing utility to determine the days on which the sun is more than 20° north of due east at sunrise.

28. A triangular parcel of land has borders of lengths 60 meters, 70 meters, and 82 meters. Find the area of the parcel of land.

29. An airplane flies 370 miles from point A to point B with a bearing of 24°. It then flies 240 miles from point B to point C with a bearing of 37° (see figure). Find the distance and bearing from point A to point C.

FIGURE FOR 29

Proofs in Mathematics

Proof

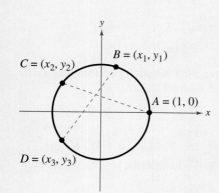

You can use the figures at the left for the proofs of the formulas for $\cos(u \pm v)$. In the top figure, let A be the point $(1, 0)$ and then use u and v to locate the points $B = (x_1, y_1)$, $C = (x_2, y_2)$, and $D = (x_3, y_3)$ on the unit circle. So, $x_i^2 + y_i^2 = 1$ for $i = 1, 2,$ and 3. For convenience, assume that $0 < v < u < 2\pi$. In the bottom figure, note that arcs AC and BD have the same length. So, line segments AC and BD are also equal in length, which implies that

$$\sqrt{(x_2 - 1)^2 + (y_2 - 0)^2} = \sqrt{(x_3 - x_1)^2 + (y_3 - y_1)^2}$$

$$x_2^2 - 2x_2 + 1 + y_2^2 = x_3^2 - 2x_1x_3 + x_1^2 + y_3^2 - 2y_1y_3 + y_1^2$$

$$(x_2^2 + y_2^2) + 1 - 2x_2 = (x_3^2 + y_3^2) + (x_1^2 + y_1^2) - 2x_1x_3 - 2y_1y_3$$

$$1 + 1 - 2x_2 = 1 + 1 - 2x_1x_3 - 2y_1y_3$$

$$x_2 = x_3x_1 + y_3y_1.$$

Finally, by substituting the values $x_2 = \cos(u - v)$, $x_3 = \cos u$, $x_1 = \cos v$, $y_3 = \sin u$, and $y_1 = \sin v$, you obtain $\cos(u - v) = \cos u \cos v + \sin u \sin v$. The formula for $\cos(u + v)$ can be established by considering $u + v = u - (-v)$ and using the formula just derived to obtain

$$\cos(u + v) = \cos[u - (-v)] = \cos u \cos(-v) + \sin u \sin(-v)$$

$$= \cos u \cos v - \sin u \sin v.$$

You can use the sum and difference formulas for sine and cosine to prove the formulas for $\tan(u \pm v)$.

$$\tan(u \pm v) = \frac{\sin(u \pm v)}{\cos(u \pm v)} \qquad \text{Quotient identity}$$

$$= \frac{\sin u \cos v \pm \cos u \sin v}{\cos u \cos v \mp \sin u \sin v} \qquad \text{Sum and difference formulas}$$

$$= \frac{\dfrac{\sin u \cos v \pm \cos u \sin v}{\cos u \cos v}}{\dfrac{\cos u \cos v \mp \sin u \sin v}{\cos u \cos v}} \qquad \begin{array}{l}\text{Divide numerator and denominator}\\ \text{by } \cos u \cos v.\end{array}$$

$$= \dfrac{\dfrac{\sin u \cos v}{\cos u \cos v} \pm \dfrac{\cos u \sin v}{\cos u \cos v}}{\dfrac{\cos u \cos v}{\cos u \cos v} \mp \dfrac{\sin u \sin v}{\cos u \cos v}} \qquad \text{Write as separate fractions.}$$

$$= \dfrac{\dfrac{\sin u}{\cos u} \pm \dfrac{\sin v}{\cos v}}{1 \mp \dfrac{\sin u}{\cos u} \cdot \dfrac{\sin v}{\cos v}} \qquad \text{Product of fractions}$$

$$= \dfrac{\tan u \pm \tan v}{1 \mp \tan u \tan v} \qquad \text{Quotient identity}$$

Trigonometry and Astronomy

Trigonometry and Astronomy

Trigonometry was used by early astronomers to calculate measurements in the universe. Trigonometry was used to calculate the circumference of Earth and the distance from Earth to the moon. Another major accomplishment in astronomy using trigonometry was computing distances to stars.

Double-Angle Formulas (p. 407)

$$\sin 2u = 2 \sin u \cos u \qquad\qquad \cos 2u = \cos^2 u - \sin^2 u$$

$$\tan 2u = \dfrac{2 \tan u}{1 - \tan^2 u} \qquad\qquad\quad = 2 \cos^2 u - 1 = 1 - 2 \sin^2 u$$

Proof

To prove all three formulas, let $v = u$ in the corresponding sum formulas.

$$\sin 2u = \sin(u + u) = \sin u \cos u + \cos u \sin u = 2 \sin u \cos u$$

$$\cos 2u = \cos(u + u) = \cos u \cos u - \sin u \sin u = \cos^2 u - \sin^2 u$$

$$\tan 2u = \tan(u + u) = \dfrac{\tan u + \tan u}{1 - \tan u \tan u} = \dfrac{2 \tan u}{1 - \tan^2 u}$$

Power-Reducing Formulas (p. 409)

$$\sin^2 u = \dfrac{1 - \cos 2u}{2} \qquad \cos^2 u = \dfrac{1 + \cos 2u}{2} \qquad \tan^2 u = \dfrac{1 - \cos 2u}{1 + \cos 2u}$$

Proof

To prove the first formula, solve for $\sin^2 u$ in the double-angle formula $\cos 2u = 1 - 2 \sin^2 u$, as follows.

$$\cos 2u = 1 - 2 \sin^2 u \qquad\qquad \text{Write double-angle formula.}$$

$$2 \sin^2 u = 1 - \cos 2u \qquad\qquad \text{Subtract } \cos 2u \text{ from, and add } 2 \sin^2 u \text{ to, each side.}$$

$$\sin^2 u = \dfrac{1 - \cos 2u}{2} \qquad\qquad \text{Divide each side by 2.}$$

443

In a similar way you can prove the second formula, by solving for $\cos^2 u$ in the double-angle formula $\cos 2u = 2 \cos^2 u - 1$. To prove the third formula, use a quotient identity, as follows.

$$\tan^2 u = \frac{\sin^2 u}{\cos^2 u} = \frac{\dfrac{1 - \cos 2u}{2}}{\dfrac{1 + \cos 2u}{2}} = \frac{1 - \cos 2u}{1 + \cos 2u}$$

Sum-to-Product Formulas   *(p. 412)*

$$\sin u + \sin v = 2 \sin\left(\frac{u + v}{2}\right) \cos\left(\frac{u - v}{2}\right)$$

$$\sin u - \sin v = 2 \cos\left(\frac{u + v}{2}\right) \sin\left(\frac{u - v}{2}\right)$$

$$\cos u + \cos v = 2 \cos\left(\frac{u + v}{2}\right) \cos\left(\frac{u - v}{2}\right)$$

$$\cos u - \cos v = -2 \sin\left(\frac{u + v}{2}\right) \sin\left(\frac{u - v}{2}\right)$$

Proof

To prove the first formula, let $x = u + v$ and $y = u - v$. Then substitute $u = (x + y)/2$ and $v = (x - y)/2$ in the product-to-sum formula.

$$\sin u \cos v = \frac{1}{2}\left[\sin(u + v) + \sin(u - v)\right]$$

$$\sin\left(\frac{x + y}{2}\right) \cos\left(\frac{x - y}{2}\right) = \frac{1}{2}(\sin x + \sin y)$$

$$2 \sin\left(\frac{x + y}{2}\right) \cos\left(\frac{x - y}{2}\right) = \sin x + \sin y$$

The other sum-to-product formulas can be proved in a similar manner.

Law of Sines   *(p. 419)*

If ABC is a triangle with sides a, b, and c, then $\dfrac{a}{\sin A} = \dfrac{b}{\sin B} = \dfrac{c}{\sin C}$.

A is acute.

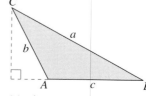

A is obtuse.

Proof

Let h be the altitude of either triangle found in the figure on the previous page. Then you have

$$\sin A = \frac{h}{b} \quad \text{or} \quad h = b \sin A \qquad \text{and} \qquad \sin B = \frac{h}{a} \quad \text{or} \quad h = a \sin B.$$

Equating these two values of h, you have

$$a \sin B = b \sin A \qquad \text{or} \qquad \frac{a}{\sin A} = \frac{b}{\sin B}.$$

A is acute.

Note that $\sin A \neq 0$ and $\sin B \neq 0$ because no angle of a triangle can have a measure of $0°$ or $180°$. In a similar manner, construct an altitude from vertex B to side AC (extended in the obtuse triangle), as shown at the left. Then you have

$$\sin A = \frac{h}{c} \quad \text{or} \quad h = c \sin A \qquad \text{and} \qquad \sin C = \frac{h}{a} \quad \text{or} \quad h = a \sin C.$$

Equating these two values of h, you have

$$a \sin C = c \sin A \qquad \text{or} \qquad \frac{a}{\sin A} = \frac{c}{\sin C}.$$

By the Transitive Property of Equality you know that

$$\frac{a}{\sin A} = \frac{b}{\sin B} = \frac{c}{\sin C}.$$

So, the Law of Sines is established.

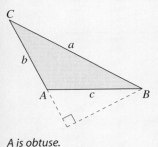

A is obtuse.

Law of Cosines (p. 428)

Standard Form	Alternative Form
$a^2 = b^2 + c^2 - 2bc \cos A$	$\cos A = \dfrac{b^2 + c^2 - a^2}{2bc}$
$b^2 = a^2 + c^2 - 2ac \cos B$	$\cos B = \dfrac{a^2 + c^2 - b^2}{2ac}$
$c^2 = a^2 + b^2 - 2ab \cos C$	$\cos C = \dfrac{a^2 + b^2 - c^2}{2ab}$

Proof

To prove the first formula, consider the triangle at the left, which has three acute angles. Note that vertex B has coordinates $(c, 0)$. Furthermore, C has coordinates (x, y), where $x = b \cos A$ and $y = b \sin A$. Because a is the distance from vertex C to vertex B, it follows that

$$a = \sqrt{(x - c)^2 + (y - 0)^2} \qquad \text{Distance Formula}$$

$$a^2 = (x - c)^2 + (y - 0)^2 \qquad \text{Square each side.}$$

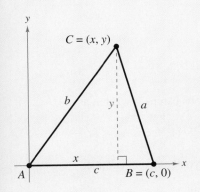

445

$$a^2 = (b \cos A - c)^2 + (b \sin A)^2 \qquad \text{Substitute for } x \text{ and } y.$$

$$a^2 = b^2 \cos^2 A - 2bc \cos A + c^2 + b^2 \sin^2 A \qquad \text{Expand.}$$

$$a^2 = b^2(\sin^2 A + \cos^2 A) + c^2 - 2bc \cos A \qquad \text{Factor out } b^2.$$

$$a^2 = b^2 + c^2 - 2bc \cos A. \qquad \sin^2 A + \cos^2 A = 1$$

Similar arguments can be used to establish the second and third formulas.

Heron's Area Formula *(p. 431)*

Given any triangle with sides of lengths a, b, and c, the area of the triangle is

$$\text{Area} = \sqrt{s(s-a)(s-b)(s-c)}$$

where $s = \dfrac{(a+b+c)}{2}$.

Proof

From Section 5.6, you know that

$$\text{Area} = \frac{1}{2} bc \sin A \qquad \text{Formula for the area of an oblique triangle}$$

$$(\text{Area})^2 = \frac{1}{4} b^2 c^2 \sin^2 A \qquad \text{Square each side.}$$

$$\text{Area} = \sqrt{\frac{1}{4} b^2 c^2 \sin^2 A} \qquad \text{Take the square root of each side.}$$

$$= \sqrt{\frac{1}{4} b^2 c^2 (1 - \cos^2 A)} \qquad \text{Pythagorean Identity}$$

$$= \sqrt{\left[\frac{1}{2} bc(1 + \cos A)\right]\left[\frac{1}{2} bc(1 - \cos A)\right]}. \qquad \text{Factor.}$$

Using the Law of Cosines, you can show that

$$\frac{1}{2} bc(1 + \cos A) = \frac{a+b+c}{2} \cdot \frac{-a+b+c}{2}$$

and

$$\frac{1}{2} bc(1 - \cos A) = \frac{a-b+c}{2} \cdot \frac{a+b-c}{2}.$$

Letting $s = (a+b+c)/2$, these two equations can be rewritten as

$$\frac{1}{2} bc(1 + \cos A) = s(s-a) \qquad \text{and} \qquad \frac{1}{2} bc(1 - \cos A) = (s-b)(s-c).$$

By substituting into the last formula for area, you can conclude that

$$\text{Area} = \sqrt{s(s-a)(s-b)(s-c)}.$$

This collection of thought-provoking and challenging exercises further explores and expands upon concepts learned in this chapter.

1. (a) Write each of the other trigonometric functions of θ in terms of $\sin \theta$.

   (b) Write each of the other trigonometric functions of θ in terms of $\cos \theta$.

2. Verify that for all integers n, $\cos\left[\dfrac{(2n+1)\pi}{2}\right] = 0$.

3. Verify that for all integers n, $\sin\left[\dfrac{(12n+1)\pi}{6}\right] = \dfrac{1}{2}$.

4. A particular sound wave is modeled by

$$p(t) = \frac{1}{4\pi}\left(p_1(t) + 30p_2(t) + p_3(t) + p_5(t) + 30p_6(t)\right)$$

   where $p_n(t) = \dfrac{1}{n}\sin(524n\pi t)$, and t is the time (in seconds).

   (a) Find the sine components $p_n(t)$ and use a graphing utility to graph each component. Then verify the graph of p that is shown.

   (b) Find the period of each sine component of p. Is p periodic? If so, what is its period?

   (c) Use the *zero* or *root* feature or the *zoom* and *trace* features of a graphing utility to find the t-intercepts of the graph of p over one cycle.

   (d) Use the *maximum* and *minimum* features of a graphing utility to approximate the absolute maximum and absolute minimum values of p over one cycle.

5. Three squares of side s are placed side by side (see figure). Make a conjecture about the relationship between the sum $u + v$ and w. Prove your conjecture by using the identity for the tangent of the sum of two angles.

6. The path traveled by an object (neglecting air resistance) that is projected at an initial height of h_0 feet, an initial velocity of v_0 feet per second, and an initial angle θ is given by

$$y = -\frac{16}{v_0^2 \cos^2 \theta}x^2 + (\tan \theta)x + h_0$$

   where x and y are measured in feet. Find a formula for the maximum height of an object projected from ground level at velocity v_0 and angle θ. To do this, find half of the horizontal distance

$$\frac{1}{32}v_0^2 \sin 2\theta$$

   and then substitute it for x in the general model for the path of a projectile (where $h_0 = 0$).

7. Use the figure to derive the formulas for

$$\sin \frac{\theta}{2}, \cos \frac{\theta}{2}, \text{ and } \tan \frac{\theta}{2}$$

   where θ is an acute angle.

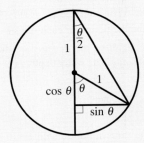

8. The force F (in pounds) on a person's back when he or she bends over at an angle θ is modeled by

$$F = \frac{0.6W \sin(\theta + 90°)}{\sin 12°}$$

   where W is the person's weight (in pounds).

   (a) Simplify the model.

   (b) Use a graphing utility to graph the model, where $W = 185$ and $0° < \theta < 90°$.

   (c) At what angle is the force a maximum? At what angle is the force a minimum?

9. The number of hours of daylight that occur at any location on Earth depends on the time of year and the latitude of the location. The following equations model the numbers of hours of daylight in Seward, Alaska (60° latitude) and New Orleans, Louisiana (30° latitude).

$$D = 12.2 - 6.4 \cos\left[\frac{\pi(t + 0.2)}{182.6}\right] \quad \text{Seward}$$

$$D = 12.2 - 1.9 \cos\left[\frac{\pi(t + 0.2)}{182.6}\right] \quad \text{New Orleans}$$

In these models, D represents the number of hours of daylight and t represents the day, with $t = 0$ corresponding to January 1.

 (a) Use a graphing utility to graph both models in the same viewing window. Use a viewing window of $0 \le t \le 365$.

(b) Find the days of the year on which both cities receive the same amount of daylight. What are these days called?

(c) Which city has the greater variation in the number of daylight hours? Which constant in each model would you use to determine the difference between the greatest and least numbers of hours of daylight?

(d) Determine the period of each model.

10. The tide, or depth of the ocean near the shore, changes throughout the day. The water depth d (in feet) of a bay can be modeled by

$$d = 35 - 28 \cos\frac{\pi}{6.2}t$$

where t is the time in hours, with $t = 0$ corresponding to 12:00 A.M.

(a) Algebraically find the times at which the high and low tides occur.

(b) Algebraically find the time(s) at which the water depth is 3.5 feet.

 (c) Use a graphing utility to verify your results from parts (a) and (b).

11. Find the solution of each inequality in the interval $[0, 2\pi]$.

(a) $\sin x \ge 0.5$ (b) $\cos x \le -0.5$

(c) $\tan x < \sin x$ (d) $\cos x \ge \sin x$

12. (a) Write a sum formula for $\sin(u + v + w)$.

(b) Write a sum formula for $\tan(u + v + w)$.

13. (a) Derive a formula for $\cos 3\theta$.

(b) Derive a formula for $\cos 4\theta$.

14. The heights h (in inches) of pistons 1 and 2 in an automobile engine can be modeled by

$$h_1 = 3.75 \sin 733t + 7.5$$

and

$$h_2 = 3.75 \sin 733\left(t + \frac{4\pi}{3}\right) + 7.5$$

where t is measured in seconds.

 (a) Use a graphing utility to graph the heights of these two pistons in the same viewing window for $0 \le t \le 1$.

(b) How often are the pistons at the same height?

15. In the figure, a beam of light is directed at the blue mirror, reflected to the red mirror, and then reflected back to the blue mirror. Find the distance PT that the light travels from the red mirror back to the blue mirror.

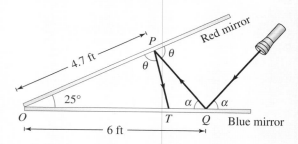

16. A triathlete sets a course to swim S 25° E from a point on shore to a buoy $\frac{3}{4}$ mile away. After swimming 300 yards through a strong current, the triathlete is off course at a bearing of S 35° E. Find the bearing and distance the triathlete needs to swim to correct her course.

Topics in Analytic Geometry

6

The nine planets move about the sun in elliptical orbits. You can use the techniques presented in this chapter to determine the distances between the planets and the center of the sun.

Kauko Helavuo/Getty Images

SELECTED APPLICATIONS

Analytic geometry concepts have many real-life applications. The applications listed below represent a small sample of the applications in this chapter.

6.1 Lines

What you should learn

- Find the inclination of a line.
- Find the angle between two lines.
- Find the distance between a point and a line.

Why you should learn it

The inclination of a line can be used to measure heights indirectly. For instance, in Exercise 56 on page 456, the inclination of a line can be used to determine the change in elevation from the base to the top of the Johnstown Inclined Plane.

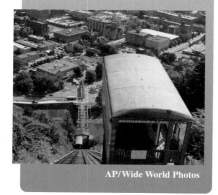

AP/Wide World Photos

The *HM mathSpace*® CD-ROM and *Eduspace*® for this text contain additional resources related to the concepts discussed in this chapter.

Inclination of a Line

In Section 1.3, you learned that the graph of the linear equation

$$y = mx + b$$

is a nonvertical line with slope m and y-intercept $(0, b)$. There, the slope of a line was described as the rate of change in y with respect to x. In this section, you will look at the slope of a line in terms of the angle of inclination of the line.

Every nonhorizontal line must intersect the x-axis. The angle formed by such an intersection determines the **inclination** of the line, as specified in the following definition.

Definition of Inclination

The **inclination** of a nonhorizontal line is the positive angle θ (less than π) measured counterclockwise from the x-axis to the line. (See Figure 6.1.)

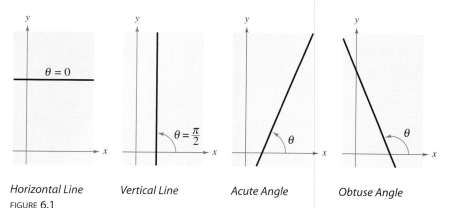

Horizontal Line   Vertical Line   Acute Angle   Obtuse Angle
FIGURE 6.1

The inclination of a line is related to its slope in the following manner.

Inclination and Slope

If a nonvertical line has inclination θ and slope m, then

$$m = \tan \theta.$$

For a proof of the relation between inclination and slope, see Proofs in Mathematics on page 522.

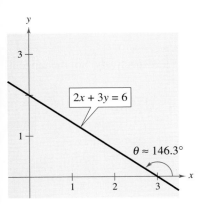

FIGURE **6.2**

Example 1   **Finding the Inclination of a Line**

Find the inclination of the line $2x + 3y = 6$.

Solution

The slope of this line is $m = -\frac{2}{3}$. So, its inclination is determined from the equation

$$\tan \theta = -\frac{2}{3}.$$

From Figure 6.2, it follows that $\frac{\pi}{2} < \theta < \pi$. This means that

$$\theta = \pi + \arctan\left(-\frac{2}{3}\right)$$

$$\approx \pi + (-0.588)$$

$$= \pi - 0.588$$

$$\approx 2.554.$$

The angle of inclination is about 2.554 radians or about 146.3°.

   Now try Exercise 19.

The Angle Between Two Lines

Two distinct lines in a plane are either parallel or intersecting. If they intersect and are nonperpendicular, their intersection forms two pairs of opposite angles. One pair is acute and the other pair is obtuse. The smaller of these angles is called the **angle between the two lines.** As shown in Figure 6.3, you can use the inclinations of the two lines to find the angle between the two lines. If two lines have inclinations θ_1 and θ_2, where $\theta_1 < \theta_2$ and $\theta_2 - \theta_1 < \pi/2$, the angle between the two lines is

$$\theta = \theta_2 - \theta_1.$$

You can use the formula for the tangent of the difference of two angles

$$\tan \theta = \tan(\theta_2 - \theta_1)$$

$$= \frac{\tan \theta_2 - \tan \theta_1}{1 + \tan \theta_1 \tan \theta_2}$$

to obtain the formula for the angle between two lines.

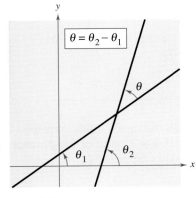

FIGURE **6.3**

Angle Between Two Lines

If two nonperpendicular lines have slopes m_1 and m_2, the angle between the two lines is

$$\tan \theta = \left| \frac{m_2 - m_1}{1 + m_1 m_2} \right|.$$

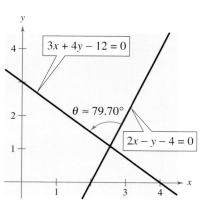

FIGURE **6.4**

Example 2   **Finding the Angle Between Two Lines**

Find the angle between the two lines.

$$\text{Line 1: } 2x - y - 4 = 0 \qquad \text{Line 2: } 3x + 4y - 12 = 0$$

Solution

The two lines have slopes of $m_1 = 2$ and $m_2 = -\frac{3}{4}$, respectively. So, the tangent of the angle between the two lines is

$$\tan \theta = \left| \frac{m_2 - m_1}{1 + m_1 m_2} \right| = \left| \frac{(-3/4) - 2}{1 + (2)(-3/4)} \right| = \left| \frac{-11/4}{-2/4} \right| = \frac{11}{2}.$$

Finally, you can conclude that the angle is

$$\theta = \arctan \frac{11}{2} \approx 1.391 \text{ radians} \approx 79.70°$$

as shown in Figure 6.4.

✔*CHECKPOINT*   Now try Exercise 27.

The Distance Between a Point and a Line

Finding the distance between a line and a point not on the line is an application of perpendicular lines. This distance is defined as the length of the perpendicular line segment joining the point and the line, as shown in Figure 6.5.

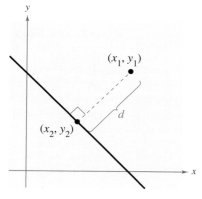

FIGURE **6.5**

> **Distance Between a Point and a Line**
>
> The distance between the point (x_1, y_1) and the line $Ax + By + C = 0$ is
>
> $$d = \frac{|Ax_1 + By_1 + C|}{\sqrt{A^2 + B^2}}.$$

Remember that the values of A, B, and C in this distance formula correspond to the general equation of a line, $Ax + By + C = 0$. For a proof of the distance between a point and a line, see Proofs in Mathematics on page 522.

Example 3   **Finding the Distance Between a Point and a Line**

Find the distance between the point $(4, 1)$ and the line $y = 2x + 1$.

Solution

The general form of the equation is

$$-2x + y - 1 = 0.$$

So, the distance between the point and the line is

$$d = \frac{|-2(4) + 1(1) + (-1)|}{\sqrt{(-2)^2 + 1^2}} = \frac{8}{\sqrt{5}} \approx 3.58 \text{ units.}$$

The line and the point are shown in Figure 6.6.

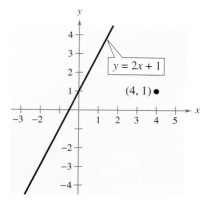

FIGURE **6.6**

✔*CHECKPOINT*   Now try Exercise 39.

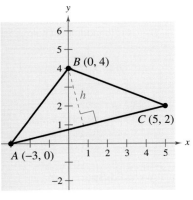

FIGURE 6.7

Example 4   **An Application of Two Distance Formulas**

Figure 6.7 shows a triangle with vertices $A(-3, 0)$, $B(0, 4)$, and $C(5, 2)$.

a. Find the altitude h from vertex B to side AC.

b. Find the area of the triangle.

Solution

a. To find the altitude, use the formula for the distance between line AC and the point $(0, 4)$. The equation of line AC is obtained as follows.

$$\text{Slope: } m = \frac{2 - 0}{5 - (-3)} = \frac{2}{8} = \frac{1}{4}$$

$$\text{Equation: } \qquad y - 0 = \frac{1}{4}(x + 3) \qquad \text{Point-slope form}$$

$$4y = x + 3 \qquad \text{Multiply each side by 4.}$$

$$x - 4y + 3 = 0 \qquad \text{General form}$$

So, the distance between this line and the point $(0, 4)$ is

$$\text{Altitude} = h = \frac{|1(0) + (-4)(4) + 3|}{\sqrt{1^2 + (-4)^2}} = \frac{13}{\sqrt{17}} \text{ units.}$$

b. Using the formula for the distance between two points, you can find the length of the base AC to be

$$b = \sqrt{[5 - (-3)]^2 + (2 - 0)^2} \qquad \text{Distance Formula}$$

$$= \sqrt{8^2 + 2^2} \qquad \text{Simplify.}$$

$$= \sqrt{68} \qquad \text{Simplify.}$$

$$= 2\sqrt{17} \text{ units.} \qquad \text{Simplify.}$$

Finally, the area of the triangle in Figure 6.7 is

$$A = \frac{1}{2}bh \qquad \text{Formula for the area of a triangle}$$

$$= \frac{1}{2}\left(2\sqrt{17}\right)\left(\frac{13}{\sqrt{17}}\right) \qquad \text{Substitute for } b \text{ and } h.$$

$$= 13 \text{ square units.} \qquad \text{Simplify.}$$

✓**CHECKPOINT**   Now try Exercise 45.

WRITING ABOUT **M**ATHEMATICS

Inclination and the Angle Between Two Lines Discuss why the inclination of a line can be an angle that is larger than $\pi/2$, but the angle between two lines cannot be larger than $\pi/2$. Decide whether the following statement is true or false: "The inclination of a line is the angle between the line and the x-axis." Explain.

6.1 Exercises

The *HM mathSpace®* CD-ROM and *Eduspace®* for this text contain step-by-step solutions to all odd-numbered exercises. They also provide Tutorial Exercises for additional help.

VOCABULARY CHECK: Fill in the blanks.

1. The _____ of a nonhorizontal line is the positive angle θ (less than π) measured counterclockwise from the x-axis to the line.

2. If a nonvertical line has inclination θ and slope m, then $m =$ _____ .

3. If two nonperpendicular lines have slopes m_1 and m_2, the angle between the two lines is tan $\theta =$ _____ .

4. The distance between the point (x_1, y_1) and the line $Ax + By + C = 0$ is given by $d =$ _____ .

PREREQUISITE SKILLS REVIEW: Practice and review algebra skills needed for this section at **www.Eduspace.com.**

In Exercises 1–8, find the slope of the line with inclination θ.

1.

2.

3.

4.

5. $\theta = \dfrac{\pi}{3}$ radians

6. $\theta = \dfrac{5\pi}{6}$ radians

7. $\theta = 1.27$ radians

8. $\theta = 2.88$ radians

In Exercises 9–14, find the inclination θ (in radians and degrees) of the line with a slope of m.

9. $m = -1$

10. $m = -2$

11. $m = 1$

12. $m = 2$

13. $m = \dfrac{3}{4}$

14. $m = -\dfrac{5}{2}$

In Exercises 15–18, find the inclination θ (in radians and degrees) of the line passing through the points.

15. $(6, 1), (10, 8)$

16. $(12, 8), (-4, -3)$

17. $(-2, 20), (10, 0)$

18. $(0, 100), (50, 0)$

In Exercises 19–22, find the inclination θ (in radians and degrees) of the line.

19. $6x - 2y + 8 = 0$

20. $4x + 5y - 9 = 0$

21. $5x + 3y = 0$

22. $x - y - 10 = 0$

In Exercises 23–32, find the angle θ (in radians and degrees) between the lines.

23. $3x + y = 3$
    $x - y = 2$

24. $x + 3y = 2$
    $x - 2y = -3$

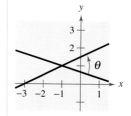

25. $x - y = 0$
    $3x - 2y = -1$

26. $2x - y = 2$
    $4x + 3y = 24$

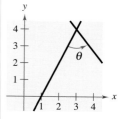

27. $x - 2y = 7$
    $6x + 2y = 5$

28. $5x + 2y = 16$
    $3x - 5y = -1$

29. $x + 2y = 8$
    $x - 2y = 2$

30. $3x - 5y = 3$
    $3x + 5y = 12$

31. $0.05x - 0.03y = 0.21$
$0.07x + 0.02y = 0.16$

32. $0.02x - 0.05y = -0.19$
$0.03x + 0.04y = 0.52$

Angle Measurement   In Exercises 33–36, find the slope of each side of the triangle and use the slopes to find the measures of the interior angles.

33.

34.

35.

36.

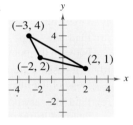

In Exercises 37–44, find the distance between the point and the line.

	Point	Line
37.	$(0, 0)$	$4x + 3y = 0$
38.	$(0, 0)$	$2x - y = 4$
39.	$(2, 3)$	$4x + 3y = 10$
40.	$(-2, 1)$	$x - y = 2$
41.	$(6, 2)$	$x + 1 = 0$
42.	$(10, 8)$	$y - 4 = 0$
43.	$(0, 8)$	$6x - y = 0$
44.	$(4, 2)$	$x - y = 20$

In Exercises 45–48, the points represent the vertices of a triangle. (a) Draw triangle *ABC* in the coordinate plane, (b) find the altitude from vertex *B* of the triangle to side *AC*, and (c) find the area of the triangle.

45. $A = (0, 0)$, $B = (1, 4)$, $C = (4, 0)$

46. $A = (0, 0)$, $B = (4, 5)$, $C = (5, -2)$

47. $A = \left(-\frac{1}{2}, \frac{1}{2}\right)$, $B = (2, 3)$, $C = \left(\frac{5}{2}, 0\right)$

48. $A = (-4, -5)$, $B = (3, 10)$, $C = (6, 12)$

In Exercises 49 and 50, find the distance between the parallel lines.

49. $x + y = 1$
$x + y = 5$

50. $3x - 4y = 1$
$3x - 4y = 10$

51. *Road Grade*   A straight road rises with an inclination of 0.10 radian from the horizontal (see figure). Find the slope of the road and the change in elevation over a two-mile stretch of the road.

52. *Road Grade*   A straight road rises with an inclination of 0.20 radian from the horizontal. Find the slope of the road and the change in elevation over a one-mile stretch of the road.

53. *Pitch of a Roof*   A roof has a rise of 3 feet for every horizontal change of 5 feet (see figure). Find the inclination of the roof.

54. Conveyor Design A moving conveyor is built so that it rises 1 meter for each 3 meters of horizontal travel.

(a) Draw a diagram that gives a visual representation of the problem.

(b) Find the inclination of the conveyor.

(c) The conveyor runs between two floors in a factory. The distance between the floors is 5 meters. Find the length of the conveyor.

55. Truss Find the angles α and β shown in the drawing of the roof truss.

Model It

56. Inclined Plane The Johnstown Inclined Plane in Johnstown, Pennsylvania is an inclined railway that was designed to carry people to the hilltop community of Westmont. It also proved useful in carrying people and vehicles to safety during severe floods. The railway is 896.5 feet long with a 70.9% uphill grade (see figure).

Not drawn to scale

(a) Find the inclination θ of the railway.

(b) Find the change in elevation from the base to the top of the railway.

(c) Using the origin of a rectangular coordinate system as the base of the inclined plane, find the equation of the line that models the railway track.

(d) Sketch a graph of the equation you found in part (c).

Synthesis

True or False? In Exercises 57 and 58, determine whether the statement is true or false. Justify your answer.

57. A line that has an inclination greater than $\pi/2$ radians has a negative slope.

58. To find the angle between two lines whose angles of inclination θ_1 and θ_2 are known, substitute θ_1 and θ_2 for m_1 and m_2, respectively, in the formula for the angle between two lines.

59. Exploration Consider a line with slope m and y-intercept $(0, 4)$.

(a) Write the distance d between the origin and the line as a function of m.

(b) Graph the function in part (a).

(c) Find the slope that yields the maximum distance between the origin and the line.

(d) Find the asymptote of the graph in part (b) and interpret its meaning in the context of the problem.

60. Exploration Consider a line with slope m and y-intercept $(0, 4)$.

(a) Write the distance d between the point $(3, 1)$ and the line as a function of m.

(b) Graph the function in part (a).

(c) Find the slope that yields the maximum distance between the point and the line.

(d) Is it possible for the distance to be 0? If so, what is the slope of the line that yields a distance of 0?

(e) Find the asymptote of the graph in part (b) and interpret its meaning in the context of the problem.

Skills Review

In Exercises 61–66, find all x-intercepts and y-intercepts of the graph of the quadratic function.

61. $f(x) = (x - 7)^2$

62. $f(x) = (x + 9)^2$

63. $f(x) = (x - 5)^2 - 5$

64. $f(x) = (x + 11)^2 + 12$

65. $f(x) = x^2 - 7x - 1$

66. $f(x) = x^2 + 9x - 22$

In Exercises 67–72, write the quadratic function in standard form by completing the square. Identify the vertex of the function.

67. $f(x) = 3x^2 + 2x - 16$

68. $f(x) = 2x^2 - x - 21$

69. $f(x) = 5x^2 + 34x - 7$

70. $f(x) = -x^2 - 8x - 15$

71. $f(x) = 6x^2 - x - 12$

72. $f(x) = -8x^2 - 34x - 21$

In Exercises 73–76, graph the quadratic function.

73. $f(x) = (x - 4)^2 + 3$

74. $f(x) = 6 - (x + 1)^2$

75. $g(x) = 2x^2 - 3x + 1$

76. $g(x) = -x^2 + 6x - 8$

6.2   Introduction to Conics: Parabolas

Conics

Conic sections were discovered during the classical Greek period, 600 to 300 B.C. The early Greeks were concerned largely with the geometric properties of conics. It was not until the 17th century that the broad applicability of conics became apparent and played a prominent role in the early development of calculus.

A **conic section** (or simply **conic**) is the intersection of a plane and a double-napped cone. Notice in Figure 6.8 that in the formation of the four basic conics, the intersecting plane does not pass through the vertex of the cone. When the plane does pass through the vertex, the resulting figure is a **degenerate conic,** as shown in Figure 6.9.

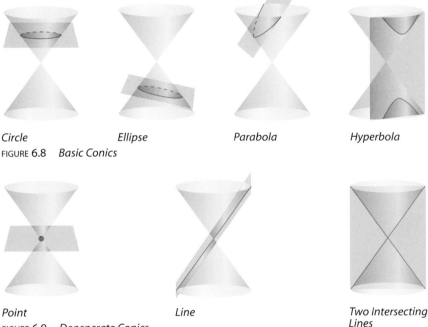

Circle   Ellipse   Parabola   Hyperbola

FIGURE **6.8**   *Basic Conics*

Point   Line   Two Intersecting Lines

FIGURE **6.9**   *Degenerate Conics*

There are several ways to approach the study of conics. You could begin by defining conics in terms of the intersections of planes and cones, as the Greeks did, or you could define them algebraically, in terms of the general second-degree equation

$$Ax^2 + Bxy + Cy^2 + Dx + Ey + F = 0.$$

However, you will study a third approach, in which each of the conics is defined as a **locus** (collection) of points satisfying a geometric property. For example, in Section 1.2, you learned that a circle is defined as the collection of all points (x, y) that are equidistant from a fixed point (h, k). This leads to the standard form of the equation of a circle

$$(x - h)^2 + (y - k)^2 = r^2. \qquad \text{Equation of circle}$$

Parabolas

In Section 2.1, you learned that the graph of the quadratic function

$$f(x) = ax^2 + bx + c$$

is a parabola that opens upward or downward. The following definition of a parabola is more general in the sense that it is independent of the orientation of the parabola.

> ### Definition of Parabola
>
> A **parabola** is the set of all points (x, y) in a plane that are equidistant from a fixed line (**directrix**) and a fixed point (**focus**) not on the line.

FIGURE 6.10 *Parabola*

The midpoint between the focus and the directrix is called the **vertex,** and the line passing through the focus and the vertex is called the **axis** of the parabola. Note in Figure 6.10 that a parabola is symmetric with respect to its axis. Using the definition of a parabola, you can derive the following **standard form** of the equation of a parabola whose directrix is parallel to the *x*-axis or to the *y*-axis.

> ### Standard Equation of a Parabola
>
> The **standard form of the equation of a parabola** with vertex at (h, k) is as follows.
>
> $$(x - h)^2 = 4p(y - k), \ p \neq 0 \qquad \text{Vertical axis, directrix: } y = k - p$$
> $$(y - k)^2 = 4p(x - h), \ p \neq 0 \qquad \text{Horizontal axis, directrix: } x = h - p$$
>
> The focus lies on the axis p units (*directed distance*) from the vertex. If the vertex is at the origin $(0, 0)$, the equation takes one of the following forms.
>
> $$x^2 = 4py \qquad \text{Vertical axis}$$
> $$y^2 = 4px \qquad \text{Horizontal axis}$$
>
> See Figure 6.11.

For a proof of the standard form of the equation of a parabola, see Proofs in Mathematics on page 523.

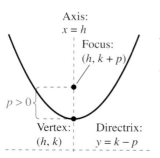

(a) $(x - h)^2 = 4p(y - k)$
Vertical axis: $p > 0$

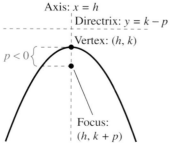

(b) $(x - h)^2 = 4p(y - k)$
Vertical axis: $p < 0$

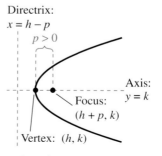

(c) $(y - k)^2 = 4p(x - h)$
Horizontal axis: $p > 0$

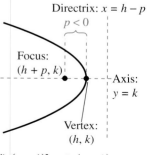

(d) $(y - k)^2 = 4p(x - h)$
Horizontal axis: $p < 0$

FIGURE 6.11

STUDY TIP

You may want to review the technique of completing the square found in Appendix A.5 (on our website *college.hmco.com*), which will be used to rewrite each of the conics in standard form.

Example 1   **Vertex at the Origin**

Find the standard equation of the parabola with vertex at the origin and focus $(2, 0)$.

Solution

The axis of the parabola is horizontal, passing through $(0, 0)$ and $(2, 0)$, as shown in Figure 6.12.

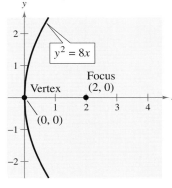

FIGURE 6.12

So, the standard form is $y^2 = 4px$, where $h = 0$, $k = 0$, and $p = 2$. So, the equation is $y^2 = 8x$.

✓**CHECKPOINT**   Now try Exercise 33.

Example 2   **Finding the Focus of a Parabola**

Find the focus of the parabola given by $y = -\frac{1}{2}x^2 - x + \frac{1}{2}$.

Solution

To find the focus, convert to standard form by completing the square.

$y = -\frac{1}{2}x^2 - x + \frac{1}{2}$	Write original equation.
$-2y = x^2 + 2x - 1$	Multiply each side by –2.
$1 - 2y = x^2 + 2x$	Add 1 to each side.
$1 + 1 - 2y = x^2 + 2x + 1$	Complete the square.
$2 - 2y = x^2 + 2x + 1$	Combine like terms.
$-2(y - 1) = (x + 1)^2$	Standard form

Comparing this equation with

$$(x - h)^2 = 4p(y - k)$$

you can conclude that $h = -1$, $k = 1$, and $p = -\frac{1}{2}$. Because p is negative, the parabola opens downward, as shown in Figure 6.13. So, the focus of the parabola is $(h, k + p) = \left(-1, \frac{1}{2}\right)$.

✓**CHECKPOINT**   Now try Exercise 21.

FIGURE 6.13

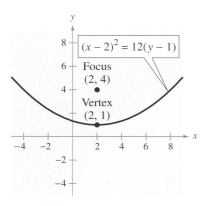

$(x - 2)^2 = 12(y - 1)$

Focus
(2, 4)

Vertex
(2, 1)

FIGURE **6.14**

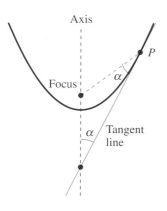

Light source
at focus

Focus   Axis

Parabolic reflector:
Light is reflected
in parallel rays.

FIGURE **6.15**

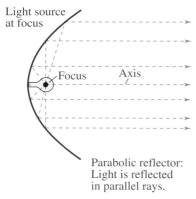

Axis

P

Focus α

α Tangent
line

FIGURE **6.16**

| Example 3 | Finding the Standard Equation of a Parabola |

Find the standard form of the equation of the parabola with vertex (2, 1) and focus (2, 4).

Solution

Because the axis of the parabola is vertical, passing through (2, 1) and (2, 4), consider the equation

$$(x - h)^2 = 4p(y - k)$$

where $h = 2$, $k = 1$, and $p = 4 - 1 = 3$. So, the standard form is

$$(x - 2)^2 = 12(y - 1).$$

You can obtain the more common quadratic form as follows.

$(x - 2)^2 = 12(y - 1)$	Write original equation.
$x^2 - 4x + 4 = 12y - 12$	Multiply.
$x^2 - 4x + 16 = 12y$	Add 12 to each side.
$\dfrac{1}{12}(x^2 - 4x + 16) = y$	Divide each side by 12.

The graph of this parabola is shown in Figure 6.14.

✓**CHECKPOINT**   Now try Exercise 45.

Application

A line segment that passes through the focus of a parabola and has endpoints on the parabola is called a **focal chord.** The specific focal chord perpendicular to the axis of the parabola is called the **latus rectum.**

    Parabolas occur in a wide variety of applications. For instance, a parabolic reflector can be formed by revolving a parabola around its axis. The resulting surface has the property that all incoming rays parallel to the axis are reflected through the focus of the parabola. This is the principle behind the construction of the parabolic mirrors used in reflecting telescopes. Conversely, the light rays emanating from the focus of a parabolic reflector used in a flashlight are all parallel to one another, as shown in Figure 6.15.

    A line is **tangent** to a parabola at a point on the parabola if the line intersects, but does not cross, the parabola at the point. Tangent lines to parabolas have special properties related to the use of parabolas in constructing reflective surfaces.

Reflective Property of a Parabola

The tangent line to a parabola at a point P makes equal angles with the following two lines (see Figure 6.16).

1. The line passing through P and the focus

2. The axis of the parabola

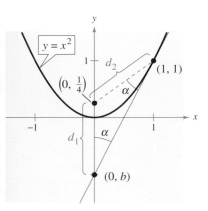

FIGURE **6.17**

Example 4   Finding the Tangent Line at a Point on a Parabola

Find the equation of the tangent line to the parabola given by $y = x^2$ at the point $(1, 1)$.

Solution

For this parabola, $p = \frac{1}{4}$ and the focus is $\left(0, \frac{1}{4}\right)$, as shown in Figure 6.17. You can find the y-intercept $(0, b)$ of the tangent line by equating the lengths of the two sides of the isosceles triangle shown in Figure 6.17:

$$d_1 = \frac{1}{4} - b$$

and

$$d_2 = \sqrt{(1 - 0)^2 + \left[1 - \left(\frac{1}{4}\right)\right]^2} = \frac{5}{4}.$$

Note that $d_1 = \frac{1}{4} - b$ rather than $b - \frac{1}{4}$. The order of subtraction for the distance is important because the distance must be positive. Setting $d_1 = d_2$ produces

$$\frac{1}{4} - b = \frac{5}{4}$$

$$b = -1.$$

So, the slope of the tangent line is

$$m = \frac{1 - (-1)}{1 - 0} = 2$$

and the equation of the tangent line in slope-intercept form is

$$y = 2x - 1.$$

✓CHECKPOINT   Now try Exercise 55.

Technology

Use a graphing utility to confirm the result of Example 4. By graphing

$$y_1 = x^2 \quad \text{and} \quad y_2 = 2x - 1$$

in the same viewing window, you should be able to see that the line touches the parabola at the point $(1, 1)$.

WRITING ABOUT MATHEMATICS

Television Antenna Dishes Cross sections of television antenna dishes are parabolic in shape. Use the figure shown to write a paragraph explaining why these dishes are parabolic.

6.2 | Exercises

VOCABULARY CHECK: Fill in the blanks.

1. A _____ is the intersection of a plane and a double-napped cone.

2. A collection of points satisfying a geometric property can also be referred to as a _____ of points.

3. A _____ is defined as the set of all points (x, y) in a plane that are equidistant from a fixed line, called the _____, and a fixed point, called the _____, not on the line.

4. The line that passes through the focus and vertex of a parabola is called the _____ of the parabola.

5. The _____ of a parabola is the midpoint between the focus and the directrix.

6. A line segment that passes through the focus of a parabola and has endpoints on the parabola is called a _____ _____ .

7. A line is _____ to a parabola at a point on the parabola if the line intersects, but does not cross, the parabola at the point.

PREREQUISITE SKILLS REVIEW: Practice and review algebra skills needed for this section at **www.Eduspace.com.**

In Exercises 1–4, describe in words how a plane could intersect with the double-napped cone shown to form the conic section.

1. Circle **2.** Ellipse

3. Parabola **4.** Hyperbola

In Exercises 5–10, match the equation with its graph. [The graphs are labeled (a), (b), (c), (d), (e), and (f).]

(a)

(b)

(c)

(d)

(e)

(f)

5. $y^2 = -4x$ **6.** $x^2 = 2y$

7. $x^2 = -8y$ **8.** $y^2 = -12x$

9. $(y - 1)^2 = 4(x - 3)$ **10.** $(x + 3)^2 = -2(y - 1)$

In Exercises 11–24, find the vertex, focus, and directrix of the parabola and sketch its graph.

11. $y = \frac{1}{2}x^2$ **12.** $y = -2x^2$

13. $y^2 = -6x$ **14.** $y^2 = 3x$

15. $x^2 + 6y = 0$ **16.** $x + y^2 = 0$

17. $(x - 1)^2 + 8(y + 2) = 0$

18. $(x + 5) + (y - 1)^2 = 0$

19. $\left(x + \frac{3}{2}\right)^2 = 4(y - 2)$ **20.** $\left(x + \frac{1}{2}\right)^2 = 4(y - 1)$

21. $y = \frac{1}{4}(x^2 - 2x + 5)$ **22.** $x = \frac{1}{4}(y^2 + 2y + 33)$

23. $y^2 + 6y + 8x + 25 = 0$

24. $y^2 - 4y - 4x = 0$

In Exercises 25–28, find the vertex, focus, and directrix of the parabola. Use a graphing utility to graph the parabola.

25. $x^2 + 4x + 6y - 2 = 0$

26. $x^2 - 2x + 8y + 9 = 0$

27. $y^2 + x + y = 0$

28. $y^2 - 4x - 4 = 0$

In Exercises 29–40, find the standard form of the equation of the parabola with the given characteristic(s) and vertex at the origin.

29.

30.

31. Focus: $\left(0, -\frac{3}{2}\right)$

32. Focus: $\left(\frac{5}{2}, 0\right)$

33. Focus: $(-2, 0)$

34. Focus: $(0, -2)$

35. Directrix: $y = -1$

36. Directrix: $y = 3$

37. Directrix: $x = 2$

38. Directrix: $x = -3$

39. Horizontal axis and passes through the point $(4, 6)$

40. Vertical axis and passes through the point $(-3, -3)$

In Exercises 41–50, find the standard form of the equation of the parabola with the given characteristics.

41.

42.

43.

44.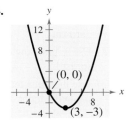

45. Vertex: $(5, 2)$; focus: $(3, 2)$

46. Vertex: $(-1, 2)$; focus: $(-1, 0)$

47. Vertex: $(0, 4)$; directrix: $y = 2$

48. Vertex: $(-2, 1)$; directrix: $x = 1$

49. Focus: $(2, 2)$; directrix: $x = -2$

50. Focus: $(0, 0)$; directrix: $y = 8$

In Exercises 51 and 52, change the equation of the parabola so that its graph matches the description.

51. $(y - 3)^2 = 6(x + 1)$; upper half of parabola

52. $(y + 1)^2 = 2(x - 4)$; lower half of parabola

 In Exercises 53 and 54, the equations of a parabola and a tangent line to the parabola are given. Use a graphing utility to graph both equations in the same viewing window. Determine the coordinates of the point of tangency.

Parabola	Tangent Line
53. $y^2 - 8x = 0$	$x - y + 2 = 0$
54. $x^2 + 12y = 0$	$x + y - 3 = 0$

In Exercises 55–58, find an equation of the tangent line to the parabola at the given point, and find the x-intercept of the line.

55. $x^2 = 2y$, $(4, 8)$

56. $x^2 = 2y$, $\left(-3, \frac{9}{2}\right)$

57. $y = -2x^2$, $(-1, -2)$

58. $y = -2x^2$, $(2, -8)$

59. *Revenue* The revenue R (in dollars) generated by the sale of x units of a patio furniture set is given by

$$(x - 106)^2 = -\frac{4}{5}(R - 14{,}045).$$

Use a graphing utility to graph the function and approximate the number of sales that will maximize revenue.

60. *Revenue* The revenue R (in dollars) generated by the sale of x units of a digital camera is given by

$$(x - 135)^2 = -\frac{5}{7}(R - 25{,}515).$$

Use a graphing utility to graph the function and approximate the number of sales that will maximize revenue.

61. *Satellite Antenna* The receiver in a parabolic television dish antenna is 4.5 feet from the vertex and is located at the focus (see figure). Write an equation for a cross section of the reflector. (Assume that the dish is directed upward and the vertex is at the origin.)

Model It

62. Suspension Bridge Each cable of the Golden Gate Bridge is suspended (in the shape of a parabola) between two towers that are 1280 meters apart. The top of each tower is 152 meters above the roadway. The cables touch the roadway midway between the towers.

(a) Draw a sketch of the bridge. Locate the origin of a rectangular coordinate system at the center of the roadway. Label the coordinates of the known points.

(b) Write an equation that models the cables.

(c) Complete the table by finding the height y of the suspension cables over the roadway at a distance of x meters from the center of the bridge.

Distance, x	Height, y
0	
250	
400	
500	
1000	

63. Road Design Roads are often designed with parabolic surfaces to allow rain to drain off. A particular road that is 32 feet wide is 0.4 foot higher in the center than it is on the sides (see figure).

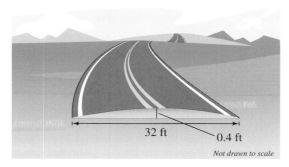

32 ft   0.4 ft

Not drawn to scale

Cross section of road surface

(a) Find an equation of the parabola that models the road surface. (Assume that the origin is at the center of the road.)

(b) How far from the center of the road is the road surface 0.1 foot lower than in the middle?

64. Highway Design Highway engineers design a parabolic curve for an entrance ramp from a straight street to an interstate highway (see figure). Find an equation of the parabola.

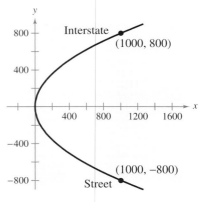

Interstate (1000, 800)

Street (1000, −800)

FIGURE FOR 64

65. Satellite Orbit A satellite in a 100-mile-high circular orbit around Earth has a velocity of approximately 17,500 miles per hour. If this velocity is multiplied by $\sqrt{2}$, the satellite will have the minimum velocity necessary to escape Earth's gravity and it will follow a parabolic path with the center of Earth as the focus (see figure).

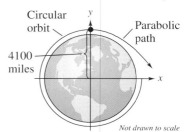

Circular orbit

4100 miles

Parabolic path

Not drawn to scale

(a) Find the escape velocity of the satellite.

(b) Find an equation of the parabolic path of the satellite (assume that the radius of Earth is 4000 miles).

66. Path of a Softball The path of a softball is modeled by

$$-12.5(y - 7.125) = (x - 6.25)^2$$

where the coordinates x and y are measured in feet, with $x = 0$ corresponding to the position from which the ball was thrown.

(a) Use a graphing utility to graph the trajectory of the softball.

(b) Use the *trace* feature of the graphing utility to approximate the highest point and the range of the trajectory.

Projectile Motion **In Exercises 67 and 68, consider the path of a projectile projected horizontally with a velocity of v feet per second at a height of s feet, where the model for the path is**

$$x^2 = -\frac{v^2}{16}(y - s).$$

In this model (in which air resistance is disregarded), y is the height (in feet) of the projectile and x is the horizontal distance (in feet) the projectile travels.

67. A ball is thrown from the top of a 75-foot tower with a velocity of 32 feet per second.

  (a) Find the equation of the parabolic path.

  (b) How far does the ball travel horizontally before striking the ground?

68. A cargo plane is flying at an altitude of 30,000 feet and a speed of 540 miles per hour. A supply crate is dropped from the plane. How many *feet* will the crate travel horizontally before it hits the ground?

Synthesis

True or False?   In Exercises 69 and 70, determine whether the statement is true or false. Justify your answer.

69. It is possible for a parabola to intersect its directrix.

70. If the vertex and focus of a parabola are on a horizontal line, then the directrix of the parabola is vertical.

71. *Exploration*   Consider the parabola $x^2 = 4py$.

  (a) Use a graphing utility to graph the parabola for $p = 1$, $p = 2$, $p = 3$, and $p = 4$. Describe the effect on the graph when p increases.

  (b) Locate the focus for each parabola in part (a).

  (c) For each parabola in part (a), find the length of the chord passing through the focus and parallel to the directrix (see figure). How can the length of this chord be determined directly from the standard form of the equation of the parabola?

  (d) Explain how the result of part (c) can be used as a sketching aid when graphing parabolas.

72. *Geometry*   The area of the shaded region in the figure is

$$A = \frac{8}{3}p^{1/2}b^{3/2}.$$

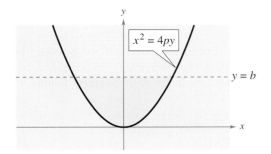

  (a) Find the area when $p = 2$ and $b = 4$.

  (b) Give a geometric explanation of why the area approaches 0 as p approaches 0.

73. *Exploration*   Let (x_1, y_1) be the coordinates of a point on the parabola $x^2 = 4py$. The equation of the line tangent to the parabola at the point is

$$y - y_1 = \frac{x_1}{2p}(x - x_1).$$

What is the slope of the tangent line?

74. *Writing*   In your own words, state the reflective property of a parabola.

Skills Review

In Exercises 75–78, list the possible rational zeros of f given by the Rational Zero Test.

75. $f(x) = x^3 - 2x^2 + 2x - 4$

76. $f(x) = 2x^3 + 4x^2 - 3x + 10$

77. $f(x) = 2x^5 + x^2 + 16$

78. $f(x) = 3x^3 - 12x + 22$

79. Find a polynomial with real coefficients that has the zeros $3, 2 + i$, and $2 - i$.

80. Find all the zeros of

$$f(x) = 2x^3 - 3x^2 + 50x - 75$$

if one of the zeros is $x = \frac{3}{2}$.

81. Find all the zeros of the function

$$g(x) = 6x^4 + 7x^3 - 29x^2 - 28x + 20$$

if two of the zeros are $x = \pm 2$.

82. Use a graphing utility to graph the function given by

$$h(x) = 2x^4 + x^3 - 19x^2 - 9x + 9.$$

Use the graph to approximate the zeros of h.

In Exercises 83–90, use the information to solve the triangle. Round your answers to two decimal places.

83. $A = 35°, a = 10, b = 7$

84. $B = 54°, b = 18, c = 11$

85. $A = 40°, B = 51°, c = 3$

86. $B = 26°, C = 104°, a = 19$

87. $a = 7, b = 10, c = 16$

88. $a = 58, b = 28, c = 75$

89. $A = 65°, b = 5, c = 12$

90. $B = 71°, a = 21, c = 29$

6.3 Ellipses

What you should learn

- Write equations of ellipses in standard form and graph ellipses.
- Use properties of ellipses to model and solve real-life problems.
- Find eccentricities of ellipses.

Why you should learn it

Ellipses can be used to model and solve many types of real-life problems. For instance, in Exercise 59 on page 473, an ellipse is used to model the orbit of Halley's comet.

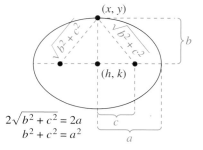

Harvard College Observatory/
SPL/Photo Researchers, Inc.

Introduction

The second type of conic is called an **ellipse,** and is defined as follows.

> ### Definition of Ellipse
>
> An **ellipse** is the set of all points (x, y) in a plane, the sum of whose distances from two distinct fixed points **(foci)** is constant. See Figure 6.18.

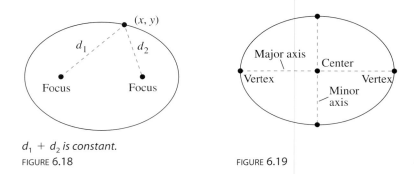

$d_1 + d_2$ is constant.
FIGURE 6.18

FIGURE 6.19

The line through the foci intersects the ellipse at two points called **vertices.** The chord joining the vertices is the **major axis,** and its midpoint is the **center** of the ellipse. The chord perpendicular to the major axis at the center is the **minor axis** of the ellipse. See Figure 6.19.

You can visualize the definition of an ellipse by imagining two thumbtacks placed at the foci, as shown in Figure 6.20. If the ends of a fixed length of string are fastened to the thumbtacks and the string is *drawn taut* with a pencil, the path traced by the pencil will be an ellipse.

FIGURE 6.20

To derive the standard form of the equation of an ellipse, consider the ellipse in Figure 6.21 with the following points: center, (h, k); vertices, $(h \pm a, k)$; foci, $(h \pm c, k)$. Note that the center is the midpoint of the segment joining the foci.

$$2\sqrt{b^2 + c^2} = 2a$$
$$b^2 + c^2 = a^2$$

FIGURE 6.21

The sum of the distances from any point on the ellipse to the two foci is constant. Using a vertex point, this constant sum is

$$(a + c) + (a - c) = 2a \qquad \text{Length of major axis}$$

or simply the length of the major axis. Now, if you let (x, y) be *any* point on the ellipse, the sum of the distances between (x, y) and the two foci must also be $2a$. That is,

$$\sqrt{[x - (h - c)]^2 + (y - k)^2} + \sqrt{[x - (h + c)]^2 + (y - k)^2} = 2a.$$

Finally, in Figure 6.21, you can see that $b^2 = a^2 - c^2$, which implies that the equation of the ellipse is

$$b^2(x - h)^2 + a^2(y - k)^2 = a^2 b^2$$

$$\frac{(x - h)^2}{a^2} + \frac{(y - k)^2}{b^2} = 1.$$

You would obtain a similar equation in the derivation by starting with a vertical major axis. Both results are summarized as follows.

STUDY TIP

Consider the equation of the ellipse

$$\frac{(x - h)^2}{a^2} + \frac{(y - k)^2}{b^2} = 1.$$

If you let $a = b$, then the equation can be rewritten as

$$(x - h)^2 + (y - k)^2 = a^2$$

which is the standard form of the equation of a circle with radius $r = a$ (see Section 1.2). Geometrically, when $a = b$ for an ellipse, the major and minor axes are of equal length, and so the graph is a circle.

Standard Equation of an Ellipse

The **standard form of the equation of an ellipse,** with center (h, k) and major and minor axes of lengths $2a$ and $2b$, respectively, where $0 < b < a$, is

$$\frac{(x - h)^2}{a^2} + \frac{(y - k)^2}{b^2} = 1 \qquad \text{Major axis is horizontal.}$$

$$\frac{(x - h)^2}{b^2} + \frac{(y - k)^2}{a^2} = 1. \qquad \text{Major axis is vertical.}$$

The foci lie on the major axis, c units from the center, with $c^2 = a^2 - b^2$. If the center is at the origin $(0, 0)$, the equation takes one of the following forms.

$$\frac{x^2}{a^2} + \frac{y^2}{b^2} = 1 \qquad \begin{array}{l}\text{Major axis is}\\ \text{horizontal.}\end{array} \qquad \frac{x^2}{b^2} + \frac{y^2}{a^2} = 1 \qquad \begin{array}{l}\text{Major axis is}\\ \text{vertical.}\end{array}$$

Figure 6.22 shows both the horizontal and vertical orientations for an ellipse.

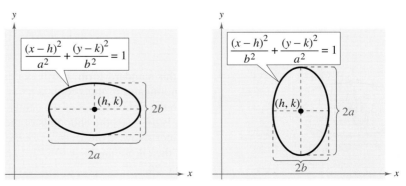

Major axis is horizontal.   Major axis is vertical.

FIGURE 6.22

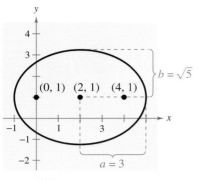

FIGURE 6.23

Example 1   **Finding the Standard Equation of an Ellipse**

Find the standard form of the equation of the ellipse having foci at $(0, 1)$ and $(4, 1)$ and a major axis of length 6, as shown in Figure 6.23.

Solution

Because the foci occur at $(0, 1)$ and $(4, 1)$, the center of the ellipse is $(2, 1)$ and the distance from the center to one of the foci is $c = 2$. Because $2a = 6$, you know that $a = 3$. Now, from $c^2 = a^2 - b^2$, you have

$$b = \sqrt{a^2 - c^2} = \sqrt{3^2 - 2^2} = \sqrt{5}.$$

Because the major axis is horizontal, the standard equation is

$$\frac{(x - 2)^2}{3^2} + \frac{(y - 1)^2}{(\sqrt{5})^2} = 1.$$

This equation simplifies to

$$\frac{(x - 2)^2}{9} + \frac{(y - 1)^2}{5} = 1.$$

✓CHECKPOINT   Now try Exercise 49.

Example 2   **Sketching an Ellipse**

Sketch the ellipse given by $x^2 + 4y^2 + 6x - 8y + 9 = 0$.

Solution

Begin by writing the original equation in standard form. In the fourth step, note that 9 and 4 are added to *both* sides of the equation when completing the squares.

$$x^2 + 4y^2 + 6x - 8y + 9 = 0 \quad \text{Write original equation.}$$

$$\left(x^2 + 6x + \quad\right) + \left(4y^2 - 8y + \quad\right) = -9 \quad \text{Group terms.}$$

$$\left(x^2 + 6x + \quad\right) + 4\left(y^2 - 2y + \quad\right) = -9 \quad \text{Factor 4 out of } y\text{-terms.}$$

$$(x^2 + 6x + 9) + 4(y^2 - 2y + 1) = -9 + 9 + 4(1)$$

$$(x + 3)^2 + 4(y - 1)^2 = 4 \quad \text{Write in completed square form.}$$

$$\frac{(x + 3)^2}{4} + \frac{(y - 1)^2}{1} = 1 \quad \text{Divide each side by 4.}$$

$$\frac{(x + 3)^2}{2^2} + \frac{(y - 1)^2}{1^2} = 1 \quad \text{Write in standard form.}$$

From this standard form, it follows that the center is $(h, k) = (-3, 1)$. Because the denominator of the x-term is $a^2 = 2^2$, the endpoints of the major axis lie two units to the right and left of the center. Similarly, because the denominator of the y-term is $b^2 = 1^2$, the endpoints of the minor axis lie one unit up and down from the center. Now, from $c^2 = a^2 - b^2$, you have $c = \sqrt{2^2 - 1^2} = \sqrt{3}$. So, the foci of the ellipse are $\left(-3 - \sqrt{3}, 1\right)$ and $\left(-3 + \sqrt{3}, 1\right)$. The ellipse is shown in Figure 6.24.

✓CHECKPOINT   Now try Exercise 25.

FIGURE 6.24

Example 3   **Analyzing an Ellipse**

Find the center, vertices, and foci of the ellipse $4x^2 + y^2 - 8x + 4y - 8 = 0$.

Solution

By completing the square, you can write the original equation in standard form.

$$4x^2 + y^2 - 8x + 4y - 8 = 0 \quad \text{Write original equation.}$$

$$\left(4x^2 - 8x + \boxed{}\right) + \left(y^2 + 4y + \boxed{}\right) = 8 \quad \text{Group terms.}$$

$$4\left(x^2 - 2x + \boxed{}\right) + \left(y^2 + 4y + \boxed{}\right) = 8 \quad \text{Factor 4 out of } \quad \text{terms.}$$

$$4(x^2 - 2x + 1) + (y^2 + 4y + 4) = 8 + 4(1) + 4$$

$$4(x - 1)^2 + (y + 2)^2 = 16 \quad \text{Write in completed square form.}$$

$$\frac{(x - 1)^2}{4} + \frac{(y + 2)^2}{16} = 1 \quad \text{Divide each side by 16.}$$

$$\frac{(x - 1)^2}{2^2} + \frac{(y + 2)^2}{4^2} = 1 \quad \text{Write in standard form.}$$

The major axis is vertical, where $h = 1$, $k = -2$, $a = 4$, $b = 2$, and

$$c = \sqrt{a^2 - b^2} = \sqrt{16 - 4} = \sqrt{12} = 2\sqrt{3}.$$

So, you have the following.

Center: $(1, -2)$ Vertices: $(1, -6)$ Foci: $\left(1, -2 - 2\sqrt{3}\right)$

$(1, 2)$ $\left(1, -2 + 2\sqrt{3}\right)$

The graph of the ellipse is shown in Figure 6.25.

✔CHECKPOINT   Now try Exercise 29.

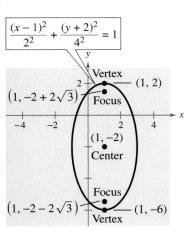

$$\frac{(x-1)^2}{2^2} + \frac{(y+2)^2}{4^2} = 1$$

FIGURE **6.25**

Technology

You can use a graphing utility to graph an ellipse by graphing the upper and lower portions in the same viewing window. For instance, to graph the ellipse in Example 3, first solve for y to get

$$y_1 = -2 + 4\sqrt{1 - \frac{(x - 1)^2}{4}} \quad \text{and} \quad y_2 = -2 - 4\sqrt{1 - \frac{(x - 1)^2}{4}}.$$

Use a viewing window in which $-6 \le x \le 9$ and $-7 \le y \le 3$. You should obtain the graph shown below.

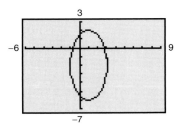

Application

Ellipses have many practical and aesthetic uses. For instance, machine gears, supporting arches, and acoustic designs often involve elliptical shapes. The orbits of satellites and planets are also ellipses. Example 4 investigates the elliptical orbit of the moon about Earth.

Example 4   **An Application Involving an Elliptical Orbit**

The moon travels about Earth in an elliptical orbit with Earth at one focus, as shown in Figure 6.26. The major and minor axes of the orbit have lengths of 768,800 kilometers and 767,640 kilometers, respectively. Find the greatest and smallest distances (the *apogee* and *perigee*), respectively from Earth's center to the moon's center.

Solution

Because $2a = 768,800$ and $2b = 767,640$, you have

$$a = 384,400 \text{ and } b = 383,820$$

which implies that

$$c = \sqrt{a^2 - b^2}$$
$$= \sqrt{384,400^2 - 383,820^2}$$
$$\approx 21,108.$$

So, the greatest distance between the center of Earth and the center of the moon is

$$a + c \approx 384,400 + 21,108 = 405,508 \text{ kilometers}$$

and the smallest distance is

$$a - c \approx 384,400 - 21,108 = 363,292 \text{ kilometers.}$$

✓*CHECKPOINT*   Now try Exercise 59.

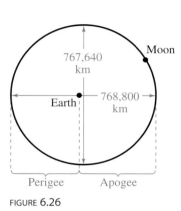

FIGURE 6.26

STUDY TIP

Note in Example 4 and Figure 6.26 that Earth *is not* the center of the moon's orbit.

Eccentricity

One of the reasons it was difficult for early astronomers to detect that the orbits of the planets are ellipses is that the foci of the planetary orbits are relatively close to their centers, and so the orbits are nearly circular. To measure the ovalness of an ellipse, you can use the concept of **eccentricity.**

Definition of Eccentricity

The **eccentricity** e of an ellipse is given by the ratio

$$e = \frac{c}{a}.$$

Note that $0 < e < 1$ for *every* ellipse.

To see how this ratio is used to describe the shape of an ellipse, note that because the foci of an ellipse are located along the major axis between the vertices and the center, it follows that

$$0 < c < a.$$

For an ellipse that is nearly circular, the foci are close to the center and the ratio c/a is small, as shown in Figure 6.27. On the other hand, for an elongated ellipse, the foci are close to the vertices, and the ratio c/a is close to 1, as shown in Figure 6.28.

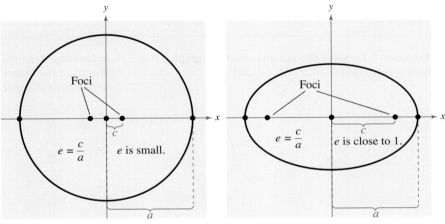

FIGURE **6.27**   FIGURE **6.28**

The orbit of the moon has an eccentricity of $e \approx 0.0549$, and the eccentricities of the nine planetary orbits are as follows.

Mercury:	$e \approx 0.2056$	Saturn:	$e \approx 0.0542$
Venus:	$e \approx 0.0068$	Uranus:	$e \approx 0.0472$
Earth:	$e \approx 0.0167$	Neptune:	$e \approx 0.0086$
Mars:	$e \approx 0.0934$	Pluto:	$e \approx 0.2488$
Jupiter:	$e \approx 0.0484$		

The time it takes Saturn to orbit the sun is equal to 29.4 Earth years.

WRITING ABOUT MATHEMATICS

Ellipses and Circles

a. Show that the equation of an ellipse can be written as

$$\frac{(x - h)^2}{a^2} + \frac{(y - k)^2}{a^2(1 - e^2)} = 1.$$

b. For the equation in part (a), let $a = 4$, $h = 1$, and $k = 2$, and use a graphing utility to graph the ellipse for $e = 0.95$, $e = 0.75$, $e = 0.5$, $e = 0.25$, and $e = 0.1$. Discuss the changes in the shape of the ellipse as e approaches 0.

c. Make a conjecture about the shape of the graph in part (b) when $e = 0$. What is the equation of this ellipse? What is another name for an ellipse with an eccentricity of 0?

6.3 Exercises

VOCABULARY CHECK: Fill in the blanks.

1. An _____ is the set of all points (x, y) in a plane, the sum of whose distances from two distinct fixed points, called _____, is constant.

2. The chord joining the vertices of an ellipse is called the _____ _____, and its midpoint is the _____ of the ellipse.

3. The chord perpendicular to the major axis at the center of the ellipse is called the _____ _____ of the ellipse.

4. The concept of _____ is used to measure the ovalness of an ellipse.

PREREQUISITE SKILLS REVIEW: Practice and review algebra skills needed for this section at **www.Eduspace.com.**

In Exercises 1–6, match the equation with its graph. [The graphs are labeled (a), (b), (c), (d), (e), and (f).]

(a)

(b)

(c)

(d)

(e)

(f)

1. $\dfrac{x^2}{4} + \dfrac{y^2}{9} = 1$

2. $\dfrac{x^2}{9} + \dfrac{y^2}{4} = 1$

3. $\dfrac{x^2}{4} + \dfrac{y^2}{25} = 1$

4. $\dfrac{x^2}{4} + \dfrac{y^2}{4} = 1$

5. $\dfrac{(x - 2)^2}{16} + (y + 1)^2 = 1$

6. $\dfrac{(x + 2)^2}{9} + \dfrac{(y + 2)^2}{4} = 1$

In Exercises 7–30, identify the conic as a circle or an ellipse. Then find the center, radius, vertices, foci, and eccentricity of the conic (if applicable), and sketch its graph.

7. $\dfrac{x^2}{25} + \dfrac{y^2}{16} = 1$

8. $\dfrac{x^2}{81} + \dfrac{y^2}{144} = 1$

9. $\dfrac{x^2}{25} + \dfrac{y^2}{25} = 1$

10. $\dfrac{x^2}{9} + \dfrac{y^2}{9} = 1$

11. $\dfrac{x^2}{5} + \dfrac{y^2}{9} = 1$

12. $\dfrac{x^2}{64} + \dfrac{y^2}{28} = 1$

13. $\dfrac{(x + 3)^2}{16} + \dfrac{(y - 5)^2}{25} = 1$ **14.** $\dfrac{(x - 4)^2}{12} + \dfrac{(y + 3)^2}{16} = 1$

15. $\dfrac{x^2}{4/9} + \dfrac{(y + 1)^2}{4/9} = 1$ **16.** $\dfrac{(x + 5)^2}{9/4} + (y - 1)^2 = 1$

17. $(x + 2)^2 + \dfrac{(y + 4)^2}{1/4} = 1$ **18.** $\dfrac{(x - 3)^2}{25/4} + \dfrac{(y - 1)^2}{25/4} = 1$

19. $9x^2 + 4y^2 + 36x - 24y + 36 = 0$

20. $9x^2 + 4y^2 - 54x + 40y + 37 = 0$

21. $x^2 + y^2 - 2x + 4y - 31 = 0$

22. $x^2 + 5y^2 - 8x - 30y - 39 = 0$

23. $3x^2 + y^2 + 18x - 2y - 8 = 0$

24. $6x^2 + 2y^2 + 18x - 10y + 2 = 0$

25. $x^2 + 4y^2 - 6x + 20y - 2 = 0$

26. $x^2 + y^2 - 4x + 6y - 3 = 0$

27. $9x^2 + 9y^2 + 18x - 18y + 14 = 0$

28. $16x^2 + 25y^2 - 32x + 50y + 16 = 0$

29. $9x^2 + 25y^2 - 36x - 50y + 60 = 0$

30. $16x^2 + 16y^2 - 64x + 32y + 55 = 0$

In Exercises 31–34, use a graphing utility to graph the ellipse. Find the center, foci, and vertices. (Recall that it may be necessary to solve the equation for y and obtain two equations.)

31. $5x^2 + 3y^2 = 15$ **32.** $3x^2 + 4y^2 = 12$

33. $12x^2 + 20y^2 - 12x + 40y - 37 = 0$

34. $36x^2 + 9y^2 + 48x - 36y - 72 = 0$

In Exercises 35–42, find the standard form of the equation of the ellipse with the given characteristics and center at the origin.

35.

36.

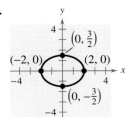

37. Vertices: $(\pm 6, 0)$; foci: $(\pm 2, 0)$

38. Vertices: $(0, \pm 8)$; foci: $(0, \pm 4)$

39. Foci: $(\pm 5, 0)$; major axis of length 12

40. Foci: $(\pm 2, 0)$; major axis of length 8

41. Vertices: $(0, \pm 5)$; passes through the point $(4, 2)$

42. Major axis vertical; passes through the points $(0, 4)$ and $(2, 0)$

In Exercises 43–54, find the standard form of the equation of the ellipse with the given characteristics.

43.

44.

45.

46.

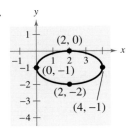

47. Vertices: $(0, 4)$, $(4, 4)$; minor axis of length 2

48. Foci: $(0, 0)$, $(4, 0)$; major axis of length 8

49. Foci: $(0, 0)$, $(0, 8)$; major axis of length 16

50. Center: $(2, -1)$; vertex: $\left(2, \frac{1}{2}\right)$; minor axis of length 2

51. Center: $(0, 4)$; $a = 2c$; vertices: $(-4, 4)$, $(4, 4)$

52. Center: $(3, 2)$; $a = 3c$; foci: $(1, 2)$, $(5, 2)$

53. Vertices: $(0, 2)$, $(4, 2)$; endpoints of the minor axis: $(2, 3)$, $(2, 1)$

54. Vertices: $(5, 0)$, $(5, 12)$; endpoints of the minor axis: $(1, 6)$, $(9, 6)$

55. Find an equation of the ellipse with vertices $(\pm 5, 0)$ and eccentricity $e = \frac{3}{5}$.

56. Find an equation of the ellipse with vertices $(0, \pm 8)$ and eccentricity $e = \frac{1}{2}$.

57. *Architecture* A semielliptical arch over a tunnel for a one-way road through a mountain has a major axis of 50 feet and a height at the center of 10 feet.

(a) Draw a rectangular coordinate system on a sketch of the tunnel with the center of the road entering the tunnel at the origin. Identify the coordinates of the known points.

(b) Find an equation of the semielliptical arch over the tunnel.

(c) You are driving a moving truck that has a width of 8 feet and a height of 9 feet. Will the moving truck clear the opening of the arch?

58. *Architecture* A fireplace arch is to be constructed in the shape of a semiellipse. The opening is to have a height of 2 feet at the center and a width of 6 feet along the base (see figure). The contractor draws the outline of the ellipse using tacks as described at the beginning of this section. Give the required positions of the tacks and the length of the string.

Model It

59. *Comet Orbit* Halley's comet has an elliptical orbit, with the sun at one focus. The eccentricity of the orbit is approximately 0.967. The length of the major axis of the orbit is approximately 35.88 astronomical units. (An astronomical unit is about 93 million miles.)

(a) Find an equation of the orbit. Place the center of the orbit at the origin, and place the major axis on the x-axis.

 (b) Use a graphing utility to graph the equation of the orbit.

(c) Find the greatest (aphelion) and smallest (perihelion) distances from the sun's center to the comet's center.

60. Satellite Orbit The first artificial satellite to orbit Earth was Sputnik I (launched by the former Soviet Union in 1957). Its highest point above Earth's surface was 947 kilometers, and its lowest point was 228 kilometers (see figure). The center of Earth was the focus of the elliptical orbit, and the radius of Earth is 6378 kilometers. Find the eccentricity of the orbit.

Focus

228 km — 947 km

61. Motion of a Pendulum The relation between the velocity y (in radians per second) of a pendulum and its angular displacement θ from the vertical can be modeled by a semiellipse. A 12-centimeter pendulum crests $(y = 0)$ when the angular displacement is -0.2 radian and 0.2 radian. When the pendulum is at equilibrium $(\theta = 0)$, the velocity is -1.6 radians per second.

(a) Find an equation that models the motion of the pendulum. Place the center at the origin.

(b) Graph the equation from part (a).

(c) Which half of the ellipse models the motion of the pendulum?

62. Geometry A line segment through a focus of an ellipse with endpoints on the ellipse and perpendicular to the major axis is called a **latus rectum** of the ellipse. Therefore, an ellipse has two latera recta. Knowing the length of the latera recta is helpful in sketching an ellipse because it yields other points on the curve (see figure). Show that the length of each latus rectum is $2b^2/a$.

Latera recta

In Exercises 63–66, sketch the graph of the ellipse, using latera recta (see Exercise 62).

63. $\dfrac{x^2}{9} + \dfrac{y^2}{16} = 1$

64. $\dfrac{x^2}{4} + \dfrac{y^2}{1} = 1$

65. $5x^2 + 3y^2 = 15$

66. $9x^2 + 4y^2 = 36$

Synthesis

True or False? In Exercises 67 and 68, determine whether the statement is true or false. Justify your answer.

67. The graph of $x^2 + 4y^4 - 4 = 0$ is an ellipse.

68. It is easier to distinguish the graph of an ellipse from the graph of a circle if the eccentricity of the ellipse is large (close to 1).

69. Exploration Consider the ellipse

$$\frac{x^2}{a^2} + \frac{y^2}{b^2} = 1, \quad a + b = 20.$$

(a) The area of the ellipse is given by $A = \pi ab$. Write the area of the ellipse as a function of a.

(b) Find the equation of an ellipse with an area of 264 square centimeters.

(c) Complete the table using your equation from part (a), and make a conjecture about the shape of the ellipse with maximum area.

a	8	9	10	11	12	13
A						

 (d) Use a graphing utility to graph the area function and use the graph to support your conjecture in part (c).

70. Think About It At the beginning of this section it was noted that an ellipse can be drawn using two thumbtacks, a string of fixed length (greater than the distance between the two tacks), and a pencil. If the ends of the string are fastened at the tacks and the string is drawn taut with a pencil, the path traced by the pencil is an ellipse.

(a) What is the length of the string in terms of a?

(b) Explain why the path is an ellipse.

Skills Review

In Exercises 71–74, use the power-reducing formulas to rewrite the expression in terms of the first power of the cosine.

71. $\sin^6 x$

72. $\cos^6 x$

73. $\cos^4 2x$

74. $\sin^4 2x$

In Exercises 75–78, find the area of the triangle with the given characteristics.

75. $A = 35°, b = 24, c = 52$

76. $a = 7.1, b = 4.8, c = 10.2$

77. $a = 14.4, b = 9.8, c = 9.8$

78. $C = 108°, a = 8, b = 12$

6.4   Hyperbolas

What you should learn

- Write equations of hyperbolas in standard form.
- Find asymptotes of and graph hyperbolas.
- Use properties of hyperbolas to solve real-life problems.
- Classify conics from their general equations.

Why you should learn it

Hyperbolas can be used to model and solve many types of real-life problems. For instance, in Exercise 42 on page 483, hyperbolas are used in long distance radio navigation for aircraft and ships.

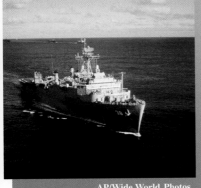

AP/Wide World Photos

Introduction

The third type of conic is called a **hyperbola.** The definition of a hyperbola is similar to that of an ellipse. The difference is that for an ellipse the *sum* of the distances between the foci and a point on the ellipse is fixed, whereas for a hyperbola the *difference* of the distances between the foci and a point on the hyperbola is fixed.

Definition of Hyperbola

A **hyperbola** is the set of all points (x, y) in a plane, the difference of whose distances from two distinct fixed points **(foci)** is a positive constant. See Figure 6.29.

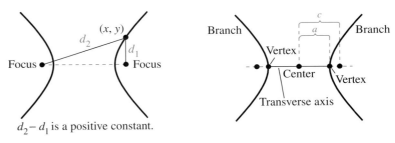

$d_2 - d_1$ is a positive constant.

FIGURE 6.29   FIGURE 6.30

The graph of a hyperbola has two disconnected **branches.** The line through the two foci intersects the hyperbola at its two **vertices.** The line segment connecting the vertices is the **transverse axis,** and the midpoint of the transverse axis is the **center** of the hyperbola. See Figure 6.30. The development of the standard form of the equation of a hyperbola is similar to that of an ellipse. Note in the definition below that a, b, and c are related differently for hyperbolas than for ellipses.

Standard Equation of a Hyperbola

The **standard form of the equation of a hyperbola** with center (h, k) is

$$\frac{(x - h)^2}{a^2} - \frac{(y - k)^2}{b^2} = 1 \qquad \text{Transverse axis is horizontal.}$$

$$\frac{(y - k)^2}{a^2} - \frac{(x - h)^2}{b^2} = 1. \qquad \text{Transverse axis is vertical.}$$

The vertices are a units from the center, and the foci are c units from the center. Moreover, $c^2 = a^2 + b^2$. If the center of the hyperbola is at the origin $(0, 0)$, the equation takes one of the following forms.

$$\frac{x^2}{a^2} - \frac{y^2}{b^2} = 1 \quad \begin{array}{l}\text{Transverse axis}\\ \text{is horizontal.}\end{array} \qquad \frac{y^2}{a^2} - \frac{x^2}{b^2} = 1 \quad \begin{array}{l}\text{Transverse axis}\\ \text{is vertical.}\end{array}$$

Figure 6.31 shows both the horizontal and vertical orientations for a hyperbola.

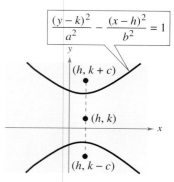

Transverse axis is horizontal.   *Transverse axis is vertical.*

FIGURE 6.31

Example 1   **Finding the Standard Equation of a Hyperbola**

Find the standard form of the equation of the hyperbola with foci $(-1, 2)$ and $(5, 2)$ and vertices $(0, 2)$ and $(4, 2)$.

Solution

By the Midpoint Formula, the center of the hyperbola occurs at the point $(2, 2)$. Furthermore, $c = 5 - 2 = 3$ and $a = 4 - 2 = 2$, and it follows that

$$b = \sqrt{c^2 - a^2} = \sqrt{3^2 - 2^2} = \sqrt{9 - 4} = \sqrt{5}.$$

So, the hyperbola has a horizontal transverse axis and the standard form of the equation is

$$\frac{(x - 2)^2}{2^2} - \frac{(y - 2)^2}{\left(\sqrt{5}\right)^2} = 1. \qquad \text{See Figure 6.32.}$$

This equation simplifies to

$$\frac{(x - 2)^2}{4} - \frac{(y - 2)^2}{5} = 1.$$

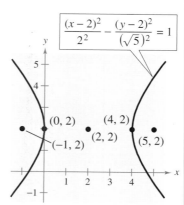

FIGURE 6.32

✓*CHECKPOINT*   Now try Exercise 27.

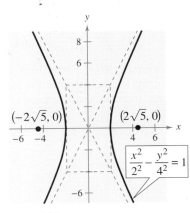

Conjugate
axis

$(h, k + b)$

Asymptote

(h, k)

$(h, k - b)$

Asymptote

$(h - a, k)$ $(h + a, k)$

FIGURE **6.33**

Asymptotes of a Hyperbola

Each hyperbola has two **asymptotes** that intersect at the center of the hyperbola, as shown in Figure 6.33. The asymptotes pass through the vertices of a rectangle of dimensions $2a$ by $2b$, with its center at (h, k). The line segment of length $2b$ joining $(h, k + b)$ and $(h, k - b)$ [or $(h + b, k)$ and $(h - b, k)$] is the **conjugate axis** of the hyperbola.

Asymptotes of a Hyperbola

The equations of the asymptotes of a hyperbola are

$$y = k \pm \frac{b}{a}(x - h) \qquad \text{Transverse axis is horizontal.}$$

$$y = k \pm \frac{a}{b}(x - h). \qquad \text{Transverse axis is vertical.}$$

Example 2   **Using Asymptotes to Sketch a Hyperbola**

Sketch the hyperbola whose equation is $4x^2 - y^2 = 16$.

Solution

Divide each side of the original equation by 16, and rewrite the equation in standard form.

$$\frac{x^2}{2^2} - \frac{y^2}{4^2} = 1 \qquad \text{Write in standard form.}$$

From this, you can conclude that $a = 2$, $b = 4$, and the transverse axis is horizontal. So, the vertices occur at $(-2, 0)$ and $(2, 0)$, and the endpoints of the conjugate axis occur at $(0, -4)$ and $(0, 4)$. Using these four points, you are able to sketch the rectangle shown in Figure 6.34. Now, from $c^2 = a^2 + b^2$, you have $c = \sqrt{2^2 + 4^2} = \sqrt{20} = 2\sqrt{5}$. So, the foci of the hyperbola are $\left(-2\sqrt{5}, 0\right)$ and $\left(2\sqrt{5}, 0\right)$. Finally, by drawing the asymptotes through the corners of this rectangle, you can complete the sketch shown in Figure 6.35. Note that the asymptotes are $y = 2x$ and $y = -2x$.

FIGURE **6.34**

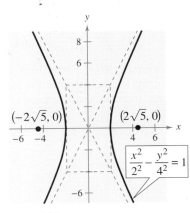

FIGURE **6.35**

✓CHECKPOINT   Now try Exercise 7.

Example 3 **Finding the Asymptotes of a Hyperbola**

Sketch the hyperbola given by $4x^2 - 3y^2 + 8x + 16 = 0$ and find the equations of its asymptotes and the foci.

Solution

$$4x^2 - 3y^2 + 8x + 16 = 0 \qquad \text{Write original equation.}$$
$$(4x^2 + 8x) - 3y^2 = -16 \qquad \text{Group terms.}$$
$$4(x^2 + 2x) - 3y^2 = -16 \qquad \text{Factor 4 from } x\text{-terms.}$$
$$4(x^2 + 2x + 1) - 3y^2 = -16 + 4 \qquad \text{Add 4 to each side.}$$
$$4(x + 1)^2 - 3y^2 = -12 \qquad \text{Write in completed square form.}$$
$$-\frac{(x + 1)^2}{3} + \frac{y^2}{4} = 1 \qquad \text{Divide each side by } -12.$$
$$\frac{y^2}{2^2} - \frac{(x + 1)^2}{(\sqrt{3})^2} = 1 \qquad \text{Write in standard form.}$$

From this equation you can conclude that the hyperbola has a vertical transverse axis, centered at $(-1, 0)$, has vertices $(-1, 2)$ and $(-1, -2)$, and has a conjugate axis with endpoints $(-1 - \sqrt{3}, 0)$ and $(-1 + \sqrt{3}, 0)$. To sketch the hyperbola, draw a rectangle through these four points. The asymptotes are the lines passing through the corners of the rectangle. Using $a = 2$ and $b = \sqrt{3}$, you can conclude that the equations of the asymptotes are

$$y = \frac{2}{\sqrt{3}}(x + 1) \qquad \text{and} \qquad y = -\frac{2}{\sqrt{3}}(x + 1).$$

Finally, you can determine the foci by using the equation $c^2 = a^2 + b^2$. So, you have $c = \sqrt{2^2 + (\sqrt{3})^2} = \sqrt{7}$, and the foci are $(-1, -2 - \sqrt{7})$ and $(-1, -2 + \sqrt{7})$. The hyperbola is shown in Figure 6.36.

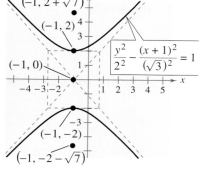

FIGURE 6.36

✓CHECKPOINT   Now try Exercise 13.

Technology

You can use a graphing utility to graph a hyperbola by graphing the upper and lower portions in the same viewing window. For instance, to graph the hyperbola in Example 3, first solve for y to get

$$y_1 = 2\sqrt{1 + \frac{(x + 1)^2}{3}} \qquad \text{and} \qquad y_2 = -2\sqrt{1 + \frac{(x + 1)^2}{3}}.$$

Use a viewing window in which $-9 \le x \le 9$ and $-6 \le y \le 6$. You should obtain the graph shown below. Notice that the graphing utility does not draw the asymptotes. However, if you trace along the branches, you will see that the values of the hyperbola approach the asymptotes.

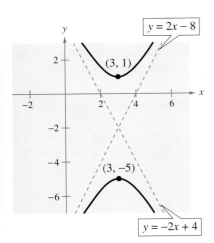

$y = 2x - 8$

(3, 1)

x

-2 2   4   6

-2

-4

(3, -5)

-6

$y = -2x + 4$

FIGURE 6.37

Example 4   **Using Asymptotes to Find the Standard Equation**

Find the standard form of the equation of the hyperbola having vertices $(3, -5)$ and $(3, 1)$ and having asymptotes

$$y = 2x - 8 \quad \text{and} \quad y = -2x + 4$$

as shown in Figure 6.37.

Solution

By the Midpoint Formula, the center of the hyperbola is $(3, -2)$. Furthermore, the hyperbola has a vertical transverse axis with $a = 3$. From the original equations, you can determine the slopes of the asymptotes to be

$$m_1 = 2 = \frac{a}{b} \quad \text{and} \quad m_2 = -2 = -\frac{a}{b}$$

and, because $a = 3$ you can conclude

$$2 = \frac{a}{b} \quad \implies \quad 2 = \frac{3}{b} \quad \implies \quad b = \frac{3}{2}.$$

So, the standard form of the equation is

$$\frac{(y + 2)^2}{3^2} - \frac{(x - 3)^2}{\left(\dfrac{3}{2}\right)^2} = 1.$$

✓**CHECKPOINT**   Now try Exercise 35.

As with ellipses, the *eccentricity* of a hyperbola is

$$e = \frac{c}{a} \qquad \text{Eccentricity}$$

and because $c > a$, it follows that $e > 1$. If the eccentricity is large, the branches of the hyperbola are nearly flat, as shown in Figure 6.38. If the eccentricity is close to 1, the branches of the hyperbola are more narrow, as shown in Figure 6.39.

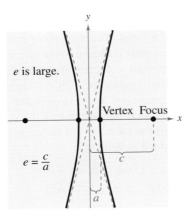

e is large.

Vertex Focus

$e = \dfrac{c}{a}$

c

a

FIGURE 6.38

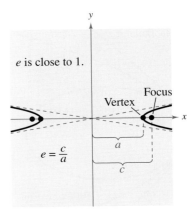

e is close to 1.

Focus

Vertex

x

$e = \dfrac{c}{a}$

a

c

FIGURE 6.39

Applications

The following application was developed during World War II. It shows how the properties of hyperbolas can be used in radar and other detection systems.

Example 5 **An Application Involving Hyperbolas**

Two microphones, 1 mile apart, record an explosion. Microphone A receives the sound 2 seconds before microphone B. Where did the explosion occur? (Assume sound travels at 1100 feet per second.)

Solution

Assuming sound travels at 1100 feet per second, you know that the explosion took place 2200 feet farther from B than from A, as shown in Figure 6.40. The locus of all points that are 2200 feet closer to A than to B is one branch of the hyperbola

$$\frac{x^2}{a^2} - \frac{y^2}{b^2} = 1$$

where

$$c = \frac{5280}{2} = 2640$$

and

$$a = \frac{2200}{2} = 1100.$$

So, $b^2 = c^2 - a^2 = 2640^2 - 1100^2 = 5,759,600$, and you can conclude that the explosion occurred somewhere on the right branch of the hyperbola

$$\frac{x^2}{1,210,000} - \frac{y^2}{5,759,600} = 1.$$

✓**CHECKPOINT** Now try Exercise 41.

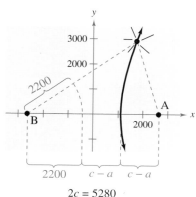

$2c = 5280$
$2200 + 2(c - a) = 5280$

FIGURE **6.40**

Another interesting application of conic sections involves the orbits of comets in our solar system. Of the 610 comets identified prior to 1970, 245 have elliptical orbits, 295 have parabolic orbits, and 70 have hyperbolic orbits. The center of the sun is a focus of each of these orbits, and each orbit has a vertex at the point where the comet is closest to the sun, as shown in Figure 6.41. Undoubtedly, there have been many comets with parabolic or hyperbolic orbits that were not identified. We only get to see such comets *once*. Comets with elliptical orbits, such as Halley's comet, are the only ones that remain in our solar system.

If p is the distance between the vertex and the focus (in meters), and v is the velocity of the comet at the vertex in (meters per second), then the type of orbit is determined as follows.

1. Ellipse: $v < \sqrt{2GM/p}$
2. Parabola: $v = \sqrt{2GM/p}$
3. Hyperbola: $v > \sqrt{2GM/p}$

In each of these relations, $M = 1.989 \times 10^{30}$ kilograms (the mass of the sun) and $G \approx 6.67 \times 10^{-11}$ cubic meter per kilogram-second squared (the universal gravitational constant).

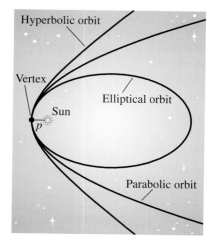

FIGURE **6.41**

General Equations of Conics

> ### Classifying a Conic from Its General Equation
>
> The graph of $Ax^2 + Cy^2 + Dx + Ey + F = 0$ is one of the following.
>
> **1.** *Circle:* $A = C$
>
> **2.** *Parabola:* $AC = 0$ $A = 0$ or $C = 0$, but not both.
>
> **3.** *Ellipse:* $AC > 0$ A and C have like signs.
>
> **4.** *Hyperbola:* $AC < 0$ A and C have unlike signs.

The test above is valid *if* the graph is a conic. The test does not apply to equations such as $x^2 + y^2 = -1$, whose graph is not a conic.

Example 6   Classifying Conics from General Equations

Classify the graph of each equation.

a. $4x^2 - 9x + y - 5 = 0$

b. $4x^2 - y^2 + 8x - 6y + 4 = 0$

c. $2x^2 + 4y^2 - 4x + 12y = 0$

d. $2x^2 + 2y^2 - 8x + 12y + 2 = 0$

Solution

a. For the equation $4x^2 - 9x + y - 5 = 0$, you have

$$AC = 4(0) = 0. \qquad \text{Parabola}$$

So, the graph is a parabola.

b. For the equation $4x^2 - y^2 + 8x - 6y + 4 = 0$, you have

$$AC = 4(-1) < 0. \qquad \text{Hyperbola}$$

So, the graph is a hyperbola.

c. For the equation $2x^2 + 4y^2 - 4x + 12y = 0$, you have

$$AC = 2(4) > 0. \qquad \text{Ellipse}$$

So, the graph is an ellipse.

d. For the equation $2x^2 + 2y^2 - 8x + 12y + 2 = 0$, you have

$$A = C = 2. \qquad \text{Circle}$$

So, the graph is a circle.

✓**CHECKPOINT**   Now try Exercise 49.

Historical Note
Caroline Herschel (1750–1848) was the first woman to be credited with detecting a new comet. During her long life, this English astronomer discovered a total of eight new comets.

The Granger Collection

> *W*RITING ABOUT *M*ATHEMATICS
>
> **Sketching Conics** Sketch each of the conics described in Example 6. Write a paragraph describing the procedures that allow you to sketch the conics efficiently.

6.4 | Exercises

VOCABULARY CHECK: Fill in the blanks.

1. A _____ is the set of all points (x, y) in a plane, the difference of whose distances from two distinct fixed points, called _____, is a positive constant.

2. The graph of a hyperbola has two disconnected parts called _____.

3. The line segment connecting the vertices of a hyperbola is called the _____ _____, and the midpoint of the line segment is the _____ of the hyperbola.

4. Each hyperbola has two _____ that intersect at the center of the hyperbola.

5. The general form of the equation of a conic is given by _____.

PREREQUISITE SKILLS REVIEW: Practice and review algebra skills needed for this section at **www.Eduspace.com.**

In Exercises 1–4, match the equation with its graph. [The graphs are labeled (a), (b), (c), and (d).]

(a)

(b)

(c)

(d)
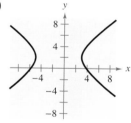

1. $\dfrac{y^2}{9} - \dfrac{x^2}{25} = 1$

2. $\dfrac{y^2}{25} - \dfrac{x^2}{9} = 1$

3. $\dfrac{(x-1)^2}{16} - \dfrac{y^2}{4} = 1$

4. $\dfrac{(x+1)^2}{16} - \dfrac{(y-2)^2}{9} = 1$

In Exercises 5–16, find the center, vertices, foci, and the equations of the asymptotes of the hyperbola, and sketch its graph using the asymptotes as an aid.

5. $x^2 - y^2 = 1$

6. $\dfrac{x^2}{9} - \dfrac{y^2}{25} = 1$

7. $\dfrac{y^2}{25} - \dfrac{x^2}{81} = 1$

8. $\dfrac{x^2}{36} - \dfrac{y^2}{4} = 1$

9. $\dfrac{(x-1)^2}{4} - \dfrac{(y+2)^2}{1} = 1$

10. $\dfrac{(x+3)^2}{144} - \dfrac{(y-2)^2}{25} = 1$

11. $\dfrac{(y+6)^2}{1/9} - \dfrac{(x-2)^2}{1/4} = 1$

12. $\dfrac{(y-1)^2}{1/4} - \dfrac{(x+3)^2}{1/16} = 1$

13. $9x^2 - y^2 - 36x - 6y + 18 = 0$

14. $x^2 - 9y^2 + 36y - 72 = 0$

15. $x^2 - 9y^2 + 2x - 54y - 80 = 0$

16. $16y^2 - x^2 + 2x + 64y + 63 = 0$

In Exercises 17–20, find the center, vertices, foci, and the equations of the asymptotes of the hyperbola. Use a graphing utility to graph the hyperbola and its asymptotes.

17. $2x^2 - 3y^2 = 6$

18. $6y^2 - 3x^2 = 18$

19. $9y^2 - x^2 + 2x + 54y + 62 = 0$

20. $9x^2 - y^2 + 54x + 10y + 55 = 0$

In Exercises 21–26, find the standard form of the equation of the hyperbola with the given characteristics and center at the origin.

21. Vertices: $(0, \pm 2)$; foci: $(0, \pm 4)$

22. Vertices: $(\pm 4, 0)$; foci: $(\pm 6, 0)$

23. Vertices: $(\pm 1, 0)$; asymptotes: $y = \pm 5x$

24. Vertices: $(0, \pm 3)$; asymptotes: $y = \pm 3x$

25. Foci: $(0, \pm 8)$; asymptotes: $y = \pm 4x$

26. Foci: $(\pm 10, 0)$; asymptotes: $y = \pm \frac{3}{4}x$

In Exercises 27–38, find the standard form of the equation of the hyperbola with the given characteristics.

27. Vertices: $(2, 0), (6, 0)$; foci: $(0, 0), (8, 0)$

28. Vertices: $(2, 3), (2, -3)$; foci: $(2, 6), (2, -6)$

29. Vertices: $(4, 1)$, $(4, 9)$; foci: $(4, 0)$, $(4, 10)$

30. Vertices: $(-2, 1)$, $(2, 1)$; foci: $(-3, 1)$, $(3, 1)$

31. Vertices: $(2, 3)$, $(2, -3)$;
passes through the point $(0, 5)$

32. Vertices: $(-2, 1)$, $(2, 1)$;
passes through the point $(5, 4)$

33. Vertices: $(0, 4)$, $(0, 0)$;
passes through the point $\left(\sqrt{5}, -1\right)$

34. Vertices: $(1, 2)$, $(1, -2)$;
passes through the point $\left(0, \sqrt{5}\right)$

35. Vertices: $(1, 2)$, $(3, 2)$;
asymptotes: $y = x$, $y = 4 - x$

36. Vertices: $(3, 0)$, $(3, 6)$;
asymptotes: $y = 6 - x$, $y = x$

37. Vertices: $(0, 2)$, $(6, 2)$;
asymptotes: $y = \frac{2}{3}x$, $y = 4 - \frac{2}{3}x$

38. Vertices: $(3, 0)$, $(3, 4)$;
asymptotes: $y = \frac{2}{3}x$, $y = 4 - \frac{2}{3}x$

39. *Art* A sculpture has a hyperbolic cross section (see figure).

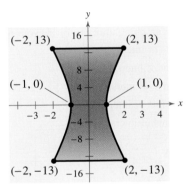

(a) Write an equation that models the curved sides of the sculpture.

(b) Each unit in the coordinate plane represents 1 foot. Find the width of the sculpture at a height of 5 feet.

40. *Sound Location* You and a friend live 4 miles apart (on the same "east-west" street) and are talking on the phone. You hear a clap of thunder from lightning in a storm, and 18 seconds later your friend hears the thunder. Find an equation that gives the possible places where the lightning could have occurred. (Assume that the coordinate system is measured in feet and that sound travels at 1100 feet per second.)

41. *Sound Location* Three listening stations located at $(3300, 0)$, $(3300, 1100)$, and $(-3300, 0)$ monitor an explosion. The last two stations detect the explosion 1 second and 4 seconds after the first, respectively. Determine the coordinates of the explosion. (Assume that the coordinate system is measured in feet and that sound travels at 1100 feet per second.)

Model It

42. *LORAN* Long distance radio navigation for aircraft and ships uses synchronized pulses transmitted by widely separated transmitting stations. These pulses travel at the speed of light (186,000 miles per second). The difference in the times of arrival of these pulses at an aircraft or ship is constant on a hyperbola having the transmitting stations as foci. Assume that two stations, 300 miles apart, are positioned on the rectangular coordinate system at points with coordinates $(-150, 0)$ and $(150, 0)$, and that a ship is traveling on a hyperbolic path with coordinates $(x, 75)$ (see figure).

(a) Find the x-coordinate of the position of the ship if the time difference between the pulses from the transmitting stations is 1000 microseconds (0.001 second).

(b) Determine the distance between the ship and station 1 when the ship reaches the shore.

(c) The ship wants to enter a bay located between the two stations. The bay is 30 miles from station 1. What should the time difference be between the pulses?

(d) The ship is 60 miles offshore when the time difference in part (c) is obtained. What is the position of the ship?

43. *Hyperbolic Mirror* A hyperbolic mirror (used in some telescopes) has the property that a light ray directed at a focus will be reflected to the other focus. The focus of a hyperbolic mirror (see figure) has coordinates (24, 0). Find the vertex of the mirror if the mount at the top edge of the mirror has coordinates (24, 24).

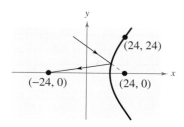

44. *Running Path* Let $(0, 0)$ represent a water fountain located in a city park. Each day you run through the park along a path given by

$$x^2 + y^2 - 200x - 52,500 = 0$$

where x and y are measured in meters.

(a) What type of conic is your path? Explain your reasoning.

(b) Write the equation of the path in standard form. Sketch a graph of the equation.

(c) After you run, you walk to the water fountain. If you stop running at $(-100, 150)$, how far must you walk for a drink of water?

In Exercises 45–60, classify the graph of the equation as a circle, a parabola, an ellipse, or a hyperbola.

45. $x^2 + y^2 - 6x + 4y + 9 = 0$

46. $x^2 + 4y^2 - 6x + 16y + 21 = 0$

47. $4x^2 - y^2 - 4x - 3 = 0$

48. $y^2 - 6y - 4x + 21 = 0$

49. $y^2 - 4x^2 + 4x - 2y - 4 = 0$

50. $x^2 + y^2 - 4x + 6y - 3 = 0$

51. $x^2 - 4x - 8y + 2 = 0$

52. $4x^2 + y^2 - 8x + 3 = 0$

53. $4x^2 + 3y^2 + 8x - 24y + 51 = 0$

54. $4y^2 - 2x^2 - 4y - 8x - 15 = 0$

55. $25x^2 - 10x - 200y - 119 = 0$

56. $4y^2 + 4x^2 - 24x + 35 = 0$

57. $4x^2 + 16y^2 - 4x - 32y + 1 = 0$

58. $2y^2 + 2x + 2y + 1 = 0$

59. $100x^2 + 100y^2 - 100x + 400y + 409 = 0$

60. $4x^2 - y^2 + 4x + 2y - 1 = 0$

Synthesis

True or False? **In Exercises 61 and 62, determine whether the statement is true or false. Justify your answer.**

61. In the standard form of the equation of a hyperbola, the larger the ratio of b to a, the larger the eccentricity of the hyperbola.

62. In the standard form of the equation of a hyperbola, the trivial solution of two intersecting lines occurs when $b = 0$.

63. Consider a hyperbola centered at the origin with a horizontal transverse axis. Use the definition of a hyperbola to derive its standard form.

64. *Writing* Explain how the central rectangle of a hyperbola can be used to sketch its asymptotes.

65. *Think About It* Change the equation of the hyperbola so that its graph is the bottom half of the hyperbola.

$$9x^2 - 54x - 4y^2 + 8y + 41 = 0$$

66. *Exploration* A circle and a parabola can have 0, 1, 2, 3, or 4 points of intersection. Sketch the circle given by $x^2 + y^2 = 4$. Discuss how this circle could intersect a parabola with an equation of the form $y = x^2 + C$. Then find the values of C for each of the five cases described below. Use a graphing utility to verify your results.

(a) No points of intersection

(b) One point of intersection

(c) Two points of intersection

(d) Three points of intersection

(e) Four points of intersection

Skills Review

In Exercises 67–72, factor the polynomial completely.

67. $x^3 - 16x$

68. $x^2 + 14x + 49$

69. $2x^3 - 24x^2 + 72x$

70. $6x^3 - 11x^2 - 10x$

71. $16x^3 + 54$

72. $4 - x + 4x^2 - x^3$

In Exercises 73–76, sketch a graph of the function. Include two full periods.

73. $y = 2 \cos x + 1$

74. $y = \sin \pi x$

75. $y = \tan 2x$

76. $y = -\frac{1}{2} \sec x$

6.5 Parametric Equations

What you should learn

- Evaluate sets of parametric equations for given values of the parameter.
- Sketch curves that are represented by sets of parametric equations.
- Rewrite sets of parametric equations as single rectangular equations by eliminating the parameter.
- Find sets of parametric equations for graphs.

Why you should learn it

Parametric equations are useful for modeling the path of an object. For instance, in Exercise 59 on page 491, you will use a set of parametric equations to model the path of a baseball.

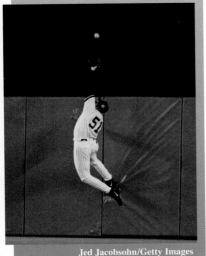

Jed Jacobsohn/Getty Images

Plane Curves

Up to this point you have been representing a graph by a single equation involving the *two* variables x and y. In this section, you will study situations in which it is useful to introduce a *third* variable to represent a curve in the plane.

To see the usefulness of this procedure, consider the path followed by an object that is propelled into the air at an angle of 45°. If the initial velocity of the object is 48 feet per second, it can be shown that the object follows the parabolic path

$$y = -\frac{x^2}{72} + x \qquad \text{Rectangular equation}$$

as shown in Figure 6.42. However, this equation does not tell the whole story. Although it does tell you *where* the object has been, it doesn't tell you *when* the object was at a given point (x, y) on the path. To determine this time, you can introduce a third variable t, called a **parameter.** It is possible to write both x and y as functions of t to obtain the **parametric equations**

$$x = 24\sqrt{2}\,t \qquad \text{Parametric equation for } x$$

$$y = -16t^2 + 24\sqrt{2}\,t. \qquad \text{Parametric equation for } y$$

From this set of equations you can determine that at time $t = 0$, the object is at the point $(0, 0)$. Similarly, at time $t = 1$, the object is at the point $\left(24\sqrt{2}, 24\sqrt{2} - 16\right)$, and so on, as shown in Figure 6.42.

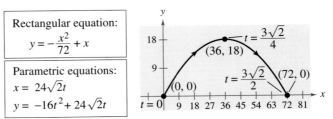

Rectangular equation:
$$y = -\frac{x^2}{72} + x$$

Parametric equations:
$$x = 24\sqrt{2}\,t$$
$$y = -16t^2 + 24\sqrt{2}\,t$$

Curvilinear Motion: Two Variables for Position, One Variable for Time
FIGURE **6.42**

For this particular motion problem, x and y are continuous functions of t, and the resulting path is a **plane curve.** (Recall that a *continuous function* is one whose graph can be traced without lifting the pencil from the paper.)

> ### Definition of Plane Curve
>
> If f and g are continuous functions of t on an interval I, the set of ordered pairs $(f(t), g(t))$ is a **plane curve** C. The equations
>
> $$x = f(t) \qquad \text{and} \qquad y = g(t)$$
>
> are **parametric equations** for C, and t is the **parameter.**

Sketching a Plane Curve

When sketching a curve represented by a pair of parametric equations, you still plot points in the xy-plane. Each set of coordinates (x, y) is determined from a value chosen for the parameter t. Plotting the resulting points in the order of *increasing* values of t traces the curve in a specific direction. This is called the **orientation** of the curve.

Example 1   Sketching a Curve

Sketch the curve given by the parametric equations

$$x = t^2 - 4 \quad \text{and} \quad y = \frac{t}{2}, \quad -2 \le t \le 3.$$

Solution

Using values of t in the interval, the parametric equations yield the points (x, y) shown in the table.

t	x	y
-2	0	-1
-1	-3	$-1/2$
0	-4	0
1	-3	$1/2$
2	0	1
3	5	$3/2$

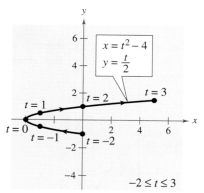

FIGURE 6.43

By plotting these points in the order of increasing t, you obtain the curve C shown in Figure 6.43. Note that the arrows on the curve indicate its orientation as t increases from -2 to 3. So, if a particle were moving on this curve, it would start at $(0, -1)$ and then move along the curve to the point $\left(5, \frac{3}{2}\right)$.

✔CHECKPOINT   Now try Exercises 1(a) and (b).

Note that the graph shown in Figure 6.43 does not define y as a function of x. This points out one benefit of parametric equations—they can be used to represent graphs that are more general than graphs of functions.

It often happens that two different sets of parametric equations have the same graph. For example, the set of parametric equations

$$x = 4t^2 - 4 \quad \text{and} \quad y = t, \quad -1 \le t \le \frac{3}{2}$$

has the same graph as the set given in Example 1. However, by comparing the values of t in Figures 6.43 and 6.44, you see that this second graph is traced out more *rapidly* (considering t as time) than the first graph. So, in applications, different parametric representations can be used to represent various *speeds* at which objects travel along a given path.

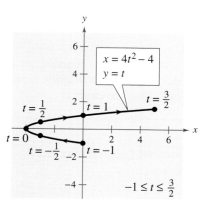

FIGURE 6.44

Eliminating the Parameter

Example 1 uses simple point plotting to sketch the curve. This tedious process can sometimes be simplified by finding a rectangular equation (in x and y) that has the same graph. This process is called **eliminating the parameter.**

Parametric equations	⇨	Solve for t in one equation.	⇨	Substitute in other equation.	⇨	Rectangular equation

$x = t^2 - 4$ $t = 2y$ $x = (2y)^2 - 4$ $x = 4y^2 - 4$
$y = t/2$

Now you can recognize that the equation $x = 4y^2 - 4$ represents a parabola with a horizontal axis and vertex $(-4, 0)$.

When converting equations from parametric to rectangular form, you may need to alter the domain of the rectangular equation so that its graph matches the graph of the parametric equations. Such a situation is demonstrated in Example 2.

Exploration

Most graphing utilities have a *parametric* mode. If yours does, enter the parametric equations from Example 2. Over what values should you let t vary to obtain the graph shown in Figure 6.45?

Example 2   Eliminating the Parameter

Sketch the curve represented by the equations

$$x = \frac{1}{\sqrt{t + 1}} \quad \text{and} \quad y = \frac{t}{t + 1}$$

by eliminating the parameter and adjusting the domain of the resulting rectangular equation.

Solution

Solving for t in the equation for x produces

$$x = \frac{1}{\sqrt{t + 1}} \quad \Rightarrow \quad x^2 = \frac{1}{t + 1}$$

which implies that

$$t = \frac{1 - x^2}{x^2}.$$

Now, substituting in the equation for y, you obtain the rectangular equation

$$y = \frac{t}{t + 1} = \frac{\dfrac{(1 - x^2)}{x^2}}{\left[\dfrac{(1 - x^2)}{x^2}\right] + 1} = \frac{\dfrac{1 - x^2}{x^2}}{\dfrac{1 - x^2}{x^2} + 1} \cdot \frac{x^2}{x^2} = 1 - x^2.$$

From this rectangular equation, you can recognize that the curve is a parabola that opens downward and has its vertex at $(0, 1)$. Also, this rectangular equation is defined for all values of x, but from the parametric equation for x you can see that the curve is defined only when $t > -1$. This implies that you should restrict the domain of x to positive values, as shown in Figure 6.45.

✓CHECKPOINT   Now try Exercise 1(c).

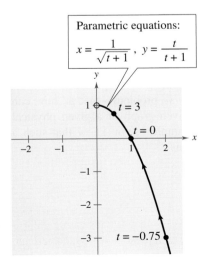

Parametric equations:

$$x = \frac{1}{\sqrt{t + 1}}, \quad y = \frac{t}{t + 1}$$

$t = 3$

$t = 0$

$t = -0.75$

FIGURE 6.45

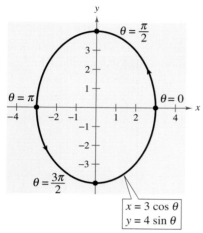

FIGURE 6.46

It is not necessary for the parameter in a set of parametric equations to represent time. The next example uses an *angle* as the parameter.

Example 3   **Eliminating an Angle Parameter**

Sketch the curve represented by

$$x = 3 \cos \theta \qquad \text{and} \qquad y = 4 \sin \theta, \qquad 0 \le \theta \le 2\pi$$

by eliminating the parameter.

Solution

Begin by solving for $\cos \theta$ and $\sin \theta$ in the equations.

$$\cos \theta = \frac{x}{3} \qquad \text{and} \qquad \sin \theta = \frac{y}{4} \qquad \text{Solve for } \cos \theta \text{ and } \sin \theta.$$

Use the identity $\sin^2 \theta + \cos^2 \theta = 1$ to form an equation involving only x and y.

$$\cos^2 \theta + \sin^2 \theta = 1 \qquad\qquad \text{Pythagorean identity}$$

$$\left(\frac{x}{3}\right)^2 + \left(\frac{y}{4}\right)^2 = 1 \qquad\qquad \text{Substitute } \frac{x}{3} \text{ for } \cos \theta \text{ and } \frac{y}{4} \text{ for } \sin \theta.$$

$$\frac{x^2}{9} + \frac{y^2}{16} = 1 \qquad\qquad \text{Rectangular equation}$$

From this rectangular equation, you can see that the graph is an ellipse centered at $(0, 0)$, with vertices $(0, 4)$ and $(0, -4)$ and minor axis of length $2b = 6$, as shown in Figure 6.46. Note that the elliptic curve is traced out *counterclockwise* as θ varies from 0 to 2π.

✓CHECKPOINT   Now try Exercise 13.

In Examples 2 and 3, it is important to realize that eliminating the parameter is primarily an *aid to curve sketching*. If the parametric equations represent the path of a moving object, the graph alone is not sufficient to describe the object's motion. You still need the parametric equations to tell you the *position*, *direction*, and *speed* at a given time.

Finding Parametric Equations for a Graph

You have been studying techniques for sketching the graph represented by a set of parametric equations. Now consider the *reverse* problem—that is, how can you find a set of parametric equations for a given graph or a given physical description? From the discussion following Example 1, you know that such a representation is not unique. That is, the equations

$$x = 4t^2 - 4 \qquad \text{and} \qquad y = t, \quad -1 \le t \le \frac{3}{2}$$

produced the same graph as the equations

$$x = t^2 - 4 \qquad \text{and} \qquad y = \frac{t}{2}, \quad -2 \le t \le 3.$$

This is further demonstrated in Example 4.

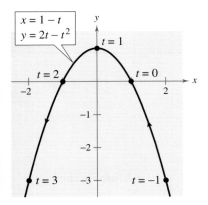

FIGURE **6.47**

Example 4   Finding Parametric Equations for a Graph

Find a set of parametric equations to represent the graph of $y = 1 - x^2$, using the following parameters.

a. $t = x$ **b.** $t = 1 - x$

Solution

a. Letting $t = x$, you obtain the parametric equations
$$x = t   \text{and}   y = 1 - x^2 = 1 - t^2.$$

b. Letting $t = 1 - x$, you obtain the parametric equations
$$x = 1 - t   \text{and}   y = 1 - x^2 = 1 - (1 - t)^2 = 2t - t^2.$$

In Figure 6.47, note how the resulting curve is oriented by the increasing values of t. For part (a), the curve would have the opposite orientation.

✓*CHECKPOINT*   Now try Exercise 37.

Example 5   Parametric Equations for a Cycloid

Describe the **cycloid** traced out by a point P on the circumference of a circle of radius a as the circle rolls along a straight line in a plane.

Solution

As the parameter, let θ be the measure of the circle's rotation, and let the point $P = (x, y)$ begin at the origin. When $\theta = 0$, P is at the origin; when $\theta = \pi$, P is at a maximum point $(\pi a, 2a)$; and when $\theta = 2\pi$, P is back on the x-axis at $(2\pi a, 0)$. From Figure 6.48, you can see that $\angle APC = 180° - \theta$. So, you have

$$\sin \theta = \sin(180° - \theta) = \sin(\angle APC) = \frac{AC}{a} = \frac{BD}{a}$$

$$\cos \theta = -\cos(180° - \theta) = -\cos(\angle APC) = \frac{AP}{-a}$$

which implies that $AP = -a \cos \theta$ and $BD = a \sin \theta$. Because the circle rolls along the x-axis, you know that $OD = \overset{\frown}{PD} = a\theta$. Furthermore, because $BA = DC = a$, you have

$$x = OD - BD = a\theta - a \sin \theta   \text{and}   y = BA + AP = a - a \cos \theta.$$

So, the parametric equations are $x = a(\theta - \sin \theta)$ and $y = a(1 - \cos \theta)$.

STUDY TIP

In Example 5, $\overset{\frown}{PD}$ represents the arc of the circle between points P and D.

Technology

Use a graphing utility in *parametric* mode to obtain a graph similar to Figure 6.48 by graphing the following equations.

$$X_{1T} = T - \sin T$$

$$Y_{1T} = 1 - \cos T$$

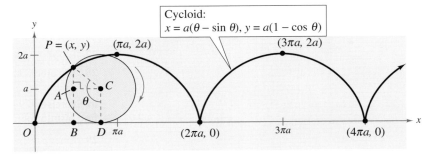

FIGURE **6.48**

✓*CHECKPOINT*   Now try Exercise 63.

6.5 | Exercises

VOCABULARY CHECK: Fill in the blanks.

1. If f and g are continuous functions of t on an interval I, the set of ordered pairs $(f(t), g(t))$ is a _____ _____ C. The equations $x = f(t)$ and $y = g(t)$ are _____ equations for C, and t is the _____.

2. The _____ of a curve is the direction in which the curve is traced out for increasing values of the parameter.

3. The process of converting a set of parametric equations to a corresponding rectangular equation is called the _____.

PREREQUISITE SKILLS REVIEW: Practice and review algebra skills needed for this section at **www.Eduspace.com.**

1. Consider the parametric equations $x = \sqrt{t}$ and $y = 3 - t$.

(a) Create a table of x- and y-values using $t = 0, 1, 2, 3$, and 4.

(b) Plot the points (x, y) generated in part (a), and sketch a graph of the parametric equations.

(c) Find the rectangular equation by eliminating the parameter. Sketch its graph. How do the graphs differ?

2. Consider the parametric equations $x = 4 \cos^2 \theta$ and $y = 2 \sin \theta$.

(a) Create a table of x- and y-values using $\theta = -\pi/2$, $-\pi/4, 0, \pi/4$, and $\pi/2$.

(b) Plot the points (x, y) generated in part (a), and sketch a graph of the parametric equations.

(c) Find the rectangular equation by eliminating the parameter. Sketch its graph. How do the graphs differ?

In Exercises 3–22, (a) sketch the curve represented by the parametric equations (indicate the orientation of the curve) and (b) eliminate the parameter and write the corresponding rectangular equation whose graph represents the curve. Adjust the domain of the resulting rectangular equation if necessary.

3. $x = 3t - 3$
$y = 2t + 1$

4. $x = 3 - 2t$
$y = 2 + 3t$

5. $x = \frac{1}{4}t$
$y = t^2$

6. $x = t$
$y = t^3$

7. $x = t + 2$
$y = t^2$

8. $x = \sqrt{t}$
$y = 1 - t$

9. $x = t + 1$
$y = \dfrac{t}{t + 1}$

10. $x = t - 1$
$y = \dfrac{t}{t - 1}$

11. $x = 2(t + 1)$
$y = |t - 2|$

12. $x = |t - 1|$
$y = t + 2$

13. $x = 3 \cos \theta$
$y = 3 \sin \theta$

14. $x = 2 \cos \theta$
$y = 3 \sin \theta$

15. $x = 4 \sin 2\theta$
$y = 2 \cos 2\theta$

16. $x = \cos \theta$
$y = 2 \sin 2\theta$

17. $x = 4 + 2 \cos \theta$
$y = -1 + \sin \theta$

18. $x = 4 + 2 \cos \theta$
$y = 2 + 3 \sin \theta$

19. $x = e^{-t}$
$y = e^{3t}$

20. $x = e^{2t}$
$y = e^t$

21. $x = t^3$
$y = 3 \ln t$

22. $x = \ln 2t$
$y = 2t^2$

In Exercises 23 and 24, determine how the plane curves differ from each other.

23. (a) $x = t$
$y = 2t + 1$

(b) $x = \cos \theta$
$y = 2 \cos \theta + 1$

(c) $x = e^{-t}$
$y = 2e^{-t} + 1$

(d) $x = e^t$
$y = 2e^t + 1$

24. (a) $x = t$
$y = t^2 - 1$

(b) $x = t^2$
$y = t^4 - 1$

(c) $x = \sin t$
$y = \sin^2 t - 1$

(d) $x = e^t$
$y = e^{2t} - 1$

In Exercises 25–28, eliminate the parameter and obtain the standard form of the rectangular equation.

25. Line through (x_1, y_1) and (x_2, y_2):
$x = x_1 + t(x_2 - x_1)$, $y = y_1 + t(y_2 - y_1)$

26. Circle: $x = h + r \cos \theta$, $y = k + r \sin \theta$

27. Ellipse: $x = h + a \cos \theta$, $y = k + b \sin \theta$

28. Hyperbola: $x = h + a \sec \theta$, $y = k + b \tan \theta$

In Exercises 29–36, use the results of Exercises 25–28 to find a set of parametric equations for the line or conic.

29. Line: passes through $(0, 0)$ and $(6, -3)$

30. Line: passes through $(2, 3)$ and $(6, -3)$

31. Circle: center: $(3, 2)$; radius: 4

32. Circle: center: $(-3, 2)$; radius: 5

33. Ellipse: vertices: $(\pm 4, 0)$; foci: $(\pm 3, 0)$

34. Ellipse: vertices: $(4, 7), (4, -3)$;

       foci: $(4, 5), (4, -1)$

35. Hyperbola: vertices: $(\pm 4, 0)$; foci: $(\pm 5, 0)$

36. Hyperbola: vertices: $(\pm 2, 0)$; foci: $(\pm 4, 0)$

In Exercises 37–44, find a set of parametric equations for the rectangular equation using (a) $t = x$ and (b) $t = 2 - x$.

37. $y = 3x - 2$ **38.** $x = 3y - 2$

39. $y = x^2$ **40.** $y = x^3$

41. $y = x^2 + 1$ **42.** $y = 2 - x$

43. $y = \dfrac{1}{x}$ **44.** $y = \dfrac{1}{2x}$

In Exercises 45–52, use a graphing utility to graph the curve represented by the parametric equations.

45. Cycloid: $x = 4(\theta - \sin \theta), \ y = 4(1 - \cos \theta)$

46. Cycloid: $x = \theta + \sin \theta, \ y = 1 - \cos \theta$

47. Prolate cycloid: $x = \theta - \frac{3}{2} \sin \theta, \ y = 1 - \frac{3}{2} \cos \theta$

48. Prolate cycloid: $x = 2\theta - 4 \sin \theta, \ y = 2 - 4 \cos \theta$

49. Hypocycloid: $x = 3 \cos^3 \theta, \ y = 3 \sin^3 \theta$

50. Curtate cycloid: $x = 8\theta - 4 \sin \theta, \ y = 8 - 4 \cos \theta$

51. Witch of Agnesi: $x = 2 \cot \theta, \ y = 2 \sin^2 \theta$

52. Folium of Descartes: $x = \dfrac{3t}{1 + t^3}, \ y = \dfrac{3t^2}{1 + t^3}$

In Exercises 53–56, match the parametric equations with the correct graph and describe the domain and range. [The graphs are labeled (a), (b), (c), and (d).]

(a)

(b)

(c)

(d)

53. Lissajous curve: $x = 2 \cos \theta, \ y = \sin 2\theta$

54. Evolute of ellipse: $x = 4 \cos^3 \theta, \ y = 6 \sin^3 \theta$

55. Involute of circle: $x = \frac{1}{2}(\cos \theta + \theta \sin \theta)$

                       $y = \frac{1}{2}(\sin \theta - \theta \cos \theta)$

56. Serpentine curve: $x = \frac{1}{2} \cot \theta, \ y = 4 \sin \theta \cos \theta$

Projectile Motion **A projectile is launched at a height of h feet above the ground at an angle of θ with the horizontal. The initial velocity is v_0 feet per second and the path of the projectile is modeled by the parametric equations**

$$x = (v_0 \cos \theta)t \quad \text{and} \quad y = h + (v_0 \sin \theta)t - 16t^2.$$

In Exercises 57 and 58, use a graphing utility to graph the paths of a projectile launched from ground level at each value of θ and v_0. For each case, use the graph to approximate the maximum height and the range of the projectile.

57. (a) $\theta = 60°, \quad v_0 = 88$ feet per second

     (b) $\theta = 60°, \quad v_0 = 132$ feet per second

     (c) $\theta = 45°, \quad v_0 = 88$ feet per second

     (d) $\theta = 45°, \quad v_0 = 132$ feet per second

58. (a) $\theta = 15°, \quad v_0 = 60$ feet per second

     (b) $\theta = 15°, \quad v_0 = 100$ feet per second

     (c) $\theta = 30°, \quad v_0 = 60$ feet per second

     (d) $\theta = 30°, \quad v_0 = 100$ feet per second

Model It

59. *Sports* The center field fence in Yankee Stadium is 7 feet high and 408 feet from home plate. A baseball is hit at a point 3 feet above the ground. It leaves the bat at an angle of θ degrees with the horizontal at a speed of 100 miles per hour (see figure).

Not drawn to scale

     (a) Write a set of parametric equations that model the path of the baseball.

     (b) Use a graphing utility to graph the path of the baseball when $\theta = 15°$. Is the hit a home run?

     (c) Use a graphing utility to graph the path of the baseball when $\theta = 23°$. Is the hit a home run?

     (d) Find the minimum angle required for the hit to be a home run.

60. Sports An archer releases an arrow from a bow at a point 5 feet above the ground. The arrow leaves the bow at an angle of 10° with the horizontal and at an initial speed of 240 feet per second.

(a) Write a set of parametric equations that model the path of the arrow.

(b) Assuming the ground is level, find the distance the arrow travels before it hits the ground. (Ignore air resistance.)

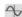 (c) Use a graphing utility to graph the path of the arrow and approximate its maximum height.

(d) Find the total time the arrow is in the air.

61. Projectile Motion Eliminate the parameter t from the parametric equations

$$x = (v_0 \cos \theta)t \quad \text{and} \quad y = h + (v_0 \sin \theta)t - 16t^2$$

for the motion of a projectile to show that the rectangular equation is

$$y = -\frac{16 \sec^2 \theta}{v_0^2}x^2 + (\tan \theta)x + h.$$

62. Path of a Projectile The path of a projectile is given by the rectangular equation

$$y = 7 + x - 0.02x^2.$$

(a) Use the result of Exercise 61 to find h, v_0, and θ. Find the parametric equations of the path.

 (b) Use a graphing utility to graph the rectangular equation for the path of the projectile. Confirm your answer in part (a) by sketching the curve represented by the parametric equations.

 (c) Use a graphing utility to approximate the maximum height of the projectile and its range.

63. Curtate Cycloid A wheel of radius a units rolls along a straight line without slipping. The curve traced by a point P that is b units from the center ($b < a$) is called a **curtate cycloid** (see figure). Use the angle θ shown in the figure to find a set of parametric equations for the curve.

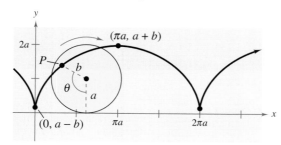

64. Epicycloid A circle of radius one unit rolls around the outside of a circle of radius two units without slipping. The curve traced by a point on the circumference of the smaller circle is called an **epicycloid** (see figure). Use the angle θ shown in the figure to find a set of parametric equations for the curve.

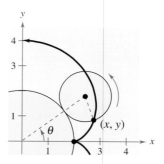

Synthesis

True or False? **In Exercises 65 and 66, determine whether the statement is true or false. Justify your answer.**

65. The two sets of parametric equations $x = t$, $y = t^2 + 1$ and $x = 3t$, $y = 9t^2 + 1$ have the same rectangular equation.

66. The graph of the parametric equations $x = t^2$ and $y = t^2$ is the line $y = x$.

67. Writing Write a short paragraph explaining why parametric equations are useful.

68. Writing Explain the process of sketching a plane curve given by parametric equations. What is meant by the orientation of the curve?

Skills Review

In Exercises 69–72, find the reference angle θ', and sketch θ and θ' in standard position.

69. $\theta = 105°$

70. $\theta = 230°$

71. $\theta = -\dfrac{2\pi}{3}$

72. $\theta = \dfrac{5\pi}{6}$

6.6 Polar Coordinates

Introduction

So far, you have been representing graphs of equations as collections of points (x, y) on the rectangular coordinate system, where x and y represent the directed distances from the coordinate axes to the point (x, y). In this section, you will study a different system called the **polar coordinate system.**

To form the polar coordinate system in the plane, fix a point O, called the **pole** (or **origin**), and construct from O an initial ray called the **polar axis,** as shown in Figure 6.49. Then each point P in the plane can be assigned **polar coordinates** (r, θ) as follows.

1. $r = directed\ distance$ from O to P

2. $\theta = directed\ angle$, counterclockwise from polar axis to segment $\overline{OP}$

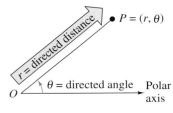

FIGURE 6.49

Example 1   Plotting Points on the Polar Coordinate System

a. The point $(r, \theta) = (2, \pi/3)$ lies two units from the pole on the terminal side of the angle $\theta = \pi/3$, as shown in Figure 6.50.

b. The point $(r, \theta) = (3, -\pi/6)$ lies three units from the pole on the terminal side of the angle $\theta = -\pi/6$, as shown in Figure 6.51.

c. The point $(r, \theta) = (3, 11\pi/6)$ coincides with the point $(3, -\pi/6)$, as shown in Figure 6.52.

FIGURE 6.50

FIGURE 6.51

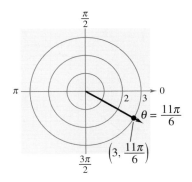

FIGURE 6.52

✓CHECKPOINT   Now try Exercise 1.

In rectangular coordinates, each point (x, y) has a unique representation. This is not true for polar coordinates. For instance, the coordinates (r, θ) and $(r, \theta + 2\pi)$ represent the same point, as illustrated in Example 1. Another way to obtain multiple representations of a point is to use negative values for r. Because r is a *directed distance*, the coordinates (r, θ) and $(-r, \theta + \pi)$ represent the same point. In general, the point (r, θ) can be represented as

$$(r, \theta) = (r, \theta \pm 2n\pi) \qquad \text{or} \qquad (r, \theta) = (-r, \theta \pm (2n + 1)\pi)$$

where n is any integer. Moreover, the pole is represented by $(0, \theta)$, where θ is any angle.

Example 2   Multiple Representations of Points

Plot the point $(3, -3\pi/4)$ and find three additional polar representations of this point, using $-2\pi < \theta < 2\pi$.

Solution

The point is shown in Figure 6.53. Three other representations are as follows.

$$\left(3, -\frac{3\pi}{4} + 2\pi\right) = \left(3, \frac{5\pi}{4}\right) \qquad \text{Add } 2\pi \text{ to } \theta.$$

$$\left(-3, -\frac{3\pi}{4} - \pi\right) = \left(-3, -\frac{7\pi}{4}\right) \qquad \text{Replace } r \text{ by } -r; \text{ subtract } \pi \text{ from } \theta.$$

$$\left(-3, -\frac{3\pi}{4} + \pi\right) = \left(-3, \frac{\pi}{4}\right) \qquad \text{Replace } r \text{ by } -r; \text{ add } \pi \text{ to } \theta.$$

✓**CHECKPOINT**   Now try Exercise 3.

Coordinate Conversion

To establish the relationship between polar and rectangular coordinates, let the polar axis coincide with the positive x-axis and the pole with the origin, as shown in Figure 6.54. Because (x, y) lies on a circle of radius r, it follows that $r^2 = x^2 + y^2$. Moreover, for $r > 0$, the definitions of the trigonometric functions imply that

$$\tan \theta = \frac{y}{x}, \qquad \cos \theta = \frac{x}{r}, \qquad \text{and} \qquad \sin \theta = \frac{y}{r}.$$

If $r < 0$, you can show that the same relationships hold.

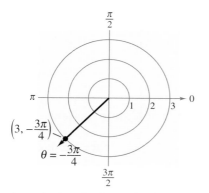

$$\left(3, -\frac{3\pi}{4}\right) = \left(3, \frac{5\pi}{4}\right) = \left(-3, -\frac{7\pi}{4}\right) = \left(-3, \frac{\pi}{4}\right) = \ldots$$

FIGURE 6.53

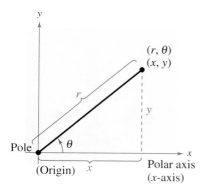

FIGURE 6.54

Coordinate Conversion

The polar coordinates (r, θ) are related to the rectangular coordinates (x, y) as follows.

Polar-to-Rectangular	*Rectangular-to-Polar*
$x = r \cos \theta$	$\tan \theta = \dfrac{y}{x}$
$y = r \sin \theta$	$r^2 = x^2 + y^2$

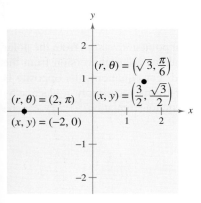

FIGURE **6.55**

Example 3   Polar-to-Rectangular Conversion

Convert each point to rectangular coordinates.

a. $(2, \pi)$ **b.** $\left(\sqrt{3}, \dfrac{\pi}{6} \right)$

Solution

a. For the point $(r, \theta) = (2, \pi)$, you have the following.

$$x = r \cos \theta = 2 \cos \pi = -2$$

$$y = r \sin \theta = 2 \sin \pi = 0$$

The rectangular coordinates are $(x, y) = (-2, 0)$. (See Figure 6.55.)

b. For the point $(r, \theta) = \left(\sqrt{3}, \dfrac{\pi}{6} \right)$, you have the following.

$$x = \sqrt{3} \cos \frac{\pi}{6} = \sqrt{3}\left(\frac{\sqrt{3}}{2} \right) = \frac{3}{2}$$

$$y = \sqrt{3} \sin \frac{\pi}{6} = \sqrt{3}\left(\frac{1}{2} \right) = \frac{\sqrt{3}}{2}$$

The rectangular coordinates are $(x, y) = \left(\dfrac{3}{2}, \dfrac{\sqrt{3}}{2} \right)$. (See Figure 6.55.)

✓CHECKPOINT   Now try Exercise 13.

Example 4   Rectangular-to-Polar Conversion

Convert each point to polar coordinates.

a. $(-1, 1)$ **b.** $(0, 2)$

Solution

a. For the second-quadrant point $(x, y) = (-1, 1)$, you have

$$\tan \theta = \frac{y}{x} = -1$$

$$\theta = \frac{3\pi}{4}.$$

Because θ lies in the same quadrant as (x, y), use positive r.

$$r = \sqrt{x^2 + y^2} = \sqrt{(-1)^2 + (1)^2} = \sqrt{2}$$

So, *one* set of polar coordinates is $(r, \theta) = \left(\sqrt{2}, 3\pi/4 \right)$, as shown in Figure 6.56.

b. Because the point $(x, y) = (0, 2)$ lies on the positive y-axis, choose

$$\theta = \frac{\pi}{2} \quad \text{and} \quad r = 2.$$

This implies that *one* set of polar coordinates is $(r, \theta) = (2, \pi/2)$, as shown in Figure 6.57.

✓CHECKPOINT   Now try Exercise 19.

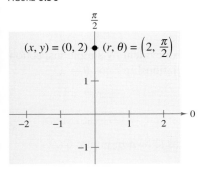

FIGURE **6.56**

FIGURE **6.57**

Equation Conversion

By comparing Examples 3 and 4, you can see that point conversion from the polar to the rectangular system is straightforward, whereas point conversion from the rectangular to the polar system is more involved. For equations, the opposite is true. To convert a rectangular equation to polar form, you simply replace x by $r \cos \theta$ and y by $r \sin \theta$. For instance, the rectangular equation $y = x^2$ can be written in polar form as follows.

$y = x^2$	Rectangular equation
$r \sin \theta = (r \cos \theta)^2$	Polar equation
$r = \sec \theta \tan \theta$	Simplest form

On the other hand, converting a polar equation to rectangular form requires considerable ingenuity.

Example 5 demonstrates several polar-to-rectangular conversions that enable you to sketch the graphs of some polar equations.

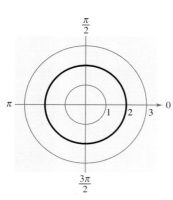

FIGURE 6.58

Example 5   Converting Polar Equations to Rectangular Form

Describe the graph of each polar equation and find the corresponding rectangular equation.

a. $r = 2$ **b.** $\theta = \dfrac{\pi}{3}$ **c.** $r = \sec \theta$

Solution

a. The graph of the polar equation $r = 2$ consists of all points that are two units from the pole. In other words, this graph is a circle centered at the origin with a radius of 2, as shown in Figure 6.58. You can confirm this by converting to rectangular form, using the relationship $r^2 = x^2 + y^2$.

$$\underbrace{r = 2}_{\text{Polar equation}} \quad\Longrightarrow\quad r^2 = 2^2 \quad\Longrightarrow\quad \underbrace{x^2 + y^2 = 2^2}_{\text{Rectangular equation}}$$

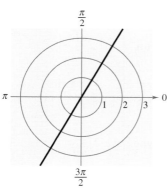

FIGURE 6.59

b. The graph of the polar equation $\theta = \pi/3$ consists of all points on the line that makes an angle of $\pi/3$ with the positive polar axis, as shown in Figure 6.59. To convert to rectangular form, make use of the relationship $\tan \theta = y/x$.

$$\underbrace{\theta = \dfrac{\pi}{3}}_{\text{Polar equation}} \quad\Longrightarrow\quad \tan \theta = \sqrt{3} \quad\Longrightarrow\quad \underbrace{y = \sqrt{3}\,x}_{\text{Rectangular equation}}$$

c. The graph of the polar equation $r = \sec \theta$ is not evident by simple inspection, so convert to rectangular form by using the relationship $r \cos \theta = x$.

$$\underbrace{r = \sec \theta}_{\text{Polar equation}} \quad\Longrightarrow\quad r \cos \theta = 1 \quad\Longrightarrow\quad \underbrace{x = 1}_{\text{Rectangular equation}}$$

Now you see that the graph is a vertical line, as shown in Figure 6.60.

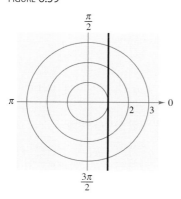

FIGURE 6.60

✔**CHECKPOINT**   Now try Exercise 65.

6.6 | Exercises

VOCABULARY CHECK: Fill in the blanks.

1. The origin of the polar coordinate system is called the _____.
2. For the point (r, θ), r is the _____ _____ from O to P and θ is the _____ _____ counterclockwise from the polar axis to the line segment $\overline{OP}$.
3. To plot the point (r, θ), use the _____ coordinate system.
4. The polar coordinates (r, θ) are related to the rectangular coordinates (x, y) as follows:

$x =$ _____ $\tan \theta =$ _____

$y =$ _____ $r^2 =$ _____

PREREQUISITE SKILLS REVIEW: Practice and review algebra skills needed for this section at **www.Eduspace.com**.

In Exercises 1–8, plot the point given in polar coordinates and find two additional polar representations of the point, using $-2\pi < \theta < 2\pi$.

1. $\left(4, -\dfrac{\pi}{3}\right)$

2. $\left(-1, -\dfrac{3\pi}{4}\right)$

3. $\left(0, -\dfrac{7\pi}{6}\right)$

4. $\left(16, \dfrac{5\pi}{2}\right)$

5. $\left(\sqrt{2}, 2.36\right)$

6. $(-3, -1.57)$

7. $\left(2\sqrt{2}, 4.71\right)$

8. $(-5, -2.36)$

In Exercises 9–16, a point in polar coordinates is given. Convert the point to rectangular coordinates.

9. $\left(3, \dfrac{\pi}{2}\right)$

10. $\left(3, \dfrac{3\pi}{2}\right)$

11. $\left(-1, \dfrac{5\pi}{4}\right)$

12. $(0, -\pi)$

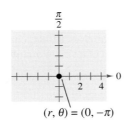

13. $\left(2, \dfrac{3\pi}{4}\right)$

14. $\left(-2, \dfrac{7\pi}{6}\right)$

15. $(-2.5, 1.1)$

16. $(8.25, 3.5)$

In Exercises 17–26, a point in rectangular coordinates is given. Convert the point to polar coordinates.

17. $(1, 1)$

18. $(-3, -3)$

19. $(-6, 0)$

20. $(0, -5)$

21. $(-3, 4)$

22. $(3, -1)$

23. $\left(-\sqrt{3}, -\sqrt{3}\right)$

24. $\left(\sqrt{3}, -1\right)$

25. $(6, 9)$

26. $(5, 12)$

 In Exercises 27–32, use a graphing utility to find one set of polar coordinates for the point given in rectangular coordinates.

27. $(3, -2)$

28. $(-5, 2)$

29. $\left(\sqrt{3}, 2\right)$

30. $\left(3, \sqrt{2}, 3\sqrt{2}\right)$

31. $\left(\dfrac{5}{2}, \dfrac{4}{3}\right)$

32. $\left(\dfrac{7}{4}, \dfrac{3}{2}\right)$

In Exercises 33–48, convert the rectangular equation to polar form. Assume $a > 0$.

33. $x^2 + y^2 = 9$

34. $x^2 + y^2 = 16$

35. $y = 4$

36. $y = x$

37. $x = 10$

38. $x = 4a$

39. $3x - y + 2 = 0$

40. $3x + 5y - 2 = 0$

41. $xy = 16$

42. $2xy = 1$

43. $y^2 - 8x - 16 = 0$

44. $(x^2 + y^2)^2 = 9(x^2 - y^2)$

45. $x^2 + y^2 = a^2$

46. $x^2 + y^2 = 9a^2$

47. $x^2 + y^2 - 2ax = 0$

48. $x^2 + y^2 - 2ay = 0$

In Exercises 49–64, convert the polar equation to rectangular form.

49. $r = 4 \sin \theta$

50. $r = 2 \cos \theta$

51. $\theta = \dfrac{2\pi}{3}$

52. $\theta = \dfrac{5\pi}{3}$

53. $r = 4$

54. $r = 10$

55. $r = 4 \csc \theta$

56. $r = -3 \sec \theta$

57. $r^2 = \cos \theta$

58. $r^2 = \sin 2\theta$

59. $r = 2 \sin 3\theta$

60. $r = 3 \cos 2\theta$

61. $r = \dfrac{2}{1 + \sin \theta}$

62. $r = \dfrac{1}{1 - \cos \theta}$

63. $r = \dfrac{6}{2 - 3 \sin \theta}$

64. $r = \dfrac{6}{2 \cos \theta - 3 \sin \theta}$

In Exercises 65–70, describe the graph of the polar equation and find the corresponding rectangular equation. Sketch its graph.

65. $r = 6$

66. $r = 8$

67. $\theta = \dfrac{\pi}{6}$

68. $\theta = \dfrac{3\pi}{4}$

69. $r = 3 \sec \theta$

70. $r = 2 \csc \theta$

Synthesis

True or False? **In Exercises 71 and 72, determine whether the statement is true or false. Justify your answer.**

71. If $\theta_1 = \theta_2 + 2\pi n$ for some integer n, then (r, θ_1) and (r, θ_2) represent the same point on the polar coordinate system.

72. If $|r_1| = |r_2|$, then (r_1, θ) and (r_2, θ) represent the same point on the polar coordinate system.

73. Convert the polar equation $r = 2(h \cos \theta + k \sin \theta)$ to rectangular form and verify that it is the equation of a circle. Find the radius of the circle and the rectangular coordinates of the center of the circle.

74. Convert the polar equation $r = \cos \theta + 3 \sin \theta$ to rectangular form and identify the graph.

75. *Think About It*

(a) Show that the distance between the points (r_1, θ_1) and (r_2, θ_2) is $\sqrt{r_1^2 + r_2^2 - 2r_1 r_2 \cos(\theta_1 - \theta_2)}$.

(b) Describe the positions of the points relative to each other for $\theta_1 = \theta_2$. Simplify the Distance Formula for this case. Is the simplification what you expected? Explain.

(c) Simplify the Distance Formula for $\theta_1 - \theta_2 = 90°$. Is the simplification what you expected? Explain.

(d) Choose two points on the polar coordinate system and find the distance between them. Then choose different polar representations of the same two points and apply the Distance Formula again. Discuss the result.

 76. *Exploration*

(a) Set the window format of your graphing utility on rectangular coordinates and locate the cursor at any position off the coordinate axes. Move the cursor horizontally and observe any changes in the displayed coordinates of the points. Explain the changes in the coordinates. Now repeat the process moving the cursor vertically.

(b) Set the window format of your graphing utility on polar coordinates and locate the cursor at any position off the coordinate axes. Move the cursor horizontally and observe any changes in the displayed coordinates of the points. Explain the changes in the coordinates. Now repeat the process moving the cursor vertically.

(c) Explain why the results of parts (a) and (b) are not the same.

Skills Review

In Exercises 77–80, use the properties of logarithms to expand the expression as a sum, difference, and/or constant multiple of logarithms. (Assume all variables are positive.)

77. $\log_6 \dfrac{x^2 z}{3y}$

78. $\log_4 \dfrac{\sqrt{2x}}{y}$

79. $\ln x(x + 4)^2$

80. $\ln 5x^2(x^2 + 1)$

In Exercises 81–84, condense the expression to the logarithm of a single quantity.

81. $\log_7 x - \log_7 3y$

82. $\log_5 a + 8 \log_5(x + 1)$

83. $\dfrac{1}{2} \ln x + \ln(x - 2)$

84. $\ln 6 + \ln y - \ln(x - 3)$

6.7   Graphs of Polar Equations

What you should learn

- Graph polar equations by point plotting.
- Use symmetry to sketch graphs of polar equations.
- Use zeros and maximum *r*-values to sketch graphs of polar equations.
- Recognize special polar graphs.

Why you should learn it

Equations of several common figures are simpler in polar form than in rectangular form. For instance, Exercise 6 on page 505 shows the graph of a circle and its polar equation.

Introduction

In previous chapters, you spent a lot of time learning how to sketch graphs on rectangular coordinate systems. You began with the basic point-plotting method, which was then enhanced by sketching aids such as symmetry, intercepts, asymptotes, periods, and shifts. This section approaches curve sketching on the polar coordinate system similarly, beginning with a demonstration of point plotting.

Example 1   **Graphing a Polar Equation by Point Plotting**

Sketch the graph of the polar equation $r = 4 \sin \theta$.

Solution

The sine function is periodic, so you can get a full range of *r*-values by considering values of θ in the interval $0 \leq \theta \leq 2\pi$, as shown in the following table.

θ	0	$\frac{\pi}{6}$	$\frac{\pi}{3}$	$\frac{\pi}{2}$	$\frac{2\pi}{3}$	$\frac{5\pi}{6}$	π	$\frac{7\pi}{6}$	$\frac{3\pi}{2}$	$\frac{11\pi}{6}$	2π
r	0	2	$2\sqrt{3}$	4	$2\sqrt{3}$	2	0	-2	-4	-2	0

If you plot these points as shown in Figure 6.61, it appears that the graph is a circle of radius 2 whose center is at the point $(x, y) = (0, 2)$.

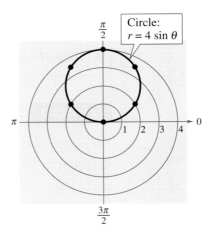

FIGURE **6.61**

✓CHECKPOINT   Now try Exercise 21.

You can confirm the graph in Figure 6.61 by converting the polar equation to rectangular form and then sketching the graph of the rectangular equation. You can also use a graphing utility set to *polar* mode and graph the polar equation or set the graphing utility to *parametric* mode and graph a parametric representation.

Symmetry

In Figure 6.61, note that as θ increases from 0 to 2π the graph is traced out twice. Moreover, note that the graph is *symmetric with respect to the line* $\theta = \pi/2$. Had you known about this symmetry and retracing ahead of time, you could have used fewer points.

Symmetry with respect to the line $\theta = \pi/2$ is one of three important types of symmetry to consider in polar curve sketching. (See Figure 6.62.)

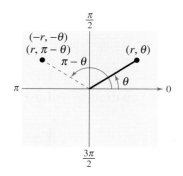

Symmetry with Respect to the Line $\theta = \dfrac{\pi}{2}$

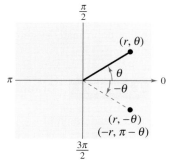

Symmetry with Respect to the Polar Axis

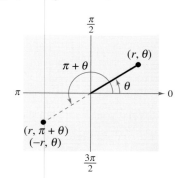

Symmetry with Respect to the Pole

FIGURE **6.62**

STUDY TIP

Note in Example 2 that $\cos(-\theta) = \cos\theta$. This is because the cosine function is *even*. Recall from Section 4.2 that the cosine function is even and the sine function is odd. That is, $\sin(-\theta) = -\sin\theta$.

Tests for Symmetry in Polar Coordinates

The graph of a polar equation is symmetric with respect to the following if the given substitution yields an equivalent equation.

1. *The line* $\theta = \pi/2$:   Replace (r, θ) by $(r, \pi - \theta)$ or $(-r, -\theta)$.

2. *The polar axis:*   Replace (r, θ) by $(r, -\theta)$ or $(-r, \pi - \theta)$.

3. *The pole:*   Replace (r, θ) by $(r, \pi + \theta)$ or $(-r, \theta)$.

Example 2   **Using Symmetry to Sketch a Polar Graph**

Use symmetry to sketch the graph of $r = 3 + 2\cos\theta$.

Solution

Replacing (r, θ) by $(r, -\theta)$ produces $r = 3 + 2\cos(-\theta) = 3 + 2\cos\theta$. So, you can conclude that the curve is symmetric with respect to the polar axis. Plotting the points in the table and using polar axis symmetry, you obtain the graph shown in Figure 6.63. This graph is called a **limaçon.**

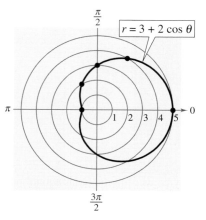

$r = 3 + 2\cos\theta$

FIGURE **6.63**

θ	0	$\dfrac{\pi}{3}$	$\dfrac{\pi}{2}$	$\dfrac{2\pi}{3}$	π
r	5	4	3	2	1

✓**CHECKPOINT**   Now try Exercise 27.

The three tests for symmetry in polar coordinates listed on page 500 are sufficient to guarantee symmetry, but they are not necessary. For instance, Figure 6.64 shows the graph of $r = \theta + 2\pi$ to be symmetric with respect to the line $\theta = \pi/2$, and yet the tests on page 500 fail to indicate symmetry because neither of the following replacements yields an equivalent equation.

Original Equation	Replacement	New Equation
$r = \theta + 2\pi$	(r, θ) by $(-r, -\theta)$	$-r = -\theta + 2\pi$
$r = \theta + 2\pi$	(r, θ) by $(r, \pi - \theta)$	$r = -\theta + 3\pi$

The equations discussed in Examples 1 and 2 are of the form

$$r = 4 \sin \theta = f(\sin \theta) \quad \text{and} \quad r = 3 + 2 \cos \theta = g(\cos \theta).$$

The graph of the first equation is symmetric with respect to the line $\theta = \pi/2$, and the graph of the second equation is symmetric with respect to the polar axis. This observation can be generalized to yield the following tests.

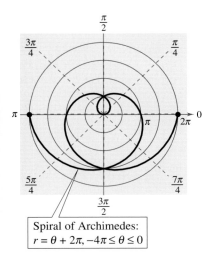

Spiral of Archimedes:
$r = \theta + 2\pi, \; -4\pi \le \theta \le 0$

FIGURE **6.64**

Quick Tests for Symmetry in Polar Coordinates

1. The graph of $r = f(\sin \theta)$ is symmetric with respect to the line $\theta = \dfrac{\pi}{2}$.

2. The graph of $r = g(\cos \theta)$ is symmetric with respect to the polar axis.

Zeros and Maximum *r*-Values

Two additional aids to graphing of polar equations involve knowing the θ-values for which $|r|$ is maximum and knowing the θ-values for which $r = 0$. For instance, in Example 1, the maximum value of $|r|$ for $r = 4 \sin \theta$ is $|r| = 4$, and this occurs when $\theta = \pi/2$, as shown in Figure 6.61. Moreover, $r = 0$ when $\theta = 0$.

Example 3   Sketching a Polar Graph

Sketch the graph of $r = 1 - 2 \cos \theta$.

Solution

From the equation $r = 1 - 2 \cos \theta$, you can obtain the following.

Symmetry: With respect to the polar axis
Maximum value of $|r|$: $r = 3$ when $\theta = \pi$
Zero of r: $r = 0$ when $\theta = \pi/3$

The table shows several θ-values in the interval $[0, \pi]$. By plotting the corresponding points, you can sketch the graph shown in Figure 6.65.

θ	0	$\dfrac{\pi}{6}$	$\dfrac{\pi}{3}$	$\dfrac{\pi}{2}$	$\dfrac{2\pi}{3}$	$\dfrac{5\pi}{6}$	π
r	-1	-0.73	0	1	2	2.73	3

Note how the negative r-values determine the *inner loop* of the graph in Figure 6.65. This graph, like the one in Figure 6.63, is a limaçon.

✔CHECKPOINT   Now try Exercise 29.

Limaçon:
$r = 1 - 2 \cos \theta$

FIGURE **6.65**

Some curves reach their zeros and maximum *r*-values at more than one point, as shown in Example 4.

Example 4 Sketching a Polar Graph

Sketch the graph of $r = 2 \cos 3\theta$.

Solution

Symmetry: With respect to the polar axis

Maximum value of $|r|$: $|r| = 2$ when $3\theta = 0, \pi, 2\pi, 3\pi$ or $\theta = 0, \pi/3, 2\pi/3, \pi$

Zeros of r: $r = 0$ when $3\theta = \pi/2, 3\pi/2, 5\pi/2$ or $\theta = \pi/6, \pi/2, 5\pi/6$

θ	0	$\dfrac{\pi}{12}$	$\dfrac{\pi}{6}$	$\dfrac{\pi}{4}$	$\dfrac{\pi}{3}$	$\dfrac{5\pi}{12}$	$\dfrac{\pi}{2}$
r	2	$\sqrt{2}$	0	$-\sqrt{2}$	-2	$-\sqrt{2}$	0

By plotting these points and using the specified symmetry, zeros, and maximum values, you can obtain the graph shown in Figure 6.66. This graph is called a **rose curve,** and each of the loops on the graph is called a *petal* of the rose curve. Note how the entire curve is generated as θ increases from 0 to π.

Exploration

Notice that the rose curve in Example 4 has three petals. How many petals do the rose curves given by $r = 2 \cos 4\theta$ and $r = 2 \sin 3\theta$ have? Determine the numbers of petals for the curves given by $r = 2 \cos n\theta$ and $r = 2 \sin n\theta$, where *n* is a positive integer.

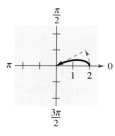

$0 \le \theta \le \dfrac{\pi}{6}$

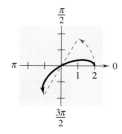

$0 \le \theta \le \dfrac{\pi}{3}$

$0 \le \theta \le \dfrac{\pi}{2}$

$0 \le \theta \le \dfrac{2\pi}{3}$

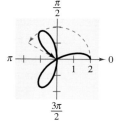

$0 \le \theta \le \dfrac{5\pi}{6}$

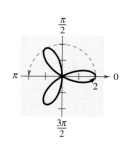

$0 \le \theta \le \pi$

FIGURE 6.66

Technology

Use a graphing utility in *polar* mode to verify the graph of $r = 2 \cos 3\theta$ shown in Figure 6.66.

✓**CHECKPOINT**   Now try Exercise 33.

Special Polar Graphs

Several important types of graphs have equations that are simpler in polar form than in rectangular form. For example, the circle

$$r = 4 \sin \theta$$

in Example 1 has the more complicated rectangular equation

$$x^2 + (y - 2)^2 = 4.$$

Several other types of graphs that have simple polar equations are shown below.

Limaçons

$r = a \pm b \cos \theta$

$r = a \pm b \sin \theta$

$(a > 0, b > 0)$

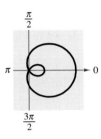
$\dfrac{a}{b} < 1$
Limaçon with
inner loop

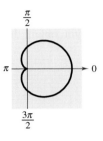
$\dfrac{a}{b} = 1$
Cardioid
(heart-shaped)

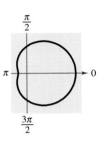
$1 < \dfrac{a}{b} < 2$
Dimpled
limaçon

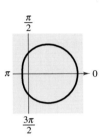
$\dfrac{a}{b} \geq 2$
Convex
limaçon

Rose Curves

n petals if n is odd,
$2n$ petals if n is even
$(n \geq 2)$

$r = a \cos n\theta$
Rose curve

$r = a \cos n\theta$
Rose curve

$r = a \sin n\theta$
Rose curve

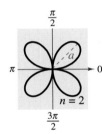
$r = a \sin n\theta$
Rose curve

Circles and Lemniscates

$r = a \cos \theta$
Circle

$r = a \sin \theta$
Circle

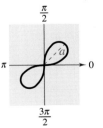
$r^2 = a^2 \sin 2\theta$
Lemniscate

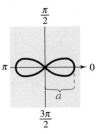
$r^2 = a^2 \cos 2\theta$
Lemniscate

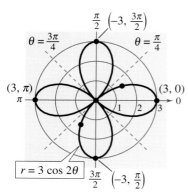

FIGURE **6.67**

Example 5 Sketching a Rose Curve

Sketch the graph of $r = 3 \cos 2\theta$.

Solution

Type of curve:	Rose curve with $2n = 4$ petals
Symmetry:	With respect to polar axis, the line $\theta = \pi/2$, and the pole
Maximum value of $|r|$:	$|r| = 3$ when $\theta = 0, \pi/2, \pi, 3\pi/2$
Zeros of r:	$r = 0$ when $\theta = \pi/4, 3\pi/4$

Using this information together with the additional points shown in the following table, you obtain the graph shown in Figure 6.67.

θ	0	$\dfrac{\pi}{6}$	$\dfrac{\pi}{4}$	$\dfrac{\pi}{3}$
r	3	$\dfrac{3}{2}$	0	$-\dfrac{3}{2}$

✔CHECKPOINT   Now try Exercise 35.

Example 6 Sketching a Lemniscate

Sketch the graph of $r^2 = 9 \sin 2\theta$.

Solution

Type of curve:	Lemniscate
Symmetry:	With respect to the pole

Maximum value of $|r|$: $|r| = 3$ when $\theta = \dfrac{\pi}{4}$

Zeros of r: $r = 0$ when $\theta = 0, \dfrac{\pi}{2}$

If $\sin 2\theta < 0$, this equation has no solution points. So, you restrict the values of θ to those for which $\sin 2\theta \geq 0$.

$$0 \leq \theta \leq \frac{\pi}{2} \quad \text{or} \quad \pi \leq \theta \leq \frac{3\pi}{2}$$

Moreover, using symmetry, you need to consider only the first of these two intervals. By finding a few additional points (see table below), you can obtain the graph shown in Figure 6.68.

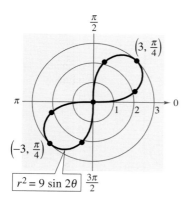

FIGURE **6.68**

θ	0	$\dfrac{\pi}{12}$	$\dfrac{\pi}{4}$	$\dfrac{5\pi}{12}$	$\dfrac{\pi}{2}$
$r = \pm 3\sqrt{\sin 2\theta}$	0	$\dfrac{\pm 3}{\sqrt{2}}$	± 3	$\dfrac{\pm 3}{\sqrt{2}}$	0

✔CHECKPOINT   Now try Exercise 39.

6.7 | Exercises

VOCABULARY CHECK: Fill in the blanks.

1. The graph of $r = f(\sin \theta)$ is symmetric with respect to the line _____.

2. The graph of $r = g(\cos \theta)$ is symmetric with respect to the _____ _____.

3. The equation $r = 2 + \cos \theta$ represents a _____ _____.

4. The equation $r = 2 \cos \theta$ represents a _____.

5. The equation $r^2 = 4 \sin 2\theta$ represents a _____.

6. The equation $r = 1 + \sin \theta$ represents a _____.

PREREQUISITE SKILLS REVIEW: Practice and review algebra skills needed for this section at **www.Eduspace.com**.

In Exercises 1–6, identify the type of polar graph.

1.

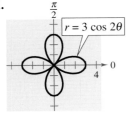

$r = 3 \cos 2\theta$

2.

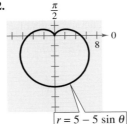

$r = 5 - 5 \sin \theta$

3.

$r = 3(1 - 2 \cos \theta)$

4.

$r^2 = 16 \cos 2\theta$

5.

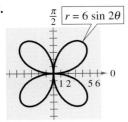

$r = 6 \sin 2\theta$

6.

$r = 3 \cos \theta$

In Exercises 7–12, test for symmetry with respect to $\theta = \pi/2$, the polar axis, and the pole.

7. $r = 5 + 4 \cos \theta$

8. $r = 16 \cos 3\theta$

9. $r = \dfrac{2}{1 + \sin \theta}$

10. $r = \dfrac{3}{2 + \cos \theta}$

11. $r^2 = 16 \cos 2\theta$

12. $r^2 = 36 \sin 2\theta$

In Exercises 13–16, find the maximum value of $|r|$ and any zeros of r.

13. $r = 10(1 - \sin \theta)$

14. $r = 6 + 12 \cos \theta$

15. $r = 4 \cos 3\theta$

16. $r = 3 \sin 2\theta$

In Exercises 17–40, sketch the graph of the polar equation using symmetry, zeros, maximum r-values, and any other additional points.

17. $r = 5$

18. $r = 2$

19. $r = \dfrac{\pi}{6}$

20. $r = -\dfrac{3\pi}{4}$

21. $r = 3 \sin \theta$

22. $r = 4 \cos \theta$

23. $r = 3(1 - \cos \theta)$

24. $r = 4(1 - \sin \theta)$

25. $r = 4(1 + \sin \theta)$

26. $r = 2(1 + \cos \theta)$

27. $r = 3 + 6 \sin \theta$

28. $r = 4 - 3 \sin \theta$

29. $r = 1 - 2 \sin \theta$

30. $r = 1 - 2 \cos \theta$

31. $r = 3 - 4 \cos \theta$

32. $r = 4 + 3 \cos \theta$

33. $r = 5 \sin 2\theta$

34. $r = 3 \cos 2\theta$

35. $r = 2 \sec \theta$

36. $r = 5 \csc \theta$

37. $r = \dfrac{3}{\sin \theta - 2 \cos \theta}$

38. $r = \dfrac{6}{2 \sin \theta - 3 \cos \theta}$

39. $r^2 = 9 \cos 2\theta$

40. $r^2 = 4 \sin \theta$

In Exercises 41–46, use a graphing utility to graph the polar equation. Describe your viewing window.

41. $r = 8 \cos \theta$

42. $r = \cos 2\theta$

43. $r = 3(2 - \sin \theta)$

44. $r = 2 \cos(3\theta - 2)$

45. $r = 8 \sin \theta \cos^2 \theta$

46. $r = 2 \csc \theta + 5$

In Exercises 47–52, use a graphing utility to graph the polar equation. Find an interval for θ for which the graph is traced *only once*.

47. $r = 3 - 4 \cos \theta$

48. $r = 5 + 4 \cos \theta$

49. $r = 2\cos\left(\dfrac{3\theta}{2}\right)$

50. $r = 3\sin\left(\dfrac{5\theta}{2}\right)$

51. $r^2 = 9\sin 2\theta$

52. $r^2 = \dfrac{1}{\theta}$

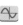 **In Exercises 53–56, use a graphing utility to graph the polar equation and show that the indicated line is an asymptote of the graph.**

Name of Graph	Polar Equation	Asymptote
53. Conchoid	$r = 2 - \sec\theta$	$x = -1$
54. Conchoid	$r = 2 + \csc\theta$	$y = 1$
55. Hyperbolic spiral	$r = \dfrac{3}{\theta}$	$y = 3$
56. Strophoid	$r = 2\cos 2\theta \sec\theta$	$x = -2$

Synthesis

True or False? **In Exercises 57 and 58, determine whether the statement is true or false. Justify your answer.**

57. In the polar coordinate system, if a graph that has symmetry with respect to the polar axis were folded on the line $\theta = 0$, the portion of the graph above the polar axis would coincide with the portion of the graph below the polar axis.

58. In the polar coordinate system, if a graph that has symmetry with respect to the pole were folded on the line $\theta = 3\pi/4$, the portion of the graph on one side of the fold would coincide with the portion of the graph on the other side of the fold.

59. ***Exploration*** Sketch the graph of $r = 6\cos\theta$ over each interval. Describe the part of the graph obtained in each case.

(a) $0 \le \theta \le \dfrac{\pi}{2}$

(b) $\dfrac{\pi}{2} \le \theta \le \pi$

(c) $-\dfrac{\pi}{2} \le \theta \le \dfrac{\pi}{2}$

(d) $\dfrac{\pi}{4} \le \theta \le \dfrac{3\pi}{4}$

60. ***Graphical Reasoning*** Use a graphing utility to graph the polar equation $r = 6[1 + \cos(\theta - \phi)]$ for (a) $\phi = 0$, (b) $\phi = \pi/4$, and (c) $\phi = \pi/2$. Use the graphs to describe the effect of the angle ϕ. Write the equation as a function of $\sin\theta$ for part (c).

61. The graph of $r = f(\theta)$ is rotated about the pole through an angle ϕ. Show that the equation of the rotated graph is $r = f(\theta - \phi)$.

62. Consider the graph of $r = f(\sin\theta)$.

(a) Show that if the graph is rotated counterclockwise $\pi/2$ radians about the pole, the equation of the rotated graph is $r = f(-\cos\theta)$.

(b) Show that if the graph is rotated counterclockwise π radians about the pole, the equation of the rotated graph is $r = f(-\sin\theta)$.

(c) Show that if the graph is rotated counterclockwise $3\pi/2$ radians about the pole, the equation of the rotated graph is $r = f(\cos\theta)$.

In Exercises 63–66, use the results of Exercises 61 and 62.

63. Write an equation for the limaçon $r = 2 - \sin\theta$ after it has been rotated through the given angle.

(a) $\dfrac{\pi}{4}$ (b) $\dfrac{\pi}{2}$ (c) π (d) $\dfrac{3\pi}{2}$

64. Write an equation for the rose curve $r = 2\sin 2\theta$ after it has been rotated through the given angle.

(a) $\dfrac{\pi}{6}$ (b) $\dfrac{\pi}{2}$ (c) $\dfrac{2\pi}{3}$ (d) π

65. Sketch the graph of each equation.

(a) $r = 1 - \sin\theta$

(b) $r = 1 - \sin\left(\theta - \dfrac{\pi}{4}\right)$

66. Sketch the graph of each equation.

(a) $r = 3\sec\theta$

(b) $r = 3\sec\left(\theta - \dfrac{\pi}{4}\right)$

(c) $r = 3\sec\left(\theta + \dfrac{\pi}{3}\right)$

(d) $r = 3\sec\left(\theta - \dfrac{\pi}{2}\right)$

 67. ***Exploration*** Use a graphing utility to graph and identify $r = 2 + k\sin\theta$ for $k = 0, 1, 2,$ and 3.

68. ***Exploration*** Consider the equation $r = 3\sin k\theta$.

(a) Use a graphing utility to graph the equation for $k = 1.5$. Find the interval for θ over which the graph is traced only once.

(b) Use a graphing utility to graph the equation for $k = 2.5$. Find the interval for θ over which the graph is traced only once.

(c) Is it possible to find an interval for θ over which the graph is traced only once for any rational number k? Explain.

Skills Review

In Exercises 69–72, find the zeros (if any) of the rational function.

69. $f(x) = \dfrac{x^2 - 9}{x + 1}$

70. $f(x) = 6 + \dfrac{4}{x^2 + 4}$

71. $f(x) = 5 - \dfrac{3}{x - 2}$

72. $f(x) = \dfrac{x^3 - 27}{x^2 + 4}$

In Exercises 73 and 74, find the standard form of the equation of the ellipse with the given characteristics. Then sketch the ellipse.

73. Vertices: $(-4, 2), (2, 2)$; minor axis of length 4

74. Foci: $(3, 2), (3, -4)$; major axis of length 8

6.8   Polar Equations of Conics

What you should learn

- Define conics in terms of eccentricity.
- Write and graph equations of conics in polar form.
- Use equations of conics in polar form to model real-life problems.

Why you should learn it

The orbits of planets and satellites can be modeled with polar equations. For instance, in Exercise 58 on page 512, a polar equation is used to model the orbit of a satellite.

Alternative Definition of Conic

In Sections 6.3 and 6.4, you learned that the rectangular equations of ellipses and hyperbolas take simple forms when the origin lies at their *centers*. As it happens, there are many important applications of conics in which it is more convenient to use one of the *foci* as the origin. In this section, you will learn that polar equations of conics take simple forms if one of the foci lies at the pole.

To begin, consider the following alternative definition of conic that uses the concept of eccentricity.

Alternative Definition of Conic

The locus of a point in the plane that moves so that its distance from a fixed point (focus) is in a constant ratio to its distance from a fixed line (directrix) is a **conic**. The constant ratio is the **eccentricity** of the conic and is denoted by e. Moreover, the conic is an **ellipse** if $e < 1$, a **parabola** if $e = 1$, and a **hyperbola** if $e > 1$. (See Figure 6.69.)

In Figure 6.69, note that for each type of conic, the focus is at the pole.

Ellipse: $0 < e < 1$

$$\frac{PF}{PQ} < 1$$

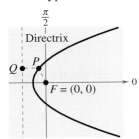

Parabola: $e = 1$

$$\frac{PF}{PQ} = 1$$

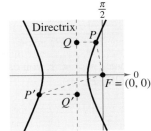

Hyperbola $e > 1$

$$\frac{PF}{PQ} = \frac{P'F}{P'Q'} > 1$$

FIGURE 6.69

Polar Equations of Conics

The benefit of locating a focus of a conic at the pole is that the equation of the conic takes on a simpler form. For a proof of the polar equations of conics, see Proofs in Mathematics on page 524.

Polar Equations of Conics

The graph of a polar equation of the form

1. $r = \dfrac{ep}{1 \pm e \cos \theta}$ or   **2.** $r = \dfrac{ep}{1 \pm e \sin \theta}$

is a conic, where $e > 0$ is the eccentricity and $|p|$ is the distance between the focus (pole) and the directrix.

Equations of the form

$$r = \frac{ep}{1 \pm e \cos \theta} = g(\cos \theta) \qquad \text{Vertical directrix}$$

correspond to conics with a vertical directrix and symmetry with respect to the polar axis. Equations of the form

$$r = \frac{ep}{1 \pm e \sin \theta} = g(\sin \theta) \qquad \text{Horizontal directrix}$$

correspond to conics with a horizontal directrix and symmetry with respect to the line $\theta = \pi/2$. Moreover, the converse is also true—that is, any conic with a focus at the pole and having a horizontal or vertical directrix can be represented by one of the given equations.

Example 1 Identifying a Conic from Its Equation

Identify the type of conic represented by the equation $r = \dfrac{15}{3 - 2 \cos \theta}$.

Algebraic Solution

To identify the type of conic, rewrite the equation in the form $r = (ep)/(1 \pm e \cos \theta)$.

$$r = \frac{15}{3 - 2 \cos \theta} \qquad \text{Write original equation.}$$

$$= \frac{5}{1 - (2/3) \cos \theta} \qquad \begin{array}{l}\text{Divide numerator and}\\ \text{denominator by 3.}\end{array}$$

Because $e = \frac{2}{3} < 1$, you can conclude that the graph is an ellipse.

✓**CHECKPOINT**   Now try Exercise 11.

Graphical Solution

You can start sketching the graph by plotting points from $\theta = 0$ to $\theta = \pi$. Because the equation is of the form $r = g(\cos \theta)$, the graph of r is symmetric with respect to the polar axis. So, you can complete the sketch, as shown in Figure 6.70. From this, you can conclude that the graph is an ellipse.

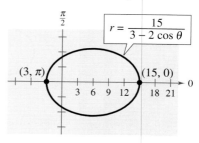

FIGURE **6.70**

For the ellipse in Figure 6.70, the major axis is horizontal and the vertices lie at $(15, 0)$ and $(3, \pi)$. So, the length of the *major* axis is $2a = 18$. To find the length of the *minor* axis, you can use the equations $e = c/a$ and $b^2 = a^2 - c^2$ to conclude that

$$b^2 = a^2 - c^2$$

$$= a^2 - (ea)^2$$

$$= a^2(1 - e^2). \qquad \text{Ellipse}$$

Because $e = \frac{2}{3}$, you have $b^2 = 9^2\left[1 - \left(\frac{2}{3}\right)^2\right] = 45$, which implies that $b = \sqrt{45} = 3\sqrt{5}$. So, the length of the minor axis is $2b = 6\sqrt{5}$. A similar analysis for hyperbolas yields

$$b^2 = c^2 - a^2$$

$$= (ea)^2 - a^2$$

$$= a^2(e^2 - 1). \qquad \text{Hyperbola}$$

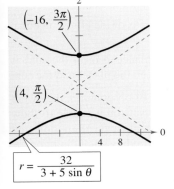

$$r = \frac{32}{3 + 5 \sin \theta}$$

FIGURE **6.71**

Example 2   Sketching a Conic from Its Polar Equation

Identify the conic $r = \dfrac{32}{3 + 5 \sin \theta}$ and sketch its graph.

Solution

Dividing the numerator and denominator by 3, you have

$$r = \frac{32/3}{1 + (5/3) \sin \theta}.$$

Because $e = \frac{5}{3} > 1$, the graph is a hyperbola. The transverse axis of the hyperbola lies on the line $\theta = \pi/2$, and the vertices occur at $(4, \pi/2)$ and $(-16, 3\pi/2)$. Because the length of the transverse axis is 12, you can see that $a = 6$. To find b, write

$$b^2 = a^2(e^2 - 1) = 6^2\left[\left(\frac{5}{3}\right)^2 - 1 \right] = 64.$$

So, $b = 8$. Finally, you can use a and b to determine that the asymptotes of the hyperbola are $y = 10 \pm \frac{3}{4}x$. The graph is shown in Figure 6.71.

✓CHECKPOINT   Now try Exercise 19.

Technology

Use a graphing utility set in *polar* mode to verify the four orientations shown at the right. Remember that e must be positive, but p can be positive or negative.

In the next example, you are asked to find a polar equation of a specified conic. To do this, let p be the distance between the pole and the directrix.

1. *Horizontal directrix above the pole:* $r = \dfrac{ep}{1 + e \sin \theta}$

2. *Horizontal directrix below the pole:* $r = \dfrac{ep}{1 - e \sin \theta}$

3. *Vertical directrix to the right of the pole:* $r = \dfrac{ep}{1 + e \cos \theta}$

4. *Vertical directrix to the left of the pole:* $r = \dfrac{ep}{1 - e \cos \theta}$

Example 3   Finding the Polar Equation of a Conic

Find the polar equation of the parabola whose focus is the pole and whose directrix is the line $y = 3$.

Solution

From Figure 6.72, you can see that the directrix is horizontal and above the pole, so you can choose an equation of the form

$$r = \frac{ep}{1 + e \sin \theta}.$$

Moreover, because the eccentricity of a parabola is $e = 1$ and the distance between the pole and the directrix is $p = 3$, you have the equation

$$r = \frac{3}{1 + \sin \theta}.$$

✓CHECKPOINT   Now try Exercise 33.

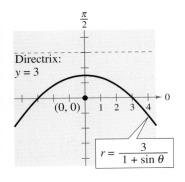

FIGURE **6.72**

Applications

Kepler's Laws (listed below), named after the German astronomer Johannes Kepler (1571–1630), can be used to describe the orbits of the planets about the sun.

1. Each planet moves in an elliptical orbit with the sun at one focus.
2. A ray from the sun to the planet sweeps out equal areas of the ellipse in equal times.
3. The square of the period (the time it takes for a planet to orbit the sun) is proportional to the cube of the mean distance between the planet and the sun.

Although Kepler simply stated these laws on the basis of observation, they were later validated by Isaac Newton (1642–1727). In fact, Newton was able to show that each law can be deduced from a set of universal laws of motion and gravitation that govern the movement of all heavenly bodies, including comets and satellites. This is illustrated in the next example, which involves the comet named after the English mathematician and physicist Edmund Halley (1656–1742).

   If you use Earth as a reference with a period of 1 year and a distance of 1 astronomical unit (an *astronomical unit* is defined as the mean distance between Earth and the sun, or about 93 million miles), the proportionality constant in Kepler's third law is 1. For example, because Mars has a mean distance to the sun of $d = 1.524$ astronomical units, its period P is given by $d^3 = P^2$. So, the period of Mars is $P \approx 1.88$ years.

Example 4   Halley's Comet

Halley's comet has an elliptical orbit with an eccentricity of $e \approx 0.967$. The length of the major axis of the orbit is approximately 35.88 astronomical units. Find a polar equation for the orbit. How close does Halley's comet come to the sun?

Solution

Using a vertical axis, as shown in Figure 6.73, choose an equation of the form $r = ep/(1 + e \sin \theta)$. Because the vertices of the ellipse occur when $\theta = \pi/2$ and $\theta = 3\pi/2$, you can determine the length of the major axis to be the sum of the r-values of the vertices. That is,

$$2a = \frac{0.967p}{1 + 0.967} + \frac{0.967p}{1 - 0.967} \approx 29.79p \approx 35.88.$$

So, $p \approx 1.204$ and $ep \approx (0.967)(1.204) \approx 1.164$. Using this value of ep in the equation, you have

$$r = \frac{1.164}{1 + 0.967 \sin \theta}$$

where r is measured in astronomical units. To find the closest point to the sun (the focus), substitute $\theta = \pi/2$ in this equation to obtain

$$r = \frac{1.164}{1 + 0.967 \sin(\pi/2)} \approx 0.59 \text{ astronomical unit} \approx 55,000,000 \text{ miles.}$$

✓CHECKPOINT   Now try Exercise 57.

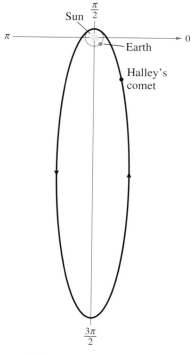

FIGURE 6.73

6.8 | Exercises

VOCABULARY CHECK:

In Exercises 1–3, fill in the blanks.

1. The locus of a point in the plane that moves so that its distance from a fixed point (focus) is in a constant ratio to its distance from a fixed line (directrix) is a _____.

2. The constant ratio is the _____ of the conic and is denoted by _____.

3. An equation of the form $r = \dfrac{ep}{1 + e \cos \theta}$ has a _____ directrix to the _____ of the pole.

4. Match the conic with its eccentricity.

   (a) $e < 1$ (b) $e = 1$ (c) $e > 1$

   (i) parabola   (ii) hyperbola   (iii) ellipse

PREREQUISITE SKILLS REVIEW: Practice and review algebra skills needed for this section at **www.Eduspace.com.**

In Exercises 1–4, write the polar equation of the conic for $e = 1$, $e = 0.5$, and $e = 1.5$. Identify the conic for each equation. Verify your answers with a graphing utility.

1. $r = \dfrac{4e}{1 + e \cos \theta}$

2. $r = \dfrac{4e}{1 - e \cos \theta}$

3. $r = \dfrac{4e}{1 - e \sin \theta}$

4. $r = \dfrac{4e}{1 + e \sin \theta}$

In Exercises 5–10, match the polar equation with its graph. [The graphs are labeled (a), (b), (c), (d), (e), and (f).]

(a)

(b)

(c)

(d)

(e)

(f)

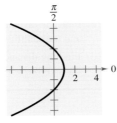

5. $r = \dfrac{2}{1 + \cos \theta}$

6. $r = \dfrac{3}{2 - \cos \theta}$

7. $r = \dfrac{3}{1 + 2 \sin \theta}$

8. $r = \dfrac{2}{1 - \sin \theta}$

9. $r = \dfrac{4}{2 + \cos \theta}$

10. $r = \dfrac{4}{1 - 3 \sin \theta}$

In Exercises 11–24, identify the conic and sketch its graph.

11. $r = \dfrac{2}{1 - \cos \theta}$

12. $r = \dfrac{3}{1 + \sin \theta}$

13. $r = \dfrac{5}{1 + \sin \theta}$

14. $r = \dfrac{6}{1 + \cos \theta}$

15. $r = \dfrac{2}{2 - \cos \theta}$

16. $r = \dfrac{3}{3 + \sin \theta}$

17. $r = \dfrac{6}{2 + \sin \theta}$

18. $r = \dfrac{9}{3 - 2 \cos \theta}$

19. $r = \dfrac{3}{2 + 4 \sin \theta}$

20. $r = \dfrac{5}{-1 + 2 \cos \theta}$

21. $r = \dfrac{3}{2 - 6 \cos \theta}$

22. $r = \dfrac{3}{2 + 6 \sin \theta}$

23. $r = \dfrac{4}{2 - \cos \theta}$

24. $r = \dfrac{2}{2 + 3 \sin \theta}$

In Exercises 25–28, use a graphing utility to graph the polar equation. Identify the graph.

25. $r = \dfrac{-1}{1 - \sin \theta}$

26. $r = \dfrac{-5}{2 + 4 \sin \theta}$

27. $r = \dfrac{3}{-4 + 2 \cos \theta}$

28. $r = \dfrac{4}{1 - 2 \cos \theta}$

In Exercises 29–32, use a graphing utility to graph the rotated conic.

29. $r = \dfrac{2}{1 - \cos(\theta - \pi/4)}$ (See Exercise 11.)

30. $r = \dfrac{3}{3 + \sin(\theta - \pi/3)}$ (See Exercise 16.)

31. $r = \dfrac{6}{2 + \sin(\theta + \pi/6)}$ (See Exercise 17.)

32. $r = \dfrac{5}{-1 + 2\cos(\theta + 2\pi/3)}$ (See Exercise 20.)

In Exercises 33–48, find a polar equation of the conic with its focus at the pole.

Conic	Eccentricity	Directrix
33. Parabola	$e = 1$	$x = -1$
34. Parabola	$e = 1$	$y = -2$
35. Ellipse	$e = \frac{1}{2}$	$y = 1$
36. Ellipse	$e = \frac{3}{4}$	$y = -3$
37. Hyperbola	$e = 2$	$x = 1$
38. Hyperbola	$e = \frac{3}{2}$	$x = -1$

Conic	Vertex or Vertices
39. Parabola	$(1, -\pi/2)$
40. Parabola	$(6, 0)$
41. Parabola	$(5, \pi)$
42. Parabola	$(10, \pi/2)$
43. Ellipse	$(2, 0), (10, \pi)$
44. Ellipse	$(2, \pi/2), (4, 3\pi/2)$
45. Ellipse	$(20, 0), (4, \pi)$
46. Hyperbola	$(2, 0), (8, 0)$
47. Hyperbola	$(1, 3\pi/2), (9, 3\pi/2)$
48. Hyperbola	$(4, \pi/2), (1, \pi/2)$

49. *Planetary Motion* The planets travel in elliptical orbits with the sun at one focus. Assume that the focus is at the pole, the major axis lies on the polar axis, and the length of the major axis is $2a$ (see figure). Show that the polar equation of the orbit is $r = a(1 - e^2)/(1 - e\cos\theta)$ where e is the eccentricity.

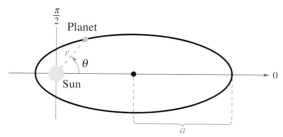

50. *Planetary Motion* Use the result of Exercise 49 to show that the minimum distance (*perihelion distance*) from the sun to the planet is $r = a(1 - e)$ and the maximum distance (*aphelion distance*) is $r = a(1 + e)$.

Planetary Motion In Exercises 51–56, use the results of Exercises 49 and 50 to find the polar equation of the planet's orbit and the perihelion and aphelion distances.

51. Earth $a = 95.956 \times 10^6$ miles, $e = 0.0167$

52. Saturn $a = 1.427 \times 10^9$ kilometers, $e = 0.0542$

53. Venus $a = 108.209 \times 10^6$ kilometers, $e = 0.0068$

54. Mercury $a = 35.98 \times 10^6$ miles, $e = 0.2056$

55. Mars $a = 141.63 \times 10^6$ miles, $e = 0.0934$

56. Jupiter $a = 778.41 \times 10^6$ kilometers, $e = 0.0484$

57. *Astronomy* The comet Encke has an elliptical orbit with an eccentricity of $e \approx 0.847$. The length of the major axis of the orbit is approximately 4.42 astronomical units. Find a polar equation for the orbit. How close does the comet come to the sun?

Model It

58. *Satellite Tracking* A satellite in a 100-mile-high circular orbit around Earth has a velocity of approximately 17,500 miles per hour. If this velocity is multiplied by $\sqrt{2}$, the satellite will have the minimum velocity necessary to escape Earth's gravity and it will follow a parabolic path with the center of Earth as the focus (see figure).

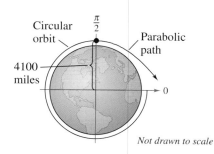

Not drawn to scale

(a) Find a polar equation of the parabolic path of the satellite (assume the radius of Earth is 4000 miles).

(b) Use a graphing utility to graph the equation you found in part (a).

(c) Find the distance between the surface of the Earth and the satellite when $\theta = 30°$.

(d) Find the distance between the surface of Earth and the satellite when $\theta = 60°$.

Synthesis

True or False? **In Exercises 59–61, determine whether the statement is true or false. Justify your answer.**

59. For a given value of $e > 1$ over the interval $\theta = 0$ to $\theta = 2\pi$, the graph of

$$r = \frac{ex}{1 - e \cos \theta}$$

is the same as the graph of

$$r = \frac{e(-x)}{1 + e \cos \theta}.$$

60. The graph of

$$r = \frac{4}{-3 - 3 \sin \theta}$$

has a horizontal directrix above the pole.

61. The conic represented by the following equation is an ellipse.

$$r^2 = \frac{16}{9 - 4 \cos\left(\theta + \frac{\pi}{4}\right)}$$

62. *Writing*   In your own words, define the term *eccentricity* and explain how it can be used to classify conics.

63. Show that the polar equation of the ellipse

$$\frac{x^2}{a^2} + \frac{y^2}{b^2} = 1 \quad \text{is} \quad r^2 = \frac{b^2}{1 - e^2 \cos^2 \theta}.$$

64. Show that the polar equation of the hyperbola

$$\frac{x^2}{a^2} - \frac{y^2}{b^2} = 1 \quad \text{is} \quad r^2 = \frac{-b^2}{1 - e^2 \cos^2 \theta}.$$

In Exercises 65–70, use the results of Exercises 63 and 64 to write the polar form of the equation of the conic.

65. $\dfrac{x^2}{169} + \dfrac{y^2}{144} = 1$

66. $\dfrac{x^2}{25} + \dfrac{y^2}{16} = 1$

67. $\dfrac{x^2}{9} - \dfrac{y^2}{16} = 1$

68. $\dfrac{x^2}{36} - \dfrac{y^2}{4} = 1$

69. Hyperbola   One focus: $(5, \pi/2)$
Vertices: $(4, \pi/2), (4, -\pi/2)$

70. Ellipse   One focus: $(4, 0)$
Vertices: $(5, 0), (5, \pi)$

71. *Exploration*   Consider the polar equation

$$r = \frac{4}{1 - 0.4 \cos \theta}.$$

(a) Identify the conic without graphing the equation.

(b) Without graphing the following polar equations, describe how each differs from the given polar equation.

$$r = \frac{4}{1 + 0.4 \cos \theta}, \quad r_2 = \frac{4}{1 - 0.4 \sin \theta}$$

(c) Use a graphing utility to verify your results in part (b).

72. *Exploration*   The equation

$$r = \frac{ep}{1 \pm e \sin \theta}$$

is the equation of an ellipse with $e < 1$. What happens to the lengths of both the major axis and the minor axis when the value of e remains fixed and the value of p changes? Use an example to explain your reasoning.

Skills Review

In Exercises 73–78, solve the trigonometric equation.

73. $4\sqrt{3} \tan \theta - 3 = 1$

74. $6 \cos x - 2 = 1$

75. $12 \sin^2 \theta = 9$

76. $9 \csc^2 x - 10 = 2$

77. $2 \cot x = 5 \cos \dfrac{\pi}{2}$

78. $\sqrt{2} \sec \theta = 2 \csc \dfrac{\pi}{4}$

In Exercises 79–82, find the exact value of the trigonometric function given that u and v are in Quadrant IV and $\sin u = -\frac{3}{5}$ and $\cos v = 1/\sqrt{2}$.

79. $\cos(u + v)$

80. $\sin(u + v)$

81. $\cos(u - v)$

82. $\sin(u - v)$

In Exercises 83 and 84, find the exact values of sin 2u, cos 2u, and tan 2u using the double-angle formulas.

83. $\sin u = \dfrac{4}{5}, \dfrac{\pi}{2} < u < \pi$

84. $\tan u = -\sqrt{3}, \dfrac{3\pi}{2} < u < 2\pi$

6 Chapter Summary

What did you learn?

6   Review Exercises

6.1 In Exercises 1–4, find the inclination θ (in radians and degrees) of the line with the given characteristics.

1. Passes through the points $(-1, 2)$ and $(2, 5)$
2. Passes through the points $(3, 4)$ and $(-2, 7)$
3. Equation: $y = 2x + 4$
4. Equation: $6x - 7y - 5 = 0$

In Exercises 5–8, find the angle θ (in radians and degrees) between the lines.

5. $\begin{aligned} 4x + y &= 2 \\ -5x + y &= -1 \end{aligned}$

6. $\begin{aligned} -5x + 3y &= 3 \\ -2x + 3y &= 1 \end{aligned}$

7. $\begin{aligned} 2x - 7y &= 8 \\ 0.4x + y &= 0 \end{aligned}$

8. $\begin{aligned} 0.02x + 0.07y &= 0.18 \\ 0.09x - 0.04y &= 0.17 \end{aligned}$

In Exercises 9 and 10, find the distance between the point and the line.

Point	Line
9. $(1, 2)$	$x - y - 3 = 0$
10. $(0, 4)$	$x + 2y - 2 = 0$

6.2 In Exercises 11 and 12, state what type of conic is formed by the intersection of the plane and the double-napped cone.

11.

12.

In Exercises 13–16, find the standard form of the equation of the parabola with the given characteristics. Then graph the parabola.

13. Vertex: $(0, 0)$
    Focus: $(4, 0)$
14. Vertex: $(2, 0)$
    Focus: $(0, 0)$
15. Vertex: $(0, 2)$
    Directrix: $x = -3$
16. Vertex: $(2, 2)$
    Directrix: $y = 0$

In Exercises 17 and 18, find an equation of the tangent line to the parabola at the given point, and find the x-intercept of the line.

17. $x^2 = -2y$, $(2, -2)$
18. $x^2 = -2y$, $(-4, -8)$

19. **Architecture** A parabolic archway is 12 meters high at the vertex. At a height of 10 meters, the width of the archway is 8 meters (see figure). How wide is the archway at ground level?

FIGURE FOR 19

FIGURE FOR 20

20. **Flashlight** The light bulb in a flashlight is at the focus of its parabolic reflector, 1.5 centimeters from the vertex of the reflector (see figure). Write an equation of a cross section of the flashlight's reflector with its focus on the positive x-axis and its vertex at the origin.

6.3 In Exercises 21–24, find the standard form of the equation of the ellipse with the given characteristics. Then graph the ellipse.

21. Vertices: $(-3, 0)$, $(7, 0)$; foci: $(0, 0)$, $(4, 0)$
22. Vertices: $(2, 0)$, $(2, 4)$; foci: $(2, 1)$, $(2, 3)$
23. Vertices: $(0, 1)$, $(4, 1)$; endpoints of the minor axis: $(2, 0)$, $(2, 2)$
24. Vertices: $(-4, -1)$, $(-4, 11)$; endpoints of the minor axis: $(-6, 5)$, $(-2, 5)$

25. **Architecture** A semielliptical archway is to be formed over the entrance to an estate. The arch is to be set on pillars that are 10 feet apart and is to have a height (atop the pillars) of 4 feet. Where should the foci be placed in order to sketch the arch?

26. **Wading Pool** You are building a wading pool that is in the shape of an ellipse. Your plans give an equation for the elliptical shape of the pool measured in feet as

$$\frac{x^2}{324} + \frac{y^2}{196} = 1.$$

Find the longest distance across the pool, the shortest distance, and the distance between the foci.

In Exercises 27–30, find the center, vertices, foci, and eccentricity of the ellipse.

27. $\dfrac{(x + 2)^2}{81} + \dfrac{(y - 1)^2}{100} = 1$

28. $\dfrac{(x - 5)^2}{1} + \dfrac{(y + 3)^2}{36} = 1$

29. $16x^2 + 9y^2 - 32x + 72y + 16 = 0$

30. $4x^2 + 25y^2 + 16x - 150y + 141 = 0$

6.4   In Exercises 31–34, find the standard form of the equation of the hyperbola with the given characteristics.

31. Vertices: $(0, \pm 1)$; foci: $(0, \pm 3)$

32. Vertices: $(2, 2), (-2, 2)$; foci: $(4, 2), (-4, 2)$

33. Foci: $(0, 0), (8, 0)$; asymptotes: $y = \pm 2(x - 4)$

34. Foci: $(3, \pm 2)$; asymptotes: $y = \pm 2(x - 3)$

In Exercises 35–38, find the center, vertices, foci, and the equations of the asymptotes of the hyperbola, and sketch its graph using the asymptotes as an aid.

35. $\dfrac{(x - 3)^2}{16} - \dfrac{(y + 5)^2}{4} = 1$

36. $\dfrac{(y - 1)^2}{4} - x^2 = 1$

37. $9x^2 - 16y^2 - 18x - 32y - 151 = 0$

38. $-4x^2 + 25y^2 - 8x + 150y + 121 = 0$

39. *LORAN*   Radio transmitting station A is located 200 miles east of transmitting station B. A ship is in an area to the north and 40 miles west of station A. Synchronized radio pulses transmitted at 186,000 miles per second by the two stations are received 0.0005 second sooner from station A than from station B. How far north is the ship?

40. *Locating an Explosion*   Two of your friends live 4 miles apart and on the same "east-west" street, and you live halfway between them. You are having a three-way phone conversation when you hear an explosion. Six seconds later, your friend to the east hears the explosion, and your friend to the west hears it 8 seconds after you do. Find equations of two hyperbolas that would locate the explosion. (Assume that the coordinate system is measured in feet and that sound travels at 1100 feet per second.)

In Exercises 41–44, classify the graph of the equation as a circle, a parabola, an ellipse, or a hyperbola.

41. $5x^2 - 2y^2 + 10x - 4y + 17 = 0$

42. $-4y^2 + 5x + 3y + 7 = 0$

43. $3x^2 + 2y^2 - 12x + 12y + 29 = 0$

44. $4x^2 + 4y^2 - 4x + 8y - 11 = 0$

6.5   In Exercises 45 and 46, complete the table for each set of parametric equations. Plot the points (x, y) and sketch a graph of the parametric equations.

45. $x = 3t - 2$ and $y = 7 - 4t$

t	-3	-2	-1	0	1	2	3
x							
y							

46. $x = \dfrac{1}{5}t$ and $y = \dfrac{4}{t - 1}$

t	-1	0	2	3	4	5
x						
y						

In Exercises 47–52, (a) sketch the curve represented by the parametric equations (indicate the orientation of the curve) and (b) eliminate the parameter and write the corresponding rectangular equation whose graph represents the curve. Adjust the domain of the resulting rectangular equation, if necessary. (c) Verify your result with a graphing utility.

47. $x = 2t$
      $y = 4t$

48. $x = 1 + 4t$
      $y = 2 - 3t$

49. $x = t^2$
      $y = \sqrt{t}$

50. $x = t + 4$
      $y = t^2$

51. $x = 6 \cos \theta$
      $y = 6 \sin \theta$

52. $x = 3 + 3 \cos \theta$
      $y = 2 + 5 \sin \theta$

53. Find a parametric representation of the circle with center $(5, 4)$ and radius 6.

54. Find a parametric representation of the ellipse with center $(-3, 4)$, major axis horizontal and eight units in length, and minor axis six units in length.

55. Find a parametric representation of the hyperbola with vertices $(0, \pm 4)$ and foci $(0, \pm 5)$.

56. *Involute of a Circle*   The *involute* of a circle is described by the endpoint P of a string that is held taut as it is unwound from a spool (see figure). The spool does not rotate. Show that a parametric representation of the involute of a circle is

$$x = r(\cos \theta + \theta \sin \theta)$$

$$y = r(\sin \theta - \theta \cos \theta).$$

6.6 In Exercises 57–60, plot the point given in polar coordinates and find two additional polar representations of the point, using $-2\pi < \theta < 2\pi$.

57. $\left(2, \dfrac{\pi}{4}\right)$

58. $\left(-5, -\dfrac{\pi}{3}\right)$

59. $(-7, 4.19)$

60. $\left(\sqrt{3}, 2.62\right)$

In Exercises 61–64, a point in polar coordinates is given. Convert the point to rectangular coordinates.

61. $\left(-1, \dfrac{\pi}{3}\right)$

62. $\left(2, \dfrac{5\pi}{4}\right)$

63. $\left(3, \dfrac{3\pi}{4}\right)$

64. $\left(0, \dfrac{\pi}{2}\right)$

In Exercises 65–68, a point in rectangular coordinates is given. Convert the point to polar coordinates.

65. $(0, 2)$
66. $\left(-\sqrt{5}, \sqrt{5}\right)$
67. $(4, 6)$
68. $(3, -4)$

In Exercises 69–74, convert the rectangular equation to polar form.

69. $x^2 + y^2 = 49$

70. $x^2 + y^2 = 20$

71. $x^2 + y^2 - 6y = 0$

72. $x^2 + y^2 - 4x = 0$

73. $xy = 5$

74. $xy = -2$

In Exercises 75–80, convert the polar equation to rectangular form.

75. $r = 5$

76. $r = 12$

77. $r = 3 \cos \theta$

78. $r = 8 \sin \theta$

79. $r^2 = \sin \theta$

80. $r^2 = \cos 2\theta$

6.7 In Exercises 81–90, determine the symmetry of r, the maximum value of $|r|$, and any zeros of r. Then sketch the graph of the polar equation (plot additional points if necessary).

81. $r = 4$

82. $r = 11$

83. $r = 4 \sin 2\theta$

84. $r = \cos 5\theta$

85. $r = -2(1 + \cos \theta)$

86. $r = 3 - 4 \cos \theta$

87. $r = 2 + 6 \sin \theta$

88. $r = 5 - 5 \cos \theta$

89. $r = -3 \cos 2\theta$

90. $r = \cos 2\theta$

 In Exercises 91–94, identify the type of polar graph and use a graphing utility to graph the equation.

91. $r = 3(2 - \cos \theta)$

92. $r = 3(1 - 2 \cos \theta)$

93. $r = 4 \cos 3\theta$

94. $r^2 = 9 \cos 2\theta$

6.8 In Exercises 95–98, identify the conic and sketch its graph.

95. $r = \dfrac{1}{1 + 2 \sin \theta}$

96. $r = \dfrac{2}{1 + \sin \theta}$

97. $r = \dfrac{4}{5 - 3 \cos \theta}$

98. $r = \dfrac{16}{4 + 5 \cos \theta}$

In Exercises 99–102, find a polar equation of the conic with its focus at the pole.

99. Parabola   Vertex: $(2, \pi)$

100. Parabola   Vertex: $(2, \pi/2)$

101. Ellipse   Vertices: $(5, 0), (1, \pi)$

102. Hyperbola   Vertices: $(1, 0), (7, 0)$

103. *Explorer 18*   On November 26, 1963, the United States launched Explorer 18. Its low and high points above the surface of Earth were 119 miles and 122,800 miles, respectively (see figure). The center of Earth was at one focus of the orbit. Find the polar equation of the orbit and find the distance between the surface of Earth (assume Earth has a radius of 4000 miles) and the satellite when $\theta = \pi/3$.

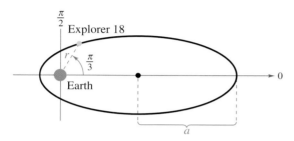

104. *Asteroid*   An asteroid takes a parabolic path with Earth as its focus. It is about 6,000,000 miles from Earth at its closest approach. Write the polar equation of the path of the asteroid with its vertex at $\theta = \pi/2$. Find the distance between the asteroid and Earth when $\theta = -\pi/3$.

Synthesis

True or False?   **In Exercises 105–107, determine whether the statement is true or false. Justify your answer.**

105. The graph of $\frac{1}{4}x^2 - y^4 = 1$ is a hyperbola.

106. Only one set of parametric equations can represent the line $y = 3 - 2x$.

107. There is a unique polar coordinate representation of each point in the plane.

108. Consider an ellipse with the major axis horizontal and 10 units in length. The number b in the standard form of the equation of the ellipse must be less than what real number? Explain the change in the shape of the ellipse as b approaches this number.

109. The graph of the parametric equations $x = 2 \sec t$ and $y = 3 \tan t$ is shown in the figure. How would the graph change for the equations $x = 2 \sec(-t)$ and $y = 3 \tan(-t)$?

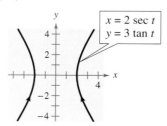

110. A moving object is modeled by the parametric equations $x = 4 \cos t$ and $y = 3 \sin t$, where t is time (see figure). How would the path change for the following?

(a) $x = 4 \cos 2t$, $y = 3 \sin 2t$

(b) $x = 5 \cos t$, $y = 3 \sin t$

111. Identify the type of symmetry each of the following polar points has with the point in the figure.

(a) $\left(-4, \dfrac{\pi}{6}\right)$ (b) $\left(4, -\dfrac{\pi}{6}\right)$ (c) $\left(-4, -\dfrac{\pi}{6}\right)$

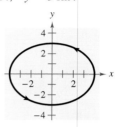

112. What is the relationship between the graphs of the rectangular and polar equations?

(a) $x^2 + y^2 = 25$, $r = 5$ (b) $x - y = 0$, $\theta = \dfrac{\pi}{4}$

113. *Geometry*   The area of the ellipse in the figure is twice the area of the circle. What is the length of the major axis? (*Hint:* The area of an ellipse is $A = \pi ab$.)

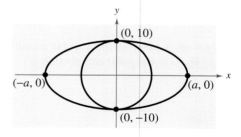

6 Chapter Test

Take this test as you would take a test in class. When you are finished, check your work against the answers given in the back of the book.

1. Find the inclination of the line $2x - 7y + 3 = 0$.
2. Find the angle between the lines $3x + 2y - 4 = 0$ and $4x - y + 6 = 0$.
3. Find the distance between the point $(7, 5)$ and the line $y = 5 - x$.

In Exercises 4–7, classify the conic and write the equation in standard form. Identify the center, vertices, foci, and asymptotes (if applicable). Then sketch the graph of the conic.

4. $y^2 - 4x + 4 = 0$
5. $x^2 - 4y^2 - 4x = 0$
6. $9x^2 + 16y^2 + 54x - 32y - 47 = 0$
7. $2x^2 + 2y^2 - 8x - 4y + 9 = 0$

8. Find the standard form of the equation of the parabola with vertex $(3, -2)$, with a vertical axis, and passing through the point $(0, 4)$.
9. Find the standard form of the equation of the hyperbola with foci $(0, 0)$ and $(0, 4)$ and asymptotes $y = \pm\frac{1}{2}x + 2$.
10. Sketch the curve represented by the parametric equations $x = 2 + 3\cos\theta$ and $y = 2\sin\theta$. Eliminate the parameter and write the corresponding rectangular equation.
11. Find a set of parametric equations of the line passing through the points $(2, -3)$ and $(6, 4)$. (There are many correct answers.)
12. Convert the polar coordinate $\left(-2, \frac{5\pi}{6}\right)$ to rectangular form.
13. Convert the rectangular coordinate $(2, -2)$ to polar form and find two additional polar representations of this point.
14. Convert the rectangular equation $x^2 + y^2 - 4y = 0$ to polar form.

In Exercises 15–18, sketch the graph of the polar equation. Identify the type of graph.

15. $r = \dfrac{4}{1 + \cos\theta}$
16. $r = \dfrac{4}{2 + \cos\theta}$
17. $r = 2 + 3\sin\theta$
18. $r = 3\sin 2\theta$

19. Find a polar equation of the ellipse with focus at the pole, eccentricity $e = \frac{1}{4}$, and directrix $y = 4$.
20. A straight road rises with an inclination of 0.15 radian from the horizontal. Find the slope of the road and the change in elevation over a one-mile stretch of the road.
21. A baseball is hit at a point 3 feet above the ground toward the left field fence. The fence is 10 feet high and 375 feet from home plate. The path of the baseball can be modeled by the parametric equations $x = (115\cos\theta)t$ and $y = 3 + (115\sin\theta)t - 16t^2$. Will the baseball go over the fence if it is hit at an angle of $\theta = 30°$? Will the baseball go over the fence if $\theta = 35°$?

6 Cumulative Test for Chapters 4–6

Take this test to review the material from earlier chapters. When you are finished, check your work against the answers given in the back of the book.

1. Consider the angle $\theta = -120°$.
   (a) Sketch the angle in standard position.
   (b) Determine a coterminal angle in the interval $[0°, 360°)$.
   (c) Convert the angle to radian measure.
   (d) Find the reference angle θ'.
   (e) Find the exact values of the six trigonometric functions of θ.

2. Convert the angle $\theta = 2.35$ radians to degrees. Round the answer to one decimal place.

3. Find $\cos \theta$ if $\tan \theta = -\frac{4}{3}$ and $\sin \theta < 0$.

In Exercises 4–6, sketch the graph of the function. (Include two full periods.)

4. $f(x) = 3 - 2 \sin \pi x$
5. $g(x) = \dfrac{1}{2} \tan\left(x - \dfrac{\pi}{2}\right)$
6. $h(x) = -\sec(x + \pi)$

FIGURE FOR 7

7. Find a, b, and c such that the graph of the function $h(x) = a \cos(bx + c)$ matches the graph in the figure.

8. Sketch the graph of the function $f(x) = \frac{1}{2}x \sin x$ over the interval $-3\pi \le x \le 3\pi$.

In Exercises 9 and 10, find the exact value of the expression without using a calculator.

9. $\tan(\arctan 6.7)$

10. $\tan\left(\arcsin \frac{3}{5}\right)$

11. Write an algebraic expression equivalent to $\sin(\arccos 2x)$.

12. Use the fundamental identities to simplify: $\cos\left(\dfrac{\pi}{2} - x\right) \csc x$.

13. Subtract and simplify: $\dfrac{\sin \theta - 1}{\cos \theta} - \dfrac{\cos \theta}{\sin \theta - 1}$.

In Exercises 14–16, verify the identity.

14. $\cot^2 \alpha(\sec^2 \alpha - 1) = 1$
15. $\sin(x + y) \sin(x - y) = \sin^2 x - \sin^2 y$
16. $\sin^2 x \cos^2 x = \frac{1}{8}(1 - \cos 4x)$

In Exercises 17 and 18, find all solutions of the equation in the interval $[0, 2\pi)$.

17. $2 \cos^2 \beta - \cos \beta = 0$
18. $3 \tan \theta - \cot \theta = 0$

19. Use the Quadratic Formula to solve the equation in the interval $[0, 2\pi)$: $\sin^2 x + 2 \sin x + 1 = 0$.

20. Given that $\sin u = \frac{12}{13}$, $\cos v = \frac{3}{5}$, and angles u and v are both in Quadrant I, find $\tan(u - v)$.

21. If $\tan \theta = \frac{1}{2}$, find the exact value of $\tan(2\theta)$.

22. If $\tan \theta = \dfrac{4}{3}$, find the exact value of $\sin \dfrac{\theta}{2}$.

23. Write the product $5 \sin \dfrac{3\pi}{4} \cdot \cos \dfrac{7\pi}{4}$ as a sum or difference.

24. Write $\cos 8x + \cos 4x$ as a product.

In Exercises 25–28, use the information to solve the triangle shown in the figure. Round your answers to two decimal places.

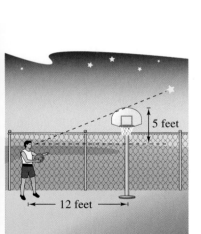

FIGURE FOR 25–28

25. $A = 30°$, $a = 9$, $b = 8$

26. $A = 30°$, $b = 8$, $c = 10$

27. $A = 30°$, $C = 90°$, $b = 10$

28. $a = 4$, $b = 8$, $c = 9$

29. Two sides of a triangle have lengths 7 inches and 12 inches. Their included angle measures $60°$. Find the area of the triangle.

30. Find the area of a triangle with sides of lengths 11 inches, 16 inches, and 17 inches.

In Exercises 31 and 32, identify the conic and sketch its graph.

31. $\dfrac{(x-2)^2}{4} + \dfrac{(y+1)^2}{9} = 1$

32. $x^2 + y^2 - 2x - 4y + 1 = 0$

33. Find the standard form of the equation of the ellipse with vertices $(0, 0)$ and $(0, 4)$ and endpoints of the minor axis $(1, 2)$ and $(-1, 2)$.

34. Sketch the curve represented by parametric equations $x = 4 \ln t$ and $y = \frac{1}{2}t^2$. Then eliminate the parameter and write the corresponding rectangular equation whose graph represents the curve.

35. Plot the point $(-2, -3\pi/4)$ and find three additional polar representations for $-2\pi < \theta < 2\pi$.

36. Convert the rectangular equation $-8x - 3y + 5 = 0$ to polar form.

37. Convert the polar equation $r = \dfrac{2}{4 - 5 \cos \theta}$ to rectangular form.

In Exercises 38–40, sketch the graph of the polar equation. Identify the type of graph.

38. $r = -\dfrac{\pi}{6}$

39. $r = 3 - 2 \sin \theta$

40. $r = 2 + 5 \cos \theta$

41. A ceiling fan with 21-inch blades makes 63 revolutions per minute. Find the angular speed of the fan in radians per minute. Find the linear speed of the tips of the blades in inches per minute.

42. Find the area of the sector of a circle with a radius of 8 yards and a central angle of $114°$.

43. From a point 200 feet from a flagpole, the angles of elevation to the bottom and top of the flag are $16° \, 45'$ and $18°$, respectively. Approximate the height of the flag to the nearest foot.

44. To determine the angle of elevation of a star in the sky, you get the star in your line of vision with the backboard of a basketball hoop that is 5 feet higher than your eyes (see figure). Your horizontal distance from the backboard is 12 feet. What is the angle of elevation of the star?

45. Write a model for a particle in simple harmonic motion with a displacement of 4 inches and a period of 8 seconds.

FIGURE FOR 44

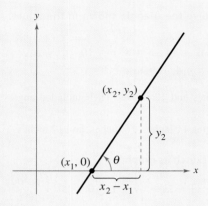

Inclination and Slope *(p. 450)*

If a nonvertical line has inclination θ and slope m, then $m = \tan \theta$.

Proof

If $m = 0$, the line is horizontal and $\theta = 0$. So, the result is true for horizontal lines because $m = 0 = \tan 0$.

If the line has a positive slope, it will intersect the x-axis. Label this point $(x_1, 0)$, as shown in the figure. If (x_2, y_2) is a second point on the line, the slope is

$$m = \frac{y_2 - 0}{x_2 - x_1} = \frac{y_2}{x_2 - x_1} = \tan \theta.$$

The case in which the line has a negative slope can be proved in a similar manner.

Distance Between a Point and a Line *(p. 452)*

The distance between the point (x_1, y_1) and the line $Ax + By + C = 0$ is

$$d = \frac{|Ax_1 + By_1 + C|}{\sqrt{A^2 + B^2}}.$$

Proof

For simplicity's sake, assume that the given line is neither horizontal nor vertical (see figure). By writing the equation $Ax + By + C = 0$ in slope-intercept form

$$y = -\frac{A}{B}x - \frac{C}{B}$$

you can see that the line has a slope of $m = -A/B$. So, the slope of the line passing through (x_1, y_1) and perpendicular to the given line is B/A, and its equation is $y - y_1 = (B/A)(x - x_1)$. These two lines intersect at the point (x_2, y_2), where

$$x_2 = \frac{B(Bx_1 - Ay_1) - AC}{A^2 + B^2} \quad \text{and} \quad y_2 = \frac{A(-Bx_1 + Ay_1) - BC}{A^2 + B^2}.$$

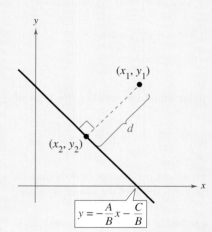

Finally, the distance between (x_1, y_1) and (x_2, y_2) is

$$d = \sqrt{(x_2 - x_1)^2 + (y_2 - y_1)^2}$$

$$= \sqrt{\left(\frac{B^2 x_1 - ABy_1 - AC}{A^2 + B^2} - x_1\right)^2 + \left(\frac{-ABx_1 + A^2 y_1 - BC}{A^2 + B^2} - y_1\right)^2}$$

$$= \sqrt{\frac{A^2(Ax_1 + By_1 + C)^2 + B^2(Ax_1 + By_1 + C)^2}{(A^2 + B^2)^2}}$$

$$= \frac{|Ax_1 + By_1 + C|}{\sqrt{A^2 + B^2}}.$$

Parabolic Paths

There are many natural occurrences of parabolas in real life. For instance, the famous astronomer Galileo discovered in the 17th century that an object that is projected upward and obliquely to the pull of gravity travels in a parabolic path. Examples of this are the center of gravity of a jumping dolphin and the path of water molecules in a drinking fountain.

Standard Equation of a Parabola (p. 458)

The standard form of the equation of a parabola with vertex at (h, k) is as follows.

$$(x - h)^2 = 4p(y - k), \quad p \neq 0 \qquad \text{Vertical axis, directrix: } y = k - p$$

$$(y - k)^2 = 4p(x - h), \quad p \neq 0 \qquad \text{Horizontal axis, directrix: } x = h - p$$

The focus lies on the axis p units (*directed distance*) from the vertex. If the vertex is at the origin $(0, 0)$, the equation takes one of the following forms.

$$x^2 = 4py \qquad \text{Vertical axis}$$

$$y^2 = 4px \qquad \text{Horizontal axis}$$

Proof

For the case in which the directrix is parallel to the x-axis and the focus lies above the vertex, as shown in the top figure, if (x, y) is any point on the parabola, then, by definition, it is equidistant from the focus $(h, k + p)$ and the directrix $y = k - p$. So, you have

$$\sqrt{(x - h)^2 + [y - (k + p)]^2} = y - (k - p)$$

$$(x - h)^2 + [y - (k + p)]^2 = [y - (k - p)]^2$$

$$(x - h)^2 + y^2 - 2y(k + p) + (k + p)^2 = y^2 - 2y(k - p) + (k - p)^2$$

$$(x - h)^2 + y^2 - 2ky - 2py + k^2 + 2pk + p^2 = y^2 - 2ky + 2py + k^2 - 2pk + p^2$$

$$(x - h)^2 - 2py + 2pk = 2py - 2pk$$

$$(x - h)^2 = 4p(y - k).$$

For the case in which the directrix is parallel to the y-axis and the focus lies to the right of the vertex, as shown in the bottom figure, if (x, y) is any point on the parabola, then, by definition, it is equidistant from the focus $(h + p, k)$ and the directrix $x = h - p$. So, you have

$$\sqrt{[x - (h + p)]^2 + (y - k)^2} = x - (h - p)$$

$$[x - (h + p)]^2 + (y - k)^2 = [x - (h - p)]^2$$

$$x^2 - 2x(h + p) + (h + p)^2 + (y - k)^2 = x^2 - 2x(h - p) + (h - p)^2$$

$$x^2 - 2hx - 2px + h^2 + 2ph + p^2 + (y - k)^2 = x^2 - 2hx + 2px + h^2 - 2ph + p^2$$

$$-2px + 2ph + (y - k)^2 = 2px - 2ph$$

$$(y - k)^2 = 4p(x - h).$$

Note that if a parabola is centered at the origin, then the two equations above would simplify to $x^2 = 4py$ and $y^2 = 4px$, respectively.

Parabola with vertical axis

Parabola with horizontal axis

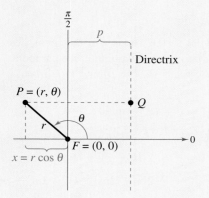

Polar Equations of Conics *(p. 507)*

The graph of a polar equation of the form

1. $r = \dfrac{ep}{1 \pm e \cos \theta}$

or

2. $r = \dfrac{ep}{1 \pm e \sin \theta}$

is a conic, where $e > 0$ is the eccentricity and $|p|$ is the distance between the focus (pole) and the directrix.

Proof

A proof for $r = ep/(1 + e \cos \theta)$ with $p > 0$ is shown here. The proofs of the other cases are similar. In the figure, consider a vertical directrix, p units to the right of the focus $F = (0, 0)$. If $P = (r, \theta)$ is a point on the graph of

$$r = \frac{ep}{1 + e \cos \theta}$$

the distance between P and the directrix is

$$
\begin{aligned}
PQ &= |p - x| \\
&= |p - r \cos \theta| \\
&= \left| p - \left(\frac{ep}{1 + e \cos \theta} \right) \cos \theta \right| \\
&= \left| p \left(1 - \frac{e \cos \theta}{1 + e \cos \theta} \right) \right| \\
&= \left| \frac{p}{1 + e \cos \theta} \right| \\
&= \left| \frac{r}{e} \right|.
\end{aligned}
$$

Moreover, because the distance between P and the pole is simply $PF = |r|$, the ratio of PF to PQ is

$$
\begin{aligned}
\frac{PF}{PQ} &= \frac{|r|}{\left| \dfrac{r}{e} \right|} \\
&= |e| \\
&= e
\end{aligned}
$$

and, by definition, the graph of the equation must be a conic.

This collection of thought-provoking and challenging exercises further explores and expands upon concepts learned in this chapter.

1. Several mountain climbers are located in a mountain pass between two peaks. The angles of elevation to the two peaks are 0.84 radian and 1.10 radians. A range finder shows that the distances to the peaks are 3250 feet and 6700 feet, respectively (see figure).

1.10 radians   3250 ft   0.84 radian
6700 ft

(a) Find the angle between the two lines of sight to the peaks.

(b) Approximate the amount of vertical climb that is necessary to reach the summit of each peak.

2. Statuary Hall is an elliptical room in the United States Capitol in Washington D.C. The room is also called the Whispering Gallery because a person standing at one focus of the room can hear even a whisper spoken by a person standing at the other focus. This occurs because any sound that is emitted from one focus of an ellipse will reflect off the side of the ellipse to the other focus. Statuary Hall is 46 feet wide and 97 feet long.

(a) Find an equation that models the shape of the room.

(b) How far apart are the two foci?

(c) What is the area of the floor of the room? (The area of an ellipse is $A = \pi ab$.)

3. Find the equation(s) of all parabolas that have the x-axis as the axis of symmetry and focus at the origin.

4. Find the area of the square inscribed in the ellipse below.

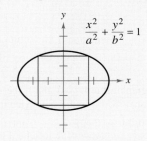

$$\frac{x^2}{a^2} + \frac{y^2}{b^2} = 1$$

5. A tour boat travels between two islands that are 12 miles apart (see figure). For a trip between the islands, there is enough fuel for a 20-mile trip.

Island 1   Island 2
$\longmapsto$ 12 mi $\longmapsto$
Not drawn to scale

(a) Explain why the region in which the boat can travel is bounded by an ellipse.

(b) Let $(0, 0)$ represent the center of the ellipse. Find the coordinates of each island.

(c) The boat travels from one island, straight past the other island to the vertex of the ellipse, and back to the second island. How many miles does the boat travel? Use your answer to find the coordinates of the vertex.

(d) Use the results from parts (b) and (c) to write an equation for the ellipse that bounds the region in which the boat can travel.

6. Find an equation of the hyperbola such that for any point on the hyperbola, the difference between its distances from the points $(2, 2)$ and $(10, 2)$ is 6.

7. Prove that the graph of the equation

$$Ax^2 + Cy^2 + Dx + Ey + F = 0$$

is one of the following (except in degenerate cases).

	Conic	Condition
(a)	Circle	$A = C$
(b)	Parabola	$A = 0$ or $C = 0$ (but not both)
(c)	Ellipse	$AC > 0$
(d)	Hyperbola	$AC < 0$

8. The following sets of parametric equations model projectile motion.

$x = (v_0 \cos \theta)t$ $x = (v_0 \cos \theta)t$

$y = (v_0 \sin \theta)t$ $y = h + (v_0 \sin \theta)t - 16t^2$

(a) Under what circumstances would you use each model?

(b) Eliminate the parameter for each set of equations.

(c) In which case is the path of the moving object not affected by a change in the velocity v? Explain.

525

9. As t increases, the ellipse given by the parametric equations

$$x = \cos t \quad \text{and} \quad y = 2 \sin t$$

is traced out *counterclockwise*. Find a parametric representation for which the same ellipse is traced out *clockwise*.

 10. A **hypocycloid** has the parametric equations

$$x = (a - b) \cos t + b \cos\left(\frac{a - b}{b}t\right)$$

and

$$y = (a - b) \sin t - b \sin\left(\frac{a - b}{b}t\right).$$

Use a graphing utility to graph the hypocycloid for each value of a and b. Describe each graph.

(a) $a = 2, b = 1$ (b) $a = 3, b = 1$

(c) $a = 4, b = 1$ (d) $a = 10, b = 1$

(e) $a = 3, b = 2$ (f) $a = 4, b = 3$

11. The curve given by the parametric equations

$$x = \frac{1 - t^2}{1 + t^2}$$

and

$$y = \frac{t(1 - t^2)}{1 + t^2}$$

is called a **strophoid.**

(a) Find a rectangular equation of the strophoid.

(b) Find a polar equation of the strophoid.

 (c) Use a graphing utility to graph the strophoid.

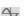 **12.** The rose curves described in this chapter are of the form

$$r = a \cos n\theta \quad \text{or} \quad r = a \sin n\theta$$

where n is a positive integer that is greater than or equal to 2. Use a graphing utility to graph $r = a \cos n\theta$ and $r = a \sin n\theta$ for some noninteger values of n. Describe the graphs.

13. What conic section is represented by the polar equation

$$r = a \sin \theta + b \cos \theta?$$

14. The graph of the polar equation

$$r = e^{\cos \theta} - 2 \cos 4\theta + \sin^5\left(\frac{\theta}{12}\right)$$

is called the *butterfly curve*, as shown in the figure.

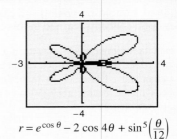

$$r = e^{\cos \theta} - 2 \cos 4\theta + \sin^5\left(\frac{\theta}{12}\right)$$

FIGURE FOR **14**

(a) The graph above was produced using $0 \le \theta \le 2\pi$. Does this show the entire graph? Explain your reasoning.

(b) Approximate the maximum r-value of the graph. Does this value change if you use $0 \le \theta \le 4\pi$ instead of $0 \le \theta \le 2\pi$? Explain.

 15. Use a graphing utility to graph the polar equation

$$r = \cos 5\theta + n \cos \theta$$

for $0 \le \theta \le \pi$ for the integers $n = -5$ to $n = 5$. As you graph these equations, you should see the graph change shape from a heart to a bell. Write a short paragraph explaining what values of n produce the heart portion of the curve and what values of n produce the bell portion of the curve.

16. The planets travel in elliptical orbits with the sun at one focus. The polar equation of the orbit of a planet with one focus at the pole and major axis of length $2a$ is

$$r = \frac{(1 - e^2)a}{1 - e \cos \theta}$$

where e is the eccentricity. The minimum distance (perihelion) from the sun to a planet is $r = a(1 - e)$ and the maximum distance (aphelion) is $r = a(1 + e)$. The length of the major axis for the planet Neptune is $a = 9.000 \times 10^9$ kilometers and the eccentricity is $e = 0.0086$. The length of the major axis for the planet Pluto is $a = 10.813 \times 10^9$ kilometers and the eccentricity is $e = 0.2488$.

(a) Find the polar equation of the orbit of each planet.

(b) Find the perihelion and aphelion distances for each planet.

(c) Use a graphing utility to graph the polar equation of each planet's orbit in the same viewing window.

(d) Do the orbits of the two planets intersect? Will the two planets ever collide? Why or why not?

(e) Is Pluto ever closer to the sun than Neptune? Why is Pluto called the ninth planet and Neptune the eighth planet?

Answers to Odd-Numbered Exercises and Tests

Chapter 1

Section 1.1   *(page 9)*

Vocabulary Check   *(page 9)*

1. (a) v   (b) vi   (c) i   (d) iv   (e) iii   (f) ii
2. Cartesian   **3.** Distance Formula
4. Midpoint Formula

---

1. A: $(2, 6)$, B: $(-6, -2)$, C: $(4, -4)$, D: $(-3, 2)$
3.   **5.**

   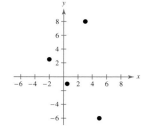

7. $(-3, 4)$ **9.** $(-5, -5)$ **11.** Quadrant IV
13. Quadrant II   **15.** Quadrant III or IV
17. Quadrant III   **19.** Quadrant I or III
21.

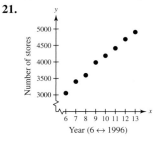

23. 8   **25.** 5
27. (a) 4, 3, 5   (b) $4^2 + 3^2 = 5^2$
29. (a) 10, 3, $\sqrt{109}$ (b) $10^2 + 3^2 = \left(\sqrt{109}\right)^2$
31. (a)   (b) 10
                                         (c) $(5, 4)$

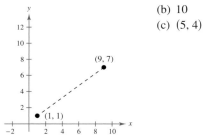

33. (a)   (b) 17
                                         (c) $\left(0, \frac{5}{2}\right)$

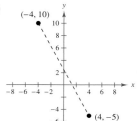

35. (a)   (b) $2\sqrt{10}$
                                         (c) $(2, 3)$

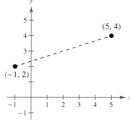

37. (a)   (b) $\dfrac{\sqrt{82}}{3}$
                                         (c) $\left(-1, \frac{7}{6}\right)$

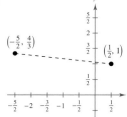

39. (a)   (b) $\sqrt{110.97}$
                                         (c) $(1.25, 3.6)$

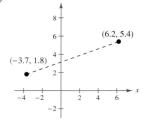

41. $\left(\sqrt{5}\right)^2 + \left(\sqrt{45}\right)^2 = \left(\sqrt{50}\right)^2$
43. $(2x_m - x_1, 2y_m - y_1)$
45. $\left(\dfrac{3x_1 + x_2}{4}, \dfrac{3y_1 + y_2}{4}\right)$, $\left(\dfrac{x_1 + x_2}{2}, \dfrac{y_1 + y_2}{2}\right)$,
$\left(\dfrac{x_1 + 3x_2}{4}, \dfrac{y_1 + 3y_2}{4}\right)$
47. $2\sqrt{505} \approx 45$ yards   **49.** \$3803.5 million
51. $(0, 1)$, $(4, 2)$, $(1, 4)$ **53.** $(-3, 6)$, $(2, 10)$, $(2, 4)$, $(-3, 4)$
55. \$3.31 per pound; 2001   **57.** $\approx 250\%$

59. (a) The number of artists elected each year seems to be nearly steady except for the first few years. From six to eight artists will be elected in 2008.

    (b) The Rock and Roll Hall of Fame was opened in 1986.

61. 1998: \$19,384.5 million; 2000: \$20,223.0 million; 2002: \$21,061.5 million

63. $\sqrt[3]{\dfrac{4.47}{\pi}} \approx 1.12$ inches

65. Length of side $= 43$ centimeters; area $= 800.64$ square centimeters

67. (a) 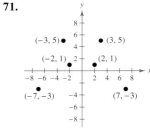   (b) $l = 1.5w$; $p = 5w$

    (c) 7.5 meters $\times$ 5 meters

69. (a)   (b) 2002

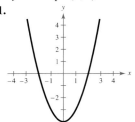

    (c) Answers will vary. Sample answer: Technology now enables us to transport information in many ways other than by mail. The Internet is one example.

71.

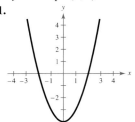

    (a) The point is reflected through the y-axis.

    (b) The point is reflected through the x-axis.

    (c) The point is reflected through the origin.

73. False. The Midpoint Formula would be used 15 times.

75. No. It depends on the magnitudes of the quantities measured.

77. b   **78.** c   **79.** d   **80.** a   **81.** $x = 1$

83. $x = 2 \pm \sqrt{11}$ **85.** $x < \frac{3}{5}$ **87.** $14 < x < 22$

Section 1.2   (page 22)

Vocabulary Check   (page 22)

1. solution or solution point   **2.** graph

3. intercepts   **4.** y-axis   **5.** circle; (h, k); r

6. numerical

---

1. (a) Yes   (b) Yes   **3.** (a) No   (b) Yes

5.

x	-1	0	1	2	$\frac{5}{2}$
y	7	5	3	1	0
(x, y)	$(-1, 7)$	$(0, 5)$	$(1, 3)$	$(2, 1)$	$\left(\frac{5}{2}, 0\right)$

7.

x	-1	0	1	2	3
y	4	0	-2	-2	0
(x, y)	$(-1, 4)$	$(0, 0)$	$(1, -2)$	$(2, -2)$	$(3, 0)$

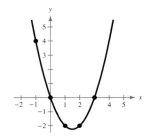

9. x-intercepts: $(\pm 2, 0)$ **11.** x-intercept: $\left(\frac{6}{5}, 0\right)$

    y-intercept: $(0, 16)$ y-intercept: $(0, -6)$

13. x-intercept: $(-4, 0)$ **15.** x-intercept: $\left(\frac{7}{3}, 0\right)$

    y-intercept: $(0, 2)$ y-intercept: $(0, 7)$

17. x-intercepts: $(0, 0), (2, 0)$ **19.** x-intercept: $(6, 0)$

    y-intercept: $(0, 0)$ y-intercepts: $\left(0, \pm\sqrt{6}\right)$

21.   **23.**

25. y-axis symmetry   **27.** Origin symmetry

29. Origin symmetry   **31.** x-axis symmetry

33.

35.

37.

39.

41.

43.

45.

Intercepts: $(6, 0), (0, 3)$

47.

Intercepts: $(3, 0), (1, 0), (0, 3)$

49.

Intercept: $(0, 0)$

51.

Intercept: $(0, 0)$

53.

Intercepts: $(0, 0), (-6, 0)$

55.

Intercepts: $(-3, 0), (0, 3)$

57. $x^2 + y^2 = 16$ **59.** $(x - 2)^2 + (y + 1)^2 = 16$
61. $(x + 1)^2 + (y - 2)^2 = 5$
63. $(x - 3)^2 + (y - 4)^2 = 25$
65. Center: $(0, 0)$; Radius: 5 **67.** Center: $(1, -3)$; Radius: 3

 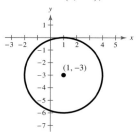

69. Center: $\left(\frac{1}{2}, \frac{1}{2}\right)$; Radius: $\frac{3}{2}$ **71.**

73. (a) 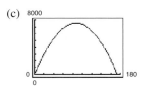 (b) Answers will vary.

(c) (d) $x = 86\frac{2}{3}, y = 86\frac{2}{3}$

(e) A regulation NFL playing field is 120 yards long and $53\frac{1}{3}$ yards wide. The actual area is 6400 square yards.

75. (a) and (b)

(c) 66.0 years (d) 2005: 77.0 years; 2010: 77.1 years
(e) Answers will vary.

77. False. A graph is symmetric with respect to the x-axis if, whenever (x, y) is on the graph $(x, -y)$ is also on the graph.

79. The viewing window is incorrect. Change the viewing window. Answers will vary.

81. $9x^5,\ 4x^3,\ -7$ **83.** $2\sqrt{2x}$

85. $\dfrac{10\sqrt{7x}}{x}$ **87.** $\sqrt[3]{|t|}$

Section 1.3   *(page 34)*

Vocabulary Check   *(page 34)*

1. linear   **2.** slope   **3.** parallel
4. perpendicular   **5.** rate or rate of change
6. linear extrapolation
7. a. iii   b. i   c. v   d. ii   e. iv

1. (a) L_2 (b) L_3 (c) L_1

3.
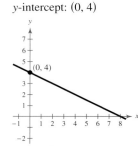

5. $\frac{3}{2}$ **7.** -4

9. $m = 5$;
y-intercept: $(0, 3)$

11. $m = -\frac{1}{2}$;
y-intercept: $(0, 4)$
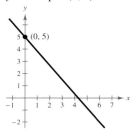

13. m is undefined.
There is no y-intercept.

15. $m = -\frac{7}{6}$;
y-intercept: $(0, 5)$

17. $m = 0$;
y-intercept: $(0, 3)$
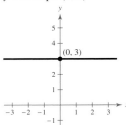

19. m is undefined.
There is no y-intercept.

21.

$m = 2$

23.

m is undefined.

25.

$m = -\frac{1}{7}$

27.

$m = 0.15$

29. $(0, 1), (3, 1), (-1, 1)$
31. $(6, -5), (7, -4), (8, -3)$
33. $(-8, 0), (-8, 2), (-8, 3)$
35. $(-4, 6), (-3, 8), (-2, 10)$
37. $(9, -1), (11, 0), (13, 1)$
39. $y = 3x - 2$

41. $y = -2x$
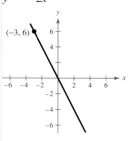

43. $y = -\frac{1}{3}x + \frac{4}{3}$

45. $x = 6$

63. $x = \frac{7}{3}$

47. $y = \frac{5}{2}$

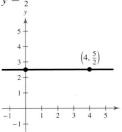

49. $y = 5x + 27.3$

65. Perpendicular   **67.** Parallel

69. (a) $y = 2x - 3$ (b) $y = -\frac{1}{2}x + 2$

71. (a) $y = -\frac{3}{4}x + \frac{3}{8}$ (b) $y = \frac{4}{3}x + \frac{127}{72}$

73. (a) $y = 0$ (b) $x = -1$

75. (a) $x = 2$ (b) $y = 5$

77. (a) $y = x + 4.3$ (b) $y = -x + 9.3$

79. $3x + 2y - 6 = 0$ **81.** $12x + 3y + 2 = 0$

83. $x + y - 3 = 0$

85. Line (b) is perpendicular to line (c).

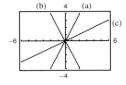

87. Line (a) is parallel to line (b).
Line (c) is perpendicular to line (a) and line (b).

51. $y = -\frac{3}{5}x + 2$

53. $x = -8$

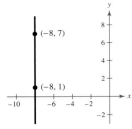

55. $y = -\frac{1}{2}x + \frac{3}{2}$

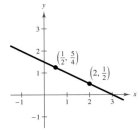

57. $y = -\frac{6}{5}x - \frac{18}{25}$

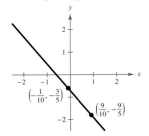

89. $3x - 2y - 1 = 0$ **91.** $80x + 12y + 139 = 0$

93. (a) Sales increasing 135 units per year
(b) No change in sales
(c) Sales decreasing 40 units per year

95. (a) Salary increased greatest from 1990 to 1992; Least from 1992 to 1994
(b) Slope of line from 1990 to 2002 is about 2351.83
(c) Salary increased an average of $2351.83 over the 12 years between 1990 and 2002

97. 12 feet   **99.** $V(t) = 3165 - 125t$

101. b; The slope is -20, which represents the decrease in the amount of the loan each week. The y-intercept is $(0, 200)$ which represents the original amount of the loan.

102. c; The slope is 2, which represents the hourly wage per unit produced. The y-intercept is $(0, 8.50)$ which represents the initial hourly wage.

103. a; The slope is 0.32, which represents the increase in travel cost for each mile driven. The y-intercept is $(0, 30)$ which represents the amount per day for food.

59. $y = 0.4x + 0.2$

61. $y = -1$

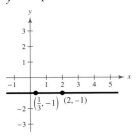

CHAPTER 1

104. d; The slope is -100, which represents the decrease in the value of the word processor each year. The y-intercept is $(0, 750)$ which represents the initial purchase price of the computer.

105. $y = 0.4825t - 2.2325$; $y(18) \approx \$6.45$; $y(20) \approx \$7.42$

107. $V = -175t + 875$

109. (a) $y(t) = 179.5t + 40,571$
(b) $y(8) = 42,007$; $y(10) = 42,366$ (c) $m = 179.5$

111. $S = 0.85L$

113. (a) $C = 16.75t + 36,500$ (b) $R = 27t$
(c) $P = 10.25t - 36,500$ (d) $t \approx 3561$ hours

115. (a) (b) $y = 8x + 50$

(c) (d) $m = 8$, 8 meters

117. $C = 0.38x + 120$

119. (a) and (b)

(c) Answers will vary. Sample answer:
$y = 11.72x - 14.1$
(d) Answers will vary. Sample answer: The y-intercept indicates that initially there were -14.1 million subscribers which doesn't make sense in the context of this problem. Each year, the number of cellular phone subscribers increases by 11.72 million.
(e) The model is accurate.
(f) Answers will vary. Sample answer: 196.9 million

121. False. The slope with the greatest magnitude corresponds to the steepest line.

123. Find the distance between each two points and use the Pythagorean Theorem.

125. No. The slope cannot be determined without knowing the scale on the y-axis. The slopes could be the same.

127. V-intercept: initial cost; Slope: annual depreciation

129. d **130.** c **131.** a **132.** b

133. -1 **135.** $\frac{7}{2}, 7$ **137.** No solution

139. Answers will vary.

Section 1.4 *(page 48)*

Vocabulary Check *(page 48)*

1. domain; range; function
2. verbally; numerically; graphically; algebraically
3. independent; dependent **4.** piecewise-defined
5. implied domain **6.** difference quotient

1. Yes **3.** No

5. Yes, each input value has exactly one output value.

7. No, the input values of 7 and 10 each have two different output values.

9. (a) Function
(b) Not a function, because the element 1 in A corresponds to two elements, -2 and 1, in B.
(c) Function
(d) Not a function, because not every element in A is matched with an element in B.

11. Each is a function. For each year there corresponds one and only one circulation.

13. Not a function **15.** Function **17.** Function

19. Not a function **21.** Function **23.** Not a function

25. (a) -1 (b) -9 (c) $2x - 5$

27. (a) 36π (b) $\frac{9}{2}\pi$ (c) $\frac{32}{3}\pi r^3$

29. (a) 1 (b) 2.5 (c) $3 - 2|x|$

31. (a) $-\dfrac{1}{9}$ (b) Undefined (c) $\dfrac{1}{y^2 + 6y}$

33. (a) 1 (b) -1 (c) $\dfrac{|x - 1|}{x - 1}$

35. (a) -1 (b) 2 (c) 6

37. (a) -7 (b) 4 (c) 9

39.

x	-2	-1	0	1	2
$f(x)$	1	-2	-3	-2	1

41.

t	-5	-4	-3	-2	-1
$h(t)$	1	$\frac{1}{2}$	0	$\frac{1}{2}$	1

43.

x	-2	-1	0	1	2
$f(x)$	5	$\frac{9}{2}$	4	1	0

45. 5 **47.** $\frac{4}{3}$ **49.** ± 3 **51.** $0, \pm 1$ **53.** $2, -1$

55. $3, 0$ **57.** All real numbers

59. All real numbers t except $t = 0$

61. All real numbers y such that $y \geq 0$

63. All real numbers x such that $-1 \leq x \leq 1$

65. All real numbers x except $x = 0, -2$

67. All real numbers s such that $s \geq 1$ except $s = 4$

69. All real numbers x such that $x > 0$

71. $\{(-2, 4), (-1, 1), (0, 0), (1, 1), (2, 4)\}$

73. $\{(-2, 4), (-1, 3), (0, 2), (1, 3), (2, 4)\}$

75. $g(x) = cx^2$; $c = -2$ **76.** $f(x) = cx$; $c = \frac{1}{4}$

77. $r(x) = \dfrac{c}{x}$; $c = 32$ **78.** $h(x) = c\sqrt{|x|}$; $c = 3$

79. $3 + h$, $h \neq 0$ **81.** $3x^2 + 3xh + h^2 + 3$, $h \neq 0$

83. $-\dfrac{x + 3}{9x^2}$, $x \neq 3$ **85.** $\dfrac{\sqrt{5x} - 5}{x - 5}$ **87.** $A = \dfrac{P^2}{16}$

89. (a) The maximum volume is 1024 cubic centimeters.

(b)

Yes, V is a function of x.

(c) $V = x(24 - 2x)^2$, $0 < x < 12$

91. $A = \dfrac{x^2}{2(x - 2)}$, $x > 2$

93. Yes, the ball will be at a height of 6 feet.

95. 1990: \$27,300
1991: \$28,052
1992: \$29,168
1993: \$30,648
1994: \$32,492
1995: \$34,700
1996: \$37,272
1997: \$40,208
1998: \$41,300
1999: \$43,800
2000: \$46,300
2001: \$48,800
2002: \$51,300

97. (a) $C = 12.30x + 98,000$
(b) $R = 17.98x$
(c) $P = 5.68x - 98,000$

99. (a) $R = \dfrac{240n - n^2}{20}$, $n \geq 80$

(b)

n	90	100	110	120	130	140	150
$R(n)$	\$675	\$700	\$715	\$720	\$715	\$700	\$675

The revenue is maximum when 120 people take the trip.

101. (a)

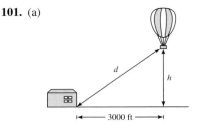

(b) $h = \sqrt{d^2 - 3000^2}$, $d \geq 3000$

103. False. The range is $[-1, \infty)$.

105. The domain is the set of inputs of the function, and the range is the set of outputs.

107. (a) Yes. The amount you pay in sales tax will increase as the price of the item purchased increases.
(b) No. The length of time that you study will not necessarily determine how well you do on an exam.

109. $\frac{15}{8}$ **111.** $-\frac{1}{5}$ **113.** $2x - 3y - 11 = 0$

115. $10x + 9y + 15 = 0$

Section 1.5   *(page 61)*

Vocabulary Check   *(page 61)*

1. ordered pairs   2. Vertical Line Test
3. zeros   4. decreasing
5. maximum   6. average rate of change; secant
7. odd   8. even

1. Domain: $(-\infty, -1]$, $[1, \infty)$ **3.** Domain: $[-4, 4]$
Range: $[0, \infty)$ Range: $[0, 4]$

5. (a) 0   (b) -1 (c) 0   (d) -2

7. (a) -3 (b) 0   (c) 1   (d) -3 **9.** Function

11. Not a function   **13.** Function   **15.** $-\frac{5}{2}, 6$

17. 0   **19.** $0, \pm\sqrt{2}$ **21.** $\pm\frac{1}{2}, 6$ **23.** $\frac{1}{2}$

25.

$-\frac{5}{3}$

27.

$-\frac{11}{2}$

29.

$\frac{1}{3}$

31. Increasing on $(-\infty, \infty)$

33. Increasing on $(-\infty, 0)$ and $(2, \infty)$
Decreasing on $(0, 2)$

CHAPTER 1

35. Increasing on $(-\infty, 0)$ and $(2, \infty)$; Constant on $(0, 2)$

37. Increasing on $(1, \infty)$; Decreasing on $(-\infty, -1)$
Constant on $(-1, 1)$

39.

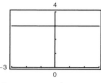

Constant on $(-\infty, \infty)$

41.

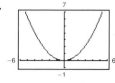

Decreasing on $(-\infty, 0)$
Increasing on $(0, \infty)$

43.

Increasing on $(-\infty, 0)$
Decreasing on $(0, \infty)$

45.

Decreasing on $(-\infty, 1)$

47.

Increasing on $(0, \infty)$

49.

Relative minimum:
$(1, -9)$

51.

Relative maximum:
$(1.5, 0.25)$

53.

Relative maximum: $(-1.79, 8.21)$
Relative minimum: $(1.12, -4.06)$

55.

$(-\infty, 4]$

57.

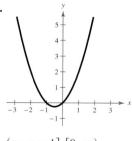

$(-\infty, -1], [0, \infty)$

59.

$[1, \infty)$

61.

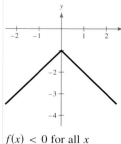

$f(x) < 0$ for all x

63. The average rate of change from $x_1 = 0$ to $x_2 = 3$ is -2.

65. The average rate of change from $x_1 = 1$ to $x_2 = 5$ is 18.

67. The average rate of change from $x_1 = 1$ to $x_2 = 3$ is 0.

69. The average rate of change from $x_1 = 3$ to $x_2 = 11$ is $-\frac{1}{4}$.

71. Even; y-axis symmetry   **73.** Odd; origin symmetry

75. Neither even nor odd; no symmetry

77. $h = -x^2 + 4x - 3$ **79.** $h = 2x - x^2$

81. $L = \frac{1}{2}y^2$ **83.** $L = 4 - y^2$

85. (a)

(b) 30 watts

87. (a) Ten thousands   (b) Ten millions   (c) Percents

89. (a)

(b) The average rate of change from 2002 to 2007 is 408.56. The estimated revenue is increasing each year at a fast pace.

91. (a) $s = -16t^2 + 64t + 6$

(b)

(c) Average rate of change $= 16$

(d) The slope of the secant line is positive.

(e) Secant line: $16t + 6$

(f)

93. (a) $s = -16t^2 + 120t$

(b)
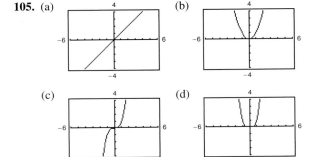

(c) Average rate of change $= -8$

(d) The slope of the secant line is negative.

(e) Secant line: $-8t + 240$

(f)

95. (a) $s = -16t^2 + 120$

(b)

(c) Average rate of change $= -32$

(d) The slope of the secant line is negative.

(e) Secant line: $-32t + 120$

(f)

97. False. The function $f(x) = \sqrt{x^2 + 1}$ has a domain of all real numbers.

99. (a) Even. The graph is a reflection in the x-axis.

(b) Even. The graph is a reflection in the y-axis.

(c) Even. The graph is a vertical translation of f.

(d) Neither. The graph is a horizontal translation of f.

101. (a) $\left(\frac{3}{2}, 4\right)$ (b) $\left(\frac{3}{2}, -4\right)$

103. (a) $(-4, 9)$ (b) $(-4, -9)$

105. (a) (b)

(c) (d)

(e)

(f)

All the graphs pass through the origin. The graphs of the odd powers of x are symmetric with respect to the origin, and the graphs of the even powers are symmetric with respect to the y-axis. As the powers increase, the graphs become flatter in the interval $-1 < x < 1$.

107. $0, 10$ **109.** $0, \pm 1$

111. (a) 37 (b) -28 (c) $5x - 43$

113. (a) -9 (b) $2\sqrt{7} - 9$

(c) The given value is not in the domain of the function.

115. $h + 4, \ h \neq 0$

Section 1.6   *(page 71)*

Vocabulary Check   *(page 71)*

1. g   **2.** i   **3.** h   **4.** a   **5.** b

6. e   **7.** f   **8.** c   **9.** d

1. (a) $f(x) = -2x + 6$ **3.** (a) $f(x) = -3x + 11$

(b) (b)
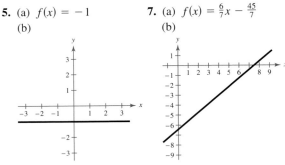

5. (a) $f(x) = -1$ **7.** (a) $f(x) = \frac{6}{7}x - \frac{45}{7}$

(b) (b)

9. **11.**

13.

15.

17.

19.

21.

23.

25.

27.

29. (a) 2   (b) 2   (c) −4   (d) 3
31. (a) 1   (b) 3   (c) 7   (d) −19
33. (a) 6   (b) −11   (c) 6   (d) −22
35. (a) −10   (b) −4   (c) −1   (d) 41

37.

39.

41.

43.

45.

47.

49.

51. (a)

(b) Domain: $(-\infty, \infty)$;
Range: $[0, 2)$

(c) Sawtooth pattern

53. (a) $f(x) = |x|$ (b) $g(x) = |x + 2| - 1$
55. (a) $f(x) = x^3$ (b) $g(x) = (x - 1)^3 - 2$
57. (a) $f(x) = 2$ (b) $g(x) = 2$
59. (a) $f(x) = x$ (b) $g(x) = x - 2$

61. (a)

(b) $5.64

63. (a)

(b) $50.25

65. (a) $W(30) = 360$; $W(40) = 480$;
$W(45) = 570$; $W(50) = 660$

(b) $W(h) = \begin{cases} 12h, & 0 < h \le 45 \\ 18(h - 45) + 540, & h > 45 \end{cases}$

67. (a) $f(x) = \begin{cases} 0.505x^2 - 1.47x + 6.3, & 1 \le x \le 6 \\ -1.97x + 26.3, & 6 < x \le 12 \end{cases}$

Answers will vary. Sample answer: The domain is determined by inspection of a graph of the data with the two models.

(b)

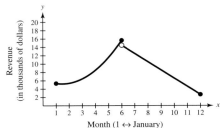

(c) $f(5) = 11.575, f(11) = 4.63$; These values represent the revenue for the months of May and November, respectively.

(d) These values are quite close to the actual data values.

69. False. A piecewise-defined function is a function that is defined by two or more equations over a specified domain. That domain may or may not include x- and y-intercepts.

71. $f(x) = \begin{cases} -\frac{4}{3}x + 6, & 0 \le x \le 3 \\ -\frac{2}{5}x + \frac{16}{5}, & 3 < x \le 8 \end{cases}$

73. $x \le 1$

75. Neither

Section 1.7 *(page 79)*

1. (a)

(b)

(c)

3. (a)

(b)

(c)

5. (a)

(b)

(c)

(d)

(e)

(f)

CHAPTER 1

(g)

7. (a)

(b)

(c)

(d)

(e)

(f)

(g)

9. (a) $y = x^2 - 1$ (b) $y = 1 - (x + 1)^2$
(c) $y = -(x - 2)^2 + 6$ (d) $y = (x - 5)^2 - 3$
11. (a) $y = |x| + 5$ (b) $y = -|x + 3|$
(c) $y = |x - 2| - 4$ (d) $y = -|x - 6| - 1$
13. Horizontal shift of $y = x^3$; $y = (x - 2)^3$
15. Reflection in the x-axis of $y = x^2$; $y = -x^2$
17. Reflection in the x-axis and vertical shift of $y = \sqrt{x}$;
$y = 1 - \sqrt{x}$
19. (a) $f(x) = x^2$
(b) Reflection in the x-axis, and vertical shift 12 units upward, of $f(x) = x^2$
(c)   (d) $g(x) = 12 - f(x)$

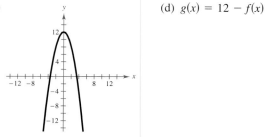

21. (a) $f(x) = x^3$
(b) Vertical shift seven units upward, of $f(x) = x^3$
(c)   (d) $g(x) = f(x) + 7$

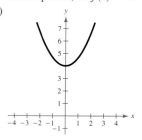

23. (a) $f(x) = x^2$
(b) Vertical shrink of two-thirds, and vertical shift four units upward, of $f(x) = x^2$
(c)   (d) $g(x) = \frac{2}{3}f(x) + 4$

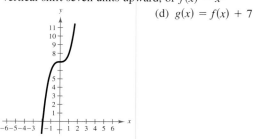

25. (a) $f(x) = x^2$
(b) Reflection in the x-axis, horizontal shift five units to the left, and vertical shift two units upward, of $f(x) = x^2$

(c)

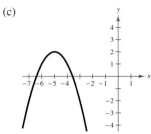

(d) $g(x) = 2 - f(x + 5)$

(c)

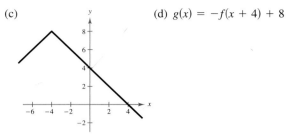

(d) $g(x) = -f(x + 4) + 8$

27. (a) $f(x) = \sqrt{x}$
(b) Horizontal shrink of $\frac{1}{3}$, of $f(x) = \sqrt{x}$
(c)

(d) $g(x) = f(3x)$

29. (a) $f(x) = x^3$
(b) Vertical shift two units upward, and horizontal shift one unit to the right, of $f(x) = x^3$
(c)

(d) $g(x) = f(x - 1) + 2$

31. (a) $f(x) = |x|$
(b) Reflection in the x-axis, and vertical shift two units downward, of $f(x) = |x|$
(c)

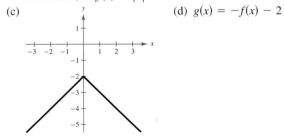

(d) $g(x) = -f(x) - 2$

33. (a) $f(x) = |x|$
(b) Reflection in the x-axis, horizontal shift four units to the left, and vertical shift eight units upward, of $f(x) = |x|$

35. (a) $f(x) = [\![x]\!]$
(b) Reflection in the x-axis, and vertical shift three units upward, of $f(x) = [\![x]\!]$
(c)

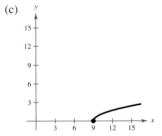

(d) $g(x) = 3 - f(x)$

37. (a) $f(x) = \sqrt{x}$
(b) Horizontal shift of nine units to the right, of $f(x) = \sqrt{x}$
(c)

(d) $g(x) = f(x - 9)$

39. (a) $f(x) = \sqrt{x}$
(b) Reflection in the y-axis, horizontal shift of seven units to the right, and vertical shift two units downward, of $f(x) = \sqrt{x}$
(c)

(d) $g(x) = f(7 - x) - 2$

41. (a) $f(x) = \sqrt{x}$
(b) Horizontal stretch, and vertical shift four units downward, of $f(x) = \sqrt{x}$

CHAPTER 1

(c)

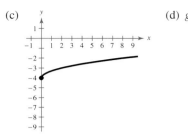

(d) $g(x) = f\left(\frac{1}{2}x\right) - 4$

43. $f(x) = (x - 2)^2 - 8$ **45.** $f(x) = (x - 13)^3$
47. $f(x) = -|x| - 10$ **49.** $f(x) = -\sqrt{-x + 6}$
51. (a) $y = -3x^2$ (b) $y = 4x^2 + 3$
53. (a) $y = -\frac{1}{2}|x|$ (b) $y = 3|x| - 3$
55. Vertical stretch of $y = x^3$; $y = 2x^3$
57. Reflection in the x-axis and vertical shrink of $y = x^2$;
$y = -\frac{1}{2}x^2$
59. Reflection in the y-axis and vertical shrink of $y = \sqrt{x}$;
$y = \frac{1}{2}\sqrt{-x}$
61. $y = -(x - 2)^3 + 2$ **63.** $y = -\sqrt{x} - 3$
65. (a)

(b)

(c)

(d)

(e)

(f)

67. (a) Horizontal stretch of 0.035 and a vertical shift of 20.6 units upward.

(b) 0.77-billion-gallon increase in fuel usage by trucks each year
(c) $f(t) = 20.6 + 0.035(t + 10)^2$. The graph is shifted 10 units to the left.
(d) 52.1 billion gallons. Yes.
69. True. $|-x| = |x|$
71. (a) $g(t) = \frac{3}{4}f(t)$ (b) $g(t) = f(t) + 10{,}000$
(c) $g(t) = f(t - 2)$

73. $(-2, 0), (-1, 1), (0, 2)$ **75.** $\dfrac{4}{x(1 - x)}$

77. $\dfrac{3x - 2}{x(x - 1)}$ **79.** $\dfrac{(x - 4)\sqrt{x^2 - 4}}{x^2 - 4}$

81. $5(x - 3), x \neq -3$
83. (a) 38   (b) $\frac{57}{4}$ (c) $x^2 - 12x + 38$
85. All real numbers x except $x = 1$
87. All real numbers x such that $-9 \leq x \leq 9$

Section 1.8   *(page 89)*

Vocabulary Check   *(page 89)*

1. addition; subtraction; multiplication; division
2. composition   **3.** $g(x)$ **4.** inner; outer

1.

3.

5. (a) $2x$ (b) 4   (c) $x^2 - 4$
(d) $\dfrac{x + 2}{x - 2}$; all real numbers x except $x = 2$
7. (a) $x^2 + 4x - 5$ (b) $x^2 - 4x + 5$ (c) $4x^3 - 5x^2$
(d) $\dfrac{x^2}{4x - 5}$; all real numbers x except $x = \dfrac{5}{4}$

9. (a) $x^2 + 6 + \sqrt{1 - x}$ (b) $x^2 + 6 - \sqrt{1 - x}$

(c) $(x^2 + 6)\sqrt{1 - x}$

(d) $\dfrac{(x^2 + 6)\sqrt{1 - x}}{1 - x}$; all real numbers x such that $x < 1$

11. (a) $\dfrac{x + 1}{x^2}$ (b) $\dfrac{x - 1}{x^2}$ (c) $\dfrac{1}{x^3}$

(d) x; all real numbers x except $x = 0$

13. 3   **15.** 5   **17.** $9t^2 - 3t + 5$ **19.** 74

21. 26   **23.** $\frac{3}{5}$

25.

27.

29.

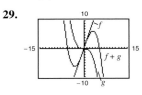

$f(x),\ g(x)$

31. (a) $(x - 1)^2$ (b) $x^2 - 1$ (c) x^4

33. (a) x (b) x (c) $\sqrt[3]{\sqrt[3]{x - 1} - 1}$

35. (a) $\sqrt{x^2 + 4}$ (b) $x + 4$

Domains of f and $g \circ f$: $x \geq -4$

Domains of g and $f \circ g$: all real numbers

37. (a) $x + 1$ (b) $\sqrt{x^2 + 1}$

Domains of f and $g \circ f$: all real numbers

Domains of g and $f \circ g$: all real numbers x such that $x \geq 0$

39. (a) $|x + 6|$ (b) $|x| + 6$

Domains of f, g, $f \circ g$, and $g \circ f$: all real numbers

41. (a) $\dfrac{1}{x + 3}$ (b) $\dfrac{1}{x} + 3$

Domains of f and $g \circ f$: all real numbers x except $x = 0$

Domains of g: all real numbers

Domains of $f \circ g$: all real numbers x except $x = -3$

43. (a) 3   (b) 0   **45.** (a) 0   (b) 4

47. $f(x) = x^2,\ g(x) = 2x + 1$

49. $f(x) = \sqrt[3]{x},\ g(x) = x^2 - 4$

51. $f(x) = \dfrac{1}{x},\ g(x) = x + 2$

53. $f(x) = \dfrac{x + 3}{4 + x},\ g(x) = -x^2$

55. $T = \frac{3}{4}x + \frac{1}{15}x^2$

57. (a) $c(t) = \dfrac{p(t) + b(t) - d(t)}{p(t)} \times 100$

(b) $c(5)$ is the population change in the year 2005.

59. (a) $(A + N)(t) = 5.31t^2 - 102.0t + 1338$

$(A + N)(4) = 1014.96$

$(A + N)(8) = 861.84$

$(A + N)(12) = 878.64$

(b) $(A - N)(t) = 1.41t^2 - 17.6t + 132$

$(A - N)(4) = 84.16$

$(A - N)(8) = 81.44$

$(A - N)(12) = 123.84$

61. (a) $y_1 = 10.20t + 92.7$

$y_2 = 3.357t^2 - 26.46t + 379.5$

$y_3 = -0.465t^2 + 9.71t + 7.4$

(b) $y_1 + y_2 + y_3 = 2.892t^2 - 6.55t + 479.6$; this amount represents the amount spent on health care in the United States.

(c)

(d) In 2008, \$1298.708 billion is estimated to be spent on health services and supplies, and in 2010, \$1505.4 billion is estimated.

63. (a) $r(x) = \dfrac{x}{2}$ (b) $A(r) = \pi r^2$

(c) $(A \circ r)(x) = \pi\left(\dfrac{x}{2}\right)^2$; $(A \circ r)(x)$ represents the area of the circular base of the tank on the square foundation with side length x.

65. (a) $N(T(t)) = 30(3t^2 + 2t + 20)$ This represents the number of bacteria in the food as a function of time.

(b) $t = 2.846$ hours

67. $g(f(x))$ represents 3 percent of an amount over \$500,000.

69. False. $(f \circ g)(x) = 6x + 1$ and $(g \circ f)(x) = 6x + 6$

71. Answers will vary.   **73.** 3   **75.** $\dfrac{-4}{x(x + h)}$

CHAPTER 1

77. $3x - y - 10 = 0$ **79.** $3x + 2y - 22 = 0$

Section 1.9   *(page 99)*

1. $f^{-1}(x) = \frac{1}{6}x$ **3.** $f^{-1}(x) = x - 9$

5. $f^{-1}(x) = \dfrac{x - 1}{3}$ **7.** $f^{-1}(x) = x^3$

9. c   **10.** b   **11.** a   **12.** d

13. (a) $f(g(x)) = f\left(\dfrac{x}{2}\right) = 2\left(\dfrac{x}{2}\right) = x$

$g(f(x)) = g(2x) = \dfrac{(2x)}{2} = x$

(b)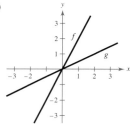

15. (a) $f(g(x)) = f\left(\dfrac{x - 1}{7}\right) = 7\left(\dfrac{x - 1}{7}\right) + 1 = x$

$g(f(x)) = g(7x + 1) = \dfrac{(7x + 1) - 1}{7} = x$

(b)

17. (a) $f(g(x)) = f\left(\sqrt[3]{8x}\right) = \dfrac{\left(\sqrt[3]{8x}\right)^3}{8} = x$

$g(f(x)) = g\left(\dfrac{x^3}{8}\right) = \sqrt[3]{8\left(\dfrac{x^3}{8}\right)} = x$

(b)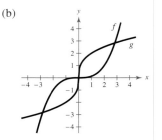

19. (a) $f(g(x)) = f(x^2 + 4), \ x \geq 0$

$= \sqrt{(x^2 + 4) - 4} = x$

$g(f(x)) = g\left(\sqrt{x - 4}\right)$

$= \left(\sqrt{x - 4}\right)^2 + 4 = x$

(b)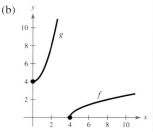

21. (a) $f(g(x)) = f\left(\sqrt{9 - x}\right), \ x \leq 9$

$= 9 - \left(\sqrt{9 - x}\right)^2 = x$

$g(f(x)) = g(9 - x^2), \ x \geq 0$

$= \sqrt{9 - (9 - x^2)} = x$

(b)

23. (a) $f(g(x)) = f\left(-\dfrac{5x + 1}{x - 1}\right) = \dfrac{-\left(\dfrac{5x + 1}{x - 1}\right) - 1}{-\left(\dfrac{5x + 1}{x - 1}\right) + 5}$

$= \dfrac{-5x - 1 - x + 1}{-5x - 1 + 5x - 5} = x$

$g(f(x)) = g\left(\dfrac{x - 1}{x + 5}\right) = \dfrac{-5\left(\dfrac{x - 1}{x + 5}\right) - 1}{\dfrac{x - 1}{x + 5} - 1}$

$= \dfrac{-5x + 5 - x - 5}{x - 1 - x - 5} = x$

(b)

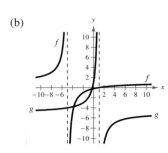

25. No **27.**

x	-2	0	2	4	6	8
$f^{-1}(x)$	-2	-1	0	1	2	3

29. Yes **31.** No

33.

The function has an inverse.

35.

The function does not have an inverse.

37.

The function does not have an inverse.

39. (a) $f^{-1}(x) = \dfrac{x + 3}{2}$

(b)

(c) The graph of f^{-1} is the reflection of the graph of f in the line $y = x$.

(d) The domains and ranges of f and f^{-1} are all real numbers.

41. (a) $f^{-1}(x) = \sqrt[5]{x + 2}$

(b)

(c) The graph of f^{-1} is the reflection of the graph of f in the line $y = x$.

(d) The domains and ranges of f and f^{-1} are all real numbers.

43. (a) $f^{-1}(x) = x^2, \ x \ge 0$

(b)

(c) The graph of f^{-1} is the reflection of the graph of f in the line $y = x$.

(d) The domains and ranges of f and f^{-1} are all real numbers x such that $x \ge 0$.

45. (a) $f^{-1}(x) = \sqrt{4 - x^2}, \ 0 \le x \le 2$

(b)

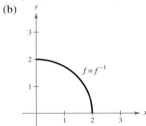

(c) The graph of f^{-1} is the same as the graph of f.

(d) The domains and ranges of f and f^{-1} are all real numbers x such that $0 \le x \le 2$.

47. (a) $f^{-1}(x) = \dfrac{4}{x}$

(b)

(c) The graph of f^{-1} is the same as the graph of f.

(d) The domains and ranges of f and f^{-1} are all real numbers x except $x = 0$.

49. (a) $f^{-1}(x) = \dfrac{2x + 1}{x - 1}$

CHAPTER 1

(b)

(c) The graph of f^{-1} is the reflection of the graph of f in the line $y = x$.

(d) The domain of f and the range of f^{-1} are all real numbers x except $x = 2$. The domain of f^{-1} and the range of f are all real numbers x except $x = 1$.

51. (a) $f^{-1}(x) = x^3 + 1$

(b)

(c) The graph of f^{-1} is the reflection of the graph of f in the line $y = x$.

(d) The domains and ranges of f and f^{-1} are all real numbers.

53. (a) $f^{-1}(x) = \dfrac{5x - 4}{6 - 4x}$

(b)

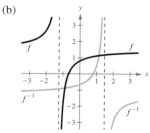

(c) The graph of f^{-1} is the reflection of the graph of f in the line $y = x$.

(d) The domain of f and the range of f^{-1} are all real numbers x except $x = -\frac{5}{4}$. The domain of f^{-1} and the range of f are all real numbers x except $x = \frac{3}{2}$.

55. No inverse   **57.** $g^{-1}(x) = 8x$ **59.** No inverse

61. $f^{-1}(x) = \sqrt{x} - 3$ **63.** No inverse

65. No inverse   **67.** $f^{-1}(x) = \dfrac{x^2 - 3}{2}, \quad x \geq 0$

69. 32   **71.** 600   **73.** $2\sqrt[3]{x + 3}$

75. $\dfrac{x + 1}{2}$ **77.** $\dfrac{x + 1}{2}$

79. (a) $f^{-1}(108{,}209) = 11$

(b) f^{-1} represents the year for a given number of households in the United States.

(c) $y = 1578.68t + 90{,}183.63$

(d) $f^{-1} = \dfrac{t - 90{,}183.63}{1578.68}$ (e) $f^{-1}(117{,}022) = 17$

(f) $f^{-1}(108{,}209) = 11.418$; the results are similar.

81. (a) Yes

(b) f^{-1} yields the year for a given number of miles traveled by motor vehicles.

(c) $f^{-1}(2632) = 8$

(d) No. $f(t)$ would not pass the Horizontal Line Test.

83. (a) $y = \sqrt{\dfrac{x - 245.50}{0.03}}, \quad 245.5 < x < 545.5$

$x = $ degrees Fahrenheit; $y = \%$ load

(b)

(c) $0 < x < 92.11$

85. False. $f(x) = x^2$ has no inverse.

87. Answers will vary.

89.

x	1	3	4	6
y	1	2	6	7

x	1	2	6	7
$f^{-1}(x)$	1	3	4	6

91.

x	-2	-1	3	4
y	6	0	-2	-3

x	-3	-2	0	6
$f^{-1}(x)$	4	3	-1	-2

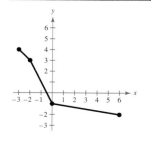

93. $k = \frac{1}{4}$ **95.** ± 8 **97.** $\frac{3}{2}$ **99.** $3 \pm \sqrt{5}$

101. $5, -\frac{10}{3}$ **103.** 16, 18

Section 1.10   *(page 109)*

Vocabulary Check   *(page 109)*

1. variation; regression   **2.** sum of square differences
3. correlation coefficient   **4.** directly proportional
5. constant of variation   **6.** directly proportional
7. inverse   **8.** combined   **9.** jointly proportional

1.

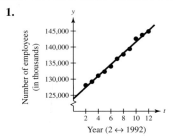

The model is a good fit for the actual data.

3.

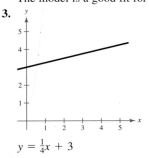

$y = \frac{1}{4}x + 3$

5.

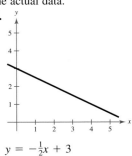

$y = -\frac{1}{2}x + 3$

7. (a) and (b)

$y = t + 130$
(c) $y = 1.03t + 130.3$ (d) The models are similar.
(e) Part (b): 238 feet; Part (c): 241.51 feet
(f) Answers will vary.

9. (a)

(b) $S = 38.4t + 224$

(c)

The model is a good fit.
(d) 2005: $800 million; 2007: $876.8 million
(e) Each year the annual gross ticket sales for Broadway shows in New York City increase by $38.4 million.

11. Inversely

13.

x	2	4	6	8	10
$y = kx^2$	4	16	36	64	100

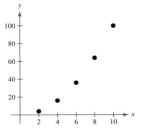

15.

x	2	4	6	8	10
$y = kx^2$	2	8	18	32	50

CHAPTER 1

17.

x	2	4	6	8	10
$y = k/x^2$	$\frac{1}{2}$	$\frac{1}{8}$	$\frac{1}{18}$	$\frac{1}{32}$	$\frac{1}{50}$

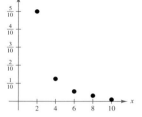

19.

x	2	4	6	8	10
$y = k/x^2$	$\frac{5}{2}$	$\frac{5}{8}$	$\frac{5}{18}$	$\frac{5}{32}$	$\frac{1}{10}$

21. $y = \dfrac{5}{x}$ **23.** $y = -\dfrac{7}{10}x$ **25.** $y = \dfrac{12}{5}x$

27. $y = 205x$ **29.** $I = 0.035P$

31. Model: $y = \frac{33}{13}x$; 25.4 centimeters, 50.8 centimeters

33. $y = 0.0368x$; \$7360

35. (a) 0.05 meter   (b) $176\frac{2}{3}$ newtons

37. 39.47 pounds   **39.** $A = kr^2$ **41.** $y = \dfrac{k}{x^2}$

43. $F = \dfrac{kg}{r^2}$ **45.** $P = \dfrac{k}{V}$ **47.** $F = \dfrac{km_1 m_2}{r^2}$

49. The area of a triangle is jointly proportional to its base and height.

51. The volume of a sphere varies directly as the cube of its radius.

53. Average speed is directly proportional to the distance and inversely proportional to the time.

55. $A = \pi r^2$ **57.** $y = \dfrac{28}{x}$ **59.** $F = 14rs^3$

61. $z = \dfrac{2x^2}{3y}$ **63.** ≈ 0.61 mile per hour   **65.** 506 feet

67. 1470 joules   **69.** The velocity is increased by one-third.

71. (a)

Temperature (in °C) vs Depth (in meters)

(b) Yes. $k_1 = 4200$, $k_2 = 3800$, $k_3 = 4200$, $k_4 = 4800$, $k_5 = 4500$

(c) $C = \dfrac{4300}{d}$

(d) [graph]   (e) ≈ 1433 meters

73. (a) [graph]   (b) 0.2857 microwatt per square centimeter

75. False. y will increase if k is positive and y will decrease if k is negative.

77. True. The closer the value of $|r|$ is to 1, the better the fit.

79. The accuracy is questionable when based on such limited data.

81. $x > 5$ **83.** $-4 < x < 5$

85. (a) $-\frac{5}{3}$ (b) $-\frac{7}{3}$ (c) 21   **87.** Answers will vary.

Review Exercises   *(page 117)*

1. [graph]   **3.** Quadrant IV

5. (a)

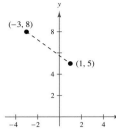

(b) 5

(c) $\left(-1, \frac{13}{2}\right)$

7. (a)

(b) 9.9

(c) $(2.8, 4.1)$

9. $(2, 5), (4, 5), (2, 0), (4, 0)$ **11.** $656.45 million

13. Radius $\approx$ 22.5 centimeters

15.

x	-2	-1	0	1	2
y	-11	-8	-5	-2	1

17.

x	-1	0	1	2	3	4
y	4	0	-2	-2	0	4

19.

21.

23.

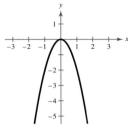

25. x-intercept: $\left(-\frac{7}{2}, 0\right)$
y-intercept: $(0, 7)$

27. x-intercepts: $(1, 0), (5, 0)$
y-intercept: $(0, 5)$

29. No symmetry

31. y-axis symmetry

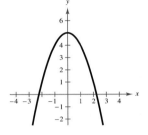

33. No symmetry

35. No symmetry

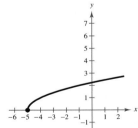

37. Center: $(0, 0)$;
Radius: 3

39. Center: $(-2, 0)$;
Radius: 4

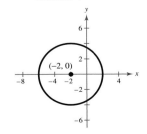

41. Center: $\left(\frac{1}{2}, -1\right)$; Radius: 6

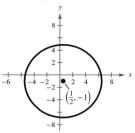

43. $(x - 2)^2 + (y + 3)^2 = 13$

45. (a)

x	0	4	8	12	16	20
F	0	5	10	15	20	25

(b)

(c) 12.5 pounds

47. slope: 0
y-intercept: 6

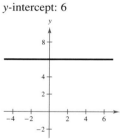

49. slope: 3
y-intercept: 13

51.

$m = -\frac{1}{2}$

53.

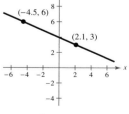

$m = -\frac{5}{11}$

55. $y = \frac{3}{2}x - 5$

57. $y = -\frac{1}{2}x + 2$

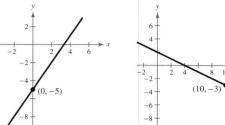

59. $x = 0$ **61.** $y = -\frac{4}{3}x + \frac{8}{3}$

63. (a) $y = \frac{5}{4}x - \frac{23}{4}$ (b) $y = -\frac{4}{5}x + \frac{2}{5}$

65. $V = 850t + 7400$, $6 \le t \le 11$ **67.** No **69.** Yes

71. (a) 5 (b) 17 (c) $t^4 + 1$ (d) $t^2 + 2t + 2$

73. All real numbers x such that $-5 \le x \le 5$

75. All real numbers x except $x = 3, -2$

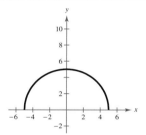

77. (a) 16 feet per second (b) 1.5 seconds
(c) -16 feet per second

79. $4x + 2h + 3$, $h \ne 0$ **81.** Function

83. Not a function **85.** $\frac{7}{3}$, 3 **87.** $-\frac{3}{8}$

89. Increasing on $(0, \infty)$
Decreasing on $(-\infty, -1)$
Constant on $(-1, 0)$

91.

93.

95. 4   **97.** $\dfrac{1 - \sqrt{2}}{2}$ **99.** Neither even nor odd

101. Odd

103. $f(x) = -3x$ **105.**

107.   **109.**

111.   **113.**

115. $y = x^3$

117. (a) $f(x) = x^2$

(b) Vertical shift of nine units downward

(c)

(d) $h(x) = f(x) - 9$

119. (a) $f(x) = \sqrt{x}$

(b) Horizontal shift of seven units to the right

(c)

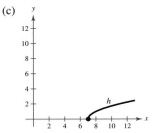

(d) $h(x) = f(x - 7)$

121. (a) $f(x) = x^2$

(b) Reflection in the x-axis, horizontal shift of three units to the left, and vertical shift of one unit upward

(c)

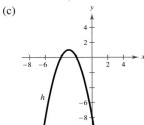

(d) $h(x) = -f(x + 3) + 1$

123. (a) $f(x) = [\![x]\!]$

(b) Reflection in the x-axis and vertical shift of six units upward

(c)

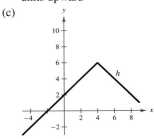

(d) $h(x) = -f(x) + 6$

125. (a) $f(x) = |x|$

(b) Reflections in the x-axis and the y-axis, horizontal shift of four units to the right, and vertical shift of six units upward

(c)

(d) $h(x) = -f(-x + 4) + 6$

CHAPTER 1

127. (a) $f(x) = [\![x]\!]$
  (b) Horizontal shift of nine units to the right and vertical stretch
  (c)
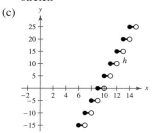
  (d) $h(x) = 5f(x - 9)$

129. (a) $f(x) = \sqrt{x}$
  (b) Reflection in the x-axis, vertical stretch, and horizontal shift of four units to the right
  (c)
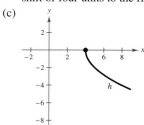
  (d) $h(x) = -2f(x - 4)$

131. (a) $x^2 + 2x + 2$ (b) $x^2 - 2x + 4$
  (c) $2x^3 - x^2 + 6x - 3$
  (d) $\dfrac{x^2 + 3}{2x - 1}$; all real numbers x except $x = \dfrac{1}{2}$

133. (a) $x - \frac{8}{3}$ (b) $x - 8$
  Domains of $f, g, f \circ g$, and $g \circ f$: all real numbers

135. $f(x) = x^3, g(x) = 6x - 5$

137. (a) $(v + d)(t) = -36.04t^2 + 804.6t - 1112$
  (b)

  (c) $(v + d)(10) = 3330$

139. $f^{-1}(x) = x + 7$ **141.** The function has an inverse.

143.

The function has an inverse.

145.

The function has an inverse.

147. (a) $f^{-1}(x) = 2x + 6$
  (b)
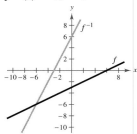
  (c) The graph of f^{-1} is the reflection of the graph of f in the line $y = x$.
  (d) Both f and f^{-1} have domains and ranges that are all real numbers.

149. (a) $f^{-1}(x) = x^2 - 1, \ x \geq 0$
  (b)
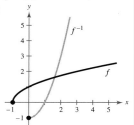
  (c) The graph of f^{-1} is the reflection of the graph of f in the line $y = x$.
  (d) f has a domain of $[-1, \infty)$ and a range of $[0, \infty)$; f^{-1} has a domain of $[0, \infty)$ and a range of $[-1, \infty)$.

151. $x \geq 4; \ f^{-1}(x) = \sqrt{\dfrac{x}{2}} + 4$

153. (a)

  (b) The model is a good fit for the actual data.

155. Model: $m = \frac{8}{5}k$; 3.2 kilometers, 16 kilometers

157. A factor of 4   **159.** $\approx$ 2 hours, 26 minutes

161. False. The graph is reflected in the *x*-axis, shifted nine units to the left, and then shifted 13 units downward.

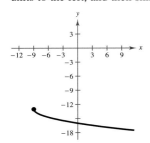

163. True. If *y* is directly proportional to *x*, then $y = kx$, so $x = (1/k)y$. Therefore, *x* is directly proportional to *y*.

165. A function from a set *A* to a set *B* is a relation that assigns to each element *x* in the set *A* exactly one element *y* in the set *B*.

Chapter Test   *(page 123)*

1.

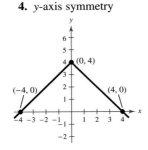

Midpoint: $\left(2, \frac{5}{2}\right)$; Distance: $\sqrt{89}$

2. ≈ 11.937 centimeters

3. No symmetry

4. *y*-axis symmetry

5. *y*-axis symmetry

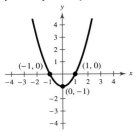

6. $(x - 1)^2 + (y - 3)^2 = 16$ **7.** $2x + y - 1 = 0$

8. $17x + 10y - 59 = 0$

9. (a) $4x - 7y + 44 = 0$ (b) $7x + 4y - 53 = 0$

10. (a) $-\dfrac{1}{8}$ (b) $-\dfrac{1}{28}$ (c) $\dfrac{\sqrt{x}}{x^2 - 18x}$

11. $-10 \le x \le 10$

12. (a) $0, \pm 0.4314$

(b)

(c) Increasing on $(-0.31, 0), (0.31, \infty)$
Decreasing on $(-\infty, -0.31), (0, 0.31)$

(d) Even

13. (a) $0, 3$

(b)

(c) Increasing on $(-\infty, 2)$
Decreasing on $(2, 3)$

(d) Neither even nor odd

14. (a) -5

(b)

(c) Increasing on $(-5, \infty)$
Decreasing on $(-\infty, -5)$

(d) Neither even nor odd

15.

16. Reflection in the x-axis of $y = [\![x]\!]$

17. Reflection in the x-axis, horizontal shift, and vertical shift of $y = \sqrt{x}$

18. (a) $2x^2 - 4x - 2$ (b) $4x^2 + 4x - 12$

(c) $-3x^4 - 12x^3 + 22x^2 + 28x - 35$

(d) $\dfrac{3x^2 - 7}{-x^2 - 4x + 5}$, $x \neq -5, 1$

(e) $3x^4 + 24x^3 + 18x^2 - 120x + 68$

(f) $-9x^4 + 30x^2 - 16$

19. (a) $\dfrac{1 + 2x^{3/2}}{x}$, $x > 0$ (b) $\dfrac{1 - 2x^{3/2}}{x}$, $x > 0$

(c) $\dfrac{2\sqrt{x}}{x}$, $x > 0$ (d) $\dfrac{1}{2x^{3/2}}$, $x > 0$

(e) $\dfrac{\sqrt{x}}{2x}$, $x > 0$ (f) $\dfrac{2\sqrt{x}}{x}$, $x > 0$

20. $f^{-1}(x) = \sqrt[3]{x - 8}$ **21.** No inverse

22. $f^{-1}(x) = \left(\frac{1}{3}x\right)^{2/3}$, $x \geq 0$ **23.** $v = 6\sqrt{s}$

24. $A = \dfrac{25}{6}xy$ **25.** $b = \dfrac{48}{a}$

Problem Solving   (page 125)

1. (a) $W_1 = 2000 + 0.07S$ (b) $W_2 = 2300 + 0.05S$

(c)

Both jobs pay the same monthly salary if sales equal $15,000.

(d) No. Job 1 would pay $3400 and job 2 would pay $3300.

3. (a) The function will be even.

(b) The function will be odd.

(c) The function will be neither even nor odd.

5. $f(x) = a_{2n}x^{2n} + a_{2n-2}x^{2n-2} + \cdots + a_2 x^2 + a_0$

$f(-x) = a_{2n}(-x)^{2n} + a_{2n-2}(-x)^{2n-2}$

$\qquad + \cdots + a_2(-x)^2 + a_0$

$\qquad = f(x)$

7. (a) $81\frac{2}{3}$ hours   (b) $25\frac{5}{7}$ miles per hour

(c) $y = \dfrac{-180}{7}x + 3400$

Domain: $0 \leq x \leq \dfrac{1190}{9}$

Range: $0 \leq y \leq 3400$

(d)

9. (a) $(f \circ g)(x) = 4x + 24$ (b) $(f \circ g)^{-1}(x) = \frac{1}{4}x - 6$

(c) $f^{-1}(x) = \frac{1}{4}x$; $g^{-1}(x) = x - 6$

(d) $(g^{-1} \circ f^{-1})(x) = \frac{1}{4}x - 6$

(e) $(f \circ g)(x) = 8x^3 + 1$; $(f \circ g)^{-1}(x) = \frac{1}{2}\sqrt[3]{x - 1}$;

$f^{-1}(x) = \sqrt[3]{x - 1}$; $g^{-1}(x) = \frac{1}{2}x$;

$(g^{-1} \circ f^{-1})(x) = \frac{1}{2}\sqrt[3]{x - 1}$

(f) Answers will vary.   (g) $(f \circ g)^{-1}(x) = (g^{-1} \circ f^{-1})(x)$

11. (a)   (b)

(e)

(f)

13. Proof

15. (a)

x	-4	-2	0	4
$f(f^{-1}(x))$	-4	-2	0	4

(b)

x	-3	-2	0	1
$(f + f^{-1})(x)$	5	1	-3	-5

(c)

x	-3	-2	0	1
$(f \circ f^{-1})(x)$	4	0	2	6

(d)

x	-4	-3	0	4
$\left| f^{-1}(x) \right|$	2	1	1	3

Chapter 2

Section 2.1   *(page 134)*

Vocabulary Check   *(page 134)*

1. nonnegative integer; real   **2.** quadratic; parabola
3. axis   **4.** positive; minimum
5. negative; maximum

1. g   **2.** c   **3.** b   **4.** h
5. f   **6.** a   **7.** e   **8.** d
9. (a)

(b)

Vertical shrink

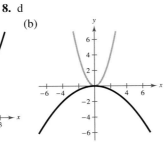

Vertical shrink and
reflection in the *x*-axis

(c)

Vertical stretch

(d)

Vertical stretch and
reflection in the *x*-axis

11. (a)

Horizontal shift

(b)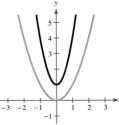

Horizontal shrink and
vertical shift

(c)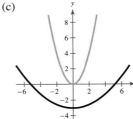

Horizontal stretch and
vertical shift

(d)

Horizontal shift

13.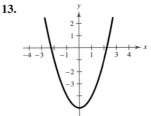

Vertex: $(0, -5)$
Axis of symmetry: *y*-axis
x-intercepts: $\left(\pm\sqrt{5}, 0 \right)$

15.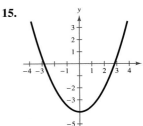

Vertex: $(0, -4)$
Axis of symmetry: *y*-axis
x-intercepts: $\left(\pm 2\sqrt{2}, 0 \right)$

17.

Vertex: $(-5, -6)$
Axis of symmetry: $x = -5$
x-intercepts: $\left(-5 \pm \sqrt{6}, 0\right)$

19.

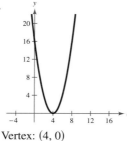

Vertex: $(4, 0)$
Axis of symmetry: $x = 4$
x-intercept: $(4, 0)$

21.

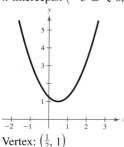

Vertex: $\left(\frac{1}{2}, 1\right)$
Axis of symmetry: $x = \frac{1}{2}$
No x-intercept

23.

Vertex: $(1, 6)$
Axis of symmetry: $x = 1$
x-intercepts: $\left(1 \pm \sqrt{6}, 0\right)$

25.

Vertex: $\left(\frac{1}{2}, 20\right)$
Axis of symmetry: $x = \frac{1}{2}$
No x-intercept

27.

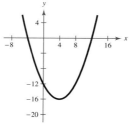

Vertex: $(4, -16)$
Axis of symmetry: $x = 4$
x-intercepts: $(-4, 0), (12, 0)$
Vertex: $(-1, 4)$
Axis of symmetry: $x = -1$
x-intercepts: $(1, 0), (-3, 0)$

29.

31.

Vertex: $(-4, -5)$
Axis of symmetry: $x = -4$
x-intercepts: $\left(-4 \pm \sqrt{5}, 0\right)$

33.

Vertex: $(4, -1)$
Axis of symmetry: $x = 4$
x-intercepts: $\left(4 \pm \frac{1}{2}\sqrt{2}, 0\right)$

35.

Vertex: $(-2, -3)$
Axis of symmetry: $x = -2$
x-intercepts: $\left(-2 \pm \sqrt{6}, 0\right)$

37. $y = (x - 1)^2$ **39.** $y = -(x + 1)^2 + 4$
41. $y = -2(x + 2)^2 + 2$ **43.** $f(x) = (x + 2)^2 + 5$
45. $f(x) = -\frac{1}{2}(x - 3)^2 + 4$ **47.** $f(x) = \frac{3}{4}(x - 5)^2 + 12$
49. $f(x) = -\frac{24}{49}\left(x + \frac{1}{4}\right)^2 + \frac{3}{2}$ **51.** $f(x) = -\frac{16}{3}\left(x + \frac{5}{2}\right)^2$
53. $(\pm 4, 0)$ **55.** $(5, 0), (-1, 0)$

57.

$(0, 0), (4, 0)$

59.

$(3, 0), (6, 0)$

61.

$\left(-\frac{5}{2}, 0\right), (6, 0)$

63.

$(7, 0), (-1, 0)$

65. $f(x) = x^2 - 2x - 3$
$g(x) = -x^2 + 2x + 3$
67. $f(x) = x^2 - 10x$
$g(x) = -x^2 + 10x$
69. $f(x) = 2x^2 + 7x + 3$
$g(x) = -2x^2 - 7x - 3$
71. $55, 55$ **73.** $12, 6$
75. (a) $A = \dfrac{8x(50 - x)}{3}$

(b)

x	5	10	15	20	25	30
A	600	1067	1400	1600	1667	1600

$x = 25$ feet, $y = 33\frac{1}{3}$ feet

(c)

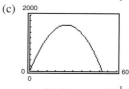

$x = 25$ feet, $y = 33\frac{1}{3}$ feet

(d) $A = -\frac{8}{3}(x - 25)^2 + \frac{5000}{3}$ (e) They are identical.
77. 16 feet   **79.** 20 fixtures   **81.** 350,000 units
83. (a) \$14,000,000; \$14,375,000; \$13,500,000
(b) 24; \$14,400
85. (a)

(b) 4299; answers will vary.
(c) 8879; 24

87. (a)   (b) 69.6 miles per hour

89. True. The equation has no real solutions, so the graph has no x-intercepts.

91. $f(x) = a\left(x + \dfrac{b}{2a}\right)^2 + \dfrac{4ac - b^2}{4a}$

93. Yes. A graph of a quadratic equation whose vertex is on the x-axis has only one x-intercept.

95. $y = -\frac{1}{3}x + \frac{5}{3}$ **97.** $y = \frac{5}{4}x + 3$ **99.** 27

101. $-\frac{1408}{49}$ **103.** 109   **105.** Answers will vary.

Section 2.2   (page 148)

Vocabulary Check   (page 148)

1. continuous   **2.** Leading Coefficient Test
3. n; $n - 1$ **4.** (a) solution; (b) $(x - a)$; (c) x-intercept
5. touches; crosses   **6.** standard
7. Intermediate Value

1. c   **2.** g   **3.** h   **4.** f
5. a   **6.** e   **7.** d   **8.** b
9. (a)   (b)

(c)   (d)

11. (a)   (b)

(c)   (d)

(e)   (f)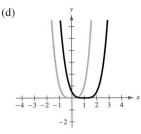

13. Falls to the left, rises to the right
15. Falls to the left, falls to the right
17. Rises to the left, falls to the right
19. Rises to the left, falls to the right
21. Falls to the left, falls to the right
23.   **25.**

27. (a) ± 5
  (b) odd multiplicity; number of turning points: 1
  (c)

29. (a) 3
  (b) even multiplicity; number of turning points: 1
  (c)

31. (a) $-2, 1$
  (b) odd multiplicity; number of turning points: 1
  (c)

CHAPTER 2

33. (a) $0, 2 \pm \sqrt{3}$

(b) odd multiplicity; number of turning points: 2

(c)

35. (a) $0, 2$

(b) 0, odd multiplicity; 2, even multiplicity; number of turning points: 2

(c)

37. (a) $0, \pm\sqrt{3}$

(b) 0, odd multiplicity; $\pm\sqrt{3}$, even multiplicity; number of turning points: 4

(c)

39. (a) No real zeros

(b) number of turning points: 1

(c)

41. (a) $\pm 2, -3$

(b) odd multiplicity; number of turning points: 2

(c)

43. (a)

(b) x-intercepts: $(0, 0), \left(\frac{5}{2}, 0\right)$ (c) $x = 0, \frac{5}{2}$

(d) The answers in part (c) match the x-intercepts.

45. (a)

(b) x-intercepts: $(0, 0), (\pm 1, 0), (\pm 2, 0)$

(c) $x = 0, 1, -1, 2, -2$

(d) The answers in part (c) match the x-intercepts.

47. $f(x) = x^2 - 10x$ **49.** $f(x) = x^2 + 4x - 12$

51. $f(x) = x^3 + 5x^2 + 6x$

53. $f(x) = x^4 - 4x^3 - 9x^2 + 36x$

55. $f(x) = x^2 - 2x - 2$ **57.** $f(x) = x^2 + 4x + 4$

59. $f(x) = x^3 + 2x^2 - 3x$ **61.** $f(x) = x^3 - 3x$

63. $f(x) = x^4 + x^3 - 15x^2 + 23x - 10$

65. $f(x) = x^5 + 16x^4 + 96x^3 + 256x^2 + 256x$

67. (a) Falls to the left, rises to the right

(b) $0, \pm 3$ (c) Answers will vary.

(d)

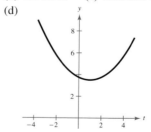

69. (a) Rises to the left, rises to the right

(b) No zeros   (c) Answers will vary.

(d)

71. (a) Falls to the left, rises to the right

(b) $0, 3$ (c) Answers will vary.

(d)

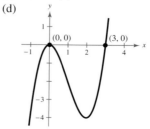

73. (a) Falls to the left, rises to the right
(b) 0, 2, 3   (c) Answers will vary.
(d)

75. (a) Rises to the left, falls to the right
(b) $-5, 0$ (c) Answers will vary.
(d)
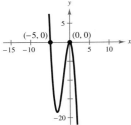

77. (a) Falls to the left, rises to the right
(b) 0, 4   (c) Answers will vary.
(d)
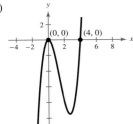

79. (a) Falls to the left, falls to the right
(b) ± 2 (c) Answers will vary.
(d)

81.

Zeros: $0, \pm 2$,
odd multiplicity

83.

Zeros: -1,
even multiplicity;
$3, \frac{9}{2}$, odd multiplicity

85. $[-1, 0], [1, 2], [2, 3]; \approx -0.879, 1.347, 2.532$

87. $[-2, -1], [0, 1]; \approx -1.585, 0.779$

89. (a) $V = l \times w \times h$
$= (36 - 2x)(36 - 2x)x$
$= x(36 - 2x)^2$
(b) Domain: $0 < x < 18$
(c)

x	1	2	3	4	5	6	7
V	1156	2048	2700	3136	3380	3456	3388

6 inches $\times$ 24 inches $\times$ 24 inches
(d)
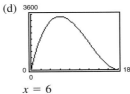
$x = 6$

91. (a) $A = -2x^2 + 12x$ (b) $V = -384x^2 + 2304x$
(c) 0 inches $< x < 6$ inches
(d)

When $x = 3$, the volume is maximum at $V = 3456$;
dimensions of gutter are 3 inches $\times$ 6 inches $\times$ 3 inches.
(e)

The maximum value is the same.
(f) No. Answers will vary.

93.

The model is a good fit.

95. Region 1: 259,370
Region 2: 223,470
Answers will vary.

97. (a)

(b) $t \approx 15$ (c) Vertex: $(15.22, 2.54)$
(d) The results are approximately equal.

99. False. A fifth-degree polynomial can have at most four turning points.

101. True. The degree of the function is odd and its leading coefficient is negative, so the graph rises to the left and falls to the right.

103.

(a) Vertical shift of two units; Even
(b) Horizontal shift of two units; Neither even nor odd
(c) Reflection in the y-axis; Even
(d) Reflection in the x-axis; Even
(e) Horizontal stretch; Even
(f) Vertical shrink; Even
(g) $g(x) = x^3$; Neither odd nor even
(h) $g(x) = x^{16}$; Even

105. $(5x - 8)(x + 3)$ **107.** $x^2(4x + 5)(x - 3)$

109. $-\frac{7}{2}, 4$ **111.** $-\frac{5}{4}, \frac{1}{3}$ **113.** $1 \pm \sqrt{22}$

115. $\dfrac{-5 \pm \sqrt{185}}{4}$

117. Horizontal translation four units to the left of $y = x^2$

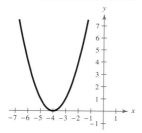

119. Horizontal translation one unit left and vertical translation five units down of $y = \sqrt{x}$

121. Vertical stretch by a factor of 2 and vertical translation nine units up of $y = [\![x]\!]$

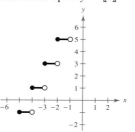

Section 2.3   (page 159)

Vocabulary Check   (page 159)

1. dividend; divisor; quotient; remainder
2. improper; proper   **3.** synthetic division
4. factor   **5.** remainder

1. Answers will vary.

3.

5. $2x + 4$

7. $x^2 - 3x + 1$ **9.** $x^3 + 3x^2 - 1$ **11.** $7 - \dfrac{11}{x + 2}$

13. $3x + 5 - \dfrac{2x - 3}{2x^2 + 1}$ **15.** $x^2 + 2x + 4 + \dfrac{2x - 11}{x^2 - 2x + 3}$

17. $x + 3 + \dfrac{6x^2 - 8x + 3}{(x - 1)^3}$ **19.** $3x^2 - 2x + 5$

21. $4x^2 - 9$ **23.** $-x^2 + 10x - 25$

25. $5x^2 + 14x + 56 + \dfrac{232}{x - 4}$

27. $10x^3 + 10x^2 + 60x + 360 + \dfrac{1360}{x - 6}$

29. $x^2 - 8x + 64$

31. $-3x^3 - 6x^2 - 12x - 24 - \dfrac{48}{x - 2}$

33. $-x^3 - 6x^2 - 36x - 36 - \dfrac{216}{x - 6}$

35. $4x^2 + 14x - 30$

37. $f(x) = (x - 4)(x^2 + 3x - 2) + 3, \quad f(4) = 3$

39. $f(x) = \left(x + \frac{2}{3}\right)(15x^3 - 6x + 4) + \frac{34}{3}, \quad f\left(-\frac{2}{3}\right) = \frac{34}{3}$

41. $f(x) = \left(x - \sqrt{2}\right)\left[x^2 + \left(3 + \sqrt{2}\right)x + 3\sqrt{2}\right] - 8,$
$f\left(\sqrt{2}\right) = -8$

43. $f(x) = \left(x - 1 + \sqrt{3}\right)\left[-4x^2 + \left(2 + 4\sqrt{3}\right)x + \left(2 + 2\sqrt{3}\right)\right],$
$f\left(1 - \sqrt{3}\right) = 0$

45. (a) 1   (b) 4   (c) 4   (d) 1954

47. (a) 97   (b) $-\frac{5}{3}$ (c) 17   (d) -199

49. $(x - 2)(x + 3)(x - 1)$; Zeros: $2, -3, 1$
51. $(2x - 1)(x - 5)(x - 2)$; Zeros: $\frac{1}{2}, 5, 2$
53. $\left(x + \sqrt{3}\right)\left(x - \sqrt{3}\right)(x + 2)$; Zeros: $-\sqrt{3}, \sqrt{3}, -2$
55. $(x - 1)\left(x - 1 - \sqrt{3}\right)\left(x - 1 + \sqrt{3}\right)$;
   Zeros: $1, 1 + \sqrt{3}, 1 - \sqrt{3}$
57. (a) Answers will vary.   (b) $2x - 1$
   (c) $f(x) = (2x - 1)(x + 2)(x - 1)$ (d) $\frac{1}{2}, -2, 1$
   (e)

59. (a) Answers will vary.   (b) $(x - 1), (x - 2)$
   (c) $f(x) = (x - 1)(x - 2)(x - 5)(x + 4)$
   (d) $1, 2, 5, -4$
   (e)

61. (a) Answers will vary.   (b) $x + 7$
   (c) $f(x) = (x + 7)(2x + 1)(3x - 2)$
   (d) $-7, -\frac{1}{2}, \frac{2}{3}$
   (e)

63. (a) Answers will vary.   (b) $\left(x - \sqrt{5}\right)$
   (c) $f(x) = \left(x - \sqrt{5}\right)\left(x + \sqrt{5}\right)(2x - 1)$ (d) $\pm\sqrt{5}, \frac{1}{2}$
   (e)

65. (a) Zeros are 2 and $\approx \pm 2.236$.
   (b) $x = 2$ (c) $f(x) = (x - 2)\left(x - \sqrt{5}\right)\left(x + \sqrt{5}\right)$
67. (a) Zeros are -2, ≈ 0.268, and ≈ 3.732.
   (b) $x = -2$
   (c) $h(t) = (t + 2)\left[t - \left(2 + \sqrt{3}\right)\right]\left[t - \left(2 - \sqrt{3}\right)\right]$
69. $2x^2 - x - 1$, $x \neq \frac{3}{2}$ **71.** $x^2 + 3x$, $x \neq -2, -1$
73. (a) and (b)

$M = -0.242x^3 + 12.43x^2 - 173.4x + 2118$

(c)

t	3	4	5	6	7	8
$M(t)$	1703	1608	1531	1473	1430	1402

t	9	10	11	12	13
$M(t)$	1388	1385	1392	1409	1433

Answers will vary.
   (d) 1614 thousand. No, because the model will approach negative infinity quickly.
75. False. $-\frac{4}{7}$ is a zero of f.
77. True. The degree of the numerator is greater than the degree of the denominator.
79. $x^{2n} + 6x^n + 9$ **81.** The remainder is 0.
83. $c = -210$ **85.** 0; $x + 3$ is a factor of f.
87. $\pm\frac{5}{3}$ **89.** $-\frac{7}{5}, 2$ **91.** $\dfrac{-3 \pm \sqrt{3}}{2}$
93. $f(x) = x^3 - 7x^2 + 12x$
95. $f(x) = x^3 + x^2 - 7x - 3$

Section 2.4   *(page 167)*

Vocabulary Check   *(page 167)*

1. (a) iii   (b) i   (c) ii   **2.** $\sqrt{-1}$; -1
3. complex numbers; $a + bi$ **4.** principal square
5. complex conjugates

1. $a = -10$, $b = 6$ **3.** $a = 6$, $b = 5$ **5.** $4 + 3i$
7. $2 - 3\sqrt{3}i$ **9.** $5\sqrt{3}i$ **11.** 8
13. $-1 - 6i$ **15.** $0.3i$ **17.** $11 - i$ **19.** 4
21. $3 - 3\sqrt{2}i$ **23.** $-14 + 20i$ **25.** $\frac{1}{6} + \frac{7}{6}i$
27. $5 + i$ **29.** $12 + 30i$ **31.** 24   **33.** $-9 + 40i$
35. -10 **37.** $6 - 3i, 45$ **39.** $-1 + \sqrt{5}i, 6$
41. $-2\sqrt{5}i, 20$ **43.** $\sqrt{8}, 8$ **45.** $-5i$
47. $\frac{8}{41} + \frac{10}{41}i$ **49.** $\frac{4}{5} + \frac{3}{5}i$ **51.** $-5 - 6i$
53. $-\frac{120}{1681} - \frac{27}{1681}i$ **55.** $-\frac{1}{2} - \frac{5}{2}i$ **57.** $\frac{62}{949} + \frac{297}{949}i$
59. $-2\sqrt{3}$ **61.** -10
63. $\left(21 + 5\sqrt{2}\right) + \left(7\sqrt{5} - 3\sqrt{10}\right)i$ **65.** $1 \pm i$
67. $-2 \pm \frac{1}{2}i$ **69.** $-\frac{5}{2}, -\frac{3}{2}$ **71.** $2 \pm \sqrt{2}i$
73. $\frac{5}{7} \pm \frac{5\sqrt{15}}{7}$ **75.** $-1 + 6i$
77. $-5i$ **79.** $-375\sqrt{3}i$ **81.** i
83. (a) $z_1 = 9 + 16i$, $z_2 = 20 - 10i$
   (b) $z = \dfrac{11{,}240}{877} + \dfrac{4630}{877}i$
85. (a) 16   (b) 16   (c) 16   (d) 16
87. False. If the complex number is real, the number equals its conjugate.

CHAPTER 2

89. False.
$$i^{44} + i^{150} - i^{74} - i^{109} + i^{61} = 1 - 1 + 1 - i + i = 1$$
91. Proof   **93.** $-x^2 - 3x + 12$ **95.** $3x^2 + \frac{23}{2}x - 2$
97. -31 **99.** $\dfrac{27}{2}$ **101.** $a = \dfrac{\sqrt{3V\pi b}}{2\pi b}$ **103.** 1 liter

Section 2.5   *(page 179)*

Vocabulary Check   *(page 179)*

1. Fundamental Theorem of Algebra
2. Linear Factorization Theorem   **3.** Rational Zero
4. conjugate   **5.** irreducible over the reals
6. Descartes' Rule of Signs   **7.** lower; upper

---

1. $0, 6$ **3.** $2, -4$ **5.** $-6, \pm i$ **7.** $\pm 1, \pm 3$
9. $\pm 1, \pm 3, \pm 5, \pm 9, \pm 15, \pm 45, \pm\frac{1}{2}, \pm\frac{3}{2}, \pm\frac{5}{2}, \pm\frac{9}{2}, \pm\frac{15}{2}, \pm\frac{45}{2}$
11. $1, 2, 3$ **13.** $1, -1, 4$ **15.** $-1, -10$ **17.** $\frac{1}{2}, -1$
19. $-2, 3, \pm\frac{2}{3}$ **21.** $-1, 2$ **23.** $-6, \frac{1}{2}, 1$
25. (a) $\pm 1, \pm 2, \pm 4$
(b)   (c) $-2, -1, 2$

27. (a) $\pm 1, \pm 3, \pm\frac{1}{2}, \pm\frac{3}{2}, \pm\frac{1}{4}, \pm\frac{3}{4}$
(b)   (c) $-\frac{1}{4}, 1, 3$

29. (a) $\pm 1, \pm 2, \pm 4, \pm 8, \pm\frac{1}{2}$
(b)   (c) $-\frac{1}{2}, 1, 2, 4$

31. (a) $\pm 1, \pm 3, \pm\frac{1}{2}, \pm\frac{3}{2}, \pm\frac{1}{4}, \pm\frac{3}{4}, \pm\frac{1}{8}, \pm\frac{3}{8}, \pm\frac{1}{16}, \pm\frac{3}{16}, \pm\frac{1}{32}, \pm\frac{3}{32}$
(b)   (c) $1, \frac{3}{4}, -\frac{1}{8}$

33. (a) $\pm 1, \approx\pm 1.414$
(b) $f(x) = (x + 1)(x - 1)\left(x + \sqrt{2}\right)\left(x - \sqrt{2}\right)$
35. (a) $0, 3, 4, \approx\pm 1.414$
(b) $h(x) = x(x - 3)(x - 4)\left(x + \sqrt{2}\right)\left(x - \sqrt{2}\right)$
37. $x^3 - x^2 + 25x - 25$ **39.** $x^3 + 4x^2 - 31x - 174$
41. $3x^4 - 17x^3 + 25x^2 + 23x - 22$
43. (a) $(x^2 + 9)(x^2 - 3)$
(b) $(x^2 + 9)\left(x + \sqrt{3}\right)\left(x - \sqrt{3}\right)$
(c) $(x + 3i)(x - 3i)\left(x + \sqrt{3}\right)\left(x - \sqrt{3}\right)$
45. (a) $(x^2 - 2x - 2)(x^2 - 2x + 3)$
(b) $\left(x - 1 + \sqrt{3}\right)\left(x - 1 - \sqrt{3}\right)(x^2 - 2x + 3)$
(c) $\left(x - 1 + \sqrt{3}\right)\left(x - 1 - \sqrt{3}\right)\left(x - 1 + \sqrt{2}i\right)$
$\left(x - 1 - \sqrt{2}i\right)$
47. $-\frac{3}{2}, \pm 5i$ **49.** $\pm 2i, 1, -\frac{1}{2}$ **51.** $-3 \pm i, \frac{1}{4}$
53. $2, -3 \pm \sqrt{2}i, 1$ **55.** $\pm 5i$; $(x + 5i)(x - 5i)$
57. $2 \pm \sqrt{3}$; $\left(x - 2 - \sqrt{3}\right)\left(x - 2 + \sqrt{3}\right)$
59. $\pm 3, \pm 3i$; $(x + 3)(x - 3)(x + 3i)(x - 3i)$
61. $1 \pm i$; $(z - 1 + i)(z - 1 - i)$
63. $2, 2 \pm i$; $(x - 2)(x - 2 + i)(x - 2 - i)$
65. $-2, 1 \pm \sqrt{2}i$; $(x + 2)\left(x - 1 + \sqrt{2}i\right)\left(x - 1 - \sqrt{2}i\right)$
67. $-\frac{1}{5}, 1 \pm \sqrt{5}i$; $(5x + 1)\left(x - 1 + \sqrt{5}i\right)\left(x - 1 - \sqrt{5}i\right)$
69. $2, \pm 2i$; $(x - 2)^2(x + 2i)(x - 2i)$
71. $\pm i, \pm 3i$; $(x + i)(x - i)(x + 3i)(x - 3i)$
73. $-10, -7 \pm 5i$ **75.** $-\frac{3}{4}, 1 \pm \frac{1}{2}i$
77. $-2, -\frac{1}{2}, \pm i$ **79.** No real zeros
81. No real zeros   **83.** One positive zero
85. One or three positive zeros
87. Answers will vary.   **89.** Answers will vary.
91. $1, -\frac{1}{2}$ **93.** $-\frac{3}{4}$ **95.** $\pm 2, \pm\frac{3}{2}$ **97.** $\pm 1, \frac{1}{4}$
99. d   **100.** a   **101.** b   **102.** c
103. (a)

(b) $V = x(9 - 2x)(15 - 2x)$
Domain: $0 < x < \frac{9}{2}$
(c)

1.82 centimeters $\times$ 5.36 centimeters $\times$ 11.36 centimeters
(d) $\frac{1}{2}, \frac{7}{2}, 8$; 8 is not in the domain of V.
105. $x \approx 38.4$, or \$384,000

107. (a) $V = x^3 + 9x^2 + 26x + 24 = 120$
   (b) 4 feet by 5 feet by 6 feet
109. $x \approx 40$, or 4000 units
111. No. Setting $p = 9{,}000{,}000$ and solving the resulting equation yields imaginary roots.
113. False. The most complex zeros it can have is two, and the Linear Factorization Theorem guarantees that there are three linear factors, so one zero must be real.
115. r_1, r_2, r_3 **117.** $5 + r_1, 5 + r_2, 5 + r_3$
119. The zeros cannot be determined.
121. (a) $0 < k < 4$ (b) $k = 4$ (c) $k < 0$ (d) $k > 4$
123. Answers will vary. There are infinitely many possible functions for f. Sample equation and graph:
   $f(x) = -2x^3 + 3x^2 + 11x - 6$

125. Answers will vary.
127. (a) $x^2 + b$ (b) $x^2 - 2ax + a^2 + b^2$
129. $-11 + 9i$ **131.** $20 + 40i$
133.   **135.**

137.

Section 2.6 *(page 193)*

1. (a)

x	$f(x)$	x	$f(x)$	x	$f(x)$
0.5	-2	1.5	2	5	0.25
0.9	-10	1.1	10	10	$0.\overline{1}$
0.99	-100	1.01	100	100	$0.\overline{01}$
0.999	-1000	1.001	1000	1000	$0.\overline{001}$

   (b) Vertical asymptote: $x = 1$
       Horizontal asymptote: $y = 0$
   (c) Domain: all real numbers x except $x = 1$
3. (a)

x	$f(x)$	x	$f(x)$	x	$f(x)$
0.5	-1	1.5	5.4	5	3.125
0.9	-12.79	1.1	17.29	10	$3.\overline{03}$
0.99	-147.8	1.01	152.3	100	$3.\overline{0003}$
0.999	-1498	1.001	1502	1000	3

   (b) Vertical asymptotes: $x = \pm 1$
       Horizontal asymptote: $y = 3$
   (c) Domain: all real numbers x except $x = \pm 1$
5. Domain: all real numbers x except $x = 0$
   Vertical asymptote: $x = 0$
   Horizontal asymptote: $y = 0$
7. Domain: all real numbers x except $x = 2$
   Vertical asymptote: $x = 2$
   Horizontal asymptote: $y = -1$
9. Domain: all real numbers x except $x = \pm 1$
   Vertical asymptotes: $x = \pm 1$
11. Domain: all real numbers x
   Horizontal asymptote: $y = 3$
13. d **14.** a **15.** c **16.** b
17. 1 **19.** 6
21. Domain: all real numbers x except $x = \pm 4$;
   Vertical asymptote: $x = -4$; horizontal asymptote: $y = 0$
23. Domain: all real numbers x except $x = -1, 3$;
   Vertical asymptote: $x = 3$; horizontal asymptote: $y = 1$
25. Domain: all real numbers x except $x = -1, \frac{1}{2}$;
   Vertical asymptote: $x = \frac{1}{2}$; horizontal asymptote: $y = \frac{1}{2}$
27. (a) Domain: all real numbers x except $x = -2$
   (b) y-intercept: $\left(0, \frac{1}{2}\right)$
   (c) Vertical asymptote: $x = -2$
       Horizontal asymptote: $y = 0$

CHAPTER 2

(d)

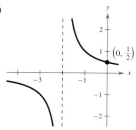

29. (a) Domain: all real numbers x except $x = -2$
(b) y-intercept: $\left(0, -\frac{1}{2}\right)$
(c) Vertical asymptote: $x = -2$
Horizontal asymptote: $y = 0$
(d)

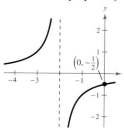

31. (a) Domain: all real numbers x except $x = -1$
(b) x-intercept: $\left(-\frac{5}{2}, 0\right)$
y-intercept: $(0, 5)$
(c) Vertical asymptote: $x = -1$
Horizontal asymptote: $y = 2$
(d)

33. (a) Domain: all real numbers x
(b) Intercept: $(0, 0)$
(c) Horizontal asymptote: $y = 1$
(d)

35. (a) Domain: all real numbers s
(b) Intercept: $(0, 0)$ (c) Horizontal asymptote: $y = 0$
(d)

37. (a) Domain: all real numbers x except $x = \pm2$
(b) x-intercepts: $(1, 0)$ and $(4, 0)$
y-intercept: $(0, -1)$
(c) Vertical asymptotes: $x = \pm2$
Horizontal asymptote: $y = 1$
(d)

39. (a) Domain: all real numbers x except $x = \pm1, 2$
(b) x-intercept: $(3, 0), \left(-\frac{1}{2}, 0\right)$
y-intercept: $\left(0, -\frac{3}{2}\right)$
(c) Vertical asymptotes: $x = 2, x = \pm1$
Horizontal asymptote: $y = 0$
(d)

41. (a) Domain: all real numbers x except $x = 2, -3$
(b) Intercept: $(0, 0)$
(c) Vertical asymptote: $x = 2$
Horizontal asymptote: $y = 1$
(d)

43. (a) Domain: all real numbers x except $x = -\frac{3}{2}, 2$
  (b) x-intercept: $\left(\frac{1}{2}, 0\right)$
   y-intercept: $\left(0, -\frac{1}{3}\right)$
  (c) Vertical asymptote: $x = -\frac{3}{2}$
   Horizontal asymptote: $y = 1$
  (d)

45. (a) Domain: all real numbers t except $t = -1$
  (b) t-intercept: $(1, 0)$
   y-intercept: $(0, -1)$
  (c) Vertical asymptote: None
   Horizontal asymptote: None
  (d)

47. (a) Domain of f: all real numbers x except $x = -1$
   Domain of g: all real numbers x
  (b) $x - 1$; Vertical asymptotes: none
  (c)

x	-3	-2	-1.5	-1	-0.5	0	1
$f(x)$	-4	-3	-2.5	Undef.	-1.5	-1	0
$g(x)$	-4	-3	-2.5	-2	-1.5	-1	0

  (d)

  (e) Because there are only a finite number of pixels, the graphing utility may not attempt to evaluate the function where it does not exist.
49. (a) Domain of f: all real numbers x except $x = 0, 2$
   Domain of g: all real numbers x except $x = 0$

(b) $\frac{1}{x}$; Vertical asymptote: $x = 0$
(c)

x	-0.5	0	0.5	1	1.5	2	3
$f(x)$	-2	Undef.	2	1	$\frac{2}{3}$	Undef.	$\frac{1}{3}$
$g(x)$	-2	Undef.	2	1	$\frac{2}{3}$	$\frac{1}{2}$	$\frac{1}{3}$

(d)

(e) Because there are only a finite number of pixels, the graphing utility may not attempt to evaluate the function where it does not exist.
51. (a) Domain: all real numbers x except $x = 0$
  (b) x-intercepts: $(2, 0), (-2, 0)$
  (c) Vertical asymptote: $x = 0$
   Slant asymptote: $y = x$
  (d)

53. (a) Domain: all real numbers x except $x = 0$
  (b) No intercepts
  (c) Vertical asymptote: $x = 0$
   Slant asymptote: $y = 2x$
  (d)

55. (a) Domain: all real numbers x except $x = 0$
  (b) No intercepts
  (c) Vertical asymptote: $x = 0$
   Slant asymptote: $y = x$

CHAPTER 2

(d)

57. (a) Domain: all real numbers t except $t = -5$
(b) y-intercept: $(0, -0.2)$
(c) Vertical asymptote: $t = -5$
  Slant asymptote: $y = -t + 5$
(d)

59. (a) Domain: all real numbers x except $x = \pm 1$
(b) Intercept: $(0, 0)$
(c) Vertical asymptotes: $x = \pm 1$
  Slant asymptote: $y = x$
(d)

61. (a) Domain: all real numbers x except $x = 1$
(b) y-intercept: $(0, -1)$
(c) Vertical asymptote: $x = 1$
  Slant asymptote: $y = x$
(d)

63. (a) Domain: all real numbers x except $x = -1, -2$
(b) y-intercept: $(0, 0.5)$
  x-intercepts: $(0.5, 0), (1, 0)$

(c) Vertical asymptote: $x = -2$
  Slant asymptote: $y = 2x - 7$
(d)

65.

Domain: all real numbers x except $x = -3$
Vertical asymptote: $x = -3$
Slant asymptote: $y = x + 2$
$y = x + 2$

67.

Domain: all real numbers x except $x = 0$
Vertical asymptote: $x = 0$
Slant asymptote: $y = -x + 3$
$y = -x + 3$

69. (a) $(-1, 0)$ (b) -1
71. (a) $(1, 0), (-1, 0)$ (b) ± 1
73. (a)

(b) \$28.33 million; \$170 million; \$765 million
(c) No. The function is undefined at $p = 100$.
75. (a) 333 deer, 500 deer, 800 deer (b) 1500 deer
77. (a) Answers will vary. (b) $(4, \infty)$
(c)

11.75 inches × 5.87 inches

79. (a) Answers will vary.

(b) Vertical asymptote: $x = 25$

Horizontal asymptote: $y = 25$

(c)

(d)

x	30	35	40	45	50	55	60
y	150	87.5	66.7	56.3	50	45.8	42.9

(e) Yes. You would expect the average speed for the round trip to be the average of the average speeds for the two parts of the trip.

(f) No. At 20 miles per hour you would use more time in one direction than is required for the round trip at an average speed of 50 miles per hour.

81. False. Polynomials do not have vertical asymptotes.

83. Answers will vary. Sample answer: $f(x) = \dfrac{2x^2}{x^2 + 1}$

85. $(x - 7)(x - 8)$

87. $(x - 5)(x + 2i)(x - 2i)$

89. $x \geq \dfrac{10}{3}$

91. $-3 < x < 7$

93. Answers will vary.

Section 2.7   *(page 204)*

Vocabulary Check   *(page 204)*

1. critical; test intervals   **2.** zeros; undefined values

3. $P = R - C$

1. (a) No   (b) Yes   (c) Yes   (d) No

3. (a) Yes   (b) No   (c) No   (d) Yes

5. $2, -\dfrac{3}{2}$ **7.** $\dfrac{7}{2}, 5$

9. $[-3, 3]$

11. $(-7, 3)$

13. $(-\infty, -5] \cup [1, \infty)$

15. $(-3, 2)$

17. $(-3, 1)$

19. $\left(-\infty, -4 - \sqrt{21}\,\right] \cup \left[-4 + \sqrt{21}, \infty\right)$

21. $(-1, 1) \cup (3, \infty)$

23. $[-3, 2] \cup [3, \infty)$

25. $x = \dfrac{1}{2}$ **27.** $(-\infty, 0) \cup \left(0, \dfrac{3}{2}\right)$

29. $[-2, 0] \cup [2, \infty)$ **31.** $[-2, \infty)$

33.   **35.**

(a) $x \leq -1$, $x \geq 3$ (a) $-2 \leq x \leq 0$,

(b) $0 \leq x \leq 2$ $2 \leq x < \infty$

(b) $x \leq 4$

37. $(-\infty, -1) \cup (0, 1)$ **39.** $(-\infty, -1) \cup (4, \infty)$

41. $(5, 15)$ **43.** $\left(-5, -\dfrac{3}{2}\right) \cup (-1, \infty)$

45. $\left(-\dfrac{3}{4}, 3\right) \cup [6, \infty)$ **47.** $(-3, -2] \cup [0, 3)$

49. $(-\infty, -1) \cup \left(-\dfrac{2}{3}, 1\right) \cup (3, \infty)$

51.   **53.**

(a) $0 \leq x < 2$ (a) $|x| \geq 2$

(b) $2 < x \leq 4$ (b) $-\infty < x < \infty$

CHAPTER 2

55. $[-2, 2]$ **57.** $(-\infty, 3] \cup [4, \infty)$
59. $(-5, 0] \cup (7, \infty)$ **61.** $(-3.51, 3.51)$
63. $(-0.13, 25.13)$ **65.** $(2.26, 2.39)$
67. (a) $t = 10$ seconds   (b) 4 seconds $< t < 6$ seconds
69. 13.8 meters $\leq L \leq 36.2$ meters
71. $40,000 \leq x \leq 50,000;\ 50.00 \leq p \leq 55.00$
73. (a)

(b)

t	24	26	28	30	32	34
C	70.5	71.6	72.9	74.6	76.8	79.6

2011

(c) $t \approx 31$

(d)

t	36	37	38	39
C	83.2	85.4	87.8	90.5

t	40	41	42	43
C	93.5	96.8	100.4	104.4

2016 to 2021

(e) $37 \leq t \leq 41$ (f) Answers will vary.
75. $R_1 \geq 2$ ohms
77. True. The test intervals are $(-\infty, -3), (-3, 1), (1, 4),$ and $(4, \infty)$.
79. $(-\infty, -4] \cup [4, \infty)$ **81.** $\left(-\infty, -2\sqrt{30}\right] \cup \left[2\sqrt{30}, \infty\right)$
83. (a) If $a > 0$ and $c \leq 0$, b can be any real number. If $a > 0$ and $c > 0$, $b < -2\sqrt{ac}$ or $b > 2\sqrt{ac}$.
    (b) 0
85. $(2x + 5)^2$ **87.** $(x + 3)(x + 2)(x - 2)$ **89.** $2x^2 + x$

Review Exercises   *(page 208)*

1. (a)

Vertical stretch

(b)

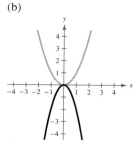

Vertical stretch and reflection in the x-axis

(c)

Vertical shift

(d)

Horizontal shift

3. $g(x) = (x - 1)^2 - 1$

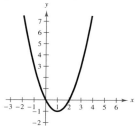

Vertex: $(1, -1)$
Axis of symmetry: $x = 1$
x-intercepts: $(0, 0), (2, 0)$

5. $f(x) = (x + 4)^2 - 6$

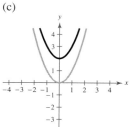

Vertex: $(-4, -6)$
Axis of symmetry: $x = -4$
x-intercepts: $\left(-4 \pm \sqrt{6}, 0\right)$

7. $f(t) = -2(t - 1)^2 + 3$

Vertex: $(1, 3)$
Axis of symmetry: $t = 1$
t-intercepts: $\left(1 \pm \dfrac{\sqrt{6}}{2}, 0\right)$

9. $h(x) = 4\left(x + \tfrac{1}{2}\right)^2 + 12$

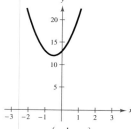

Vertex: $\left(-\tfrac{1}{2}, 12\right)$
Axis of symmetry: $x = -\tfrac{1}{2}$
No x-intercept

11. $h(x) = \left(x + \tfrac{5}{2}\right)^2 - \tfrac{41}{4}$

Vertex: $\left(-\tfrac{5}{2}, -\tfrac{41}{4}\right)$
Axis of symmetry: $x = -\tfrac{5}{2}$
x-intercepts: $\left(\dfrac{\pm\sqrt{41} - 5}{2}, 0\right)$

13. $f(x) = \tfrac{1}{3}\left(x + \tfrac{5}{2}\right)^2 - \tfrac{41}{12}$

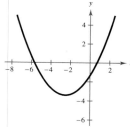

Vertex: $\left(-\tfrac{5}{2}, -\tfrac{41}{12}\right)$
Axis of symmetry: $x = -\tfrac{5}{2}$
x-intercepts: $\left(\dfrac{\pm\sqrt{41} - 5}{2}, 0\right)$

15. $f(x) = -\frac{1}{2}(x - 4)^2 + 1$　**17.** $f(x) = (x - 1)^2 - 4$

19. (a)

(b) $y = 100 - x$
$A = 100x - x^2$
(c) $x = 50, \; y = 50$

21. 1091 units

23.

25.

27.

29. Falls to the left, falls to the right

31. Rises to the left, rises to the right

33. $-7, \frac{3}{2}$, odd multiplicity; turning point: 1

35. $0, \pm\sqrt{3}$, odd multiplicity; turning points: 2

37. 0, even multiplicity; $\frac{5}{3}$, odd multiplicity; turning points: 2

39. (a) Rises to the left, falls to the right　(b) -1
(c) Answers will vary.
(d)

41. (a) Rises to the right, rises to the left　(b) $-3, 0, 1$
(c) Answers will vary.
(d)

43. (a) $[-1, 0]$　(b) ≈ -0.900

45. (a) $[-1, 0], [1, 2]$　(b) $\approx -0.200, \approx 1.772$

47. $8x + 5 + \dfrac{2}{3x - 2}$　**49.** $5x + 2$

51. $x^2 - 3x + 2 - \dfrac{1}{x^2 + 2}$

53. $6x^3 + 8x^2 - 11x - 4 - \dfrac{8}{x - 2}$

55. $2x^2 - 11x - 6$

57. (a) Yes　(b) Yes　(c) Yes　(d) No

59. (a) -421　(b) -9

61. (a) Answers will vary.　(b) $(x + 7), (x + 1)$
(c) $f(x) = (x + 7)(x + 1)(x - 4)$　(d) $-7, -1, 4$
(e)

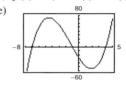

63. (a) Answers will vary.　(b) $(x + 1), (x - 4)$
(c) $f(x) = (x + 1)(x - 4)(x + 2)(x - 3)$
(d) $-2, -1, 3, 4$
(e)

65. $6 + 2i$　**67.** $-1 + 3i$　**69.** $3 + 7i$

71. $40 + 65i$　**73.** $-4 - 46i$　**75.** $\frac{23}{17} + \frac{10}{17}i$

77. $\frac{21}{13} - \frac{1}{13}i$　**79.** $\pm\dfrac{\sqrt{3}}{3}i$　**81.** $1 \pm 3i$

83. $0, 2$　**85.** $8, 1$　**87.** $-4, 6, \pm 2i$

89. $\pm 1, \pm 3, \pm 5, \pm 15, \pm\frac{1}{2}, \pm\frac{3}{2}, \pm\frac{5}{2}, \pm\frac{15}{2}, \pm\frac{1}{4}, \pm\frac{3}{4}, \pm\frac{5}{4}, \pm\frac{15}{4}$

91. $-1, -3, 6$　**93.** $1, 8$　**95.** $-4, 3$

97. $3x^4 - 14x^3 + 17x^2 - 42x + 24$

99. $4, \pm i$　**101.** $-3, \frac{1}{2}, 2 \pm i$

103. $0, 1, -5; f(x) = x(x - 1)(x + 5)$

105. $-4, 2 \pm 3i; g(x) = (x + 4)^2(x - 2 - 3i)(x - 2 + 3i)$

107. Two or no positive zeros, one negative zero

109. Answers will vary.

111. Domain: all real numbers x except $x = -12$

113. Domain: all real numbers x except $x = 6, 4$

115. Vertical asymptote: $x = -3$
Horizontal asymptote: $y = 0$

117. Vertical asymptote: $x = -3$
Horizontal asymptote: $y = 0$

119. (a) Domain: all real numbers x except $x = 0$
(b) No intercepts
(c) Vertical asymptote: $x = 0$
Horizontal asymptote: $y = 0$

CHAPTER 2

(d)

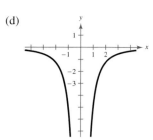

121. (a) Domain: all real numbers x except $x = 1$
   (b) x-intercept: $(-2, 0)$
       y-intercept: $(0, 2)$
   (c) Vertical asymptote: $x = 1$
       Horizontal asymptote: $y = -1$
   (d)

123. (a) Domain: all real numbers x (b) Intercept: $(0, 0)$
   (c) Horizontal asymptote: $y = 1$
   (d)

125. (a) Domain: all real numbers x (b) Intercept: $(0, 0)$
   (c) Horizontal asymptote: $y = 0$
   (d)

127. (a) Domain: all real numbers x (b) Intercept: $(0, 0)$
   (c) Horizontal asymptote: $y = -6$

(d)

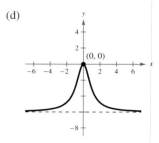

129. (a) Domain: all real numbers x except $x = 0, \frac{1}{3}$
   (b) x-intercept: $(1.5, 0)$
   (c) Vertical asymptote: $x = 0$
       Horizontal asymptote: $y = 2$
   (d)

131. (a) Domain: all real numbers x
   (b) Intercept: $(0, 0)$ (c) Slant asymptote: $y = 2x$
   (d)

133. (a) Domain: all real numbers x except $x = \frac{4}{3}$
   (b) y-intercept: $(0, -0.5)$
       x-intercepts: $\left(\frac{2}{3}, 0\right), (1, 0)$
   (c) Vertical asymptote: $x = \frac{4}{3}$
       Slant asymptote: $y = x - \frac{1}{3}$
   (d)

135. $0.50 is the horizontal asymptote of the function.

137. (a)

2 in.

2 in. y 2 in.

2 in.

x

(b) $(x - 4)(y - 4) = 30$

$$y = \frac{4x + 14}{x - 4}$$

$$\text{Area} = x\left(\frac{4x + 14}{x - 4}\right)$$

$$= \frac{2x(2x + 7)}{x - 4}$$

(c) $4 < x < \infty$

(d)

9.48 inches × 9.48 inches

139. $\left(-\frac{4}{3}, \frac{1}{2}\right)$ **141.** $[-4, 0] \cup [4, \infty)$

143. $[-5, -1) \cup (1, \infty)$ **145.** $[-4, -3] \cup (0, \infty)$

147. 4.9%

149. False. A fourth-degree polynomial can have at most four zeros, and complex zeros occur in conjugate pairs.

151. Find the vertex of the quadratic function and write the function in standard form. If the leading coefficient is positive, the vertex is a minimum. If the leading coefficient is negative, the vertex is a maximum.

153. An asymptote of a graph is a line to which the graph becomes arbitrarily close as x increases or decreases without bound.

Chapter Test *(page 212)*

1. (a) Reflection in the x-axis followed by a vertical translation

(b) Horizontal translation

2. $y = (x - 3)^2 - 6$

3. (a) 50 feet

(b) 5. Yes, changing the constant term results in a vertical translation of the graph and therefore changes the maximum height.

4. Rises to the left, falls to the right

5. $3x + \dfrac{x - 1}{x^2 + 1}$ **6.** $2x^3 + 4x^2 + 3x + 6 + \dfrac{9}{x - 2}$

7. $(4x - 1)\left(x - \sqrt{3}\right)\left(x + \sqrt{3}\right)$;

Solutions: $\frac{1}{4}, \pm\sqrt{3}$

8. (a) $-3 + 5i$ (b) 7 **9.** $2 - i$

10. $f(x) = x^4 - 9x^3 + 28x^2 - 30x$

11. $f(x) = x^4 - 6x^3 + 16x^2 - 24x + 16$

12. $-2, \pm\sqrt{5}i$ **13.** $-2, 4, -1 \pm \sqrt{2}i$

14. x-intercepts: $(-2, 0), (2, 0)$

No y-intercept

Vertical asymptote: $x = 0$

Horizontal asymptote: $y = -1$

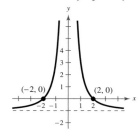

15. x-intercept: $(-1.5, 0)$

y-intercept: $(0, 0.75)$

Vertical asymptote: $x = -4$

Horizontal asymptote: $y = 2$

16. No x-intercept

y-intercept: $(0, -2)$

Vertical asymptote: $x = 1$

Slant asymptote: $y = x + 1$

17. $x < -4$ or $x > \frac{3}{2}$ **18.** $x < -6$ or $0 < x < 4$

Problem Solving *(page 215)*

1. Answers will vary.
3. 2 inches × 2 inches × 5 inches
5. (a) and (b) $y = -x^2 + 5x - 4$
7. (a) $f(x) = (x - 2)x^2 + 5 = x^3 - 2x^2 + 5$
   (b) $f(x) = -(x + 3)x^2 + 1 = -x^3 - 3x^2 + 1$
9. $(a + bi)(a - bi) = a^2 + abi - abi - b^2i^2$
   $$= a^2 + b^2$$
11. (a) As $|a|$ increases, the graph stretches vertically. For $a < 0$, the graph is reflected in the x-axis.
   (b) As $|b|$ increases, the vertical asymptote is translated. For $b > 0$, the graph is translated to the right. For $b < 0$, the graph is reflected in the x-axis and is translated to the left.

Chapter 3

Section 3.1 *(page 226)*

Vocabulary Check *(page 226)*

1. algebraic   2. transcendental

3. natural exponential; natural   4. $A = P\left(1 + \dfrac{r}{n}\right)^{nt}$

5. $A = Pe^{rt}$

---

1. 946.852   3. 0.006   5. 1767.767
7. d   8. c   9. a   10. b
11.

x	-2	-1	0	1	2
$f(x)$	4	2	1	0.5	0.25

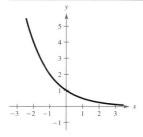

13.

x	-2	-1	0	1	2
$f(x)$	36	6	1	0.167	0.028

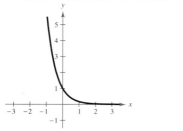

15.

x	-2	-1	0	1	2
$f(x)$	0.125	0.25	0.5	1	2

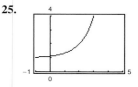

17. Shift the graph of f four units to the right.
19. Shift the graph of f five units upward.
21. Reflect the graph of f in the x-axis and y-axis and shift six units to the right.

23.   25.

27. 0.472   29. 3.857×10^{-22} 31. 7166.647

33.

x	-2	-1	0	1	2
$f(x)$	0.135	0.368	1	2.718	7.389

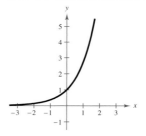

35.

x	-8	-7	-6	-5	-4
$f(x)$	0.055	0.149	0.406	1.104	3

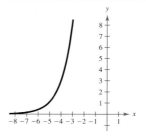

37.

x	−2	−1	0	1	2
f(x)	4.037	4.100	4.271	4.736	6

39.

41.

43.

45. $x = 2$ **47.** $x = -3$ **49.** $x = \frac{1}{3}$ **51.** $x = 3, -1$

53.

n	1	2	4
A	\$3200.21	\$3205.09	\$3207.57

n	12	365	Continuous
A	\$3209.23	\$3210.06	\$3210.06

55.

n	1	2	4
A	\$4515.28	\$4535.05	\$4545.11

n	12	365	Continuous
A	\$4551.89	\$4555.18	\$4555.30

57.

t	10	20	30
A	\$17,901.90	\$26,706.49	\$39,841.40

t	40	50
A	\$59,436.39	\$88,668.67

59.

t	10	20	30
A	\$22,986.49	\$44,031.56	\$84,344.25

t	40	50
A	\$161,564.86	\$309,484.08

61. \$222,822.57   **63.** \$35.45

65. (a) $V(1) = 10,000.298$ (b) $V(1.5) = 100,004.47$
(c) $V(2) = 1,000,059.6$

67. (a) 25 grams   (b) 16.21 grams
(c)

69. (a)

(b)

x	0	25	50	75	100
Model	12.5	44.5	81.82	96.19	99.3
Actual	12	44	81	96	99

(c) 63.14%   (d) 38 masses

71. True. As $x \to -\infty$, $f(x) \to -2$ but never reaches -2.

73. $f(x) = h(x)$ **75.** $f(x) = g(x) = h(x)$

77.   (a) $x < 0$ (b) $x > 0$

79.

As $x \to \infty$, $f(x) \to g(x)$.
As $x \to -\infty$, $f(x) \to g(x)$.

81. $y = \pm\sqrt{25 - x^2}$

83.

85. Answers will vary.

Section 3.2   *(page 236)*

Vocabulary Check   *(page 236)*

1. logarithmic   **2.** 10   **3.** natural; e

4. $a^{\log_a x} = x$ **5.** $x = y$

---

1. $4^3 = 64$ **3.** $7^{-2} = \frac{1}{49}$ **5.** $32^{2/5} = 4$

7. $36^{1/2} = 6$ **9.** $\log_5 125 = 3$ **11.** $\log_{81} 3 = \frac{1}{4}$

13. $\log_6 \frac{1}{36} = -2$ **15.** $\log_7 1 = 0$ **17.** 4   **19.** 0

21. 2   **23.** -0.0972 **25.** 1.097   **27.** 4   **29.** 1

31.

Domain: $(0, \infty)$
x-intercept: $(1, 0)$
Vertical asymptote: $x = 0$

33.

Domain: $(0, \infty)$
x-intercept: $(9, 0)$
Vertical asymptote: $x = 0$

35.

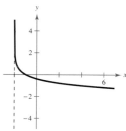

Domain: $(-2, \infty)$
x-intercept: $(-1, 0)$
Vertical asymptote: $x = -2$

37.

Domain: $(0, \infty)$
x-intercept: $(5, 0)$
Vertical asymptote: $x = 0$

39. c   **40.** f   **41.** d   **42.** e   **43.** b   **44.** a

45. $e^{-0.693\cdots} = \frac{1}{2}$ **47.** $e^{1.386\cdots} = 4$

49. $e^{5.521\cdots} = 250$ **51.** $e^0 = 1$

53. $\ln 20.0855\ldots = 3$ **55.** $\ln 1.6487\ldots = \frac{1}{2}$

57. $\ln 0.6065\ldots = -0.5$ **59.** $\ln 4 = x$ **61.** 2.913

63. -0.575 **65.** 3   **67.** $-\frac{2}{3}$

69.

Domain: $(1, \infty)$
x-intercept: $(2, 0)$
Vertical asymptote: $x = 1$

71.

Domain: $(-\infty, 0)$
x-intercept: $(-1, 0)$
Vertical asymptote: $x = 0$

73.

75.

77.

79. $x = 3$ **81.** $x = 7$ **83.** $x = 4$ **85.** $x = -5, 5$

87. (a) 30 years; 20 years   (b) \$396,234; \$301,123.20
(c) \$246,234; \$151,123.20
(d) $x = 1000$; The monthly payment must be greater than
\$1000.

89. (a)

(b) 80
(c) 68.1
(d) 62.3

91. False. Reflecting $g(x)$ about the line $y = x$ will determine the graph of $f(x)$.

93.   **95.**

The functions f and g are inverses.   The functions f and g are inverses.

97. (a)

$g(x)$; The natural log function grows at a slower rate than the square root function.

(b)

$g(x)$; The natural log function grows at a slower rate than the fourth root function.

99. (a) False   (b) True   (c) True   (d) False

101. (a)

(b) Increasing: $(1, \infty)$
Decreasing: $(0, 1)$

(c) Relative minimum: $(1, 0)$

103. 15   **105.** 4300   **107.** 1028

Section 3.3   *(page 243)*

Vocabulary Check   *(page 243)*

1. change-of-base   **2.** $\dfrac{\log x}{\log a} = \dfrac{\ln x}{\ln a}$

3. c   **4.** a   **5.** b

1. (a) $\dfrac{\log x}{\log 5}$ (b) $\dfrac{\ln x}{\ln 5}$ **3.** (a) $\dfrac{\log x}{\log \frac{1}{5}}$ (b) $\dfrac{\ln x}{\ln \frac{1}{5}}$

5. (a) $\dfrac{\log \frac{3}{10}}{\log x}$ (b) $\dfrac{\ln \frac{3}{10}}{\ln x}$ **7.** (a) $\dfrac{\log x}{\log 2.6}$ (b) $\dfrac{\ln x}{\ln 2.6}$

9. 1.771   **11.** -2.000 **13.** -0.417 **15.** 2.633

17. $\frac{3}{2}$ **19.** $-3 - \log_5 2$ **21.** $6 + \ln 5$ **23.** 2

25. $\frac{3}{4}$ **27.** 2.4   **29.** -9 is not in the domain of $\log_3 x$.

31. 4.5   **33.** $-\frac{1}{2}$ **35.** 7   **37.** 2

39. $\log_4 5 + \log_4 x$ **41.** $4 \log_8 x$ **43.** $1 - \log_5 x$

45. $\frac{1}{2} \ln z$ **47.** $\ln x + \ln y + 2 \ln z$

49. $\ln z + 2 \ln(z - 1)$ **51.** $\frac{1}{2} \log_2(a - 1) - 2 \log_2 3$

53. $\frac{1}{3} \ln x - \frac{1}{3} \ln y$ **55.** $4 \ln x + \frac{1}{2} \ln y - 5 \ln z$

57. $2 \log_5 x - 2 \log_5 y - 3 \log_5 z$

59. $\dfrac{3}{4} \ln x + \dfrac{1}{4} \ln(x^2 + 3)$ **61.** $\ln 3x$ **63.** $\log_4 \dfrac{z}{y}$

65. $\log_2(x + 4)^2$ **67.** $\log_3 \sqrt[4]{5x}$ **69.** $\ln \dfrac{x}{(x + 1)^3}$

71. $\log \dfrac{xz^3}{y^2}$ **73.** $\ln \dfrac{x}{(x^2 - 4)^4}$ **75.** $\ln \sqrt[3]{\dfrac{x(x + 3)^2}{x^2 - 1}}$

77. $\log_8 \dfrac{\sqrt[3]{y(y + 4)^2}}{y - 1}$

79. $\log_2 \frac{32}{4} = \log_2 32 - \log_2 4$; Property 2

81. $\beta = 10(\log I + 12)$; 60 dB   **83.** ≈ 3

85. $y = 256.24 - 20.8 \ln x$

87. False. $\ln 1 = 0$ **89.** False. $\ln(x - 2) \ne \ln x - \ln 2$

91. False. $u = v^2$ **93.** Answers will vary.

95. $f(x) = \dfrac{\log x}{\log 2} = \dfrac{\ln x}{\ln 2}$ **97.** $f(x) = \dfrac{\log x}{\log \frac{1}{2}} = \dfrac{\ln x}{\ln \frac{1}{2}}$

99. $f(x) = \dfrac{\log x}{\log 11.8} = \dfrac{\ln x}{\ln 11.8}$

101. $f(x) = h(x)$; Property 2

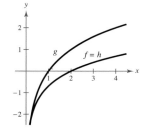

103. $\dfrac{3x^4}{2y^3}$, $x \neq 0$ **105.** $1, x \neq 0, y \neq 0$

107. $-1, \dfrac{1}{3}$ **109.** $\dfrac{-1 \pm \sqrt{97}}{6}$

Section 3.4 *(page 253)*

Vocabulary Check *(page 253)*

1. solve
2. (a) $x = y$ (b) $x = y$ (c) x (d) x
3. extraneous

---

1. (a) Yes   (b) No
3. (a) No   (b) Yes   (c) Yes, approximate
5. (a) Yes, approximate   (b) No   (c) Yes
7. (a) No   (b) Yes   (c) Yes, approximate
9. 2   **11.** -5 **13.** 2   **15.** $\ln 2 \approx 0.693$
17. $e^{-1} \approx 0.368$ **19.** 64   **21.** $(3, 8)$ **23.** $(9, 2)$
25. $2, -1$ **27.** $\approx 1.618, \approx -0.618$
29. $\dfrac{\ln 5}{\ln 3} \approx 1.465$ **31.** $\ln 5 \approx 1.609$ **33.** $\ln 28 \approx 3.332$
35. $\dfrac{\ln 80}{2 \ln 3} \approx 1.994$ **37.** 2   **39.** 4
41. $3 - \dfrac{\ln 565}{\ln 2} \approx -6.142$ **43.** $\dfrac{1}{3}\log\left(\dfrac{3}{2}\right) \approx 0.059$
45. $1 + \dfrac{\ln 7}{\ln 5} \approx 2.209$ **47.** $\dfrac{\ln 12}{3} \approx 0.828$
49. $-\ln \dfrac{3}{5} \approx 0.511$ **51.** 0   **53.** $\dfrac{\ln \frac{8}{3}}{3 \ln 2} + \dfrac{1}{3} \approx 0.805$
55. $\ln 5 \approx 1.609$ **57.** $\ln 4 \approx 1.386$
59. $2 \ln 75 \approx 8.635$ **61.** $\dfrac{1}{2} \ln 1498 \approx 3.656$
63. $\dfrac{\ln 4}{365 \ln\left(1 + \frac{0.065}{365}\right)} \approx 21.330$
65. $\dfrac{\ln 2}{12 \ln\left(1 + \frac{0.10}{12}\right)} \approx 6.960$

67.
-0.427

69.
3.847

71.
12.207

73.
16.636

75. $e^{-3} \approx 0.050$ **77.** $\dfrac{e^{2.4}}{2} \approx 5.512$ **79.** 1,000,000
81. $\dfrac{e^{10/3}}{5} \approx 5.606$ **83.** $e^2 - 2 \approx 5.389$
85. $e^{-2/3} \approx 0.513$ **87.** $2(3^{11/6}) \approx 14.988$
89. No solution   **91.** $1 + \sqrt{1 + e} \approx 2.928$
93. No solution   **95.** 7   **97.** $\dfrac{-1 + \sqrt{17}}{2} \approx 1.562$
99. 2   **101.** $\dfrac{725 + 125\sqrt{33}}{8} \approx 180.384$

103.
2.807

105.
20.086

107. (a) 8.2 years   (b) 12.9 years
109. (a) 1426 units   (b) 1498 units
111. (a)
(b) $V = 6.7$; The yield will approach 6.7 million cubic feet per acre.
(c) 29.3 years

113. 2001
115. (a) $y = 100$ and $y = 0$; The range falls between 0% and 100%.
(b) Males: 69.71 inches   Females: 64.51 inches
117. (a)

x	0.2	0.4	0.6	0.8	1.0
y	162.6	78.5	52.5	40.5	33.9

(b) The model appears to fit the data well.

(c) 1.2 meters
(d) No. According to the model, when the number of g's is less than 23, x is between 2.276 meters and 4.404 meters, which isn't realistic in most vehicles.
119. $\log_b uv = \log_b u + \log_b v$
True by Property 1 in Section 5.3.
121. $\log_b(u - v) = \log_b u - \log_b v$
False.
$1.95 \approx \log(100 - 10) \neq \log 100 - \log 10 = 1$
123. Yes. See Exercise 93.
125. Yes. Time to double: $t = \dfrac{\ln 2}{r}$;
Time to quadruple: $t = \dfrac{\ln 4}{r} = 2\left(\dfrac{\ln 2}{r}\right)$

127. $4|x|y^2\sqrt{3y}$ **129.** $5\sqrt[3]{3}$
131.

133.

135. 1.226 **137.** -5.595

Section 3.5 (page 264)

Vocabulary Check (page 264)

1. $y = ae^{bx}$; $y = ae^{-bx}$
2. $y = a + b \ln x$; $y = a + b \log x$
3. normally distributed **4.** bell; average value
5. sigmoidal

1. c **2.** e **3.** b **4.** a **5.** d **6.** f

	Initial Investment	Annual % Rate	Time to Double	Amount After 10 years
7.	$1000	3.5%	19.8 yr	$1419.07
9.	$750	8.9438%	7.75 yr	$1834.36
11.	$500	11.0%	6.3 yr	$1505.00
13.	$6376.28	4.5%	15.4 yr	$10,000.00

15. $112,087.09
17. (a) 6.642 years (b) 6.330 years
 (c) 6.302 years (d) 6.301 years
19.

r	2%	4%	6%	8%	10%	12%
t	54.93	27.47	18.31	13.73	10.99	9.16

21.

r	2%	4%	6%	8%	10%	12%
t	55.48	28.01	18.85	14.27	11.53	9.69

23. Continuous compounding

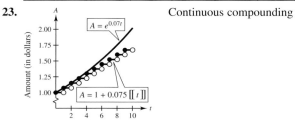

	Half-life (years)	Initial Quantity	Amount After 1000 Years
25.	1599	10 g	6.48 g
27.	5715	2.26 g	2 g
29.	24,100	2.16 g	2.1 g

31. $y = e^{0.7675x}$ **33.** $y = 5e^{-0.4024x}$
35. (a) Decreasing due to the negative exponent.
 (b) 2000: population of 2430 thousand
 2003: population of 2408.95 thousand
 (c) 2018
37. $k = 0.2988$; $\approx 5,309,734$ hits **39.** 3.15 hours
41. (a) $\approx 12,180$ years old (b) ≈ 4797 years old
43. (a) $V = -6394t + 30,788$ (b) $V = 30,788e^{-0.268t}$
 (c)

The exponential model depreciates faster.

 (d)

t	1	3
$V = -6394t + 30,788$	24,394	11,606
$V = 30,788e^{-0.268t}$	23,550	13,779

 (e) Answers will vary.
45. (a) $S(t) = 100(1 - e^{-0.1625t})$
 (b)

 (c) 55,625

47. (a)

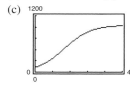

 (b) 100

49. (a) 203 animals (b) 13 years
 (c) 1200

Horizontal asymptotes: $y = 0$, $y = 1000$. The population size will approach 1000 as time increases.

51. (a) $10^{7.9} \approx 79,432,823$ (b) $10^{8.3} \approx 199,526,231$
 (c) $10^{4.2} \approx 15,849$
53. (a) 20 decibels (b) 70 decibels
 (c) 40 decibels (d) 120 decibels
55. 95% **57.** 4.64 **59.** 1.58×10^{-6} moles per liter
61. $10^{5.1}$ **63.** 3:00 A.M.
65. (a) 150,000

 (b) ≈ 21 years; Yes

67. False. The domain can be the set of real numbers for a logistic growth function.

69. False. The graph of $f(x)$ is the graph of $g(x)$ shifted upward five units.

71. (a) Logarithmic   (b) Logistic   (c) Exponential
(d) Linear   (e) None of the above   (f) Exponential

73. (a)

(b) $\sqrt{10}$
(c) $\left(-\frac{1}{2}, \frac{7}{2}\right)$
(d) 3

75. (a)

(b) $\sqrt{146}$
(c) $\left(\frac{17}{2}, \frac{1}{2}\right)$
(d) $-\frac{5}{11}$

77. (a)

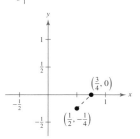

(b) $\sqrt{\frac{1}{8}}$
(c) $\left(\frac{5}{8}, -\frac{1}{8}\right)$
(d) 1

79.

81.

83.

85.

87.

89.

91.

93. Answers will vary.

Review Exercises   *(page 271)*

1. 76.699   **3.** 0.337   **5.** 1456.529
7. c   **8.** d   **9.** a   **10.** b
11. Shift the graph of f one unit to the right.
13. Reflect f in the x-axis and shift two units to the left.

15.

x	-1	0	1	2	3
$f(x)$	8	5	4.25	4.063	4.016

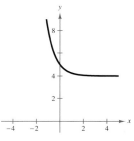

17.

x	-2	-1	0	1	2
$f(x)$	-0.377	-1	-2.65	-7.023	-18.61

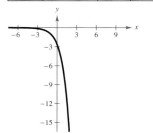

19.

x	-1	0	1	2	3
$f(x)$	4.008	4.04	4.2	5	9

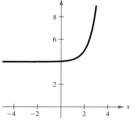

21.

x	-2	-1	0	1	2
$f(x)$	3.25	3.5	4	5	7

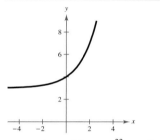

23. $x = -4$ **25.** $x = \frac{22}{5}$ **27.** 2980.958   **29.** 0.183

31.

x	-2	-1	0	1	2
$h(x)$	2.72	1.65	1	0.61	0.37

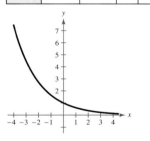

33.

x	-3	-2	-1	0	1
$f(x)$	0.37	1	2.72	7.39	20.09

35.

n	1	2	4	12
A	\$6569.98	\$6635.43	\$6669.46	\$6692.64

n	365	Continuous
A	\$6704.00	\$6704.39

37. (a) 0.154   (b) 0.487   (c) 0.811
39. (a) \$1,069,047.14   (b) 7.9 years
41. $\log_4 64 = 3$ **43.** $\ln 2.2255 \ldots = 0.8$
45. 3   **47.** -3 **49.** $x = 7$ **51.** $x = -5$
53. Domain: $(0, \infty)$ **55.** Domain: $(0, \infty)$
x-intercept: $(1, 0)$ x-intercept: $(3, 0)$
Vertical asymptote: $x = 0$ Vertical asymptote: $x = 0$

57. Domain: $(-5, \infty)$
x-intercept: $(9995, 0)$
Vertical asymptote: $x = -5$

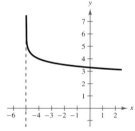

59. 3.118   **61.** -12 **63.** 2.034
65. Domain: $(0, \infty)$ **67.** Domain: $(-\infty, 0), (0, \infty)$
x-intercept: $(e^{-3}, 0)$ x-intercept: $(\pm 1, 0)$
Vertical asymptote: $x = 0$ Vertical asymptote: $x = 0$

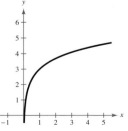

69. 53.4 inches   **71.** 1.585   **73.** -2.322
75. $\log 2 + 2 \log 3 \approx 1.255$ **77.** $2 \ln 2 + \ln 5 \approx 2.996$

79. $1 + 2 \log_5 x$ **81.** $1 + \log_3 2 - \frac{1}{3} \log_3 x$

83. $2 \ln x + 2 \ln y + \ln z$ **85.** $\ln(x + 3) - \ln x - \ln y$

87. $\log_2 5x$ **89.** $\ln \dfrac{x}{\sqrt[4]{y}}$ **91.** $\log_8 y^7 \sqrt[3]{x + 4}$

93. $\ln \dfrac{\sqrt{2x - 1}}{(x + 1)^2}$

95. (a) $0 \le h < 18,000$

(b)   Vertical asymptote:
$h = 18,000$

(c) The plane is climbing at a slower rate, so the time required increases.

(d) 5.46 minutes

97. 3   **99.** $\ln 3 \approx 1.099$ **101.** 16

103. $e^4 \approx 54.598$ **105.** $\ln 12 \approx 2.485$ **107.** $x = 1, 3$

109. $\dfrac{\ln 22}{\ln 2} \approx 4.459$ **111.** $\dfrac{\ln 17}{\ln 5} \approx 1.760$

113. $\ln 2 \approx 0.693, \ln 5 \approx 1.609$

115.   **117.**

7.480; 0.392   2.447

119. $\frac{1}{3}e^{8.2} \approx 1213.650$ **121.** $\frac{1}{4}e^{7.5} \approx 452.011$

123. $3e^2 \approx 22.167$ **125.** $e^4 - 1 \approx 53.598$

127. No solution   **129.** 0.900

131.   **133.**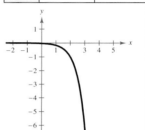

1.643   No solution

135. 15.2 years   **137.** e   **138.** b   **139.** f

140. d   **141.** a   **142.** c   **143.** $y = 2e^{0.1014x}$

145. 2008   **147.** (a) 13.8629%   (b) \$11,486.98

149. (a) 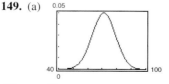   (b) 71

151. $10^{-3.5}$ watt per square centimeter

153. True by the inverse properties

155. b and d are negative.
a and c are positive.
Answers will vary.

Chapter Test   *(page 275)*

1. 1123.690   **2.** 687.291   **3.** 0.497   **4.** 22.198

5.

x	-1	$-\frac{1}{2}$	0	$\frac{1}{2}$	1
$f(x)$	10	3.162	1	0.316	0.1

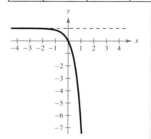

6.

x	-1	0	1	2	3
$f(x)$	-0.005	-0.028	-0.167	-1	-6

7.

x	-1	$-\frac{1}{2}$	0	$\frac{1}{2}$	1
$f(x)$	0.865	0.632	0	-1.718	-6.389

8. (a) -0.89 (b) 9.2

9.

x	$\frac{1}{2}$	1	$\frac{3}{2}$	2	4
$f(x)$	-5.699	-6	-6.176	-6.301	-6.602

Vertical asymptote: $x = 0$

10.

x	5	7	9	11	13
f(x)	0	1.099	1.609	1.946	2.197

Vertical asymptote: $x = 4$

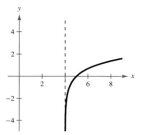

11.

x	−5	−3	−1	0	1
f(x)	1	2.099	2.609	2.792	2.946

Vertical asymptote: $x = -6$

12. 1.945 **13.** 0.115 **14.** 1.328

15. $\log_2 3 + 4 \log_2 |a|$ **16.** $\ln 5 + \frac{1}{2}\ln x - \ln 6$

17. $(\log 7 + 2 \log x) - (\log y + 3 \log z)$

18. $\log_3 13y$ **19.** $\ln \dfrac{x^4}{y^4}$ **20.** $\ln \dfrac{x^2(x-5)}{y^3}$

21. $x = -2$ **22.** $x = \dfrac{\ln 44}{-5} \approx -0.757$

23. $\dfrac{\ln 197}{4} \approx 1.321$ **24.** $e^{1/2} \approx 1.649$

25. $e^{-11/4} \approx 0.0639$ **26.** $\frac{800}{501} \approx 1.597$

27. $y = 2745e^{0.1570x}$ **28.** 55%

29. (a)

x	$\frac{1}{4}$	1	2	4	5	6
H	58.720	75.332	86.828	103.43	110.59	117.38

(b) 103 centimeters; 103.43 centimeters

Cumulative Test for Chapters 1–3 *(page 276)*

1. (a) Midpoint: $\left(1, \frac{3}{2}\right)$; Distance: $\sqrt{41}$

2.

3.

4.

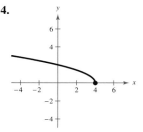

5. $y = 2x + 2$

6. For some values of x there correspond two values of y.

7. (a) $\dfrac{3}{2}$ (b) Division by 0 is undefined. (c) $\dfrac{s+2}{s}$

8. (a) Vertical shrink by $\frac{1}{2}$
(b) Vertical shift of two units upward
(c) Horizontal shift of two units to the left

9. (a) $5x - 2$ (b) $-3x - 4$ (c) $4x^2 - 11x - 3$
(d) $\dfrac{x-3}{4x+1}$; Domain: all real numbers x except $x = -\dfrac{1}{4}$

10. (a) $\sqrt{x-1} + x^2 + 1$ (b) $\sqrt{x-1} - x^2 - 1$
(c) $x^2\sqrt{x-1} + \sqrt{x-1}$
(d) $\dfrac{\sqrt{x-1}}{x^2+1}$; Domain: all real numbers x such that $x \geq 1$

11. (a) $2x + 12$ (b) $\sqrt{2x^2 + 6}$
Domain of $f \circ g$: all real numbers x such that $x \geq -6$
Domain of $g \circ f$: all real numbers

12. (a) $|x| - 2$ (b) $|x - 2|$
Domain of $f \circ g$ and $g \circ f$: all real numbers

13. Yes; $h^{-1}(x) = \frac{1}{5}(x + 2)$ **14.** 2438.65 kilowatts

15. $y = -\frac{3}{4}(x + 8)^2 + 5$

16.

17.

18.

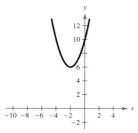

19. $-2, \pm 2i; (x + 2)(x + 2i)(x - 2i)$
20. $-7, 0, 3; x(x)(x - 3)(x + 7)$
21. $4, -\frac{1}{2}, 1 \pm 3i; (x - 4)(2x + 1)(x - 1 + 3i)(x - 1 - 3i)$

22. $3x - 2 - \dfrac{3x - 2}{2x^2 + 1}$

23. $2x^3 - x^2 + 2x - 10 + \dfrac{25}{x + 2}$

24.

Interval: $[1, 2]$; 1.20
25. Intercept: $(0, 0)$
Vertical asymptotes: $x = \pm 3$
Horizontal asymptote: $y = 0$

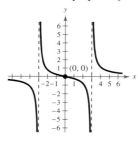

26. y-intercept: $(0, -1)$
x-intercept: $(1, 0)$
Horizontal asymptote: $y = 1$
Vertical asymptote: $x = -1$

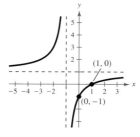

27. y-intercept: $(0, 6)$
x-intercepts: $(-2, 0), (-3, 0)$
Slant asymptote: $y = x + 4$
Vertical asymptote: $x = -1$

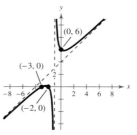

28. $x \le -2$ or $0 \le x \le 2$

29. All real numbers x such that $x < -5$ or $x > -1$

30. Reflect f in the x-axis and y-axis, and shift three units to the right.

31. Reflect f in the x-axis, and shift four units upward.

32. 1.991   **33.** -0.067 **34.** 1.717   **35.** 0.281
36. $\ln(x + 4) + \ln(x - 4) - 4 \ln x, x > 4$

37. $\ln \dfrac{x^2}{\sqrt{x + 5}}, x > 0$ **38.** $x = \dfrac{\ln 12}{2} \approx 1.242$

39. $\ln 3 \approx 1.099$ or $3 \ln 2 \approx 2.079$
40. $e^6 - 2 \approx 401.429$
41. (a)

(b) $S = 0.274t^2 - 4.08t + 50.6$

(c)

The model is a good fit for the data.

(d) 65.9 Yes, this is a reasonable answer.

Problem Solving *(page 279)*

1.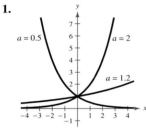

$y = 0.5^x$ and $y = 1.2^x$

$0 \le a \le 1.44$

3. As $x \to \infty$, the graph of e^x increases at a greater rate than the graph of x^n.

5. Answers will vary.

7. (a)   (b)

(c)

9.

$$f^{-1}(x) = \ln\left(\frac{x + \sqrt{x^2 + 4}}{2}\right)$$

11. c

13. $t = \dfrac{\ln c_1 - \ln c_2}{\left(\dfrac{1}{k_2} - \dfrac{1}{k_1}\right)\ln\dfrac{1}{2}}$

15. (a) $y_1 = 252{,}606(1.0310)^t$

(b) $y_2 = 400.88t^2 - 1464.6t + 291{,}782$

(c)

(d) The exponential model is a better fit. No, because the model is rapidly approaching infinity.

17. $1, e^2$

19. $y_4 = (x - 1) - \frac{1}{2}(x - 1)^2 + \frac{1}{3}(x - 1)^3 - \frac{1}{4}(x - 1)^4$

The pattern implies that

$\ln x = (x - 1) - \frac{1}{2}(x - 1)^2 + \frac{1}{3}(x - 1)^3 - \cdots$.

21.

17.7 cubic feet per minute

23. (a)   **25.** (a)

(b)–(e)   (b)–(e)
Answers will vary.   Answers will vary.

Chapter 4

Section 4.1 *(page 290)*

Vocabulary Check *(page 290)*

1. Trigonometry   **2.** angle   **3.** coterminal
4. radian   **5.** acute; obtuse
6. complementary; supplementary   **7.** degree
8. linear   **9.** angular   **10.** $A = \frac{1}{2}r^2\theta$

---

1. 2 radians   **3.** -3 radians   **5.** 1 radian
7. (a) Quadrant I   (b) Quadrant III
9. (a) Quadrant IV   (b) Quadrant III
11. (a) Quadrant III   (b) Quadrant II

CHAPTER 4

13. (a)   (b)

15. (a)   (b)

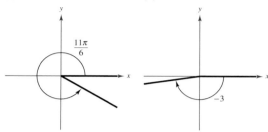

17. (a) $\dfrac{13\pi}{6}, -\dfrac{11\pi}{6}$ (b) $\dfrac{17\pi}{6}, -\dfrac{7\pi}{6}$

19. (a) $\dfrac{8\pi}{3}, -\dfrac{4\pi}{3}$ (b) $\dfrac{25\pi}{12}, -\dfrac{23\pi}{12}$

21. (a) Complement: $\dfrac{\pi}{6}$; Supplement: $\dfrac{2\pi}{3}$

     (b) Complement: none; Supplement: $\dfrac{\pi}{4}$

23. (a) Complement: $\dfrac{\pi}{2} - 1 \approx 0.57$;

       Supplement: $\pi - 1 \approx 2.14$

     (b) Complement: none; Supplement: $\pi - 2 \approx 1.14$

25. $210°$ **27.** $-60°$ **29.** $165°$

31. (a) Quadrant II   (b) Quadrant IV

33. (a) Quadrant III   (b) Quadrant I

35. (a)   (b)

37. (a)   (b)

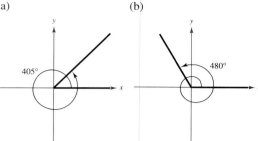

39. (a) $405°, -315°$ (b) $324°, -396°$

41. (a) $600°, -120°$ (b) $180°, -540°$

43. (a) Complement: $72°$; Supplement: $162°$

     (b) Complement: none; Supplement: $65°$

45. (a) Complement: $11°$; Supplement: $101°$

     (b) Complement: none; Supplement: $30°$

47. (a) $\dfrac{\pi}{6}$ (b) $\dfrac{5\pi}{6}$ **49.** (a) $-\dfrac{\pi}{9}$ (b) $-\dfrac{4\pi}{3}$

51. (a) $270°$ (b) $210°$ **53.** (a) $420°$ (b) $-66°$

55. 2.007 **57.** -3.776 **59.** 9.285 **61.** -0.014

63. $25.714°$ **65.** $337.500°$ **67.** $-756.000°$

69. $-114.592°$ **71.** (a) $54.75°$ (b) $-128.5°$

73. (a) $85.308°$ (b) $330.007°$

75. (a) $240° 36'$ (b) $-145° 48'$

77. (a) $2° 30'$ (b) $-3° 34' 48''$

79. $\frac{6}{5}$ radians   **81.** $\frac{32}{7}$ radians   **83.** $\frac{2}{9}$ radian

85. $\frac{50}{29}$ radians   **87.** 15π inches ≈ 47.12 inches

89. 3 meters   **91.** $\dfrac{8\pi}{3}$ square inches ≈ 8.38 square inches

93. 12.27 square feet   **95.** 591.3 miles

97. 0.071 radian $\approx 4.04°$ **99.** $\frac{5}{12}$ radian

101. (a) 728.3 revolutions per minute

      (b) 4576 radians per minute

103. (a) $10,400\pi$ radians per minute

          $\approx 32,672.56$ radians per minute

      (b) $9425\pi/3$ feet per minute ≈ 9869.84 feet per minute

105. (a) $[400\pi, 1000\pi]$ radians per minute

      (b) $[2400\pi, 6000\pi]$ centimeters per minute

107.

     $A = 476.39\pi$ square meters ≈ 1496.62 square meters

109. False. A measurement of 4π radians corresponds to two complete revolutions from the initial to the terminal side of an angle.

111. False. The terminal side of the angle lies on the *x*-axis.

113. Increases. The linear velocity is proportional to the radius.

115. The arc length is increasing. If θ is constant, the length of the arc is proportional to the radius $(s = r\theta)$.

117. $\dfrac{\sqrt{2}}{2}$ **119.** $2\sqrt{10}$

121.

$y = x^5$

$y = (x - 2)^5$

123.

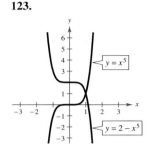

$y = x^5$

$y = 2 - x^5$

Section 4.2   *(page 299)*

Vocabulary Check   *(page 299)*

1. unit circle   **2.** periodic

3. period   **4.** odd; even

1. $\sin\theta = \frac{15}{17}$ $\csc\theta = \frac{17}{15}$
$\cos\theta = -\frac{8}{17}$ $\sec\theta = -\frac{17}{8}$
$\tan\theta = -\frac{15}{8}$ $\cot\theta = -\frac{8}{15}$

3. $\sin\theta = -\frac{5}{13}$ $\csc\theta = -\frac{13}{5}$
$\cos\theta = \frac{12}{13}$ $\sec\theta = \frac{13}{12}$
$\tan\theta = -\frac{5}{12}$ $\cot\theta = -\frac{12}{5}$

5. $\left(\dfrac{\sqrt{2}}{2}, \dfrac{\sqrt{2}}{2}\right)$ **7.** $\left(-\dfrac{\sqrt{3}}{2}, -\dfrac{1}{2}\right)$ **9.** $\left(-\dfrac{1}{2}, -\dfrac{\sqrt{3}}{2}\right)$

11. $(0, -1)$

13. $\sin\dfrac{\pi}{4} = \dfrac{\sqrt{2}}{2}$

$\cos\dfrac{\pi}{4} = \dfrac{\sqrt{2}}{2}$

$\tan\dfrac{\pi}{4} = 1$

15. $\sin\left(-\dfrac{\pi}{6}\right) = -\dfrac{1}{2}$

$\cos\left(-\dfrac{\pi}{6}\right) = \dfrac{\sqrt{3}}{2}$

$\tan\left(-\dfrac{\pi}{6}\right) = -\dfrac{\sqrt{3}}{3}$

17. $\sin\left(-\dfrac{7\pi}{4}\right) = \dfrac{\sqrt{2}}{2}$

$\cos\left(-\dfrac{7\pi}{4}\right) = \dfrac{\sqrt{2}}{2}$

$\tan\left(-\dfrac{7\pi}{4}\right) = 1$

19. $\sin\dfrac{11\pi}{6} = -\dfrac{1}{2}$

$\cos\dfrac{11\pi}{6} = \dfrac{\sqrt{3}}{2}$

$\tan\dfrac{11\pi}{6} = -\dfrac{\sqrt{3}}{3}$

21. $\sin\left(-\dfrac{3\pi}{2}\right) = 1$

$\cos\left(-\dfrac{3\pi}{2}\right) = 0$

$\tan\left(-\dfrac{3\pi}{2}\right)$ is undefined.

23. $\sin\dfrac{3\pi}{4} = \dfrac{\sqrt{2}}{2}$ $\csc\dfrac{3\pi}{4} = \sqrt{2}$

$\cos\dfrac{3\pi}{4} = -\dfrac{\sqrt{2}}{2}$ $\sec\dfrac{3\pi}{4} = -\sqrt{2}$

$\tan\dfrac{3\pi}{4} = -1$ $\cot\dfrac{3\pi}{4} = -1$

25. $\sin\left(-\dfrac{\pi}{2}\right) = -1$ $\csc\left(-\dfrac{\pi}{2}\right) = -1$

$\cos\left(-\dfrac{\pi}{2}\right) = 0$ $\sec\left(-\dfrac{\pi}{2}\right)$ is undefined.

$\tan\left(-\dfrac{\pi}{2}\right)$ is undefined. $\cot\left(-\dfrac{\pi}{2}\right) = 0$

27. $\sin\left(\dfrac{4\pi}{3}\right) = -\dfrac{\sqrt{3}}{2}$ $\csc\left(\dfrac{4\pi}{3}\right) = -\dfrac{2\sqrt{3}}{3}$

$\cos\left(\dfrac{4\pi}{3}\right) = -\dfrac{1}{2}$ $\sec\left(\dfrac{4\pi}{3}\right) = -2$

$\tan\left(\dfrac{4\pi}{3}\right) = \sqrt{3}$ $\cot\left(\dfrac{4\pi}{3}\right) = \dfrac{\sqrt{3}}{3}$

29. $\sin 5\pi = \sin \pi = 0$ **31.** $\cos\dfrac{8\pi}{3} = \cos\dfrac{2\pi}{3} = -\dfrac{1}{2}$

33. $\cos\left(-\dfrac{15\pi}{2}\right) = \cos\dfrac{\pi}{2} = 0$

35. $\sin\left(-\dfrac{9\pi}{4}\right) = \sin\dfrac{7\pi}{4} = -\dfrac{\sqrt{2}}{2}$

37. (a) $-\frac{1}{3}$ (b) -3 **39.** (a) $-\frac{1}{5}$ (b) -5

41. (a) $\frac{4}{5}$ (b) $-\frac{4}{5}$ **43.** 0.7071   **45.** 1.0378

47. -0.1288 **49.** 1.3940   **51.** -1.4486

53. (a) -1 (b) -0.4

55. (a) 0.25 or 2.89   (b) 1.82 or 4.46

57. (a)

t	0	$\frac{1}{4}$	$\frac{1}{2}$	$\frac{3}{4}$	1
y	0.25	0.0138	-0.1501	-0.0249	0.0883

(b) $t \approx 5.5$ (c) The displacement decreases.

59. False. $\sin(-t) = -\sin t$ means that the function is odd, not that the sine of a negative angle is a negative number.

61. (a) *y*-axis symmetry   (b) $\sin t_1 = \sin(\pi - t_1)$
(c) $\cos(\pi - t_1) = -\cos t_1$

63. $f^{-1}(x) = \frac{2}{3}(x + 1)$ **65.** $f^{-1}(x) = \sqrt{x^2 + 4}$, $x \geq 0$

67.

69.

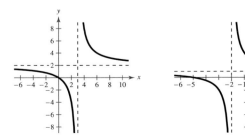

Section 4.3   *(page 308)*

Vocabulary Check   *(page 308)*

1. (a) v   (b) iv   (c) vi   (d) iii   (e) i   (f) ii
2. opposite; adjacent; hypotenuse
3. elevation; depression

1. $\sin \theta = \frac{3}{5}$ $\csc \theta = \frac{5}{3}$
   $\cos \theta = \frac{4}{5}$ $\sec \theta = \frac{5}{4}$
   $\tan \theta = \frac{3}{4}$ $\cot \theta = \frac{4}{3}$

3. $\sin \theta = \frac{9}{41}$ $\csc \theta = \frac{41}{9}$
   $\cos \theta = \frac{40}{41}$ $\sec \theta = \frac{41}{40}$
   $\tan \theta = \frac{9}{40}$ $\cot \theta = \frac{40}{9}$

5. $\sin \theta = \frac{1}{3}$ $\csc \theta = 3$
   $\cos \theta = \frac{2\sqrt{2}}{3}$ $\sec \theta = \frac{3\sqrt{2}}{4}$
   $\tan \theta = \frac{\sqrt{2}}{4}$ $\cot \theta = 2\sqrt{2}$

The triangles are similar, and corresponding sides are proportional.

7. $\sin \theta = \frac{3}{5}$ $\csc \theta = \frac{5}{3}$
   $\cos \theta = \frac{4}{5}$ $\sec \theta = \frac{5}{4}$
   $\tan \theta = \frac{3}{4}$ $\cot \theta = \frac{4}{3}$

The triangles are similar, and corresponding sides are proportional.

9.

$\cos \theta = \frac{\sqrt{7}}{4}$ $\sec \theta = \frac{4\sqrt{7}}{7}$
$\tan \theta = \frac{3\sqrt{7}}{7}$ $\cot \theta = \frac{\sqrt{7}}{3}$
$\csc \theta = \frac{4}{3}$

11.
$\sin \theta = \frac{\sqrt{3}}{2}$ $\csc \theta = \frac{2\sqrt{3}}{3}$
$\cos \theta = \frac{1}{2}$ $\cot \theta = \frac{\sqrt{3}}{3}$
$\tan \theta = \sqrt{3}$

13.

$\sin \theta = \frac{3\sqrt{10}}{10}$ $\sec \theta = \sqrt{10}$
$\cos \theta = \frac{\sqrt{10}}{10}$ $\cot \theta = \frac{1}{3}$
$\csc \theta = \frac{\sqrt{10}}{3}$

15.

$\sin \theta = \frac{2\sqrt{13}}{13}$ $\csc \theta = \frac{\sqrt{13}}{2}$
$\cos \theta = \frac{3\sqrt{13}}{13}$ $\sec \theta = \frac{\sqrt{13}}{3}$
$\tan \theta = \frac{2}{3}$

17. $\frac{\pi}{6}; \frac{1}{2}$ **19.** $60°; \sqrt{3}$ **21.** $60°; \frac{\pi}{3}$ **23.** $30°; \frac{\sqrt{3}}{2}$

25. $45°; \frac{\pi}{4}$ **27.** (a) $\sqrt{3}$ (b) $\frac{1}{2}$ (c) $\frac{\sqrt{3}}{2}$ (d) $\frac{\sqrt{3}}{3}$

29. (a) $\frac{2\sqrt{13}}{13}$ (b) $\frac{3\sqrt{13}}{13}$ (c) $\frac{2}{3}$ (d) $\frac{\sqrt{13}}{2}$

31. (a) 3   (b) $\frac{2\sqrt{2}}{3}$ (c) $\frac{\sqrt{2}}{4}$ (d) $\frac{1}{3}$

33–41. Answers will vary.   **43.** (a) 0.1736   (b) 0.1736
45. (a) 0.2815   (b) 3.5523
47. (a) 1.3499   (b) 1.3432
49. (a) 5.0273   (b) 0.1989
51. (a) 1.8527   (b) 0.9817
53. (a) $30° = \frac{\pi}{6}$ (b) $30° = \frac{\pi}{6}$

55. (a) $60° = \frac{\pi}{3}$ (b) $45° = \frac{\pi}{4}$

57. (a) $60° = \frac{\pi}{3}$ (b) $45° = \frac{\pi}{4}$

59. $30\sqrt{3}$ **61.** $\frac{32\sqrt{3}}{3}$

63. 443.2 meters; 323.3 meters   **65.** $30° = \frac{\pi}{6}$

67. (a) 371.1 feet   (b) 341.6 feet
   (c) Moving down line at 61.8 feet per second
      Dropping vertically at 24.2 feet per second
69. $(x_1, y_1) = (28\sqrt{3}, 28)$
   $(x_2, y_2) = (28, 28\sqrt{3})$

71. (a)

(b) $\sin 85° = \frac{h}{20}$
(c) 19.9 meters

(d) The side of the triangle labeled h will become shorter.
(e)

Angle, θ	80°	70°	60°	50°
Height	19.7	18.8	17.3	15.3

Angle, θ	40°	30°	20°	10°
Height	12.9	10.0	6.8	3.5

(f) As $\theta \to 0°$, $h \to 0$.

73. True, $\csc x = \dfrac{1}{\sin x}$. **75.** False, $\dfrac{\sqrt{2}}{2} + \dfrac{\sqrt{2}}{2} \neq 1$.

77. False, $1.7321 \neq 0.0349$.

79. Corresponding sides of similar triangles are proportional.

81. (a)

θ	0.1	0.2	0.3	0.4	0.5
$\sin \theta$	0.0998	0.1987	0.2955	0.3894	0.4794

(b) θ (c) As θ approaches 0, $\sin \theta$ approaches 0.

83. $\dfrac{x}{x-2}$, $x \neq \pm 6$ **85.** $\dfrac{2(x^2 - 5x - 10)}{(x-2)(x+2)^2}$

Section 4.4 *(page 318)*

Vocabulary Check *(page 318)*

1. $\dfrac{y}{r}$ **2.** $\csc \theta$ **3.** $\dfrac{y}{x}$ **4.** $\dfrac{r}{x}$ **5.** $\cos \theta$

6. $\cot \theta$ **7.** reference

---

1. (a) $\sin \theta = \dfrac{3}{5}$ (b) $\sin \theta = -\dfrac{15}{17}$
$\cos \theta = \dfrac{4}{5}$ $\cos \theta = \dfrac{8}{17}$
$\tan \theta = \dfrac{3}{4}$ $\tan \theta = -\dfrac{15}{8}$
$\csc \theta = \dfrac{5}{3}$ $\csc \theta = -\dfrac{17}{15}$
$\sec \theta = \dfrac{5}{4}$ $\sec \theta = \dfrac{17}{8}$
$\cot \theta = \dfrac{4}{3}$ $\cot \theta = -\dfrac{8}{15}$

3. (a) $\sin \theta = -\dfrac{1}{2}$ (b) $\sin \theta = \dfrac{\sqrt{17}}{17}$
$\cos \theta = -\dfrac{\sqrt{3}}{2}$ $\cos \theta = -\dfrac{4\sqrt{17}}{17}$
$\tan \theta = \dfrac{\sqrt{3}}{3}$ $\tan \theta = -\dfrac{1}{4}$
$\csc \theta = -2$ $\csc \theta = \sqrt{17}$
$\sec \theta = -\dfrac{2\sqrt{3}}{3}$ $\sec \theta = -\dfrac{\sqrt{17}}{4}$
$\cot \theta = \sqrt{3}$ $\cot \theta = -4$

5. $\sin \theta = \dfrac{24}{25}$ $\csc \theta = \dfrac{25}{24}$
$\cos \theta = \dfrac{7}{25}$ $\sec \theta = \dfrac{25}{7}$
$\tan \theta = \dfrac{24}{7}$ $\cot \theta = \dfrac{7}{24}$

7. $\sin \theta = \dfrac{5\sqrt{29}}{29}$ $\csc \theta = \dfrac{\sqrt{29}}{5}$
$\cos \theta = -\dfrac{2\sqrt{29}}{29}$ $\sec \theta = -\dfrac{\sqrt{29}}{2}$
$\tan \theta = -\dfrac{5}{2}$ $\cot \theta = -\dfrac{2}{5}$

9. $\sin \theta = \dfrac{68\sqrt{5849}}{5849}$ $\csc \theta = \dfrac{\sqrt{5849}}{68}$
$\cos \theta = -\dfrac{35\sqrt{5849}}{5849}$ $\sec \theta = -\dfrac{\sqrt{5849}}{35}$
$\tan \theta = -\dfrac{68}{35}$ $\cot \theta = -\dfrac{35}{68}$

11. Quadrant III **13.** Quadrant II

15. $\sin \theta = \dfrac{3}{5}$ $\csc \theta = \dfrac{5}{3}$
$\cos \theta = -\dfrac{4}{5}$ $\sec \theta = -\dfrac{5}{4}$
$\tan \theta = -\dfrac{3}{4}$ $\cot \theta = -\dfrac{4}{3}$

17. $\sin \theta = -\dfrac{15}{17}$ $\csc \theta = -\dfrac{17}{15}$
$\cos \theta = \dfrac{8}{17}$ $\sec \theta = \dfrac{17}{8}$
$\tan \theta = -\dfrac{15}{8}$ $\cot \theta = -\dfrac{8}{15}$

19. $\sin \theta = -\dfrac{\sqrt{10}}{10}$ $\csc \theta = -\sqrt{10}$
$\cos \theta = \dfrac{3\sqrt{10}}{10}$ $\sec \theta = \dfrac{\sqrt{10}}{3}$
$\tan \theta = -\dfrac{1}{3}$ $\cot \theta = -3$

21. $\sin \theta = \dfrac{\sqrt{3}}{2}$ $\csc \theta = \dfrac{2\sqrt{3}}{3}$
$\cos \theta = -\dfrac{1}{2}$ $\sec \theta = -2$
$\tan \theta = -\sqrt{3}$ $\cot \theta = -\dfrac{\sqrt{3}}{3}$

23. $\sin \theta = 0$ $\csc \theta$ is undefined.
$\cos \theta = -1$ $\sec \theta = -1$
$\tan \theta = 0$ $\cot \theta$ is undefined.

25. $\sin \theta = \dfrac{\sqrt{2}}{2}$ $\csc \theta = \sqrt{2}$
$\cos \theta = -\dfrac{\sqrt{2}}{2}$ $\sec \theta = -\sqrt{2}$
$\tan \theta = -1$ $\cot \theta = -1$

27. $\sin \theta = -\dfrac{2\sqrt{5}}{5}$ $\csc \theta = -\dfrac{\sqrt{5}}{2}$
$\cos \theta = -\dfrac{\sqrt{5}}{5}$ $\sec \theta = -\sqrt{5}$
$\tan \theta = 2$ $\cot \theta = \dfrac{1}{2}$

29. 0 **31.** Undefined **33.** 1 **35.** Undefined

37. $\theta' = 23°$ **39.** $\theta' = 65°$

41. $\theta' = \dfrac{\pi}{3}$ **43.** $\theta' = 3.5 - \pi$

45. $\sin 225° = -\dfrac{\sqrt{2}}{2}$

$\cos 225° = -\dfrac{\sqrt{2}}{2}$

$\tan 225° = 1$

47. $\sin 750° = \dfrac{1}{2}$

$\cos 750° = \dfrac{\sqrt{3}}{2}$

$\tan 750° = \dfrac{\sqrt{3}}{3}$

49. $\sin(-150°) = -\dfrac{1}{2}$

$\cos(-150°) = -\dfrac{\sqrt{3}}{2}$

$\tan(-150°) = \dfrac{\sqrt{3}}{3}$

51. $\sin \dfrac{4\pi}{3} = -\dfrac{\sqrt{3}}{2}$

$\cos \dfrac{4\pi}{3} = -\dfrac{1}{2}$

$\tan \dfrac{4\pi}{3} = \sqrt{3}$

53. $\sin\left(-\dfrac{\pi}{6}\right) = -\dfrac{1}{2}$

$\cos\left(-\dfrac{\pi}{6}\right) = \dfrac{\sqrt{3}}{2}$

$\tan\left(-\dfrac{\pi}{6}\right) = -\dfrac{\sqrt{3}}{3}$

55. $\sin \dfrac{11\pi}{4} = \dfrac{\sqrt{2}}{2}$

$\cos \dfrac{11\pi}{4} = -\dfrac{\sqrt{2}}{2}$

$\tan \dfrac{11\pi}{4} = -1$

57. $\sin\left(-\dfrac{3\pi}{2}\right) = 1$

$\cos\left(-\dfrac{3\pi}{2}\right) = 0$

$\tan\left(-\dfrac{3\pi}{2}\right)$ is undefined.

59. $\dfrac{4}{5}$ **61.** $-\dfrac{\sqrt{13}}{2}$ **63.** $\dfrac{8}{5}$ **65.** 0.1736

67. -0.3420 **69.** -1.4826 **71.** 3.2361

73. 4.6373 **75.** 0.3640 **77.** -0.6052

79. -0.4142

81. (a) $30° = \dfrac{\pi}{6},\ 150° = \dfrac{5\pi}{6}$ (b) $210° = \dfrac{7\pi}{6},\ 330° = \dfrac{11\pi}{6}$

83. (a) $60° = \dfrac{\pi}{3},\ 120° = \dfrac{2\pi}{3}$ (b) $135° = \dfrac{3\pi}{4},\ 315° = \dfrac{7\pi}{4}$

85. (a) $45° = \dfrac{\pi}{4},\ 225° = \dfrac{5\pi}{4}$ (b) $150° = \dfrac{5\pi}{6},\ 330° = \dfrac{11\pi}{6}$

87. (a) $N = 22.099 \sin(0.522t - 2.219) + 55.008$
$F = 36.641 \sin(0.502t - 1.831) + 25.610$

(b) February: $N = 34.6°,\ F = -1.4°$
March: $N = 41.6°,\ F = 13.9°$
May: $N = 63.4°,\ F = 48.6°$
June: $N = 72.5°,\ F = 59.5°$
August: $N = 75.5°,\ F = 55.6°$
September: $N = 68.6°,\ F = 41.7°$
November: $N = 46.8°,\ F = 6.5°$

(c) Answers will vary.

89. (a) 2 centimeters (b) 0.14 centimeter
(c) -1.98 centimeters

91. 0.79 ampere

93. False. In each of the four quadrants, the signs of the secant function and cosine function will be the same, because these functions are reciprocals of each other.

95. As θ increases from $0°$ to $90°$, x decreases from 12 cm to 0 cm and y increases from 0 cm to 12 cm. Therefore, $\sin \theta = y/12$ increases from 0 to 1 and $\cos \theta = x/12$ decreases from 1 to 0. Thus, $\tan \theta = y/x$ and increases without bound. When $\theta = 90°$, the tangent is undefined.

97.

x-intercepts:
$(1, 0), (-4, 0)$
y-intercept: $(0, -4)$
Domain: all real numbers x

99.

x-intercept: $(-2, 0)$
y-intercept: $(0, 8)$
Domain: all real numbers x

101.

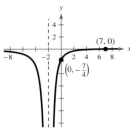

x-intercept: $(7, 0)$
y-intercept: $\left(0, -\frac{7}{4}\right)$
Vertical asymptote:
$\quad x = -2$
Horizontal asymptote:
$\quad y = 0$
Domain: all real numbers
$\quad\quad x$ except $x = -2$

103.

y-intercept: $\left(0, \frac{1}{2}\right)$
Horizontal asymptote:
$\quad y = 0$
Domain: all real numbers x

105.

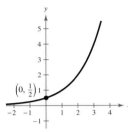

x-intercepts: $(\pm 1, 0)$
Vertical asymptote: $x = 0$
Domain: all real numbers x
$\quad\quad$ except $x = 0$

Section 4.5   (page 328)

Vocabulary Check   (page 328)

1. cycle **2.** amplitude **3.** $\dfrac{2\pi}{b}$

4. phase shift **5.** vertical shift

1. Period: π **3.** Period: 4π **5.** Period: 6
Amplitude: 3   Amplitude: $\frac{5}{2}$ Amplitude: $\frac{1}{2}$

7. Period: 2π **9.** Period: $\dfrac{\pi}{5}$
Amplitude: 3   Amplitude: 3

11. Period: 3π **13.** Period: 1
Amplitude: $\frac{1}{2}$ Amplitude: $\frac{1}{4}$

15. g is a shift of f π units to the right.

17. g is a reflection of f in the x-axis.

19. The period of f is twice the period of g.

21. g is a shift of f three units upward.

23. The graph of g has twice the amplitude of the graph of f.

25. The graph of g is a horizontal shift of the graph of f
π units to the right.

27.

29.

31.

33.

35.

37.

39.

41.

43.

45.

CHAPTER 4

47.

49.

51.

53.

55.

57.

59.

61.

63. $a = 2, d = 1$ **65.** $a = -4, d = 4$

67. $a = -3, b = 2, c = 0$ **69.** $a = 2, b = 1, c = -\dfrac{\pi}{4}$

71.

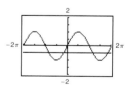

$$x = -\frac{\pi}{6}, -\frac{5\pi}{6}, \frac{7\pi}{6}, \frac{11\pi}{6}$$

73. (a) 6 seconds   (b) 10 cycles per minute

(c)

75. (a) $C(t) = 56.55 + 26.95 \cos\left(\dfrac{\pi}{6}t - 3.67\right)$

(b)

The model is a good fit.

(c)

The model is a good fit.

(d) Tallahassee: 77.90°; Chicago: 56.55°
   The constant term gives the annual average temperature.

(e) 12; yes; one full period is one year.

(f) Chicago; amplitude; the greater the amplitude, the greater the variability in temperature.

77. (a) $\dfrac{1}{440}$ second   (b) 440 cycles per second

79. (a) 365; answers will vary.

(b) 30.3 gallons; the constant term

(c)

$124 < t < 252$

81. False. The graph of $f(x) = \sin(x + 2\pi)$ translates the graph of $f(x) = \sin x$ exactly one period to the left so that the two graphs look identical.

83. True. Because $\cos x = \sin\left(x + \dfrac{\pi}{2}\right)$, $y = -\cos x$ is a reflection in the x-axis of $y = \sin\left(x + \dfrac{\pi}{2}\right)$.

85.

Conjecture: $\sin x = \cos\left(x - \dfrac{\pi}{2}\right)$

87. (a)

The graphs appear to coincide from $-\dfrac{\pi}{2}$ to $\dfrac{\pi}{2}$.

(b)

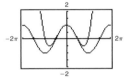

The graphs appear to coincide from $-\dfrac{\pi}{2}$ to $\dfrac{\pi}{2}$.

(c) $-\dfrac{x^7}{7!}, \ -\dfrac{x^6}{6!}$

 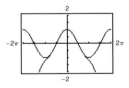

The interval of accuracy increased.

89. $\frac{1}{2} \log_{10}(x - 2)$　　**91.** $3 \ln t - \ln(t - 1)$

93. $\log_{10} \sqrt{xy}$　　**95.** $\ln \dfrac{3x}{y^4}$　　**97.** Answers will vary.

Section 4.6　(page 339)

┌───┐
Vocabulary Check　*(page 339)*

　1. vertical　　**2.** reciprocal　　**3.** damping

　4. π　　**5.** $x \neq n\pi$　　**6.** $(-\infty, -1] \cup [1, \infty)$

　7. 2π
└───┘

1. e, π　　**2.** c, 2π　　**3.** a, 1　　**4.** d, 2π
5. f, 4　　**6.** b, 4

7.

9.

11.

13.

15.

17.

19.

21.

23.

25.

27.

29.

55.

The expressions are equivalent.

57. d, $f \to 0$ as $x \to 0$.   **58.** a, $f \to 0$ as $x \to 0$.

59. b, $g \to 0$ as $x \to 0$.   **60.** c, $g \to 0$ as $x \to 0$.

31.

33.

61.

63.

The functions are equal.   The functions are equal.

35.

37.

65.

67.
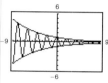

As $x \to \infty$, $g(x) \to 0$.   As $x \to \infty$, $f(x) \to 0$.

39.

41. $-\dfrac{7\pi}{4}, -\dfrac{3\pi}{4}, \dfrac{\pi}{4}, \dfrac{5\pi}{4}$

69.

71.

As $x \to 0$, $y \to \infty$.   As $x \to 0$, $g(x) \to 1$.

43. $-\dfrac{4\pi}{3}, -\dfrac{\pi}{3}, \dfrac{2\pi}{3}, \dfrac{5\pi}{3}$ **45.** $-\dfrac{4\pi}{3}, -\dfrac{2\pi}{3}, \dfrac{2\pi}{3}, \dfrac{4\pi}{3}$

47. $-\dfrac{7\pi}{4}, -\dfrac{5\pi}{4}, \dfrac{\pi}{4}, \dfrac{3\pi}{4}$ **49.** Even

73.

As $x \to 0$, $f(x)$ oscillates between 1 and -1.

75. $d = 7 \cot x$

51. (a)
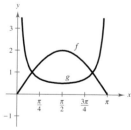

(b) $\dfrac{\pi}{6} < x < \dfrac{5\pi}{6}$

(c) f approaches 0 and g approaches $+\infty$ because the cosecant is the reciprocal of the sine.

53.

The expressions are equivalent except that when $\sin x = 0$, y_1 is undefined.

77. (a)

(b) As the predator population increases, the number of prey decreases. When the number of prey is small, the number of predators decreases.

(c) C: 24 months; R: 24 months

79. (a) H: 12 months; L: 12 months

(b) Summer; winter   (c) 1 month

81. True. For a given value of x, the y-coordinate of csc x is the reciprocal of the y-coordinate of sin x.

83. As x approaches $\pi/2$ from the left, f approaches ∞. As x approaches $\pi/2$ from the right, f approaches $-\infty$.

85. (a)

0.7391

(b) 1, 0.5403, 0.8576, 0.6543, 0.7935, 0.7014, 0.7640, 0.7221, 0.7504, 0.7314, . . . ; 0.7391

87.

The graphs appear to coincide on the interval $-1.1 \le x \le 1.1$.

89. $\dfrac{\ln 54}{2} \approx 1.994$ **91.** $-\ln 2 \approx -0.693$

93. $\dfrac{2 + e^{73}}{3} \approx 1.684 \times 10^{31}$

95. $\pm\sqrt{e^{3.2} - 1} \approx \pm 4.851$ **97.** 2

Section 4.7   *(page 349)*

Vocabulary Check   *(page 349)*

1. $y = \sin^{-1} x; \ -1 \le x \le 1$

2. $y = \arccos x; \ 0 \le y \le \pi$

3. $y = \tan^{-1} x; \ -\infty < x < \infty; \ -\dfrac{\pi}{2} < y < \dfrac{\pi}{2}$

1. $\dfrac{\pi}{6}$ **3.** $\dfrac{\pi}{3}$ **5.** $\dfrac{\pi}{6}$ **7.** $\dfrac{5\pi}{6}$ **9.** $-\dfrac{\pi}{3}$

11. $\dfrac{2\pi}{3}$ **13.** $\dfrac{\pi}{3}$ **15.** 0

17.

19. 1.29   **21.** -0.85 **23.** -1.25 **25.** 0.32

27. 1.99   **29.** 0.74   **31.** 0.85   **33.** 1.29

35. $-\dfrac{\pi}{3}, \ -\dfrac{\sqrt{3}}{3}, \ 1$ **37.** $\theta = \arctan\dfrac{x}{4}$

39. $\theta = \arcsin\dfrac{x + 2}{5}$ **41.** $\theta = \arccos\dfrac{x + 3}{2x}$

43. 0.3   **45.** -0.1 **47.** 0   **49.** $\dfrac{3}{5}$ **51.** $\dfrac{\sqrt{5}}{5}$

53. $\dfrac{12}{13}$ **55.** $\dfrac{\sqrt{34}}{5}$ **57.** $\dfrac{\sqrt{5}}{3}$ **59.** $\dfrac{1}{x}$

61. $\sqrt{1 - 4x^2}$ **63.** $\sqrt{1 - x^2}$ **65.** $\dfrac{\sqrt{9 - x^2}}{x}$

67. $\dfrac{\sqrt{x^2 + 2}}{x}$

69.

Asymptotes: $y = \pm 1$

71. $\dfrac{9}{\sqrt{x^2 + 81}}, \ x > 0; \ \dfrac{-9}{\sqrt{x^2 + 81}}, \ x < 0$

73. $\dfrac{|x - 1|}{\sqrt{x^2 - 2x + 10}}$

75.   **77.**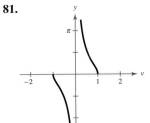

The graph of g is a horizontal shift one unit to the right of f.

79.   **81.**

83.

85.

87.

89. $3\sqrt{2}\sin\left(2t + \dfrac{\pi}{4}\right)$

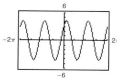

The graph implies that the identity is true.

91. (a) $\theta = \arcsin\dfrac{5}{s}$ (b) 0.13, 0.25

93. (a)

(b) 2 feet (c) $\beta = 0$; As x increases, β approaches 0.

95. (a) $\theta \approx 26.0°$ (b) 24.4 feet

97. (a) $\theta = \arctan\dfrac{x}{20}$ (b) 14.0°, 31.0°

99. False. $\dfrac{5\pi}{4}$ is not in the range of the arctangent.

101. Domain: $(-\infty, \infty)$
Range: $(0, \pi)$

103. Domain: $(-\infty, -1] \cup [1, \infty)$
Range: $[-\pi/2, 0) \cup (0, \pi/2]$

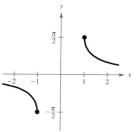

105. (a) $\dfrac{\pi}{4}$ (b) $\dfrac{\pi}{2}$ (c) 1.25 (d) 2.03

107. (a) $f \circ f^{-1}$ $f^{-1} \circ f$

(b) The domains and ranges of the functions are restricted. The graphs of $f \circ f^{-1}$ and $f^{-1} \circ f$ differ because of the domains and ranges of f and f^{-1}.

109. 1279.284 **111.** 117.391

113.

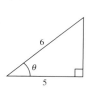

$\cos\theta = \dfrac{\sqrt{7}}{4}$ $\sec\theta = \dfrac{4\sqrt{7}}{7}$

$\tan\theta = \dfrac{3\sqrt{7}}{7}$ $\cot\theta = \dfrac{\sqrt{7}}{3}$

$\csc\theta = \dfrac{4}{3}$

115.

$\sin\theta = \dfrac{\sqrt{11}}{6}$ $\sec\theta = \dfrac{6}{5}$

$\tan\theta = \dfrac{\sqrt{11}}{5}$ $\cot\theta = \dfrac{5\sqrt{11}}{11}$

$\csc\theta = \dfrac{6\sqrt{11}}{11}$

117. Eight people

119. (a) $21,253.63 (b) $21,275.17
(c) $21,285.66 (d) $21,286.01

Section 4.8 *(page 359)*

Vocabulary Check *(page 359)*

1. elevation; depression **2.** bearing
3. harmonic motion

1. $a \approx 3.64$
$c \approx 10.64$
$B = 70°$

3. $a \approx 8.26$
$c \approx 25.38$
$A = 19°$

5. $c \approx 11.66$
$A \approx 30.96°$
$B \approx 59.04°$

7. $a \approx 49.48$
$A \approx 72.08°$
$B \approx 17.92°$

9. $a \approx 91.34$
$b \approx 420.70$
$B \approx 77°45'$

11. 2.56 inches

13. 19.99 inches   **15.** 107.2 feet   **17.** 19.7 feet

19. (a)

(b) $h = 50(\tan 47°40' - \tan 35°)$ (c) 19.9 feet

21. 2236.8 feet

23. (a)

(b) $\tan \theta = \dfrac{12\frac{1}{2}}{17\frac{1}{3}}$ (c) 35.8°

25. 2.06°   **27.** 0.73 mile

29. 554 miles north; 709 miles east

31. (a) 58.18 nautical miles west;
        104.95 nautical miles south
  (b) S 36.7° W; distance = 130.9 nautical miles

33. (a) N 58° E   (b) 68.82 meters

35. N 56.31° W   **37.** 1933.3 feet

39. ≈ 3.23 miles or $\approx 17{,}054$ feet

41. 78.7°   **43.** 35.3°   **45.** 29.4 inches

47. $y = \sqrt{3}\,r$ **49.** $a \approx 12.2, b \approx 7$

51. $d = 4\sin(\pi t)$ **53.** $d = 3\cos\left(\dfrac{4\pi t}{3}\right)$

55. (a) 4   (b) 4   (c) 4   (d) $\frac{1}{16}$

57. (a) $\frac{1}{16}$ (b) 60   (c) 0   (d) $\frac{1}{120}$ **59.** $\omega = 528\pi$

61. (a)

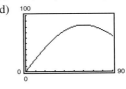

(b) $\dfrac{\pi}{8}$ (c) $\dfrac{\pi}{32}$

63. (a)

Base 1	Base 2	Altitude	Area
8	8 + 16 cos 30°	8 sin 30°	59.7
8	8 + 16 cos 40°	8 sin 40°	72.7
8	8 + 16 cos 50°	8 sin 50°	80.5
8	8 + 16 cos 60°	8 sin 60°	83.1
8	8 + 16 cos 70°	8 sin 70°	80.7
8	8 + 16 cos 80°	8 sin 80°	74.0
8	8 + 16 cos 90°	8 sin 90°	64.0

(b)

Base 1	Base 2	Altitude	Area
8	8 + 16 cos 56°	8 sin 56°	82.73
8	8 + 16 cos 58°	8 sin 58°	83.04
8	8 + 16 cos 59°	8 sin 59°	83.11
8	8 + 16 cos 60°	8 sin 60°	83.14
8	8 + 16 cos 61°	8 sin 61°	83.11
8	8 + 16 cos 62°	8 sin 62°	83.04

83.14 square feet

(c) $A = 64(1 + \cos \theta)(\sin \theta)$

(d)

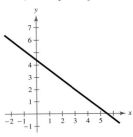

≈ 83.1 square feet when $\theta = 60°$
The answers are the same.

65. False. The tower is leaning, so it is not perfectly vertical and does not form a right angle with the ground.

67. No. N 24° E means 24 degrees east of north.

69. $y = 4x + 6$ **71.** $y = -\frac{4}{5}x + \frac{22}{5}$

Review Exercises *(page 365)*

1. 0.5 radian

3.

(b) Quadrant II

(c) $\dfrac{3\pi}{4}, -\dfrac{5\pi}{4}$

5.

(b) Quadrant II

(c) $\dfrac{2\pi}{3}, -\dfrac{10\pi}{3}$

7.

(b) Quadrant I

(c) $430°, -290°$

9.

(b) Quadrant III

(c) $250°, -470°$

11. 8.378   **13.** -0.589 **15.** $128.571°$

17. $-200.535°$ **19.** 478.17 inches

21. (a) $66\frac{2}{3}\pi$ radians per minute

(b) 400π inches per minute

23. Area = 339.28 square inches

25. $\left(-\dfrac{1}{2}, \dfrac{\sqrt{3}}{2}\right)$ **27.** $\left(-\dfrac{\sqrt{3}}{2}, \dfrac{1}{2}\right)$

29. $\sin\dfrac{7\pi}{6} = -\dfrac{1}{2}$ $\csc\dfrac{7\pi}{6} = -2$

$\cos\dfrac{7\pi}{6} = -\dfrac{\sqrt{3}}{2}$ $\sec\dfrac{7\pi}{6} = -\dfrac{2\sqrt{3}}{3}$

$\tan\dfrac{7\pi}{6} = \dfrac{\sqrt{3}}{3}$ $\cot\dfrac{7\pi}{6} = \sqrt{3}$

31. $\sin\left(-\dfrac{2\pi}{3}\right) = -\dfrac{\sqrt{3}}{2}$ $\csc\left(-\dfrac{2\pi}{3}\right) = -\dfrac{2\sqrt{3}}{3}$

$\cos\left(-\dfrac{2\pi}{3}\right) = -\dfrac{1}{2}$ $\sec\left(-\dfrac{2\pi}{3}\right) = -2$

$\tan\left(-\dfrac{2\pi}{3}\right) = \sqrt{3}$ $\cot\left(-\dfrac{2\pi}{3}\right) = \dfrac{\sqrt{3}}{3}$

33. $\sin\dfrac{11\pi}{4} = \sin\dfrac{3\pi}{4} = \dfrac{\sqrt{2}}{2}$

35. $\sin\left(-\dfrac{17\pi}{6}\right) = \sin\dfrac{7\pi}{6} = -\dfrac{1}{2}$

37. -75.3130 **39.** 3.2361

41. $\sin\theta = \dfrac{4\sqrt{41}}{41}$

$\cos\theta = \dfrac{5\sqrt{41}}{41}$

$\tan\theta = \dfrac{4}{5}$

$\csc\theta = \dfrac{\sqrt{41}}{4}$

$\sec\theta = \dfrac{\sqrt{41}}{5}$

$\cot\theta = \dfrac{5}{4}$

43. $\sin\theta = \dfrac{\sqrt{3}}{2}$

$\cos\theta = \dfrac{1}{2}$

$\tan\theta = \sqrt{3}$

$\csc\theta = \dfrac{2\sqrt{3}}{3}$

$\sec\theta = 2$

$\cot\theta = \dfrac{\sqrt{3}}{3}$

45. (a) 3   (b) $\dfrac{2\sqrt{2}}{3}$ (c) $\dfrac{3\sqrt{2}}{4}$ (d) $\dfrac{\sqrt{2}}{4}$

47. (a) $\dfrac{1}{4}$ (b) $\dfrac{\sqrt{15}}{4}$ (c) $\dfrac{4\sqrt{15}}{15}$ (d) $\dfrac{\sqrt{15}}{15}$

49. 0.6494   **51.** 0.5621   **53.** 3.6722   **55.** 71.3 meters

57. $\sin\theta = \frac{4}{5}$ $\csc\theta = \frac{5}{4}$

$\cos\theta = \frac{3}{5}$ $\sec\theta = \frac{5}{3}$

$\tan\theta = \frac{4}{3}$ $\cot\theta = \frac{3}{4}$

59. $\sin\theta = \dfrac{15\sqrt{241}}{241}$ $\csc\theta = \dfrac{\sqrt{241}}{15}$

$\cos\theta = \dfrac{4\sqrt{241}}{241}$ $\sec\theta = \dfrac{\sqrt{241}}{4}$

$\tan\theta = \dfrac{15}{4}$ $\cot\theta = \dfrac{4}{15}$

61. $\sin\theta = \dfrac{9\sqrt{82}}{82}$ $\csc\theta = \dfrac{\sqrt{82}}{9}$

$\cos\theta = \dfrac{-\sqrt{82}}{82}$ $\sec\theta = -\sqrt{82}$

$\tan\theta = -9$ $\cot\theta = -\dfrac{1}{9}$

63. $\sin\theta = \dfrac{4\sqrt{17}}{17}$ $\csc\theta = \dfrac{\sqrt{17}}{4}$

$\cos\theta = \dfrac{\sqrt{17}}{17}$ $\sec\theta = \sqrt{17}$

$\tan\theta = 4$ $\cot\theta = \dfrac{1}{4}$

65. $\sin\theta = -\dfrac{\sqrt{11}}{6}$

$\cos\theta = \dfrac{5}{6}$

$\tan\theta = -\dfrac{\sqrt{11}}{5}$

$\csc\theta = -\dfrac{6\sqrt{11}}{11}$

$\cot\theta = -\dfrac{5\sqrt{11}}{11}$

67. $\cos\theta = -\dfrac{\sqrt{55}}{8}$

$\tan\theta = -\dfrac{3\sqrt{55}}{55}$

$\csc\theta = \dfrac{8}{3}$

$\sec\theta = -\dfrac{8\sqrt{55}}{55}$

$\cot\theta = -\dfrac{\sqrt{55}}{3}$

69. $\sin \theta = \dfrac{\sqrt{21}}{5}$

$\tan \theta = -\dfrac{\sqrt{21}}{2}$

$\csc \theta = \dfrac{5\sqrt{21}}{21}$

$\sec \theta = -\dfrac{5}{2}$

$\cot \theta = -\dfrac{2\sqrt{21}}{21}$

71. $\theta' = 84°$

73. $\theta' = \dfrac{\pi}{5}$

75. $\sin \dfrac{\pi}{3} = \dfrac{\sqrt{3}}{2}$; $\cos \dfrac{\pi}{3} = \dfrac{1}{2}$; $\tan \dfrac{\pi}{3} = \sqrt{3}$

77. $\sin\left(-\dfrac{7\pi}{3}\right) = -\dfrac{\sqrt{3}}{2}$; $\cos\left(-\dfrac{7\pi}{3}\right) = \dfrac{1}{2}$;

$\tan\left(-\dfrac{7\pi}{3}\right) = -\sqrt{3}$

79. $\sin 495° = \dfrac{\sqrt{2}}{2}$; $\cos 495° = -\dfrac{\sqrt{2}}{2}$; $\tan 495° = -1$

81. $\sin(-240°) = \dfrac{\sqrt{3}}{2}$; $\cos(-240°) = -\dfrac{1}{2}$;

$\tan(-240°) = -\sqrt{3}$

83. -0.7568 **85.** 0.0584 **87.** 3.2361

89.

91.

93.

95.

97. (a) $y = 2 \sin 528\pi x$ (b) 264 cycles per second

99.

101.

103.

105.

107.

As $x \to +\infty$, $f(x) \to +\infty$

109. $-\dfrac{\pi}{6}$ **111.** 0.41 **113.** -0.46 **115.** $\dfrac{\pi}{6}$

117. π **119.** 1.24 **121.** -0.98

123.

125.

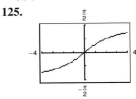

127. $\dfrac{4}{5}$ **129.** $\dfrac{13}{5}$ **131.** $\dfrac{\sqrt{4 - x^2}}{x}$ **133.** $66.8°$

135. 1221 miles, 85.6°

137. False. The sine or cosine function is often useful for modeling simple harmonic motion.

139. False. For each θ there corresponds exactly one value of y.

141. d; The period is 2π and the amplitude is 3.

143. b; The period is 2 and the amplitude is 2.

145. The function is undefined because $\sec \theta = 1/\cos \theta$.

147. The ranges of the other four trigonometric functions are $(-\infty, \infty)$ or $(-\infty, -1] \cup [1, \infty)$.

149. (a) $A = 0.4r^2, r > 0;$ (b) $A = 50\theta, \theta > 0;$
$s = 0.8r, r > 0$ $s = 10\theta, \theta > 0$

 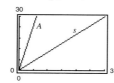

The area function increases more rapidly.

Chapter Test   *(page 369)*

1. (a)

(b) $\dfrac{13\pi}{4}, -\dfrac{3\pi}{4}$

(c) $225°$

2. 3000 radians per minute   **3.** ≈ 709.04 square feet

4. $\sin \theta = \dfrac{3\sqrt{10}}{10}$ $\csc \theta = \dfrac{\sqrt{10}}{3}$

$\cos \theta = -\dfrac{\sqrt{10}}{10}$ $\sec \theta = -\sqrt{10}$

$\tan \theta = -3$ $\cot \theta = -\dfrac{1}{3}$

5. For $0 \le \theta < \dfrac{\pi}{2}$:   For $\pi \le \theta < \dfrac{3\pi}{2}$:

$\sin \theta = \dfrac{3\sqrt{13}}{13}$ $\sin \theta = -\dfrac{3\sqrt{13}}{13}$

$\cos \theta = \dfrac{2\sqrt{13}}{13}$ $\cos \theta = -\dfrac{2\sqrt{13}}{13}$

$\csc \theta = \dfrac{\sqrt{13}}{3}$ $\csc \theta = -\dfrac{\sqrt{13}}{3}$

$\sec \theta = \dfrac{\sqrt{13}}{2}$ $\sec \theta = -\dfrac{\sqrt{13}}{2}$

$\cot \theta = \dfrac{2}{3}$ $\cot \theta = \dfrac{2}{3}$

6. $\theta' = 70°$

7. Quadrant III   **8.** $150°, 210°$ **9.** 1.33, 1.81

10. $\sin \theta = -\dfrac{4}{5}$ **11.** $\sin \theta = \dfrac{15}{17}$

$\tan \theta = -\dfrac{4}{3}$ $\cos \theta = -\dfrac{8}{17}$

$\csc \theta = -\dfrac{5}{4}$ $\tan \theta = -\dfrac{15}{8}$

$\sec \theta = \dfrac{5}{3}$ $\csc \theta = \dfrac{17}{15}$

$\cot \theta = -\dfrac{3}{4}$ $\cot \theta = -\dfrac{8}{15}$

12.

13.

14.

Period: 2

15.

Not periodic

16. $a = -2, b = \dfrac{1}{2}, c = -\dfrac{\pi}{4}$ **17.** $\dfrac{\sqrt{5}}{2}$

18.

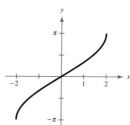

19. $310.1°$ **20.** $d = -6 \cos \pi t$

Problem Solving   *(page 371)*

1. (a) $\dfrac{11\pi}{2}$ radians or $990°$ (b) ≈ 816.42 feet

3. (a) 4767 feet   (b) 3705 feet
  (c) $w = 2183$ feet,
  $$\tan 63° = \frac{w + 3705}{3000}$$

5. (a)   (b)

  Even   Even

7. $h = 51 - 50 \sin\left(8\pi t + \dfrac{\pi}{2}\right)$

9. (a)

  (b)

  (c) $P(7369) = 0.631$
    $E(7369) = 0.901$
    $I(7369) = 0.945$

11. (a) 3.35, 7.35   (b) -0.65
  (c) Yes. There is a difference of nine periods between the values.

13. (a) $40.5°$ (b) $x \approx 1.71$ feet; $y \approx 3.46$ feet
  (c) ≈ 1.75 feet
  (d) As you move closer to the rock, d must get smaller and smaller. The angles θ_1 and θ_2 will decrease along with the distance y, so d will decrease.

Chapter 5

Section 5.1   *(page 379)*

Vocabulary Check   *(page 379)*

1. $\tan u$ **2.** $\cos u$ **3.** $\cot u$ **4.** $\csc u$
5. $\cot^2 u$ **6.** $\sec^2 u$ **7.** $\cos u$ **8.** $\csc u$
9. $\cos u$ **10.** $-\tan u$

1. $\sin x = \dfrac{\sqrt{3}}{2}$
  $\cos x = -\dfrac{1}{2}$
  $\tan x = -\sqrt{3}$
  $\csc x = \dfrac{2\sqrt{3}}{3}$
  $\sec x = -2$
  $\cot x = -\dfrac{\sqrt{3}}{3}$

3. $\sin \theta = -\dfrac{\sqrt{2}}{2}$
  $\cos \theta = \dfrac{\sqrt{2}}{2}$
  $\tan \theta = -1$
  $\sec \theta = \sqrt{2}$
  $\csc \theta = -\sqrt{2}$
  $\cot \theta = -1$

5. $\sin x = -\dfrac{5}{13}$
  $\cos x = -\dfrac{12}{13}$
  $\tan x = \dfrac{5}{12}$
  $\sec x = -\dfrac{13}{12}$
  $\csc x = -\dfrac{13}{5}$
  $\cot x = \dfrac{12}{5}$

7. $\sin \phi = -\dfrac{\sqrt{5}}{3}$
  $\cos \phi = \dfrac{2}{3}$
  $\tan \phi = -\dfrac{\sqrt{5}}{2}$
  $\sec \phi = \dfrac{3}{2}$
  $\csc \phi = -\dfrac{3\sqrt{5}}{5}$
  $\cot \phi = -\dfrac{2\sqrt{5}}{5}$

9. $\sin x = \dfrac{1}{3}$
  $\cos x = -\dfrac{2\sqrt{2}}{3}$
  $\tan x = -\dfrac{\sqrt{2}}{4}$
  $\csc x = 3$
  $\sec x = -\dfrac{3\sqrt{2}}{4}$
  $\cot x = -2\sqrt{2}$

11. $\sin \theta = -\dfrac{2\sqrt{5}}{5}$
  $\cos \theta = -\dfrac{\sqrt{5}}{5}$
  $\tan \theta = 2$
  $\csc \theta = -\dfrac{\sqrt{5}}{2}$
  $\sec \theta = -\sqrt{5}$
  $\cot \theta = \dfrac{1}{2}$

13. $\sin \theta = -1$
  $\cos \theta = 0$
  $\tan \theta$ is undefined.
  $\cot \theta = 0$
  $\csc \theta = -1$
  $\sec \theta$ is undefined.

15. d   **16.** a   **17.** b   **18.** f   **19.** e   **20.** c
21. b   **22.** c   **23.** f   **24.** a   **25.** e   **26.** d
27. $\csc \theta$ **29.** $\cos^2 \phi$ **31.** $\cos x$ **33.** $\sin^2 x$
35. 1   **37.** $\tan x$ **39.** $1 + \sin y$ **41.** $\sec \beta$
43. $\cos u + \sin u$ **45.** $\sin^2 x$ **47.** $\sin^2 x \tan^2 x$
49. $\sec x + 1$ **51.** $\sec^4 x$ **53.** $\sin^2 x - \cos^2 x$
55. $\cot^2 x(\csc x - 1)$ **57.** $1 + 2\sin x \cos x$
59. $4\cot^2 x$ **61.** $2\csc^2 x$ **63.** $2\sec x$
65. $1 + \cos y$ **67.** $3(\sec x + \tan x)$

69.

x	0.2	0.4	0.6	0.8	1.0
y_1	0.1987	0.3894	0.5646	0.7174	0.8415
y_2	0.1987	0.3894	0.5646	0.7174	0.8415

x	1.2	1.4
y_1	0.9320	0.9854
y_2	0.9320	0.9854

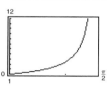

$y_1 = y_2$

71.

x	0.2	0.4	0.6	0.8	1.0
y_1	1.2230	1.5085	1.8958	2.4650	3.4082
y_2	1.2230	1.5085	1.8958	2.4650	3.4082

x	1.2	1.4
y_1	5.3319	11.6814
y_2	5.3319	11.6814

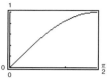

$y_1 = y_2$

73. $\csc x$ **75.** $\tan x$ **77.** $3 \sin \theta$ **79.** $3 \tan \theta$

81. $5 \sec \theta$ **83.** $3 \cos \theta = 3; \sin \theta = 0; \cos \theta = 1$

85. $4 \sin \theta = 2\sqrt{2}; \sin \theta = \dfrac{\sqrt{2}}{2}; \cos \theta = \dfrac{\sqrt{2}}{2}$

87. $0 \le \theta \le \pi$ **89.** $0 \le \theta < \dfrac{\pi}{2}, \dfrac{3\pi}{2} < \theta < 2\pi$

91. $\ln|\cot x|$ **93.** $\ln|\csc t \sec t|$

95. (a) $\csc^2 132° - \cot^2 132° \approx 1.8107 - 0.8107 = 1$

(b) $\csc^2 \dfrac{2\pi}{7} - \cot^2 \dfrac{2\pi}{7} \approx 1.6360 - 0.6360 = 1$

97. (a) $\cos(90° - 80°) = \sin 80° \approx 0.9848$

(b) $\cos\left(\dfrac{\pi}{2} - 0.8\right) = \sin 0.8 \approx 0.7174$

99. $\mu = \tan \theta$

101. True. For example, $\sin(-x) = -\sin x$.

103. 1, 1 **105.** $\infty, 0$

107. Not an identity because $\cos \theta = \pm\sqrt{1 - \sin^2 \theta}$

109. Not an identity because $\dfrac{\sin k\theta}{\cos k\theta} = \tan k\theta$

111. An identity because $\sin \theta \cdot \dfrac{1}{\sin \theta} = 1$

113. Answers will vary. **115.** $x - 25$

117. $\dfrac{x^2 + 6x - 8}{(x + 5)(x - 8)}$ **119.** $\dfrac{-5x^2 + 8x + 28}{(x^2 - 4)(x + 4)}$

121.

123.

Section 5.2 *(page 387)*

Vocabulary Check *(page 387)*

1. identity **2.** conditional equation **3.** $\tan u$

4. $\cot u$ **5.** $\cos^2 u$ **6.** $\sin u$ **7.** $-\csc u$

8. $\sec u$

1–37. Answers will vary.

39. (a)

(b)

Identity

(c) Answers will vary.

41. (a)

(b)

Not an identity

(c) Answers will vary.

43. (a)

(b)

Identity

(c) Answers will vary.

45. (a)

(b)

Not an identity

(c) Answers will vary.

47 and 49. Answers will vary.   **51.** 1

53. 2   **55.** Answers will vary.

57. False. An identity is an equation that is true for all real values of θ.

59. The equation is not an identity because $\sin \theta = \pm\sqrt{1 - \cos^2 \theta}$.

Possible answer: $\dfrac{7\pi}{4}$

61. $2 + \left(3 - \sqrt{26}\right)i$ **63.** $-8 + 4i$

65. $-3 \pm \sqrt{21}$ **67.** $1 \pm \sqrt{5}$

Section 5.3 *(page 396)*

> **Vocabulary Check** *(page 396)*
>
> **1.** general   **2.** quadratic   **3.** extraneous

1–5. Answers will vary.   **7.** $\dfrac{2\pi}{3} + 2n\pi, \dfrac{4\pi}{3} + 2n\pi$

9. $\dfrac{\pi}{3} + 2n\pi, \dfrac{2\pi}{3} + 2n\pi$ **11.** $\dfrac{\pi}{6} + n\pi, \dfrac{5\pi}{6} + n\pi$

13. $n\pi, \dfrac{3\pi}{2} + 2n\pi$ **15.** $\dfrac{\pi}{3} + n\pi, \dfrac{2\pi}{3} + n\pi$

17. $\dfrac{\pi}{8} + \dfrac{n\pi}{2}, \dfrac{3\pi}{8} + \dfrac{n\pi}{2}$ **19.** $\dfrac{n\pi}{3}, \dfrac{\pi}{4} + n\pi$

21. $0, \dfrac{\pi}{2}, \pi, \dfrac{3\pi}{2}$ **23.** $0, \pi, \dfrac{\pi}{6}, \dfrac{5\pi}{6}, \dfrac{7\pi}{6}, \dfrac{11\pi}{6}$

25. $\dfrac{\pi}{3}, \dfrac{5\pi}{3}, \pi$ **27.** No solution   **29.** $\pi, \dfrac{\pi}{3}, \dfrac{5\pi}{3}$

31. $\dfrac{\pi}{6}, \dfrac{5\pi}{6}, \dfrac{7\pi}{6}, \dfrac{11\pi}{6}$ **33.** $\dfrac{\pi}{2}$ **35.** $\dfrac{\pi}{6} + n\pi, \dfrac{5\pi}{6} + n\pi$

37. $\dfrac{\pi}{12} + \dfrac{n\pi}{3}$ **39.** $\dfrac{\pi}{2} + 4n\pi, \dfrac{7\pi}{2} + 4n\pi$

41. $-1 + 4n$ **43.** $-2 + 6n, 2 + 6n$

45. 2.678, 5.820   **47.** 1.047, 5.236   **49.** 0.860, 3.426

51. 0, 2.678, 3.142, 5.820   **53.** 0.983, 1.768, 4.124, 4.910

55. 0.3398, 0.8481, 2.2935, 2.8018

57. 1.9357, 2.7767, 5.0773, 5.9183

59. $\dfrac{\pi}{4}, \dfrac{5\pi}{4}$, arctan 5, arctan $5 + \pi$ **61.** $\dfrac{\pi}{3}, \dfrac{5\pi}{3}$

63. (a)

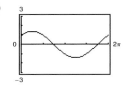

(b) $\dfrac{\pi}{4} \approx 0.7854$

$\dfrac{5\pi}{4} \approx 3.9270$

Maximum: (0.7854, 1.4142)

Minimum: (3.9270, −1.4142)

65. 1

67. (a) All real numbers x except $x = 0$

(b) y-axis symmetry; Horizontal asymptote: $y = 1$

(c) Oscillates   (d) Infinitely many solutions

(e) Yes, 0.6366

69. 0.04 second, 0.43 second, 0.83 second

71. February, March, and April   **73.** 36.9°, 53.1°

75. (a) Between $t = 8$ seconds and $t = 24$ seconds

(b) 5 times: $t = 16, 48, 80, 112, 144$ seconds

77. (a)

(b) $0.6 < x < 1.1$

$A \approx 1.12$

79. True. The first equation has a smaller period than the second equation, so it will have more solutions in the interval $[0, 2\pi)$.

81. 1

83. $C = 24°$

$a \approx 54.8$

$b \approx 50.1$

85. $\sin 390° = \dfrac{1}{2}$ **87.** $\sin(-1845°) = -\dfrac{\sqrt{2}}{2}$

$\cos 390° = \dfrac{\sqrt{3}}{2}$ $\cos(-1845°) = \dfrac{\sqrt{2}}{2}$

$\tan 390° = \dfrac{\sqrt{3}}{3}$ $\tan(-1845°) = -1$

89. 1.36°   **91.** Answers will vary.

Section 5.4 *(page 404)*

> **Vocabulary Check** *(page 404)*
>
> **1.** $\sin u \cos v - \cos u \sin v$
>
> **2.** $\cos u \cos v - \sin u \sin v$ **3.** $\dfrac{\tan u + \tan v}{1 - \tan u \tan v}$
>
> **4.** $\sin u \cos v + \cos u \sin v$
>
> **5.** $\cos u \cos v + \sin u \sin v$ **6.** $\dfrac{\tan u - \tan v}{1 + \tan u \tan v}$

1. (a) $\dfrac{-\sqrt{2} - \sqrt{6}}{4}$ (b) $\dfrac{-1 + \sqrt{2}}{2}$

3. (a) $\dfrac{\sqrt{2} - \sqrt{6}}{4}$ (b) $\dfrac{\sqrt{2} + 1}{2}$

5. (a) $\dfrac{1}{2}$ (b) $\dfrac{-\sqrt{3} - 1}{2}$

7. $\sin 105° = \dfrac{\sqrt{2}}{4}\left(\sqrt{3} + 1\right)$

$\cos 105° = \dfrac{\sqrt{2}}{4}\left(1 - \sqrt{3}\right)$

$\tan 105° = -2 - \sqrt{3}$

CHAPTER 5

9. $\sin 195° = \dfrac{\sqrt{2}}{4}\left(1 - \sqrt{3}\right)$

$\cos 195° = -\dfrac{\sqrt{2}}{4}\left(\sqrt{3} + 1\right)$

$\tan 195° = 2 - \sqrt{3}$

11. $\sin \dfrac{11\pi}{12} = \dfrac{\sqrt{2}}{4}\left(\sqrt{3} - 1\right)$

$\cos \dfrac{11\pi}{12} = -\dfrac{\sqrt{2}}{4}\left(\sqrt{3} + 1\right)$

$\tan \dfrac{11\pi}{12} = -2 + \sqrt{3}$

13. $\sin \dfrac{17\pi}{12} = -\dfrac{\sqrt{2}}{4}\left(\sqrt{3} + 1\right)$

$\cos \dfrac{17\pi}{12} = \dfrac{\sqrt{2}}{4}\left(1 - \sqrt{3}\right)$

$\tan \dfrac{17\pi}{12} = 2 + \sqrt{3}$

15. $\sin 285° = -\dfrac{\sqrt{2}}{4}\left(\sqrt{3} + 1\right)$

$\cos 285° = \dfrac{\sqrt{2}}{4}\left(\sqrt{3} - 1\right)$

$\tan 285° = -\left(2 + \sqrt{3}\right)$

17. $\sin(-165°) = -\dfrac{\sqrt{2}}{4}\left(\sqrt{3} - 1\right)$

$\cos(-165°) = -\dfrac{\sqrt{2}}{4}\left(1 + \sqrt{3}\right)$

$\tan(-165°) = 2 - \sqrt{3}$

19. $\sin \dfrac{13\pi}{12} = \dfrac{\sqrt{2}}{4}\left(1 - \sqrt{3}\right)$

$\cos \dfrac{13\pi}{12} = -\dfrac{\sqrt{2}}{4}\left(1 + \sqrt{3}\right)$

$\tan \dfrac{13\pi}{12} = 2 - \sqrt{3}$

21. $\sin\left(-\dfrac{13\pi}{12}\right) = \dfrac{\sqrt{2}}{4}\left(\sqrt{3} - 1\right)$

$\cos\left(-\dfrac{13\pi}{12}\right) = -\dfrac{\sqrt{2}}{4}\left(\sqrt{3} + 1\right)$

$\tan\left(-\dfrac{13\pi}{12}\right) = -2 + \sqrt{3}$

23. $\cos 40°$ **25.** $\tan 239°$ **27.** $\sin 1.8$ **29.** $\tan 3x$

31. $-\dfrac{\sqrt{3}}{2}$ **33.** $\dfrac{\sqrt{3}}{2}$ **35.** -1 **37.** $-\dfrac{63}{65}$

39. $\dfrac{16}{65}$ **41.** $-\dfrac{63}{16}$ **43.** $\dfrac{65}{56}$ **45.** $\dfrac{3}{5}$ **47.** $-\dfrac{44}{117}$

49. $\dfrac{5}{3}$ **51.** 1 **53.** 0 **55–63.** Answers will vary.

65. $-\sin x$ **67.** $-\cos \theta$

69. $\dfrac{\pi}{2}$ **71.** $\dfrac{5\pi}{4}, \dfrac{7\pi}{4}$ **73.** $\dfrac{\pi}{4}, \dfrac{7\pi}{4}$

75. (a) $y = \dfrac{5}{12}\sin(2t + 0.6435)$

(b) $\dfrac{5}{12}$ feet   (c) $\dfrac{1}{\pi}$ cycle per second

77. False. $\sin(u \pm v) = \sin u \cos v \pm \cos u \sin v$

79. False.

$\cos\left(x - \dfrac{\pi}{2}\right) = \cos x \cos \dfrac{\pi}{2} + \sin x \sin \dfrac{\pi}{2} = \sin x$

81 and 83. Answers will vary.

85. (a) $\sqrt{2}\sin\left(\theta + \dfrac{\pi}{4}\right)$ (b) $\sqrt{2}\cos\left(\theta - \dfrac{\pi}{4}\right)$

87. (a) $13\sin(3\theta + 0.3948)$ (b) $13\cos(3\theta - 1.1760)$

89. $2\cos \theta$ **91.** Proof   **93.** $15°$

95.

$\sin^2\left(\theta + \dfrac{\pi}{4}\right) + \sin^2\left(\theta - \dfrac{\pi}{4}\right) = 1$

97. $f^{-1}(x) = \dfrac{x + 15}{5}$

99. Because f is not one-to-one, f^{-1} does not exist.
101. $4x - 3$ **103.** $6x - 3$

Section 5.5   (page 415)

Vocabulary Check   (page 415)

1. $2\sin u \cos u$ **2.** $\cos^2 u$
3. $\cos^2 u - \sin^2 u = 2\cos^2 u - 1 = 1 - 2\sin^2 u$
4. $\tan^2 u$ **5.** $\pm\sqrt{\dfrac{1 - \cos u}{2}}$
6. $\dfrac{1 - \cos u}{\sin u} = \dfrac{\sin u}{1 + \cos u}$
7. $\frac{1}{2}\left[\cos(u - v) + \cos(u + v)\right]$
8. $\frac{1}{2}\left[\sin(u + v) + \sin(u - v)\right]$
9. $2\sin\left(\dfrac{u + v}{2}\right)\cos\left(\dfrac{u - v}{2}\right)$
10. $-2\sin\left(\dfrac{u + v}{2}\right)\sin\left(\dfrac{u - v}{2}\right)$

1. $\dfrac{\sqrt{17}}{17}$ **3.** $\dfrac{15}{17}$ **5.** $\dfrac{8}{15}$ **7.** $\dfrac{17}{8}$

9. $0, \dfrac{\pi}{3}, \pi, \dfrac{5\pi}{3}$ **11.** $\dfrac{\pi}{12}, \dfrac{5\pi}{12}, \dfrac{13\pi}{12}, \dfrac{17\pi}{12}$

13. $0, \dfrac{2\pi}{3}, \dfrac{4\pi}{3}$ **15.** $\dfrac{\pi}{2}, \dfrac{\pi}{6}, \dfrac{5\pi}{6}, \dfrac{7\pi}{6}, \dfrac{3\pi}{2}, \dfrac{11\pi}{6}$

17. $0, \dfrac{\pi}{2}, \pi, \dfrac{3\pi}{2}$ **19.** $3\sin 2x$ **21.** $4\cos 2x$

23. $\sin 2u = \dfrac{24}{25}$

$\cos 2u = -\dfrac{7}{25}$

$\tan 2u = -\dfrac{24}{7}$

25. $\sin 2u = \dfrac{24}{25}$

$\cos 2u = \dfrac{7}{25}$

$\tan 2u = \dfrac{24}{7}$

27. $\sin 2u = -\dfrac{4\sqrt{21}}{25}$

$\cos 2u = -\dfrac{17}{25}$

$\tan 2u = \dfrac{4\sqrt{21}}{17}$

29. $\frac{1}{8}(3 + 4\cos 2x + \cos 4x)$ **31.** $\frac{1}{8}(1 - \cos 4x)$

33. $\frac{1}{16}(1 + \cos 2x - \cos 4x - \cos 2x \cos 4x)$

35. $\dfrac{4\sqrt{17}}{17}$ **37.** $\dfrac{1}{4}$ **39.** $\sqrt{17}$

41. $\sin 75° = \frac{1}{2}\sqrt{2 + \sqrt{3}}$

$\cos 75° = \frac{1}{2}\sqrt{2 - \sqrt{3}}$

$\tan 75° = 2 + \sqrt{3}$

43. $\sin 112° 30' = \frac{1}{2}\sqrt{2 + \sqrt{2}}$

$\cos 112° 30' = -\frac{1}{2}\sqrt{2 - \sqrt{2}}$

$\tan 112° 30' = -1 - \sqrt{2}$

45. $\sin \dfrac{\pi}{8} = \frac{1}{2}\sqrt{2 - \sqrt{2}}$

$\cos \dfrac{\pi}{8} = \frac{1}{2}\sqrt{2 + \sqrt{2}}$

$\tan \dfrac{\pi}{8} = \sqrt{2} - 1$

47. $\sin \dfrac{3\pi}{8} = \frac{1}{2}\sqrt{2 + \sqrt{2}}$

$\cos \dfrac{3\pi}{8} = \frac{1}{2}\sqrt{2 - \sqrt{2}}$

$\tan \dfrac{3\pi}{8} = \sqrt{2} + 1$

49. $\sin \dfrac{u}{2} = \dfrac{5\sqrt{26}}{26}$

$\cos \dfrac{u}{2} = \dfrac{\sqrt{26}}{26}$

$\tan \dfrac{u}{2} = 5$

51. $\sin \dfrac{u}{2} = \sqrt{\dfrac{89 - 8\sqrt{89}}{178}}$

$\cos \dfrac{u}{2} = -\sqrt{\dfrac{89 + 8\sqrt{89}}{178}}$

$\tan \dfrac{u}{2} = \dfrac{8 - \sqrt{89}}{5}$

53. $\sin \dfrac{u}{2} = \dfrac{3\sqrt{10}}{10}$

$\cos \dfrac{u}{2} = -\dfrac{\sqrt{10}}{10}$

$\tan \dfrac{u}{2} = -3$

55. $|\sin 3x|$ **57.** $-|\tan 4x|$

59. π

61. $\dfrac{\pi}{3}, \pi, \dfrac{5\pi}{3}$

63. $3\left(\sin \dfrac{\pi}{2} + \sin 0\right)$ **65.** $5(\cos 60° + \cos 90°)$

67. $\frac{1}{2}(\sin 10\theta + \sin 2\theta)$ **69.** $\frac{5}{2}(\cos 8\beta + \cos 2\beta)$

71. $\frac{1}{2}(\cos 2y - \cos 2x)$ **73.** $\frac{1}{2}(\sin 2\theta + \sin 2\pi)$

75. $2\cos 4\theta \sin \theta$ **77.** $2\cos 4x \cos 2x$

79. $2\cos \alpha \sin \beta$ **81.** $-2\sin \theta \sin \dfrac{\pi}{2}$

83. $\dfrac{\sqrt{3} + 1}{2}$ **85.** $-\sqrt{2}$

87. $0, \dfrac{\pi}{4}, \dfrac{\pi}{2}, \dfrac{3\pi}{4}, \pi, \dfrac{5\pi}{4}, \dfrac{3\pi}{2}, \dfrac{7\pi}{4}$

89. $\dfrac{\pi}{6}, \dfrac{5\pi}{6}$

91. $\frac{25}{169}$ **93.** $\frac{4}{13}$ **95–109.** Answers will vary.

111.

113.

115.

117. $2x\sqrt{1 - x^2}$ **119.** $23.85°$

121. (a) π (b) 0.4482

(c) 760 miles per hour; 3420 miles per hour

(d) $\theta = 2\sin^{-1}\left(\dfrac{1}{M}\right)$

123. False. For $u < 0$,

$\sin 2u = -\sin(-2u)$

$= -2\sin(-u)\cos(-u)$

$= -2(-\sin u)\cos u$

$= 2\sin u \cos u.$

CHAPTER 5

125. (a)   (b) π

Maximum: $(\pi, 3)$

127. (a) $\frac{1}{4}(3 + \cos 4x)$ (b) $2 \cos^4 x - 2 \cos^2 x + 1$
(c) $1 - 2 \sin^2 x \cos^2 x$ (d) $1 - \frac{1}{2} \sin^2 2x$
(e) No. There is often more than one way to rewrite a trigonometric expression.

129. (a)   (b) Distance $= 2\sqrt{10}$
(c) Midpoint: $(2, 3)$

131. (a) (b) Distance $= \frac{2}{3}\sqrt{13}$
(c) Midpoint: $\left(\frac{2}{3}, \frac{3}{2}\right)$

133. (a) Complement: $35°$; supplement: $125°$
(b) No complement; supplement: $18°$

135. (a) Complement: $\frac{4\pi}{9}$; supplement: $\frac{17\pi}{18}$
(b) Complement: $\frac{\pi}{20}$; supplement: $\frac{11\pi}{20}$

137. September: \$235,000; October: \$272,600
139. ≈ 127 feet

Section 5.6 *(page 425)*

Vocabulary Check *(page 425)*

1. oblique 2. $\dfrac{b}{\sin B}$ 3. $\dfrac{1}{2} ac \sin B$

1. $C = 105°, b \approx 28.28, c \approx 38.64$
3. $C = 120°, b \approx 4.75, c \approx 7.17$
5. $B \approx 21.55°, C \approx 122.45°, c \approx 11.49$
7. $B = 60.9°, b \approx 19.32, c \approx 6.36$
9. $B = 42°4', a \approx 22.05, b \approx 14.88$
11. $A \approx 10°11', C \approx 154°19', c \approx 11.03$
13. $A \approx 25.57°, B \approx 9.43°, a \approx 10.53$
15. $B \approx 18°13', C \approx 51°32', c \approx 40.06$

17. $C = 83°, a \approx 0.62, b \approx 0.51$
19. $B \approx 48.74°, C \approx 21.26°, c \approx 48.23$
21. No solution
23. Two solutions:
$B \approx 72.21°, C \approx 49.79°, c \approx 10.27$
$B \approx 107.79°, C \approx 14.21°, c \approx 3.30$

25. (a) $b \le 5, b = \dfrac{5}{\sin 36°}$ (b) $5 < b < \dfrac{5}{\sin 36°}$
(c) $b > \dfrac{5}{\sin 36°}$

27. (a) $b \le 10.8, b = \dfrac{10.8}{\sin 10°}$ (b) $10.8 < b < \dfrac{10.8}{\sin 10°}$
(c) $b > \dfrac{10.8}{\sin 10°}$

29. 10.4 **31.** 1675.2 **33.** 3204.5 **35.** 15.3 meters
37. 16.1° **39.** 77 meters
41. (a) 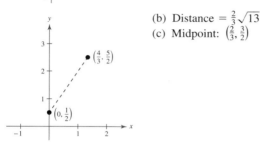 (b) 22.6 miles
(c) 21.4 miles
(d) 7.3 miles

Not drawn to scale

43. 3.2 miles
45. True. If an angle of a triangle is obtuse (greater than 90°), then the other two angles must be acute and therefore less than 90°. The triangle is oblique.
47. (a) $\alpha = \arcsin(0.5 \sin \beta)$
(b) Domain: $0 < \beta < \pi$
Range: $0 < \alpha < \dfrac{\pi}{6}$
(c) $c = \dfrac{18 \sin[\pi - \beta - \arcsin(0.5 \sin \beta)]}{\sin \beta}$
(d) Domain: $0 < \beta < \pi$
Range: $9 < c < 27$

(e)

β	0.4	0.8	1.2	1.6
α	0.1960	0.3669	0.4848	0.5234
c	25.95	23.07	19.19	15.33

β	2.0	2.4	2.8
α	0.4720	0.3445	0.1683
c	12.29	10.31	9.27

As β increases from 0 to π, α increases and then decreases, and c decreases from 27 to 9.

49. $\cos x$ **51.** $\sin^2 x$

Section 5.7 (page 432)

1. $A \approx 23.07°, B \approx 34.05°, C \approx 122.88°$
3. $B \approx 23.79°, C \approx 126.21°, a \approx 18.59$
5. $A \approx 31.99°, B \approx 42.39°, C \approx 105.63°$
7. $A \approx 92.94°, B \approx 43.53°, C \approx 43.53°$
9. $B \approx 13.45°, C \approx 31.55°, a \approx 12.16$
11. $A \approx 141°45', C \approx 27°40', b \approx 11.87$
13. $A \approx 27°10', C \approx 27°10', b \approx 56.94$
15. $A \approx 33.80°, B \approx 103.20°, c \approx 0.54$

	a	b	c	d	θ	ϕ
17.	5	8	12.07	5.69	45°	135.1°
19.	10	14	20	13.86	68.2°	111.8°
21.	15	16.96	25	20	77.2°	102.8°

23. 16.25   **25.** 10.4   **27.** 52.11
29.   N 37.1° E, S 63.1° E

31. 373.3 meters   **33.** 72.3°   **35.** 43.3 miles
37. (a) N 58.4° W   (b) S 81.5° W
39. 63.7 feet   **41.** 24.2 miles
43. $\overline{PQ} \approx 9.4, \overline{QS} = 5, \overline{RS} \approx 12.8$
45.

d (inches)	9	10	12	13	14
θ (degrees)	60.9°	69.5°	88.0°	98.2°	109.6°
s (inches)	20.88	20.28	18.99	18.28	17.48

d (inches)	15	16
θ (degrees)	122.9°	139.8°
s (inches)	16.55	15.37

47. 46,837.5 square feet   **49.** $83,336.37
51. False. For s to be the average of the lengths of the three
sides of the triangle, s would be equal to $(a + b + c)/3$.
53. False. The three side lengths do not form a triangle.
55. (a) 570.60   (b) 5910   (c) 177

57. Answers will vary.   **59.** $-\dfrac{\pi}{2}$ **61.** $\dfrac{\pi}{3}$

63. $-\dfrac{\pi}{3}$ **65.** $\dfrac{1}{\sqrt{1 - 4x^2}}$ **67.** $\dfrac{1}{x - 2}$

69. $\cos \theta = 1$ **71.** $\tan \theta = -\dfrac{\sqrt{3}}{3}$

   $\sec \theta = 1$ $\sec \theta = \dfrac{2\sqrt{3}}{3}$

   $\csc \theta$ is undefined. $\csc \theta = -2$

73. $-2 \sin \dfrac{7\pi}{12} \sin \dfrac{\pi}{4}$

Review Exercises (page 437)

1. $\sec x$ **3.** $\cos x$ **5.** $\cot x$

7. $\tan x = \dfrac{3}{4}$ **9.** $\cos x = \dfrac{\sqrt{2}}{2}$

   $\csc x = \dfrac{5}{3}$ $\tan x = -1$

   $\sec x = \dfrac{5}{4}$ $\csc x = -\sqrt{2}$

   $\cot x = \dfrac{4}{3}$ $\sec x = \sqrt{2}$

                                                 $\cot x = -1$

11. $\sin^2 x$ **13.** 1   **15.** $\cot \theta$ **17.** $\cot^2 x$
19. $\sec x + 2 \sin x$
21. $-2 \tan^2 \theta$ **23–31.** Answers will vary.

33. $\dfrac{\pi}{3} + 2n\pi, \dfrac{2\pi}{3} + 2n\pi$ **35.** $\dfrac{\pi}{6} + n\pi$

37. $\dfrac{\pi}{3} + n\pi, \dfrac{2\pi}{3} + n\pi$ **39.** $0, \dfrac{2\pi}{3}, \dfrac{4\pi}{3}$ **41.** $0, \dfrac{\pi}{2}, \pi$

43. $\dfrac{\pi}{8}, \dfrac{3\pi}{8}, \dfrac{9\pi}{8}, \dfrac{11\pi}{8}$

45. $0, \dfrac{\pi}{8}, \dfrac{3\pi}{8}, \dfrac{5\pi}{8}, \dfrac{7\pi}{8}, \dfrac{9\pi}{8}, \dfrac{11\pi}{8}, \dfrac{13\pi}{8}, \dfrac{15\pi}{8}$ **47.** $0, \pi$

49. $\arctan(-4) + \pi, \arctan(-4) + 2\pi, \arctan 3,$
   $\pi + \arctan 3$

51. $\sin 285° = -\dfrac{\sqrt{2}}{4}(\sqrt{3} + 1)$

   $\cos 285° = \dfrac{\sqrt{2}}{4}(\sqrt{3} - 1)$

   $\tan 285° = -2 - \sqrt{3}$

53. $\sin \dfrac{25\pi}{12} = \dfrac{\sqrt{2}}{4}(\sqrt{3} - 1)$

   $\cos \dfrac{25\pi}{12} = \dfrac{\sqrt{2}}{4}(\sqrt{3} + 1)$

   $\tan \dfrac{25\pi}{12} = 2 - \sqrt{3}$

55. $\sin 15°$ **57.** $\tan 35°$ **59.** $-\frac{3}{52}(5 + 4\sqrt{7})$

61. $\dfrac{1}{52}(5\sqrt{7} + 36)$ **63.** $\dfrac{1}{52}(5\sqrt{7} - 36)$

65–69. Answers will vary.

71. $\dfrac{\pi}{4}, \dfrac{7\pi}{4}$ **73.** $\dfrac{\pi}{6}, \dfrac{11\pi}{6}$

CHAPTER 5

75. $\sin 2u = \frac{24}{25}$
$\cos 2u = -\frac{7}{25}$
$\tan 2u = -\frac{24}{7}$

77.

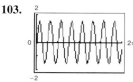

79. $\dfrac{1 - \cos 4x}{1 + \cos 4x}$ **81.** $\dfrac{3 - 4\cos 2x + \cos 4x}{4(1 + \cos 2x)}$

83. $\sin(-75°) = -\frac{1}{2}\sqrt{2 + \sqrt{3}}$
$\cos(-75°) = \frac{1}{2}\sqrt{2 - \sqrt{3}}$
$\tan(-75°) = -2 - \sqrt{3}$

85. $\sin\dfrac{19\pi}{12} = -\frac{1}{2}\sqrt{2 + \sqrt{3}}$ **87.** $\sin\dfrac{u}{2} = \dfrac{\sqrt{10}}{10}$

$\cos\dfrac{19\pi}{12} = \frac{1}{2}\sqrt{2 - \sqrt{3}}$ $\cos\dfrac{u}{2} = \dfrac{3\sqrt{10}}{10}$

$\tan\dfrac{19\pi}{12} = -2 - \sqrt{3}$ $\tan\dfrac{u}{2} = \dfrac{1}{3}$

89. $\sin\dfrac{u}{2} = \dfrac{3\sqrt{14}}{14}$

$\cos\dfrac{u}{2} = \dfrac{\sqrt{70}}{14}$

$\tan\dfrac{u}{2} = \dfrac{3\sqrt{5}}{5}$

91. $-|\cos 5x|$ **93.** $\dfrac{1}{2}\sin\dfrac{\pi}{3}$ **95.** $\dfrac{1}{2}(\cos 2\theta + \cos 8\theta)$

97. $2\cos 3\theta \sin \theta$ **99.** $-2\sin x \sin \dfrac{\pi}{6}$

101. $\theta = 15°$ or $\dfrac{\pi}{12}$

103.

105. $\frac{1}{2}\sqrt{10}$ feet   **107.** $A = 26°, a \approx 24.89, c \approx 56.23$

109. $C = 66°, a \approx 2.53, b \approx 9.11$

111. $B = 108°, a \approx 11.76, c \approx 21.49$

113. $A \approx 20.41°, C \approx 9.59°, a \approx 20.92$

115. $B \approx 39.48°, C \approx 65.52°, c \approx 48.24$

117. 7.9   **119.** 33.5

121. 31.1 meters   **123.** 31.01 feet

125. $A \approx 29.69°, B \approx 52.41°, C \approx 97.90°$

127. $A \approx 29.92°, B \approx 86.18°, C \approx 63.90°$

129. $A = 35°, C = 35°, b \approx 6.55$

131. $A \approx 48.24°, B \approx 88.76°, c \approx 21.42$

133. 615.1 meters   **135.** 9.80   **137.** 8.36

139. False. If $(\pi/2) < \theta < \pi$, then $\cos(\theta/2) > 0$. The sign of $\cos(\theta/2)$ depends on the quadrant in which $\theta/2$ lies.

141. True. $4\sin(-x)\cos(-x) = 4(-\sin x)\cos x$
$= -4\sin x \cos x$
$= -2(2\sin x \cos x)$
$= -2\sin 2x$

143. True. $\sin 90°$ is defined in the Law of Sines.

145. Reciprocal identities:

$$\sin\theta = \frac{1}{\csc\theta},\ \cos\theta = \frac{1}{\sec\theta},\ \tan\theta = \frac{1}{\cot\theta},$$

$$\csc\theta = \frac{1}{\sin\theta},\ \sec\theta = \frac{1}{\cos\theta},\ \cot\theta = \frac{1}{\tan\theta}$$

Quotient identities: $\tan\theta = \dfrac{\sin\theta}{\cos\theta}, \cot\theta = \dfrac{\cos\theta}{\sin\theta}$

Pythagorean identities: $\sin^2\theta + \cos^2\theta = 1$,
$1 + \tan^2\theta = \sec^2\theta, 1 + \cot^2\theta = \csc^2\theta$

147. $-1 \le \sin x \le 1$ for all x **149.** $y_1 = y_2 + 1$

151. $-1.8431, 2.1758, 3.9903, 8.8935, 9.8820$

Chapter Test   *(page 441)*

1. $\sin\theta = -\dfrac{3\sqrt{13}}{13}$ **2.** 1   **3.** 1   **4.** $\csc\theta \sec\theta$

$\cos\theta = -\dfrac{2\sqrt{13}}{13}$

$\csc\theta = -\dfrac{\sqrt{13}}{3}$

$\sec\theta = -\dfrac{\sqrt{13}}{2}$

$\cot\theta = \dfrac{2}{3}$

5–10. Answers will vary.

11. $\dfrac{1}{16}\left(\dfrac{10 - 15\cos 2x + 6\cos 4x - \cos 6x}{1 + \cos 2x}\right)$ **12.** $\tan 2\theta$

13. $2(\sin 6\theta + \sin 2\theta)$ **14.** $-2\cos\dfrac{7\theta}{2}\sin\dfrac{\theta}{2}$

15. $0, \dfrac{3\pi}{4}, \pi, \dfrac{7\pi}{4}$ **16.** $\dfrac{\pi}{6}, \dfrac{\pi}{2}, \dfrac{5\pi}{6}, \dfrac{3\pi}{2}$

17. $\dfrac{\pi}{6}, \dfrac{5\pi}{6}, \dfrac{7\pi}{6}, \dfrac{11\pi}{6}$ **18.** $\dfrac{\pi}{6}, \dfrac{5\pi}{6}, \dfrac{3\pi}{2}$ **19.** $\dfrac{\sqrt{2} - \sqrt{6}}{4}$

20. $\sin 2u = \frac{4}{5}, \tan 2u = -\frac{4}{3}, \cos 2u = -\frac{3}{5}$

21. $C = 88°, b \approx 27.81, c \approx 29.98$

22. $A = 43°, b \approx 25.75, c \approx 14.45$

23. Two solutions:
$B \approx 29.12°, C \approx 126.88°, c \approx 22.03$
$B \approx 150.88°, C \approx 5.12°, c \approx 2.46$

24. No solution

25. $A \approx 39.96°, C \approx 40.04°, c \approx 15.02$

26. $A \approx 23.43°, B \approx 33.57°, c \approx 86.46$

27. Day 123 to day 223

28. 2052.5 square meters   **29.** 606.3 miles; 29.1°

Problem Solving   (page 447)

1.

(a) $\cos \theta = \pm \sqrt{1 - \sin^2 \theta}$

$\tan \theta = \pm \dfrac{\sin \theta}{\sqrt{1 - \sin^2 \theta}}$

$\cot \theta = \pm \dfrac{\sqrt{1 - \sin^2 \theta}}{\sin \theta}$

$\sec \theta = \pm \dfrac{1}{\sqrt{1 - \sin^2 \theta}}$

$\csc \theta = \dfrac{1}{\sin \theta}$

(b) $\sin \theta = \pm \sqrt{1 - \cos^2 \theta}$

$\tan \theta = \pm \dfrac{\sqrt{1 - \cos^2 \theta}}{\cos \theta}$

$\csc \theta = \pm \dfrac{1}{\sqrt{1 - \cos^2 \theta}}$

$\sec \theta = \dfrac{1}{\cos \theta}$

$\cot \theta = \pm \dfrac{\cos \theta}{\sqrt{1 - \cos^2 \theta}}$

3. Answers will vary.   **5.** $u + v = w$

7. $\sin \dfrac{\theta}{2} = \sqrt{\dfrac{1 - \cos \theta}{2}}$

$\cos \dfrac{\theta}{2} = \sqrt{\dfrac{1 + \cos \theta}{2}}$

$\tan \dfrac{\theta}{2} = \dfrac{\sin \theta}{1 + \cos \theta}$

9. (a)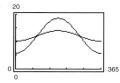

(b) $t = 91, t = 274$; Spring Equinox and Fall Equinox

(c) Seward; The amplitudes: 6.4 and 1.9

(d) 365.2 days

11. (a) $\dfrac{\pi}{6} \le x \le \dfrac{5\pi}{6}$

(b) $\dfrac{2\pi}{3} \le x \le \dfrac{4\pi}{3}$

(c) $\dfrac{\pi}{2} < x < \pi, \dfrac{3\pi}{2} < x < 2\pi$

(d) $0 \le x \le \dfrac{\pi}{4}, \dfrac{5\pi}{4} \le x \le 2\pi$

13. (a) $\cos 3\theta = \cos \theta - 4 \sin^2 \theta \cos \theta$

(b) $\cos 4\theta = \cos^4 \theta - 6 \sin^2 \theta \cos^2 \theta + \sin^4 \theta$

15. 2.01 feet

Chapter 6

Section 6.1   (page 454)

1. $\dfrac{\sqrt{3}}{3}$ **3.** -1 **5.** $\sqrt{3}$ **7.** 3.2236

9. $\dfrac{3\pi}{4}$ radians, 135°   **11.** $\dfrac{\pi}{4}$ radian, 45°

13. 0.6435 radian, 36.9°   **15.** 1.0517 radians, 60.3°

17. 2.1112 radians, 121.0°   **19.** 1.2490 radians, 71.6°

21. 2.1112 radians, 121.0°   **23.** 1.1071 radians, 63.4°

25. 0.1974 radian, 11.3°   **27.** 1.4289 radians, 81.9°

29. 0.9273 radian, 53.1°   **31.** 0.8187 radian, 46.9°

33. $(2, 1) \leftrightarrow (4, 4)$: slope $= \dfrac{3}{2}$

$(4, 4) \leftrightarrow (6, 2)$: slope $= -1$

$(6, 2) \leftrightarrow (2, 1)$: slope $= \dfrac{1}{4}$

$(2, 1)$: 42.3°; $(4, 4)$: 78.7°; $(6, 2)$: 59.0°

35. $(-4, -1) \leftrightarrow (3, 2)$: slope $= \dfrac{3}{7}$

$(3, 2) \leftrightarrow (1, 0)$: slope $= 1$

$(1, 0) \leftrightarrow (-4, -1)$: slope $= \dfrac{1}{5}$

$(-4, -1)$: 11.9°; $(3, 2)$: 21.8°; $(1, 0)$: 146.3°

37. 0   **39.** $\dfrac{7}{5}$ **41.** 7

43. $\dfrac{8\sqrt{37}}{37} \approx 1.3152$

45. (a)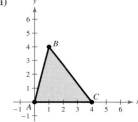

(b) 4

(c) 8

47. (a)

(b) $\dfrac{35\sqrt{37}}{74}$

(c) $\dfrac{35}{8}$

49. $2\sqrt{2}$ **51.** 0.1003, 1054 feet   **53.** 31.0°

55. $\alpha \approx 33.69°$; $\beta \approx 56.31°$

57. True. The inclination of a line is related to its slope by $m = \tan \theta$. If the angle is greater than $\pi/2$ but less than π, then the angle is in the second quadrant, where the tangent function is negative.

59. (a) $d = \dfrac{4}{\sqrt{m^2 + 1}}$

(b)

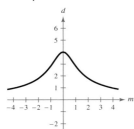

(c) $m = 0$

(d) The graph has a horizontal asymptote of $d = 0$. As the slope becomes larger, the distance between the origin and the line, $y = mx + 4$, becomes smaller and approaches 0.

61. x-intercept: $(7, 0)$ **63.** x-intercepts: $(5 \pm \sqrt{5}, 0)$
y-intercept: $(0, 49)$ y-intercept: $(0, 20)$

65. x-intercepts: $\left(\dfrac{7 \pm \sqrt{53}}{2}, 0\right)$

y-intercept: $(0, -1)$

67. $f(x) = 3\left(x + \tfrac{1}{3}\right)^2 - \tfrac{49}{3}$ **69.** $f(x) = 5\left(x + \tfrac{17}{5}\right)^2 - \tfrac{324}{5}$
Vertex: $\left(-\tfrac{1}{3}, -\tfrac{49}{3}\right)$ Vertex: $\left(-\tfrac{17}{5}, -\tfrac{324}{5}\right)$

71. $f(x) = 6\left(x - \tfrac{1}{12}\right)^2 - \tfrac{289}{24}$
Vertex: $\left(\tfrac{1}{12}, -\tfrac{289}{24}\right)$

73.   **75.**

Section 6.2   *(page 462)*

1. A circle is formed when a plane intersects the top or bottom half of a double-napped cone and is perpendicular to the axis of the cone.

3. A parabola is formed when a plane intersects the top or bottom half of a double-napped cone, is parallel to the side of the cone, and does not intersect the vertex.

5. e   **6.** b   **7.** d   **8.** f   **9.** a   **10.** c

11. Vertex: $(0, 0)$
Focus: $\left(0, \tfrac{1}{2}\right)$
Directrix: $y = -\tfrac{1}{2}$

13. Vertex: $(0, 0)$
Focus: $\left(-\tfrac{3}{2}, 0\right)$
Directrix: $x = \tfrac{3}{2}$

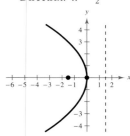

15. Vertex: $(0, 0)$
Focus: $\left(0, -\tfrac{3}{2}\right)$
Directrix: $y = \tfrac{3}{2}$

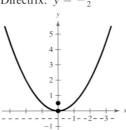

17. Vertex: $(1, -2)$
Focus: $(1, -4)$
Directrix: $y = 0$

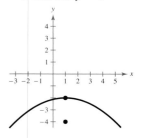

19. Vertex: $\left(-\tfrac{3}{2}, 2\right)$
Focus: $\left(-\tfrac{3}{2}, 3\right)$
Directrix: $y = 1$

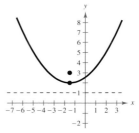

21. Vertex: $(1, 1)$
Focus: $(1, 2)$
Directrix: $y = 0$

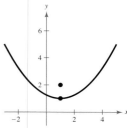

23. Vertex: $(-2, -3)$
Focus: $(-4, -3)$
Directrix: $x = 0$

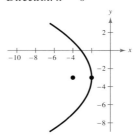

25. Vertex: $(-2, 1)$
Focus: $\left(-2, -\frac{1}{2}\right)$
Directrix: $y = \frac{5}{2}$

27. Vertex: $\left(\frac{1}{4}, -\frac{1}{2}\right)$
Focus: $\left(0, -\frac{1}{2}\right)$
Directrix: $x = \frac{1}{2}$

29. $x^2 = \frac{3}{2}y$ **31.** $x^2 = -6y$ **33.** $y^2 = -8x$
35. $x^2 = 4y$ **37.** $y^2 = -8x$ **39.** $y^2 = 9x$
41. $(x - 3)^2 = -(y - 1)$ **43.** $y^2 = 4(x + 4)$
45. $(y - 2)^2 = -8(x - 5)$ **47.** $x^2 = 8(y - 4)$
49. $(y - 2)^2 = 8x$ **51.** $y = \sqrt{6(x + 1)} + 3$
53.

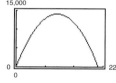

$(2, 4)$
55. $4x - y - 8 = 0;\ (2, 0)$
57. $4x - y + 2 = 0;\ \left(-\frac{1}{2}, 0\right)$
59.

$x = 106$ units
63. (a) $y = -\frac{1}{640}x^2$ (b) 8 feet
65. (a) $17{,}500\sqrt{2}$ miles per hour $\approx 24{,}750$ miles per hour
(b) $x^2 = -16{,}400(y - 4100)$
67. (a) $x^2 = -64(y - 75)$ (b) 69.3 feet
69. False. If the graph crossed the directrix, there would exist points closer to the directrix than the focus.
71. (a)

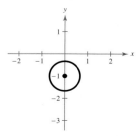

As p increases, the graph becomes wider.
(b) $(0, 1),\ (0, 2),\ (0, 3),\ (0, 4)$
(c) $4, 8, 12, 16;\ 4|p|$
(d) Easy way to determine two additional points on the graph

73. $m = \dfrac{x_1}{2p}$ **75.** $\pm 1, \pm 2, \pm 4$
77. $\pm\frac{1}{2}, \pm 1, \pm 2, \pm 4, \pm 8, \pm 16$
79. $f(x) = x^3 - 7x^2 + 17x - 15$ **81.** $\frac{1}{2}, -\frac{5}{3}, \pm 2$
83. $B \approx 23.67°,\ C \approx 121.33°,\ c \approx 14.89$
85. $C = 89°,\ a \approx 1.93,\ b \approx 2.33$

87. $A \approx 16.39°,\ B \approx 23.77°,\ C \approx 139.84°$
89. $B \approx 24.62°,\ C \approx 90.38°,\ a \approx 10.88$

Section 6.3 *(page 472)*

Vocabulary Check *(page 472)*
1. ellipse; foci **2.** major axis; center
3. minor axis **4.** eccentricity

1. b **2.** c **3.** d **4.** f **5.** a **6.** e
7. Ellipse
Center: $(0, 0)$
Vertices: $(\pm 5, 0)$
Foci: $(\pm 3, 0)$
Eccentricity: $\dfrac{3}{5}$

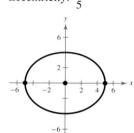

9. Circle
Center: $(0, 0)$
Radius: 5

11. Ellipse
Center: $(0, 0)$
Vertices: $(0, \pm 3)$
Foci: $(0, \pm 2)$
Eccentricity: $\frac{2}{3}$

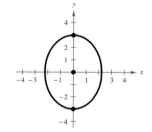

13. Ellipse
Center: $(-3, 5)$
Vertices: $(-3, 10),\ (-3, 0)$
Foci: $(-3, 8),\ (-3, 2)$
Eccentricity: $\frac{3}{5}$

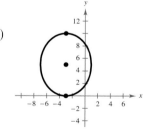

15. Circle
Center: $(0, -1)$
Radius: $\frac{2}{3}$

17. Ellipse

Center: $(-2, -4)$

Vertices: $(-3, -4), (-1, -4)$

Foci: $\left(\dfrac{-4 \pm \sqrt{3}}{2}, -4\right)$

Eccentricity: $\dfrac{\sqrt{3}}{2}$

19. Ellipse

Center: $(-2, 3)$

Vertices: $(-2, 6), (-2, 0)$

Foci: $(-2, 3 \pm \sqrt{5})$

Eccentricity: $\dfrac{\sqrt{5}}{3}$

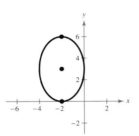

21. Circle

Center: $(1, -2)$

Radius: 6

Foci: $(3, -5 \pm 2\sqrt{5})$

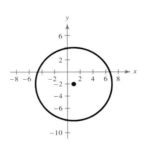

23. Ellipse

Center: $(-3, 1)$

Vertices: $(-3, 7), (-3, -5)$

Foci: $(-3, 1 \pm 2\sqrt{6})$

Eccentricity: $\dfrac{\sqrt{6}}{3}$

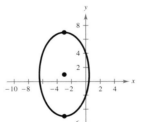

25. Ellipse

Center: $\left(3, -\dfrac{5}{2}\right)$

Vertices: $\left(9, -\dfrac{5}{2}\right), \left(-3, -\dfrac{5}{2}\right)$

Foci: $\left(3 \pm 3\sqrt{3}, -\dfrac{5}{2}\right)$

Eccentricity: $\dfrac{\sqrt{3}}{2}$

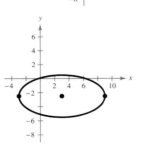

27. Circle

Center: $(-1, 1)$

Radius: $\dfrac{2}{3}$

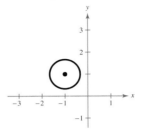

29. Ellipse

Center: $(2, 1)$

Vertices: $\left(\dfrac{7}{3}, 1\right), \left(\dfrac{5}{3}, 1\right)$

Foci: $\left(\dfrac{34}{15}, 1\right), \left(\dfrac{26}{15}, 1\right)$

Eccentricity: $\dfrac{4}{5}$

31.

Center: $(0, 0)$

Vertices: $(0, \pm\sqrt{5})$

Foci: $(0, \pm\sqrt{2})$

33.

Center: $\left(\dfrac{1}{2}, -1\right)$

Vertices: $\left(\dfrac{1}{2} \pm \sqrt{5}, -1\right)$

Foci: $\left(\dfrac{1}{2} \pm \sqrt{2}, -1\right)$

35. $\dfrac{x^2}{4} + \dfrac{y^2}{16} = 1$ **37.** $\dfrac{x^2}{36} + \dfrac{y^2}{32} = 1$

39. $\dfrac{x^2}{36} + \dfrac{y^2}{11} = 1$ **41.** $\dfrac{21x^2}{400} + \dfrac{y^2}{25} = 1$

43. $\dfrac{(x-2)^2}{1} + \dfrac{(y-3)^2}{9} = 1$

45. $\dfrac{(x+2)^2}{16} + \dfrac{(y-3)^2}{9} = 1$

47. $\dfrac{(x-2)^2}{4} + \dfrac{(y-4)^2}{1} = 1$

49. $\dfrac{x^2}{48} + \dfrac{(y-4)^2}{64} = 1$ **51.** $\dfrac{x^2}{16} + \dfrac{(y-4)^2}{12} = 1$

53. $\dfrac{(x-2)^2}{4} + \dfrac{(y-2)^2}{1} = 1$ **55.** $\dfrac{x^2}{25} + \dfrac{y^2}{16} = 1$

57. (a)

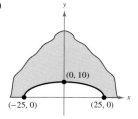

(0, 10)

(−25, 0)   (25, 0)

(b) $\dfrac{x^2}{625} + \dfrac{y^2}{100} = 1$ (c) Yes

59. (a) $\dfrac{x^2}{321.84} + \dfrac{y^2}{20.89} = 1$

(b)

(c) Aphelion: 35.29 astronomical units
Perihelion: 0.59 astronomical unit

61. (a) $\dfrac{x^2}{0.04} + \dfrac{y^2}{2.56} = 1$

(b)

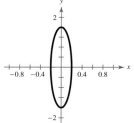

(c) The bottom half

63.

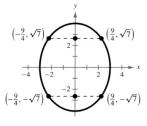

$\left(-\frac{9}{4}, \sqrt{7}\right)$ $\left(\frac{9}{4}, \sqrt{7}\right)$

$\left(-\frac{9}{4}, -\sqrt{7}\right)$ $\left(\frac{9}{4}, -\sqrt{7}\right)$

65.

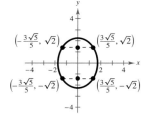

$\left(-\frac{3\sqrt{5}}{5}, \sqrt{2}\right)$ $\left(\frac{3\sqrt{5}}{5}, \sqrt{2}\right)$

$\left(-\frac{3\sqrt{5}}{5}, -\sqrt{2}\right)$ $\left(\frac{3\sqrt{5}}{5}, -\sqrt{2}\right)$

67. False. The graph of $x^2/4 + y^4 = 1$ is not an ellipse. The degree of y is 4, not 2.

69. (a) $A = \pi a(20 - a)$ (b) $\dfrac{x^2}{196} + \dfrac{y^2}{36} = 1$

(c)

a	8	9	10	11	12	13
A	301.6	311.0	314.2	311.0	301.6	285.9

$a = 10$, circle

(d)

350

0   20
 0

The shape of an ellipse with a maximum area is a circle. The maximum area is found when $a = 10$, (verified in part (c), and therefore $b = 10$, so the equation produces a circle.

71. $\frac{1}{32}(10 - 15\cos 2x + 6\cos 4x - \cos 6x)$

73. $\frac{1}{4}\left(\frac{3}{2} + 2\cos 4x + \frac{1}{2}\cos 8x\right)$

75. Area $= 357.9$ **77.** Area $= 47.9$

Section 6.4   (page 482)

1. b   **2.** c   **3.** a   **4.** d

5. Center: $(0, 0)$
Vertices: $(\pm 1, 0)$
Foci: $\left(\pm\sqrt{2}, 0\right)$
Asymptotes: $y = \pm x$

7. Center: $(0, 0)$
Vertices: $(0, \pm 5)$
Foci: $\left(0, \pm\sqrt{106}\right)$
Asymptotes: $y = \pm\frac{5}{9}x$

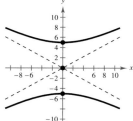

9. Center: $(1, -2)$
Vertices: $(3, -2), (-1, -2)$
Foci: $\left(1 \pm \sqrt{5}, -2\right)$
Asymptotes:
$y = -2 \pm \frac{1}{2}(x - 1)$

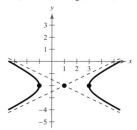

CHAPTER 6

11. Center: $(2, -6)$

Vertices:

$$\left(2, -\frac{17}{3}\right), \left(2, -\frac{19}{3}\right)$$

Foci: $\left(2, -6 \pm \dfrac{\sqrt{13}}{6}\right)$

Asymptotes:

$$y = -6 \pm \frac{2}{3}(x - 2)$$

13. Center: $(2, -3)$

Vertices: $(3, -3), (1, -3)$

Foci: $\left(2 \pm \sqrt{10}, -3\right)$

Asymptotes:

$$y = -3 \pm 3(x - 2)$$

15. The graph of this equation is two lines intersecting at $(-1, -3)$.

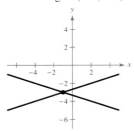

17. Center: $(0, 0)$

Vertices: $\left(\pm\sqrt{3}, 0\right)$

Foci: $\left(\pm\sqrt{5}, 0\right)$

Asymptotes: $y = \pm\dfrac{\sqrt{6}}{3}x$

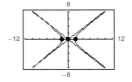

19. Center: $(1, -3)$

Vertices: $\left(1, -3 \pm \sqrt{2}\right)$

Foci: $\left(1, -3 \pm 2\sqrt{5}\right)$

Asymptotes: $y = -3 \pm \frac{1}{3}(x - 1)$

21. $\dfrac{y^2}{4} - \dfrac{x^2}{12} = 1$ **23.** $\dfrac{x^2}{1} - \dfrac{y^2}{25} = 1$

25. $\dfrac{17y^2}{1024} - \dfrac{17x^2}{64} = 1$ **27.** $\dfrac{(x - 4)^2}{4} - \dfrac{y^2}{12} = 1$

29. $\dfrac{(y - 5)^2}{16} - \dfrac{(x - 4)^2}{9} = 1$ **31.** $\dfrac{y^2}{9} - \dfrac{4(x - 2)^2}{9} = 1$

33. $\dfrac{(y - 2)^2}{4} - \dfrac{x^2}{4} = 1$ **35.** $\dfrac{(x - 2)^2}{1} - \dfrac{(y - 2)^2}{1} = 1$

37. $\dfrac{(x - 3)^2}{9} - \dfrac{(y - 2)^2}{4} = 1$

39. (a) $\dfrac{x^2}{1} - \dfrac{y^2}{169/3} = 1$ (b) ≈ 2.403 feet

41. $(3300, -2750)$

43. $\left(12\left(\sqrt{5} - 1\right), 0\right) \approx (14.83, 0)$

45. Circle   **47.** Hyperbola   **49.** Hyperbola

51. Parabola   **53.** Ellipse   **55.** Parabola

57. Ellipse   **59.** Circle

61. True. For a hyperbola, $c^2 = a^2 + b^2$. The larger the ratio of b to a, the larger the eccentricity of the hyperbola, $e = c/a$.

63. Answers will vary.   **65.** $y = 1 - 3\sqrt{\dfrac{(x - 3)^2}{4} - 1}$

67. $x(x + 4)(x - 4)$

69. $2x(x - 6)^2$ **71.** $2(2x + 3)(4x^2 - 6x + 9)$

73.

75.

Section 6.5 *(page 490)*

Vocabulary Check *(page 490)*

1. plane curve; parametric; parameter
2. orientation   3. eliminating the parameter

1. (a)

t	0	1	2	3	4
x	0	1	$\sqrt{2}$	$\sqrt{3}$	2
y	3	2	1	0	-1

(b)

(c) $y = 3 - x^2$

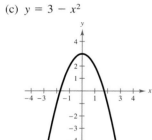

The graph of the rectangular equation shows the entire parabola rather than just the right half.

3. (a)

(b) $y = \frac{2}{3}x + 3$

5. (a)

(b) $y = 16x^2$

7. (a)

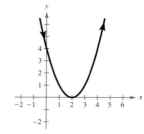

(b) $y = x^2 - 4x + 4$

9. (a)

(b) $y = \dfrac{(x-1)}{x}$

11. (a)

(b) $y = \left| \dfrac{x}{2} - 3 \right|$

13. (a)

(b) $\dfrac{y^2}{9} + \dfrac{x^2}{9} = 1$

15. (a)

(b) $\dfrac{x^2}{16} + \dfrac{y^2}{4} = 1$

17. (a)

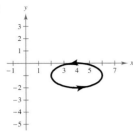

(b) $\dfrac{(x-4)^2}{4} + (y+1)^2 = 1$

19. (a)

(b) $y = \dfrac{1}{x^3}$

21. (a)

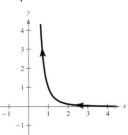

(b) $y = \ln x$

23. Each curve represents a portion of the line $y = 2x + 1$.

        Domain   *Orientation*
   (a) $(-\infty, \infty)$ Left to right
   (b) $[-1, 1]$ Depends on θ
   (c) $(0, \infty)$ Right to left
   (d) $(0, \infty)$ Left to right

25. $y - y_1 = m(x - x_1)$

27. $\dfrac{(x-h)^2}{a^2} + \dfrac{(y-k)^2}{b^2} = 1$

29. $x = 6t$ **31.** $x = 3 + 4\cos\theta$
     $y = -3t$ $y = 2 + 4\sin\theta$

33. $x = 4\cos\theta$ **35.** $x = 4\sec\theta$
     $y = \sqrt{7}\sin\theta$ $y = 3\tan\theta$

37. (a) $x = t,\ y = 3t - 2$ (b) $x = -t + 2,\ y = -3t + 4$

39. (a) $x = t,\ y = t^2$ (b) $x = -t + 2,\ y = t^2 - 4t + 4$

41. (a) $x = t,\ y = t^2 + 1$ (b) $x = -t + 2,\ y = t^2 - 4t + 5$

43. (a) $x = t,\ y = \dfrac{1}{t}$ (b) $x = -t + 2,\ y = -\dfrac{1}{t - 2}$

45.

47.

49.

51.

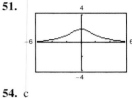

53. b
    Domain: $[-2, 2]$
    Range: $[-1, 1]$

54. c
    Domain: $[-4, 4]$
    Range: $[-6, 6]$

55. d
    Domain: $(-\infty, \infty)$
    Range: $(-\infty, \infty)$

56. a
    Domain: $(-\infty, \infty)$
    Range: $[-2, 2]$

57. (a)

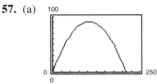

    Maximum height: 90.7 feet
    Range: 209.6 feet

(b)

    Maximum height: 204.2 feet
    Range: 471.6 feet

(c)

    Maximum height: 60.5 feet
    Range: 242.0 feet

(d)

    Maximum height: 136.1 feet
    Range: 544.5 feet

59. (a) $x = (146.67 \cos \theta)t$
$y = 3 + (146.67 \sin \theta)t - 16t^2$

(b)   No

(c) 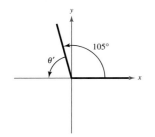   Yes

(d) $19.3°$

61. Answers will vary.

63. $x = a\theta - b \sin \theta$
$y = a - b \cos \theta$

65. True
$x = t$
$y = t^2 + 1 \Longrightarrow y = x^2 + 1$
$x = 3t$
$y = 9t^2 + 1 \Longrightarrow y = x^2 + 1$

67. Parametric equations are useful when graphing two functions simultaneously on the same coordinate system. For example, they are useful when tracking the path of an object so that the position and the time associated with that position can be determined.

69. $\theta' = 75°$ **71.** $\theta' = \dfrac{\pi}{3}$

Section 6.6   *(page 497)*

Vocabulary Check   *(page 497)*

1. pole   **2.** directed distance; directed angle

3. polar   **4.** $x = r \cos \theta$ $\tan \theta = \dfrac{y}{x}$
$y = r \sin \theta$ $r^2 = x^2 + y^2$

1.   **3.**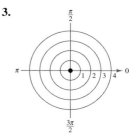

$\left(4, \dfrac{5\pi}{3}\right), \left(-4, -\dfrac{4\pi}{3}\right)$ $\left(0, \dfrac{5\pi}{6}\right), \left(0, -\dfrac{13\pi}{6}\right)$

5.   **7.**

$\left(\sqrt{2}, 8.64\right), \left(-\sqrt{2}, -0.78\right)$ $\left(2\sqrt{2}, 10.99\right), \left(-2\sqrt{2}, 7.85\right)$

9. $(0, 3)$ **11.** $\left(\dfrac{\sqrt{2}}{2}, \dfrac{\sqrt{2}}{2}\right)$

13. $\left(-\sqrt{2}, \sqrt{2}\right)$ **15.** $(-1.1340, -2.2280)$

17. $\left(\sqrt{2}, \dfrac{\pi}{4}\right)$ **19.** $(6, \pi)$ **21.** $(5, 2.2143)$

23. $\left(\sqrt{6}, \dfrac{5\pi}{4}\right)$ **25.** $\left(3\sqrt{13}, 0.9828\right)$

27. $\left(\sqrt{13}, 5.6952\right)$ **29.** $\left(\sqrt{7}, 0.8571\right)$

31. $\left(\tfrac{17}{6}, 0.4900\right)$ **33.** $r = 3$ **35.** $r = 4 \csc \theta$

37. $r = 10 \sec \theta$ **39.** $r = \dfrac{-2}{3 \cos \theta - \sin \theta}$

41. $r^2 = 16 \sec \theta \csc \theta = 32 \csc 2\theta$

43. $r = \dfrac{4}{1 - \cos \theta}$ or $-\dfrac{4}{1 + \cos \theta}$

45. $r = a$ **47.** $r = 2a \cos \theta$ **49.** $x^2 + y^2 - 4y = 0$

51. $\sqrt{3}x + y = 0$ **53.** $x^2 + y^2 = 16$

55. $y = 4$ **57.** $x^2 + y^2 - x^{2/3} = 0$

59. $(x^2 + y^2)^2 = 6x^2y - 2y^3$ **61.** $x^2 + 4y - 4 = 0$

63. $4x^2 - 5y^2 - 36y - 36 = 0$

65. The graph of the polar equation consists of all points that are six units from the pole.
$x^2 + y^2 = 36$

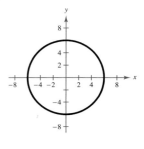

67. The graph of the polar
equation consists of all
points on the line that make
an angle of $\pi/6$ with the
positive polar axis.
$-\sqrt{3}x + 3y = 0$

69. The graph of the polar
equation is not evident by
simple inspection, so convert
to rectangular form.
$x - 3 = 0$

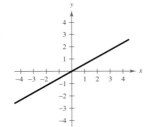

71. True. Because r is a directed distance, the point (r, θ) can
be represented as $(r, \theta \pm 2\pi n)$.

73. $(x - h)^2 + (y - k)^2 = h^2 + k^2$
Radius: $\sqrt{h^2 + k^2}$
Center: (h, k)

75. (a) Answers will vary.
   (b) $(r_1, \theta_1), (r_2, \theta_2)$ and the pole are collinear.
   $d = \sqrt{r_1^2 + r_2^2 - 2r_1 r_2} = |r_1 - r_2|$
   This represents the distance between two points on the
   line $\theta = \theta_1 = \theta_2$.
   (c) $d = \sqrt{r_1^2 + r_2^2}$
   This is the result of the Pythagorean Theorem.
   (d) Answers will vary. For example:
   Points: $(3, \pi/6), (4, \pi/3)$
   Distance: 2.053
   Points: $(-3, 7\pi/6), (-4, 4\pi/3)$
   Distance: 2.053

77. $2 \log_6 x + \log_6 z - \log_6 3 - \log_6 y$

79. $\ln x + 2 \ln(x + 4)$ **81.** $\log_7 \dfrac{x}{3y}$

83. $\ln \sqrt{x}(x - 2)$

Section 6.7   (page 505)

1. Rose curve with 4 petals   **3.** Limaçon with inner loop
5. Rose curve with 4 petals

7. Polar axis   **9.** $\theta = \dfrac{\pi}{2}$ **11.** $\theta = \dfrac{\pi}{2}$, polar axis, pole

13. Maximum: $|r| = 20$ when $\theta = \dfrac{3\pi}{2}$

Zero: $r = 0$ when $\theta = \dfrac{\pi}{2}$

15. Maximum: $|r| = 4$ when $\theta = 0, \dfrac{\pi}{3}, \dfrac{2\pi}{3}$

Zero: $r = 0$ when $\theta = \dfrac{\pi}{6}, \dfrac{\pi}{2}, \dfrac{5\pi}{6}$

17.   **19.**

21.   **23.**

25.   **27.**

29.   **31.**

33.

35.

37.

39.

41.

43.

45.

47.
$0 \leq \theta < 2\pi$

49.
$0 \leq \theta < 4\pi$

51.
$0 \leq \theta < \pi$

53.

55.

57. True. For a graph to have polar axis symmetry, replace (r, θ) by $(r, -\theta)$ or $(-r, \pi - \theta)$.

59. (a) 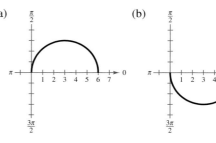 (b)

Upper half of circle   Lower half of circle

(c) (d)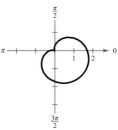

Full circle   Left half of circle

61. Answers will vary.

63. (a) $r = 2 - \dfrac{\sqrt{2}}{2}(\sin \theta - \cos \theta)$ (b) $r = 2 + \cos \theta$
(c) $r = 2 + \sin \theta$ (d) $r = 2 - \cos \theta$

65. (a) (b)

67.
$k = 0$, circle
$k = 1$, convex limaçon
$k = 2$, cardioid
$k = 3$, limaçon with inner loop

69. ± 3 **71.** $\frac{13}{5}$

73. $\dfrac{(x + 1)^2}{9} + \dfrac{(y - 2)^2}{4} = 1$

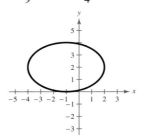

CHAPTER 6

Section 6.8   *(page 511)*

Vocabulary Check   *(page 511)*

1. conic   **2.** eccentricity; e **3.** vertical; right

4. (a) iii   (b) i   (c) ii

1. $e = 1$: $r = \dfrac{4}{1 + \cos \theta}$, parabola

$e = 0.5$: $r = \dfrac{2}{1 + 0.5 \cos \theta}$, ellipse

$e = 1.5$: $r = \dfrac{6}{1 + 1.5 \cos \theta}$, hyperbola

3. $e = 1$: $r = \dfrac{4}{1 - \sin \theta}$, parabola

$e = 0.5$: $r = \dfrac{2}{1 - 0.5 \sin \theta}$, ellipse

$e = 1.5$: $r = \dfrac{6}{1 - 1.5 \sin \theta}$, hyperbola

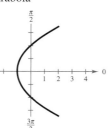

5. f   **6.** c   **7.** d   **8.** e   **9.** a   **10.** b

11. Parabola   **13.** Parabola

15. Ellipse   **17.** Ellipse

19. Hyperbola   **21.** Hyperbola

23. Ellipse

25.   **27.**

Parabola   Ellipse

29.   **31.**

33. $r = \dfrac{1}{1 - \cos \theta}$ **35.** $r = \dfrac{1}{2 + \sin \theta}$

37. $r = \dfrac{2}{1 + 2 \cos \theta}$ **39.** $r = \dfrac{2}{1 - \sin \theta}$

41. $r = \dfrac{10}{1 - \cos \theta}$ **43.** $r = \dfrac{10}{3 + 2 \cos \theta}$

45. $r = \dfrac{20}{3 - 2 \cos \theta}$ **47.** $r = \dfrac{9}{4 - 5 \sin \theta}$

49. Answers will vary.

51. $r = \dfrac{9.5929 \times 10^7}{1 - 0.0167 \cos \theta}$

Perihelion: 9.4354×10^7 miles

Aphelion: 9.7558×10^7 miles

53. $r = \dfrac{1.0820 \times 10^8}{1 - 0.0068 \cos \theta}$

Perihelion: 1.0747×10^8 kilometers

Aphelion: 1.0894×10^8 kilometers

55. $r = \dfrac{1.4039 \times 10^8}{1 - 0.0934 \cos \theta}$

Perihelion: 1.2840×10^8 miles

Aphelion: 1.5486×10^8 miles

57. $r = \dfrac{0.624}{1 + 0.847 \sin \pi/2}; r = 0.338$ astronomical unit

59. True. The graphs represent the same hyperbola.

61. True. The conic is an ellipse because the eccentricity is less than 1.

63. Answers will vary.

65. $r^2 = \dfrac{24,336}{169 - 25 \cos^2 \theta}$ **67.** $r^2 = \dfrac{144}{25 \cos^2 \theta - 9}$

69. $r^2 = \dfrac{144}{25 \sin^2 \theta - 16}$

71. (a) Ellipse

(b) The given polar equation, r, has a vertical directrix to the left of the pole. The equation, r_1, has a vertical directrix to the right of the pole, and the equation, r_2, has a horizontal directrix below the pole.

(c)

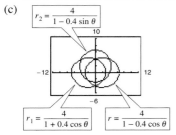

73. $\dfrac{\pi}{6} + n\pi$ **75.** $\dfrac{\pi}{3} + n\pi, \dfrac{2\pi}{3} + n\pi$

77. $\dfrac{\pi}{2} + n\pi$ **79.** $\dfrac{\sqrt{2}}{10}$ **81.** $\dfrac{7\sqrt{2}}{10}$

83. $\sin 2u = -\dfrac{24}{25}$

$\cos 2u = -\dfrac{7}{25}$

$\tan 2u = \dfrac{24}{7}$

Review Exercises *(page 515)*

1. $\dfrac{\pi}{4}$ radian, $45°$ **3.** 1.1071 radians, $63.43°$

5. 0.4424 radian, $25.35°$ **7.** 0.6588 radian, $37.75°$

9. $2\sqrt{2}$ **11.** Hyperbola

13. $y^2 = 16x$

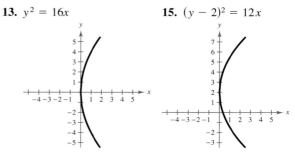

15. $(y - 2)^2 = 12x$

17. $y = -2x + 2; (1, 0)$ **19.** $8\sqrt{6}$ meters

21. $\dfrac{(x - 2)^2}{25} + \dfrac{y^2}{21} = 1$ **23.** $\dfrac{(x - 2)^2}{4} + (y - 1)^2 = 1$

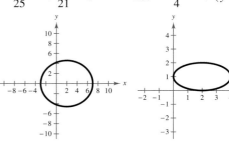

25. The foci occur 3 feet from the center of the arch on a line connecting the tops of the pillars.

27. Center: $(-2, 1)$

Vertices: $(-2, 11), (-2, -9)$

Foci: $\left(-2, 1 \pm \sqrt{19}\right)$

Eccentricity: $\dfrac{\sqrt{19}}{10}$

29. Center: $(1, -4)$

Vertices: $(1, 0), (1, -8)$

Foci: $\left(1, -4 \pm \sqrt{7}\right)$

Eccentricity: $\dfrac{\sqrt{7}}{4}$

31. $y^2 - \dfrac{x^2}{8} = 1$ **33.** $\dfrac{5(x - 4)^2}{16} - \dfrac{5y^2}{64} = 1$

35. Center: $(3, -5)$

Vertices: $(7, -5), (-1, -5)$

Foci: $\left(3 \pm 2\sqrt{5}, -5\right)$

Asymptotes:

$y = -5 \pm \tfrac{1}{2}(x - 3)$

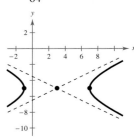

CHAPTER 6

37. Center: $(1, -1)$
Vertices: $(5, -1), (-3, -1)$
Foci: $(6, -1), (-4, -1)$
Asymptotes:
$y = -1 \pm \frac{3}{4}(x - 1)$

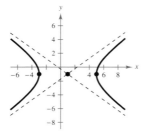

39. 72 miles
41. Hyperbola   **43.** Ellipse
45.

t	-3	-2	-1	0	1	2	3
x	-11	-8	-5	-2	1	4	7
y	19	15	11	7	3	-1	-5

47. (a)

(b) $y = 2x$

49. (a)

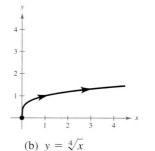

(b) $y = \sqrt[4]{x}$

51. (a)

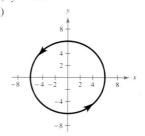

(b) $x^2 + y^2 = 36$

53. $x = 5 + 6\cos\theta$
$y = 4 + 6\sin\theta$

55. $x = 3\tan\theta$
$y = 4\sec\theta$

57.

59.

$\left(2, \frac{9\pi}{4}\right), \left(-2, \frac{5\pi}{4}\right)$ $(7, 1.05), (-7, 10.47)$

61. $\left(-\frac{1}{2}, -\frac{\sqrt{3}}{2}\right)$ **63.** $\left(-\frac{3\sqrt{2}}{2}, \frac{3\sqrt{2}}{2}\right)$

65. $\left(2, \frac{\pi}{2}\right)$ **67.** $\left(2\sqrt{13}, 0.9828\right)$ **69.** $r = 7$

71. $r = 6\sin\theta$ **73.** $r^2 = 10\csc 2\theta$
75. $x^2 + y^2 = 25$ **77.** $x^2 + y^2 = 3x$
79. $x^2 + y^2 = y^{2/3}$

81. Symmetry: $\theta = \frac{\pi}{2}$, polar axis, pole

Maximum value of $|r|$: $|r| = 4$ when $\theta = 0, \frac{\pi}{2}, \pi, \frac{3\pi}{2}$

No zeros of r

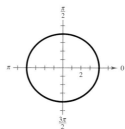

83. Symmetry: $\theta = \frac{\pi}{2}$, polar axis, pole

Maximum value of $|r|$: $|r| = 4$ when $\theta = \frac{\pi}{4}, \frac{3\pi}{4}, \frac{5\pi}{4}, \frac{7\pi}{4}$

Zeros of r: $r = 0$ when $\theta = 0, \frac{\pi}{2}, \pi, \frac{3\pi}{2}$

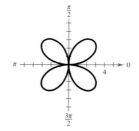

85. Symmetry: polar axis
Maximum value of $|r|$: $|r| = 4$ when $\theta = 0$
Zeros of r: $r = 0$ when $\theta = \pi$

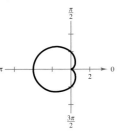

87. Symmetry: $\theta = \dfrac{\pi}{2}$

Maximum value of $|r|$: $|r| = 8$ when $\theta = \dfrac{\pi}{2}$

Zeros of r: $r = 0$ when $\theta = 3.4814,\ 5.9433$

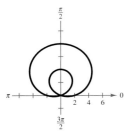

89. Symmetry: $\theta = \dfrac{\pi}{2}$, polar axis, pole

Maximum value of $|r|$: $|r| = 3$ when $\theta = 0,\ \dfrac{\pi}{2},\ \pi,\ \dfrac{3\pi}{2}$

Zeros of r: $r = 0$ when $\theta = \dfrac{\pi}{4},\ \dfrac{3\pi}{4},\ \dfrac{5\pi}{4},\ \dfrac{7\pi}{4}$

91. Limaçon

93. Rose curve

95. Hyperbola

97. Ellipse

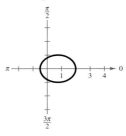

99. $r = \dfrac{4}{1 - \cos\theta}$

101. $r = \dfrac{5}{3 - 2\cos\theta}$

103. $r = \dfrac{7978.81}{1 - 0.937\cos\theta}$; $11{,}011.87$ miles

105. False. The equation of a hyperbola is a second-degree equation.

107. False. $(2, \pi/4)$, $(-2, 5\pi/4)$, and $(2, 9\pi/4)$ all represent the same point.

109. The orientation would be reversed.

111. (a) Symmetric to the pole
(b) Symmetric to the polar axis
(c) Symmetric to $\theta = \pi/2$

113. 40

Chapter Test   *(page 519)*

1. 0.2783 radian, $15.9°$ **2.** 0.8330 radian, $47.7°$

3. $\dfrac{7\sqrt{2}}{2}$

4. Parabola: $y^2 = 4(x - 1)$
Vertex: $(1, 0)$
Focus: $(2, 0)$

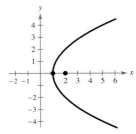

5. Hyperbola: $\dfrac{(x - 2)^2}{4} - y^2 = 1$

Center: $(2, 0)$
Vertices: $(0, 0),\ (4, 0)$
Foci: $\left(2 \pm \sqrt{5}, 0\right)$
Asymptotes: $y = \pm\tfrac{1}{2}(x - 2)$

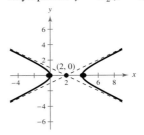

6. Ellipse: $\dfrac{(x+3)^2}{16} + \dfrac{(y-1)^2}{9} = 1$

Center: $(-3, 1)$

Vertices: $(1, 1), (-7, 1)$

Foci: $\left(-3 \pm \sqrt{7}, 1\right)$

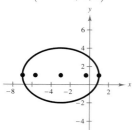

7. Circle: $(x-2)^2 + (y-1)^2 = \frac{1}{2}$

Center: $(2, 1)$

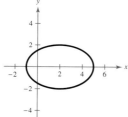

8. $(x-3)^2 = \dfrac{3}{2}(y+2)$ **9.** $\dfrac{5(y-2)^2}{4} - \dfrac{5x^2}{16} = 1$

10.

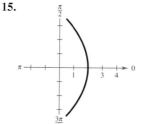

11. $x = 6 + 4t$
$y = 4 + 7t$

$\dfrac{(x-2)^2}{9} + \dfrac{y^2}{4} = 1$

12. $\left(\sqrt{3}, -1\right)$ **13.** $\left(2\sqrt{2}, \dfrac{7\pi}{4}\right), \left(-2\sqrt{2}, \dfrac{3\pi}{4}\right), \left(2\sqrt{2}, -\dfrac{\pi}{4}\right)$

14. $r = 4 \sin \theta$

15.

Parabola

16.

Ellipse

17.

18.

Limaçon with inner loop   Rose curve

19. Answers will vary. For example: $r = \dfrac{1}{1 + 0.25 \sin \theta}$

20. Slope: 0.1511; Change in elevation: 789 feet

21. No; Yes

Cumulative Test for Chapters 4–6   *(page 520)*

1. (a)

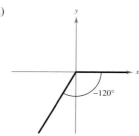

(b) $240°$

(c) $-\dfrac{2\pi}{3}$

(d) $60°$

(e) $\sin(-120°) = -\dfrac{\sqrt{3}}{2}$ $\csc(-120°) = -\dfrac{2\sqrt{3}}{3}$

$\cos(-120°) = -\dfrac{1}{2}$ $\sec(-120°) = -2$

$\tan(-120°) = \sqrt{3}$ $\cot(-120°) = \dfrac{\sqrt{3}}{3}$

2. $134.6°$ **3.** $\frac{3}{5}$

4. Ellipse   **5.** Circle

6.

7. $a = -3, b = \pi, c = 0$

8.

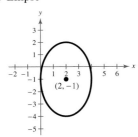

9. 6.7   **10.** $\frac{3}{4}$

11. $\sqrt{1 - 4x^2}$ **12.** 1   **13.** $2 \tan \theta$

14–16. Answers will vary.   **17.** $\frac{\pi}{3}, \frac{\pi}{2}, \frac{3\pi}{2}, \frac{5\pi}{3}$

18. $\frac{\pi}{6}, \frac{5\pi}{6}, \frac{7\pi}{6}, \frac{11\pi}{6}$ **19.** $\frac{3\pi}{2}$ **20.** $\frac{16}{63}$ **21.** $\frac{4}{3}$

22. $\frac{\sqrt{5}}{5}, \frac{2\sqrt{5}}{5}$ **23.** $\frac{5}{2}\left(\sin \frac{5\pi}{2} - \sin \pi\right)$

24. $2 \cos(6x) \cos(2x)$

25. $B \approx 26.39°, C \approx 123.61°, c \approx 15.0$

26. $B \approx 52.48°, C \approx 97.52°, a \approx 5.04$

27. $B = 60°, a \approx 5.77, c \approx 11.55$

28. $A \approx 26.38°, B \approx 62.72°, C \approx 90.90°$

29. 36.4 square inches   **30.** 85.2 square inches

31. Ellipse   **32.** Circle

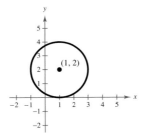

33. $\frac{x^2}{1} + \frac{(y - 2)^2}{4} = 1$

34.

The corresponding rectangular equation is $y = \dfrac{\sqrt{e^x}}{2}$.

35. $\left(-2, \frac{5\pi}{4}\right), \left(-2, -\frac{7\pi}{4}\right), \left(-2, \frac{\pi}{4}\right)$

36. $-8r \cos \theta - 3r \sin \theta + 5 = 0$

37. $9x^2 + 20x - 16y^2 + 4 = 0$

38.

Circle

39.

Dimpled limaçon

40.

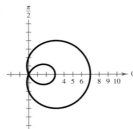

Limaçon with an open loop

41. $\approx$ 395.8 radians per minute; $\approx$ 8312.6 inches per minute

42. Area $\approx$ 63.67 square yards   **43.** 5 feet   **44.** 22.6°

45. $d = 4 \cos \frac{\pi}{4}t$

Problem Solving   (page 525)

1. (a) 1.2016 radians   (b) 2420 feet, 5971 feet

3. $y^2 = 4p(x + p)$

5. (a) Since $d_1 + d_z \leq 20$, by definition, the outer bound that the boat can travel is an ellipse. The islands are the foci.

   (b) Island 1: $(-6, 0)$; Island 2: $(6, 0)$

   (c) 20 miles; Vertex: $(10, 0)$ (d) $\frac{x^2}{100} + \frac{y^2}{64} = 1$

7. Answers will vary.

9. Answers will vary. For example: $x = \cos(-t)$; $y = 2 \sin(-t)$

11. (a) $y^2 = x^2\left(\dfrac{1 - x}{1 + x}\right)$ (b) $r = \cos 2\theta \sec \theta$

   (c)

13. Circle

15.

For $n \geq 1$, a bell is produced. For $n \leq -1$, a heart is produced. For $n = 0$, a rose curve is produced.

CHAPTER 6

Index

Appendix A:
Review of Fundamental Concepts of Algebra

Appendix B:
Concepts of Statistics

A.1 Real Numbers and Their Properties

What you should learn

- Represent and classify real numbers.
- Order real numbers and use inequalities.
- Find the absolute values of real numbers and find the distance between two real numbers.
- Evaluate algebraic expressions.
- Use the basic rules and properties of algebra.

Why you should learn it

Real numbers are used to represent many real-life quantities. For example, in Exercise 65 on page A9, you will use real numbers to represent the federal deficit.

The *HM mathSpace*® CD-ROM and *Eduspace*® for this text contain additional resources related to the concepts discussed in this chapter.

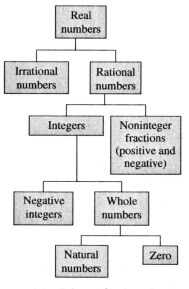

FIGURE A.1 *Subsets of real numbers*

Real Numbers

Real numbers are used in everyday life to describe quantities such as age, miles per gallon, and population. Real numbers are represented by symbols such as

$$-5, 9, 0, \frac{4}{3}, 0.666\ldots, 28.21, \sqrt{2}, \pi, \text{ and } \sqrt[3]{-32}.$$

Here are some important **subsets** (each member of subset B is also a member of set A) of the real numbers. The three dots, called *ellipsis points*, indicate that the pattern continues indefinitely.

$$\{1, 2, 3, 4, \ldots\} \qquad \text{Set of natural numbers}$$
$$\{0, 1, 2, 3, 4, \ldots\} \qquad \text{Set of whole numbers}$$
$$\{\ldots, -3, -2, -1, 0, 1, 2, 3, \ldots\} \qquad \text{Set of integers}$$

A real number is **rational** if it can be written as the ratio p/q of two integers, where $q \neq 0$. For instance, the numbers

$$\frac{1}{3} = 0.3333\ldots = 0.\overline{3}, \frac{1}{8} = 0.125, \text{ and } \frac{125}{111} = 1.126126\ldots = 1.\overline{126}$$

are rational. The decimal representation of a rational number either repeats $\left(\text{as in } \frac{173}{55} = 3.1\overline{45}\right)$ or terminates $\left(\text{as in } \frac{1}{2} = 0.5\right)$. A real number that cannot be written as the ratio of two integers is called **irrational.** Irrational numbers have infinite nonrepeating decimal representations. For instance, the numbers

$$\sqrt{2} = 1.4142135\ldots \approx 1.41 \quad \text{and} \quad \pi = 3.1415926\ldots \approx 3.14$$

are irrational. (The symbol $\approx$ means "is approximately equal to.") Figure A.1 shows subsets of real numbers and their relationships to each other.

Real numbers are represented graphically by a **real number line.** The point 0 on the real number line is the **origin.** Numbers to the right of 0 are positive, and numbers to the left of 0 are negative, as shown in Figure A.2. The term **nonnegative** describes a number that is either positive or zero.

FIGURE A.2 *The real number line*

As illustrated in Figure A.3, there is a *one-to-one correspondence* between real numbers and points on the real number line.

Every real number corresponds to exactly one point on the real number line.

Every point on the real number line corresponds to exactly one real number.

FIGURE A.3 *One-to-one*

A1

Ordering Real Numbers

One important property of real numbers is that they are *ordered*.

> ### Definition of Order on the Real Number Line
>
> If a and b are real numbers, a is less than b if $b - a$ is positive. The **order** of a and b is denoted by the **inequality** $a < b$. This relationship can also be described by saying that b is *greater than* a and writing $b > a$. The inequality $a \leq b$ means that a is *less than or equal to* b, and the inequality $b \geq a$ means that b is *greater than or equal to* a. The symbols $<$, $>$, $\leq$, and $\geq$ are *inequality symbols*.

FIGURE A.4 $a < b$ *if and only if a lies to the left of b.*

Geometrically, this definition implies that $a < b$ if and only if a lies to the *left* of b on the real number line, as shown in Figure A.4.

FIGURE A.5

FIGURE A.6

Example 1 **Interpreting Inequalities**

Describe the subset of real numbers represented by each inequality.

a. $x \leq 2$ **b.** $-2 \leq x < 3$

Solution

a. The inequality $x \leq 2$ denotes all real numbers less than or equal to 2, as shown in Figure A.5.

b. The inequality $-2 \leq x < 3$ means that $x \geq -2$ *and* $x < 3$. This "double inequality" denotes all real numbers between -2 and 3, including -2 but not including 3, as shown in Figure A.6.

✓*CHECKPOINT*   Now try Exercise 19.

Inequalities can be used to describe subsets of real numbers called **intervals.** In the bounded intervals below, the real numbers a and b are the **endpoints** of each interval. The endpoints of a closed interval are included in the interval, whereas the endpoints of an open interval are not included in the interval.

> ### Bounded Intervals on the Real Number Line
>
> | Notation | Interval Type | Inequality | Graph |
> |---|---|---|---|
> | $[a, b]$ | Closed | $a \leq x \leq b$ | |
> | (a, b) | Open | $a < x < b$ | |
> | $[a, b)$ | | $a \leq x < b$ | |
> | $(a, b]$ | | $a < x \leq b$ | |

STUDY TIP

The reason that the four types of intervals at the right are called *bounded* is that each has a finite length. An interval that does not have a finite length is *unbounded* (see page A3).

The symbols ∞, **positive infinity,** and $-\infty$, **negative infinity,** do not represent real numbers. They are simply convenient symbols used to describe the unboundedness of an interval such as $(1, \infty)$ or $(-\infty, 3]$.

Unbounded Intervals on the Real Number Line

Notation	Interval Type	Inequality	Graph
$[a, \infty)$		$x \geq a$	
(a, ∞)	Open	$x > a$	
$(-\infty, b]$		$x \leq b$	
$(-\infty, b)$	Open	$x < b$	
$(-\infty, \infty)$	Entire real line	$-\infty < x < \infty$	

Example 2   **Using Inequalities to Represent Intervals**

Use inequality notation to describe each of the following.

a. c is at most 2.   **b.** m is at least -3.

c. All x in the interval $(-3, 5]$

Solution

a. The statement "c is at most 2" can be represented by $c \leq 2$.

b. The statement "m is at least -3" can be represented by $m \geq -3$.

c. "All x in the interval $(-3, 5]$" can be represented by $-3 < x \leq 5$.

✓CHECKPOINT   Now try Exercise 31.

Example 3   **Interpreting Intervals**

Give a verbal description of each interval.

a. $(-1, 0)$ **b.** $[2, \infty)$ **c.** $(-\infty, 0)$

Solution

a. This interval consists of all real numbers that are greater than -1 and less than 0.

b. This interval consists of all real numbers that are greater than or equal to 2.

c. This interval consists of all negative real numbers.

✓CHECKPOINT   Now try Exercise 29.

The **Law of Trichotomy** states that for any two real numbers a and b, *precisely* one of three relationships is possible:

$$a = b, \quad a < b, \quad \text{or} \quad a > b. \qquad \text{Law of Trichotomy}$$

Absolute Value and Distance

The **absolute value** of a real number is its *magnitude,* or the distance between the origin and the point representing the real number on the real number line.

Definition of Absolute Value

If a is a real number, then the absolute value of a is

$$|a| = \begin{cases} a, & \text{if } a \geq 0 \\ -a, & \text{if } a < 0 \end{cases}.$$

Notice in this definition that the absolute value of a real number is never negative. For instance, if $a = -5$, then $|-5| = -(-5) = 5$. The absolute value of a real number is either positive or zero. Moreover, 0 is the only real number whose absolute value is 0. So, $|0| = 0$.

Example 4   **Evaluating the Absolute Value of a Number**

Evaluate $\dfrac{|x|}{x}$ for (a) $x > 0$ and (b) $x < 0$.

Solution

a. If $x > 0$, then $|x| = x$ and $\dfrac{|x|}{x} = \dfrac{x}{x} = 1$.

b. If $x < 0$, then $|x| = -x$ and $\dfrac{|x|}{x} = \dfrac{-x}{x} = -1$.

✓*CHECKPOINT*   Now try Exercise 47.

Properties of Absolute Values

1. $|a| \geq 0$ **2.** $|-a| = |a|$

3. $|ab| = |a||b|$ **4.** $\left|\dfrac{a}{b}\right| = \dfrac{|a|}{|b|}, \quad b \neq 0$

Absolute value can be used to define the distance between two points on the real number line. For instance, the distance between -3 and 4 is

$$|-3 - 4| = |-7|$$
$$= 7$$

as shown in Figure A.7.

FIGURE A.7   *The distance between -3 and 4 is 7.*

Distance Between Two Points on the Real Number Line

Let a and b be real numbers. The **distance between a and b** is

$$d(a, b) = |b - a| = |a - b|.$$

Algebraic Expressions

One characteristic of algebra is the use of letters to represent numbers. The letters are **variables,** and combinations of letters and numbers are **algebraic expressions.** Here are a few examples of algebraic expressions.

$$5x, \qquad 2x - 3, \qquad \frac{4}{x^2 + 2}, \qquad 7x + y$$

Definition of an Algebraic Expression

An **algebraic expression** is a collection of letters (**variables**) and real numbers (**constants**) combined using the operations of addition, subtraction, multiplication, division, and exponentiation.

The **terms** of an algebraic expression are those parts that are separated by *addition.* For example,

$$x^2 - 5x + 8 = x^2 + (-5x) + 8$$

has three terms: x^2 and $-5x$ are the **variable terms** and 8 is the **constant term.** The numerical factor of a variable term is the **coefficient** of the variable term. For instance, the coefficient of $-5x$ is -5, and the coefficient of x^2 is 1.

To **evaluate** an algebraic expression, substitute numerical values for each of the variables in the expression. Here are two examples.

Expression	Value of Variable	Substitute	Value of Expression
$-3x + 5$	$x = 3$	$-3(3) + 5$	$-9 + 5 = -4$
$3x^2 + 2x - 1$	$x = -1$	$3(-1)^2 + 2(-1) - 1$	$3 - 2 - 1 = 0$

When an algebraic expression is evaluated, the **Substitution Principle** is used. It states that "If $a = b$, then a can be replaced by b in any expression involving a." In the first evaluation shown above, for instance, 3 is *substituted* for x in the expression $-3x + 5$.

Basic Rules of Algebra

There are four arithmetic operations with real numbers: *addition, multiplication, subtraction,* and *division,* denoted by the symbols $+$, $\times$ or $\cdot$, $-$, and $\div$ or $/$. Of these, addition and multiplication are the two primary operations. Subtraction and division are the inverse operations of addition and multiplication, respectively.

Definitions of Subtraction and Division

Subtraction: Add the opposite.   **Division:** Multiply by the reciprocal.

$$a - b = a + (-b) \qquad\qquad \text{If } b \neq 0, \text{ then } a/b = a\left(\frac{1}{b}\right) = \frac{a}{b}.$$

In these definitions, $-b$ is the **additive inverse** (or opposite) of b, and $1/b$ is the **multiplicative inverse** (or reciprocal) of b. In the fractional form a/b, a is the **numerator** of the fraction and b is the **denominator.**

Because the properties of real numbers below are true for variables and algebraic expressions as well as for real numbers, they are often called the **Basic Rules of Algebra.** Try to formulate a verbal description of each property. For instance, the first property states that *the order in which two real numbers are added does not affect their sum.*

Basic Rules of Algebra

Let a, b, and c be real numbers, variables, or algebraic expressions.

Property		*Example*
Commutative Property of Addition:	$a + b = b + a$	$4x + x^2 = x^2 + 4x$
Commutative Property of Multiplication:	$ab = ba$	$(4 - x)x^2 = x^2(4 - x)$
Associative Property of Addition:	$(a + b) + c = a + (b + c)$	$(x + 5) + x^2 = x + (5 + x^2)$
Associative Property of Multiplication:	$(ab)c = a(bc)$	$(2x \cdot 3y)(8) = (2x)(3y \cdot 8)$
Distributive Properties:	$a(b + c) = ab + ac$	$3x(5 + 2x) = 3x \cdot 5 + 3x \cdot 2x$
	$(a + b)c = ac + bc$	$(y + 8)y = y \cdot y + 8 \cdot y$
Additive Identity Property:	$a + 0 = a$	$5y^2 + 0 = 5y^2$
Multiplicative Identity Property:	$a \cdot 1 = a$	$(4x^2)(1) = 4x^2$
Additive Inverse Property:	$a + (-a) = 0$	$5x^3 + (-5x^3) = 0$
Multiplicative Inverse Property:	$a \cdot \dfrac{1}{a} = 1, \quad a \neq 0$	$(x^2 + 4)\left(\dfrac{1}{x^2 + 4}\right) = 1$

Because subtraction is defined as "adding the opposite," the Distributive Properties are also true for subtraction. For instance, the "subtraction form" of $a(b + c) = ab + ac$ is $a(b - c) = ab - ac$.

STUDY TIP

Notice the difference between the *opposite of a number* and a *negative number*. If a is already negative, then its opposite, $-a$, is positive. For instance, if $a = -5$, then

$$-a = -(-5) = 5.$$

Properties of Negation and Equality

Let a and b be real numbers, variables, or algebraic expressions.

Property	*Example*
1. $(-1)a = -a$	$(-1)7 = -7$
2. $-(-a) = a$	$-(-6) = 6$
3. $(-a)b = -(ab) = a(-b)$	$(-5)3 = -(5 \cdot 3) = 5(-3)$
4. $(-a)(-b) = ab$	$(-2)(-x) = 2x$
5. $-(a + b) = (-a) + (-b)$	$-(x + 8) = (-x) + (-8)$
	$\qquad\qquad\quad = -x - 8$
6. If $a = b$, then $a \pm c = b \pm c$.	$\frac{1}{2} + 3 = 0.5 + 3$
7. If $a = b$, then $ac = bc$.	$4^2 \cdot 2 = 16 \cdot 2$
8. If $a \pm c = b \pm c$, then $a = b$.	$1.4 - 1 = \frac{7}{5} - 1 \implies 1.4 = \frac{7}{5}$
9. If $ac = bc$ and $c \neq 0$, then $a = b$.	$3x = 3 \cdot 4 \implies x = 4$

Properties of Zero

Let a and b be real numbers, variables, or algebraic expressions.

1. $a + 0 = a$ and $a - 0 = a$ **2.** $a \cdot 0 = 0$

3. $\dfrac{0}{a} = 0, \quad a \neq 0$ **4.** $\dfrac{a}{0}$ is undefined.

5. Zero-Factor Property: If $ab = 0$, then $a = 0$ or $b = 0$.

Properties and Operations of Fractions

Let a, b, c, and d be real numbers, variables, or algebraic expressions such that $b \neq 0$ and $d \neq 0$.

1. Equivalent Fractions: $\dfrac{a}{b} = \dfrac{c}{d}$ if and only if $ad = bc$.

2. Rules of Signs: $-\dfrac{a}{b} = \dfrac{-a}{b} = \dfrac{a}{-b}$ and $\dfrac{-a}{-b} = \dfrac{a}{b}$

3. Generate Equivalent Fractions: $\dfrac{a}{b} = \dfrac{ac}{bc}, \quad c \neq 0$

4. Add or Subtract with Like Denominators: $\dfrac{a}{b} \pm \dfrac{c}{b} = \dfrac{a \pm c}{b}$

5. Add or Subtract with Unlike Denominators: $\dfrac{a}{b} \pm \dfrac{c}{d} = \dfrac{ad \pm bc}{bd}$

6. Multiply Fractions: $\dfrac{a}{b} \cdot \dfrac{c}{d} = \dfrac{ac}{bd}$

7. Divide Fractions: $\dfrac{a}{b} \div \dfrac{c}{d} = \dfrac{a}{b} \cdot \dfrac{d}{c} = \dfrac{ad}{bc}, \quad c \neq 0$

Example 5   **Properties and Operations of Fractions**

a. Equivalent fractions: $\dfrac{x}{5} = \dfrac{3 \cdot x}{3 \cdot 5} = \dfrac{3x}{15}$ **b.** Divide fractions: $\dfrac{7}{x} \div \dfrac{3}{2} = \dfrac{7}{x} \cdot \dfrac{2}{3} = \dfrac{14}{3x}$

c. Add fractions with unlike denominators: $\dfrac{x}{3} + \dfrac{2x}{5} = \dfrac{5 \cdot x + 3 \cdot 2x}{3 \cdot 5} = \dfrac{11x}{15}$

✓**CHECKPOINT**   Now try Exercise 103.

If a, b, and c are integers such that $ab = c$, then a and b are **factors** or **divisors** of c. A **prime number** is an integer that has exactly two positive factors—itself and 1—such as 2, 3, 5, 7, and 11. The numbers 4, 6, 8, 9, and 10 are **composite** because each can be written as the product of two or more prime numbers. The number 1 is neither prime nor composite. The **Fundamental Theorem of Arithmetic** states that every positive integer greater than 1 can be written as the product of prime numbers in precisely one way (disregarding order). For instance, the *prime factorization* of 24 is $24 = 2 \cdot 2 \cdot 2 \cdot 3$.

A.1 | Exercises

The *HM mathSpace®* CD-ROM and *Eduspace®* for this text contain step-by-step solutions to all odd-numbered exercises. They also provide Tutorial Exercises for additional help.

VOCABULARY CHECK: Fill in the blanks.

1. A real number is _____ if it can be written as the ratio $\frac{p}{q}$ of two integers, where $q \neq 0$.

2. _____ numbers have infinite nonrepeating decimal representations.

3. The distance between a point on the real number line and the origin is the _____ _____ of the real number.

4. A number that can be written as the product of two or more prime numbers is called a _____ number.

5. An integer that has exactly two positive factors, the integer itself and 1, is called a _____ number.

6. An algebraic expression is a collection of letters called _____ and real numbers called _____.

7. The _____ of an algebraic expression are those parts separated by addition.

8. The numerical factor of a variable term is the _____ of the variable term.

9. The _____ _____ states that if $ab = 0$, then $a = 0$ or $b = 0$.

In Exercises 1–6, determine which numbers in the set are (a) natural numbers, (b) whole numbers, (c) integers, (d) rational numbers, and (e) irrational numbers.

1. $-9, -\frac{7}{2}, 5, \frac{2}{3}, \sqrt{2}, 0, 1, -4, 2, -11$
2. $\sqrt{5}, -7, -\frac{7}{3}, 0, 3.12, \frac{5}{4}, -3, 12, 5$
3. $2.01, 0.666 \ldots, -13, 0.010110111 \ldots, 1, -6$
4. $2.3030030003 \ldots, 0.7575, -4.63, \sqrt{10}, -75, 4$
5. $-\pi, -\frac{1}{3}, \frac{6}{3}, \frac{1}{2}\sqrt{2}, -7.5, -1, 8, -22$
6. $25, -17, -\frac{12}{5}, \sqrt{9}, 3.12, \frac{1}{2}\pi, 7, -11.1, 13$

In Exercises 7–10, use a calculator to find the decimal form of the rational number. If it is a nonterminating decimal, write the repeating pattern.

7. $\frac{5}{8}$
8. $\frac{1}{3}$
9. $\frac{41}{333}$
10. $\frac{6}{11}$

In Exercises 11 and 12, approximate the numbers and place the correct symbol (< or >) between them.

11.
12.

In Exercises 13–18, plot the two real numbers on the real number line. Then place the appropriate inequality symbol (< or >) between them.

13. $-4, -8$
14. $-3.5, 1$
15. $\frac{3}{2}, 7$
16. $1, \frac{16}{3}$
17. $\frac{5}{6}, \frac{2}{3}$
18. $-\frac{8}{7}, -\frac{3}{7}$

In Exercises 19–30, (a) give a verbal description of the subset of real numbers represented by the inequality or the interval, (b) sketch the subset on the real number line, and (c) state whether the interval is bounded or unbounded.

19. $x \leq 5$
20. $x \geq -2$
21. $x < 0$
22. $x > 3$
23. $[4, \infty)$
24. $(-\infty, 2)$
25. $-2 < x < 2$
26. $0 \leq x \leq 5$
27. $-1 \leq x < 0$
28. $0 < x \leq 6$
29. $[-2, 5)$
30. $(-1, 2]$

In Exercises 31–38, use inequality notation to describe the set.

31. All x in the interval $(-2, 4]$
32. All y in the interval $[-6, 0)$
33. y is nonnegative.
34. y is no more than 25.
35. t is at least 10 and at most 22.
36. k is less than 5 but no less than -3.
37. The dog's weight W is more than 65 pounds.
38. The annual rate of inflation r is expected to be at least 2.5% but no more than 5%.

In Exercises 39–48, evaluate the expression.

39. $|-10|$
40. $|0|$
41. $|3 - 8|$
42. $|4 - 1|$
43. $|-1| - |-2|$
44. $-3 - |-3|$
45. $\dfrac{-5}{|-5|}$
46. $-3|-3|$
47. $\dfrac{|x + 2|}{x + 2}, \quad x < -2$
48. $\dfrac{|x - 1|}{x - 1}, \quad x > 1$

In Exercises 49–54, place the correct symbol (<, >, or =) between the pair of real numbers.

49. $|-3|$ ___ $-|-3|$

50. $|-4|$ ___ $|4|$

51. -5 ___ $-|5|$

52. $-|-6|$ ___ $|-6|$

53. $-|-2|$ ___ $-|2|$

54. $-(-2)$ ___ -2

In Exercises 55–60, find the distance between a and b.

55. $a = 126, b = 75$

56. $a = -126, b = -75$

57. $a = -\frac{5}{2}, b = 0$

58. $a = \frac{1}{4}, b = \frac{11}{4}$

59. $a = \frac{16}{5}, b = \frac{112}{75}$

60. $a = 9.34, b = -5.65$

Budget Variance   **In Exercises 61–64, the accounting department of a sports drink bottling company is checking to see whether the actual expenses of a department differ from the budgeted expenses by more than $500 or by more than 5%. Fill in the missing parts of the table, and determine whether each actual expense passes the "budget variance test."**

	Budgeted Expense, b	Actual Expense, a	$\|a - b\|$	$0.05b$
61. Wages	$112,700	$113,356		
62. Utilities	$9,400	$9,772		
63. Taxes	$37,640	$37,335		
64. Insurance	$2,575	$2,613		

65. *Federal Deficit*   The bar graph shows the federal government receipts (in billions of dollars) for selected years from 1960 through 2000.   (Source: U.S. Office of Management and Budget)

(a) Complete the table. (*Hint:* Find $|$Receipts – Expenditures$|$.)

Year	Expenditures (in billions)	Surplus or deficit (in billions)
1960	$92.2	
1970	$195.6	
1980	$590.9	
1990	$1253.2	
2000	$1788.8	

(b) Use the table in part (a) to construct a bar graph showing the magnitude of the surplus or deficit for each year.

66. *Veterans*   The table shows the number of living veterans (in thousands) in the United States in 2002 by age group. Construct a circle graph showing the percent of living veterans by age group as a fraction of the total number of living veterans.   (Source: Department of Veteran Affairs)

Age group	Number of veterans
Under 35	2213
35–44	3290
45–54	4666
55–64	5665
65 and older	9784

In Exercises 67–72, use absolute value notation to describe the situation.

67. The distance between x and 5 is no more than 3.

68. The distance between x and -10 is at least 6.

69. y is at least six units from 0.

70. y is at most two units from a.

71. While traveling on the Pennsylvania Turnpike, you pass milepost 326 near Valley Forge, then milepost 351 near Philadelphia. How many miles do you travel during that time period?

72. The temperature in Chicago, Illinois was 48° last night at midnight, then 82° at noon today. What was the change in temperature over the 12-hour period?

In Exercises 73–78, identify the terms. Then identify the coefficients of the variable terms of the expression.

73. $7x + 4$

74. $6x^3 - 5x$

75. $\sqrt{3}x^2 - 8x - 11$

76. $3\sqrt{3}x^2 + 1$

77. $4x^3 + \dfrac{x}{2} - 5$

78. $3x^4 - \dfrac{x^2}{4}$

In Exercises 79–84, evaluate the expression for each value of x. (If not possible, state the reason.)

Expression	*Values*
79. $4x - 6$	(a) $x = -1$ (b) $x = 0$
80. $9 - 7x$	(a) $x = -3$ (b) $x = 3$
81. $x^2 - 3x + 4$	(a) $x = -2$ (b) $x = 2$
82. $-x^2 + 5x - 4$	(a) $x = -1$ (b) $x = 1$
83. $\dfrac{x + 1}{x - 1}$	(a) $x = 1$ (b) $x = -1$
84. $\dfrac{x}{x + 2}$	(a) $x = 2$ (b) $x = -2$

In Exercises 85–96, identify the rule(s) of algebra illustrated by the statement.

85. $x + 9 = 9 + x$

86. $2\left(\frac{1}{2}\right) = 1$

87. $\dfrac{1}{h + 6}(h + 6) = 1, \quad h \neq -6$

88. $(x + 3) - (x + 3) = 0$

89. $2(x + 3) = 2 \cdot x + 2 \cdot 3$

90. $(z - 2) + 0 = z - 2$

91. $1 \cdot (1 + x) = 1 + x$

92. $(z + 5)x = z \cdot x + 5 \cdot x$

93. $x + (y + 10) = (x + y) + 10$

94. $x(3y) = (x \cdot 3)y = (3x)y$

95. $3(t - 4) = 3 \cdot t - 3 \cdot 4$

96. $\frac{1}{7}(7 \cdot 12) = \left(\frac{1}{7} \cdot 7\right)12 = 1 \cdot 12 = 12$

In Exercises 97–104, perform the operation(s). (Write fractional answers in simplest form.)

97. $\frac{3}{16} + \frac{5}{16}$

98. $\frac{6}{7} - \frac{4}{7}$

99. $\frac{5}{8} - \frac{5}{12} + \frac{1}{6}$

100. $\frac{10}{11} + \frac{6}{33} - \frac{13}{66}$

101. $12 \div \frac{1}{4}$

102. $-\left(6 \cdot \frac{4}{8}\right)$

103. $\dfrac{2x}{3} - \dfrac{x}{4}$

104. $\dfrac{5x}{6} \cdot \dfrac{2}{9}$

105. (a) Use a calculator to complete the table.

n	1	0.5	0.01	0.0001	0.000001
$5/n$					

(b) Use the result from part (a) to make a conjecture about the value of $5/n$ as n approaches 0.

106. (a) Use a calculator to complete the table.

n	1	10	100	10,000	100,000
$5/n$					

(b) Use the result from part (a) to make a conjecture about the value of $5/n$ as n increases without bound.

Synthesis

True or False? **In Exercises 107 and 108, determine whether the statement is true or false. Justify your answer.**

107. If $a < b$, then $\dfrac{1}{a} < \dfrac{1}{b}$, where $a \neq b \neq 0$.

108. Because $\dfrac{a + b}{c} = \dfrac{a}{c} + \dfrac{b}{c}$, then $\dfrac{c}{a + b} = \dfrac{c}{a} + \dfrac{c}{b}$.

109. ***Exploration***   Consider $|u + v|$ and $|u| + |v|$, where $u \neq v \neq 0$.

(a) Are the values of the expressions always equal? If not, under what conditions are they unequal?

(b) If the two expressions are not equal for certain values of u and v, is one of the expressions always greater than the other? Explain.

110. ***Think About It***   Is there a difference between saying that a real number is positive and saying that a real number is nonnegative? Explain.

111. ***Think About It***   Because every even number is divisible by 2, is it possible that there exist any even prime numbers? Explain.

112. ***Writing***   Describe the differences among the sets of natural numbers, whole numbers, integers, rational numbers, and irrational numbers.

In Exercises 113 and 114, use the real numbers A, B, and C shown on the number line. Determine the sign of each expression.

113. (a) $-A$

(b) $B - A$

114. (a) $-C$

(b) $A - C$

115. ***Writing***   Can it ever be true that $|a| = -a$ for a real number a? Explain.

A.2   Exponents and Radicals

What you should learn

- Use properties of exponents.
- Use scientific notation to represent real numbers.
- Use properties of radicals.
- Simplify and combine radicals.
- Rationalize denominators and numerators.
- Use properties of rational exponents.

Why you should learn it

Real numbers and algebraic expressions are often written with exponents and radicals. For instance, in Exercise 105 on page A22, you will use an expression involving rational exponents to find the time required for a funnel to empty for different water heights.

Integer Exponents

Repeated *multiplication* can be written in **exponential form**.

Repeated Multiplication	*Exponential Form*
$a \cdot a \cdot a \cdot a \cdot a$	a^5
$(-4)(-4)(-4)$	$(-4)^3$
$(2x)(2x)(2x)(2x)$	$(2x)^4$

Exponential Notation

If a is a real number and n is a positive integer, then

$$a^n = \underbrace{a \cdot a \cdot a \cdots a}_{n \text{ factors}}$$

where n is the **exponent** and a is the **base**. The expression a^n is read "a to the nth **power**."

An exponent can also be negative. In Property 3 below, be sure you see how to use a negative exponent.

Technology

You can use a calculator to evaluate exponential expressions. When doing so, it is important to know when to use parentheses because the calculator follows the order of operations. For instance, evaluate $(-2)^4$ as follows

Scientific:

(2 [+/−]) [y^x] 4 [=]

Graphing:

([(−)] 2) [^] 4 [ENTER]

The display will be 16. If you omit the parentheses, the display will be -16.

Properties of Exponents

Let a and b be real numbers, variables, or algebraic expressions, and let m and n be integers. (All denominators and bases are nonzero.)

Property	*Example*
1. $a^m a^n = a^{m+n}$	$3^2 \cdot 3^4 = 3^{2+4} = 3^6 = 729$
2. $\dfrac{a^m}{a^n} = a^{m-n}$	$\dfrac{x^7}{x^4} = x^{7-4} = x^3$
3. $a^{-n} = \dfrac{1}{a^n} = \left(\dfrac{1}{a}\right)^n$	$y^{-4} = \dfrac{1}{y^4} = \left(\dfrac{1}{y}\right)^4$
4. $a^0 = 1, \quad a \neq 0$	$(x^2 + 1)^0 = 1$
5. $(ab)^m = a^m b^m$	$(5x)^3 = 5^3 x^3 = 125x^3$
6. $(a^m)^n = a^{mn}$	$(y^3)^{-4} = y^{3(-4)} = y^{-12} = \dfrac{1}{y^{12}}$
7. $\left(\dfrac{a}{b}\right)^m = \dfrac{a^m}{b^m}$	$\left(\dfrac{2}{x}\right)^3 = \dfrac{2^3}{x^3} = \dfrac{8}{x^3}$
8. $|a^2| = |a|^2 = a^2$	$|(-2)^2| = |-2|^2 = (2)^2 = 4$

It is important to recognize the difference between expressions such as $(-2)^4$ and -2^4. In $(-2)^4$, the parentheses indicate that the exponent applies to the negative sign as well as to the 2, but in $-2^4 = -(2^4)$, the exponent applies only to the 2. So, $(-2)^4 = 16$ and $-2^4 = -16$.

The properties of exponents listed on the preceding page apply to *all* integers m and n, not just to positive integers as shown in the examples in this section.

Example 1 Using Properties of Exponents

Use the properties of exponents to simplify each expression.

a. $(-3ab^4)(4ab^{-3})$ **b.** $(2xy^2)^3$ **c.** $3a(-4a^2)^0$ **d.** $\left(\dfrac{5x^3}{y}\right)^2$

Solution

a. $(-3ab^4)(4ab^{-3}) = (-3)(4)(a)(a)(b^4)(b^{-3}) = -12a^2b$

b. $(2xy^2)^3 = 2^3(x)^3(y^2)^3 = 8x^3y^6$

c. $3a(-4a^2)^0 = 3a(1) = 3a, \quad a \neq 0$

d. $\left(\dfrac{5x^3}{x}\right)^2 = \dfrac{5^2(x^3)^2}{y^2} = \dfrac{25x^6}{y^2}$

CHECKPOINT Now try Exercise 25.

Example 2 Rewriting with Positive Exponents

Rewrite each expression with positive exponents.

a. x^{-1} **b.** $\dfrac{1}{3x^{-2}}$ **c.** $\dfrac{12a^3b^{-4}}{4a^{-2}b}$ **d.** $\left(\dfrac{3x^2}{y}\right)^{-2}$

Solution

a. $x^{-1} = \dfrac{1}{x}$ Property 3

b. $\dfrac{1}{3x^{-2}} = \dfrac{1(x^2)}{3} = \dfrac{x^2}{3}$ The exponent -2 does not apply to 3.

c. $\dfrac{12a^3b^{-4}}{4a^{-2}b} = \dfrac{12a^3 \cdot a^2}{4b \cdot b^4} = \dfrac{3a^5}{b^5}$ Properties 3 and 1

d. $\left(\dfrac{3x^2}{y}\right)^{-2} = \dfrac{3^{-2}(x^2)^{-2}}{y^{-2}}$ Properties 5 and 7

        $= \dfrac{3^{-2}x^{-4}}{y^{-2}}$ Property 6

        $= \dfrac{y^2}{3^2x^4}$ Property 3

        $= \dfrac{y^2}{9x^4}$ Simplify.

CHECKPOINT Now try Exercise 33.

STUDY TIP

Rarely in algebra is there only one way to solve a problem. Don't be concerned if the steps you use to solve a problem are not exactly the same as the steps presented in this text. The important thing is to use steps that you understand and, of course, steps that are justified by the rules of algebra. For instance, you might prefer the following steps for Example 2(d).

$$\left(\frac{3x^2}{y}\right)^{-2} = \left(\frac{y}{3x^2}\right)^2 = \frac{y^2}{9x^4}$$

Note how Property 3 is used in the first step of this solution. The fractional form of this property is

$$\left(\frac{a}{b}\right)^{-m} = \left(\frac{b}{a}\right)^m.$$

Scientific Notation

Exponents provide an efficient way of writing and computing with very large (or very small) numbers. For instance, there are about 359 billion billion gallons of water on Earth—that is, 359 followed by 18 zeros.

$$359,000,000,000,000,000,000$$

It is convenient to write such numbers in **scientific notation.** This notation has the form $\pm c \times 10^n$, where $1 \le c < 10$ and n is an integer. So, the number of gallons of water on Earth can be written in scientific notation as

$$3.59 \times 100,000,000,000,000,000,000 = 3.59 \times 10^{20}.$$

The *positive* exponent 20 indicates that the number is *large* (10 or more) and that the decimal point has been moved 20 places. A *negative* exponent indicates that the number is *small* (less than 1). For instance, the mass (in grams) of one electron is approximately

$$9.0 \times 10^{-28} = 0.\underbrace{0000000000000000000000000009}_{28 \text{ decimal places}}.$$

Example 3   **Scientific Notation**

Write each number in scientific notation.

a. 0.0000782   **b.** 836,100,000

Solution

a. $0.0000782 = 7.82 \times 10^{-5}$ **b.** $836,100,000 = 8.361 \times 10^8$

✓CHECKPOINT   Now try Exercise 37.

Example 4   **Decimal Notation**

Write each number in decimal notation.

a. 9.36×10^{-6} **b.** 1.345×10^2

Solution

a. $9.36 \times 10^{-6} = 0.00000936$ **b.** $1.345 \times 10^2 = 134.5$

✓CHECKPOINT   Now try Exercise 41.

Technology

Most calculators automatically switch to scientific notation when they are showing large (or small) numbers that exceed the display range.

To *enter* numbers in scientific notation, your calculator should have an exponential entry key labeled

[EE]   or   [EXP].

Consult the user's guide for your calculator for instructions on keystrokes and how numbers in scientific notation are displayed.

Radicals and Their Properties

A **square root** of a number is one of its two equal factors. For example, 5 is a square root of 25 because 5 is one of the two equal factors of 25. In a similar way, a **cube root** of a number is one of its three equal factors, as in $125 = 5^3$.

Definition of *n*th Root of a Number

Let a and b be real numbers and let $n \geq 2$ be a positive integer. If

$$a = b^n$$

then b is an ***n*th root of *a*.** If $n = 2$, the root is a **square root.** If $n = 3$, the root is a **cube root.**

Some numbers have more than one *n*th root. For example, both 5 and -5 are square roots of 25. The *principal square root* of 25, written as $\sqrt{25}$, is the positive root, 5. The **principal *n*th root** of a number is defined as follows.

Principal *n*th Root of a Number

Let a be a real number that has at least one *n*th root. The **principal *n*th root of *a*** is the *n*th root that has the same sign as a. It is denoted by a **radical symbol**

$$\sqrt[n]{a}. \qquad \text{Principal } n\text{th root}$$

The positive integer n is the **index** of the radical, and the number a is the **radicand.** If $n = 2$, omit the index and write $\sqrt{a}$ rather than $\sqrt[2]{a}$. (The plural of index is *indices*.)

A common misunderstanding is that the square root sign implies both negative and positive roots. This is not correct. The square root sign implies only a positive root. When a negative root is needed, you must use the negative sign with the square root sign.

Incorrect: $\sqrt{4} = \pm 2$ *Correct:* $-\sqrt{4} = -2$ *and* $\sqrt{4} = 2$

Example 5   Evaluating Expressions Involving Radicals

a. $\sqrt{36} = 6$ because $6^2 = 36$.

b. $-\sqrt{36} = -6$ because $-\left(\sqrt{36}\right) = -\left(\sqrt{6^2}\right) = -(6) = -6$.

c. $\sqrt[3]{\dfrac{125}{64}} = \dfrac{5}{4}$ because $\left(\dfrac{5}{4}\right)^3 = \dfrac{5^3}{4^3} = \dfrac{125}{64}$.

d. $\sqrt[5]{-32} = -2$ because $(-2)^5 = -32$.

e. $\sqrt[4]{-81}$ is not a real number because there is no real number that can be raised to the fourth power to produce -81.

✓**CHECKPOINT**   Now try Exercise 51.

Here are some generalizations about the nth roots of real numbers.

Generalizations About nth Roots of Real Numbers

Real Number a	Integer n	Root(s) of a	Example
$a > 0$	$n > 0$, is even.	$\sqrt[n]{a}, \ -\sqrt[n]{a}$	$\sqrt[4]{81} = 3, \ -\sqrt[4]{81} = -3$
$a > 0$ or $a < 0$	n is odd.	$\sqrt[n]{a}$	$\sqrt[3]{-8} = -2$
$a < 0$	n is even.	No real roots	$\sqrt{-4}$ is not a real number.
$a = 0$	n is even or odd.	$\sqrt[n]{0} = 0$	$\sqrt[5]{0} = 0$

Integers such as 1, 4, 9, 16, 25, and 36 are called **perfect squares** because they have integer square roots. Similarly, integers such as 1, 8, 27, 64, and 125 are called **perfect cubes** because they have integer cube roots.

Properties of Radicals

Let a and b be real numbers, variables, or algebraic expressions such that the indicated roots are real numbers, and let m and n be positive integers.

Property

1. $\sqrt[n]{a^m} = \left(\sqrt[n]{a}\right)^m$

2. $\sqrt[n]{a} \cdot \sqrt[n]{b} = \sqrt[n]{ab}$

3. $\dfrac{\sqrt[n]{a}}{\sqrt[n]{b}} = \sqrt[n]{\dfrac{a}{b}}, \quad b \neq 0$

4. $\sqrt[m]{\sqrt[n]{a}} = \sqrt[mn]{a}$

5. $\left(\sqrt[n]{a}\right)^n = a$

6. For n even, $\sqrt[n]{a^n} = |a|$.

   For n odd, $\sqrt[n]{a^n} = a$.

Example

$\sqrt[3]{8^2} = \left(\sqrt[3]{8}\right)^2 = (2)^2 = 4$

$\sqrt{5} \cdot \sqrt{7} = \sqrt{5 \cdot 7} = \sqrt{35}$

$\dfrac{\sqrt[4]{27}}{\sqrt[4]{9}} = \sqrt[4]{\dfrac{27}{9}} = \sqrt[4]{3}$

$\sqrt[3]{\sqrt{10}} = \sqrt[6]{10}$

$\left(\sqrt{3}\right)^2 = 3$

$\sqrt{(-12)^2} = |-12| = 12$

$\sqrt[3]{(-12)^3} = -12$

A common special case of Property 6 is $\sqrt{a^2} = |a|$.

Example 6   **Using Properties of Radicals**

Use the properties of radicals to simplify each expression.

a. $\sqrt{8} \cdot \sqrt{2}$ **b.** $\left(\sqrt[3]{5}\right)^3$ **c.** $\sqrt[3]{x^3}$ **d.** $\sqrt[6]{y^6}$

Solution

a. $\sqrt{8} \cdot \sqrt{2} = \sqrt{8 \cdot 2} = \sqrt{16} = 4$

b. $\left(\sqrt[3]{5}\right)^3 = 5$

c. $\sqrt[3]{x^3} = x$

d. $\sqrt[6]{y^6} = |y|$

CHECKPOINT   Now try Exercise 61.

Simplifying Radicals

An expression involving radicals is in **simplest form** when the following conditions are satisfied.

1. All possible factors have been removed from the radical.

2. All fractions have radical-free denominators (accomplished by a process called *rationalizing the denominator*).

3. The index of the radical is reduced.

To simplify a radical, factor the radicand into factors whose exponents are multiples of the index. The roots of these factors are written outside the radical, and the "leftover" factors make up the new radicand.

Example 7   **Simplifying Even Roots**

a. $\sqrt[4]{48} = \sqrt[4]{16 \cdot 3} = \sqrt[4]{2^4 \cdot 3} = 2\sqrt[4]{3}$

      Perfect 4th power   Leftover factor

b. $\sqrt{75x^3} = \sqrt{25x^2 \cdot 3x}$ Find largest square factor.

     $= \sqrt{(5x)^2 \cdot 3x}$

     $= 5x\sqrt{3x}$ Find root of perfect square.

c. $\sqrt[4]{(5x)^4} = |5x| = 5|x|$

CHECKPOINT   Now try Exercise 63(a).

Example 8   **Simplifying Odd Roots**

a. $\sqrt[3]{24} = \sqrt[3]{8 \cdot 3} = \sqrt[3]{2^3 \cdot 3} = 2\sqrt[3]{3}$

      Perfect cube   Leftover factor

b. $\sqrt[3]{24a^4} = \sqrt[3]{8a^3 \cdot 3a}$ Find largest cube factor.

     $= \sqrt[3]{(2a)^3 \cdot 3a}$

     $= 2a\sqrt[3]{3a}$ Find root of perfect cube.

c. $\sqrt[3]{-40x^6} = \sqrt[3]{(-8x^6) \cdot 5}$ Find largest cube factor.

     $= \sqrt[3]{(-2x^2)^3 \cdot 5}$

     $= -2x^2\sqrt[3]{5}$ Find root of perfect cube.

CHECKPOINT   Now try Exercise 63(b).

Radical expressions can be combined (added or subtracted) if they are **like radicals**—that is, if they have the same index and radicand. For instance, $\sqrt{2}$, $3\sqrt{2}$, and $\frac{1}{2}\sqrt{2}$ are like radicals, but $\sqrt{3}$ and $\sqrt{2}$ are unlike radicals. To determine whether two radicals can be combined, you should first simplify each radical.

Example 9   Combining Radicals

a.
$$2\sqrt{48} - 3\sqrt{27} = 2\sqrt{16 \cdot 3} - 3\sqrt{9 \cdot 3}$$

Find square factors.

$$= 8\sqrt{3} - 9\sqrt{3}$$

Find square roots and multiply by coefficients.

$$= (8 - 9)\sqrt{3}$$

Combine like terms.

$$= -\sqrt{3}$$

Simplify.

b.
$$\sqrt[3]{16x} - \sqrt[3]{54x^4} = \sqrt[3]{8 \cdot 2x} - \sqrt[3]{27 \cdot x^3 \cdot 2x}$$

Find cube factors.

$$= 2\sqrt[3]{2x} - 3x\sqrt[3]{2x}$$

Find cube roots.

$$= (2 - 3x)\sqrt[3]{2x}$$

Combine like terms.

CHECKPOINT   Now try Exercise 71.

Rationalizing Denominators and Numerators

To rationalize a denominator or numerator of the form $a - b\sqrt{m}$ or $a + b\sqrt{m}$, multiply both numerator and denominator by a **conjugate:** $a + b\sqrt{m}$ and $a - b\sqrt{m}$ are conjugates of each other. If $a = 0$, then the rationalizing factor for $\sqrt{m}$ is itself, $\sqrt{m}$. For cube roots, choose a rationalizing factor that generates a perfect cube.

Example 10   Rationalizing Single-Term Denominators

Rationalize the denominator of each expression.

a. $\dfrac{5}{2\sqrt{3}}$ **b.** $\dfrac{2}{\sqrt[3]{5}}$

Solution

a.
$$\frac{5}{2\sqrt{3}} = \frac{5}{2\sqrt{3}} \cdot \frac{\sqrt{3}}{\sqrt{3}}$$

$\sqrt{3}$ is rationalizing factor.

$$= \frac{5\sqrt{3}}{2(3)}$$

Multiply.

$$= \frac{5\sqrt{3}}{6}$$

Simplify.

b.
$$\frac{2}{\sqrt[3]{5}} = \frac{2}{\sqrt[3]{5}} \cdot \frac{\sqrt[3]{5^2}}{\sqrt[3]{5^2}}$$

$\sqrt[3]{5^2}$ is rationalizing factor.

$$= \frac{2\sqrt[3]{5^2}}{\sqrt[3]{5^3}}$$

Multiply.

$$= \frac{2\sqrt[3]{25}}{5}$$

Simplify.

CHECKPOINT   Now try Exercise 79.

Additional Examples

a. $\dfrac{3}{\sqrt{7}} = \dfrac{3}{\sqrt{7}} \cdot \dfrac{\sqrt{7}}{\sqrt{7}} = \dfrac{3\sqrt{7}}{7}$

b. $\dfrac{2}{\sqrt[3]{4}} = \dfrac{2}{\sqrt[3]{4}} \cdot \dfrac{\sqrt[3]{2}}{\sqrt[3]{2}}$

$= \dfrac{2\sqrt[3]{2}}{\sqrt[3]{8}}$

$= \dfrac{2\sqrt[3]{2}}{2}$

$= \sqrt[3]{2}$

c. $\dfrac{6}{\sqrt{2} + \sqrt{3}}$

$= \dfrac{6}{\sqrt{2} + \sqrt{3}} \cdot \dfrac{\sqrt{2} - \sqrt{3}}{\sqrt{2} - \sqrt{3}}$

$= \dfrac{6(\sqrt{2} - \sqrt{3})}{-1}$

$= -6\sqrt{2} + 6\sqrt{3}$

Example 11   Rationalizing a Denominator with Two Terms

$\dfrac{2}{3 + \sqrt{7}} = \dfrac{2}{3 + \sqrt{7}} \cdot \dfrac{3 - \sqrt{7}}{3 - \sqrt{7}}$ Multiply numerator and denominator by conjugate of denominator.

$= \dfrac{2(3 - \sqrt{7})}{3(3) + 3(-\sqrt{7}) + \sqrt{7}(3) - (\sqrt{7})(\sqrt{7})}$ Use Distributive Property.

$= \dfrac{2(3 - \sqrt{7})}{(3)^2 - (\sqrt{7})^2}$ Simplify.

$= \dfrac{2(3 - \sqrt{7})}{9 - 7}$ Square terms of denominator.

$= \dfrac{2(3 - \sqrt{7})}{2} = 3 - \sqrt{7}$ Simplify.

✓**CHECKPOINT**   Now try Exercise 81.

Sometimes it is necessary to rationalize the numerator of an expression. For instance, in Appendix A.4 you will use the technique shown in the next example to rationalize the numerator of an expression from calculus.

STUDY TIP

Do not confuse the expression $\sqrt{5} + \sqrt{7}$ with the expression $\sqrt{5 + 7}$. In general, $\sqrt{x + y}$ does not equal $\sqrt{x} + \sqrt{y}$. Similarly, $\sqrt{x^2 + y^2}$ does not equal $x + y$.

Example 12   Rationalizing a Numerator

$\dfrac{\sqrt{5} - \sqrt{7}}{2} = \dfrac{\sqrt{5} - \sqrt{7}}{2} \cdot \dfrac{\sqrt{5} + \sqrt{7}}{\sqrt{5} + \sqrt{7}}$ Multiply numerator and denominator by conjugate of numerator.

$= \dfrac{(\sqrt{5})^2 - (\sqrt{7})^2}{2(\sqrt{5} + \sqrt{7})}$ Simplify.

$= \dfrac{5 - 7}{2(\sqrt{5} + \sqrt{7})}$ Square terms of numerator.

$= \dfrac{-2}{2(\sqrt{5} + \sqrt{7})} = \dfrac{-1}{\sqrt{5} + \sqrt{7}}$ Simplify.

✓**CHECKPOINT**   Now try Exercise 85.

Rational Exponents

> ### Definition of Rational Exponents
>
> If a is a real number and n is a positive integer such that the principal nth root of a exists, then $a^{1/n}$ is defined as
>
> $a^{1/n} = \sqrt[n]{a}$, where $1/n$ is the **rational exponent** of a.
>
> Moreover, if m is a positive integer that has no common factor with n, then
>
> $$a^{m/n} = (a^{1/n})^m = (\sqrt[n]{a})^m \quad \text{and} \quad a^{m/n} = (a^m)^{1/n} = \sqrt[n]{a^m}.$$

The symbol ∫ indicates an example or exercise that highlights algebraic techniques specifically used in calculus.

The numerator of a rational exponent denotes the *power* to which the base is raised, and the denominator denotes the *index* or the *root* to be taken.

$$\text{—Power—}$$
$$\lceil\text{Index}\rceil$$
$$b^{m/n} = \left(\sqrt[n]{b}\right)^m = \sqrt[n]{b^m}$$

When you are working with rational exponents, the properties of integer exponents still apply. For instance,

$$2^{1/2}2^{1/3} = 2^{(1/2)+(1/3)} = 2^{5/6}.$$

Example 13 **Changing from Radical to Exponential Form**

a. $\sqrt{3} = 3^{1/2}$

b. $\sqrt{(3xy)^5} = \sqrt[2]{(3xy)^5} = (3xy)^{(5/2)}$

c. $2x\sqrt[4]{x^3} = (2x)(x^{3/4}) = 2x^{1+(3/4)} = 2x^{7/4}$

✓**CHECKPOINT**   Now try Exercise 87.

Example 14 **Changing from Exponential to Radical Form**

a. $(x^2 + y^2)^{3/2} = \left(\sqrt{x^2 + y^2}\right)^3 = \sqrt{(x^2 + y^2)^3}$

b. $2y^{3/4}z^{1/4} = 2(y^3z)^{1/4} = 2\sqrt[4]{y^3z}$

c. $a^{-3/2} = \dfrac{1}{a^{3/2}} = \dfrac{1}{\sqrt{a^3}}$ d. $x^{0.2} = x^{1/5} = \sqrt[5]{x}$

✓**CHECKPOINT**   Now try Exercise 89.

Rational exponents are useful for evaluating roots of numbers on a calculator, for reducing the index of a radical, and for simplifying expressions in calculus.

Example 15 **Simplifying with Rational Exponents**

a. $(-32)^{-4/5} = \left(\sqrt[5]{-32}\right)^{-4} = (-2)^{-4} = \dfrac{1}{(-2)^4} = \dfrac{1}{16}$

b. $(-5x^{5/3})(3x^{-3/4}) = -15x^{(5/3)-(3/4)} = -15x^{11/12}, \quad x \neq 0$

c. $\sqrt[9]{a^3} = a^{3/9} = a^{1/3} = \sqrt[3]{a}$ Reduce index.

d. $\sqrt[3]{\sqrt{125}} = \sqrt[6]{125} = \sqrt[6]{(5)^3} = 5^{3/6} = 5^{1/2} = \sqrt{5}$

e. $(2x - 1)^{4/3}(2x - 1)^{-1/3} = (2x - 1)^{(4/3)-(1/3)}$

$$= 2x - 1, \qquad x \neq \frac{1}{2}$$

f. $\dfrac{x - 1}{(x - 1)^{-1/2}} = \dfrac{x - 1}{(x - 1)^{-1/2}} \cdot \dfrac{(x - 1)^{1/2}}{(x - 1)^{1/2}}$

$$= \dfrac{(x - 1)^{3/2}}{(x - 1)^0}$$

$$= (x - 1)^{3/2}, \qquad x \neq 1$$

✓**CHECKPOINT**   Now try Exercise 99.

A.2 | Exercises

VOCABULARY CHECK: Fill in the blanks.

1. In the exponential form a^n, n is the _____ and a is the _____.
2. A convenient way of writing very large or very small numbers is called _____ _____.
3. One of the two equal factors of a number is called a _____ _____ of the number.
4. The _____ _____ _____ of a number is the nth root that has the same sign as a, and is denoted by $\sqrt[n]{a}$.
5. In the radical form, $\sqrt[n]{a}$ the positive integer n is called the _____ of the radical and the number a is called the _____.
6. When an expression involving radicals has all possible factors removed, radical-free denominators, and a reduced index, it is in _____ _____.
7. The expressions $a + b\sqrt{m}$ and $a - b\sqrt{m}$ are _____ of each other.
8. The process used to create a radical-free denominator is know as _____ the denominator.
9. In the expression $b^{m/n}$, m denotes the _____ to which the base is raised and n denotes the _____ or root to be taken.

In Exercises 1 and 2, write the expression as a repeated multiplication problem.

1. 8^5
2. $(-2)^7$

In Exercises 3 and 4, write the expression using exponential notation.

3. $(4.9)(4.9)(4.9)(4.9)(4.9)(4.9)$
4. $(-10)(-10)(-10)(-10)(-10)$

In Exercises 5–12, evaluate each expression.

5. (a) $3^2 \cdot 3$ (b) $3 \cdot 3^3$
6. (a) $\dfrac{5^5}{5^2}$ (b) $\dfrac{3^2}{3^4}$
7. (a) $(3^3)^0$ (b) -3^2
8. (a) $(2^3 \cdot 3^2)^2$ (b) $\left(-\frac{3}{5}\right)^3\left(\frac{5}{3}\right)^2$
9. (a) $\dfrac{3 \cdot 4^{-4}}{3^{-4} \cdot 4^{-1}}$ (b) $32(-2)^{-5}$
10. (a) $\dfrac{4 \cdot 3^{-2}}{2^{-2} \cdot 3^{-1}}$ (b) $(-2)^0$
11. (a) $2^{-1} + 3^{-1}$ (b) $(2^{-1})^{-2}$
12. (a) $3^{-1} + 2^{-2}$ (b) $(3^{-2})^2$

In Exercises 13–16, use a calculator to evaluate the expression. (If necessary, round your answer to three decimal places.)

13. $(-4)^3(5^2)$
14. $(8^{-4})(10^3)$
15. $\dfrac{3^6}{7^3}$
16. $\dfrac{4^3}{3^{-4}}$

In Exercises 17–24, evaluate the expression for the given value of x.

Expression	Value
17. $-3x^3$	$x = 2$
18. $7x^{-2}$	$x = 4$
19. $6x^0$	$x = 10$
20. $5(-x)^3$	$x = 3$
21. $2x^3$	$x = -3$
22. $-3x^4$	$x = -2$
23. $4x^2$	$x = -\frac{1}{2}$
24. $5(-x)^3$	$x = -\frac{1}{3}$

In Exercises 25–30, simplify each expression.

25. (a) $(-5z)^3$ (b) $5x^4(x^2)$
26. (a) $(3x)^2$ (b) $(4x^3)^0$
27. (a) $6y^2(2y^0)^2$ (b) $\dfrac{3x^5}{x^3}$
28. (a) $(-z)^3(3z^4)$ (b) $\dfrac{25y^8}{10y^4}$
29. (a) $\dfrac{7x^2}{x^3}$ (b) $\dfrac{12(x + y)^3}{9(x + y)}$
30. (a) $\dfrac{r^4}{r^6}$ (b) $\left(\dfrac{4}{y}\right)^3\left(\dfrac{3}{y}\right)^4$

In Exercises 31–36, rewrite each expression with positive exponents and simplify.

31. (a) $(x + 5)^0$, $x \neq -5$ (b) $(2x^2)^{-2}$
32. (a) $(2x^5)^0$, $x \neq 0$ (b) $(z + 2)^{-3}(z + 2)^{-1}$

33. (a) $(-2x^2)^3(4x^3)^{-1}$ (b) $\left(\dfrac{x}{10}\right)^{-1}$

34. (a) $(4y^{-2})(8y^4)$ (b) $\left(\dfrac{x^{-3}y^4}{5}\right)^{-3}$

35. (a) $3^n \cdot 3^{2n}$ (b) $\left(\dfrac{a^{-2}}{b^{-2}}\right)\left(\dfrac{b}{a}\right)^3$

36. (a) $\dfrac{x^2 \cdot x^n}{x^3 \cdot x^n}$ (b) $\left(\dfrac{a^{-3}}{b^{-3}}\right)\left(\dfrac{a}{b}\right)^3$

In Exercises 37–40, write the number in scientific notation.

37. Land area of Earth: 57,300,000 square miles

38. Light year: 9,460,000,000,000 kilometers

39. Relative density of hydrogen: 0.0000899 gram per cubic centimeter

40. One micron (millionth of a meter): 0.00003937 inch

In Exercises 41–44, write the number in decimal notation.

41. Worldwide daily consumption of Coca-Cola: 4.568×10^9 ounces   (Source: The Coca-Cola Company)

42. Interior temperature of the sun: 1.5×10^7 degrees Celsius

43. Charge of an electron: 1.6022×10^{-19} coulomb

44. Width of a human hair: 9.0×10^{-5} meter

In Exercises 45 and 46, evaluate each expression without using a calculator.

45. (a) $\sqrt{25 \times 10^8}$ (b) $\sqrt[3]{8 \times 10^{15}}$

46. (a) $(1.2 \times 10^7)(5 \times 10^{-3})$ (b) $\dfrac{(6.0 \times 10^8)}{(3.0 \times 10^{-3})}$

In Exercises 47–50, use a calculator to evaluate each expression. (Round your answer to three decimal places.)

47. (a) $750\left(1 + \dfrac{0.11}{365}\right)^{800}$

(b) $\dfrac{67,000,000 + 93,000,000}{0.0052}$

48. (a) $(9.3 \times 10^6)^3(6.1 \times 10^{-4})$

(b) $\dfrac{(2.414 \times 10^4)^6}{(1.68 \times 10^5)^5}$

49. (a) $\sqrt{4.5 \times 10^9}$ (b) $\sqrt[3]{6.3 \times 10^4}$

50. (a) $(2.65 \times 10^{-4})^{1/3}$ (b) $\sqrt{9 \times 10^{-4}}$

In Exercises 51–56, evaluate each expression without using a calculator.

51. (a) $\sqrt{9}$ (b) $\sqrt[3]{\dfrac{27}{8}}$

52. (a) $27^{1/3}$ (b) $36^{3/2}$

53. (a) $32^{-3/5}$ (b) $\left(\dfrac{16}{81}\right)^{-3/4}$

54. (a) $100^{-3/2}$ (b) $\left(\dfrac{9}{4}\right)^{-1/2}$

55. (a) $\left(-\dfrac{1}{64}\right)^{-1/3}$ (b) $\left(\dfrac{1}{\sqrt{32}}\right)^{-2/5}$

56. (a) $\left(-\dfrac{125}{27}\right)^{-1/3}$ (b) $-\left(\dfrac{1}{125}\right)^{-4/3}$

In Exercises 57–60, use a calculator to approximate the number. (Round your answer to three decimal places.)

57. (a) $\sqrt{57}$ (b) $\sqrt[5]{-27^3}$

58. (a) $\sqrt[3]{45^2}$ (b) $\sqrt[6]{125}$

59. (a) $(-12.4)^{-1.8}$ (b) $(5\sqrt{3})^{-2.5}$

60. (a) $\dfrac{7 - (4.1)^{-3.2}}{2}$ (b) $\left(\dfrac{13}{3}\right)^{-3/2} - \left(-\dfrac{3}{2}\right)^{13/3}$

In Exercises 61 and 62, use the properties of radicals to simplify each expression.

61. (a) $(\sqrt[3]{4})^3$ (b) $\sqrt[5]{96x^5}$

62. (a) $\sqrt{12} \cdot \sqrt{3}$ (b) $\sqrt[4]{(3x^2)^4}$

In Exercises 63–74, simplify each radical expression.

63. (a) $\sqrt{8}$ (b) $\sqrt[3]{54}$

64. (a) $\sqrt[3]{\dfrac{16}{27}}$ (b) $\sqrt{\dfrac{75}{4}}$

65. (a) $\sqrt{72x^3}$ (b) $\sqrt{\dfrac{18^2}{z^3}}$

66. (a) $\sqrt{54xy^4}$ (b) $\sqrt{\dfrac{32a^4}{b^2}}$

67. (a) $\sqrt[3]{16x^5}$ (b) $\sqrt{75x^2y^{-4}}$

68. (a) $\sqrt[4]{3x^4y^2}$ (b) $\sqrt[5]{160x^8z^4}$

69. (a) $2\sqrt{50} + 12\sqrt{8}$ (b) $10\sqrt{32} - 6\sqrt{18}$

70. (a) $4\sqrt{27} - \sqrt{75}$ (b) $\sqrt[3]{16} + 3\sqrt[3]{54}$

71. (a) $5\sqrt{x} - 3\sqrt{x}$ (b) $-2\sqrt{9y} + 10\sqrt{y}$

72. (a) $8\sqrt{49x} - 14\sqrt{100x}$ (b) $-3\sqrt{48x^2} + 7\sqrt{75x^2}$

73. (a) $3\sqrt{x+1} + 10\sqrt{x+1}$ (b) $7\sqrt{80x} - 2\sqrt{125x}$

74. (a) $-\sqrt{x^3 - 7} + 5\sqrt{x^3 - 7}$ (b) $11\sqrt{245x^3} - 9\sqrt{45x^3}$

In Exercises 75–78, complete the statement with <, =, or >.

75. $\sqrt{5} + \sqrt{3}$ ___ $\sqrt{5+3}$ **76.** $\sqrt{\dfrac{3}{11}}$ ___ $\dfrac{\sqrt{3}}{\sqrt{11}}$

77. 5 ___ $\sqrt{3^2 + 2^2}$ **78.** 5 ___ $\sqrt{3^2 + 4^2}$

In Exercises 79–82, rationalize the denominator of the expression. Then simplify your answer.

79. $\dfrac{1}{\sqrt{3}}$ **80.** $\dfrac{5}{\sqrt{10}}$

81. $\dfrac{2}{5 - \sqrt{3}}$

82. $\dfrac{3}{\sqrt{5} + \sqrt{6}}$

 In Exercises 83–86, rationalize the numerator of the expression. Then simplify your answer.

83. $\dfrac{\sqrt{8}}{2}$

84. $\dfrac{\sqrt{2}}{3}$

85. $\dfrac{\sqrt{5} + \sqrt{3}}{3}$

86. $\dfrac{\sqrt{7} - 3}{4}$

In Exercises 87–94, fill in the missing form of the expression.

Radical Form	Rational Exponent Form
87. $\sqrt{9}$	
88. $\sqrt[3]{64}$	
89.	$32^{1/5}$
90.	$-(144^{1/2})$
91. $\sqrt[3]{-216}$	
92.	$(-243)^{1/5}$
93. $\left(\sqrt[4]{81}\right)^3$	
94.	$16^{5/4}$

In Exercises 95–98, perform the operations and simplify.

95. $\dfrac{(2x^2)^{3/2}}{2^{1/2}x^4}$

96. $\dfrac{x^{4/3}y^{2/3}}{(xy)^{1/3}}$

97. $\dfrac{x^{-3} \cdot x^{1/2}}{x^{3/2} \cdot x^{-1}}$

98. $\dfrac{5^{-1/2} \cdot 5x^{5/2}}{(5x)^{3/2}}$

In Exercises 99 and 100, reduce the index of each radical.

99. (a) $\sqrt[4]{3^2}$ (b) $\sqrt[6]{(x + 1)^4}$

100. (a) $\sqrt[6]{x^3}$ (b) $\sqrt[4]{(3x^2)^4}$

In Exercises 101 and 102, write each expression as a single radical. Then simplify your answer.

101. (a) $\sqrt{\sqrt{32}}$ (b) $\sqrt{\sqrt[4]{2x}}$

102. (a) $\sqrt{\sqrt{243(x + 1)}}$ (b) $\sqrt{\sqrt[3]{10a^7b}}$

103. *Period of a Pendulum*   The period T (in seconds) of a pendulum is

$$T = 2\pi\sqrt{\dfrac{L}{32}}$$

where L is the length of the pendulum (in feet). Find the period of a pendulum whose length is 2 feet.

The symbol indicates an example or exercise that highlights algebraic techniques specifically used in calculus.

The symbol 🔖 indicates an exercise or a part of an exercise in which you are instructed to use a graphing utility.

104. *Erosion*   A stream of water moving at the rate of v feet per second can carry particles of size $0.03\sqrt{v}$ inches. Find the size of the largest particle that can be carried by a stream flowing at the rate of $\frac{3}{4}$ foot per second.

105. *Mathematical Modeling*   A funnel is filled with water to a height of h centimeters. The formula

$$t = 0.03[12^{5/2} - (12 - h)^{5/2}], \quad 0 \le h \le 12$$

represents the amount of time t (in seconds) that it will take for the funnel to empty.

🔖 (a) Use the table feature of a graphing utility to find the times required for the funnel to empty for water heights of $h = 0$, $h = 1$, $h = 2$, . . . $h = 12$ centimeters.

(b) What value does t appear to be approaching as the height of the water becomes closer and closer to 12 centimeters?

106. *Speed of Light*   The speed of light is approximately 11,180,000 miles per minute. The distance from the sun to Earth is approximately 93,000,000 miles. Find the time for light to travel from the sun to Earth.

Synthesis

True or False?   In Exercises 107 and 108, determine whether the statement is true or false. Justify your answer.

107. $\dfrac{x^{k+1}}{x} = x^k$

108. $(a^n)^k = a^{n^k}$

109. Verify that $a^0 = 1$, $a \ne 0$. (*Hint:* Use the property of exponents $a^m/a^n = a^{m-n}$.)

110. Explain why each of the following pairs is not equal.

(a) $(3x)^{-1} \ne \dfrac{3}{x}$ (b) $y^3 \cdot y^2 \ne y^6$

(c) $(a^2b^3)^4 \ne a^6b^7$ (d) $(a + b)^2 \ne a^2 + b^2$

(e) $\sqrt{4x^2} \ne 2x$ (f) $\sqrt{2} + \sqrt{3} \ne \sqrt{5}$

111. *Exploration*   List all possible digits that occur in the units place of the square of a positive integer. Use that list to determine whether $\sqrt{5233}$ is an integer.

112. *Think About It*   Square the real number $2/\sqrt{5}$ and note that the radical is eliminated from the denominator. Is this equivalent to rationalizing the denominator? Why or why not?

A.3   Polynomials and Factoring

What you should learn

- Write polynomials in standard form.
- Add, subtract, and multiply polynomials.
- Use special products to multiply polynomials.
- Remove common factors from polynomials.
- Factor special polynomial forms.
- Factor trinomials as the product of two binomials.
- Factor polynomials by grouping.

Why you should learn it

Polynomials can be used to model and solve real-life problems. For instance, in Exercise 210 on page A34, a polynomial is used to model the stopping distance of an automobile.

Polynomials

The most common type of algebraic expression is the **polynomial.** Some examples are $2x + 5$, $3x^4 - 7x^2 + 2x + 4$, and $5x^2y^2 - xy + 3$. The first two are *polynomials in x* and the third is a *polynomial in x and y*. The terms of a polynomial in x have the form ax^k, where a is the **coefficient** and k is the **degree** of the term. For instance, the polynomial

$$2x^3 - 5x^2 + 1 = 2x^3 + (-5)x^2 + (0)x + 1$$

has coefficients 2, -5, 0, and 1.

Definition of a Polynomial in x

Let $a_0, a_1, a_2, \ldots, a_n$ be real numbers and let n be a nonnegative integer. A polynomial in x is an expression of the form

$$a_n x^n + a_{n-1} x^{n-1} + \cdots + a_1 x + a_0$$

where $a_n \neq 0$. The polynomial is of **degree** n, a_n is the **leading coefficient,** and a_0 is the **constant term.**

Polynomials with one, two, and three terms are called **monomials, binomials,** and **trinomials,** respectively. In **standard form,** a polynomial is written with descending powers of x.

Example 1   Writing Polynomials in Standard Form

Polynomial	Standard Form	Degree
a. $4x^2 - 5x^7 - 2 + 3x$	$-5x^7 + 4x^2 + 3x - 2$	7
b. $4 - 9x^2$	$-9x^2 + 4$	2
c. 8	$8 \;(8 = 8x^0)$	0

✓**CHECKPOINT**   Now try Exercise 11.

A polynomial that has all zero coefficients is called the zero polynomial, denoted by 0. No degree is assigned to this particular polynomial. For polynomials in more than one variable, the degree of a *term* is the sum of the exponents of the variables in the term. The degree of the *polynomial* is the highest degree of its terms. For instance, the degree of the polynomial $-2x^3y^6 + 4xy - x^7y^4$ is 11 because the sum of the exponents in the last term is the greatest. The leading coefficient of the polynomial is the coefficient of the highest-degree term. Expressions are not polynomials if a variable is underneath a radical or if a polynomial expression (with degree greater than 0) is in the denominator of a term. The following expressions are not polynomials.

$$x^3 - \sqrt{3x} = x^3 - (3x)^{1/2} \qquad \text{The exponent "1/2" is not an integer.}$$

$$x^2 + \frac{5}{x} = x^2 + 5x^{-1} \qquad \text{The exponent "}{-}1\text{" is not a nonnegative integer.}$$

Operations with Polynomials

You can add and subtract polynomials in much the same way you add and subtract real numbers. Simply add or subtract the *like terms* (terms having the same variables to the same powers) by adding their coefficients. For instance, $-3xy^2$ and $5xy^2$ are like terms and their sum is

$$-3xy^2 + 5xy^2 = (-3 + 5)xy^2$$
$$= 2xy^2.$$

STUDY TIP

When an expression inside parentheses is preceded by a negative sign, remember to distribute the negative sign to each term inside the parentheses, as shown.

$$-(x^2 - x + 3)$$
$$= -x^2 + x - 3$$

Example 2 Sums and Differences of Polynomials

a. $(5x^3 - 7x^2 - 3) + (x^3 + 2x^2 - x + 8)$
$$= (5x^3 + x^3) + (-7x^2 + 2x^2) - x + (-3 + 8) \qquad \text{Group like terms.}$$
$$= 6x^3 - 5x^2 - x + 5 \qquad \text{Combine like terms.}$$

b. $(7x^4 - x^2 - 4x + 2) - (3x^4 - 4x^2 + 3x)$
$$= 7x^4 - x^2 - 4x + 2 - 3x^4 + 4x^2 - 3x \qquad \text{Distributive Property}$$
$$= (7x^4 - 3x^4) + (-x^2 + 4x^2) + (-4x - 3x) + 2 \qquad \text{Group like terms.}$$
$$= 4x^4 + 3x^2 - 7x + 2 \qquad \text{Combine like terms.}$$

✓**CHECKPOINT** Now try Exercise 33.

To find the *product* of two polynomials, use the left and right Distributive Properties. For example, if you treat $5x + 7$ as a single quantity, you can multiply $3x - 2$ by $5x + 7$ as follows.

$$(3x - 2)(5x + 7) = 3x(5x + 7) - 2(5x + 7)$$
$$= (3x)(5x) + (3x)(7) - (2)(5x) - (2)(7)$$
$$= 15x^2 + 21x - 10x - 14$$

Product of	Product of	Product of	Product of
First terms	**Outer terms**	**Inner terms**	**Last terms**

$$= 15x^2 + 11x - 14$$

Note in this **FOIL Method** (which can only be used to multiply two binomials) that the outer (O) and inner (I) terms are like terms and can be combined.

Example 3 Finding a Product by the FOIL Method

Use the FOIL Method to find the product of $2x - 4$ and $x + 5$.

Solution

$$\overset{\text{F}\qquad\text{O}\qquad\text{I}\qquad\text{L}}{(2x - 4)(x + 5) = 2x^2 + 10x - 4x - 20}$$
$$= 2x^2 + 6x - 20$$

✓**CHECKPOINT** Now try Exercise 47.

Special Products

Some binomial products have special forms that occur frequently in algebra. You do not need to memorize these formulas because you can use the Distributive Property to multiply. However, becoming familiar with these formulas will enable you to manipulate the algebra more quickly.

Special Products

Let u and v be real numbers, variables, or algebraic expressions.

Special Product   *Example*

Sum and Difference of Same Terms

$(u + v)(u - v) = u^2 - v^2$ $(x + 4)(x - 4) = x^2 - 4^2$
$ = x^2 - 16$

Square of a Binomial

$(u + v)^2 = u^2 + 2uv + v^2$ $(x + 3)^2 = x^2 + 2(x)(3) + 3^2$
$ = x^2 + 6x + 9$

$(u - v)^2 = u^2 - 2uv + v^2$ $(3x - 2)^2 = (3x)^2 - 2(3x)(2) + 2^2$
$ = 9x^2 - 12x + 4$

Cube of a Binomial

$(u + v)^3 = u^3 + 3u^2v + 3uv^2 + v^3$ $(x + 2)^3 = x^3 + 3x^2(2) + 3x(2^2) + 2^3$
$ = x^3 + 6x^2 + 12x + 8$

$(u - v)^3 = u^3 - 3u^2v + 3uv^2 - v^3$ $(x - 1)^3 = x^3 - 3x^2(1) + 3x(1^2) - 1^3$
$ = x^3 - 3x^2 + 3x - 1$

Example 4   Special Products

Find each product.

a. $5x + 9$ and $5x - 9$ **b.** $x + y - 2$ and $x + y + 2$

Solution

a. The product of a sum and a difference of the *same* two terms has no middle term and takes the form $(u + v)(u - v) = u^2 - v^2$.

$$(5x + 9)(5x - 9) = (5x)^2 - 9^2 = 25x^2 - 81$$

b. By grouping $x + y$ in parentheses, you can write the product of the trinomials as a special product.

$$\begin{matrix} & \text{Difference} & \text{Sum} \\ & \downarrow & \downarrow \end{matrix}$$

$$(x + y - 2)(x + y + 2) = [(x + y) - 2][(x + y) + 2]$$

$$= (x + y)^2 - 2^2 \qquad \text{Sum and difference of same terms}$$

$$= x^2 + 2xy + y^2 - 4$$

CHECKPOINT   Now try Exercise 67.

Polynomials with Common Factors

The process of writing a polynomial as a product is called **factoring.** It is an important tool for solving equations and for simplifying rational expressions.

Unless noted otherwise, when you are asked to factor a polynomial, you can assume that you are looking for factors with integer coefficients. If a polynomial cannot be factored using integer coefficients, then it is **prime** or **irreducible over the integers.** For instance, the polynomial $x^2 - 3$ is irreducible over the integers. Over the *real numbers*, this polynomial can be factored as

$$x^2 - 3 = (x + \sqrt{3})(x - \sqrt{3}).$$

A polynomial is **completely factored** when each of its factors is prime. For instance

$$x^3 - x^2 + 4x - 4 = (x - 1)(x^2 + 4) \qquad \text{Completely factored}$$

is completely factored, but

$$x^3 - x^2 - 4x + 4 = (x - 1)(x^2 - 4) \qquad \text{Not completely factored}$$

is not completely factored. Its complete factorization is

$$x^3 - x^2 - 4x + 4 = (x - 1)(x + 2)(x - 2).$$

The simplest type of factoring involves a polynomial that can be written as the product of a monomial and another polynomial. The technique used here is the Distributive Property, $a(b + c) = ab + ac$, in the *reverse* direction.

$$ab + ac = a(b + c) \qquad \text{a is a common factor.}$$

Removing (factoring out) any common factors is the first step in completely factoring a polynomial.

Example 5   Removing Common Factors

Factor each expression.

a. $6x^3 - 4x$

b. $-4x^2 + 12x - 16$

c. $(x - 2)(2x) + (x - 2)(3)$

Solution

a. $6x^3 - 4x = 2x(3x^2) - 2x(2)$ $2x$ is a common factor.

$$= 2x(3x^2 - 2)$$

b. $-4x^2 + 12x - 16 = -4(x^2) + (-4)(-3x) + (-4)4$ -4 is a common factor.

$$= -4(x^2 - 3x + 4)$$

c. $(x - 2)(2x) + (x - 2)(3) = (x - 2)(2x + 3)$ $(x - 2)$ is a common factor.

✓**CHECKPOINT**   Now try Exercise 91.

Factoring Special Polynomial Forms

Some polynomials have special forms that arise from the special product forms on page A25. You should learn to recognize these forms so that you can factor such polynomials easily.

Factoring Special Polynomial Forms

Factored Form	*Example*

Difference of Two Squares

$u^2 - v^2 = (u + v)(u - v)$ $9x^2 - 4 = (3x)^2 - 2^2 = (3x + 2)(3x - 2)$

Perfect Square Trinomial

$u^2 + 2uv + v^2 = (u + v)^2$ $x^2 + 6x + 9 = x^2 + 2(x)(3) + 3^2 = (x + 3)^2$

$u^2 - 2uv + v^2 = (u - v)^2$ $x^2 - 6x + 9 = x^2 - 2(x)(3) + 3^2 = (x - 3)^2$

Sum or Difference of Two Cubes

$u^3 + v^3 = (u + v)(u^2 - uv + v^2)$ $x^3 + 8 = x^3 + 2^3 = (x + 2)(x^2 - 2x + 4)$

$u^3 - v^3 = (u - v)(u^2 + uv + v^2)$ $27x^3 - 1 = (3x)^3 - 1^3 = (3x - 1)(9x^2 + 3x + 1)$

One of the easiest special polynomial forms to factor is the difference of two squares. The factored form is always a set of *conjugate pairs*.

$$u^2 - v^2 = (u + v)(u - v) \qquad \text{Conjugate pairs}$$

Difference   Opposite signs

To recognize perfect square terms, look for coefficients that are squares of integers and variables raised to *even powers*.

STUDY TIP

In Example 6, note that the first step in factoring a polynomial is to check for any common factors. Once the common factors are removed, it is often possible to recognize patterns that were not immediately obvious.

Example 6   Removing a Common Factor First

$3 - 12x^2 = 3(1 - 4x^2)$ 3 is a common factor.

$\qquad\quad = 3[1^2 - (2x)^2]$

$\qquad\quad = 3(1 + 2x)(1 - 2x)$ Difference of two squares

✓CHECKPOINT   Now try Exercise 105.

Example 7   Factoring the Difference of Two Squares

a. $(x + 2)^2 - y^2 = [(x + 2) + y][(x + 2) - y]$

$\qquad\qquad\qquad = (x + 2 + y)(x + 2 - y)$

b. $16x^4 - 81 = (4x^2)^2 - 9^2$

$\qquad\qquad = (4x^2 + 9)(4x^2 - 9)$ Difference of two squares

$\qquad\qquad = (4x^2 + 9)[(2x)^2 - 3^2]$

$\qquad\qquad = (4x^2 + 9)(2x + 3)(2x - 3)$ Difference of two squares

✓CHECKPOINT   Now try Exercise 109.

A **perfect square trinomial** is the square of a binomial, and it has the following form.

$$u^2 + 2uv + v^2 = (u + v)^2 \qquad \text{or} \qquad u^2 - 2uv + v^2 = (u - v)^2$$

Like signs   Like signs

Note that the first and last terms are squares and the middle term is twice the product of u and v.

Example 8   Factoring Perfect Square Trinomials

Factor each trinomial.

a. $x^2 - 10x + 25$

b. $16x^2 + 24x + 9$

Solution

a. $x^2 - 10x + 25 = x^2 - 2(x)(5) + 5^2 = (x - 5)^2$

b. $16x^2 + 24x + 9 = (4x)^2 + 2(4x)(3) + 3^2 = (4x + 3)^2$

✓**CHECKPOINT**   Now try Exercise 115.

The next two formulas show the sums and differences of cubes. Pay special attention to the signs of the terms.

Like signs   Like signs

$$u^3 + v^3 = (u + v)(u^2 - uv + v^2) \qquad u^3 - v^3 = (u - v)(u^2 + uv + v^2)$$

Unlike signs   Unlike signs

Example 9   Factoring the Difference of Cubes

Factor $x^3 - 27$.

Solution

$$x^3 - 27 = x^3 - 3^3 \qquad \text{Rewrite 27 as } 3^3.$$

$$= (x - 3)(x^2 + 3x + 9) \qquad \text{Factor.}$$

✓**CHECKPOINT**   Now try Exercise 123.

Example 10   Factoring the Sum of Cubes

a. $y^3 + 8 = y^3 + 2^3$ Rewrite 8 as 2^3.

$$= (y + 2)(y^2 - 2y + 4) \qquad \text{Factor.}$$

b. $3(x^3 + 64) = 3(x^3 + 4^3)$ Rewrite 64 as 4^3.

$$= 3(x + 4)(x^2 - 4x + 16) \qquad \text{Factor.}$$

✓**CHECKPOINT**   Now try Exercise 125.

Trinomials with Binomial Factors

To factor a trinomial of the form $ax^2 + bx + c$, use the following pattern.

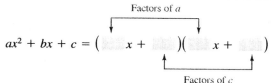

Factors of a

$$ax^2 + bx + c = (\quad x + \quad)(\quad x + \quad)$$

Factors of c

The goal is to find a combination of factors of a and c such that the outer and inner products add up to the middle term bx. For instance, in the trinomial $6x^2 + 17x + 5$, you can write all possible factorizations and determine which one has outer and inner products that add up to $17x$.

$$(6x + 5)(x + 1), (6x + 1)(x + 5), (2x + 1)(3x + 5), (2x + 5)(3x + 1)$$

You can see that $(2x + 5)(3x + 1)$ is the correct factorization because the outer (O) and inner (I) products add up to $17x$.

$$
\begin{array}{ccccc}
F & O & I & L & O+I \\
\downarrow & \downarrow & \downarrow & \downarrow & \downarrow
\end{array}
$$

$$(2x + 5)(3x + 1) = 6x^2 + 2x + 15x + 5 = 6x^2 + 17x + 5.$$

Example 11   Factoring a Trinomial: Leading Coefficient Is 1

Factor $x^2 - 7x + 12$.

Solution

The possible factorizations are

$$(x - 2)(x - 6), \quad (x - 1)(x - 12), \quad \text{and} \quad (x - 3)(x - 4).$$

Testing the middle term, you will find the correct factorization to be

$$x^2 - 7x + 12 = (x - 3)(x - 4).$$

✓**CHECKPOINT**   Now try Exercise 131.

Example 12   Factoring a Trinomial: Leading Coefficient Is Not 1

Factor $2x^2 + x - 15$.

Solution

The eight possible factorizations are as follows.

$$
\begin{array}{ll}
(2x - 1)(x + 15) & (2x + 1)(x - 15) \\
(2x - 3)(x + 5) & (2x + 3)(x - 5) \\
(2x - 5)(x + 3) & (2x + 5)(x - 3) \\
(2x - 15)(x + 1) & (2x + 15)(x - 1)
\end{array}
$$

Testing the middle term, you will find the correct factorization to be

$$2x^2 + x - 15 = (2x - 5)(x + 3). \qquad O + I = 6x - 5x = x$$

✓**CHECKPOINT**   Now try Exercise 139.

STUDY TIP

Factoring a trinomial can involve trial and error. However, once you have produced the factored form, it is an easy matter to check your answer. For instance, you can verify the factorization in Example 11 by multiplying out the expression $(x - 3)(x - 4)$ to see that you obtain the original trinomial, $x^2 - 7x + 12$.

Factoring by Grouping

Sometimes polynomials with more than three terms can be factored by a method called **factoring by grouping.** It is not always obvious which terms to group, and sometimes several different groupings will work.

Example 13   Factoring by Grouping

Use factoring by grouping to factor $x^3 - 2x^2 - 3x + 6$.

Solution

$$x^3 - 2x^2 - 3x + 6 = (x^3 - 2x^2) - (3x - 6) \qquad \text{Group terms.}$$
$$= x^2(x - 2) - 3(x - 2) \qquad \text{Factor each group.}$$
$$= (x - 2)(x^2 - 3) \qquad \text{Distributive Property}$$

CHECKPOINT   Now try Exercise 147.

Factoring a trinomial can involve quite a bit of trial and error. Some of this trial and error can be lessened by using factoring by grouping. The key to this method of factoring is knowing how to rewrite the middle term. In general, to factor a trinomial $ax^2 + bx + c$ by grouping, choose factors of the product ac that add up to b and use these factors to rewrite the middle term. This technique is illustrated in Example 14.

STUDY TIP

Another way to factor the polynomial in Example 13 is to group the terms as follows.

$$x^3 - 2x^2 - 3x + 6$$
$$= (x^3 - 3x) - (2x^2 - 6)$$
$$= x(x^2 - 3) - 2(x^2 - 3)$$
$$= (x^2 - 3)(x - 2)$$

As you can see, you obtain the same result as in Example 13.

Example 14   Factoring a Trinomial by Grouping

Use factoring by grouping to factor $2x^2 + 5x - 3$.

Solution

In the trinomial $2x^2 + 5x - 3$, $a = 2$ and $c = -3$, which implies that the product ac is -6. Now, -6 factors as $(6)(-1)$ and $6 - 1 = 5 = b$. So, you can rewrite the middle term as $5x = 6x - x$. This produces the following.

$$2x^2 + 5x - 3 = 2x^2 + 6x - x - 3 \qquad \text{Rewrite middle term.}$$
$$= (2x^2 + 6x) - (x + 3) \qquad \text{Group terms.}$$
$$= 2x(x + 3) - (x + 3) \qquad \text{Factor groups.}$$
$$= (x + 3)(2x - 1) \qquad \text{Distributive Property}$$

So, the trinomial factors as $2x^2 + 5x - 3 = (x + 3)(2x - 1)$.

CHECKPOINT   Now try Exercise 153.

Guidelines for Factoring Polynomials

1. Factor out any common factors using the Distributive Property.

2. Factor according to one of the special polynomial forms.

3. Factor as $ax^2 + bx + c = (mx + r)(nx + s)$.

4. Factor by grouping.

A.3 | Exercises

VOCABULARY CHECK: Fill in the blanks.

1. For the polynomial $a_n x^n + a_{n-1} x^{n-1} + \cdots + a_1 x + a_0$, the degree is _____, the leading coefficient is _____, and the constant term is _____.

2. A polynomial in x in standard form is written with _____ powers of x.

3. A polynomial with one term is called a _____, while a polynomial with two terms is called a _____, and a polynomial with three terms is called a _____.

4. To add or subtract polynomials, add or subtract the _____ _____ by adding their coefficients.

5. The letters in "FOIL" stand for the following.

   F _____   O _____   I _____   L _____

6. The process of writing a polynomial as a product is called _____.

7. A polynomial is _____ _____ when each of its factors is prime.

In Exercises 1–6, match the polynomial with its description. [The polynomials are labeled (a), (b), (c), (d), (e), and (f).]

(a) $3x^2$
(b) $1 - 2x^3$
(c) $x^3 + 3x^2 + 3x + 1$
(d) 12
(e) $-3x^5 + 2x^3 + x$
(f) $\frac{2}{3}x^4 + x^2 + 10$

1. A polynomial of degree 0
2. A trinomial of degree 5
3. A binomial with leading coefficient -2
4. A monomial of positive degree
5. A trinomial with leading coefficient $\frac{2}{3}$
6. A third-degree polynomial with leading coefficient 1

In Exercises 7–10, write a polynomial that fits the description. (There are many correct answers.)

7. A third-degree polynomial with leading coefficient -2
8. A fifth-degree polynomial with leading coefficient 6
9. A fourth-degree binomial with a negative leading coefficient
10. A third-degree binomial with an even leading coefficient

In Exercises 11–22, (a) write the polynomial in standard form, (b) identify the degree and leading coefficient of the polynomial, and (c) state whether the polynomial is a monomial, a binomial, or a trinomial.

11. $14x - \frac{1}{2}x^5$
12. $2x^2 - x + 1$
13. $-3x^4 + 2x^2 - 5$
14. $7x$
15. $x^5 - 1$
16. $-y + 25y^2 + 1$
17. 3
18. $t^2 + 9$
19. $1 + 6x^4 - 4x^5$
20. $3 + 2x$
21. $4x^3y$
22. $-x^5y + 2x^2y^2 + xy^4$

In Exercises 23–28, determine whether the expression is a polynomial. If so, write the polynomial in standard form.

23. $2x - 3x^3 + 8$
24. $2x^3 + x - 3x^{-1}$
25. $\dfrac{3x + 4}{x}$
26. $\dfrac{x^2 + 2x - 3}{2}$
27. $y^2 - y^4 + y^3$
28. $\sqrt{y^2 - y^4}$

In Exercises 29–46, perform the operation and write the result in standard form.

29. $(6x + 5) - (8x + 15)$
30. $(2x^2 + 1) - (x^2 - 2x + 1)$
31. $-(x^3 - 2) + (4x^3 - 2x)$
32. $-(5x^2 - 1) - (-3x^2 + 5)$
33. $(15x^2 - 6) - (-8.3x^3 - 14.7x^2 - 17)$
34. $(15.2x^4 - 18x - 19.1) - (13.9x^4 - 9.6x + 15)$
35. $5z - [3z - (10z + 8)]$
36. $(y^3 + 1) - [(y^2 + 1) + (3y - 7)]$
37. $3x(x^2 - 2x + 1)$
38. $y^2(4y^2 + 2y - 3)$
39. $-5z(3z - 1)$
40. $(-3x)(5x + 2)$
41. $(1 - x^3)(4x)$
42. $-4x(3 - x^3)$
43. $(2.5x^2 + 3)(3x)$
44. $(2 - 3.5y)(2y^3)$
45. $-4x(\frac{1}{8}x + 3)$
46. $2y(4 - \frac{7}{8}y)$

In Exercises 47–84, multiply or find the special product.

47. $(x + 3)(x + 4)$

48. $(x - 5)(x + 10)$

49. $(3x - 5)(2x + 1)$

50. $(7x - 2)(4x - 3)$

51. $(x^2 - x + 1)(x^2 + x + 1)$

52. $(x^2 + 3x - 2)(x^2 - 3x - 2)$

53. $(x + 10)(x - 10)$ **54.** $(2x + 3)(2x - 3)$

55. $(x + 2y)(x - 2y)$ **56.** $(2x + 3y)(2x - 3y)$

57. $(2x + 3)^2$ **58.** $(4x + 5)^2$

59. $(2x - 5y)^2$ **60.** $(5 - 8x)^2$

61. $(x + 1)^3$ **62.** $(x - 2)^3$

63. $(2x - y)^3$ **64.** $(3x + 2y)^3$

65. $(4x^3 - 3)^2$ **66.** $(8x + 3)^2$

67. $[(m - 3) + n][(m - 3) - n]$

68. $[(x + y) + 1][(x + y) - 1]$

69. $[(x - 3) + y]^2$ **70.** $[(x + 1) - y]^2$

71. $(2r^2 - 5)(2r^2 + 5)$ **72.** $(3a^3 - 4b^2)(3a^3 + 4b^2)$

73. $\left(\frac{1}{2}x - 3\right)^2$ **74.** $\left(\frac{2}{3}t + 5\right)^2$

75. $\left(\frac{1}{3}x - 2\right)\left(\frac{1}{3}x + 2\right)$ **76.** $\left(2x + \frac{1}{5}\right)\left(2x - \frac{1}{5}\right)$

77. $(1.2x + 3)^2$ **78.** $(1.5y - 3)^2$

79. $(1.5x - 4)(1.5x + 4)$ **80.** $(2.5y + 3)(2.5y - 3)$

81. $5x(x + 1) - 3x(x + 1)$

82. $(2x - 1)(x + 3) + 3(x + 3)$

83. $(u + 2)(u - 2)(u^2 + 4)$

84. $(x + y)(x - y)(x^2 + y^2)$

In Exercises 85–88, find the product. (The expressions are not polynomials, but the formulas can still be used.)

85. $\left(\sqrt{x} + \sqrt{y}\right)\left(\sqrt{x} - \sqrt{y}\right)$ **86.** $\left(5 + \sqrt{x}\right)\left(5 - \sqrt{x}\right)$

87. $\left(x - \sqrt{5}\right)^2$ **88.** $\left(x + \sqrt{3}\right)^2$

In Exercises 89–96, factor out the common factor.

89. $3x + 6$ **90.** $5y - 30$

91. $2x^3 - 6x$ **92.** $4x^3 - 6x^2 + 12x$

93. $x(x - 1) + 6(x - 1)$ **94.** $3x(x + 2) - 4(x + 2)$

95. $(x + 3)^2 - 4(x + 3)$ **96.** $(3x - 1)^2 + (3x - 1)$

In Exercises 97–102, find the greatest common factor such that the remaining factors have only integer coefficients.

97. $\frac{1}{2}x + 4$ **98.** $\frac{1}{3}y + 5$

99. $\frac{1}{2}x^3 + 2x^2 - 5x$ **100.** $\frac{1}{3}y^4 - 5y^2 + 2y$

101. $\frac{2}{3}x(x - 3) - 4(x - 3)$ **102.** $\frac{4}{5}y(y + 1) - 2(y + 1)$

In Exercises 103–112, completely factor the difference of two squares.

103. $x^2 - 81$

104. $x^2 - 49$

105. $32y^2 - 18$

106. $4 - 36y^2$

107. $16x^2 - \frac{1}{9}$

108. $\frac{4}{25}y^2 - 64$

109. $(x - 1)^2 - 4$ **110.** $25 - (z + 5)^2$

111. $9u^2 - 4v^2$ **112.** $25x^2 - 16y^2$

In Exercises 113–122, factor the perfect square trinomial.

113. $x^2 - 4x + 4$ **114.** $x^2 + 10x + 25$

115. $4t^2 + 4t + 1$ **116.** $9x^2 - 12x + 4$

117. $25y^2 - 10y + 1$ **118.** $36y^2 - 108y + 81$

119. $9u^2 + 24uv + 16v^2$ **120.** $4x^2 - 4xy + y^2$

121. $x^2 - \frac{4}{3}x + \frac{4}{9}$ **122.** $z^2 + z + \frac{1}{4}$

In Exercises 123–130, factor the sum or difference of cubes.

123. $x^3 - 8$ **124.** $x^3 - 27$

125. $y^3 + 64$ **126.** $z^3 + 125$

127. $8t^3 - 1$ **128.** $27x^3 + 8$

129. $u^3 + 27v^3$ **130.** $64x^3 - y^3$

In Exercises 131–144, factor the trinomial.

131. $x^2 + x - 2$ **132.** $x^2 + 5x + 6$

133. $s^2 - 5s + 6$ **134.** $t^2 - t - 6$

135. $20 - y - y^2$ **136.** $24 + 5z - z^2$

137. $x^2 - 30x + 200$ **138.** $x^2 - 13x + 42$

139. $3x^2 - 5x + 2$ **140.** $2x^2 - x - 1$

141. $5x^2 + 26x + 5$ **142.** $12x^2 + 7x + 1$

143. $-9z^2 + 3z + 2$ **144.** $-5u^2 - 13u + 6$

In Exercises 145–152, factor by grouping.

145. $x^3 - x^2 + 2x - 2$ **146.** $x^3 + 5x^2 - 5x - 25$

147. $2x^3 - x^2 - 6x + 3$ **148.** $5x^3 - 10x^2 + 3x - 6$

149. $6 + 2x - 3x^3 - x^4$ **150.** $x^5 + 2x^3 + x^2 + 2$

151. $6x^3 - 2x + 3x^2 - 1$ **152.** $8x^5 - 6x^2 + 12x^3 - 9$

In Exercises 153–158, factor the trinomial by grouping.

153. $3x^2 + 10x + 8$ **154.** $2x^2 + 9x + 9$

155. $6x^2 + x - 2$ **156.** $6x^2 - x - 15$

157. $15x^2 - 11x + 2$ **158.** $12x^2 - 13x + 1$

In Exercises 159–192, completely factor the expression.

159. $6x^2 - 54$

160. $12x^2 - 48$

161. $x^3 - 4x^2$

162. $x^3 - 9x$

163. $x^2 - 2x + 1$

164. $16 + 6x - x^2$

165. $1 - 4x + 4x^2$

166. $-9x^2 + 6x - 1$

167. $2x^2 + 4x - 2x^3$

168. $2y^3 - 7y^2 - 15y$

169. $9x^2 + 10x + 1$

170. $13x + 6 + 5x^2$

171. $\frac{1}{81}x^2 + \frac{2}{9}x - 8$

172. $\frac{1}{8}x^2 - \frac{1}{96}x - \frac{1}{16}$

173. $3x^3 + x^2 + 15x + 5$

174. $5 - x + 5x^2 - x^3$

175. $x^4 - 4x^3 + x^2 - 4x$

176. $3u - 2u^2 + 6 - u^3$

177. $\frac{1}{4}x^3 + 3x^2 + \frac{3}{4}x + 9$

178. $\frac{1}{5}x^3 + x^2 - x - 5$

179. $(t - 1)^2 - 49$

180. $(x^2 + 1)^2 - 4x^2$

181. $(x^2 + 8)^2 - 36x^2$

182. $2t^3 - 16$

183. $5x^3 + 40$

184. $4x(2x - 1) + (2x - 1)^2$

185. $5(3 - 4x)^2 - 8(3 - 4x)(5x - 1)$

186. $2(x + 1)(x - 3)^2 - 3(x + 1)^2(x - 3)$

187. $7(3x + 2)^2(1 - x)^2 + (3x + 2)(1 - x)^3$

188. $7x(2)(x^2 + 1)(2x) - (x^2 + 1)^2(7)$

189. $3(x - 2)^2(x + 1)^4 + (x - 2)^3(4)(x + 1)^3$

190. $2x(x - 5)^4 - x^2(4)(x - 5)^3$

191. $5(x^6 + 1)^4(6x^5)(3x + 2)^3 + 3(3x + 2)^2(3)(x^6 + 1)^5$

192. $\dfrac{x^2}{2}(x^2 + 1)^4 - (x^2 + 1)^5$

In Exercises 193–196, find all values of b for which the trinomial can be factored.

193. $x^2 + bx - 15$

194. $x^2 + bx + 50$

195. $x^2 + bx - 12$

196. $x^2 + bx + 24$

In Exercises 197–200, find two integer values of c such that the trinomial can be factored. (There are many correct answers.)

197. $2x^2 + 5x + c$

198. $3x^2 - 10x + c$

199. $3x^2 - x + c$

200. $2x^2 + 9x + c$

201. *Cost, Revenue, and Profit* An electronics manufacturer can produce and sell x radios per week. The total cost C (in dollars) of producing x radios is

$$C = 73x + 25{,}000$$

and the total revenue R (in dollars) is

$$R = 95x.$$

(a) Find the profit P in terms of x.

(b) Find the profit obtained by selling 5000 radios per week.

202. *Cost, Revenue, and Profit* An artisan can produce and sell x hats per month. The total cost C (in dollars) of producing x hats is

$$C = 460 + 12x$$

and the total revenue R (in dollars) is

$$R = 36x.$$

(a) Find the profit P in terms of x.

(b) Find the profit obtained by selling 42 hats per month.

203. *Compound Interest* After 2 years, an investment of $500 compounded annually at an interest rate r will yield an amount of $500(1 + r)^2$.

(a) Write this polynomial in standard form.

(b) Use a calculator to evaluate the polynomial for the values of r shown in the table.

r	$2\frac{1}{2}\%$	3%	4%	$4\frac{1}{2}\%$	5%
$500(1 + r)^2$					

(c) What conclusion can you make from the table?

204. *Compound Interest* After 3 years, an investment of $1200 compounded annually at an interest rate r will yield an amount of $1200(1 + r)^3$.

(a) Write this polynomial in standard form.

(b) Use a calculator to evaluate the polynomial for the values of r shown in the table.

r	2%	3%	$3\frac{1}{2}\%$	4%	$4\frac{1}{2}\%$
$1200(1 + r)^3$					

(c) What conclusion can you make from the table?

205. *Volume of a Box* A take-out fast-food restaurant is constructing an open box by cutting squares from the corners of a piece of cardboard that is 18 centimeters by 26 centimeters (see figure). The edge of each cut-out square is x centimeters.

(a) Find the volume of the box in terms of x.

(b) Find the volume when $x = 1$, $x = 2$, and $x = 3$.

206. *Volume of a Box* An overnight shipping company is designing a closed box by cutting along the solid lines and folding along the broken lines on the rectangular piece of corrugated cardboard shown in the figure. The length and width of the rectangle are 45 centimeters and 15 centimeters, respectively.

(a) Find the volume of the shipping box in terms of x.

(b) Find the volume when $x = 3$, $x = 5$, and $x = 7$.

Geometry **In Exercises 207 and 208, find a polynomial that represents the total number of square feet for the floor plan shown in the figure.**

207.

208.

209. *Geometry* Find the area of the shaded region in each figure. Write your result as a polynomial in standard form.

(a)

(b)

210. *Stopping Distance* The stopping distance of an automobile is the distance traveled during the driver's reaction time plus the distance traveled after the brakes are applied. In an experiment, these distances were measured (in feet) when the automobile was traveling at a speed of x miles per hour on dry, level pavement, as shown in the bar graph. The distance traveled during the reaction time R was

$$R = 1.1x$$

and the braking distance B was

$$B = 0.0475x^2 - 0.001x + 0.23.$$

(a) Determine the polynomial that represents the total stopping distance T.

(b) Use the result of part (a) to estimate the total stopping distance when $x = 30$, $x = 40$, and $x = 55$ miles per hour.

(c) Use the bar graph to make a statement about the total stopping distance required for increasing speeds.

Geometric Modeling In Exercises 211–214, draw a "geometric factoring model" to represent the factorization. For instance, a factoring model for

$$2x^2 + 3x + 1 = (2x + 1)(x + 1)$$

is shown in the figure.

211. $3x^2 + 7x + 2 = (3x + 1)(x + 2)$
212. $x^2 + 4x + 3 = (x + 3)(x + 1)$
213. $2x^2 + 7x + 3 = (2x + 1)(x + 3)$
214. $x^2 + 3x + 2 = (x + 2)(x + 1)$

Geometry In Exercises 215–218, write an expression in factored form for the area of the shaded portion of the figure.

215.

216.

217.

218.

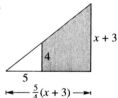

219. *Geometry* The volume V of concrete used to make the cylindrical concrete storage tank shown in the figure is $V = \pi R^2 h - \pi r^2 h$ where R is the outside radius, r is the inside radius, and h is the height of the storage tank.

(a) Factor the expression for the volume.
(b) From the result of part (a), show that the volume of concrete is

$$2\pi(\text{average radius})(\text{thickness of the tank})h.$$

220. *Chemistry* The rate of change of an autocatalytic chemical reaction is $kQx - kx^2$, where Q is the amount of the original substance, x is the amount of substance formed, and k is a constant of proportionality. Factor the expression.

Synthesis

True or False? In Exercises 221–224, determine whether the statement is true or false. Justify your answer.

221. The product of two binomials is always a second-degree polynomial.

222. The sum of two binomials is always a binomial.

223. The difference of two perfect squares can be factored as the product of conjugate pairs.

224. The sum of two perfect squares can be factored as the binomial sum squared.

225. Find the degree of the product of two polynomials of degrees m and n.

226. Find the degree of the sum of two polynomials of degrees m and n if $m < n$.

227. *Think About It* When the polynomial

$$-x^3 + 3x^2 + 2x - 1$$

is subtracted from an unknown polynomial, the difference is

$$5x^2 + 8.$$

If it is possible, find the unknown polynomial.

228. *Logical Reasoning* Verify that $(x + y)^2$ is not equal to $x^2 + y^2$ by letting $x = 3$ and $y = 4$ and evaluating both expressions. Are there any values of x and y for which $(x + y)^2 = x^2 + y^2$? Explain.

229. Factor $x^{2n} - y^{2n}$ completely.

230. Factor $x^{3n} + y^{3n}$ completely.

231. Factor $x^{3n} - y^{2n}$ completely.

232. *Writing* Explain what is meant when it is said that a polynomial is in factored form.

233. Give an example of a polynomial that is prime with respect to the integers.

A.4   Rational Expressions

What you should learn

- Find domains of algebraic expressions.
- Simplify rational expressions.
- Add, subtract, multiply, and divide rational expressions.
- Simplify complex fractions and rewrite difference quotients.

Why you should learn it

Rational expressions can be used to solve real-life problems. For instance, in Exercise 84 on page A45, a rational expression is used to model the projected number of households banking and paying bills online from 2002 through 2007.

Domain of an Algebraic Expression

The set of real numbers for which an algebraic expression is defined is the **domain** of the expression. Two algebraic expressions are **equivalent** if they have the same domain and yield the same values for all numbers in their domain. For instance, $(x + 1) + (x + 2)$ and $2x + 3$ are equivalent because

$$(x + 1) + (x + 2) = x + 1 + x + 2$$
$$= x + x + 1 + 2$$
$$= 2x + 3.$$

Example 1   Finding the Domain of an Algebraic Expression

a. The domain of the polynomial

$$2x^3 + 3x + 4$$

is the set of all real numbers. In fact, the domain of any polynomial is the set of all real numbers, unless the domain is specifically restricted.

b. The domain of the radical expression

$$\sqrt{x - 2}$$

is the set of real numbers greater than or equal to 2, because the square root of a negative number is not a real number.

c. The domain of the expression

$$\frac{x + 2}{x - 3}$$

is the set of all real numbers except $x = 3$, which would result in division by zero, which is undefined.

✓**CHECKPOINT**   Now try Exercise 1.

The quotient of two algebraic expressions is a *fractional expression*. Moreover, the quotient of two *polynomials* such as

$$\frac{1}{x}, \qquad \frac{2x - 1}{x + 1}, \qquad \text{or} \qquad \frac{x^2 - 1}{x^2 + 1}$$

is a **rational expression.** Recall that a fraction is in simplest form if its numerator and denominator have no factors in common aside from ±1. To write a fraction in simplest form, divide out common factors.

$$\frac{a \cdot \cancel{c}}{b \cdot \cancel{c}} = \frac{a}{b}, \quad c \neq 0$$

The key to success in simplifying rational expressions lies in your ability to *factor* polynomials.

Simplifying Rational Expressions

When simplifying rational expressions, be sure to factor each polynomial completely before concluding that the numerator and denominator have no factors in common.

In this text, when a rational expression is written, the domain is usually not listed with the expression. It is *implied* that the real numbers that make the denominator zero are excluded from the expression. Also, when performing operations with rational expressions, this text follows the convention of listing *by the simplified expression* all values of *x* that must be specifically excluded from the domain in order to make the domains of the simplified and original expressions agree.

Example 2   Simplifying a Rational Expression

Write $\dfrac{x^2 + 4x - 12}{3x - 6}$ in simplest form.

Solution

$$\frac{x^2 + 4x - 12}{3x - 6} = \frac{(x + 6)(x - 2)}{3(x - 2)} \qquad \text{Factor completely.}$$

$$= \frac{x + 6}{3}, \qquad x \neq 2 \qquad \text{Divide out common factors.}$$

Note that the original expression is undefined when $x = 2$ (because division by zero is undefined). To make sure that the simplified expression is *equivalent* to the original expression, you must restrict the domain of the simplified expression by excluding the value $x = 2$.

CHECKPOINT   Now try Exercise 19.

Sometimes it may be necessary to change the sign of a factor to simplify a rational expression, as shown in Example 3.

Example 3   Simplifying Rational Expressions

Write $\dfrac{12 + x - x^2}{2x^2 - 9x + 4}$ in simplest form.

Solution

$$\frac{12 + x - x^2}{2x^2 - 9x + 4} = \frac{(4 - x)(3 + x)}{(2x - 1)(x - 4)} \qquad \text{Factor completely.}$$

$$= \frac{-(x - 4)(3 + x)}{(2x - 1)(x - 4)} \qquad (4 - x) = -(x - 4)$$

$$= -\frac{3 + x}{2x - 1}, \qquad x \neq 4 \qquad \text{Divide out common factors.}$$

CHECKPOINT   Now try Exercise 25.

STUDY TIP

In Example 2, do not make the mistake of trying to simplify further by dividing out terms.

$$\frac{x + 6}{3} = \frac{x + 6}{3} = x + 2$$

Remember that to simplify fractions, divide out common *factors*, not terms.

Operations with Rational Expressions

To multiply or divide rational expressions, use the properties of fractions discussed in Appendix A.1. Recall that to divide fractions, you invert the divisor and multiply.

Example 4   Multiplying Rational Expressions

$$\frac{2x^2 + x - 6}{x^2 + 4x - 5} \cdot \frac{x^3 - 3x^2 + 2x}{4x^2 - 6x} = \frac{(2x - 3)(x + 2)}{(x + 5)(x - 1)} \cdot \frac{x(x - 2)(x - 1)}{2x(2x - 3)}$$

$$= \frac{(x + 2)(x - 2)}{2(x + 5)}, \qquad x \neq 0, x \neq 1, x \neq \tfrac{3}{2}$$

✓**CHECKPOINT**   Now try Exercise 39.

In Example 4 the restrictions $x \neq 0$, $x \neq 1$, and $x \neq \tfrac{3}{2}$ are listed with the simplified expression in order to make the two domains agree. Note that the value $x = -5$ is excluded from both domains, so it is not necessary to list this value.

Example 5   Dividing Rational Expressions

$$\frac{x^3 - 8}{x^2 - 4} \div \frac{x^2 + 2x + 4}{x^3 + 8} = \frac{x^3 - 8}{x^2 - 4} \cdot \frac{x^3 + 8}{x^2 + 2x + 4} \qquad \text{Invert and multiply.}$$

$$= \frac{(x - 2)(x^2 + 2x + 4)}{(x + 2)(x - 2)} \cdot \frac{(x + 2)(x^2 - 2x + 4)}{(x^2 + 2x + 4)}$$

$$= x^2 - 2x + 4, \qquad x \neq \pm 2 \qquad \begin{array}{l}\text{Divide out}\\\text{common factors.}\end{array}$$

✓**CHECKPOINT**   Now try Exercise 41.

To add or subtract rational expressions, you can use the LCD (least common denominator) method or the *basic definition*

$$\frac{a}{b} \pm \frac{c}{d} = \frac{ad \pm bc}{bd}, \qquad b \neq 0, d \neq 0. \qquad \text{Basic definition}$$

This definition provides an efficient way of adding or subtracting *two* fractions that have no common factors in their denominators.

Example 6   Subtracting Rational Expressions

$$\frac{x}{x - 3} - \frac{2}{3x + 4} = \frac{x(3x + 4) - 2(x - 3)}{(x - 3)(3x + 4)} \qquad \text{Basic definition}$$

$$= \frac{3x^2 + 4x - 2x + 6}{(x - 3)(3x + 4)} \qquad \text{Distributive Property}$$

$$= \frac{3x^2 + 2x + 6}{(x - 3)(3x + 4)} \qquad \text{Combine like terms.}$$

✓**CHECKPOINT**   Now try Exercise 49.

STUDY TIP

When subtracting rational expressions, remember to distribute the negative sign to all the terms in the quantity that is being subtracted.

For three or more fractions, or for fractions with a repeated factor in the denominators, the LCD method works well. Recall that the least common denominator of several fractions consists of the product of all prime factors in the denominators, with each factor given the highest power of its occurrence in any denominator. Here is a numerical example.

$$\frac{1}{6} + \frac{3}{4} - \frac{2}{3} = \frac{1 \cdot 2}{6 \cdot 2} + \frac{3 \cdot 3}{4 \cdot 3} - \frac{2 \cdot 4}{3 \cdot 4}$$ The LCD is 12.

$$= \frac{2}{12} + \frac{9}{12} - \frac{8}{12}$$

$$= \frac{3}{12}$$

$$= \frac{1}{4}$$

Sometimes the numerator of the answer has a factor in common with the denominator. In such cases the answer should be simplified. For instance, in the example above, $\frac{3}{12}$ was simplified to $\frac{1}{4}$.

Example 7   **Combining Rational Expressions: The LCD Method**

Perform the operations and simplify.

$$\frac{3}{x - 1} - \frac{2}{x} + \frac{x + 3}{x^2 - 1}$$

Solution

Using the factored denominators $(x - 1)$, x, and $(x + 1)(x - 1)$, you can see that the LCD is $x(x + 1)(x - 1)$.

$$\frac{3}{x - 1} - \frac{2}{x} + \frac{x + 3}{(x + 1)(x - 1)}$$

$$= \frac{3(x)(x + 1)}{x(x + 1)(x - 1)} - \frac{2(x + 1)(x - 1)}{x(x + 1)(x - 1)} + \frac{(x + 3)(x)}{x(x + 1)(x - 1)}$$

$$= \frac{3(x)(x + 1) - 2(x + 1)(x - 1) + (x + 3)(x)}{x(x + 1)(x - 1)}$$

$$= \frac{3x^2 + 3x - 2x^2 + 2 + x^2 + 3x}{x(x + 1)(x - 1)}$$ Distributive Property

$$= \frac{3x^2 - 2x^2 + x^2 + 3x + 3x + 2}{x(x + 1)(x - 1)}$$ Group like terms.

$$= \frac{2x^2 + 6x + 2}{x(x + 1)(x - 1)}$$ Combine like terms.

$$= \frac{2(x^2 + 3x + 1)}{x(x + 1)(x - 1)}$$ Factor.

✓**CHECKPOINT**   Now try Exercise 51.

Complex Fractions and the Difference Quotient

Fractional expressions with separate fractions in the numerator, denominator, or both are called **complex fractions.** Here are two examples.

$$\frac{\left(\dfrac{1}{x}\right)}{x^2 + 1} \quad \text{and} \quad \frac{\left(\dfrac{1}{x}\right)}{\left(\dfrac{1}{x^2 + 1}\right)}$$

A complex fraction can be simplified by combining the fractions in its numerator into a single fraction and then combining the fractions in its denominator into a single fraction. Then invert the denominator and multiply.

Example 8   Simplifying a Complex Fraction

$$\frac{\left(\dfrac{2}{x} - 3\right)}{\left(1 - \dfrac{1}{x - 1}\right)} = \frac{\left[\dfrac{2 - 3(x)}{x}\right]}{\left[\dfrac{1(x - 1) - 1}{x - 1}\right]} \qquad \text{Combine fractions.}$$

$$= \frac{\left(\dfrac{2 - 3x}{x}\right)}{\left(\dfrac{x - 2}{x - 1}\right)} \qquad \text{Simplify.}$$

$$= \frac{2 - 3x}{x} \cdot \frac{x - 1}{x - 2} \qquad \text{Invert and multiply.}$$

$$= \frac{(2 - 3x)(x - 1)}{x(x - 2)}, \qquad x \neq 1$$

✓**CHECKPOINT**   Now try Exercise 57.

Another way to simplify a complex fraction is to multiply its numerator and denominator by the LCD of all fractions in its numerator and denominator. This method is applied to the fraction in Example 8 as follows.

$$\frac{\left(\dfrac{2}{x} - 3\right)}{\left(1 - \dfrac{1}{x - 1}\right)} = \frac{\left(\dfrac{2}{x} - 3\right)}{\left(1 - \dfrac{1}{x - 1}\right)} \cdot \frac{x(x - 1)}{x(x - 1)} \qquad \text{LCD is } x(x - 1).$$

$$= \frac{\left(\dfrac{2 - 3x}{x}\right) \cdot x(x - 1)}{\left(\dfrac{x - 2}{x - 1}\right) \cdot x(x - 1)}$$

$$= \frac{(2 - 3x)(x - 1)}{x(x - 2)}, \qquad x \neq 1$$

The next three examples illustrate some methods for simplifying rational expressions involving negative exponents and radicals. These types of expressions occur frequently in calculus.

To simplify an expression with negative exponents, one method is to begin by factoring out the common factor with the *smaller* exponent. Remember that when factoring, you *subtract* exponents. For instance, in $3x^{-5/2} + 2x^{-3/2}$ the smaller exponent is $-\frac{5}{2}$ and the common factor is $x^{-5/2}$.

$$3x^{-5/2} + 2x^{-3/2} = x^{-5/2}[3(1) + 2x^{-3/2-(-5/2)}]$$

$$= x^{-5/2}(3 + 2x^1)$$

$$= \frac{3 + 2x}{x^{5/2}}$$

Example 9   **Simplifying an Expression**

Simplify the following expression containing negative exponents.

$$x(1 - 2x)^{-3/2} + (1 - 2x)^{-1/2}$$

Solution

Begin by factoring out the common factor with the *smaller exponent.*

$$x(1 - 2x)^{-3/2} + (1 - 2x)^{-1/2} = (1 - 2x)^{-3/2}[x + (1 - 2x)^{(-1/2)-(-3/2)}]$$

$$= (1 - 2x)^{-3/2}[x + (1 - 2x)^1]$$

$$= \frac{1 - x}{(1 - 2x)^{3/2}}$$

CHECKPOINT   Now try Exercise 65.

A second method for simplifying an expression with negative exponents is shown in the next example.

Example 10   **Simplifying an Expression with Negative Exponents**

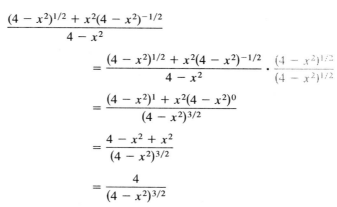

$$\frac{(4 - x^2)^{1/2} + x^2(4 - x^2)^{-1/2}}{4 - x^2}$$

$$= \frac{(4 - x^2)^{1/2} + x^2(4 - x^2)^{-1/2}}{4 - x^2} \cdot \frac{(4 - x^2)^{1/2}}{(4 - x^2)^{1/2}}$$

$$= \frac{(4 - x^2)^1 + x^2(4 - x^2)^0}{(4 - x^2)^{3/2}}$$

$$= \frac{4 - x^2 + x^2}{(4 - x^2)^{3/2}}$$

$$= \frac{4}{(4 - x^2)^{3/2}}$$

CHECKPOINT   Now try Exercise 67.

Example 11   **Rewriting a Difference Quotient**

The following expression from calculus is an example of a *difference quotient*.

$$\frac{\sqrt{x+h} - \sqrt{x}}{h}$$

Rewrite this expression by rationalizing its numerator.

Solution

$$\frac{\sqrt{x+h} - \sqrt{x}}{h} = \frac{\sqrt{x+h} - \sqrt{x}}{h} \cdot \frac{\sqrt{x+h} + \sqrt{x}}{\sqrt{x+h} + \sqrt{x}}$$

$$= \frac{\left(\sqrt{x+h}\right)^2 - \left(\sqrt{x}\right)^2}{h\left(\sqrt{x+h} + \sqrt{x}\right)}$$

$$= \frac{h}{h\left(\sqrt{x+h} + \sqrt{x}\right)}$$

$$= \frac{1}{\sqrt{x+h} + \sqrt{x}}, \qquad h \neq 0$$

Notice that the original expression is undefined when $h = 0$. So, you must exclude $h = 0$ from the domain of the simplified expression so that the expressions are equivalent.

✓**CHECKPOINT**   Now try Exercise 73.

Difference quotients, such as that in Example 11, occur frequently in calculus. Often, they need to be rewritten in an equivalent form that can be evaluated when $h = 0$. Note that the equivalent form is not simpler than the original form, but it has the advantage that it is defined when $h = 0$.

A.4 | Exercises

VOCABULARY CHECK: Fill in the blanks.

1. The set of real numbers for which an algebraic expression is defined is the _____ of the expression.

2. The quotient of two algebraic expressions is a fractional expression and the quotient of two polynomials is a _____ _____.

3. Fractional expressions with separate fractions in the numerator, denominator, or both are called _____ fractions.

4. To simplify an expression with negative exponents, it is possible to begin by factoring out the common factor with the _____ exponent.

5. Two algebraic expressions that have the same domain and yield the same values for all numbers in their domains are called _____.

6. An important rational expression, such as $\dfrac{(x+h)^2 - x^2}{h}$, that occurs in calculus is called a _____ _____.

In Exercises 1–8, find the domain of the expression.

1. $3x^2 - 4x + 7$

2. $2x^2 + 5x - 2$

3. $4x^3 + 3, \quad x \geq 0$

4. $6x^2 - 9, \quad x > 0$

5. $\dfrac{1}{x - 2}$

6. $\dfrac{x + 1}{2x + 1}$

7. $\sqrt{x + 1}$

8. $\sqrt{6 - x}$

In Exercises 9 and 10, find the missing factor in the numerator such that the two fractions are equivalent.

9. $\dfrac{5}{2x} = \dfrac{5(\quad)}{6x^2}$

10. $\dfrac{3}{4} = \dfrac{3(\quad)}{4(x + 1)}$

In Exercises 11–28, write the rational expression in simplest form.

11. $\dfrac{15x^2}{10x}$

12. $\dfrac{18y^2}{60y^5}$

13. $\dfrac{3xy}{xy + x}$

14. $\dfrac{2x^2y}{xy - y}$

15. $\dfrac{4y - 8y^2}{10y - 5}$

16. $\dfrac{9x^2 + 9x}{2x + 2}$

17. $\dfrac{x - 5}{10 - 2x}$

18. $\dfrac{12 - 4x}{x - 3}$

19. $\dfrac{y^2 - 16}{y + 4}$

20. $\dfrac{x^2 - 25}{5 - x}$

21. $\dfrac{x^3 + 5x^2 + 6x}{x^2 - 4}$

22. $\dfrac{x^2 + 8x - 20}{x^2 + 11x + 10}$

23. $\dfrac{y^2 - 7y + 12}{y^2 + 3y - 18}$

24. $\dfrac{x^2 - 7x + 6}{x^2 + 11x + 10}$

25. $\dfrac{2 - x + 2x^2 - x^3}{x^2 - 4}$

26. $\dfrac{x^2 - 9}{x^3 + x^2 - 9x - 9}$

27. $\dfrac{z^3 - 8}{z^2 + 2z + 4}$

28. $\dfrac{y^3 - 2y^2 - 3y}{y^3 + 1}$

In Exercises 29 and 30, complete the table. What can you conclude?

29.

x	0	1	2	3	4	5	6
$\dfrac{x^2 - 2x - 3}{x - 3}$							
$x + 1$							

30.

x	0	1	2	3	4	5	6
$\dfrac{x - 3}{x^2 - x - 6}$							
$\dfrac{1}{x + 2}$							

31. *Error Analysis*   Describe the error.

$$\dfrac{5x^3}{2x^3 + 4} = \dfrac{5x^3}{2x^3 + 4} = \dfrac{5}{2 + 4} = \dfrac{5}{6}$$

32. *Error Analysis*   Describe the error.

$$\dfrac{x^3 + 25x}{x^2 - 2x - 15} = \dfrac{x(x^2 + 25)}{(x - 5)(x + 3)}$$
$$= \dfrac{x(x + 5)(x - 5)}{(x - 5)(x + 3)} = \dfrac{x(x + 5)}{x + 3}$$

Geometry   **In Exercises 33 and 34, find the ratio of the area of the shaded portion of the figure to the total area of the figure.**

33.

34.

In Exercises 35–42, perform the multiplication or division and simplify.

35. $\dfrac{5}{x - 1} \cdot \dfrac{x - 1}{25(x - 2)}$

36. $\dfrac{x + 13}{x^3(3 - x)} \cdot \dfrac{x(x - 3)}{5}$

37. $\dfrac{r}{r - 1} \cdot \dfrac{r^2 - 1}{r^2}$

38. $\dfrac{4y - 16}{5y + 15} \cdot \dfrac{2y + 6}{4 - y}$

39. $\dfrac{t^2 - t - 6}{t^2 + 6t + 9} \cdot \dfrac{t + 3}{t^2 - 4}$

40. $\dfrac{x^2 + xy - 2y^2}{x^3 + x^2y} \cdot \dfrac{x}{x^2 + 3xy + 2y^2}$

41. $\dfrac{x^2 - 36}{x} \div \dfrac{x^3 - 6x^2}{x^2 + x}$

42. $\dfrac{x^2 - 14x + 49}{x^2 - 49} \div \dfrac{3x - 21}{x + 7}$

In Exercises 43–52, perform the addition or subtraction and simplify.

43. $\dfrac{5}{x-1} + \dfrac{x}{x-1}$

44. $\dfrac{2x-1}{x+3} + \dfrac{1-x}{x+3}$

45. $6 - \dfrac{5}{x+3}$

46. $\dfrac{3}{x-1} - 5$

47. $\dfrac{3}{x-2} + \dfrac{5}{2-x}$

48. $\dfrac{2x}{x-5} - \dfrac{5}{5-x}$

49. $\dfrac{1}{x^2-x-2} - \dfrac{x}{x^2-5x+6}$

50. $\dfrac{2}{x^2-x-2} + \dfrac{10}{x^2+2x-8}$

51. $-\dfrac{1}{x} + \dfrac{2}{x^2+1} + \dfrac{1}{x^3+x}$

52. $\dfrac{2}{x+1} + \dfrac{2}{x-1} + \dfrac{1}{x^2-1}$

Error Analysis **In Exercises 53 and 54, describe the error.**

53. $\dfrac{x+4}{x+2} - \dfrac{3x-8}{x+2} = \dfrac{x+4-3x-8}{x+2}$
$= \dfrac{-2x-4}{x+2} = \dfrac{-2(x+2)}{x+2} = -2$

54. $\dfrac{6-x}{x(x+2)} + \dfrac{x+2}{x^2} + \dfrac{8}{x^2(x+2)}$
$= \dfrac{x(6-x) + (x+2)^2 + 8}{x^2(x+2)}$
$= \dfrac{6x - x^2 + x^2 + 4 + 8}{x^2(x+2)}$
$= \dfrac{6(x+2)}{x^2(x+2)} = \dfrac{6}{x^2}$

In Exercises 55–60, simplify the complex fraction.

55. $\dfrac{\left(\dfrac{x}{2} - 1\right)}{(x-2)}$

56. $\dfrac{(x-4)}{\left(\dfrac{x}{4} - \dfrac{4}{x}\right)}$

57. $\dfrac{\left[\dfrac{x^2}{(x+1)^2}\right]}{\left[\dfrac{x}{(x+1)^3}\right]}$

58. $\dfrac{\left(\dfrac{x^2-1}{x}\right)}{\left[\dfrac{(x-1)^2}{x}\right]}$

59. $\dfrac{\left(\sqrt{x} - \dfrac{1}{2\sqrt{x}}\right)}{\sqrt{x}}$

60. $\dfrac{\left(\dfrac{t^2}{\sqrt{t^2+1}} - \sqrt{t^2+1}\right)}{t^2}$

In Exercises 61–66, factor the expression by removing the common factor with the smaller exponent.

61. $x^5 - 2x^{-2}$

62. $x^5 - 5x^{-3}$

63. $x^2(x^2+1)^{-5} - (x^2+1)^{-4}$

64. $2x(x-5)^{-3} - 4x^2(x-5)^{-4}$

65. $2x^2(x-1)^{1/2} - 5(x-1)^{-1/2}$

66. $4x^3(2x-1)^{3/2} - 2x(2x-1)^{-1/2}$

In Exercises 67 and 68, simplify the expression.

67. $\dfrac{3x^{1/3} - x^{-2/3}}{3x^{-2/3}}$

68. $\dfrac{-x^3(1-x^2)^{-1/2} - 2x(1-x^2)^{1/2}}{x^4}$

In Exercises 69–72, simplify the difference quotient.

69. $\dfrac{\left(\dfrac{1}{x+h} - \dfrac{1}{x}\right)}{h}$

70. $\dfrac{\left[\dfrac{1}{(x+h)^2} - \dfrac{1}{x^2}\right]}{h}$

71. $\dfrac{\left(\dfrac{1}{x+h-4} - \dfrac{1}{x-4}\right)}{h}$

72. $\dfrac{\left(\dfrac{x+h}{x+h+1} - \dfrac{x}{x+1}\right)}{h}$

In Exercises 73–76, simplify the difference quotient by rationalizing the numerator.

73. $\dfrac{\sqrt{x+2} - \sqrt{x}}{2}$

74. $\dfrac{\sqrt{z-3} - \sqrt{z}}{3}$

75. $\dfrac{\sqrt{x+h+1} - \sqrt{x+1}}{h}$

76. $\dfrac{\sqrt{x+h-2} - \sqrt{x-2}}{h}$

Probability **In Exercises 77 and 78, consider an experiment in which a marble is tossed into a box whose base is shown in the figure. The probability that the marble will come to rest in the shaded portion of the box is equal to the ratio of the shaded area to the total area of the figure. Find the probability.**

77.

78.
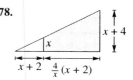

79. *Rate* A photocopier copies at a rate of 16 pages per minute.

(a) Find the time required to copy one page.

(b) Find the time required to copy x pages.

(c) Find the time required to copy 60 pages.

80. *Rate* After working together for t hours on a common task, two workers have done fractional parts of the job equal to $t/3$ and $t/5$, respectively. What fractional part of the task has been completed?

Finance **In Exercises 81 and 82, the formula that approximates the annual interest rate r of a monthly installment loan is given by**

$$r = \dfrac{\left[\dfrac{24(NM - P)}{N}\right]}{\left(P + \dfrac{NM}{12}\right)}$$

where N is the total number of payments, M is the monthly payment, and P is the amount financed.

81. (a) Approximate the annual interest rate for a four-year car loan of $16,000 that has monthly payments of $400.

(b) Simplify the expression for the annual interest rate r, and then rework part (a).

82. (a) Approximate the annual interest rate for a five-year car loan of $28,000 that has monthly payments of $525.

(b) Simplify the expression for the annual interest rate r, and then rework part (a).

83. *Refrigeration* When food (at room temperature) is placed in a refrigerator, the time required for the food to cool depends on the amount of food, the air circulation in the refrigerator, the original temperature of the food, and the temperature of the refrigerator. The model that gives the temperature of food that has an original temperature of 75°F and is placed in a 40°F refrigerator is

$$T = 10\left(\dfrac{4t^2 + 16t + 75}{t^2 + 4t + 10}\right)$$

where T is the temperature (in degrees Fahrenheit) and t is the time (in hours).

(a) Complete the table.

t	0	2	4	6	8	10
T						

t	12	14	16	18	20	22
T						

(b) What value of T does the mathematical model appear to be approaching?

84. *Interactive Money Management* The table shows the projected numbers of U.S. households (in millions) banking online and paying bills online for the years 2002 through 2007. (Source: eMarketer; Forrester Research)

Year	Banking	Paying Bills
2002	21.9	13.7
2003	26.8	17.4
2004	31.5	20.9
2005	35.0	23.9
2006	40.0	26.7
2007	45.0	29.1

Mathematical models for these data are

$$\text{Number banking online} = \dfrac{-0.728t^2 + 23.81t - 0.3}{-0.049t^2 + 0.61t + 1.0}$$

and

$$\text{Number paying bills online} = \dfrac{4.39t + 5.5}{0.002t^2 + 0.01t + 1.0}$$

where t represents the year, with $t = 2$ corresponding to 2002.

(a) Using the models, create a table to estimate the projected number of households banking online and the projected number of households paying bills online for the given years.

(b) Compare the values given by the models with the actual data.

(c) Determine a model for the ratio of the projected number of households paying bills online to the projected number of households banking online.

(d) Use the model from part (c) to find the ratio over the given years. Interpret your results.

Synthesis

True or False? **In Exercises 85 and 86, determine whether the statement is true or false. Justify your answer.**

85. $\dfrac{x^{2n} - 1^{2n}}{x^n - 1^n} = x^n + 1^n$

86. $\dfrac{x^2 - 3x + 2}{x - 1} = x - 2$, for all values of x.

87. *Think About It* How do you determine whether a rational expression is in simplest form?

A.5 Solving Equations

What you should learn

- Identify different types of equations.
- Solve linear equations in one variable and equations that lead to linear equations.
- Solve quadratic equations by factoring, extracting square roots, completing the square, and using the Quadratic Formula.
- Solve polynomial equations of degree three or greater.
- Solve equations involving radicals.
- Solve equations with absolute values.

Why you should learn it

Linear equations are used in many real-life applications. For example, in Exercise 185 on page A58, linear equations can be used to model the relationship between the length of a thigh-bone and the height of a person, helping researchers learn about ancient cultures.

Equations and Solutions of Equations

An **equation** in x is a statement that two algebraic expressions are equal. For example

$$3x - 5 = 7, \, x^2 - x - 6 = 0, \text{ and } \sqrt{2x} = 4$$

are equations. To **solve** an equation in x means to find all values of x for which the equation is true. Such values are **solutions.** For instance, $x = 4$ is a solution of the equation

$$3x - 5 = 7$$

because $3(4) - 5 = 7$ is a true statement.

The solutions of an equation depend on the kinds of numbers being considered. For instance, in the set of rational numbers, $x^2 = 10$ has no solution because there is no rational number whose square is 10. However, in the set of real numbers, the equation has the two solutions $x = \sqrt{10}$ and $x = -\sqrt{10}$.

An equation that is true for *every* real number in the *domain* of the variable is called an **identity.** The domain is the set of all real numbers for which the equation is defined. For example

$$x^2 - 9 = (x + 3)(x - 3) \qquad \text{Identity}$$

is an identity because it is a true statement for any real value of x. The equation

$$\frac{x}{3x^2} = \frac{1}{3x} \qquad \text{Identity}$$

where $x \neq 0$, is an identity because it is true for any nonzero real value of x.

An equation that is true for just *some* (or even none) of the real numbers in the domain of the variable is called a **conditional equation.** For example, the equation

$$x^2 - 9 = 0 \qquad \text{Conditional equation}$$

is conditional because $x = 3$ and $x = -3$ are the only values in the domain that satisfy the equation. The equation $2x - 4 = 2x + 1$ is conditional because there are no real values of x for which the equation is true. Learning to solve conditional equations is the primary focus of this section.

Linear Equations in One Variable

Definition of a Linear Equation

A **linear equation in one variable** x is an equation that can be written in the standard form

$$ax + b = 0$$

where a and b are real numbers with $a \neq 0$.

A linear equation has exactly one solution. To see this, consider the following steps. (Remember that $a \neq 0$.)

$$ax + b = 0 \qquad \text{Write original equation.}$$

$$ax = -b \qquad \text{Subtract } b \text{ from each side.}$$

$$x = -\frac{b}{a} \qquad \text{Divide each side by } a.$$

To solve a conditional equation in x, isolate x on one side of the equation by a sequence of **equivalent** (and usually simpler) **equations,** each having the same solution(s) as the original equation. The operations that yield equivalent equations come from the Substitution Principle (see Appendix A.1) and simplification techniques.

Generating Equivalent Equations

An equation can be transformed into an *equivalent equation* by one or more of the following steps.

	Given Equation	Equivalent Equation
1. Remove symbols of grouping, combine like terms, or simplify fractions on one or both sides of the equation.	$2x - x = 4$	$x = 4$
2. Add (or subtract) the same quantity to (from) *each* side of the equation.	$x + 1 = 6$	$x = 5$
3. Multiply (or divide) *each* side of the equation by the same *nonzero* quantity.	$2x = 6$	$x = 3$
4. Interchange the two sides of the equation.	$2 = x$	$x = 2$

Example 1 **Solving a Linear Equation**

a. $3x - 6 = 0$ Original equation

$ 3x = 6$ Add 6 to each side.

$ x = 2$ Divide each side by 3.

b. $5x + 4 = 3x - 8$ Original equation

$ 2x + 4 = -8$ Subtract $3x$ from each side.

$ 2x = -12$ Subtract 4 from each side.

$ x = -6$ Divide each side by 2.

✔CHECKPOINT   Now try Exercise 13.

STUDY TIP

An equation with a *single fraction* on each side can be cleared of denominators by **cross multiplying,** which is equivalent to multiplying by the LCD and then dividing out. To do this, multiply the left numerator by the right denominator and the right numerator by the left denominator as follows.

$$\frac{a}{b} = \frac{c}{d} \qquad \text{LCD is } bd.$$

$$\frac{a}{b} \cdot bd = \frac{c}{d} \cdot bd \qquad \text{Multiply by LCD.}$$

$$ad = cb \qquad \begin{array}{l}\text{Divide out}\\ \text{common factors.}\end{array}$$

To solve an equation involving fractional expressions, find the least common denominator (LCD) of all terms and multiply every term by the LCD. This process will clear the original equation of fractions and produce a simpler equation to work with.

Example 2 An Equation Involving Fractional Expressions

Solve $\dfrac{x}{3} + \dfrac{3x}{4} = 2$.

Solution

$$\frac{x}{3} + \frac{3x}{4} = 2 \qquad \text{Write original equation.}$$

$$(12)\frac{x}{3} + (12)\frac{3x}{4} = (12)2 \qquad \text{Multiply each term by the LCD of 12.}$$

$$4x + 9x = 24 \qquad \text{Divide out and multiply.}$$

$$13x = 24 \qquad \text{Combine like terms.}$$

$$x = \frac{24}{13} \qquad \text{Divide each side by 13.}$$

The solution is $x = \frac{24}{13}$. Check this in the original equation.

✓**CHECKPOINT** Now try Exercise 21.

When multiplying or dividing an equation by a *variable* quantity, it is possible to introduce an extraneous solution. An **extraneous solution** is one that does not satisfy the original equation. Therefore, it is essential that you check your solutions.

Example 3 An Equation with an Extraneous Solution

Solve $\dfrac{1}{x-2} = \dfrac{3}{x+2} - \dfrac{6x}{x^2 - 4}$.

Solution

The LCD is $x^2 - 4$, or $(x+2)(x-2)$. Multiply each term by this LCD.

$$\frac{1}{x-2}(x+2)(x-2) = \frac{3}{x+2}(x+2)(x-2) - \frac{6x}{x^2-4}(x+2)(x-2)$$

$$x + 2 = 3(x-2) - 6x, \qquad x \neq \pm 2$$

$$x + 2 = 3x - 6 - 6x$$

$$x + 2 = -3x - 6$$

$$4x = -8 \quad \Longrightarrow \quad x = -2 \qquad \text{Extraneous solution}$$

In the original equation, $x = -2$ yields a denominator of zero. So, $x = -2$ is an extraneous solution, and the original equation has *no solution*.

✓**CHECKPOINT** Now try Exercise 37.

STUDY TIP

Recall that the least common denominator of two or more fractions consists of the product of all prime factors in the denominators, with each factor given the highest power of its occurrence in any denominator. For instance, in Example 3, by factoring each denominator you can determine that the LCD is $(x+2)(x-2)$.

Quadratic Equations

A **quadratic equation** in x is an equation that can be written in the general form

$$ax^2 + bx + c = 0$$

where a, b, and c are real numbers, with $a \neq 0$. A quadratic equation in x is also known as a **second-degree polynomial equation** in x.

You should be familiar with the following four methods of solving quadratic equations.

Solving a Quadratic Equation

Factoring: If $ab = 0$, then $a = 0$ or $b = 0$.

Example: $x^2 - x - 6 = 0$

$$(x - 3)(x + 2) = 0$$

$$x - 3 = 0 \implies x = 3$$

$$x + 2 = 0 \implies x = -2$$

Square Root Principle: If $u^2 = c$, where $c > 0$, then $u = \pm\sqrt{c}$.

Example: $(x + 3)^2 = 16$

$$x + 3 = \pm 4$$

$$x = -3 \pm 4$$

$$x = 1 \quad \text{or} \quad x = -7$$

Completing the Square: If $x^2 + bx = c$, then

$$x^2 + bx + \left(\frac{b}{2}\right)^2 = c + \left(\frac{b}{2}\right)^2 \qquad \text{Add } \left(\frac{b}{2}\right)^2 \text{ to each side.}$$

$$\left(x + \frac{b}{2}\right)^2 = c + \frac{b^2}{4}.$$

Example: $x^2 + 6x = 5$

$$x^2 + 6x + 3^2 = 5 + 3^2 \qquad \text{Add } \left(\frac{6}{2}\right)^2 \text{ to each side.}$$

$$(x + 3)^2 = 14$$

$$x + 3 = \pm\sqrt{14}$$

$$x = -3 \pm \sqrt{14}$$

Quadratic Formula: If $ax^2 + bx + c = 0$, then $x = \dfrac{-b \pm \sqrt{b^2 - 4ac}}{2a}$.

Example: $2x^2 + 3x - 1 = 0$

$$x = \frac{-3 \pm \sqrt{3^2 - 4(2)(-1)}}{2(2)}$$

$$= \frac{-3 \pm \sqrt{17}}{4}$$

STUDY TIP

The Square Root Principle is also referred to as *extracting square roots*.

STUDY TIP

You can solve every quadratic equation by completing the square or using the Quadratic Formula.

Example 4   **Solving a Quadratic Equation by Factoring**

a. $2x^2 + 9x + 7 = 3$ Original equation

   $2x^2 + 9x + 4 = 0$ Write in general form.

   $(2x + 1)(x + 4) = 0$ Factor.

   $2x + 1 = 0$ ⟹ $x = -\dfrac{1}{2}$ Set 1st factor equal to 0.

   $x + 4 = 0$ ⟹ $x = -4$ Set 2nd factor equal to 0.

The solutions are $x = -\frac{1}{2}$ and $x = -4$. Check these in the original equation.

b. $6x^2 - 3x = 0$ Original equation

   $3x(2x - 1) = 0$ Factor.

   $3x = 0$ ⟹ $x = 0$ Set 1st factor equal to 0.

   $2x - 1 = 0$ ⟹ $x = \dfrac{1}{2}$ Set 2nd factor equal to 0.

The solutions are $x = 0$ and $x = \frac{1}{2}$. Check these in the original equation.

✓*CHECKPOINT*   Now try Exercise 57.

Note that the method of solution in Example 4 is based on the Zero-Factor Property from Appendix A.1. Be sure you see that this property works *only* for equations written in general form (in which the right side of the equation is zero). So, all terms must be collected on one side *before* factoring. For instance, in the equation $(x - 5)(x + 2) = 8$, it is *incorrect* to set each factor equal to 8. Try to solve this equation correctly.

Example 5   **Extracting Square Roots**

Solve each equation by extracting square roots.

a. $4x^2 = 12$ **b.** $(x - 3)^2 = 7$

Solution

a. $4x^2 = 12$ Write original equation.

   $x^2 = 3$ Divide each side by 4.

   $x = \pm\sqrt{3}$ Extract square roots.

When you take the square root of a variable expression, you must account for both positive and negative solutions. So, the solutions are $x = \sqrt{3}$ and $x = -\sqrt{3}$. Check these in the original equation.

b. $(x - 3)^2 = 7$ Write original equation.

   $x - 3 = \pm\sqrt{7}$ Extract square roots.

   $x = 3 \pm \sqrt{7}$ Add 3 to each side.

The solutions are $x = 3 \pm \sqrt{7}$. Check these in the original equation.

✓*CHECKPOINT*   Now try Exercise 77.

When solving quadratic equations by completing the square, you must add $(b/2)^2$ to *each side* in order to maintain equality. If the leading coefficient is *not* 1, you must divide each side of the equation by the leading coefficient *before* completing the square, as shown in Example 7.

Example 6   **Completing the Square: Leading Coefficient Is 1**

Solve $x^2 + 2x - 6 = 0$ by completing the square.

Solution

$$x^2 + 2x - 6 = 0 \qquad \text{Write original equation.}$$

$$x^2 + 2x = 6 \qquad \text{Add 6 to each side.}$$

$$x^2 + 2x + 1^2 = 6 + 1^2 \qquad \text{Add } 1^2 \text{ to each side.}$$

$$\underbrace{\hphantom{xxxx}}_{(\text{half of } 2)^2}$$

$$(x + 1)^2 = 7 \qquad \text{Simplify.}$$

$$x + 1 = \pm\sqrt{7} \qquad \text{Take square root of each side.}$$

$$x = -1 \pm \sqrt{7} \qquad \text{Subtract 1 from each side.}$$

The solutions are $x = -1 \pm \sqrt{7}$. Check these in the original equation.

✓**CHECKPOINT**   Now try Exercise 85.

Example 7   **Completing the Square: Leading Coefficient Is Not 1**

$$3x^2 - 4x - 5 = 0 \qquad \text{Original equation}$$

$$3x^2 - 4x = 5 \qquad \text{Add 5 to each side.}$$

$$x^2 - \frac{4}{3}x = \frac{5}{3} \qquad \text{Divide each side by 3.}$$

$$x^2 - \frac{4}{3}x + \left(-\frac{2}{3}\right)^2 = \frac{5}{3} + \left(-\frac{2}{3}\right)^2 \qquad \text{Add } \left(-\frac{2}{3}\right)^2 \text{ to each side.}$$

$$\underbrace{\hphantom{xxxx}}_{\left(\text{half of } -\frac{4}{3}\right)^2}$$

$$x^2 - \frac{4}{3}x + \frac{4}{9} = \frac{19}{9} \qquad \text{Simplify.}$$

$$\left(x - \frac{2}{3}\right)^2 = \frac{19}{9} \qquad \text{Perfect square trinomial.}$$

$$x - \frac{2}{3} = \pm\frac{\sqrt{19}}{3} \qquad \text{Extract square roots.}$$

$$x = \frac{2}{3} \pm \frac{\sqrt{19}}{3} \qquad \text{Solutions}$$

✓**CHECKPOINT**   Now try Exercise 91.

Example 8 **The Quadratic Formula: Two Distinct Solutions**

Use the Quadratic Formula to solve $x^2 + 3x = 9$.

Solution

$$x^2 + 3x = 9$$ Write original equation.

$$x^2 + 3x - 9 = 0$$ Write in general form.

$$x = \frac{-b \pm \sqrt{b^2 - 4ac}}{2a}$$ Quadratic Formula

$$x = \frac{-3 \pm \sqrt{(3)^2 - 4(1)(-9)}}{2(1)}$$ Substitute $a = 1$, $b = 3$, and $c = -9$.

$$x = \frac{-3 \pm \sqrt{45}}{2}$$ Simplify.

$$x = \frac{-3 \pm 3\sqrt{5}}{2}$$ Simplify.

The equation has two solutions:

$$x = \frac{-3 + 3\sqrt{5}}{2} \quad \text{and} \quad x = \frac{-3 - 3\sqrt{5}}{2}.$$

Check these in the original equation.

✓*CHECKPOINT* Now try Exercise 101.

Example 9 **The Quadratic Formula: One Solution**

Use the Quadratic Formula to solve $8x^2 - 24x + 18 = 0$.

Solution

$$8x^2 - 24x + 18 = 0$$ Write original equation.

$$4x^2 - 12x + 9 = 0$$ Divide out common factor of 2.

$$x = \frac{-b \pm \sqrt{b^2 - 4ac}}{2a}$$ Quadratic Formula

$$x = \frac{-(-12) \pm \sqrt{(-12)^2 - 4(4)(9)}}{2(4)}$$ Substitute $a = 4$, $b = -12$, and $c = 9$.

$$x = \frac{12 \pm \sqrt{0}}{8} = \frac{3}{2}$$ Simplify.

This quadratic equation has only one solution: $x = \frac{3}{2}$. Check this in the original equation.

✓*CHECKPOINT* Now try Exercise 105.

Note that Example 9 could have been solved without first dividing out a common factor of 2. Substituting $a = 8$, $b = -24$, and $c = 18$ into the Quadratic Formula produces the same result.

Polynomial Equations of Higher Degree

The methods used to solve quadratic equations can sometimes be extended to solve polynomial equations of higher degree.

Example 10   Solving a Polynomial Equation by Factoring

Solve $3x^4 = 48x^2$.

Solution

First write the polynomial equation in general form with zero on one side, factor the other side, and then set each factor equal to zero and solve.

$3x^4 = 48x^2$	Write original equation.
$3x^4 - 48x^2 = 0$	Write in general form.
$3x^2(x^2 - 16) = 0$	Factor out common factor.
$3x^2(x + 4)(x - 4) = 0$	Write in factored form.
$3x^2 = 0 \implies x = 0$	Set 1st factor equal to 0.
$x + 4 = 0 \implies x = -4$	Set 2nd factor equal to 0.
$x - 4 = 0 \implies x = 4$	Set 3rd factor equal to 0.

You can check these solutions by substituting in the original equation, as follows.

Check

$3(0)^4 = 48(0)^2$	0 checks. ✓
$3(-4)^4 = 48(-4)^2$	-4 checks. ✓
$3(4)^4 = 48(4)^2$	4 checks. ✓

So, you can conclude that the solutions are $x = 0$, $x = -4$, and $x = 4$.

✓CHECKPOINT   Now try Exercise 135.

Example 11   Solving a Polynomial Equation by Factoring

Solve $x^3 - 3x^2 - 3x + 9 = 0$.

Solution

$x^3 - 3x^2 - 3x + 9 = 0$	Write original equation.
$x^2(x - 3) - 3(x - 3) = 0$	Factor by grouping.
$(x - 3)(x^2 - 3) = 0$	Distributive Property
$x - 3 = 0 \implies x = 3$	Set 1st factor equal to 0.
$x^2 - 3 = 0 \implies x = \pm\sqrt{3}$	Set 2nd factor equal to 0.

The solutions are $x = 3$, $x = \sqrt{3}$, and $x = -\sqrt{3}$. Check these in the original equation.

✓CHECKPOINT   Now try Exercise 143.

Equations Involving Radicals

Operations such as squaring each side of an equation, raising each side of an equation to a rational power, and multiplying each side of an equation by a variable quantity all can introduce extraneous solutions. So, when you use any of these operations, checking your solutions is crucial.

Example 12   Solving Equations Involving Radicals

a.

$\sqrt{2x + 7} - x = 2$	Original equation
$\sqrt{2x + 7} = x + 2$	Isolate radical.
$2x + 7 = x^2 + 4x + 4$	Square each side.
$0 = x^2 + 2x - 3$	Write in general form.
$0 = (x + 3)(x - 1)$	Factor.
$x + 3 = 0 \quad \Longrightarrow \quad x = -3$	Set 1st factor equal to 0.
$x - 1 = 0 \quad \Longrightarrow \quad x = 1$	Set 2nd factor equal to 0.

By checking these values, you can determine that the only solution is $x = 1$.

b.

$\sqrt{2x - 5} - \sqrt{x - 3} = 1$	Original equation
$\sqrt{2x - 5} = \sqrt{x - 3} + 1$	Isolate $\sqrt{2x - 5}$.
$2x - 5 = x - 3 + 2\sqrt{x - 3} + 1$	Square each side.
$2x - 5 = x - 2 + 2\sqrt{x - 3}$	Combine like terms.
$x - 3 = 2\sqrt{x - 3}$	Isolate $2\sqrt{x - 3}$.
$x^2 - 6x + 9 = 4(x - 3)$	Square each side.
$x^2 - 10x + 21 = 0$	Write in general form.
$(x - 3)(x - 7) = 0$	Factor.
$x - 3 = 0 \quad \Longrightarrow \quad x = 3$	Set 1st factor equal to 0.
$x - 7 = 0 \quad \Longrightarrow \quad x = 7$	Set 2nd factor equal to 0.

The solutions are $x = 3$ and $x = 7$. Check these in the original equation.

✓*CHECKPOINT*   Now try Exercise 155.

STUDY TIP

When an equation contains two radicals, it may not be possible to isolate both. In such cases, you may have to raise each side of the equation to a power at *two* different stages in the solution, as shown in Example 12(b).

Example 13   Solving an Equation Involving a Rational Exponent

$(x - 4)^{2/3} = 25$	Original equation
$\sqrt[3]{(x - 4)^2} = 25$	Rewrite in radical form.
$(x - 4)^2 = 15{,}625$	Cube each side.
$x - 4 = \pm 125$	Take square root of each side.
$x = 129, \quad x = -121$	Add 4 to each side.

✓*CHECKPOINT*   Now try Exercise 163.

Equations with Absolute Values

To solve an equation involving an absolute value, remember that the expression inside the absolute value signs can be positive or negative. This results in *two* separate equations, each of which must be solved. For instance, the equation

$$|x - 2| = 3$$

results in the two equations $x - 2 = 3$ and $-(x - 2) = 3$, which implies that the equation has two solutions: $x = 5$ and $x = -1$.

Example 14 **Solving an Equation Involving Absolute Value**

Solve $|x^2 - 3x| = -4x + 6$.

Solution

Because the variable expression inside the absolute value signs can be positive or negative, you must solve the following two equations.

First Equation

$$x^2 - 3x = -4x + 6 \qquad \text{Use positive expression.}$$
$$x^2 + x - 6 = 0 \qquad \text{Write in general form.}$$
$$(x + 3)(x - 2) = 0 \qquad \text{Factor.}$$
$$x + 3 = 0 \implies x = -3 \qquad \text{Set 1st factor equal to 0.}$$
$$x - 2 = 0 \implies x = 2 \qquad \text{Set 2nd factor equal to 0.}$$

Second Equation

$$-(x^2 - 3x) = -4x + 6 \qquad \text{Use negative expression.}$$
$$x^2 - 7x + 6 = 0 \qquad \text{Write in general form.}$$
$$(x - 1)(x - 6) = 0 \qquad \text{Factor.}$$
$$x - 1 = 0 \implies x = 1 \qquad \text{Set 1st factor equal to 0.}$$
$$x - 6 = 0 \implies x = 6 \qquad \text{Set 2nd factor equal to 0.}$$

Check

$$|(-3)^2 - 3(-3)| \stackrel{?}{=} -4(-3) + 6 \qquad \text{Substitute } -3 \text{ for } x.$$
$$18 = 18 \qquad -3 \text{ checks.} ✓$$
$$|(2)^2 - 3(2)| \stackrel{?}{=} -4(2) + 6 \qquad \text{Substitute 2 for } x.$$
$$2 \neq -2 \qquad 2 \text{ does not check.}$$
$$|(1)^2 - 3(1)| \stackrel{?}{=} -4(1) + 6 \qquad \text{Substitute 1 for } x.$$
$$2 = 2 \qquad 1 \text{ checks.} ✓$$
$$|(6)^2 - 3(6)| \stackrel{?}{=} -4(6) + 6 \qquad \text{Substitute 6 for } x.$$
$$18 \neq -18 \qquad 6 \text{ does not check.}$$

The solutions are $x = -3$ and $x = 1$.

✓CHECKPOINT   Now try Exercise 181.

A.5 | Exercises

VOCABULARY CHECK: Fill in the blanks.

1. An _____ is a statement that equates two algebraic expressions.

2. To find all values that satisfy an equation is to _____ the equation.

3. There are two types of equations, _____ and _____ equations.

4. A linear equation in one variable is an equation that can be written in the standard from _____.

5. When solving an equation, it is possible to introduce an _____ solution, which is a value that does not satisfy the original equation.

6. An equation of the form $ax^2 + bx + c = 0$, $a \neq 0$ is a _____ _____, or a second-degree polynomial equation in x.

7. The four methods that can be used to solve a quadratic equation are _____, _____, _____, and the _____.

In Exercises 1–10, determine whether the equation is an identity or a conditional equation.

1. $2(x - 1) = 2x - 2$

2. $3(x + 2) = 5x + 4$

3. $-6(x - 3) + 5 = -2x + 10$

4. $3(x + 2) - 5 = 3x + 1$

5. $4(x + 1) - 2x = 2(x + 2)$

6. $-7(x - 3) + 4x = 3(7 - x)$

7. $x^2 - 8x + 5 = (x - 4)^2 - 11$

8. $x^2 + 2(3x - 2) = x^2 + 6x - 4$

9. $3 + \dfrac{1}{x + 1} = \dfrac{4x}{x + 1}$

10. $\dfrac{5}{x} + \dfrac{3}{x} = 24$

In Exercises 11–26, solve the equation and check your solution.

11. $x + 11 = 15$

12. $7 - x = 19$

13. $7 - 2x = 25$

14. $7x + 2 = 23$

15. $8x - 5 = 3x + 20$

16. $7x + 3 = 3x - 17$

17. $2(x + 5) - 7 = 3(x - 2)$

18. $3(x + 3) = 5(1 - x) - 1$

19. $x - 3(2x + 3) = 8 - 5x$

20. $9x - 10 = 5x + 2(2x - 5)$

21. $\dfrac{5x}{4} + \dfrac{1}{2} = x - \dfrac{1}{2}$

22. $\dfrac{x}{5} - \dfrac{x}{2} = 3 + \dfrac{3x}{10}$

23. $\frac{3}{2}(z + 5) - \frac{1}{4}(z + 24) = 0$

24. $\dfrac{3x}{2} + \dfrac{1}{4}(x - 2) = 10$

25. $0.25x + 0.75(10 - x) = 3$

26. $0.60x + 0.40(100 - x) = 50$

In Exercises 27–48, solve the equation and check your solution. (If not possible, explain why.)

27. $x + 8 = 2(x - 2) - x$

28. $8(x + 2) - 3(2x + 1) = 2(x + 5)$

29. $\dfrac{100 - 4x}{3} = \dfrac{5x + 6}{4} + 6$

30. $\dfrac{17 + y}{y} + \dfrac{32 + y}{y} = 100$

31. $\dfrac{5x - 4}{5x + 4} = \dfrac{2}{3}$

32. $\dfrac{10x + 3}{5x + 6} = \dfrac{1}{2}$

33. $10 - \dfrac{13}{x} = 4 + \dfrac{5}{x}$

34. $\dfrac{15}{x} - 4 = \dfrac{6}{x} + 3$

35. $3 = 2 + \dfrac{2}{z + 2}$

36. $\dfrac{1}{x} + \dfrac{2}{x - 5} = 0$

37. $\dfrac{x}{x + 4} + \dfrac{4}{x + 4} + 2 = 0$

38. $\dfrac{7}{2x + 1} - \dfrac{8x}{2x - 1} = -4$

39. $\dfrac{2}{(x - 4)(x - 2)} = \dfrac{1}{x - 4} + \dfrac{2}{x - 2}$

40. $\dfrac{4}{x - 1} + \dfrac{6}{3x + 1} = \dfrac{15}{3x + 1}$

41. $\dfrac{1}{x - 3} + \dfrac{1}{x + 3} = \dfrac{10}{x^2 - 9}$

42. $\dfrac{1}{x - 2} + \dfrac{3}{x + 3} = \dfrac{4}{x^2 + x - 6}$

43. $\dfrac{3}{x^2 - 3x} + \dfrac{4}{x} = \dfrac{1}{x - 3}$

44. $\dfrac{6}{x} - \dfrac{2}{x + 3} = \dfrac{3(x + 5)}{x^2 + 3x}$

45. $(x + 2)^2 + 5 = (x + 3)^2$

46. $(x + 1)^2 + 2(x - 2) = (x + 1)(x - 2)$

47. $(x + 2)^2 - x^2 = 4(x + 1)$

48. $(2x + 1)^2 = 4(x^2 + x + 1)$

In Exercises 49–54, write the quadratic equation in general form.

49. $2x^2 = 3 - 8x$

50. $x^2 = 16x$

51. $(x - 3)^2 = 3$

52. $13 - 3(x + 7)^2 = 0$

53. $\frac{1}{5}(3x^2 - 10) = 18x$

54. $x(x + 2) = 5x^2 + 1$

In Exercises 55–68, solve the quadratic equation by factoring.

55. $6x^2 + 3x = 0$

56. $9x^2 - 1 = 0$

57. $x^2 - 2x - 8 = 0$

58. $x^2 - 10x + 9 = 0$

59. $x^2 + 10x + 25 = 0$

60. $4x^2 + 12x + 9 = 0$

61. $3 + 5x - 2x^2 = 0$

62. $2x^2 = 19x + 33$

63. $x^2 + 4x = 12$

64. $-x^2 + 8x = 12$

65. $\frac{3}{4}x^2 + 8x + 20 = 0$

66. $\frac{1}{8}x^2 - x - 16 = 0$

67. $x^2 + 2ax + a^2 = 0$, a is a real number

68. $(x + a)^2 - b^2 = 0$, a and b are real numbers

In Exercises 69–82, solve the equation by extracting square roots.

69. $x^2 = 49$

70. $x^2 = 169$

71. $x^2 = 11$

72. $x^2 = 32$

73. $3x^2 = 81$

74. $9x^2 = 36$

75. $(x - 12)^2 = 16$

76. $(x + 13)^2 = 25$

77. $(x + 2)^2 = 14$

78. $(x - 5)^2 = 30$

79. $(2x - 1)^2 = 18$

80. $(4x + 7)^2 = 44$

81. $(x - 7)^2 = (x + 3)^2$

82. $(x + 5)^2 = (x + 4)^2$

In Exercises 83–92, solve the quadratic equation by completing the square.

83. $x^2 + 4x - 32 = 0$

84. $x^2 - 2x - 3 = 0$

85. $x^2 + 12x + 25 = 0$

86. $x^2 + 8x + 14 = 0$

87. $9x^2 - 18x = -3$

88. $9x^2 - 12x = 14$

89. $8 + 4x - x^2 = 0$

90. $-x^2 + x - 1 = 0$

91. $2x^2 + 5x - 8 = 0$

92. $4x^2 - 4x - 99 = 0$

In Exercises 93–116, use the Quadratic Formula to solve the equation.

93. $2x^2 + x - 1 = 0$

94. $2x^2 - x - 1 = 0$

95. $16x^2 + 8x - 3 = 0$

96. $25x^2 - 20x + 3 = 0$

97. $2 + 2x - x^2 = 0$

98. $x^2 - 10x + 22 = 0$

99. $x^2 + 14x + 44 = 0$

100. $6x = 4 - x^2$

101. $x^2 + 8x - 4 = 0$

102. $4x^2 - 4x - 4 = 0$

103. $12x - 9x^2 = -3$

104. $16x^2 + 22 = 40x$

105. $9x^2 + 24x + 16 = 0$

106. $36x^2 + 24x - 7 = 0$

107. $4x^2 + 4x = 7$

108. $16x^2 - 40x + 5 = 0$

109. $28x - 49x^2 = 4$

110. $3x + x^2 - 1 = 0$

111. $8t = 5 + 2t^2$

112. $25h^2 + 80h + 61 = 0$

113. $(y - 5)^2 = 2y$

114. $(z + 6)^2 = -2z$

115. $\frac{1}{2}x^2 + \frac{3}{8}x = 2$

116. $\left(\frac{5}{7}x - 14\right)^2 = 8x$

In Exercises 117–124, use the Quadratic Formula to solve the equation. (Round your answer to three decimal places.)

117. $5.1x^2 - 1.7x - 3.2 = 0$

118. $2x^2 - 2.50x - 0.42 = 0$

119. $-0.067x^2 - 0.852x + 1.277 = 0$

120. $-0.005x^2 + 0.101x - 0.193 = 0$

121. $422x^2 - 506x - 347 = 0$

122. $1100x^2 + 326x - 715 = 0$

123. $12.67x^2 + 31.55x + 8.09 = 0$

124. $-3.22x^2 - 0.08x + 28.651 = 0$

In Exercises 125–134, solve the equation using any convenient method.

125. $x^2 - 2x - 1 = 0$

126. $11x^2 + 33x = 0$

127. $(x + 3)^2 = 81$

128. $x^2 - 14x + 49 = 0$

129. $x^2 - x - \frac{11}{4} = 0$

130. $x^2 + 3x - \frac{3}{4} = 0$

131. $(x + 1)^2 = x^2$

132. $a^2x^2 - b^2 = 0$, a and b are real numbers

133. $3x + 4 = 2x^2 - 7$

134. $4x^2 + 2x + 4 = 2x + 8$

In Exercises 135–152, find all solutions of the equation. Check your solutions in the original equation.

135. $4x^4 - 18x^2 = 0$

136. $20x^3 - 125x = 0$

137. $x^4 - 81 = 0$

138. $x^6 - 64 = 0$

139. $x^3 + 216 = 0$

140. $27x^3 - 512 = 0$

141. $5x^3 + 30x^2 + 45x = 0$

142. $9x^4 - 24x^3 + 16x^2 = 0$

143. $x^3 - 3x^2 - x + 3 = 0$

144. $x^3 + 2x^2 + 3x + 6 = 0$

145. $x^4 - x^3 + x - 1 = 0$

146. $x^4 + 2x^3 - 8x - 16 = 0$

147. $x^4 - 4x^2 + 3 = 0$

148. $x^4 + 5x^2 - 36 = 0$

149. $4x^4 - 65x^2 + 16 = 0$

150. $36t^4 + 29t^2 - 7 = 0$

151. $x^6 + 7x^3 - 8 = 0$

152. $x^6 + 3x^3 + 2 = 0$

In Exercises 153–184, find all solutions of the equation. Check your solutions in the original equation.

153. $\sqrt{2x} - 10 = 0$

154. $4\sqrt{x} - 3 = 0$

155. $\sqrt{x - 10} - 4 = 0$

156. $\sqrt{5 - x} - 3 = 0$

157. $\sqrt[3]{2x + 5} + 3 = 0$

158. $\sqrt[3]{3x + 1} - 5 = 0$

159. $-\sqrt{26 - 11x} + 4 = x$

160. $x + \sqrt{31 - 9x} = 5$

161. $\sqrt{x + 1} = \sqrt{3x + 1}$

162. $\sqrt{x + 5} = \sqrt{x - 5}$

163. $(x - 5)^{3/2} = 8$

164. $(x + 3)^{3/2} = 8$

165. $(x + 3)^{2/3} = 8$

166. $(x + 2)^{2/3} = 9$

167. $(x^2 - 5)^{3/2} = 27$

168. $(x^2 - x - 22)^{3/2} = 27$

169. $3x(x - 1)^{1/2} + 2(x - 1)^{3/2} = 0$

170. $4x^2(x - 1)^{1/3} + 6x(x - 1)^{4/3} = 0$

171. $x = \dfrac{3}{x} + \dfrac{1}{2}$

172. $\dfrac{4}{x} - \dfrac{5}{3} = \dfrac{x}{6}$

173. $\dfrac{1}{x} - \dfrac{1}{x + 1} = 3$

174. $\dfrac{4}{x + 1} - \dfrac{3}{x + 2} = 1$

175. $\dfrac{20 - x}{x} = x$

176. $4x + 1 = \dfrac{3}{x}$

177. $\dfrac{x}{x^2 - 4} + \dfrac{1}{x + 2} = 3$

178. $\dfrac{x + 1}{3} - \dfrac{x + 1}{x + 2} = 0$

179. $|2x - 1| = 5$

180. $|3x + 2| = 7$

181. $|x| = x^2 + x - 3$

182. $|x^2 + 6x| = 3x + 18$

183. $|x + 1| = x^2 - 5$

184. $|x - 10| = x^2 - 10x$

185. **Anthropology** The relationship between the length of an adult's femur (thigh bone) and the height of the adult can be approximated by the linear equations

$y = 0.432x - 10.44$ Female

$y = 0.449x - 12.15$ Male

where y is the length of the femur in inches and x is the height of the adult in inches (see figure).

y in. | femur
x in.

(a) An anthropologist discovers a femur belonging to an adult human female. The bone is 16 inches long. Estimate the height of the female.

(b) From the foot bones of an adult human male, an anthropologist estimates that the person's height was 69 inches. A few feet away from the site where the foot bones were discovered, the anthropologist

discovers a male adult femur that is 19 inches long. Is it likely that both the foot bones and the thigh bone came from the same person?

(c) Complete the table to determine if there is a height of an adult for which an anthropologist would not be able to determine whether the femur belonged to a male or a female.

Height, x	Female femur length, y	Male femur length, y
60		
70		
80		
90		
100		
110		

186. **Operating Cost** A delivery company has a fleet of vans. The annual operating cost C per van is

$C = 0.32m + 2500$

where m is the number of miles traveled by a van in a year. What number of miles will yield an annual operating cost of $10,000?

187. **Flood Control** A river has risen 8 feet above its flood stage. The water begins to recede at a rate of 3 inches per hour. Write a mathematical model that shows the number of feet above flood stage after t hours. If the water continually recedes at this rate, when will the river be 1 foot above its flood stage?

188. **Floor Space** The floor of a one-story building is 14 feet longer than it is wide. The building has 1632 square feet of floor space.

(a) Draw a diagram that gives a visual representation of the floor space. Represent the width as w and show the length in terms of w.

(b) Write a quadratic equation in terms of w.

(c) Find the length and width of the floor of the building.

189. **Packaging** An open box with a square base (see figure) is to be constructed from 84 square inches of material. The height of the box is 2 inches. What are the dimensions of the box? (*Hint:* The surface area is $S = x^2 + 4xh$.)

2 in.

x

x

190. *Geometry* The hypotenuse of an isosceles right triangle is 5 centimeters long. How long are its sides?

191. *Geometry* An equilateral triangle has a height of 10 inches. How long is one of its sides? (*Hint:* Use the height of the triangle to partition the triangle into two congruent right triangles.)

192. *Flying Speed* Two planes leave simultaneously from Chicago's O'Hare Airport, one flying due north and the other due east (see figure). The northbound plane is flying 50 miles per hour faster than the eastbound plane. After 3 hours, the planes are 2440 miles apart. Find the speed of each plane.

193. *Voting Population* The total voting-age population P (in millions) in the United States from 1990 to 2002 can be modeled by

$$P = \frac{182.45 - 3.189t}{1.00 - 0.026t}, \quad 0 \le t \le 12$$

where t represents the year, with $t = 0$ corresponding to 1990. (Source: U.S. Census Bureau)

(a) In which year did the total voting-age population reach 200 million?

(b) Use the model to predict when the total voting-age population will reach 230 million. Is this prediction reasonable? Explain.

194. *Airline Passengers* An airline offers daily flights between Chicago and Denver. The total monthly cost C (in millions of dollars) of these flights is $C = \sqrt{0.2x + 1}$ where x is the number of passengers (in thousands). The total cost of the flights for June is 2.5 million dollars. How many passengers flew in June?

195. *Demand* The demand equation for a video game is modeled by $p = 40 - \sqrt{0.01x + 1}$ where x is the number of units demanded per day and p is the price per unit. Approximate the demand when the price is $37.55.

196. *Demand* The demand equation for a high definition television set is modeled by

$$p = 800 - \sqrt{0.01x + 1}$$

where x is the number of units demanded per month and p is the price per unit. Approximate the demand when the price is $750.

Synthesis

True or False? **In Exercises 197–200, determine whether the statement is true or false. Justify your answer.**

197. The equation $x(3 - x) = 10$ is a linear equation.

198. If $(2x - 3)(x + 5) = 8$, then either $2x - 3 = 8$ or $x + 5 = 8$.

199. An equation can never have more than one extraneous solution.

200. When solving an absolute value equation, you will always have to check more than one solution.

201. *Think About It* What is meant by *equivalent equations*? Give an example of two equivalent equations.

202. *Writing* Describe the steps used to transform an equation into an equivalent equation.

203. To solve the equation $2x^2 + 3x = 15x$, a student divides each side by x and solves the equation $2x + 3 = 15$. The resulting solution $(x = 6)$ satisfies the original equation. Is there an error? Explain.

204. Solve $3(x + 4)^2 + (x + 4) - 2 = 0$ in two ways.

(a) Let $u = x + 4$, and solve the resulting equation for u. Then solve the u-solution for x.

(b) Expand and collect like terms in the equation, and solve the resulting equation for x.

(c) Which method is easier? Explain.

Think About It **In Exercises 205–210, write a quadratic equation that has the given solutions. (There are many correct answers.)**

205. -3 and 6

206. -4 and -11

207. 8 and 14

208. $\frac{1}{6}$ and $-\frac{2}{5}$

209. $1 + \sqrt{2}$ and $1 - \sqrt{2}$

210. $-3 + \sqrt{5}$ and $-3 - \sqrt{5}$

In Exercises 211 and 212, consider an equation of the form $x + |x - a| = b$, where a and b are constants.

211. Find a and b when the solution of the equation is $x = 9$. (There are many correct answers.)

212. *Writing* Write a short paragraph listing the steps required to solve this equation involving absolute values and explain why it is important to check your solutions.

213. Solve each equation, given that a and b are not zero.

(a) $ax^2 + bx = 0$

(b) $ax^2 - ax = 0$

A.6 Linear Inequalities in One Variable

Introduction

Simple inequalities were discussed in Appendix A.1. There, you used the inequality symbols $<$, $\leq$, $>$, and $\geq$ to compare two numbers and to denote subsets of real numbers. For instance, the simple inequality

$$x \geq 3$$

denotes all real numbers x that are greater than or equal to 3.

Now, you will expand your work with inequalities to include more involved statements such as

$$5x - 7 < 3x + 9$$

and

$$-3 \leq 6x - 1 < 3.$$

As with an equation, you **solve an inequality** in the variable x by finding all values of x for which the inequality is true. Such values are **solutions** and are said to **satisfy** the inequality. The set of all real numbers that are solutions of an inequality is the **solution set** of the inequality. For instance, the solution set of

$$x + 1 < 4$$

is all real numbers that are less than 3.

The set of all points on the real number line that represent the solution set is the **graph of the inequality.** Graphs of many types of inequalities consist of intervals on the real number line. See Appendix A.1 to review the nine basic types of intervals on the real number line. Note that each type of interval can be classified as *bounded* or *unbounded*.

Example 1 Intervals and Inequalities

Write an inequality to represent each interval, and state whether the interval is bounded or unbounded.

a. $(-3, 5]$
b. $(-3, \infty)$
c. $[0, 2]$
d. $(-\infty, \infty)$

Solution

a. $(-3, 5]$ corresponds to $-3 < x \leq 5$.   Bounded
b. $(-3, \infty)$ corresponds to $-3 < x$.   Unbounded
c. $[0, 2]$ corresponds to $0 \leq x \leq 2$.   Bounded
d. $(-\infty, \infty)$ corresponds to $-\infty < x < \infty$.   Unbounded

✓*CHECKPOINT*   Now try Exercise 1.

Properties of Inequalities

The procedures for solving linear inequalities in one variable are much like those for solving linear equations. To isolate the variable, you can make use of the **Properties of Inequalities.** These properties are similar to the properties of equality, but there are two important exceptions. When each side of an inequality is multiplied or divided by a negative number, the direction of the inequality symbol must be reversed. Here is an example.

$$-2 < 5 \qquad \text{Original inequality}$$

$$(-3)(-2) > (-3)(5) \qquad \text{Multiply each side by } -3 \text{ and reverse inequality.}$$

$$6 > -15 \qquad \text{Simplify.}$$

Notice that if the inequality was not reversed you would obtain the false statement $6 < -15$.

Two inequalities that have the same solution set are **equivalent.** For instance, the inequalities

$$x + 2 < 5$$

and

$$x < 3$$

are equivalent. To obtain the second inequality from the first, you can subtract 2 from each side of the inequality. The following list describes the operations that can be used to create equivalent inequalities.

Properties of Inequalities

Let a, b, c, and d be real numbers.

1. Transitive Property

$$a < b \text{ and } b < c \quad \implies \quad a < c$$

2. Addition of Inequalities

$$a < b \text{ and } c < d \quad \implies \quad a + c < b + d$$

3. Addition of a Constant

$$a < b \quad \implies \quad a + c < b + c$$

4. Multiplication by a Constant

$$\text{For } c > 0, a < b \quad \implies \quad ac < bc$$

$$\text{For } c < 0, a < b \quad \implies \quad ac > bc \qquad \text{Reverse the inequality.}$$

Each of the properties above is true if the symbol $<$ is replaced by $\leq$ and the symbol $>$ is replaced by $\geq$. For instance, another form of the multiplication property would be as follows.

$$\text{For } c > 0, a \leq b \quad \implies \quad ac \leq bc$$

$$\text{For } c < 0, a \leq b \quad \implies \quad ac \geq bc$$

Solving a Linear Inequality in One Variable

The simplest type of inequality is a **linear inequality** in one variable. For instance, $2x + 3 > 4$ is a linear inequality in x.

In the following examples, pay special attention to the steps in which the inequality symbol is reversed. Remember that when you multiply or divide by a negative number, you must reverse the inequality symbol.

Example 2 Solving Linear Inequalities

Solve each inequality.

a. $5x - 7 > 3x + 9$

b. $1 - \dfrac{3x}{2} \geq x - 4$

Solution

a. $\quad 5x - 7 > 3x + 9 \qquad$ Write original inequality.

$\qquad 2x - 7 > 9 \qquad$ Subtract $3x$ from each side.

$\qquad\quad 2x > 16 \qquad$ Add 7 to each side.

$\qquad\qquad x > 8 \qquad$ Divide each side by 2.

The solution set is all real numbers that are greater than 8, which is denoted by $(8, \infty)$. The graph of this solution set is shown in Figure A.8. Note that a parenthesis at 8 on the real number line indicates that 8 *is not* part of the solution set.

Solution interval: $(8, \infty)$

FIGURE **A.8**

b. $\quad 1 - \dfrac{3x}{2} \geq x - 4 \qquad$ Write original inequality.

$\qquad 2 - 3x \geq 2x - 8 \qquad$ Multiply each side by 2.

$\qquad 2 - 5x \geq \;\; - 8 \qquad$ Subtract $2x$ from each side.

$\qquad\quad -5x \geq \;\; - 10 \qquad$ Subtract 2 from each side.

$\qquad\qquad x \leq 2 \qquad$ Divide each side by -5 and reverse the inequality.

The solution set is all real numbers that are less than or equal to 2, which is denoted by $(-\infty, 2]$. The graph of this solution set is shown in Figure A.9. Note that a bracket at 2 on the real number line indicates that 2 *is* part of the solution set.

Solution interval: $(-\infty, 2]$

FIGURE **A.9**

✓CHECKPOINT Now try Exercise 25.

Sometimes it is possible to write two inequalities as a **double inequality.** For instance, you can write the two inequalities $-4 \le 5x - 2$ and $5x - 2 < 7$ more simply as

$$-4 \le 5x - 2 < 7. \qquad \qquad \text{Double inequality}$$

This form allows you to solve the two inequalities together, as demonstrated in Example 3.

Example 3   Solving a Double Inequality

To solve a double inequality, you can isolate x as the middle term.

$$-3 \le 6x - 1 < 3 \qquad \qquad \text{Original inequality}$$

$$-3 + 1 \le 6x - 1 + 1 < 3 + 1 \qquad \qquad \text{Add 1 to each part.}$$

$$-2 \le 6x < 4 \qquad \qquad \text{Simplify.}$$

$$\frac{-2}{6} \le \frac{6x}{6} < \frac{4}{6} \qquad \qquad \text{Divide each part by 6.}$$

$$-\frac{1}{3} \le x < \frac{2}{3} \qquad \qquad \text{Simplify.}$$

The solution set is all real numbers that are greater than or equal to $-\frac{1}{3}$ and less than $\frac{2}{3}$, which is denoted by $\left[-\frac{1}{3}, \frac{2}{3}\right)$. The graph of this solution set is shown in Figure A.10.

Solution interval: $\left[-\frac{1}{3}, \frac{2}{3}\right)$

FIGURE A.10

✓CHECKPOINT   Now try Exercise 37.

The double inequality in Example 3 could have been solved in two parts as follows.

$$-3 \le 6x - 1 \qquad \text{and} \qquad 6x - 1 < 3$$

$$-2 \le 6x \qquad \qquad \qquad 6x < 4$$

$$-\frac{1}{3} \le x \qquad \qquad \qquad x < \frac{2}{3}$$

The solution set consists of all real numbers that satisfy *both* inequalities. In other words, the solution set is the set of all values of x for which

$$-\frac{1}{3} \le x < \frac{2}{3}.$$

When combining two inequalities to form a double inequality, be sure that the inequalities satisfy the Transitive Property. For instance, it is *incorrect* to combine the inequalities $3 < x$ and $x \le -1$ as $3 < x \le -1$. This "inequality" is wrong because 3 is not less than -1.

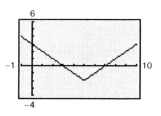
Inequalities Involving Absolute Values

Solving an Absolute Value Inequality

Let x be a variable or an algebraic expression and let a be a real number such that $a \geq 0$.

1. The solutions of $|x| < a$ are all values of x that lie between $-a$ and a.

    $|x| < a$ if and only if $-a < x < a$.   Double inequality

2. The solutions of $|x| > a$ are all values of x that are less than $-a$ or greater than a.

    $|x| > a$ if and only if $x < -a$ or $x > a$.   Compound inequality

These rules are also valid if $<$ is replaced by $\leq$ and $>$ is replaced by $\geq$.

Example 4   Solving an Absolute Value Inequality

Solve each inequality.

a. $|x - 5| < 2$ **b.** $|x + 3| \geq 7$

Solution

a. $|x - 5| < 2$ Write original inequality.

$-2 < x - 5 < 2$ Write equivalent inequalities.

$-2 + 5 < x - 5 + 5 < 2 + 5$ Add 5 to each part.

$3 < x < 7$ Simplify.

The solution set is all real numbers that are greater than 3 and less than 7, which is denoted by (3, 7). The graph of this solution set is shown in Figure A.11.

b. $|x + 3| \geq 7$ Write original inequality.

$x + 3 \leq -7$ or $x + 3 \geq 7$ Write equivalent inequalities.

$x + 3 - 3 \leq -7 - 3$ $x + 3 - 3 \geq 7 - 3$ Subtract 3 from each side.

$x \leq -10$ $x \geq 4$ Simplify.

The solution set is all real numbers that are less than or equal to -10 *or* greater than or equal to 4. The interval notation for this solution set is $(-\infty, -10] \cup [4, \infty)$. The symbol $\cup$ is called a *union* symbol and is used to denote the combining of two sets. The graph of this solution set is shown in Figure A.12.

STUDY TIP

Note that the graph of the inequality $|x - 5| < 2$ can be described as all real numbers *within* two units of 5, as shown in Figure A.11.

$|x - 5| < 2$: *Solutions lie inside* (3, 7)
FIGURE A.11

$|x + 3| \geq 7$: *Solutions lie outside* $(-10, 4)$
FIGURE A.12

✓**CHECKPOINT**   Now try Exercise 49.

Applications

A problem-solving plan can be used to model and solve real-life problems that involve inequalities, as illustrated in Example 5.

Example 5   Comparative Shopping

You are choosing between two different cell phone plans. Plan A costs $49.99 per month for 500 minutes plus $0.40 for each additional minute. Plan B costs $45.99 per month for 500 minutes plus $0.45 for each additional minute. How many *additional* minutes must you use in one month for plan B to cost more than plan A?

Solution

Verbal Model:

Monthly cost for plan B	>	Monthly cost for plan A

Labels: Minutes used (over 500) in one month $= m$ (minutes)
                Monthly cost for plan A $= 0.40m + 49.99$ (dollars)
                Monthly cost for plan B $= 0.45m + 45.99$ (dollars)

Inequality: $0.45m + 45.99 > 0.40m + 49.99$

$$0.05m > 4$$

$$m > 80 \text{ minutes}$$

Plan B costs more if you use more than 80 additional minutes in one month.

✓CHECKPOINT   Now try Exercise 91.

Example 6   Accuracy of a Measurement

You go to a candy store to buy chocolates that cost $9.89 per pound. The scale that is used in the store has a state seal of approval that indicates the scale is accurate to within half an ounce (or $\frac{1}{32}$ of a pound). According to the scale, your purchase weighs one-half pound and costs $4.95. How much might you have been undercharged or overcharged as a result of inaccuracy in the scale?

Solution

Let x represent the *true* weight of the candy. Because the scale is accurate to within half an ounce (or $\frac{1}{32}$ of a pound), the difference between the exact weight (x) and the scale weight $\left(\frac{1}{2}\right)$ is less than or equal to $\frac{1}{32}$ of a pound. That is, $\left|x - \frac{1}{2}\right| \leq \frac{1}{32}$. You can solve this inequality as follows.

$$-\tfrac{1}{32} \leq x - \tfrac{1}{2} \leq \tfrac{1}{32}$$
$$\tfrac{15}{32} \leq x \leq \tfrac{17}{32}$$
$$0.46875 \leq x \leq 0.53125$$

In other words, your "one-half pound" of candy could have weighed as little as 0.46875 pound (which would have cost $4.64) or as much as 0.53125 pound (which would have cost $5.25). So, you could have been overcharged by as much as $0.31 or undercharged by as much as $0.30.

✓CHECKPOINT   Now try Exercise 105.

A.6 Exercises

VOCABULARY CHECK: Fill in the blanks.

1. The set of all real numbers that are solutions to an inequality is the _____ _____ of the inequality.

2. The set of all points on the real number line that represent the solution set of an inequality is the _____ of the inequality.

3. To solve a linear inequality in one variable, you can use the properties of inequalities, which are identical to those used to solve equations, with the exception of multiplying or dividing each side by a _____ number.

4. Two inequalities that have the same solution set are _____ _____.

5. It is sometimes possible to write two inequalities as one inequality, called a _____ inequality.

6. The symbol $\cup$ is called a _____ symbol and is used to denote the combining of two sets.

In Exercises 1–6, (a) write an inequality that represents the interval and (b) state whether the interval is bounded or unbounded.

1. $[-1, 5]$
2. $(2, 10]$
3. $(11, \infty)$
4. $[-5, \infty)$
5. $(-\infty, -2)$
6. $(-\infty, 7]$

In Exercises 7–12, match the inequality with its graph. [The graphs are labeled (a), (b), (c), (d), (e), and (f).]

(a)

(b)

(c)

(d)

(e)

(f)

7. $x < 3$
8. $x \geq 5$
9. $-3 < x \leq 4$
10. $0 \leq x \leq \frac{9}{2}$
11. $|x| < 3$
12. $|x| > 4$

In Exercises 13–18, determine whether each value of x is a solution of the inequality.

Inequality	Values
13. $5x - 12 > 0$	(a) $x = 3$ (b) $x = -3$
	(c) $x = \frac{5}{2}$ (d) $x = \frac{3}{2}$
14. $2x + 1 < -3$	(a) $x = 0$ (b) $x = -\frac{1}{4}$
	(c) $x = -4$ (d) $x = -\frac{3}{2}$

Inequality	Values
15. $0 < \dfrac{x - 2}{4} < 2$	(a) $x = 4$ (b) $x = 10$
	(c) $x = 0$ (d) $x = \frac{7}{2}$
16. $-1 < \dfrac{3 - x}{2} \leq 1$	(a) $x = 0$ (b) $x = -5$
	(c) $x = 1$ (d) $x = 5$
17. $|x - 10| \geq 3$	(a) $x = 13$ (b) $x = -1$
	(c) $x = 14$ (d) $x = 9$
18. $|2x - 3| < 15$	(a) $x = -6$ (b) $x = 0$
	(c) $x = 12$ (d) $x = 7$

In Exercises 19–44, solve the inequality and sketch the solution on the real number line. (Some inequalities have no solutions.)

19. $4x < 12$
20. $10x < -40$
21. $-2x > -3$
22. $-6x > 15$
23. $x - 5 \geq 7$
24. $x + 7 \leq 12$
25. $2x + 7 < 3 + 4x$
26. $3x + 1 \geq 2 + x$
27. $2x - 1 \geq 1 - 5x$
28. $6x - 4 \leq 2 + 8x$
29. $4 - 2x < 3(3 - x)$
30. $4(x + 1) < 2x + 3$
31. $\frac{3}{4}x - 6 \leq x - 7$
32. $3 + \frac{2}{7}x > x - 2$
33. $\frac{1}{2}(8x + 1) \geq 3x + \frac{5}{2}$
34. $9x - 1 < \frac{3}{4}(16x - 2)$
35. $3.6x + 11 \geq -3.4$
36. $15.6 - 1.3x < -5.2$
37. $1 < 2x + 3 < 9$
38. $-8 \leq -(3x + 5) < 13$

39. $-4 < \dfrac{2x - 3}{3} < 4$

40. $0 \le \dfrac{x + 3}{2} < 5$

41. $\frac{3}{4} > x + 1 > \frac{1}{4}$

42. $-1 < 2 - \dfrac{x}{3} < 1$

43. $3.2 \le 0.4x - 1 \le 4.4$

44. $4.5 > \dfrac{1.5x + 6}{2} > 10.5$

In Exercises 45–60, solve the inequality and sketch the solution on the real number line. (Some inequalities have no solution.)

45. $|x| < 6$

46. $|x| > 4$

47. $\left|\dfrac{x}{2}\right| > 1$

48. $\left|\dfrac{x}{5}\right| > 3$

49. $|x - 5| < -1$

50. $|x - 7| < -5$

51. $|x - 20| \le 6$

52. $|x - 8| \ge 0$

53. $|3 - 4x| \ge 9$

54. $|1 - 2x| < 5$

55. $\left|\dfrac{x - 3}{2}\right| \ge 4$

56. $\left|1 - \dfrac{2x}{3}\right| < 1$

57. $|9 - 2x| - 2 < -1$

58. $|x + 14| + 3 > 17$

59. $2|x + 10| \ge 9$

60. $3|4 - 5x| \le 9$

Graphical Analysis   In Exercises 61–68, use a graphing utility to graph the inequality and identify the solution set.

61. $6x > 12$

62. $3x - 1 \le 5$

63. $5 - 2x \ge 1$

64. $3(x + 1) < x + 7$

65. $|x - 8| \le 14$

66. $|2x + 9| > 13$

67. $2|x + 7| \ge 13$

68. $\frac{1}{2}|x + 1| \le 3$

Graphical Analysis   In Exercises 69–74, use a graphing utility to graph the equation. Use the graph to approximate the values of x that satisfy each inequality.

	Equation	Inequalities	
69.	$y = 2x - 3$	(a) $y \ge 1$	(b) $y \le 0$
70.	$y = \frac{2}{3}x + 1$	(a) $y \le 5$	(b) $y \ge 0$
71.	$y = -\frac{1}{2}x + 2$	(a) $0 \le y \le 3$	(b) $y \ge 0$
72.	$y = -3x + 8$	(a) $-1 \le y \le 3$	(b) $y \le 0$
73.	$y = |x - 3|$	(a) $y \le 2$	(b) $y \ge 4$
74.	$y = \left|\frac{1}{2}x + 1\right|$	(a) $y \le 4$	(b) $y \ge 1$

In Exercises 75–80, find the interval(s) on the real number line for which the radicand is nonnegative.

75. $\sqrt{x - 5}$ **76.** $\sqrt{x - 10}$

77. $\sqrt{x + 3}$ **78.** $\sqrt{3 - x}$

79. $\sqrt[4]{7 - 2x}$ **80.** $\sqrt[4]{6x + 15}$

81. *Think About It*   The graph of $|x - 5| < 3$ can be described as all real numbers within three units of 5. Give a similar description of $|x - 10| < 8$.

82. *Think About It*   The graph of $|x - 2| > 5$ can be described as all real numbers more than five units from 2. Give a similar description of $|x - 8| > 4$.

In Exercises 83–90, use absolute value notation to define the interval (or pair of intervals) on the real number line.

83.

84.

85.

86.

87. All real numbers within 10 units of 12

88. All real numbers at least five units from 8

89. All real numbers more than four units from -3

90. All real numbers no more than seven units from -6

91. *Checking Account*   You can choose between two types of checking accounts at your local bank. Type A charges a monthly service fee of $6 plus $0.25 for each check written. Type B charges a monthly service fee of $4.50 plus $0.50 for each check written. How many checks must you write in a month in order for the monthly charges for type A to be less than that for type B?

92. *Copying Costs* Your department sends its copying to the photocopy center of your company. The center bills your department $0.10 per page. You have investigated the possibility of buying a departmental copier for $3000. With your own copier, the cost per page would be $0.03. The expected life of the copier is 4 years. How many copies must you make in the four-year period to justify buying the copier?

93. *Investment* In order for an investment of $1000 to grow to more than $1062.50 in 2 years, what must the annual interest rate be? $[A = P(1 + rt)]$

94. *Investment* In order for an investment of $750 to grow to more than $825 in 2 years, what must the annual interest rate be? $[A = P(1 + rt)]$

95. *Cost, Revenue, and Profit* The revenue for selling x units of a product is $R = 115.95x$. The cost of producing x units is

$$C = 95x + 750.$$

To obtain a profit, the revenue must be greater than the cost. For what values of x will this product return a profit?

96. *Cost, Revenue, and Profit* The revenue for selling x units of a product is $R = 24.55x$. The cost of producing x units is

$$C = 15.4x + 150,000.$$

To obtain a profit, the revenue must be greater than the cost. For what values of x will this product return a profit?

97. *Daily Sales* A doughnut shop sells a dozen doughnuts for $2.95. Beyond the fixed costs (rent, utilities, and insurance) of $150 per day, it costs $1.45 for enough materials (flour, sugar, and so on) and labor to produce a dozen doughnuts. The daily profit from doughnut sales varies between $50 and $200. Between what levels (in dozens) do the daily sales vary?

98. *Weight Loss Program* A person enrolls in a diet and exercise program that guarantees a loss of at least $1\frac{1}{2}$ pounds per week. The person's weight at the beginning of the program is 164 pounds. Find the maximum number of weeks before the person attains a goal weight of 128 pounds.

 99. *Data Analysis: IQ Scores and GPA* The admissions office of a college wants to determine whether there is a relationship between IQ scores x and grade-point averages y after the first year of school. An equation that models the data the admissions office obtained is

$$y = 0.067x - 5.638.$$

(a) Use a graphing utility to graph the model.

(b) Use the graph to estimate the values of x that predict a grade-point average of at least 3.0.

 100. *Data Analysis: Weightlifting* You want to determine whether there is a relationship between an athlete's weight x (in pounds) and the athlete's maximum bench-press weight y (in pounds). The table shows a sample of data from 12 athletes.

(a) Use a graphing utility to plot the data.

Athlete's weight, x	Bench-press weight, y
165	170
184	185
150	200
210	255
196	205
240	295
202	190
170	175
185	195
190	185
230	250
160	155

(b) A model for the data is $y = 1.3x - 36$. Use a graphing utility to graph the model in the same viewing window used in part (a).

(c) Use the graph to estimate the values of x that predict a maximum bench-press weight of at least 200 pounds.

(d) Verify your estimate from part (c) algebraically.

(e) Use the graph to write a statement about the accuracy of the model. If you think the graph indicates that an athlete's weight is not a particularly good indicator of the athlete's maximum bench-press weight, list other factors that might influence an individual's maximum bench-press weight.

101. *Teachers' Salaries* The average salary S (in thousands of dollars) for elementary school teachers in the United States from 1990 to 2002 is approximated by the model

$$S = 1.05t + 31.0, \qquad 0 \le t \le 12$$

where t represents the year, with $t = 0$ corresponding to 1990. (Source: National Education Association)

(a) According to this model, when was the average salary at least $32,000, but not more than $42,000?

(b) According to this model, when will the average salary exceed $48,000?

102. *Egg Production* The number of eggs E (in billions) produced in the United States from 1990 to 2002 can be modeled by

$$E = 1.64t + 67.2, \quad 0 \le t \le 12$$

where t represents the year, with $t = 0$ corresponding to 1990. (Source: U.S. Department of Agriculture)

(a) According to this model, when was the annual egg production 70 billion, but no more than 80 billion?

(b) According to this model, when will the annual egg production exceed 95 billion?

103. *Geometry* The side of a square is measured as 10.4 inches with a possible error of $\frac{1}{16}$ inch. Using these measurements, determine the interval containing the possible areas of the square.

104. *Geometry* The side of a square is measured as 24.2 centimeters with a possible error of 0.25 centimeter. Using these measurements, determine the interval containing the possible areas of the square.

105. *Accuracy of Measurement* You stop at a self-service gas station to buy 15 gallons of 87-octane gasoline at $1.89 a gallon. The gas pump is accurate to within $\frac{1}{10}$ of a gallon. How much might you be undercharged or overcharged?

106. *Accuracy of Measurement* You buy six T-bone steaks that cost $14.99 per pound. The weight that is listed on the package is 5.72 pounds. The scale that weighed the package is accurate to within $\frac{1}{2}$ ounce. How much might you be undercharged or overcharged?

107. *Time Study* A time study was conducted to determine the length of time required to perform a particular task in a manufacturing process. The times required by approximately two-thirds of the workers in the study satisfied the inequality

$$\left| \frac{t - 15.6}{1.9} \right| < 1$$

where t is time in minutes. Determine the interval on the real number line in which these times lie.

108. *Height* The heights h of two-thirds of the members of a population satisfy the inequality

$$\left| \frac{h - 68.5}{2.7} \right| \le 1$$

where h is measured in inches. Determine the interval on the real number line in which these heights lie.

109. *Meteorology* An electronic device is to be operated in an environment with relative humidity h in the interval defined by $|h - 50| \le 30$. What are the minimum and maximum relative humidities for the operation of this device?

110. *Music* Michael Kasha of Florida State University used physics and mathematics to design a new classical guitar. He used the model for the frequency of the vibrations on a circular plate

$$v = \frac{2.6t}{d^2} \sqrt{\frac{E}{\rho}}$$

where v is the frequency (in vibrations per second), t is the plate thickness (in millimeters), d is the diameter of the plate, E is the elasticity of the plate material, and ρ is the density of the plate material. For fixed values of d, E, and ρ, the graph of the equation is a line (see figure).

(a) Estimate the frequency when the plate thickness is 2 millimeters.

(b) Estimate the plate thickness when the frequency is 600 vibrations per second.

(c) Approximate the interval for the plate thickness when the frequency is between 200 and 400 vibrations per second.

(d) Approximate the interval for the frequency when the plate thickness is less than 3 millimeters.

Synthesis

True or False? **In Exercises 111 and 112, determine whether the statement is true or false. Justify your answer.**

111. If a, b, and c are real numbers, and $a \le b$, then $ac \le bc$.

112. If $-10 \le x \le 8$, then $-10 \ge -x$ and $-x \ge -8$.

113. Identify the graph of the inequality $|x - a| \ge 2$.

(a)
$a - 2$ a $a + 2$ $\to x$

(b)
$a - 2$ a $a + 2$ $\to x$

(c)
$2 - a$ 2 $2 + a$ $\to x$

(d)
$2 - a$ 2 $2 + a$ $\to x$

114. Find sets of values of a, b, and c such that $0 \le x \le 10$ is a solution of the inequality $|ax - b| \le c$.

A.7 Errors and the Algebra of Calculus

Algebraic Errors to Avoid

This section contains five lists of common algebraic errors: errors involving parentheses, errors involving fractions, errors involving exponents, errors involving radicals, and errors involving dividing out. Many of these errors are made because they seem to be the *easiest* things to do. For instance, the operations of subtraction and division are often believed to be commutative and associative. The following examples illustrate the fact that subtraction and division are neither commutative nor associative.

Not commutative	*Not associative*
$4 - 3 \neq 3 - 4$	$8 - (6 - 2) \neq (8 - 6) - 2$
$15 \div 5 \neq 5 \div 15$	$20 \div (4 \div 2) \neq (20 \div 4) \div 2$

Errors Involving Parentheses

Potential Error	*Correct Form*	*Comment*
$a - (x - b) = a - x - b$	$a - (x - b) = a - x + b$	Change all signs when distributing minus sign.
$(a + b)^2 = a^2 + b^2$	$(a + b)^2 = a^2 + 2ab + b^2$	Remember the middle term when squaring binomials.
$\left(\frac{1}{2}a\right)\left(\frac{1}{2}b\right) = \frac{1}{2}(ab)$	$\left(\frac{1}{2}a\right)\left(\frac{1}{2}b\right) = \frac{1}{4}(ab) = \frac{ab}{4}$	$\frac{1}{2}$ occurs twice as a factor.
$(3x + 6)^2 = 3(x + 2)^2$	$(3x + 6)^2 = [3(x + 2)]^2$ $= 3^2(x + 2)^2$	When factoring, apply exponents to all factors.

Errors Involving Fractions

Potential Error	*Correct Form*	*Comment*
	Leave as $\dfrac{a}{x + b}$.	Do not add denominators when adding fractions.
	$\dfrac{\left(\dfrac{x}{a}\right)}{b} = \left(\dfrac{x}{a}\right)\left(\dfrac{1}{b}\right) = \dfrac{x}{ab}$	Multiply by the reciprocal when dividing fractions.
	$\dfrac{1}{a} + \dfrac{1}{b} = \dfrac{b + a}{ab}$	Use the property for adding fractions.
	$\dfrac{1}{3x} = \dfrac{1}{3} \cdot \dfrac{1}{x}$	Use the property for multiplying fractions.
	$(1/3)x = \dfrac{1}{3} \cdot x = \dfrac{x}{3}$	Be careful when using a slash to denote division.
	$(1/x) + 2 = \dfrac{1}{x} + 2 = \dfrac{1 + 2x}{x}$	Be careful when using a slash to denote division and be sure to find a common denominator before you add fractions.

Errors Involving Exponents

Potential Error	Correct Form	Comment
$(x^2)^3 = x^5$	$(x^2)^3 = x^{2 \cdot 3} = x^6$	Multiply exponents when raising a power to a power.
$x^2 \cdot x^3 = x^6$	$x^2 \cdot x^3 = x^{2+3} = x^5$	Add exponents when multiplying powers with like bases.
$2x^3 = (2x)^3$	$2x^3 = 2(x^3)$	Exponents have priority over coefficients.
$\dfrac{1}{x^2 - x^3} = x^{-2} - x^{-3}$	Leave as $\dfrac{1}{x^2 - x^3}$.	Do not move term-by-term from denominator to numerator.

Errors Involving Radicals

Potential Error	Correct Form	Comment
$\sqrt{5x} = 5\sqrt{x}$	$\sqrt{5x} = \sqrt{5}\sqrt{x}$	Radicals apply to every factor inside the radical.
$\sqrt{x^2 + a^2} = x + a$	Leave as $\sqrt{x^2 + a^2}$.	Do not apply radicals term-by-term.
$\sqrt{-x + a} = -\sqrt{x - a}$	Leave as $\sqrt{-x + a}$.	Do not factor minus signs out of square roots.

Errors Involving Dividing Out

Potential Error	Correct Form	Comment
$\dfrac{a + bx}{a} = 1 + bx$	$\dfrac{a + bx}{a} = \dfrac{a}{a} + \dfrac{bx}{a} = 1 + \dfrac{b}{a}x$	Divide out common factors, not common terms.
$\dfrac{a + ax}{a} = a + x$	$\dfrac{a + ax}{a} = \dfrac{a(1 + x)}{a} = 1 + x$	Factor before dividing out.
$1 + \dfrac{x}{2x} = 1 + \dfrac{1}{x}$	$1 + \dfrac{x}{2x} = 1 + \dfrac{1}{2} = \dfrac{3}{2}$	Divide out common factors.

A good way to avoid errors is to *work slowly, write neatly,* and *talk to yourself.* Each time you write a step, ask yourself why the step is algebraically legitimate. You can justify the step below because *dividing the numerator and denominator by the same nonzero number produces an equivalent fraction.*

$$\frac{2x}{6} = \frac{2 \cdot x}{2 \cdot 3} = \frac{x}{3}$$

Example 1   Using the Property for Adding Fractions

Describe and correct the error. $\dfrac{1}{2x} + \dfrac{1}{3x} = \dfrac{1}{5x}$

Solution

When adding fractions, use the property for adding fractions: $\dfrac{1}{a} + \dfrac{1}{b} = \dfrac{b + a}{ab}$.

$$\frac{1}{2x} + \frac{1}{3x} = \frac{3x + 2x}{6x^2} = \frac{5x}{6x^2} = \frac{5}{6x}$$

✓CHECKPOINT   Now try Exercise 17.

Some Algebra of Calculus

In calculus it is often necessary to take a simplified algebraic expression and "unsimplify" it. See the following lists, taken from a standard calculus text.

Unusual Factoring

Expression	Useful Calculus Form	Comment
$\dfrac{5x^4}{8}$	$\dfrac{5}{8}x^4$	Write with fractional coefficient.
$\dfrac{x^2 + 3x}{-6}$	$-\dfrac{1}{6}(x^2 + 3x)$	Write with fractional coefficient.
$2x^2 - x - 3$	$2\left(x^2 - \dfrac{x}{2} - \dfrac{3}{2}\right)$	Factor out the leading coefficient.
$\dfrac{x}{2}(x + 1)^{-1/2} + (x + 1)^{1/2}$	$\dfrac{(x + 1)^{-1/2}}{2}[x + 2(x + 1)]$	Factor out factor with lowest power.

Writing with Negative Exponents

Expression	Useful Calculus Form	Comment
$\dfrac{9}{5x^3}$	$\dfrac{9}{5}x^{-3}$	Move the factor to the numerator and change the sign of the exponent.
$\dfrac{7}{\sqrt{2x - 3}}$	$7(2x - 3)^{-1/2}$	Move the factor to the numerator and change the sign of the exponent.

Writing a Fraction as a Sum

Expression	Useful Calculus Form	Comment
$\dfrac{x + 2x^2 + 1}{\sqrt{x}}$	$x^{1/2} + 2x^{3/2} + x^{-1/2}$	Divide each term by $x^{1/2}$.
$\dfrac{1 + x}{x^2 + 1}$	$\dfrac{1}{x^2 + 1} + \dfrac{x}{x^2 + 1}$	Rewrite the fraction as the sum of fractions.
$\dfrac{2x}{x^2 + 2x + 1}$	$\dfrac{2x + 2 - 2}{x^2 + 2x + 1}$	Add and subtract the same term.
	$= \dfrac{2x + 2}{x^2 + 2x + 1} - \dfrac{2}{(x + 1)^2}$	Rewrite the fraction as the difference of fractions.
$\dfrac{x^2 - 2}{x + 1}$	$x - 1 - \dfrac{1}{x + 1}$	Use long division. (See Section 2.3.)
$\dfrac{x + 7}{x^2 - x - 6}$	$\dfrac{2}{x - 3} - \dfrac{1}{x + 2}$	Use the method of partial fractions. (See Section 7.4.)

Inserting Factors and Terms

Expression	Useful Calculus Form	Comment
$(2x - 1)^3$	$\dfrac{1}{2}(2x - 1)^3(2)$	Multiply and divide by 2.
$7x^2(4x^3 - 5)^{1/2}$	$\dfrac{7}{12}(4x^3 - 5)^{1/2}(12x^2)$	Multiply and divide by 12.
$\dfrac{4x^2}{9} - 4y^2 = 1$	$\dfrac{x^2}{9/4} - \dfrac{y^2}{1/4} = 1$	Write with fractional denominators.
$\dfrac{x}{x + 1}$	$\dfrac{x + 1 - 1}{x + 1} = 1 - \dfrac{1}{x + 1}$	Add and subtract the same term.

The next five examples demonstrate many of the steps in the preceding lists.

Example 2   **Factors Involving Negative Exponents**

Factor $x(x + 1)^{-1/2} + (x + 1)^{1/2}$.

Solution

When multiplying factors with like bases, you add exponents. When factoring, you are undoing multiplication, and so you *subtract* exponents.

$$x(x + 1)^{-1/2} + (x + 1)^{1/2} = (x + 1)^{-1/2}[x(x + 1)^0 + (x + 1)^1]$$
$$= (x + 1)^{-1/2}[x + (x + 1)]$$
$$= (x + 1)^{-1/2}(2x + 1)$$

✓CHECKPOINT   Now try Exercise 23.

Another way to simplify the expression in Example 2 is to multiply the expression by a fractional form of 1 and then use the Distributive Property.

$$x(x + 1)^{-1/2} + (x + 1)^{1/2} = [x(x + 1)^{-1/2} + (x + 1)^{1/2}] \cdot \frac{(x + 1)^{1/2}}{(x + 1)^{1/2}}$$

$$= \frac{x(x + 1)^0 + (x + 1)^1}{(x + 1)^{1/2}} = \frac{2x + 1}{\sqrt{x + 1}}$$

Example 3   **Inserting Factors in an Expression**

Insert the required factor: $\dfrac{x + 2}{(x^2 + 4x - 3)^2} = (\ \ )\dfrac{1}{(x^2 + 4x - 3)^2}(2x + 4)$.

Solution

The expression on the right side of the equation is twice the expression on the left side. To make both sides equal, insert a factor of $\frac{1}{2}$.

$$\frac{x + 2}{(x^2 + 4x - 3)^2} = \left(\frac{1}{2}\right)\frac{1}{(x^2 + 4x - 3)^2}(2x + 4)$$ Right side is multiplied and divided by 2.

✓CHECKPOINT   Now try Exercise 25.

Example 4 **Rewriting Fractions**

Explain why the two expressions are equivalent.

$$\frac{4x^2}{9} - 4y^2 = \frac{x^2}{\frac{9}{4}} - \frac{y^2}{\frac{1}{4}}$$

Solution

To write the expression on the left side of the equation in the form given on the right side, multiply the numerators and denominators of both terms by $\frac{1}{4}$.

$$\frac{4x^2}{9} - 4y^2 = \frac{4x^2}{9}\left(\frac{\frac{1}{4}}{\frac{1}{4}}\right) - 4y^2\left(\frac{\frac{1}{4}}{\frac{1}{4}}\right) = \frac{x^2}{\frac{9}{4}} - \frac{y^2}{\frac{1}{4}}$$

✓**CHECKPOINT** Now try Exercise 29.

Example 5 **Rewriting with Negative Exponents**

Rewrite each expression using negative exponents.

a. $\dfrac{-4x}{(1 - 2x^2)^2}$ **b.** $\dfrac{2}{5x^3} - \dfrac{1}{\sqrt{x}} + \dfrac{3}{5(4x)^2}$

Solution

a. $\dfrac{-4x}{(1 - 2x^2)^2} = -4x(1 - 2x^2)^{-2}$

b. Begin by writing the second term in exponential form.

$$\frac{2}{5x^3} - \frac{1}{\sqrt{x}} + \frac{3}{5(4x)^2} = \frac{2}{5x^3} - \frac{1}{x^{1/2}} + \frac{3}{5(4x)^2}$$

$$= \frac{2}{5}x^{-3} - x^{-1/2} + \frac{3}{5}(4x)^{-2}$$

✓**CHECKPOINT** Now try Exercise 39.

Example 6 **Writing a Fraction as a Sum of Terms**

Rewrite each fraction as the sum of three terms.

a. $\dfrac{x^2 - 4x + 8}{2x}$ **b.** $\dfrac{x + 2x^2 + 1}{\sqrt{x}}$

Solution

a. $\dfrac{x^2 - 4x + 8}{2x} = \dfrac{x^2}{2x} - \dfrac{4x}{2x} + \dfrac{8}{2x}$ **b.** $\dfrac{x + 2x^2 + 1}{\sqrt{x}} = \dfrac{x}{x^{1/2}} + \dfrac{2x^2}{x^{1/2}} + \dfrac{1}{x^{1/2}}$

$$= \frac{x}{2} - 2 + \frac{4}{x}$$ $$= x^{1/2} + 2x^{3/2} + x^{-1/2}$$

✓**CHECKPOINT** Now try Exercise 43.

A.7 | Exercises

VOCABULARY CHECK: Fill in the blanks.

1. To write the expression $\dfrac{2}{\sqrt{x}}$ with negative exponents, move $\sqrt{x}$ to the _____ and change the sign of the exponent.

2. When dividing fractions, multiply by the _____.

In Exercises 1–18, describe and correct the error.

1. $\overline{2x - (3y + 4) = 2x - 3y + 4}$

2. $\overline{5z + 3(x - 2) = 5z + 3x - 2}$

3. $\dfrac{4}{16x - (2x + 1)} = \dfrac{4}{14x + 1}$

4. $\dfrac{1 - x}{(5 - x)(-x)} = \dfrac{x - 1}{x(x - 5)}$

5. $\overline{(5z)(6z) = 30z}$

6. $\overline{x(yz) = (xy)(xz)}$

7. $a\left(\dfrac{x}{y}\right) = \dfrac{ax}{ay}$

8. $\overline{(4x)^2 = 4x^2}$

9. $\overline{\sqrt{x + 9} = \sqrt{x} + 3}$

10. $\overline{\sqrt{25 - x^2} = 5 - x}$

11. $\dfrac{2x^2 + 1}{5x} = \dfrac{2x + 1}{5}$

12. $\dfrac{6x + y}{6x - y} = \dfrac{x + y}{x - y}$

13. $\dfrac{1}{a^{-1} + b^{-1}} = \left(\dfrac{1}{a + b}\right)^{-1}$

14. $\dfrac{1}{x + y^{-1}} = \dfrac{y}{x + 1}$

15. $\overline{(x^2 + 5x)^{1/2} = x(x + 5)^{1/2}}$

16. $\overline{x(2x - 1)^2 = (2x^2 - x)^2}$

17. $\dfrac{3}{x} + \dfrac{4}{y} = \dfrac{7}{x + y}$

18. $\dfrac{1}{2y} = (1/2)y$

In Exercises 19–38, insert the required factor in the parentheses.

19. $\dfrac{3x + 2}{5} = \dfrac{1}{5}(\quad)$

20. $\dfrac{7x^2}{10} = \dfrac{7}{10}(\quad)$

21. $\tfrac{2}{3}x^2 + \tfrac{1}{3}x + 5 = \tfrac{1}{3}(\quad)$

22. $\tfrac{3}{4}x + \tfrac{1}{2} = \tfrac{1}{4}(\quad)$

23. $x^2(x^3 - 1)^4 = (\quad)(x^3 - 1)^4(3x^2)$

24. $x(1 - 2x^2)^3 = (\quad)(1 - 2x^2)^3(-4x)$

25. $\dfrac{4x + 6}{(x^2 + 3x + 7)^3} = (\quad)\dfrac{1}{(x^2 + 3x + 7)^3}(2x + 3)$

26. $\dfrac{x + 1}{(x^2 + 2x - 3)^2} = (\quad)\dfrac{1}{(x^2 + 2x - 3)^2}(2x + 2)$

27. $\dfrac{3}{x} + \dfrac{5}{2x^2} - \dfrac{3}{2}x = (\quad)(6x + 5 - 3x^3)$

28. $\dfrac{(x - 1)^2}{169} + (y + 5)^2 = \dfrac{(x - 1)^3}{169(\quad)} + (y + 5)^2$

29. $\dfrac{9x^2}{25} + \dfrac{16y^2}{49} = \dfrac{x^2}{(\quad)} + \dfrac{y^2}{(\quad)}$

30. $\dfrac{3x^2}{4} - \dfrac{9y^2}{16} = \dfrac{x^2}{(\quad)} - \dfrac{y^2}{(\quad)}$

31. $\dfrac{x^2}{1/12} - \dfrac{y^2}{2/3} = \dfrac{12x^2}{(\quad)} - \dfrac{3y^2}{(\quad)}$

32. $\dfrac{x^2}{4/9} + \dfrac{y^2}{7/8} = \dfrac{9x^2}{(\quad)} + \dfrac{8y^2}{(\quad)}$

33. $x^{1/3} - 5x^{4/3} = x^{1/3}(\quad)$

34. $3(2x + 1)x^{1/2} + 4x^{3/2} = x^{1/2}(\quad)$

35. $(1 - 3x)^{4/3} - 4x(1 - 3x)^{1/3} = (1 - 3x)^{1/3}(\quad)$

36. $\dfrac{1}{2\sqrt{x}} + 5x^{3/2} - 10x^{5/2} = \dfrac{1}{2\sqrt{x}}(\quad)$

37. $\dfrac{1}{10}(2x + 1)^{5/2} - \dfrac{1}{6}(2x + 1)^{3/2} = \dfrac{(2x + 1)^{3/2}}{15}(\quad)$

38. $\dfrac{3}{7}(t + 1)^{7/3} - \dfrac{3}{4}(t + 1)^{4/3} = \dfrac{3(t + 1)^{4/3}}{28}(\quad)$

In Exercises 39–42, write the expression using negative exponents.

39. $\dfrac{3x^2}{(2x - 1)^3}$

40. $\dfrac{x + 1}{x(6 - x)^{1/2}}$

41. $\dfrac{4}{3x} + \dfrac{4}{x^4} - \dfrac{7x}{\sqrt[3]{2x}}$

42. $\dfrac{x}{x - 2} + \dfrac{1}{x^2} + \dfrac{8}{3(9x)^3}$

In Exercises 43–48, write the fraction as a sum of two or more terms.

43. $\dfrac{16 - 5x - x^2}{x}$

44. $\dfrac{x^3 - 5x^2 + 4}{x^2}$

45. $\dfrac{4x^3 - 7x^2 + 1}{x^{1/3}}$

46. $\dfrac{2x^5 - 3x^3 + 5x - 1}{x^{3/2}}$

47. $\dfrac{3 - 5x^2 - x^4}{\sqrt{x}}$

48. $\dfrac{x^3 - 5x^4}{3x^2}$

In Exercises 49–60, simplify the expression.

49. $\dfrac{-2(x^2 - 3)^{-3}(2x)(x + 1)^3 - 3(x + 1)^2(x^2 - 3)^{-2}}{[(x + 1)^3]^2}$

50. $\dfrac{x^5(-3)(x^2 + 1)^{-4}(2x) - (x^2 + 1)^{-3}(5)x^4}{(x^5)^2}$

51. $\dfrac{(6x + 1)^3(27x^2 + 2) - (9x^3 + 2x)(3)(6x + 1)^2(6)}{[(6x + 1)^3]^2}$

52. $\dfrac{(4x^2 + 9)^{1/2}(2) - (2x + 3)\left(\frac{1}{2}\right)(4x^2 + 9)^{-1/2}(8x)}{[(4x^2 + 9)^{1/2}]^2}$

53. $\dfrac{(x + 2)^{3/4}(x + 3)^{-2/3} - (x + 3)^{1/3}(x + 2)^{-1/4}}{[(x + 2)^{3/4}]^2}$

54. $(2x - 1)^{1/2} - (x + 2)(2x - 1)^{-1/2}$

55. $\dfrac{2(3x - 1)^{1/3} - (2x + 1)\left(\frac{1}{3}\right)(3x - 1)^{-2/3}(3)}{(3x - 1)^{2/3}}$

56. $\dfrac{(x + 1)\left(\frac{1}{2}\right)(2x - 3x^2)^{-1/2}(2 - 6x) - (2x - 3x^2)^{1/2}}{(x + 1)^2}$

57. $\dfrac{1}{(x^2 + 4)^{1/2}} \cdot \dfrac{1}{2}(x^2 + 4)^{-1/2}(2x)$

58. $\dfrac{1}{x^2 - 6}(2x) + \dfrac{1}{2x + 5}(2)$

59. $(x^2 + 5)^{1/2}\left(\frac{3}{2}\right)(3x - 2)^{1/2}(3)$
$\qquad + (3x - 2)^{3/2}\left(\frac{1}{2}\right)(x^2 + 5)^{-1/2}(2x)$

60. $(3x + 2)^{-1/2}(3)(x - 6)^{1/2}(1)$
$\qquad + (x - 6)^3\left(-\frac{1}{2}\right)(3x + 2)^{-3/2}(3)$

61. *Athletics* An athlete has set up a course for training as part of her regimen in preparation for an upcoming triathlon. She is dropped off by a boat 2 miles from the nearest point on shore. The finish line is 4 miles down the coast and 2 miles inland (see figure). She can swim 2 miles per hour and run 6 miles per hour. The time t (in hours) required for her to reach the finish line can be approximated by the model

$$t = \dfrac{\sqrt{x^2 + 4}}{2} + \dfrac{\sqrt{(4 - x)^2 + 4}}{6}$$

where x is the distance down the coast (in miles) to which she swims and then leaves the water to start her run.

(a) Find the times required for the triathlete to finish when she swims to the points $x = 0.5$, $x = 1.0$, ..., $x = 3.5$, and $x = 4.0$ miles down the coast.

(b) Use your results from part (a) to determine the distance down the coast that will yield the minimum amount of time required for the triathlete to reach the finish line.

(c) The expression below was obtained using calculus. It can be used to find the minimum amount of time required for the triathlete to reach the finish line. Simplify the expression.

$$\tfrac{1}{2}x(x^2 + 4)^{-1/2} + \tfrac{1}{6}(x - 4)(x^2 - 8x + 20)^{-1/2}$$

62. (a) Verify that $y_1 = y_2$ analytically.

$$y_1 = x^2\left(\frac{1}{3}\right)(x^2 + 1)^{-2/3}(2x) + (x^2 + 1)^{1/3}(2x)$$

$$y_2 = \dfrac{2x(4x^2 + 3)}{3(x^2 + 1)^{2/3}}$$

(b) Complete the table and demonstrate the equality in part (a) numerically.

x	-2	-1	$-\frac{1}{2}$	0	1	2	$\frac{5}{2}$
y_1							
y_2							

Synthesis

True or False? **In Exercises 63–66, determine whether the statement is true or false. Justify your answer.**

63. $x^{-1} + y^{-2} = \dfrac{y^2 + x}{xy^2}$

64. $\dfrac{1}{x^{-2} + y^{-1}} = x^2 + y$

65. $\dfrac{1}{\sqrt{x} + 4} = \dfrac{\sqrt{x} - 4}{x - 16}$

66. $\dfrac{x^2 - 9}{\sqrt{x} - 3} = \sqrt{x} + 3$

In Exercises 67–70, find and correct any errors. If the problem is correct, state that it is correct.

67. $x^n \cdot x^{3n} = x^{3n^2}$

68. $(x^n)^{2n} + (x^{2n})^n = 2x^{2n^2}$

69. $x^{2n} + y^{2n} = (x^n + y^n)^2$

70. $\dfrac{x^{2n} \cdot x^{3n}}{x^{3n} + x^2} = \dfrac{x^{5n}}{x^{3n} + x^2}$

71. *Think About It* You are taking a course in calculus, and for one of the homework problems you obtain the following answer.

$$\tfrac{1}{10}(2x - 1)^{5/2} + \tfrac{1}{6}(2x - 1)^{3/2}$$

The answer in the back of the book is $\tfrac{1}{15}(2x - 1)^{3/2}(3x + 1)$. Show how the second answer can be obtained from the first. Then use the same technique to simplify each of the following expressions.

(a) $\dfrac{2}{3}x(2x - 3)^{3/2} - \dfrac{2}{15}(2x - 3)^{5/2}$

(b) $\dfrac{2}{3}x(4 + x)^{3/2} - \dfrac{2}{15}(4 + x)^{5/2}$

Appendix A

Appendix A.1 *(page A8)*

Vocabulary Check *(page A8)*

1. rational **2.** irrational **3.** absolute value
4. composite **5.** prime **6.** variables; constants
7. terms **8.** coefficient **9.** Zero-Factor Property

---

1. (a) 5, 1, 2 (b) 0, 5, 1, 2
(c) $-9, 5, 0, 1, -4, 2, -11$
(d) $-\frac{7}{2}, \frac{2}{3}, -9, 5, 0, 1, -4, 2, -11$ (e) $\sqrt{2}$
2. (a) 12, 5 (b) 12, 5, 0 (c) $-7, 12, 5, 0, -3$
(d) $-7, -\frac{7}{3}, 0, 3.12, \frac{5}{4}, -3, 12, 5$ (e) $\sqrt{5}$
3. (a) 1 (b) 1 (c) $-13, 1, -6$
(d) $2.01, -13, 1, -6, 0.666\ldots$
(e) $0.010110111\ldots$
4. (a) 4 (b) 4 (c) $-75, 4$
(d) $-75, 4, -4.63, 0.7575$
(e) $2.3030030003\ldots, \sqrt{10}$
5. (a) $\frac{6}{3}, 8$ (b) $\frac{6}{3}, 8$ (c) $\frac{6}{3}, -1, 8, -22$
(d) $-\frac{1}{3}, \frac{6}{3}, -7.5, -1, 8, -22$ (e) $-\pi, \frac{1}{2}\sqrt{2}$
6. (a) $25, \sqrt{9}, 7, 13$ (b) $25, \sqrt{9}, 7, 13$
(c) $25, -17, \sqrt{9}, 7, 13$
(d) $-\dfrac{12}{5}, \sqrt{9}, 3.12, 25, -17, -11.1, 13$ (e) $\dfrac{\pi}{2}$
7. 0.625 **8.** $0.\overline{3}$ **9.** $0.\overline{123}$ **10.** $0.\overline{54}$
11. $-1 < 2.5$ **12.** $-6 < -2.5$
13. $-4 > -8$

14.
$-3.5 < 1$
15. $\frac{3}{2} < 7$

16.
$1 < \frac{16}{3}$
17. $\frac{5}{6} > \frac{2}{3}$

18.
$-\frac{8}{7} < -\frac{3}{7}$
19. (a) $x \le 5$ denotes the set of all real numbers less than or equal to 5.

(b) (c) Unbounded

20. (a) $x \ge -2$ denotes the set of all real numbers greater than or equal to -2.
(b) (c) Unbounded
21. (a) $x < 0$ denotes the set of all real numbers less than 0.
(b) (c) Unbounded
22. (a) $x > 3$ denotes the set of all real numbers greater than 3.
(b) (c) Unbounded
23. (a) $[4, \infty)$ denotes the set of all real numbers greater than or equal to 4.
(b) (c) Unbounded
24. (a) $(-\infty, 2)$ denotes the set of all real numbers less than 2.
(b) (c) Unbounded
25. (a) $-2 < x < 2$ denotes the set of all real numbers greater than -2 and less than 2.
(b) (c) Bounded
26. (a) $0 \le x \le 5$ denotes the set of all real numbers greater than or equal to zero and less than or equal to 5.
(b) (c) Bounded
27. (a) $-1 \le x < 0$ denotes the set of all real numbers greater than or equal to -1 and less than 0.
(b) (c) Bounded
28. (a) $0 < x \le 6$ denotes the set of positive real numbers less than or equal to 6.
(b) (c) Bounded
29. (a) $[-2, 5)$ denotes the set of all real numbers greater than or equal to -2 and less than 5.
(b) (c) Bounded
30. (a) $(-1, 2]$ denotes all real numbers greater than -1 and less than or equal to 2.
(b) (c) Bounded
31. $-2 < x \le 4$ **32.** $-6 \le y < 0$ **33.** $y \ge 0$
34. $y \le 25$ **35.** $10 \le t \le 22$ **36.** $-3 \le k < 5$
37. $W > 65$ **38.** $2.5\% \le r \le 5\%$ **39.** 10 **40.** 0
41. 5 **42.** 3 **43.** -1 **44.** -6 **45.** -1
46. -9 **47.** -1 **48.** 1 **49.** $|-3| > -|-3|$
50. $|-4| = |4|$ **51.** $-5 = -|5|$
52. $-|-6| < |-6|$ **53.** $-|-2| = -|2|$

54. $-(-2) > -2$ **55.** 51   **56.** 51   **57.** $\frac{5}{2}$
58. $\frac{5}{2}$ **59.** $\frac{128}{75}$ **60.** 14.99
61. $|\$113,356 - \$112,700| = \$656 > \$500$
$0.05(\$112,700) = \$5635$
Because the actual expenses differ from the budget by more than \$500, there is failure to meet the "budget variance test."
62. $|\$9772 - \$9400| = \$372 < \$500$
$0.05(\$9400) = \$470$
Because the difference between the actual expenses and the budget is less than \$500 and less than 5% of the budgeted amount, there is compliance with the "budget variance test."
63. $|\$37,335 - \$37,640| = \$305 < \$500$
$0.05(\$37,640) = \$1882$
Because the difference between the actual expenses and the budget is less than \$500 and less than 5% of the budgeted amount, there is compliance with the "budget variance test."
64. $|\$2613 - \$2575| = \$38 < \$500$
$0.05(\$2575) = \$128.75$
Because the difference between the actual expenses and the budget is less than \$500 and less than 5% of the budgeted amount, there is compliance with the "budget variance test."
65. (a)

Year	Expenditures (in billions)	Surplus or deficit (in billions)
1960	\$92.2	\$0.3 (s)
1970	\$195.6	\$2.8 (d)
1980	\$590.9	\$73.8 (d)
1990	\$1253.2	\$221.2 (d)
2000	\$1788.8	\$236.4 (s)

(b)

66.

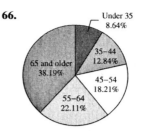

67. $|x - 5| \leq 3$ **68.** $|x + 10| \geq 6$ **69.** $|y| \geq 6$
70. $|y - a| \leq 2$ **71.** $|326 - 351| = 25$ miles
72. $|48° - 82°| = 34°$
73. $7x$ and 4 are the terms; 7 is the coefficient.
74. $6x^3$ and $-5x$ are the terms; 6 and -5 are the coefficients.
75. $\sqrt{3}x^2$, $-8x$, and -11 are the terms; $\sqrt{3}$ and -8 are the coefficients.
76. $3\sqrt{3}x^2$ and 1 are the terms; $3\sqrt{3}$ is the coefficient.
77. $4x^3$, $x/2$, and -5 are the terms; 4 and $\frac{1}{2}$ are the coefficients.
78. $3x^4$ and $-x^2/4$ are the terms; 3 and $-\frac{1}{4}$ are the coefficients.
79. (a) -10 (b) -6 **80.** (a) 30   (b) -12
81. (a) 14   (b) 2   **82.** (a) -10 (b) 0
83. (a) Division by 0 is undefined.   (b) 0
84. (a) $\frac{1}{2}$ (b) Division by 0 is undefined.
85. Commutative Property of Addition
86. Multiplicative Inverse Property
87. Multiplicative Inverse Property
88. Additive Inverse Property
89. Distributive Property
90. Additive Identity Property
91. Multiplicative Identity Property
92. Distributive Property
93. Associative Property of Addition
94. Associative and Commutative Properties of Multiplication
95. Distributive Property
96. $\frac{1}{7}(7 \cdot 12) = \left(\frac{1}{7} \cdot 7\right)12$ Associative Property of Multiplication
$= 1 \cdot 12$ Multiplicative Inverse Property
$= 12$ Multiplicative Identity Property
97. $\frac{1}{2}$ **98.** $\frac{2}{7}$ **99.** $\frac{3}{8}$ **100.** $\frac{59}{66}$ **101.** 48
102. -3 **103.** $\dfrac{5x}{12}$ **104.** $\dfrac{5x}{27}$
105. (a)

n	1	0.5	0.01	0.0001	0.000001
$5/n$	5	10	500	50,000	5,000,000

(b) The value of $5/n$ approaches infinity as n approaches 0.
106. (a)

n	1	10	100	10,000	100,000
$5/n$	5	0.5	0.05	0.0005	0.00005

(b) The value of $5/n$ approaches 0 as n increases without bound.

107. False. If $a < b$, then $\dfrac{1}{a} > \dfrac{1}{b}$, where $a \neq b \neq 0$.

108. False. The denominators cannot be added when adding fractions.

109. (a) No. If one variable is negative and the other is positive, the expressions are unequal.

(b) $|u + v| \leq |u| + |v|$

The expressions are equal when u and v have the same sign. If u and v differ in sign, $|u + v|$ is less than $|u| + |v|$.

110. Yes. y is nonnegative if $y \geq 0$. y is positive if $y > 0$.

111. The only even prime number is 2, because its only factors are itself and 1.

112.

113. (a) Negative   (b) Negative
114. (a) Positive   (b) Positive
115. Yes. $|a| = -a$ if $a < 0$.

Appendix A.2   (page A20)

Vocabulary Check   (page A20)

1. exponent; base   **2.** scientific notation
3. square root   **4.** principle nth root
5. index; radicand   **6.** simplest form
7. conjugates   **8.** rationalizing
9. power; index

1. $8 \times 8 \times 8 \times 8 \times 8$
2. $(-2) \times (-2) \times (-2) \times (-2) \times (-2) \times (-2) \times (-2)$
3. 4.9^6 **4.** $(-10)^5$ **5.** (a) 27   (b) 81
6. (a) 125   (b) $\dfrac{1}{9}$ **7.** (a) 1   (b) -9
8. (a) 5184   (b) $-\dfrac{3}{5}$ **9.** (a) $\dfrac{243}{64}$ (b) -1
10. (a) $\dfrac{16}{3}$ (b) 1   **11.** (a) $\dfrac{5}{6}$ (b) 4
12. (a) $\dfrac{7}{12}$ (b) $\dfrac{1}{81}$ **13.** -1600 **14.** 0.244
15. 2.125   **16.** 5184   **17.** -24 **18.** $\dfrac{7}{16}$ **19.** 6
20. -135 **21.** -54 **22.** -48 **23.** 1
24. $-\dfrac{5}{27}$ **25.** (a) $-125z^3$ (b) $5x^6$
26. (a) $9x^2$ (b) 1   **27.** $24y^2$ (b) $3x^2$
28. (a) $-3z^7$ (b) $\dfrac{5}{2}y^4$ **29.** (a) $\dfrac{7}{x}$ (b) $\dfrac{4}{3}(x + y)^2$

30. (a) $\dfrac{1}{r^2}$ (b) $\dfrac{5184}{y^7}$ **31.** (a) 1   (b) $\dfrac{1}{4x^4}$
32. (a) 1   (b) $\dfrac{1}{(z + 2)^4}$ **33.** (a) $-2x^3$ (b) $\dfrac{10}{x}$
34. (a) $32y^2$ (b) $\dfrac{125x^9}{y^{12}}$ **35.** (a) 3^{3n} (b) $\dfrac{b^5}{a^5}$
36. (a) $\dfrac{1}{x}$ (b) 1   **37.** 5.73×10^7 square miles
38. 9.46×10^{12} kilometers
39. 8.99×10^{-5} gram per cubic centimeter
40. 3.937×10^{-5} inch
41. 4,568,000,000 ounces   **42.** 15,000,000°C
43. 0.000000000000000000016022 coulomb
44. 0.00009 meter   **45.** (a) 50,000   (b) 200,000
46. (a) 60,000   (b) 2.0×10^{11}
47. (a) 954.448   (b) 3.077×10^{10}
48. (a) 4.907×10^{17} (b) 1.479
49. (a) 67,082.039   (b) 39.791
50. (a) 0.064   (b) 0.03   **51.** (a) 3   (b) $\dfrac{3}{2}$
52. (a) 3   (b) 216   **53.** (a) $\dfrac{1}{8}$ (b) $\dfrac{27}{8}$
54. (a) $\dfrac{1}{1000}$ (b) $\dfrac{2}{3}$ **55.** (a) -4 (b) 2
56. (a) $-\dfrac{3}{5}$ (b) -625 **57.** (a) 7.550   (b) -7.225
58. (a) 12.651   (b) 2.236
59. (a) -0.011 (b) 0.005
60. (a) 3.495   (b) 5.906   **61.** (a) 4   (b) $2\sqrt[5]{3}x$
62. (a) 6   (b) $3x^2$ **63.** (a) $2\sqrt{2}$ (b) $3\sqrt[3]{2}$
64. (a) $\dfrac{2\sqrt[3]{2}}{3}$ (b) $\dfrac{5\sqrt{3}}{2}$ **65.** (a) $6x\sqrt{2x}$ (b) $\dfrac{18\sqrt{z}}{z^2}$
66. (a) $3y^2\sqrt{6x}$ (b) $\dfrac{4a^2}{|b|}\sqrt{2}$
67. (a) $2x\sqrt[3]{2x^2}$ (b) $\dfrac{5|x|\sqrt{3}}{y^2}$
68. (a) $\sqrt[4]{3}|x|\sqrt{y}$ (b) $2x\sqrt[5]{5x^3z^4}$
69. (a) $34\sqrt{2}$ (b) $22\sqrt{2}$ **70.** (a) $7\sqrt{3}$ (b) $11\sqrt[3]{2}$
71. (a) $2\sqrt{x}$ (b) $4\sqrt{y}$
72. (a) $-84\sqrt{x}$ (b) $23|x|\sqrt{3}$
73. (a) $13\sqrt{x + 1}$ (b) $18\sqrt{5x}$
74. (a) $4\sqrt{x^3 - 7}$ (b) $50x\sqrt{5x}$
75. $\sqrt{5} + \sqrt{3} > \sqrt{5 + 3}$ **76.** $\sqrt{\dfrac{3}{11}} = \dfrac{\sqrt{3}}{\sqrt{11}}$
77. $5 > \sqrt{3^2 + 2^2}$ **78.** $5 = \sqrt{3^2 + 4^2}$ **79.** $\dfrac{\sqrt{3}}{3}$
80. $\dfrac{\sqrt{10}}{2}$ **81.** $\dfrac{5 + \sqrt{3}}{11}$ **82.** $3(\sqrt{6} - \sqrt{5})$
83. $\dfrac{2}{\sqrt{2}}$ **84.** $\dfrac{2}{3\sqrt{2}}$ **85.** $\dfrac{2}{3(\sqrt{5} - \sqrt{3})}$
86. $-\dfrac{1}{2(\sqrt{7} + 3)}$ **87.** $9^{1/2}$ **88.** $64^{1/3}$
89. $\sqrt[5]{32}$ **90.** $-\sqrt{144}$ **91.** $(-216)^{1/3}$

92. $\sqrt[5]{-243}$ **93.** $81^{3/4}$ **94.** $\sqrt[4]{16^5}$

95. $\dfrac{2}{x}$ **96.** $xy^{1/3}$ **97.** $\dfrac{1}{x^3}, \; x > 0$ **98.** x

99. (a) $\sqrt{3}$ (b) $\sqrt[3]{(x+1)^2}$ **100.** (a) $\sqrt{x}$ (b) $3x^2$

101. (a) $2\sqrt[4]{2}$ (b) $\sqrt[8]{2x}$

102. (a) $3\sqrt[4]{3(x+1)}$ (b) $a\sqrt[6]{10ab}$

103. $\dfrac{\pi}{2} \approx 1.57$ seconds   **104.** 0.026 inch

105. (a)

h	0	1	2	3	4	5	6
t	0	2.93	5.48	7.67	9.53	11.08	12.32

h	7	8	9	10	11	12
t	13.29	14.00	14.50	14.80	14.93	14.96

(b) $t \to 8.64\sqrt{3} \approx 14.96$

106. 8.32 minutes

107. True. When dividing variables, you subtract exponents.

108. False. When a power is raised to a power, you multiply the exponents: $(a^n)^k = a^{nk}$.

109. $a^0 = 1, \; a \neq 0$, using the property $\dfrac{a^m}{a^n} = a^{m-n}$:
$\dfrac{a^m}{a^m} = a^{m-m} = a^0 = 1$.

110. (a) 3 is also raised to the -1 power, so $(3x)^{-1} = \dfrac{1}{3x}$.

(b) When two powers have the same base, the exponents are added: $y^3 \cdot y^2 = y^5$.

(c) When a power is raised to a power, the exponents are multiplied: $(a^2b^3)^4 = a^8b^{12}$.

(d) The square of a binomial contains a cross-product term: $(a + b)^2 = a^2 + 2ab + b^2$.

(e) If $x < 0$, then $\sqrt{4x^2} > 0$ but $2x < 0$: $\sqrt{4x^2} = 2|x|$.

(f) Radicals can be added together only if they have the same radicand and index: $\sqrt{2} + \sqrt{2} = 2\sqrt{2}$.

111. When any positive integer is squared, the units digit is 0, 1, 4, 5, 6, or 9. Therefore, $\sqrt{5233}$ is not an integer.

112. No. Rationalizing the denominator produces a number equivalent to the original fraction; squaring does not.

Appendix A.3   *(page A31)*

Vocabulary Check   *(page A31)*

1. $n; a_n; a_0$ **2.** descending

3. monomial; binomial; trinomial   **4.** like terms

5. First terms; Outer terms; Inner terms; Last terms

6. factoring   **7.** completely factored

1. d   **2.** e   **3.** b   **4.** a   **5.** f   **6.** c

7. $-2x^3 + 4x^2 - 3x + 20$ **8.** $6x^5 + 3x + 1$

9. $-15x^4 + 1$ **10.** $20x^3 + 5$

11. (a) $-\frac{1}{2}x^5 + 14x$

(b) Degree: 5; Leading coefficient: $-\frac{1}{2}$

(c) Binomial

12. (a) $2x^2 - x + 1$

(b) Degree: 2; Leading coefficient: 2

(c) Trinomial

13. (a) $-3x^4 + 2x^2 - 5$

(b) Degree: 4; Leading coefficient: -3

(c) Trinomial

14. (a) $7x$

(b) Degree: 1; Leading coefficient: 7

(c) Monomial

15. (a) $x^5 - 1$

(b) Degree: 5; Leading coefficient: 1

(c) Binomial

16. (a) $25y^2 - y + 1$

(b) Degree: 2; Leading coefficient: 25

(c) Trinomial

17. (a) 3

(b) Degree: 0; Leading coefficient: 3

(c) Monomial

18. (a) $t^2 + 9$

(b) Degree: 2; Leading coefficient: 1

(c) Binomial

19. (a) $-4x^5 + 6x^4 + 1$

(b) Degree: 5; Leading coefficient: -4

(c) Trinomial

20. (a) $2x + 3$

(b) Degree: 1; Leading coefficient: 2

(c) Binomial

21. (a) $4x^3y$

(b) Degree: 3; Leading coefficient: 4

(c) Monomial

22. (a) $-x^5y + 2x^2y^2 + xy^4$

(b) Degree: 5; Leading coefficient: -1

(c) Trinomial

23. Polynomial: $-3x^3 + 2x + 8$

24. Not a polynomial because of the negative exponent

25. Not a polynomial because it includes a term with a negative exponent

26. Polynomial: $\frac{1}{2}x^2 + x - \frac{3}{2}$

27. Polynomial: $-y^4 + y^3 + y^2$

28. Not a polynomial because of the square root

29. $-2x - 10$ **30.** $x^2 + 2x$ **31.** $3x^3 - 2x + 2$

32. $-2x^2 - 4$ **33.** $8.3x^3 + 29.7x^2 + 11$

34. $1.3x^4 - 8.4x - 34.1$ **35.** $12z + 8$

36. $y^3 - y^2 - 3y + 7$ **37.** $3x^3 - 6x^2 + 3x$

38. $4y^4 + 2y^3 - 3y^2$ **39.** $-15z^2 + 5z$

40. $-15x^2 - 6x$ **41.** $-4x^4 + 4x$ **42.** $4x^4 - 12x$

43. $7.5x^3 + 9x$ **44.** $-7y^4 + 4y^3$ **45.** $-\frac{1}{2}x^2 - 12x$

46. $-\frac{7}{4}y^2 + 8y$ **47.** $x^2 + 7x + 12$

48. $x^2 + 5x - 50$ **49.** $6x^2 - 7x - 5$

50. $28x^2 - 29x + 6$ **51.** $x^4 + x^2 + 1$

52. $x^4 - 13x^2 + 4$ **53.** $x^2 - 100$ **54.** $4x^2 - 9$

55. $x^2 - 4y^2$ **56.** $4x^2 - 9y^2$ **57.** $4x^2 + 12x + 9$

58. $16x^2 + 40x + 25$ **59.** $4x^2 - 20xy + 25y^2$

60. $64x^2 - 80x + 25$ **61.** $x^3 + 3x^2 + 3x + 1$

62. $x^3 - 6x^2 + 12x - 8$ **63.** $8x^3 - 12x^2y + 6xy^2 - y^3$

64. $27x^3 + 54x^2y + 36xy^2 + 8y^3$ **65.** $16x^6 - 24x^3 + 9$

66. $64x^2 + 48x + 9$ **67.** $m^2 - n^2 - 6m + 9$

68. $x^2 + 2xy + y^2 - 1$

69. $x^2 + 2xy + y^2 - 6x - 6y + 9$

70. $x^2 - 2xy + y^2 + 2x - 2y + 1$ **71.** $4r^4 - 25$

72. $9a^6 - 16b^4$ **73.** $\frac{1}{4}x^2 - 3x + 9$

74. $\frac{4}{9}t^2 + \frac{20}{3}t + 25$ **75.** $\frac{1}{9}x^2 - 4$ **76.** $4x^2 - \frac{1}{25}$

77. $1.44x^2 + 7.2x + 9$ **78.** $2.25y^2 - 9y + 9$

79. $2.25x^2 - 16$ **80.** $6.25y^2 - 9$ **81.** $2x^2 + 2x$

82. $2x^2 + 8x + 6$ **83.** $u^4 - 16$ **84.** $x^4 - y^4$

85. $x - y$ **86.** $25 - x$ **87.** $x^2 - 2\sqrt{5}x + 5$

88. $x^2 + 2x\sqrt{3} + 3$ **89.** $3(x + 2)$ **90.** $5(y - 6)$

91. $2x(x^2 - 3)$ **92.** $2x(2x^2 - 3x + 6)$

93. $(x - 1)(x + 6)$ **94.** $(x + 2)(3x - 4)$

95. $(x + 3)(x - 1)$ **96.** $3x(3x - 1)$ **97.** $\frac{1}{2}(x + 8)$

98. $\frac{1}{3}(y + 15)$ **99.** $\frac{1}{2}x(x^2 + 4x - 10)$

100. $\frac{1}{3}y(y^3 - 15y + 6)$ **101.** $\frac{2}{3}(x - 6)(x - 3)$

102. $\frac{2}{5}(y + 1)(2y - 5)$ **103.** $(x + 9)(x - 9)$

104. $(x - 7)(x + 7)$ **105.** $2(4y - 3)(4y + 3)$

106. $-4(3y + 1)(3y - 1)$ **107.** $\left(4x + \frac{1}{3}\right)\left(4x - \frac{1}{3}\right)$

108. $\left(\frac{2}{5}y + 8\right)\left(\frac{2}{5}y - 8\right)$ **109.** $(x + 1)(x - 3)$

110. $-z(z + 10)$ **111.** $(3u + 2v)(3u - 2v)$

112. $(5x + 4y)(5x - 4y)$ **113.** $(x - 2)^2$

114. $(x + 5)^2$ **115.** $(2t + 1)^2$ **116.** $(3x - 2)^2$

117. $(5y - 1)^2$ **118.** $(6y - 9)^2$ **119.** $(3u + 4v)^2$

120. $(2x - y)^2$ **121.** $\left(x - \frac{2}{3}\right)^2$ **122.** $\left(z + \frac{1}{2}\right)^2$

123. $(x - 2)(x^2 + 2x + 4)$ **124.** $(x - 3)(x^2 + 3x + 9)$

125. $(y + 4)(y^2 - 4y + 16)$

126. $(z + 5)(z^2 - 5z + 25)$ **127.** $(2t - 1)(4t^2 + 2t + 1)$

128. $(3x + 2)(9x^2 - 6x + 4)$

129. $(u + 3v)(u^2 - 3uv + 9v^2)$

130. $(4x - y)(16x^2 + 4xy + y^2)$ **131.** $(x + 2)(x - 1)$

132. $(x + 2)(x + 3)$ **133.** $(s - 3)(s - 2)$

134. $(t + 2)(t - 3)$ **135.** $-(y + 5)(y - 4)$

136. $-(z - 8)(z + 3)$ **137.** $(x - 20)(x - 10)$

138. $(x - 6)(x - 7)$ **139.** $(3x - 2)(x - 1)$

140. $(2x + 1)(x - 1)$ **141.** $(5x + 1)(x + 5)$

142. $(3x + 1)(4x + 1)$ **143.** $-(3z - 2)(3z + 1)$

144. $-(5u - 2)(u + 3)$ **145.** $(x - 1)(x^2 + 2)$

146. $(x + 5)(x^2 - 5)$ **147.** $(2x - 1)(x^2 - 3)$

148. $(x - 2)(5x^2 + 3)$ **149.** $(3 + x)(2 - x^3)$

150. $(x^2 + 2)(x + 1)(x^2 - x + 1)$

151. $(3x^2 - 1)(2x + 1)$ **152.** $(4x^3 - 3)(2x^2 + 3)$

153. $(x + 2)(3x + 4)$ **154.** $(x + 3)(2x + 3)$

155. $(2x - 1)(3x + 2)$ **156.** $(2x + 3)(3x - 5)$

157. $(3x - 1)(5x - 2)$ **158.** $(x - 1)(12x - 1)$

159. $6(x + 3)(x - 3)$ **160.** $12(x + 2)(x - 2)$

161. $x^2(x - 4)$ **162.** $x(x + 3)(x - 3)$ **163.** $(x - 1)^2$

164. $(8 - x)(2 + x)$ **165.** $(1 - 2x)^2$

166. $(-3x + 1)(3x - 1)$ **167.** $-2x(x + 1)(x - 2)$

168. $y(2y + 3)(y - 5)$ **169.** $(9x + 1)(x + 1)$

170. $(5x + 3)(x + 2)$ **171.** $\frac{1}{81}(x + 36)(x - 18)$

172. $\frac{1}{96}(4x - 3)(3x + 2)$ **173.** $(3x + 1)(x^2 + 5)$

174. $(5 - x)(1 + x^2)$ **175.** $x(x - 4)(x^2 + 1)$

176. $(u + 2)(3 - u^2)$ **177.** $\frac{1}{4}(x^2 + 3)(x + 12)$

178. $\frac{1}{5}(x^2 - 5)(x + 5)$ **179.** $(t + 6)(t - 8)$

180. $(x + 1)^2(x - 1)^2$

181. $(x + 2)(x + 4)(x - 2)(x - 4)$

182. $2(t - 2)(t^2 + 2t + 4)$

183. $5(x + 2)(x^2 - 2x + 4)$ **184.** $(2x - 1)(6x - 1)$

185. $(3 - 4x)(23 - 60x)$ **186.** $-(x + 1)(x - 3)(x + 9)$

187. $5(1 - x)^2(3x + 2)(4x + 3)$

188. $7(x^2 + 1)(3x^2 - 1)$ **189.** $(x - 2)^2(x + 1)^3(7x - 5)$

190. $-2x(x - 5)^3(x + 5)$

191. $3(x^6 + 1)^4(3x + 2)^2(33x^6 + 20x^5 + 3)$

192. $-(x^2 + 1)^4\left(\dfrac{x^2}{2} + 1\right)$

193. $-14, 14, -2, 2$ **194.** $-51, 51, -15, 15, -27, 27$

195. $-11, 11, -4, 4, -1, 1$

196. $-25, 25, -14, 14, -11, 11, -10, 10$

197. Two possible answers: $2, -12$

198. Two possible answers: $3, -8$

199. Two possible answers: $-2, -4$

200. Two possible answers: $9, 7$

201. (a) $P = 22x - 25,000$ (b) \$85,000

202. (a) $P = 24x - 460$ (b) \$548

203. (a) $500r^2 + 1000r + 500$

(b)

r	$2\frac{1}{2}\%$	3%	4%
$500(1 + r)^2$	\$525.31	\$530.45	\$540.80

r	$4\frac{1}{2}\%$	5%
$500(1 + r)^2$	\$546.01	\$551.25

(c) The amount increases with increasing r.

204. (a) $1200r^3 + 3600r^2 + 3600r + 1200$

(b)

r	2%	3%	$3\frac{1}{2}\%$
$1200(1 + r)^3$	\$1273.45	\$1311.27	\$1330.46

r	4%	$4\frac{1}{2}\%$
$1200(1 + r)^3$	\$1349.84	\$1369.40

(c) The amount increases with increasing r.

205. (a) $V = 4x^3 - 88x^2 + 468x$

(b)

x (cm)	1	2	3
V (cm³)	384	616	720

206. (a) $V = \frac{1}{2}(6x^3 - 135x^2 + 675x)$

(b)

x (cm)	3	5	7
V (cm³)	486	375	84

207. $44x + 308$ **208.** $2x^2 + 46x + 252$

209. (a) $3x^2 + 8x$ (b) $30x^2$

210. (a) $T = 0.0475x^2 + 1.099x + 0.23$

(b)

x (mi/hr)	30	40	55
T (feet)	75.95	120.19	204.36

(c) The stopping distance increases at an accelerating rate as speed increases.

211.

212.

213.

214.

215. $4\pi(r + 1)$ **216.** $r^2(4 - \pi)$

217. $4(6 - x)(6 + x)$ **218.** $\frac{5}{8}(x + 7)(x - 1)$

219. (a) $\pi h(R - r)(R + r)$ (b) $V = 2\pi\left[\left(\dfrac{R + r}{2}\right)(R - r)\right]h$

220. $kx(Q - x)$

221. False. $(4x^2 + 1)(3x + 1) = 12x^3 + 4x^2 + 3x + 1$

222. False. $(4x + 3) + (-4x + 6)$

$$= 4x + 3 - 4x + 6$$
$$= 3 + 6$$
$$= 9$$

223. True. $a^2 - b^2 = (a + b)(a - b)$

224. False. A perfect square trinomial can be factored as the binomial sum squared.

225. $m + n$ **226.** n **227.** $-x^3 + 8x^2 + 2x + 7$

228. $(3 + 4)^2 = 49 \neq 25 = 3^2 + 4^2$.

If either x or y is zero, then $(x + y)^2 = x^2 + y^2$.

229. $(x^n + y^n)(x^n - y^n)$

230. $(x^n + y^n)(x^{2n} - x^n y^n + y^{2n})$

231. $x^{3n} - y^{2n}$ is completely factored.

232. Answers will vary. Sample answer: The roots of the equation can be found when a polynomial is in factored form.

233. Answers will vary. Sample answer: $x^2 - 3$

Appendix A.4   *(page A42)*

> ### Vocabulary Check   *(page A42)*
>
> **1.** domain   **2.** rational expression   **3.** complex
> **4.** smaller   **5.** equivalent   **6.** difference quotient

1. All real numbers   **2.** All real numbers

3. All nonnegative real numbers

4. All positive real numbers

5. All real numbers x such that $x \neq 2$

6. All real numbers x such that $x \neq -\frac{1}{2}$

7. All real numbers x such that $x \geq -1$

8. All real numbers x such that $x \leq 6$

9. $3x$, $x \neq 0$ **10.** $(x + 1)$, $x \neq -1$

11. $\dfrac{3x}{2}$, $x \neq 0$ **12.** $\dfrac{3}{10y^3}$ **13.** $\dfrac{3y}{y + 1}$, $x \neq 0$

14. $\dfrac{2x^2}{x - 1}$ **15.** $\dfrac{-4y}{5}$, $y \neq \frac{1}{2}$ **16.** $\dfrac{9x}{2}$, $x \neq -1$

17. $-\dfrac{1}{2}$, $x \neq 5$ **18.** $-4, x \neq 3$ **19.** $y - 4$, $y \neq -4$

20. $-(x + 5)$, $x \neq 5$ **21.** $\dfrac{x(x + 3)}{x - 2}$, $x \neq -2$

22. $\dfrac{x - 2}{x + 1}$, $x \neq -10$ **23.** $\dfrac{y - 4}{y + 6}$, $y \neq 3$

24. $\dfrac{(x - 6)(x - 1)}{(x + 10)(x + 1)}$ **25.** $\dfrac{-(x^2 + 1)}{(x + 2)}$, $x \neq 2$

26. $\dfrac{1}{x+1}$, $x \neq \pm 3$ **27.** $z - 2$

28. $\dfrac{y(y-3)}{y^2 - y + 1}$, $y \neq -1$

29.

x	0	1	2	3	4	5	6
$\dfrac{x^2 - 2x - 3}{x - 3}$	1	2	3	Undef.	5	6	7
$x + 1$	1	2	3	4	5	6	7

The expressions are equivalent except at $x = 3$.

30.

x	0	1	2	3	4	5	6
$\dfrac{x-3}{x^2 - x - 6}$	$\frac{1}{2}$	$\frac{1}{3}$	$\frac{1}{4}$	Undef.	$\frac{1}{6}$	$\frac{1}{7}$	$\frac{1}{8}$
$\dfrac{1}{x+2}$	$\frac{1}{2}$	$\frac{1}{3}$	$\frac{1}{4}$	$\frac{1}{5}$	$\frac{1}{6}$	$\frac{1}{7}$	$\frac{1}{8}$

The expressions are equivalent except at $x = 3$.

31. The expression cannot be simplified.

32. The polynomial, $x^2 + 25$, can not be factored.

33. $\dfrac{\pi}{4}$, $r \neq 0$ **34.** $\dfrac{x+5}{4(2x+3)}$, $x \neq -5$

35. $\dfrac{1}{5(x-2)}$, $x \neq 1$ **36.** $-\dfrac{x+13}{5x^2}$, $x \neq 3$

37. $\dfrac{r+1}{r}$, $r \neq 1$ **38.** $-\dfrac{8}{5}$, $y \neq -3, 4$

39. $\dfrac{t-3}{(t+3)(t-2)}$, $t \neq -2$ **40.** $\dfrac{x-y}{x(x+y)^2}$, $x \neq -2y$

41. $\dfrac{(x+6)(x+1)}{x^2}$, $x \neq 6$ **42.** $\dfrac{1}{3}$, $x \neq \pm 7$

43. $\dfrac{x+5}{x-1}$ **44.** $\dfrac{x}{x+3}$ **45.** $\dfrac{6x+13}{x+3}$ **46.** $\dfrac{8-5x}{x-1}$

47. $-\dfrac{2}{x-2}$ **48.** $\dfrac{2x+5}{x-5}$

49. $-\dfrac{x^2+3}{(x+1)(x-2)(x-3)}$ **50.** $\dfrac{6(2x+3)}{(x-2)(x+1)(x+4)}$

51. $\dfrac{2-x}{x^2+1}$, $x \neq 0$ **52.** $\dfrac{4x+1}{(x-1)(x+1)}$

53. The error was incorrect subtraction in the numerator.
54. The error was an incorrect expansion of $(x+2)^2$ in the numerator.

55. $\dfrac{1}{2}$, $x \neq 2$ **56.** $\dfrac{4x}{x+4}$, $x \neq 0, 4$

57. $x(x+1)$, $x \neq -1, 0$ **58.** $\dfrac{x+1}{x-1}$, $x \neq 0$

59. $\dfrac{2x-1}{2x}$, $x > 0$ **60.** $\dfrac{-1}{t^2\sqrt{t^2+1}}$ **61.** $\dfrac{x^7-2}{x^2}$

62. $\dfrac{x^8-5}{x^3}$ **63.** $\dfrac{-1}{(x^2+1)^5}$ **64.** $\dfrac{-2x(x+5)}{(x-5)^4}$

65. $\dfrac{2x^3 - 2x^2 - 5}{(x-1)^{1/2}}$ **66.** $\dfrac{4x^3(2x-1)^2 - 2x}{(2x-1)^{1/2}}$

67. $\dfrac{3x-1}{3}$, $x \neq 0$ **68.** $\dfrac{x^2-2}{x^3(1-x^2)^{1/2}}$

69. $\dfrac{-1}{x(x+h)}$, $h \neq 0$ **70.** $-\dfrac{2x+h}{x^2(x+h)^2}$, $h \neq 0$

71. $\dfrac{-1}{(x-4)(x+h-4)}$, $h \neq 0$

72. $\dfrac{1}{(x+h+1)(x+1)}$, $h \neq 0$ **73.** $\dfrac{1}{\sqrt{x+2} + \sqrt{x}}$

74. $\dfrac{-1}{\sqrt{z-3} + \sqrt{z}}$ **75.** $\dfrac{1}{\sqrt{x+h+1} + \sqrt{x+1}}$, $h \neq 0$

76. $\dfrac{1}{\sqrt{x+h-2} + \sqrt{x-2}}$, $h \neq 0$

77. $\dfrac{x}{2(2x+1)}$, $x \neq 0$ **78.** $\dfrac{8(x+2)}{(x+4)^2}$

79. (a) $\dfrac{1}{16}$ minute (b) $\dfrac{x}{16}$ minute(s) (c) $\dfrac{60}{16} = \dfrac{15}{4}$ minutes

80. $\dfrac{8t}{15}$ **81.** (a) 9.09% (b) $\dfrac{288(MN - P)}{N(MN + 12P)}$; 9.09%

82. (a) 4.57% (b) $\dfrac{288(MN - P)}{N(MN + 12P)}$; 4.57%

83. (a)

t	0	2	4	6	8	10
T	75	55.9	48.3	45	43.3	42.3

t	12	14	16	18	20	22
T	41.7	41.3	41.1	40.9	40.7	40.6

(b) The model is approaching a T-value of 40.

84. (a)

Year, t	Banking (millions)	Paying bills (millions)
2002	21.9	13.9
2003	27.0	17.8
2004	31.4	21.5
2005	35.6	25.0
2006	40.2	28.1
2007	45.6	31.0

(b) The estimates are fairly close to the actual numbers of households.

(c)

$$\text{Rate} = \dfrac{-0.2151t^3 + 2.408t^2 + 7.75t + 5.5}{-0.00146t^4 + 0.0403t^3 - 0.491t^2 + 23.81t - 0.3}$$

(d)

Year	2002	2003	2004
Ratio	0.6333	0.6592	0.6861

Year	2005	2006	2007
Ratio	0.7013	0.7003	0.6812

Explanation will vary.

85. False. In order for the simplified expression to be equivalent to the original expression, the domain of the simplified expression needs to be restricted. If n is even, $x \neq -1, 1$. If n is odd, $x \neq 1$.

86. False. The two expressions are equivalent for all values of x such that $x \neq 1$.

87. Completely factor each polynomial in the numerator and in the denominator. Then conclude that there are no common factors.

Appendix A.5 (page A56)

> **Vocabulary Check** *(page A56)*
>
> **1.** equation **2.** solve **3.** identities; conditional
> **4.** $ax + b = 0$ **5.** extraneous
> **6.** quadratic equation
> **7.** factoring; extracting square roots; completing the square; Quadratic Formula

1. Identity **2.** Conditional equation
3. Conditional equation **4.** Identity **5.** Identity
6. Identity **7.** Identity **8.** Identity
9. Conditional equation **10.** Conditional equation
11. 4 **12.** -12 **13.** -9 **14.** 3 **15.** 5
16. -5 **17.** 9 **18.** $-\frac{5}{8}$ **19.** No solution
20. All real numbers x **21.** -4 **22.** -5
23. $-\frac{6}{5}$ **24.** 6 **25.** 9 **26.** 50
27. No solution. The x-terms sum to zero.
28. No solution. The x-terms sum to zero. **29.** 10
30. $\frac{1}{2}$ **31.** 4 **32.** 0 **33.** 3 **34.** $\frac{9}{7}$ **35.** 0
36. $\frac{5}{3}$ **37.** No solution. The variable is divided out.
38. $\frac{11}{6}$ **39.** No solution. The solution is extraneous.
40. $-\frac{13}{3}$ **41.** 2 **42.** $\frac{7}{4}$
43. No solution. The solution is extraneous.
44. No solution. The solution is extraneous.
45. 0 **46.** $-\frac{1}{2}$ **47.** All real numbers x
48. No solution. The x-terms sum to zero.
49. $2x^2 + 8x - 3 = 0$ **50.** $x^2 - 16x = 0$
51. $x^2 - 6x + 6 = 0$ **52.** $-3x^2 - 42x - 134 = 0$
53. $3x^2 - 90x - 10 = 0$ **54.** $4x^2 - 2x + 1 = 0$
55. $0, -\frac{1}{2}$ **56.** $-\frac{1}{3}, \frac{1}{3}$ **57.** $4, -2$ **58.** $9, 1$
59. -5 **60.** $-\frac{3}{2}$ **61.** $3, -\frac{1}{2}$ **62.** $-\frac{3}{2}, 11$

63. $2, -6$ **64.** $2, 6$ **65.** $-\frac{20}{3}, -4$ **66.** $-8, 16$
67. $-a$ **68.** $-a - b, -a + b$ **69.** ± 7 **70.** ± 13
71. $\pm\sqrt{11}$ **72.** $\pm 4\sqrt{2}$ **73.** $\pm 3\sqrt{3}$ **74.** ± 2
75. $8, 16$ **76.** $-18, -8$ **77.** $-2 \pm \sqrt{14}$
78. $5 \pm \sqrt{30}$ **79.** $\dfrac{1 \pm 3\sqrt{2}}{2}$ **80.** $-\dfrac{7}{4} \pm \dfrac{\sqrt{11}}{2}$
81. 2 **82.** $-\frac{9}{2}$ **83.** $4, -8$ **84.** $3, -1$
85. $\sqrt{11} - 6, -\sqrt{11} - 6$ **86.** $-4 \pm \sqrt{2}$
87. $1 \pm \dfrac{\sqrt{6}}{3}$ **88.** $\dfrac{2}{3} \pm \sqrt{2}$ **89.** $2 \pm 2\sqrt{3}$
90. No solution **91.** $\dfrac{-5 \pm \sqrt{89}}{4}$ **92.** $\dfrac{11}{2}, -\dfrac{9}{2}$
93. $\frac{1}{2}, -1$ **94.** $1, -\frac{1}{2}$ **95.** $\frac{1}{4}, -\frac{3}{4}$ **96.** $\frac{3}{5}, \frac{1}{5}$
97. $1 \pm \sqrt{3}$ **98.** $5 \pm \sqrt{3}$ **99.** $-7 \pm \sqrt{5}$
100. $-3 \pm \sqrt{13}$ **101.** $-4 \pm 2\sqrt{5}$ **102.** $\dfrac{1}{2} \pm \dfrac{\sqrt{5}}{2}$
103. $\dfrac{2}{3} \pm \dfrac{\sqrt{7}}{3}$ **104.** $\dfrac{5}{4} \pm \dfrac{\sqrt{3}}{4}$ **105.** $-\dfrac{4}{3}$
106. $-\dfrac{1}{3} \pm \dfrac{\sqrt{11}}{6}$ **107.** $-\dfrac{1}{2} \pm \sqrt{2}$ **108.** $\dfrac{5}{4} \pm \dfrac{\sqrt{5}}{2}$
109. $\dfrac{2}{7}$ **110.** $-\dfrac{3}{2} \pm \dfrac{\sqrt{13}}{2}$ **111.** $2 \pm \dfrac{\sqrt{6}}{2}$
112. $-\dfrac{8}{5} \pm \dfrac{\sqrt{3}}{5}$ **113.** $6 \pm \sqrt{11}$ **114.** $-7 \pm \sqrt{13}$
115. $-\dfrac{3}{8} \pm \dfrac{\sqrt{265}}{8}$ **116.** $\dfrac{686 \pm 196\sqrt{6}}{25}$
117. $0.976, -0.643$ **118.** $1.400, -0.150$
119. $1.355, -14.071$ **120.** $2.137, 18.063$
121. $1.687, -0.488$ **122.** $0.672, -0.968$
123. $-0.290, -2.200$ **124.** $-2.995, 2.971$
125. $1 \pm \sqrt{2}$ **126.** $0, -3$ **127.** $6, -12$ **128.** 7
129. $\frac{1}{2} \pm \sqrt{3}$ **130.** $-\frac{3}{2} \pm \sqrt{3}$ **131.** $-\frac{1}{2}$
132. $-\dfrac{b}{a}, \dfrac{b}{a}$ **133.** $\dfrac{3}{4} \pm \dfrac{\sqrt{97}}{4}$ **134.** ± 1
135. $0, \pm\dfrac{3\sqrt{2}}{2}$ **136.** $0, \pm\dfrac{5}{2}$ **137.** ± 3 **138.** ± 2
139. -6 **140.** $\frac{8}{3}$ **141.** $-3, 0$ **142.** $0, \frac{4}{3}$
143. $3, 1, -1$ **144.** -2 **145.** ± 1 **146.** ± 2
147. $\pm\sqrt{3}, \pm 1$ **148.** ± 2 **149.** $\pm\frac{1}{2}, \pm 4$
150. $\pm\dfrac{\sqrt{7}}{6}$ **151.** $1, -2$ **152.** $-\sqrt[3]{2}$ **153.** 50
154. $\frac{9}{16}$ **155.** 26 **156.** -4 **157.** -16
158. $\frac{124}{3}$ **159.** $2, -5$ **160.** $3, -2$ **161.** 0
162. No solution **163.** 9 **164.** 1 **165.** $-3 \pm 16\sqrt{2}$
166. $-29, 25$ **167.** $\pm\sqrt{14}$ **168.** $\dfrac{1 \pm 5\sqrt{5}}{2}$ **169.** 1
170. $0, 1, \frac{3}{5}$ **171.** $2, -\frac{3}{2}$ **172.** $2, -12$
173. $\dfrac{-3 \pm \sqrt{21}}{6}$ **174.** $-3, 1$ **175.** $4, -5$

176. $\frac{3}{4}, -1$ **177.** $\frac{1 \pm \sqrt{31}}{3}$ **178.** ± 1 **179.** $3, -2$

180. $\frac{5}{3}, -3$ **181.** $\sqrt{3}, -3$ **182.** $-6, -3, 3$

183. $3, \dfrac{-1 - \sqrt{17}}{2}$ **184.** $10, -1$

185. (a) 61.2 inches
(b) Yes. The estimated height of a male with a 19-inch femur is 69.4 inches.
(c)

Height, x	Female femur length	Male femur length
60	15.48	14.79
70	19.80	19.28
80	24.12	23.77
90	28.44	28.26
100	32.76	32.75
110	37.08	37.24

100 inches
(d) $x \approx 100.59$; There would not be a problem because it is not likely for either a male or a female to be 100 inches tall (which is 8 feet 4 inches tall).

186. 23,437.5 miles

187. $y = -0.25t + 8$; after about 28 hours

188. (a)

(b) $w(w + 14) = 1632$
(c) $w = 34$ feet
$l = 48$ feet

189. 6 inches × 6 inches × 2 inches

190. $\dfrac{5\sqrt{2}}{2} \approx 3.54$ centimeters

191. $\dfrac{20\sqrt{3}}{3} \approx 11.55$ inches

192. ≈ 550 miles per hour and 600 miles per hour

193. (a) 1998 (b) During 2007

194. 26,250 passengers **195.** 500 units

196. 250,000 units

197. False. $x(3 - x) = 10$
$3x - x^2 = 10$
The equation cannot be written in the form $ax + b = 0$.

198. False. The product must equal zero for the Zero-Factor Property to be used.

199. False. See Example 14 on page A55.

200. False. $|x| = 0$ has only one solution to check, 0.

201. Equivalent equations have the same solution set, and one is derived from the other by steps for generating equivalent equations.
$2x = 5,\ 2x + 3 = 8$

202. Remove symbols of grouping, combine like terms, reduce fractions.
Add (or subtract) the same quantity to (from) each side of the equation.
Multiply (or divide) each side of the equation by the same nonzero quantity.
Interchange the two sides of the equation.

203. Yes. The student should have subtracted $15x$ from both sides to make the right side of the equation equal to zero. Factoring out an x shows that there are two solutions, $x = 0$ and $x = 6$.

204. (a) and (b) $x = -5, -\frac{10}{3}$
(c) The method used in part (a) reduces the number of algebraic steps.

205. $x^2 - 3x - 18 = 0$ **206.** $x^2 + 15x + 44 = 0$

207. $x^2 - 22x + 112 = 0$ **208.** $30x^2 + 7x - 2 = 0$

209. $x^2 - 2x - 1 = 0$ **210.** $x^2 + 6x + 4 = 0$

211. $a = 9, b = 9$

212. Isolate the absolute value by subtracting x from both sides of the equation. The expression inside the absolute value signs can be positive or negative, so two separate equations must be solved.

213. (a) $x = 0, -\dfrac{b}{a}$ (b) $x = 0, 1$

Appendix A.6 *(page A66)*

Vocabulary Check *(page A66)*

1. solution set **2.** graph **3.** negative
4. solution set **5.** double **6.** union

1. $-1 \le x \le 5$. Bounded **2.** $2 < x \le 10$. Bounded
3. $x > 11$. Unbounded **4.** $x \ge -5$. Unbounded
5. $x < -2$. Unbounded **6.** $x \le 7$. Unbounded
7. b **8.** f **9.** d **10.** c **11.** e **12.** a
13. (a) Yes (b) No (c) Yes (d) No
14. (a) No (b) No (c) Yes (d) No
15. (a) Yes (b) No (c) No (d) Yes
16. (a) No (b) No (c) Yes (d) No
17. (a) Yes (b) Yes (c) Yes (d) No
18. (a) No (b) Yes (c) No (d) Yes
19. $x < 3$ **20.** $x < -4$

21. $x < \frac{3}{2}$ **22.** $x < -\frac{5}{2}$

23. $x \ge 12$ **24.** $x \le 5$

25. $x > 2$

26. $x \geq \frac{1}{2}$

27. $x \geq \frac{2}{7}$

28. $x \geq -3$

29. $x < 5$

30. $x < -\frac{1}{2}$

31. $x \geq 4$

32. $x < 7$

33. $x \geq 2$

34. $x > \frac{1}{6}$

35. $x \geq -4$

36. $x > 16$

37. $-1 < x < 3$

38. $-6 < x \leq 1$

39. $-\frac{9}{2} < x < \frac{15}{2}$

40. $-3 \leq x < 7$

41. $-\frac{3}{4} < x < -\frac{1}{4}$

42. $3 < x < 9$

43. $10.5 \leq x \leq 13.5$

44. No solution

45. $-6 < x < 6$

46. $x < -4, x > 4$

47. $x < -2, x > 2$

48. $x < -15, x > 15$

49. No solution

50. No solution

51. $14 \leq x \leq 26$

52. All real numbers x

53. $x \leq -\frac{3}{2}, x \geq 3$

54. $-2 < x < 3$

55. $x \leq -5, x \geq 11$

56. $0 < x < 3$

57. $4 < x < 5$

58. $x < -28, x > 0$

59. $x \leq -\frac{29}{2}, x \geq -\frac{11}{2}$

60. $\frac{1}{5} \leq x \leq \frac{7}{5}$

61.

$x > 2$

62.

$x \leq 2$

63.

$x \leq 2$

64.

$x < 2$

65.

$-6 \leq x \leq 22$

66.

$x < -11, x > 2$

67.

$x \leq -\frac{27}{2}, x \geq -\frac{1}{2}$

68.

$-7 \leq x \leq 5$

69.

(a) $x \geq 2$
(b) $x \leq \frac{3}{2}$

70.

(a) $x \leq 6$
(b) $x \geq -\frac{3}{2}$

71.

(a) $-2 \leq x \leq 4$
(b) $x \leq 4$

72.

(a) $\frac{5}{3} \leq x \leq 3$
(b) $x \geq \frac{8}{3}$

APPENDIX A

73.

(a) $1 \le x \le 5$

(b) $x \le -1, x \ge 7$

74.

(a) $-10 \le x \le 6$

(b) $x \le -4, x \ge 0$

75. $[5, \infty)$ **76.** $[10, \infty)$ **77.** $[-3, \infty)$

78. $(-\infty, 3]$ **79.** $\left(-\infty, \frac{7}{2}\right]$ **80.** $\left[-\frac{5}{2}, \infty\right)$

81. All real numbers within eight units of 10

82. All real numbers more than four units from 8

83. $|x| \le 3$ **84.** $|x| > 3$ **85.** $|x - 7| \ge 3$

86. $|x + 1| \le 4$ **87.** $|x - 12| < 10$

88. $|x - 8| \ge 5$ **89.** $|x + 3| > 4$ **90.** $|x + 6| \le 7$

91. $x > 6$ **92.** More than 42,857 copies

93. $r > 3.125\%$ **94.** $r > 5\%$ **95.** $x \ge 36$

96. $x \ge 16{,}394$ **97.** $134 \le x \le 234$ **98.** 24 weeks

99. (a)

(b) $x \ge 129$

100. (a) and (b)

(c) $x \ge 182$ (d) $x \ge 181.54$

(e) An athlete's weight is not a particularly good indicator of the athlete's maximum bench-press weight. Other factors, such as muscle tone and exercise habits, influence maximum bench-press weight.

101. (a) $1 \le t \le 10$ (b) $t > 16$

102. (a) $2 \le t \le 7$ (b) $t \ge 17$

103. 106.864 square inches $\le$ area ≤ 109.464 square inches

104. 573.6025 square centimeters $\le$ area ≤ 597.8025 square centimeters

105. Might be undercharged or overcharged by $0.19.

106. $0.47

107. $13.7 < t < 17.5$

108. $65.8 \le h \le 71.2$

109. $20 \le h \le 80$

110. (a) ≈ 330 vibrations/second

(b) ≈ 3.6 millimeters

(c) 1.2 millimeters $\le t \le 2.4$ millimeters

(d) $v < 500$ vibrations/second

111. False. c has to be greater than zero.

112. False. If $-10 \le x \le 8$, then $10 \ge -x$ and $-x \ge -8$.

113. b

114. One set (the solution is not unique): $a = 1, b = 5, c = 5$

Appendix A.7 *(page A75)*

> ### Vocabulary Check *(page A75)*
>
> **1.** numerator **2.** reciprocal

1. Change all signs when distributing the minus sign.

$2x - (3y + 4) = 2x - 3y - 4$

2. The 3 is distributed to both terms.

$5z + 3(x - 2) = 5z + 3x - 6$

3. Change all signs when distributing the minus sign.

$$\frac{4}{16x - (2x + 1)} = \frac{4}{14x - 1}$$

4. The expression on the right should be negated.

$$\frac{1 - x}{(5 - x)(-x)} = -\frac{x - 1}{x(x - 5)}$$

5. z occurs twice as a factor.

$(5z)(6z) = 30z^2$

6. yz is one term, not two. $x(yz) = xyz$

7. The fraction as a whole is multiplied by a, not the numerator and denominator separately.

$$a\left(\frac{x}{y}\right) = \frac{ax}{y}$$

8. The exponent also applies to the coefficient. $(4x)^2 = 16x^2$

9. $\sqrt{x + 9}$ cannot be simplified.

10. Do not apply radicals term-by-term.

$\sqrt{25 - x^2} = \sqrt{(5 + x)(5 - x)}$

11. Divide out common factors, not common terms.

$\dfrac{2x^2 + 1}{5x}$ cannot be simplified.

12. $\dfrac{6x + y}{6x - y}$ cannot be simplified.

13. To get rid of negative exponents:

$$\frac{1}{a^{-1} + b^{-1}} = \frac{1}{a^{-1} + b^{-1}} \cdot \frac{ab}{ab} = \frac{ab}{b + a}.$$

14. The negative exponent is on a term of the denominator, not a factor.

$$\frac{1}{x + y^{-1}} = \frac{y}{xy + 1}, \quad y \ne 0$$

15. Factor within grouping symbols before applying exponent to each factor.

$(x^2 + 5x)^{1/2} = [x(x + 5)]^{1/2} = x^{1/2}(x + 5)^{1/2}$

16. Exponents are applied before multiplying.

$x(2x - 1)^2 = x(4x^2 - 4x + 1) = 4x^3 - 4x^2 + x$

17. To add fractions, first find a common denominator.

$$\frac{3}{x} + \frac{4}{y} = \frac{3y + 4x}{xy}$$

18. Be careful when using a slash to denote division.

$$(1/2)y = \frac{1}{2} \cdot y = \frac{y}{2}$$

19. $3x + 2$ **20.** x^2 **21.** $2x^2 + x + 15$

22. $3x + 2$ **23.** $\frac{1}{3}$ **24.** $-\frac{1}{4}$ **25.** 2 **26.** $\frac{1}{2}$

27. $\frac{1}{2x^2}$ **28.** $x - 1$ **29.** $\frac{25}{9}, \frac{49}{16}$ **30.** $\frac{4}{3}, \frac{16}{9}$

31. $1, 2$ **32.** $4, 7$ **33.** $1 - 5x$ **34.** $10x + 3$

35. $1 - 7x$ **36.** $1 + 10x^2 - 20x^3$ **37.** $3x - 1$

38. $4t - 3$ **39.** $3x^2(2x - 1)^{-3}$

40. $(x + 1)x^{-1}(6 - x)^{-1/2}$

41. $\frac{4}{3}x^{-1} + 4x^{-4} - 7x(2x)^{-1/3}$

42. $x(x - 2)^{-1} + x^{-2} + \frac{8}{3}(9x)^{-3}$ **43.** $\frac{16}{x} - 5 - x$

44. $x - 5 + \frac{4}{x^2}$ **45.** $4x^{8/3} - 7x^{5/3} + \frac{1}{x^{1/3}}$

46. $2x^{7/2} - 3x^{3/2} + \frac{5}{x^{1/2}} - \frac{1}{x^{3/2}}$ **47.** $\frac{3}{x^{1/2}} - 5x^{3/2} - x^{7/2}$

48. $\frac{x}{3} - \frac{5x^2}{3}$ **49.** $\frac{-7x^2 - 4x + 9}{(x^2 - 3)^3(x + 1)^4}$ **50.** $\frac{-11x^2 - 5}{x^6(x^2 + 1)^4}$

51. $\frac{27x^2 - 24x + 2}{(6x + 1)^4}$ **52.** $\frac{-6(2x - 3)}{(4x^2 + 9)^{3/2}}$

53. $\frac{-1}{(x + 3)^{2/3}(x + 2)^{7/4}}$ **54.** $\frac{x - 3}{(2x - 1)^{1/2}}$

55. $\frac{4x - 3}{(3x - 1)^{4/3}}$ **56.** $\frac{1 - 4x}{(x + 1)^2(2x - 3x^2)^{1/2}}$

57. $\frac{x}{x^2 + 4}$ **58.** $\frac{2(3x^2 + 5x - 6)}{(x^2 - 6)(2x + 5)}$

59. $\frac{(3x - 2)^{1/2}(15x^2 - 4x + 45)}{2(x^2 + 5)^{1/2}}$

60. $\frac{3(x - 6)^{1/2}[6x + 4 - (x - 6)^{5/2}]}{2(3x + 2)^{3/2}}$

61. (a)

x	0.5	1.0	1.5	2.0
t	1.70	1.72	1.78	1.89

x	2.5	3.0	3.5	4.0
t	2.02	2.18	2.36	2.57

(b) $x = 0.5$ mile

(c) $\dfrac{3x\sqrt{x^2 - 8x + 20} + (x - 4)\sqrt{x^2 + 4}}{6\sqrt{x^2 + 4}\sqrt{x^2 - 8x + 20}}$

62. (a) Answers will vary.

(b)

x	-2	-1	$-\frac{1}{2}$	0	1	2	$\frac{5}{2}$
y_1	-8.7	-2.9	-1.1	0	2.9	8.7	12.5
y_2	-8.7	-2.9	-1.1	0	2.9	8.7	12.5

63. True. $x^{-1} + y^{-2} = \dfrac{1}{x} + \dfrac{1}{y^2} = \dfrac{y^2 + x}{xy^2}$

64. False. Cannot move term-by-term from denominator to numerator.

65. True. $\dfrac{1}{\sqrt{x} + 4} = \dfrac{1}{\sqrt{x} + 4} \cdot \dfrac{\sqrt{x} - 4}{\sqrt{x} - 4} = \dfrac{\sqrt{x} - 4}{x - 16}$

66. False. $x^2 - 9$ does not factor into $\left(\sqrt{x} + 3\right)\left(\sqrt{x} - 3\right)$.

67. Add exponents when multiplying powers with like bases.
$x^n \cdot x^{3n} = x^{4n}$

68. There is no error.

69. When a binomial is squared, there is also a middle term.
$(x^n + y^n)^2 = x^{2n} + 2x^n y^n + y^{2n} \neq x^{2n} + y^{2n}$

70. There is no error.

71. The two answers are equivalent and can be obtained by factoring.

$\frac{1}{10}(2x - 1)^{5/2} + \frac{1}{6}(2x - 1)^{3/2}$

$= \frac{1}{60}(2x - 1)^{3/2}[6(2x - 1) + 10]$

$= \frac{1}{60}(2x - 1)^{3/2}(12x + 4)$

$= \frac{4}{60}(2x - 1)^{3/2}(3x + 1)$

$= \frac{1}{15}(2x - 1)^{3/2}(3x + 1)$

(a) $\frac{2}{5}(2x - 3)^{3/2}(x + 1)$ (b) $\frac{8}{15}(4 + x)^{3/2}(x - 1)$

APPENDIX A

Appendix B   Concepts in Statistics

B.1   Representing Data

▶ **What you should learn**

• Use line plots to order and analyze data.
• Use stem-and-leaf plots to organize and compare data.
• Use histograms to represent frequency distributions.

▶ **Why you should learn it**

Line plots, stem-and-leaf plots, and histograms are quick methods for determining which elements in a set of data occur with the greatest frequency. For instance, in Exercise 8 on page B4, you are asked to construct a frequency distribution and a histogram of employees' monthly salary contributions to a retirement plan.

Line Plots

Statistics is the branch of mathematics that studies techniques for collecting, organizing, and interpreting data. In this section, you will study several ways to organize data. The first is a **line plot,** which uses a portion of a real number line to order numbers. Line plots are especially useful for ordering small sets of numbers (about 50 or less) by hand.

Example 1 ▶ Constructing a Line Plot

Use a line plot to organize the following test scores. Which score occurs with the greatest frequency?

93, 70, 76, 67, 86, 93, 82, 78, 83, 86, 64, 78, 76, 66, 83,
83, 96, 74, 69, 76, 64, 74, 79, 76, 88, 76, 81, 82, 74, 70

Solution

Begin by scanning the data to find the smallest and largest numbers. For this data set, the smallest number is 64 and the largest is 96. Next, draw a portion of a real number line that includes the interval [64, 96]. To create the line plot, start with the first number, 93, and enter an × above 93 on the number line. Continue recording ×'s for each number in the list until you obtain the line plot shown in Figure B.1. From the line plot, you can see that 76 occurs with the greatest frequency.

FIGURE **B.1**

✔**CHECKPOINT**   Now try Exercise 3.

Test Scores

93, 70, 76, 58, 86, 93, 82, 78,
83, 86, 64, 78, 76, 66, 83, 83,
96, 74, 69, 76, 64, 74, 79, 76,
88, 76, 81, 82, 74, 70

Stems	Leaves
5	8
6	4 4 6 9
7	0 0 4 4 4 6 6 6 6 6 8 8 9
8	1 2 2 3 3 3 6 6 8
9	3 3 6

Stem-and-Leaf Plots

Another type of plot that can be used to organize sets of numbers by hand is a **stem-and-leaf plot.** A set of test scores and the corresponding stem-and-leaf plot are shown at the left.

Note that the *leaves* represent the units digits of the numbers and the *stems* represent the tens digits. Stem-and-leaf plots can also be used to compare two sets of data, as shown in the following example.

Example 2 ▶ Comparing Two Sets of Data

Use a stem-and-leaf plot to compare the test scores given on the previous page with the following test scores. Which set of test scores is better?

90, 81, 70, 62, 64, 73, 81, 92, 73, 81, 92, 93, 83, 75, 76, 83, 94, 96, 86, 77, 77, 86, 96, 86, 77, 86, 87, 87, 79, 88

Solution

Begin by ordering the second set of scores.

62, 64, 70, 73, 73, 75, 76, 77, 77, 77, 79, 81, 81, 81, 83, 83, 86, 86, 86, 86, 87, 87, 88, 90, 92, 92, 93, 94, 96, 96

Now that the data have been ordered, you can construct a *double* stem-and-leaf plot by letting the leaves to the right of the stems represent the units digits for the first group of test scores and letting the leaves to the left of the stems represent the units digits for the second group of test scores.

Leaves (2nd Group)	Stems	Leaves (1st Group)
	5	8
4 2	6	4 4 6 9
9 7 7 7 6 5 3 3 0	7	0 0 4 4 4 6 6 6 6 8 8 9
8 7 7 6 6 6 6 3 3 1 1 1	8	1 2 2 3 3 3 6 6 8
6 6 4 3 2 2 0	9	3 3 6

By comparing the two sets of leaves, you can see that the second group of test scores is better than the first group.

✓**CHECKPOINT**   Now try Exercise 6.

Example 3 ▶ Using a Stem-and-Leaf Plot

The table at the left above shows the percent of the population of each state and the District of Columbia that was at least 65 years old in 2003. Use a stem-and-leaf plot to organize the data.   (Source: U.S. Census Bureau)

Solution

Begin by ordering the numbers, as shown below.

6.3, 8.6, 9.5, 9.7, 9.8, 10.6, 11.2, 11.3, 11.3, 11.3, 11.4, 11.7, 11.9, 12.0, 12.0, 12.0, 12.0, 12.1, 12.1, 12.3, 12.3, 12.3, 12.4, 12.4, 12.7, 12.8, 12.9, 13.0, 13.0, 13.0, 13.0, 13.1, 13.1, 13.2, 13.3, 13.3, 13.3, 13.4, 13.5, 13.5, 13.6, 13.9, 14.0, 14.3, 14.4, 14.7, 14.8, 15.3, 15.4, 17.0

Next construct the stem-and-leaf plot using the leaves to represent the digits to the right of the decimal points, as shown at the left. From the stem-and-leaf plot, you can see that Alaska has the lowest percent and Florida has the highest percent.

✓**CHECKPOINT**   Now try Exercise 5.

AK	6.3	MT	13.6
AL	13.2	NC	12.1
AR	13.9	ND	14.8
AZ	12.8	NE	13.4
CA	10.6	NH	12.0
CO	9.7	NJ	13.0
CT	13.5	NM	12.0
DC	12.0	NV	11.2
DE	13.1	NY	13.0
FL	17.0	OH	13.3
GA	9.5	OK	13.1
HI	13.5	OR	12.7
IA	14.7	PA	15.4
ID	11.4	RI	14.0
IL	11.9	SC	12.3
IN	12.3	SD	14.3
KS	13.0	TN	12.4
KY	12.4	TX	9.8
LA	11.7	UT	8.6
MA	13.3	VA	11.3
MD	11.3	VT	12.9
ME	14.4	WA	11.3
MI	12.3	WI	13.0
MN	12.0	WV	15.3
MO	13.3	WY	12.0
MS	12.1		

Stems	Leaves
6.	3
7.	
8.	6
9.	5 7 8
10.	6
11.	2 3 3 3 4 7 9
12.	0 0 0 0 1 1 3 3 3 4 4 7 8 9
13.	0 0 0 0 1 1 2 3 3 3 4 5 5 6 9
14.	0 3 4 7 8
15.	3 4
16.	
17.	0

Histograms and Frequency Distributions

With data such as that given in Example 3, it is useful to group the numbers into intervals and plot the frequency of the data in each interval. For instance, the **frequency distribution** and **histogram** shown in Figure B.2 represent the data given in Example 3.

Frequency Distribution

Interval	Tally
[6, 8)	I
[8, 10)	IIII
[10, 12)	LHT III
[12, 14)	LHT LHT LHT LHT LHT LHT
[14, 16)	LHT I
[16, 18)	I

Histogram

FIGURE **B.2**

A histogram has a portion of a real number line as its horizontal axis. A histogram is similar to a bar graph, except that the rectangles (bars) in a bar graph can be either horizontal or vertical and the labels of the bars are not necessarily numbers.

Another difference between a bar graph and a histogram is that the bars in a bar graph are usually separated by spaces, whereas the bars in a histogram are not separated by spaces.

Interval	Tally
100–109	LHT III
110–119	I
120–129	III
130–139	III
140–149	LHT II
150–159	LHT
160–169	LHT III
170–179	LHT I
180–189	II
190–199	LHT

FIGURE **B.3**

Example 4 ▶ Constructing a Histogram

A company has 48 sales representatives who sold the following numbers of units during the first quarter of 2005. Construct a frequency distribution for this data set.

107	162	184	170	177	102	145	141
105	193	167	149	195	127	193	191
150	153	164	167	171	163	141	129
109	171	150	138	100	164	147	153
171	163	118	142	107	144	100	132
153	107	124	162	192	134	187	177

Solution

To begin constructing a frequency distribution, you must first decide on the number of intervals. There are several ways to group this data. However, because the smallest number is 100 and the largest is 195, it seems that 10 intervals would be appropriate. The first interval would be 100–109, the second interval would be 110–119, and so on. By tallying the data into the 10 intervals, you obtain the distribution shown at the left above. A histogram for the distribution is shown in Figure B.3.

✓CHECKPOINT   Now try Exercise 7.

B.1   Exercises

VOCABULARY CHECK: **Fill in the blanks.**

1. _____ is the branch of mathematics that studies techniques for collecting, organizing, and interpreting data.

2. A _____ plot and a _____ plot are useful for ordering small sets of numbers by hand.

3. A _____ has a portion of a real number line as its horizontal axis, and the bars are not separated by spaces.

4. You use a _____ _____ to create a histogram.

---

1. *Gasoline Prices* The line plot shows a sample of prices of unleaded regular gasoline from 25 different cities.

0.989 1.009 1.029 1.049 1.069 1.089 1.109 1.129 1.149 1.169 1.189

   (a) What price occurred with the greatest frequency?

   (b) What is the range of prices?

2. *Agriculture* The line plot shows the weights (to the nearest hundred pounds) of 30 head of cattle sold by a rancher.

   600   800   1000   1200   1400

   (a) What weight occurred with the greatest frequency?

   (b) What is the range of weights?

Quiz and Exam Scores **In Exercises 3–6, use the following scores from a math class of 30 students. The scores are for two 25-point quizzes and two 100-point exams.**

Quiz #1   20, 15, 14, 20, 16, 19, 10, 21, 24, 15, 15, 14, 15, 21, 19, 15, 20, 18, 18, 22, 18, 16, 18, 19, 21, 19, 16, 20, 14, 12

Quiz #2   22, 22, 23, 22, 21, 24, 22, 19, 21, 23, 23, 25, 24, 22, 22, 23, 23, 23, 23, 22, 24, 23, 22, 24, 21, 24, 16, 21, 16, 14

Exam #1   77, 100, 77, 70, 83, 89, 87, 85, 81, 84, 81, 78, 89, 78, 88, 85, 90, 92, 75, 81, 85, 100, 98, 81, 78, 75, 85, 89, 82, 75

Exam #2   76, 78, 73, 59, 70, 81, 71, 66, 66, 73, 68, 67, 63, 67, 77, 84, 87, 71, 78, 78, 90, 80, 77, 70, 80, 64, 74, 68, 68, 68

3. Construct a line plot for each quiz. For each quiz, which score occurred with the greatest frequency?

4. Construct a line plot for each exam. For each exam, which score occurred with the greatest frequency?

5. Construct a stem-and-leaf plot for Exam #1.

6. Construct a double stem-and-leaf plot to compare the scores for Exam #1 and Exam #2. Which set of scores is higher?

7. *Agriculture* The table shows the total numbers of farms (in thousands) in the 50 states in 2002. Use a frequency distribution and a histogram to organize the data. (Source: U.S. Dept. of Agriculture)

AK	1	AL	45	AR	47	AZ	7	CA	80
CO	31	CT	4	DE	2	FL	44	GA	49
HI	5	IA	91	ID	25	IL	73	IN	60
KS	64	KY	87	LA	27	MA	6	MD	12
ME	7	MI	53	MN	81	MO	107	MS	42
MT	28	NC	54	ND	31	NE	49	NH	3
NJ	10	NM	15	NV	3	NY	37	OH	78
OK	83	OR	40	PA	58	RI	1	SC	25
SD	32	TN	88	TX	229	UT	15	VA	48
VT	7	WA	36	WI	77	WV	21	WY	9

8. *Retirement Contributions* The employees of a company must contribute 7% of their monthly salaries to a company-sponsored retirement plan. The contributed amounts (in dollars) for the company's 35 employees are shown below. Use a frequency distribution and a histogram to organize the data.

100, 200, 130, 136, 161, 156, 209, 126, 135, 98, 114, 117, 168, 133, 140, 124, 172, 127, 143, 157, 124, 152, 104, 126, 155, 92, 194, 115, 120, 136, 148, 112, 116, 146, 96

9. *Meteorology* The data shows the seasonal snowfall (in inches) at Lincoln, Nebraska for the years 1975 through 2004 (the amounts are listed in order by year). How would you organize the data? Explain your reasoning. (Source: University of Nebraska–Lincoln)

21.2, 21.8, 31.0, 34.4, 23.3, 13.0, 32.3, 38.0, 47.5, 21.5, 18.9, 15.7, 13.0, 19.1, 18.7, 25.8, 23.8, 32.1, 21.3, 21.8, 30.7, 29.0, 44.6, 24.4, 11.9, 37.9, 29.5, 31.7, 35.9, 16.3

B.2   Measures of Central Tendency and Dispersion

▶ **What you should learn**

- Find and interpret the mean, median, and mode of a set of data.
- Determine the measure of central tendency that best represents a set of data.
- Find the standard deviation of a set of data.
- Create and use box-and-whisker plots.

▶ **Why you should learn it**

Measures of central tendency and dispersion provide a convenient way to describe and compare sets of data. For instance, in Exercise 36 on page B13, the mean and standard deviation are used to analyze the price of gold for the years 1984 through 2003.

Mean, Median, and Mode

In many real-life situations, it is helpful to describe data by a single number that is most representative of the entire collection of numbers. Such a number is called a **measure of central tendency.** The most commonly used measures are as follows.

1. The **mean,** or **average,** of n numbers is the sum of the numbers divided by n.
2. The numerical **median** of n numbers is the middle number when the numbers are written in order. If n is even, the median is the average of the two middle numbers.
3. The **mode** of n numbers is the number that occurs most frequently. If two numbers tie for most frequent occurrence, the collection has two modes and is called **bimodal.**

Example 1 ▶   Comparing Measures of Central Tendency

On an interview for a job, the interviewer tells you that the average annual income of the company's 25 employees is $60,849. The actual annual incomes of the 25 employees are shown below. What are the mean, median, and mode of the incomes?

$17,305,	$478,320,	$45,678,	$18,980,	$17,408,
$25,676,	$28,906,	$12,500,	$24,540,	$33,450,
$12,500,	$33,855,	$37,450,	$20,432,	$28,956,
$34,983,	$36,540,	$250,921,	$36,853,	$16,430,
$32,654,	$98,213,	$48,980,	$94,024,	$35,671

Solution

The mean of the incomes is

$$\text{Mean} = \frac{17{,}305 + 478{,}320 + 45{,}678 + 18{,}980 + \cdots + 35{,}671}{25}$$

$$= \frac{1{,}521{,}225}{25} = \$60{,}849.$$

To find the median, order the incomes as follows.

$12,500,	$12,500,	$16,430,	$17,305,	$17,408,
$18,980,	$20,432,	$24,540,	$25,676,	$28,906,
$28,956,	$32,654,	$33,450,	$33,855,	$34,983,
$35,671,	$36,540,	$36,853,	$37,450,	$45,678,
$48,980,	$94,024,	$98,213,	$250,921,	$478,320

From this list, you can see that the median income is $33,450. You can also see that $12,500 is the only income that occurs more than once. So, the mode is $12,500.

✓**CHECKPOINT**   Now try Exercise 1.

In Example 1, was the interviewer telling you the truth about the annual incomes? Technically, the person was telling the truth because the average is (generally) defined to be the mean. However, of the three measures of central tendency *mean:* $60,849 *median:* $33,450 *mode:* $12,500 it seems clear that the median is most representative. The mean is inflated by the two highest salaries.

Choosing a Measure of Central Tendency

Which of the three measures of central tendency is the most representative? The answer is that it depends on the distribution of the data *and* the way in which you plan to use the data.

For instance, in Example 1, the mean salary of $60,849 does not seem very representative to a potential employee. To a city income tax collector who wants to estimate 1% of the total income of the 25 employees, however, the mean is precisely the right measure.

Example 2 ▶ Choosing a Measure of Central Tendency

Which measure of central tendency is the most representative of the data shown in each frequency distribution?

a.

Number	1	2	3	4	5	6	7	8	9
Frequency	7	20	15	11	8	3	2	0	15

b.

Number	1	2	3	4	5	6	7	8	9
Frequency	9	8	7	6	5	6	7	8	9

c.

Number	1	2	3	4	5	6	7	8	9
Frequency	6	1	2	3	5	5	4	3	0

Solution

a. For these data, the mean is 4.23, the median is 3, and the mode is 2. Of these, the mode is probably the most representative measure.

b. For these data, the mean and median are each 5 and the modes are 1 and 9 (the distribution is bimodal). Of these, the mean or median is the most representative measure.

c. For these data, the mean is 4.59, the median is 5, and the mode is 1. Of these, the mean or median is the most representative measure.

✓*CHECKPOINT*   Now try Exercise 15.

Variance and Standard Deviation

Very different sets of numbers can have the same mean. You will now study two **measures of dispersion,** which give you an idea of how much the numbers in a data set differ from the mean of the set. These two measures are called the *variance* of the set and the *standard deviation* of the set.

Definitions of Variance and Standard Deviation

Consider a set of numbers $\{x_1, x_2, \ldots, x_n\}$ with a mean of $\bar{x}$. The **variance** of the set is

$$v = \frac{(x_1 - \bar{x})^2 + (x_2 - \bar{x})^2 + \cdots + (x_n - \bar{x})^2}{n}$$

and the **standard deviation** of the set is $\sigma = \sqrt{v}$ (σ is the lowercase Greek letter *sigma*).

The standard deviation of a data set is a measure of how much a typical number in the set differs from the mean. The greater the standard deviation, the more the numbers in the set *vary* from the mean. For instance, each of the following data sets has a mean of 5.

$$\{5, 5, 5, 5\}, \qquad \{4, 4, 6, 6\}, \qquad \text{and} \qquad \{3, 3, 7, 7\}$$

The standard deviations of the data sets are 0, 1, and 2.

$$\sigma_1 = \sqrt{\frac{(5 - 5)^2 + (5 - 5)^2 + (5 - 5)^2 + (5 - 5)^2}{4}}$$

$$= 0$$

$$\sigma_2 = \sqrt{\frac{(4 - 5)^2 + (4 - 5)^2 + (6 - 5)^2 + (6 - 5)^2}{4}}$$

$$= 1$$

$$\sigma_3 = \sqrt{\frac{(3 - 5)^2 + (3 - 5)^2 + (7 - 5)^2 + (7 - 5)^2}{4}}$$

$$= 2$$

Example 3 ▶ Estimations of Standard Deviation

Consider the three frequency distributions represented by the bar graphs in Figure B.4. Which data set has the smallest standard deviation? Which has the largest?

FIGURE **B.4**

Solution

Of the three data sets, the numbers in data set *A* are grouped most closely to the center and the numbers in data set *C* are the most dispersed. So, data set *A* has the smallest standard deviation and data set *C* has the largest standard deviation.

✓CHECKPOINT   Now try Exercise 17.

Example 4 ▶ Finding Standard Deviation

Find the standard deviation of each data set shown in Example 3.

Solution

Because of the symmetry of each bar graph, you can conclude that each has a mean of $\bar{x} = 4$. The standard deviation of data set A is

$$\sigma = \sqrt{\frac{(-3)^2 + 2(-2)^2 + 3(-1)^2 + 5(0)^2 + 3(1)^2 + 2(2)^2 + (3)^2}{17}}$$

$$\approx 1.53.$$

The standard deviation of data set B is

$$\sigma = \sqrt{\frac{2(-3)^2 + 2(-2)^2 + 2(-1)^2 + 2(0)^2 + 2(1)^2 + 2(2)^2 + 2(3)^2}{14}}$$

$$= 2.$$

The standard deviation of data set C is

$$\sigma = \sqrt{\frac{5(-3)^2 + 4(-2)^2 + 3(-1)^2 + 2(0)^2 + 3(1)^2 + 4(2)^2 + 5(3)^2}{26}}$$

$$\approx 2.22.$$

These values confirm the results of Example 3. That is, data set A has the smallest standard deviation and data set C has the largest.

✓**CHECKPOINT**   Now try Exercise 19.

The following alternative formula provides a more efficient way to compute the standard deviation.

Alternative Formula for Standard Deviation

The standard deviation of $\{x_1, x_2, \ldots, x_n\}$ is

$$\sigma = \sqrt{\frac{x_1^2 + x_2^2 + \cdots + x_n^2}{n} - \bar{x}^2}.$$

Because of lengthy computations, this formula is difficult to verify. Conceptually, however, the process is straightforward. It consists of showing that the expressions

$$\sqrt{\frac{(x_1 - \bar{x})^2 + (x_2 - \bar{x})^2 + \cdots + (x_n - \bar{x})^2}{n}}$$

and

$$\sqrt{\frac{x_1^2 + x_2^2 + \cdots + x_n^2}{n} - \bar{x}^2}$$

are equivalent. Try verifying this equivalence for the set $\{x_1, x_2, x_3\}$ with $\bar{x} = (x_1 + x_2 + x_3)/3$.

Example 5 ▶ **Using the Alternative Formula**

Use the alternative formula for standard deviation to find the standard deviation of the following set of numbers.

5, 6, 6, 7, 7, 8, 8, 8, 9, 10

Solution

Begin by finding the mean of the set, which is 7.4. So, the standard deviation is

$$\sigma = \sqrt{\frac{5^2 + 2(6^2) + 2(7^2) + 3(8^2) + 9^2 + 10^2}{10} - (7.4)^2}$$

$$= \sqrt{\frac{568}{10} - 54.76}$$

$$= \sqrt{2.04}$$

$$\approx 1.43.$$

You can use the *one-variable statistics* feature of a graphing utility to check this result.

✓CHECKPOINT   Now try Exercise 27.

A well-known theorem in statistics, called *Chebychev's Theorem*, states that at least

$$1 - \frac{1}{k^2}$$

of the numbers in a distribution must lie within k standard deviations of the mean. So, at least 75% of the numbers in a data set must lie within two standard deviations of the mean, and at least 88.9% of the numbers must lie within three standard deviations of the mean. For most distributions, these percentages are low. For instance, in all three distributions shown in Example 3, 100% of the numbers lie within two standard deviations of the mean.

Example 6 ▶ **Describing a Distribution**

The table at the left shows the number of outpatient visits to hospitals (in millions) in each state and the District of Columbia in 2002. Find the mean and standard deviation of the data. What percent of the data values lie within two standard deviations of the mean?   (Source: Health Forum)

Solution

Begin by entering the numbers into a graphing utility. Then use the *one-variable statistics* feature to obtain $\bar{x} \approx 10.91$ and $\sigma = 11.40$. The interval that contains all numbers that lie within two standard deviations of the mean is

$$[10.91 - 2(11.40), 10.91 + 2(11.40)] \quad \text{or} \quad [-11.89, 33.71].$$

From the table you can see that all but two of the data values (96%) lie in this interval—all but the data values that correspond to the numbers of outpatient visits to hospitals in California and New York.

✓CHECKPOINT   Now try Exercise 36.

AK	1.3	MT	2.7
AL	10.0	NC	13.8
AR	4.8	ND	1.9
AZ	5.1	NE	3.5
CA	53.3	NH	3.0
CO	7.0	NJ	15.9
CT	6.6	NM	4.2
DC	1.5	NV	2.5
DE	1.9	NY	46.8
FL	22.5	OH	28.4
GA	12.5	OK	4.8
HI	2.0	OR	8.2
IA	9.3	PA	32.4
ID	2.4	RI	2.2
IL	26.5	SC	7.3
IN	14.1	SD	1.5
KS	5.7	TN	10.0
KY	8.6	TX	33.5
LA	10.7	UT	4.8
MA	19.0	VA	10.8
MD	6.5	VT	1.5
ME	3.7	WA	9.7
MI	25.9	WI	11.6
MN	8.9	WV	5.7
MO	14.9	WY	0.9
MS	4.0		

Box-and-Whisker Plots

Standard deviation is the measure of dispersion that is associated with the mean. **Quartiles** measure dispersion associated with the median.

Definition of Quartiles

Consider an ordered set of numbers whose median is m. The **lower quartile** is the median of the numbers that occur before m. The **upper quartile** is the median of the numbers that occur after m.

Example 7 ► Finding Quartiles of a Data Set

Find the lower and upper quartiles for the data set.

34, 14, 24, 16, 12, 18, 20, 24, 16, 26, 13, 27

Solution

Begin by ordering the data.

12, 13, 14, 16, 16, 18, 20, 24, 24, 26, 27, 34

1st 25%   2nd 25%   3rd 25%   4th 25%

The median of the entire data set is 19. The median of the six numbers that are less than 19 is 15. So, the lower quartile is 15. The median of the six numbers that are greater than 19 is 25. So, the upper quartile is 25.

✓**CHECKPOINT**   Now try Exercise 39(a).

Quartiles are represented graphically by a **box-and-whisker plot,** as shown in Figure B.5. In the plot, notice that five numbers are listed: the smallest number, the lower quartile, the median, the upper quartile, and the largest number. Also notice that the numbers are spaced proportionally, as though they were on a real number line.

12   15   19   25   34

FIGURE **B.5**

The next example shows how to find quartiles when the number of elements in a data set is not divisible by 4.

Example 8 ▶ **Sketching Box-and-Whisker Plots**

Sketch a box-and-whisker plot for each data set.

a. 27, 28, 30, 42, 45, 50, 50, 61, 62, 64, 66

b. 82, 82, 83, 85, 87, 89, 90, 94, 95, 95, 96, 98, 99

c. 11, 13, 13, 15, 17, 18, 20, 24, 24, 27

Solution

a. This data set has 11 numbers. The median is 50 (the sixth number). The lower quartile is 30 (the median of the first five numbers). The upper quartile is 62 (the median of the last five numbers). See Figure B.6.

27   30   50   62   66

FIGURE **B.6**

b. This data set has 13 numbers. The median is 90 (the seventh number). The lower quartile is 84 (the median of the first six numbers). The upper quartile is 95.5 (the median of the last six numbers). See Figure B.7.

82   84   90   95.5   99

FIGURE **B.7**

c. This data set has 10 numbers. The median is 17.5 (the average of the fifth and sixth numbers). The lower quartile is 13 (the median of the first five numbers). The upper quartile is 24 (the median of the last five numbers). See Figure B.8.

11   13   17.5   24   27

FIGURE **B.8**

✓CHECKPOINT   Now try Exercise 41(b).

B.2 Exercises

VOCABULARY CHECK: Fill in the blanks.

1. A single number that is the most representative of a data set is called a _____ of _____ _____ .

2. The _____ of n numbers is the sum of the numbers divided by n.

3. If there is an even number of data values in a data set, then the _____ is the average of the two middle numbers.

4. If two numbers of a data set are tied for the most frequent occurrence, the collection has two _____ and is called _____.

5. Two measures of dispersion associated with the mean are called the _____ and the _____ _____ of a data set.

6. _____ measure dispersion associated with the median.

7. You can represent quartiles graphically by creating a _____ _____ .

In Exercises 1–6, find the mean, median, and mode of the set of measurements.

1. 5, 12, 7, 14, 8, 9, 7
2. 30, 37, 32, 39, 33, 34, 32
3. 5, 12, 7, 24, 8, 9, 7
4. 20, 37, 32, 39, 33, 34, 32
5. 5, 12, 7, 14, 9, 7
6. 30, 37, 32, 39, 34, 32

7. *Reasoning* Compare your answers for Exercises 1 and 3 with those for Exercises 2 and 4. Which of the measures of central tendency is sensitive to extreme measurements? Explain your reasoning.

8. *Reasoning*
   (a) Add 6 to each measurement in Exercise 1 and calculate the mean, median, and mode of the revised measurements. How are the measures of central tendency changed?
   (b) If a constant k is added to each measurement in a set of data, how will the measures of central tendency change?

9. *Electric Bills* A person had the following monthly bills for electricity. What are the mean and median of the collection of bills?

January	$67.92	February	$59.84
March	$52.00	April	$52.50
May	$57.99	June	$65.35
July	$81.76	August	$74.98
September	$87.82	October	$83.18
November	$65.35	December	$57.00

10. *Car Rental* A car rental company kept the following record of the numbers of miles a rental car was driven. What are the mean, median, and mode of the data?

Monday	410	Tuesday	260
Wednesday	320	Thursday	320
Friday	460	Saturday	150

11. *Families* A study was done on families having six children. The table shows the numbers of families in the study with the indicated numbers of girls. Determine the mean, median, and mode of this set of data.

Number of girls	0	1	2	3	4	5	6
Frequency	1	24	45	54	50	19	7

12. *Sports* A baseball fan examined the records of a favorite baseball player's performance during his last 50 games. The numbers of games in which the player had 0, 1, 2, 3, and 4 hits are recorded in the table.

Number of hits	0	1	2	3	4
Frequency	14	26	7	2	1

(a) Determine the average number of hits per game.
(b) Determine the player's batting average if he had 200 at-bats during the 50-game series.

13. *Think About It* Construct a collection of numbers that has the following properties. If this is not possible, explain why it is not.

Mean = 6, median = 4, mode = 4

14. *Think About It* Construct a collection of numbers that has the following properties. If this is not possible, explain why it is not.

Mean = 6, median = 6, mode = 4

15. *Test Scores* A professor records the following scores for a 100-point exam.

99, 64, 80, 77, 59, 72, 87, 79, 92, 88,
90, 42, 20, 89, 42, 100, 98, 84, 78, 91

Which measure of central tendency best describes these test scores?

16. *Shoe Sales* A salesman sold eight pairs of men's black dress shoes. The sizes of the eight pairs were as follows: $10\frac{1}{2}$, 8, 12, $10\frac{1}{2}$, 10, $9\frac{1}{2}$, 11, and $10\frac{1}{2}$. Which measure (or measures) of central tendency best describes the typical shoe size for the data?

In Exercises 17 and 18, line plots of sets of data are given. Determine the mean and standard deviation of each set.

17. (a)

(b)

(c)

(d)

18. (a)

(b)

(c)

(d)

In Exercises 19–26, find the mean ($\bar{x}$), variance (v), and standard deviation (σ) of the data set.

19. 4, 10, 8, 2

20. 3, 15, 6, 9, 2

21. 0, 1, 1, 2, 2, 2, 3, 3, 4

22. 2, 2, 2, 2, 2, 2

23. 1, 2, 3, 4, 5, 6, 7

24. 1, 1, 1, 5, 5, 5

25. 49, 62, 40, 29, 32, 70

26. 1.5, 0.4, 2.1, 0.7, 0.8

In Exercises 27–32, use the alternative formula to find the standard deviation of the data set.

27. 2, 4, 6, 6, 13, 5

28. 10, 25, 50, 26, 15, 33, 29, 4

29. 246, 336, 473, 167, 219, 359

30. 6.0, 9.1, 4.4, 8.7, 10.4

31. 8.1, 6.9, 3.7, 4.2, 6.1

32. 9.0, 7.5, 3.3, 7.4, 6.0

33. *Reasoning* Without calculating the standard deviation, explain why the data set {4, 4, 20, 20} has a standard deviation of 8.

34. *Reasoning* If the standard deviation of a data set of numbers is 0, what does this imply about the set?

35. *Test Scores* An instructor adds five points to each student's exam score. Will this change the mean or standard deviation of the exam scores? Explain.

36. *Price of Gold* The following data represents the average prices of gold (in dollars per fine ounce) for the years 1984 to 2003. Use a computer or graphing utility to find the mean, variance, and standard deviation of the data. What percent of the data lies within two standard deviations of the mean? (Source: U.S. Bureau of Mines and U.S. Geological Survey)

361, 318, 368, 478, 438,
383, 385, 363, 345, 361,
385, 386, 389, 332, 295,
280, 280, 272, 311, 350

37. *Think About It* The histograms represent the test scores of two classes of a college course in mathematics. Which histogram has the smaller standard deviation?

38. *Test Scores* The scores of a mathematics exam given to 600 science and engineering students at a college had a mean and standard deviation of 235 and 28, respectively. Use Chebychev's Theorem to determine the intervals containing at least $\frac{3}{4}$ and at least $\frac{8}{9}$ of the scores. How would the intervals change if the standard deviation were 16?

In Exercises 39–42, (a) find the lower and upper quartiles of the data and (b) sketch a box-and-whisker plot for the data without the aid of a graphing utility.

39. 23, 15, 14, 23, 13, 14, 13, 20, 12

40. 11, 10, 11, 14, 17, 16, 14, 11, 8, 14, 20

41. 46, 48, 48, 50, 52, 47, 51, 47, 49, 53

42. 25, 20, 22, 28, 24, 28, 25, 19, 27, 29, 28, 21

In Exercises 43–46, use a graphing utility to create a box-and-whisker plot for the data.

43. 19, 12, 14, 9, 14, 15, 17, 13, 19, 11, 10, 19

44. 9, 5, 5, 5, 6, 5, 4, 12, 7, 10, 7, 11, 8, 9, 9

45. 20.1, 43.4, 34.9, 23.9, 33.5, 24.1, 22.5, 42.4, 25.7, 17.4, 23.8, 33.3, 17.3, 36.4, 21.8

46. 78.4, 76.3, 107.5, 78.5, 93.2, 90.3, 77.8, 37.1, 97.1, 75.5, 58.8, 65.6

47. *Product Lifetime* A company has redesigned a product in an attempt to increase the lifetime of the product. The two sets of data list the lifetimes (in months) of 20 units with the original design and 20 units with the new design. Create a box-and-whisker plot for each set of data, and then comment on the differences between the plots.

Original Design

15.1	78.3	56.3	68.9	30.6
27.2	12.5	42.7	72.7	20.2
53.0	13.5	11.0	18.4	85.2
10.8	38.3	85.1	10.0	12.6

New Design

55.8	71.5	25.6	19.0	23.1
37.2	60.0	35.3	18.9	80.5
46.7	31.1	67.9	23.5	99.5
54.0	23.2	45.5	24.8	87.8

B.3 Least Squares Regression

▶ **What you should learn**

• Use the sum of squared differences to measure how well a model fits a set of data.
• Find a least squares regression line for a set of data.
• Find a least squares regression parabola for a set of data.

▶ **Why you should learn it**

The method of least squares provides a way of creating mathematical models for a set of data, which can then be analyzed. For instance, in Exercise 9 on page B15, you will find the least squares regression line for the quantity of college textbooks sold in the United States from 2000 to 2003.

In many of the examples and exercises in the text, you have been asked to use the *regression* feature of a graphing utility to find mathematical models for sets of data. The *regression* feature of a graphing utility uses the **method of least squares** to find a mathematical model for a set of data. As a measure of how well a model fits a set of data points

$$\{(x_1, y_1), (x_2, y_2), (x_3, y_3), \ldots, (x_n, y_n)\}$$

you can add the squares of the differences between the actual y-values and the values given by the model to obtain the **sum of the squared differences.** For instance, the table shows the heights x (in feet) and the diameters y (in inches) of eight trees. The table also shows the values of a linear model $y^* = 0.54x - 29.5$ for each x-value. The sum of squared differences for the model is 51.7.

x	70	72	75	76	85	78	77	80
y	8.3	10.5	11.0	11.4	12.9	14.0	16.3	18.0
y^*	8.3	9.38	11.0	11.54	16.4	12.62	12.08	13.7
$(y - y^*)^2$	0	1.2544	0	0.0196	12.25	1.9044	17.8084	18.49

The model that has the least sum of squared differences is the **least squares regression line** for the data. The least squares regression line for the data in the table is $y \approx 0.43x - 20.3$. The sum of squared differences is 43.3.

To find the least squares regression line $y = ax + b$ for the points $\{(x_1, y_1), (x_2, y_2), (x_3, y_3), \ldots, (x_n, y_n)\}$ algebraically, you need to solve the following system for a and b.

$$\begin{cases} nb + \left(\sum_{i=1}^{n} x_i\right)a = \sum_{i=1}^{n} y_i \\ \left(\sum_{i=1}^{n} x_i\right)b + \left(\sum_{i=1}^{n} x_i^2\right)a = \sum_{i=1}^{n} x_i y_i \end{cases}$$

In the system,

$$\sum_{i=1}^{n} x_i = x_1 + x_2 + \cdots + x_n$$

$$\sum_{i=1}^{n} y_i = y_1 + y_2 + \cdots + y_n$$

$$\sum_{i=1}^{n} x_i^2 = x_1^2 + x_2^2 + \cdots + x_n^2$$

$$\sum_{i=1}^{n} x_i y_i = x_1 y_1 + x_2 y_2 + \cdots + x_n y_n.$$

Example 1 ▶ Finding a Least Squares Regression Line

Find the least squares regression line for the points $(-3, 0)$, $(-1, 1)$, $(0, 2)$, and $(2, 3)$.

Solution

Begin by constructing a table like that shown below.

x	y	xy	x^2
-3	0	0	9
-1	1	-1	1
0	2	0	0
2	3	6	4
$\sum\limits_{i=1}^{n} x_i = -2$	$\sum\limits_{i=1}^{n} y_i = 6$	$\sum\limits_{i=1}^{n} x_i y_i = 5$	$\sum\limits_{i=1}^{n} x_i^2 = 14$

Applying the system for the least squares regression line with $n = 4$ produces

$$\begin{cases} nb + \left(\sum\limits_{i=1}^{n} x_i\right)a = \sum\limits_{i=1}^{n} y_i \\ \left(\sum\limits_{i=1}^{n} x_i\right)b + \left(\sum\limits_{i=1}^{n} x_i^2\right)a = \sum\limits_{i=1}^{n} x_i y_i \end{cases} \implies \begin{cases} 4b - 2a = 6 \\ -2b + 14a = 5 \end{cases}.$$

Solving this system of equations produces $a = \frac{8}{13}$ and $b = \frac{47}{26}$. So, the least squares regression line is $y = \frac{8}{13}x + \frac{47}{26}$, as shown in Figure B.9.

FIGURE **B.9**

✓CHECKPOINT   Now try Exercise 5.

The least squares regression parabola $y = ax^2 + bx + c$ for the points

$$\{(x_1, y_1), (x_2, y_2), (x_3, y_3), \ldots, (x_n, y_n)\}$$

is obtained in a similar manner by solving the following system of three equations in three unknowns for a, b, and c.

$$\begin{cases} nc + \left(\sum\limits_{i=1}^{n} x_i\right)b + \left(\sum\limits_{i=1}^{n} x_i^2\right)a = \sum\limits_{i=1}^{n} y_i \\ \left(\sum\limits_{i=1}^{n} x_i\right)c + \left(\sum\limits_{i=1}^{n} x_i^2\right)b + \left(\sum\limits_{i=1}^{n} x_i^3\right)a = \sum\limits_{i=1}^{n} x_i y_i \\ \left(\sum\limits_{i=1}^{n} x_i^2\right)c + \left(\sum\limits_{i=1}^{n} x_i^3\right)b + \left(\sum\limits_{i=1}^{n} x_i^4\right)a = \sum\limits_{i=1}^{n} x_i^2 y_i \end{cases}$$

Fortunately, graphing utilities have built-in least squares *regression* features.

B.3 Exercises

VOCABULARY CHECK: Fill in the blanks.

1. A graphing utility uses the _____ of _____ to find a mathematical model for a set of data.
2. The _____ of the _____ measures how well a model fits a set of data points.
3. The _____ line for a set of data is the linear model that has least sum of squared differences.

In Exercises 1–4, you are given a set of data points and a linear model for the data. Find the sum of squared differences for the given linear model.

1. $(-3, -1), (-1, 0), (0, 2), (2, 3), (4, 4)$
   $y = 0.5x + 0.5$
2. $(0, 2), (1, 1), (2, 2), (3, 4), (5, 6)$
   $y = 0.8x + 2$
3. $(-2, 6), (-1, 4), (0, 2), (1, 1), (2, 1)$
   $y = -1.7x + 2.7$
4. $(0, 7), (2, 5), (3, 2), (4, 3), (6, 0)$
   $y = -1.2x + 7$

In Exercises 5–8, find the least squares regression line for the points. Verify your answer with a graphing utility.

5. $(-4, 1), (-3, 3), (-2, 4), (-1, 6)$
6. $(0, -1), (2, 0), (4, 3), (6, 5)$
7. $(-3, 1), (-1, 2), (1, 2), (4, 3)$
8. $(0, -1), (2, 1), (3, 2), (5, 3)$

9. *Book Sales* The quantity of college textbooks sold in the United States from 2000 to 2003 are represented by the ordered pairs (x, y), where x represents the year, with $x = 0$ corresponding to 2000 and y represents the quantity of books sold (in millions). Find the least squares regression line for the data. What is the sum of squared differences? (Source: Book Industry Study Group, Inc.)

   $(0, 83), (1, 86), (2, 88), (3, 89)$

10. *Cell Phone Calls* The average lengths of a cell phone call from 2000 to 2003 are represented by the ordered pairs (x, y), where x represents the year, with $x = 0$ corresponding to 2000 and y represents the average length of a call (in minutes). Find the least squares regression line for the data. What is the sum of squared differences? (Source: Cellular Telecommunications & Internet Association)

    $(0, 2.56), (1, 2.74), (2, 2.73), (3, 2.87)$

In Exercises 11–14, find the least squares regression parabola for the points. Verify your answer with a graphing utility.

11. $(0, 0), (2, 4), (4, 2)$
12. $(-2, 6), (-1, 2), (1, 3)$
13. $(-1, 4), (0, 2), (1, 0), (3, 4)$
14. $(-3, -1), (-1, 2), (1, 2), (3, 0)$

Answers to Odd-Numbered Exercises for Appendix B

Appendix B.1 *(page B4)*

> **Vocabulary Check** *(page B4)*
> **1.** statistics **2.** line; stem-and-leaf **3.** histogram
> **4.** frequency distribution

1. (a) $2.109 (b) $0.19

3. Quiz 1:

Quiz 2:

5.

Stems	Leaves
7	0 5 5 5 7 7 8 8 8
8	1 1 1 1 2 3 4 5 5 5 5 7 8 9 9 9
9	0 2 8
10	0 0

7.

Interval	Tally
[0, 25)	⫿⫿⫿ ⫿⫿⫿ ⫿⫿⫿ ∥
[25, 50)	⫿⫿⫿ ⫿⫿⫿ ⫿⫿⫿ ∥
[50, 75)	⫿⫿⫿ ∣
[75, 100)	⫿⫿⫿ ∥∣
[100, 125)	∣
[125, 150)	
[150, 175)	
[175, 200)	
[200, 225)	
[225, 250)	∣

Number of farms
(in thousands)

9. A histogram would be the best way to organize the data because it would be easy to group the data into intervals and it would be easy to identify any patterns in the data by using a histogram.

Appendix B.2 *(page B11)*

> **Vocabulary Check** *(page B11)*
> **1.** measure; central; tendency **2.** mean **3.** median
> **4.** modes; bimodal **5.** variance; standard deviation
> **6.** quartiles **7.** box-and-whisker plot

1. Mean: 8.86; median: 8; mode: 7

3. Mean: 10.29; median: 8; mode: 7

5. Mean: 9; median: 8; mode: 7

7. The mean is sensitive to extreme values.

9. Mean: $67.14; median: $65.35

11. Mean: 3.07; median: 3; mode: 3

13. One possibility: $\{4, 4, 10\}$

15. The median gives the most representative description.

17. (a) $\bar{x} = 12$; $\sigma \cdot 2.83$ (b) $\bar{x} = 20$; $\sigma \cdot 2.83$
(c) $\bar{x} = 12$; $\sigma \cdot 1.41$ (d) $\bar{x} = 9$; $\sigma \cdot 1.41$

19. $\bar{x} = 6$, $v = 10$, $\sigma \cdot 3.16$

21. $\bar{x} = 2$, $v = \frac{4}{3}$, $\sigma \cdot 1.15$ **23.** $\bar{x} = 4$, $v = 4$, $\sigma = 2$

25. $\bar{x} = 47$, $v = 226$, $\sigma \cdot 15.03$ **27.** 3.42

29. 101.55 **31.** 1.65

33. $\bar{x} = 12$ and $|x_i - 12| = 8$ for all x_i

35. It will increase the mean by 5, but the standard deviation will not change.

37. First histogram

39. (a) Lower quartile: 13; upper quartile: 21.5

(b)

12 13 14   21.5 23

41. (a) Lower quartile: 47; upper quartile: 51

(b)

46 47 48.5   51   53

43.

9 11.5 14   18 19

45.

17.3 24.1 34.9 43.4
21.8

47.

From the plots, you can see that the lifetimes of the units in the sample made by the new design are greater than the lifetimes of the units in the sample made by the original design. (The median increased by more than 12 months.)

Appendix B.3   *(page B15)*

> ### Vocabulary Check   *(page B15)*
>
> **1.** method; least squares   **2.** sum; squared differences
> **3.** least squares regression

1. 6.75   **3.** 3.55   **5.** $y = 1.6x + 7.5$

7. $y = \frac{28}{107}x + \frac{207}{107}$ **9.** $y = 2x + 83.5; 1$

11. $y = -0.75x^2 + 3.5x$ **13.** $y = \frac{78}{55}x^2 - \frac{104}{55}x + \frac{10}{11}$

Definition of the Six Trigonometric Functions

Right triangle definitions, where $0 < \theta < \pi/2$

$$\sin \theta = \frac{\text{opp.}}{\text{hyp.}} \qquad \csc \theta = \frac{\text{hyp.}}{\text{opp.}}$$

$$\cos \theta = \frac{\text{adj.}}{\text{hyp.}} \qquad \sec \theta = \frac{\text{hyp.}}{\text{adj.}}$$

$$\tan \theta = \frac{\text{opp.}}{\text{adj.}} \qquad \cot \theta = \frac{\text{adj.}}{\text{opp.}}$$

Circular function definitions, where θ *is any angle*

$$\sin \theta = \frac{y}{r} \qquad \csc \theta = \frac{r}{y}$$

$$\cos \theta = \frac{x}{r} \qquad \sec \theta = \frac{r}{x}$$

$$\tan \theta = \frac{y}{x} \qquad \cot \theta = \frac{x}{y}$$

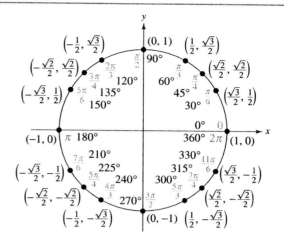

Reciprocal Identities

$$\sin u = \frac{1}{\csc u} \qquad \cos u = \frac{1}{\sec u} \qquad \tan u = \frac{1}{\cot u}$$

$$\csc u = \frac{1}{\sin u} \qquad \sec u = \frac{1}{\cos u} \qquad \cot u = \frac{1}{\tan u}$$

Quotient Identities

$$\tan u = \frac{\sin u}{\cos u} \qquad \cot u = \frac{\cos u}{\sin u}$$

Pythagorean Identities

$$\sin^2 u + \cos^2 u = 1$$
$$1 + \tan^2 u = \sec^2 u \qquad 1 + \cot^2 u = \csc^2 u$$

Cofunction Identities

$$\sin\left(\frac{\pi}{2} - u\right) = \cos u \qquad \cot\left(\frac{\pi}{2} - u\right) = \tan u$$

$$\cos\left(\frac{\pi}{2} - u\right) = \sin u \qquad \sec\left(\frac{\pi}{2} - u\right) = \csc u$$

$$\tan\left(\frac{\pi}{2} - u\right) = \cot u \qquad \csc\left(\frac{\pi}{2} - u\right) = \sec u$$

Even/Odd Identities

$$\sin(-u) = -\sin u \qquad \cot(-u) = -\cot u$$
$$\cos(-u) = \cos u \qquad \sec(-u) = \sec u$$
$$\tan(-u) = -\tan u \qquad \csc(-u) = -\csc u$$

Sum and Difference Formulas

$$\sin(u \pm v) = \sin u \cos v \pm \cos u \sin v$$
$$\cos(u \pm v) = \cos u \cos v \mp \sin u \sin v$$
$$\tan(u \pm v) = \frac{\tan u \pm \tan v}{1 \mp \tan u \tan v}$$

Double-Angle Formulas

$$\sin 2u = 2 \sin u \cos u$$
$$\cos 2u = \cos^2 u - \sin^2 u = 2 \cos^2 u - 1 = 1 - 2 \sin^2 u$$
$$\tan 2u = \frac{2 \tan u}{1 - \tan^2 u}$$

Power-Reducing Formulas

$$\sin^2 u = \frac{1 - \cos 2u}{2}$$

$$\cos^2 u = \frac{1 + \cos 2u}{2}$$

$$\tan^2 u = \frac{1 - \cos 2u}{1 + \cos 2u}$$

Sum-to-Product Formulas

$$\sin u + \sin v = 2 \sin\left(\frac{u + v}{2}\right) \cos\left(\frac{u - v}{2}\right)$$

$$\sin u - \sin v = 2 \cos\left(\frac{u + v}{2}\right) \sin\left(\frac{u - v}{2}\right)$$

$$\cos u + \cos v = 2 \cos\left(\frac{u + v}{2}\right) \cos\left(\frac{u - v}{2}\right)$$

$$\cos u - \cos v = -2 \sin\left(\frac{u + v}{2}\right) \sin\left(\frac{u - v}{2}\right)$$

Product-to-Sum Formulas

$$\sin u \sin v = \frac{1}{2}[\cos(u - v) - \cos(u + v)]$$

$$\cos u \cos v = \frac{1}{2}[\cos(u - v) + \cos(u + v)]$$

$$\sin u \cos v = \frac{1}{2}[\sin(u + v) + \sin(u - v)]$$

$$\cos u \sin v = \frac{1}{2}[\sin(u + v) - \sin(u - v)]$$

FORMULAS FROM GEOMETRY

Triangle:
$h = a \sin \theta$

$\text{Area} = \dfrac{1}{2}bh$

$c^2 = a^2 + b^2 - 2ab \cos \theta$ (Law of Cosines)

Right Triangle:
Pythagorean Theorem
$c^2 = a^2 + b^2$

Equilateral Triangle:
$h = \dfrac{\sqrt{3}s}{2}$

$\text{Area} = \dfrac{\sqrt{3}s^2}{4}$

Parallelogram:
$\text{Area} = bh$

Trapezoid:
$\text{Area} = \dfrac{h}{2}(a + b)$

Circle:
$\text{Area} = \pi r^2$

$\text{Circumference} = 2\pi r$

Sector of Circle:
$\text{Area} = \dfrac{\theta r^2}{2}$

$s = r\theta$

θ in radians

Circular Ring:
$\text{Area} = \pi(R^2 - r^2)$

$\qquad = 2\pi pw$

$p = $ average radius,

$w = $ width of ring

Sector of Circular Ring:
$\text{Area} = \theta pw$

$p = $ average radius,

$w = $ width of ring,

θ in radians

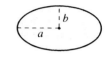

Ellipse:
$\text{Area} = \pi ab$

$\text{Circumference} \approx 2\pi \sqrt{\dfrac{a^2 + b^2}{2}}$

Cone:
$\text{Volume} = \dfrac{Ah}{3}$

$A = $ area of base

Right Circular Cone:
$\text{Volume} = \dfrac{\pi r^2 h}{3}$

$\text{Lateral Surface Area} = \pi r \sqrt{r^2 + h^2}$

Frustum of Right Circular Cone:
$\text{Volume} = \dfrac{\pi(r^2 + rR + R^2)h}{3}$

$\text{Lateral Surface Area} = \pi s(R + r)$

Right Circular Cylinder:
$\text{Volume} = \pi r^2 h$

$\text{Lateral Surface Area} = 2\pi rh$

Sphere:
$\text{Volume} = \dfrac{4}{3}\pi r^3$

$\text{Surface Area} = 4\pi r^2$

Wedge:
$A = B \sec \theta$

$A = $ area of upper face,

$B = $ area of base

ALGEBRA

Factors and Zeros of Polynomials:

Given the polynomial $p(x) = a_n x^n + a_{n-1} x^{n-1} + \cdots + a_1 x + a_0$. If $p(b) = 0$, then b is a *zero* of the polynomial and a *solution* of the equation $p(x) = 0$. Furthermore, $(x - b)$ is a *factor* of the polynomial.

Fundamental Theorem of Algebra: An nth degree polynomial has n (not necessarily distinct) zeros.

Quadratic Formula: If $p(x) = ax^2 + bx + c$, $a \neq 0$ and $b^2 - 4ac \geq 0$, then the real zeros of p are $x = \left(-b \pm \sqrt{b^2 - 4ac}\right)/2a$.

Special Factors:

Examples

$x^2 - a^2 = (x - a)(x + a)$ $x^2 - 9 = (x - 3)(x + 3)$

$x^3 - a^3 = (x - a)(x^2 + ax + a^2)$ $x^3 - 8 = (x - 2)(x^2 + 2x + 4)$

$x^3 + a^3 = (x + a)(x^2 - ax + a^2)$ $x^3 + 4 = \left(x + \sqrt[3]{4}\right)\left(x^2 - \sqrt[3]{4}x + \sqrt[3]{16}\right)$

$x^4 - a^4 = (x - a)(x + a)(x^2 + a^2)$ $x^4 - 4 = \left(x - \sqrt{2}\right)\left(x + \sqrt{2}\right)(x^2 + 2)$

$x^4 + a^4 = \left(x^2 + \sqrt{2}ax + a^2\right)\left(x^2 - \sqrt{2}ax + a^2\right)$ $x^4 + 4 = (x^2 + 2x + 2)(x^2 - 2x + 2)$

$x^n - a^n = (x - a)(x^{n-1} + ax^{n-2} + \cdots + a^{n-1})$, for n odd $x^5 - 1 = (x - 1)(x^4 + x^3 + x^2 + x + 1)$

$x^n + a^n = (x + a)(x^{n-1} - ax^{n-2} + \cdots + a^{n-1})$, for n odd $x^7 + 1 = (x + 1)(x^6 - x^5 + x^4 - x^3 + x^2 - x + 1)$

$x^{2n} - a^{2n} = (x^n - a^n)(x^n + a^n)$ $x^6 - 1 = (x^3 - 1)(x^3 + 1)$

Binomial Theorem:

Examples

$(x + a)^2 = x^2 + 2ax + a^2$ $(x + 3)^2 = x^2 + 6x + 9$

$(x - a)^2 = x^2 - 2ax + a^2$ $(x^2 - 5)^2 = x^4 - 10x^2 + 25$

$(x + a)^3 = x^3 + 3ax^2 + 3a^2x + a^3$ $(x + 2)^3 = x^3 + 6x^2 + 12x + 8$

$(x - a)^3 = x^3 - 3ax^2 + 3a^2x - a^3$ $(x - 1)^3 = x^3 - 3x^2 + 3x - 1$

$(x + a)^4 = x^4 + 4ax^3 + 6a^2x^2 + 4a^3 + a^4$ $\left(x + \sqrt{2}\right)^4 = x^4 + 4\sqrt{2}x^3 + 12x^2 + 8\sqrt{2}x + 4$

$(x - a)^4 = x^4 - 4ax^3 + 6a^2x^2 - 4a^3x + a^4$ $(x - 4)^4 = x^4 - 16x^3 + 96x^2 - 256x + 256$

$(x + a)^n = x^n + nax^{n-1} + \dfrac{n(n-1)}{2!}a^2x^{n-2} + \cdots + na^{n-1}x + a^n$ $(x + 1)^5 = x^5 + 5x^4 + 10x^3 + 10x^2 + 5x + 1$

$(x - a)^n = x^n - nax^{n-1} + \dfrac{n(n-1)}{2!}a^2x^{n-2} - \cdots \pm na^{n-1}x \mp a^n$ $(x - 1)^6 = x^6 - 6x^5 + 15x^4 - 20x^3 + 15x^2 - 6x + 1$

Rational Zero Test: If $p(x) = a_n x^n + a_{n-1} x^{n-1} + \cdots + a_1 x + a_0$ has integer coefficients, then every *rational* zero of $p(x) = 0$ is of the form $x = r/s$, where r is a factor of a_0 and s is a factor of a_n.

Exponents and Radicals:

$a^0 = 1$, $a \neq 0$ $\dfrac{a^x}{a^y} = a^{x-y}$ $\left(\dfrac{a}{b}\right)^x = \dfrac{a^x}{b^x}$ $\sqrt[n]{a^m} = a^{m/n} = \left(\sqrt[n]{a}\right)^m$

$a^{-x} = \dfrac{1}{a^x}$ $(a^x)^y = a^{xy}$ $\sqrt{a} = a^{1/2}$ $\sqrt[n]{ab} = \sqrt[n]{a}\sqrt[n]{b}$

$a^x a^y = a^{x+y}$ $(ab)^x = a^x b^x$ $\sqrt[n]{a} = a^{1/n}$ $\sqrt[n]{\left(\dfrac{a}{b}\right)} = \dfrac{\sqrt[n]{a}}{\sqrt[n]{b}}$

Conversion Table:

1 centimeter $\approx$ 0.394 inch	1 joule $\approx$ 0.738 foot-pound	1 mile $\approx$ 1.609 kilometers
1 meter $\approx$ 39.370 inches	1 gram $\approx$ 0.035 ounce	1 gallon $\approx$ 3.785 liters
$\approx$ 3.281 feet	1 kilogram $\approx$ 2.205 pounds	1 pound $\approx$ 4.448 newtons
1 kilometer $\approx$ 0.621 mile	1 inch $\approx$ 2.540 centimeters	1 foot-lb $\approx$ 1.356 joules
1 liter $\approx$ 0.264 gallon	1 foot $\approx$ 30.480 centimeters	1 ounce $\approx$ 28.350 grams
1 newton $\approx$ 0.225 pound	$\approx$ 0.305 meter	1 pound $\approx$ 0.454 kilogram